HARCOURT
Math

GRADE 6

VOLUME 1

CALIFORNIA TEACHER'S EDITION

Harcourt School Publishers

Orlando • Boston • Dallas • Chicago • San Diego

www.harcourtschool.com

Photo Credits:

Unit Overview Pages:

Unit 1 David Parker/Science Photo Library/Photo Researchers; Unit 2 Ed Young/Science Photo Library/Photo Researchers; Unit 4 Sepp Seitz/Woodfin Camp & Associates; Unit 6 Charles D. Winters/Photo Researchers; Unit 7 Robert Frerck/Woodfin Camp & Associates; Unit 8 Harcourt; Unit 9 Michal Heron/Woodfin Camp & Associates.

ISBN 0-15-315531-0

4 5 6 7 8 9 10   048   2004 2003 2002

Teacher's Edition Contents

Volume 1

Pupil Edition

UNIT 1 Number Sense and Operations

Chapters 1-4

UNIT 2 Statistics and Graphing

Chapters 5-6

UNIT 3 Fraction Concepts and Operations

Chapters 7-10

UNIT 4 Algebra: Integers

Chapters 11-13

Volume 2

Pupil Edition

UNIT 5 Algebra: Expressions and Equations

Chapters 14-16

UNIT 6 Geometry and Spatial Reasoning

Chapters 17-19

UNIT 7 Ratio, Proportion, Percent, and Probability

Chapters 20-23

UNIT 8 Measurement

Chapters 24-27

UNIT 9 Algebra: Patterns and Relationships

Chapters 28-30

Mathematics Advisors

The development of *Harcourt Math* was guided by prominent, accomplished mathematicians from across the United States. Their guidance helped ensure accurate mathematics, appropriate conceptual development, and alignment with the California Mathematics Content Standards.

Richard Askey

Professor of Mathematics
University of Wisconsin
Madison, Wisconsin
Grades 3–4

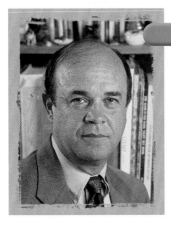

David Wright

Professor of Mathematics
Brigham Young University
Provo, Utah
Grades K–2

David Singer

Professor of Mathematics
Case Western Reserve University
Cleveland, Ohio
Grade 5

Jerome Dancis

Associate Professor of Mathematics
University of Maryland
College Park, Maryland
Grade 6

Tom Roby

Assistant Professor of Mathematics
California State University
Hayward, California
Grade 6

Contributors to the Professional Handbook

The Professional Handbook, found behind the third tab in Volume 1 of this Teacher's Edition, includes articles and essays written by leading mathematicians and researchers who share their insights into the structure of mathematics and topics important to elementary mathematics instruction.

Roger Howe
Professor of Mathematics
Yale University
New Haven, Connecticut
Marvelous Decimals
Doing Decimal Arithmetic:
   Addition

Doing Decimal Arithmetic:
   Multiplication
Estimation and Approximation
Estimation and Arithmetic

Liping Ma
Mathematics Researcher
and Educator
Palo Alto, California
A "Blind Spot" in the Order of
Operations

Tom Roby
Models for Fractions

David Wright
Geometry and Measurement

Program Consultants

Program Consultants and Specialists

Janet S. Abbott
Mathematics Consultant
California

Lois Harrison-Jones
Education and Management Consultant
Dallas, Texas

Arax Miller
Curriculum Coordinator and English Department
    Chairperson
Chamlian School
Glendale, California

Rebecca Valbuena
Language Development Specialist
Stanton Elementary School
Glendora, California

Reviewers and Field-Test Teachers

Daarina Abdus-Samad
Teacher
Norma Coombs Alternative School
Pasadena, California

Britta Abinger
Teacher
Corkery School
Chicago, Illinois

Kathy Albrecht
Teacher
Heritage Oak Elementary
Roseville, California

Terri Battenburg
Teacher
Vencil Brown Elementary
Roseville, California

Caye Baxter
Teacher
Lindbergh Schweitzer Elementary
San Diego, California

Hazel Bills
Teacher
Corkery School
Chicago, Illinois

Bonnie Bray
Teacher
Warren Road Elementary
Augusta, Georgia

Mary Couch
Teacher
Georgetown Elementary
Georgetown, California

Alison Cox
Teacher
Malcolm Elementary
Laguna Niguel, California

Erin Cronin
Teacher
San Ysidro Middle School
San Ysidro, California

Deloris Cureton
Teacher
East Lake Elementary
Decatur, Georgia

Kathleen Duarte
Teacher
Callie Kirkpatrick School
Menifee, California

Vickie Eilenberger
Teacher
Fremont Elementary
Santa Ana, California

Kelly L. Fleming
Teacher
Windy Hill Elementary
Owings, Maryland

Ellen Galdieri
Teacher
Dowell Elementary
Huntingtown, Maryland

Susan Gaspich
Teacher
Chelsea Heights Elementary
Atlantic City, New Jersey

Jerri A. Hall
Teacher
Miller Middle School
Macon, Georgia

Elizabeth Harris
Teacher
Springfield Elementary
Providence, Rhode Island

Lottie Harris
Teacher
Jackson Road Elementary
Griffin, Georgia

Sarah Hillyer
Teacher
Craddock Elementary
Aurora, Ohio

Heather Hunt
Teacher
Horizon Elementary
Hanover Park, Illinois

Maureen Irvine
Teacher
Charles Hoffman Elementary
Running Springs, California

Denise Jones
Teacher
Dobbs Elementary
Atlanta, Georgia

Sunyong Kim
Teacher
Wilton Place Elementary
Sacramento, California

and Reviewers

Inell Lemon
Math Coordinator
Jensen Scholastic Academy
Chicago, Illinois

Catherine Lewis
Teacher
John Ehrhardt Elementary
Elk Grove, California

Marie S. Massey
Teacher
Reese Road Elementary
Columbus, Georgia

Susan Milstein
Teacher
Dag Hammerskjold School
Brooklyn, New York

Marilyn Moore
Teacher
Winterville Elementary
Winterville, Georgia

Penny L. Moore
Teacher
Terrace View Elementary
Grand Terrace, California

Ethel T. Munro
Teacher
Windom Elementary
Orchard Park, New York

Edward H. Nakamura
Teacher
Lakewood School
Lodi, California

Helen Hyun-Jou Park
Teacher
Wilton Place Elementary
Los Angeles, California

Carol G. Parker
Teacher
Valley of Enchantment Elementary
Lake Arrowhead, California

Beth Peery
Learner Support Strategist
Cheatham Hill Elementary
Marietta, Georgia

Eloise Preiss
Assistant Superintendent of Curriculum and
    Instruction
Turlock School District
Turlock, California

Pauline E. Robinson
Teacher
Star Hill Elementary
Dover, Delaware

Hector Ruiz
Teacher
Luther Burbank Elementary
Artesia, California

Manwella Smith
Teacher
Prairie Elementary
Sacramento, California

Leigh Ann Spitzer
Teacher
Washington Elementary
Kingsburg, California

Sylvia Teahan
Teacher
New Albany Elementary
Cinnaminson, New Jersey

Fran Threewit
Reading and Math Specialist
Kenwood Elementary School
Kenwood, California

Beverly J. Tornberg
Teacher
Valhalla Elementary
Pleasant Hill, California

Peter Tuttle
Teacher
Noble Elementary
Cleveland Heights, Ohio

Shelia R. Wells
Teacher
Foster Elementary
Compton, California

Claudia West
Teacher
Westlake Hills Elementary
Westlake Village, California

Beverly A. White
Teacher
Cecil Elementary
Cecil, Pennsylvania

Jill Wilke
Teacher
Brea Country Hills School
Brea, California

Authors

Senior Author

Evan M. Maletsky

Professor of Mathematics
Montclair State University
Upper Montclair, New Jersey

Angela Giglio Andrews

Math Teacher, Scott School
Naperville District #203
Naperville, Illinois

Grace M. Burton

Chair, Department of Curricular Studies
Professor, School of Education
University of North Carolina
at Wilmington
Wilmington, North Carolina

Howard C. Johnson

Dean of the Graduate School
Associate Vice Chancellor for Academic Affairs
Professor, Mathematics and Mathematics Education
Syracuse University
Syracuse, New York

Lynda Luckie

Administrator/Math Specialist
Gwinnett County Public Schools
Lawrenceville, Georgia

Joyce C. McLeod

Visiting Professor
Rollins College
Winter Park, Florida

Vicki Newman

Classroom Teacher
McGaugh Elementary School
Los Alamitos Unified School District
Seal Beach, California

Janet K. Scheer

Executive Director
Create A Vision
Foster City, California

Karen A. Schultz

College of Education
Georgia State University
Atlanta, Georgia

Dear Educator,

The *Mathematics Framework for California Public Schools* states the following goal for California students: *Proficiency in mathematics*. This means that students should be able to:

- Solve meaningful, challenging problems.

- Demonstrate both a depth and breadth of mathematical understanding.

- Perform computations and mathematical procedures quickly and accurately.

These elements of proficiency form the basis for a balanced mathematics curriculum, as shown in this graphic.

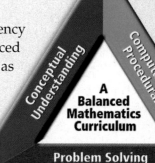

Harcourt Math **supports these goals and is based on the following principles:**

- All children can be successful at becoming proficient in mathematics.

- Problem solving is the focus of mathematics instruction and is best developed by learning problem solving strategies and by solving a balance of problems that are multistep, nonroutine, and real-world.

- Practice is necessary for mathematical proficiency and should focus on computational and procedural skills.

- Conceptual understanding of mathematical concepts is best developed through experiences that involve the use of concrete materials or pictorial models.

- Mathematical reasoning is fundamental to developing conceptual understanding and mathematical proficiency and should permeate all aspects of mathematics instruction.

- Assessing children's prior knowledge is important for determining a starting point for new learning.

- Tools for intervention should provide options for ensuring student achievement in mathematics.

- A strong partnership among home, school, and the community helps students succeed in mathematics.

- Children's competence in mathematics should be assessed through a variety of tools that are consistent, ongoing, and aligned with instruction.

- Children whose primary language is not English will benefit from regular mathematics instruction that includes English-language acquisition strategies.

Harcourt Math provides you with the resources to develop in your students mathematical proficiency and an appreciation for the beauty and power of mathematics in everyday life.

Sincerely,

The Authors

About the California Mathematics

"California mathematics educators, parents, and policy makers unanimously agree on the ultimate goal for California students in mathematics: All students need to develop proficiency in mathematics." (California Mathematics Framework, p. vi)

In December 1997 the California State Board of Education adopted the California Mathematics Content Standards. The Standards were developed as a result of a recognized need for more rigorous and focused mathematics instruction for the students of California schools. The Standards are comparable to those of other academically demanding nations and raise the expectations of what students should know and be able to do. The Standards are specific for all grade levels, kindergarten through high school, and are organized by the following five strands:

► **Number Sense**—developing number concepts, computation, numeration (systems of writing numbers), and estimation

► **Algebra and Functions**—solving mathematical equations and inequalities

► **Measurement and Geometry**—studying space and figures in space; using measurement tools

► **Statistics, Data Analysis, and Probability**—collecting data and displaying it in various ways, calculating simple averages, and performing probability experiments

► **Mathematical Reasoning**—explaining concepts, solving problems and puzzles, understanding algorithms and formulas, and justifying results in all areas of mathematics

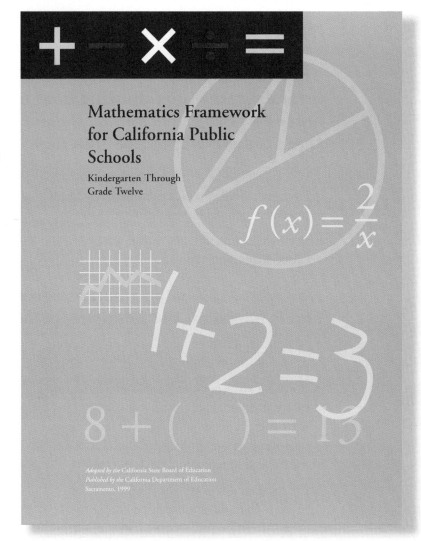

Mathematics Framework
for California Public
Schools

Kindergarten Through
Grade Twelve

$$f(x) = \frac{2}{x}$$

$$1 + 2 = 3$$

$$8 + (\ ) = 13$$

Adopted by the California State Board of Education
Published by the California Department of Education
Sacramento, 1999

In 1999 the California Department of Education published the *Mathematics Framework for California Public Schools.* Its purpose is to guide the development of a math curriculum and instructional materials. In addition to the Standards, the Framework also provides elaboration and examples of mathematical concepts. Key Standards are identified for each grade level. These are the most important Standards, and they are expected to receive additional emphasis during the school year.

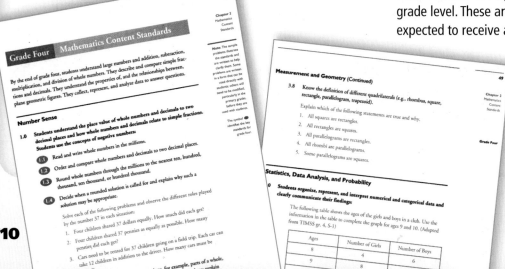

Content Standards

***Harcourt Math* was developed to meet the goals and Standards of the California Mathematics Framework, and does so in the following ways:**

▶ Instructional materials and resources for each grade, K–6, focus on and are aligned with the Standards for that grade.

▶ Each grade level is organized into units and chapters that develop the number sense, algebra and functions, measurement and geometry, statistics, data analysis, and probability strands. Standards for the mathematical reasoning strand are infused into the other strands and permeate all aspects of the program.

▶ The Key Standards receive major emphasis and are supported with focused instruction. They are clearly identified for teachers.

▶ Students learn mathematics by direct instruction, hands-on experiences, step-by-step models that build conceptual understanding, and ample practice that requires the use of problem-solving skills and strategies.

▶ The program provides a balance of computational and procedural skills, conceptual understanding, and problem solving.

▶ The materials are organized so that family and community members are encouraged to and can assist in the learning. The ***Pupil Edition*** clearly identifies for parents which Standards are taught, and the **Family Involvement Activities** component provides opportunities for extending the learning experiences.

▶ The **Intervention Strategies and Activities** component assists teachers with students who fall short of the grade-level Standards and helps to guide their transition to achieving those Standards.

▶ The program assists and supports teachers in planning and implementing a Standards-based program.

▶ Assessment guides the instruction and determines progress toward achieving the Standards.

Point-of-use correlations to the Mathematics Standards appear throughout the *Pupil Edition* and are also reproduced in this *Teacher's Edition*. A complete correlation to the Mathematics Standards is provided at the back of this *Teacher's Edition*, Volume 1.

○━ Key Standards are identified with this key logo.

SCIENCE Standards
ES 3.1

This *Teacher's Edition* also provides point-of-use correlations to California Standards in English-Language Arts, Science, and History/Social Science. Correlation charts appear at the back of this *Teacher's Edition*, Volume 1.

A System for Mathematics Instruction

Harcourt Math employs a consistent method of instruction for developing mathematical proficiency. This Standards-based instruction is provided in every lesson and includes the following four steps.

1 INTRODUCE ▶

Teachers introduce the topic by assessing prior knowledge, reviewing prerequisite skills, setting a purpose for learning, and introducing vocabulary.

> Warm-Up Resources
> or Getting Started Options
>
> Quick Review
>
> Why Learn This?
>
> Vocabulary

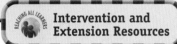
Intervention and Extension Resources

"It is important to tell students the short-term goals and sketch the long-term implications of the mathematics they are expected to learn and the contexts within which the associated competencies, when developed, can be used." (p. 185) "Mathematical terms [should be] defined and used appropriately, precisely, and accurately." (p. 230)

In INTRODUCE, *Harcourt Math* provides

- **Warm-Up Resources** or **Getting Started Options** that start each lesson and promote continual review of computation and problem solving skills.

- **Quick Review** of prerequisite skills.

- **Why Learn This?** for helping students understand short- and long-term goals.

- **Vocabulary** terms defined in context and used appropriately.

2 TEACH ▶

In this step, concrete experiences promote reasoning and provide for conceptual development. Problem solving strategies and computational procedures are taught via step-by-step, direct instruction. Strategies include:

> Guided Instruction
>
> Modifying Instruction
>
> Reasoning

Intervention and Extension Resources

"Teachers effectively organize instruction around goals that are tied to the standards and direct students' mathematical learning." (p. 12) "Concepts and procedures [should be] explained and accompanied by examples to reinforce the lessons." (p. 230)

In TEACH, *Harcourt Math* provides

- Step-by-step **Guided Instruction** to cement understanding, promote **Reasoning,** and monitor achievement of the Standards.

- **Modifying Instruction** for adapting the lesson for students with special needs.

- Questioning strategies for assessing student comprehension.

- Concrete experiences, step-by-step pictorial models, and examples that link to abstract processes and procedures.

Intervention and Extension Resources for every step provide alternative teaching strategies, ways to meet individual needs, and ways to intervene when students fall behind.

Standards with *Harcourt Math*

Each step of the *Harcourt Math* system for mathematics instruction was designed to meet the specific goals and expectations of the California Mathematics Framework.

3 PRACTICE ▶

Daily practice is essential for conceptual development, computational proficiency, and development of reasoning and problem solving strategies. Components include:

Guided Practice and Check

Common Error Alert

Independent Practice

Mixed Review and Test Prep

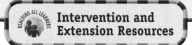 Intervention and Extension Resources

"Errors should not simply be considered mistakes to be corrected but an opportunity to understand how the student understands the problem." (p. 190) "Review and practice distributed over time . . . [should be] provided to enhance understanding and promote generalization and transfer of skill and knowledge." (p. 234) "Ample practice [should be] provided with both routine calculations and more involved multi-step procedures in order to foster the automatic use of these procedures and to foster the development of mathematical understanding. . . ." (p. 230)

In PRACTICE, *Harcourt Math* provides

- **Guided Practice** and **Check** for identifying students who are having difficulty.

- **Common Error Alert** that identifies and describes common mistakes and offers suggestions for help.

- **Independent Practice** that is conceptual, procedural, reasoning, and problem-based.

- **Mixed Review and Test Prep** that provides cumulative review in a variety of formats.

4 ASSESS

Assessment in every lesson helps students summarize their learning and check their progress. It helps teachers bring closure to the lesson, make critical decisions about future instruction, and provide appropriate interventions for individual students. Components include:

Discuss   **Lesson Quiz**

Write

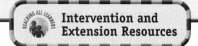 Intervention and Extension Resources

"Assessment that monitors student progress helps steer instruction in the right direction. It signals when alternative routes need to be taken or when the student needs to backtrack to gain more forward momentum." (p. 195)

In ASSESS, *Harcourt Math* provides

- Opportunities to assess in different ways, as well as to address different learning styles:
  Discuss
  Write
  Lesson Quiz

- Continuous monitoring of student achievement of the Standards.

In addition to lesson assessment, multiple means of assessment are provided for every chapter. See the end-of-chapter pages and the Assessment Guide.

Reaching All Learners

"The ultimate goal of the mathematics programs in California is to ensure universal access to high-quality curriculum and instruction so that all students can meet or exceed the state's mathematics content standards." (p. 201)

Harcourt Math provides strategies and activities for meeting the needs of all learners

Alternative Teaching Strategy

Have students **identify the multiplication property** that each equation represents. Then students can fill in the missing number or symbol.

* × 1 = __ Property of One; *

0 × * = __ Property of Zero; 0

(* × ♥) × ◇ = * × (◇ × __) Order Property; ♥

Alternative Teaching Strategies provide an alternative approach for developing lesson concepts, including addressing different learning modalities.

English Language Learners

Help students **understand the terms** *divisor, dividend, and quotient.* Use an example problem and point to the number that represents each term. Then, write the word and give the definition. Give students several other examples and have them label the divisor, dividend, and quotient in each problem. Then, have students write

Activities for English Language Learners offer a variety of ways to explain a concept by using graphics and real objects to accompany oral and written instruction. *Success for English Language Learners* also provides support and activities for addressing the needs of children acquiring English.

Advanced Learners

Challenge students to work with a partner to **write and solve decimal riddles** similar to the following:

- My decimal number is less than 0.5 but greater than 0.35.
- The digit in the tenths place is 1 less than the digit in the hundredths place.

Strategies for Advanced Learners provide challenging opportunities to go beyond the Standards and allow students to move forward in the curriculum.

Special Needs

Have students **identify the LCD and subtract mixed numbers** by completing the following activity.

Instruct students to copy these examples and match them with their equivalents. Then students can find the them by using fraction bars.

Strategies for Special Needs offer alternative suggestions that ensure the inclusion of all students in mathematics learning.

Early Finishers

Have students write and administer a survey, and **compare data sets** between their class and their school.

Ask students to think of a multiple-choice question they would like to ask their classmates and schoolmates.

When the survey is ready, have the students administer it to their class and then to the student body. Students should display the results of both surveys as circle graphs.

Activities for Early Finishers help cement the learning and provide greater depth of understanding.

Curriculum Connections

Share the following with students to help them **practice different ways to read and write numbers.**

The ancient Roman numeral system goes back to about 500 B.C. It is still used sometimes today, but its flaw is that it lacks a zero. The Romans were not consistent in how they used Roman numerals. They might write a number as XXXXVIIII, XXXXIX, or IL. We now follow certain rules when using Roman numerals. Ask:

- What number do these symbols represent? 49
- What is the correct way to write the number today? written more

Curriculum Connections offer ways to reinforce or extend the Standards in all curriculum areas and to reach learners by connecting math to other subject areas.

"When students begin to fall behind in their mastery of mathematics standards, immediate intervention is warranted. . . . In a standards-based environment, students who are struggling to learn or master mathematics need the richest and most organized type of instruction." (p. 206)

Harcourt Math provides intervention strategies for diagnosing and intervening when students have difficulty with mathematics.

Before Each Chapter Begins

The Assessing Prior Knowledge—Check What You Know section that begins each chapter assesses students' prior knowledge of previously taught, prerequisite skills. You can use the results to diagnose the nature of students' difficulties and intervene, using several options:

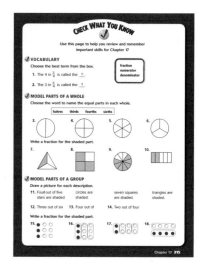

Troubleshooting

This section in the back of the *Pupil Edition*, Grades 3–6, provides a targeted minilesson for each prerequisite skill. The minilesson presents a pictorial model as a reteaching aid and includes practice to help students get back on track toward achieving the Standards.

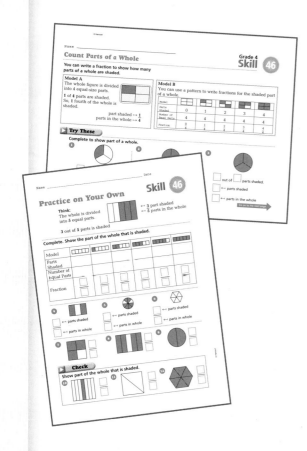

Intervention Strategies and Activities

This component provides independent learning for students who have difficulty with a particular math concept or skill. Each activity provides direct instruction, conceptual models, and scaffolded practice. Alternative teaching strategies give the teacher multiple ways to ensure student success. Built-in assessment determines whether students are ready to move on to the next level in the chapter concepts. The component is available in three formats: as a kit, as copying masters, and as a CD-ROM. (Grades 1–6)

While Teaching Each Chapter

Built-in lesson intervention ensures success at mastering the Standards.

Lesson Check

Within the Teach part of every lesson, Grades 3–6, the Check strategy provides an opportunity to ensure that students understand the lesson concept.

Alternative Teaching Strategies

These strategies may be used when students have difficulty with the lesson concept. They offer different ways to present the concept, including addressing different learning modalities.

Reteach Workbook

This component offers an additional resource that approaches each lesson concept in an alternative way. One worksheet is provided for each lesson. (Grades 1–6)

Assessment

Harcourt Math **provides a wide range of assessment tools to measure student achievement before, during, and after instruction.**

▶ Entry-Level Assessment

Inventory Test

This test, provided in the *Assessment Guide,* may be administered at the beginning of the school year to determine a baseline for student mastery of the Standards. The baseline may also be used to evaluate a student's future growth when compared to subsequent tests.

Assessing Prior Knowledge– Check What You Know

This feature appears at the beginning of every chapter. It may be used before chapter instruction begins in order to determine whether students possess crucial prerequisite skills. Tools for intervention are provided.

Pretests

The **Chapter Tests,** Form A (multiple choice) or Form B (free response), may be used as pretests to measure what students already may have mastered before instruction begins. The tests are provided in the *Assessment Guide.*

▶ Progress Monitoring

Daily Assessment

These point-of-use strategies allow you to continually adjust instruction so that all students are constantly progressing toward mastery of the Standards. These strategies, which appear in every lesson of this *Teacher's Edition,* include the **Quick Review,** the **Mixed Review and Test Prep,** and the **Assess** section of the lesson (Discuss, Write, and Lesson Quiz).

Intervention

While monitoring students' progress, you may determine that intervention is needed. The **Intervention and Extensions Resources** page for each lesson suggests several options for meeting individual needs.

Student Self-Assessment

Students evaluate their own work through checklists, portfolios, and journals. Suggestions are provided in the *Assessment Guide.*

▶ Summative Evaluation

Formal Assessment

Several options are provided to help you determine whether students have achieved the goals defined by a given Standard or set of Standards. These options are provided at the end of each chapter and unit and at the end of the year.

- Chapter Review/Test in the *Pupil Edition*

- Cumulative Review, in the *Pupil Edition,* for cumulative review

- Chapter Test, Form A and Form B in the *Assessment Guide*

- Unit Tests in the *Assessment Guide*

Performance Assessment

Performance Tasks for every unit are provided in the *Assessment Guide.*

**The Harcourt Electronic Test System—
Math Practice and Assessment**

This technology component provides you with the opportunity to make and grade chapter tests electronically. You can customize the tests to meet individual needs or create Standards-based tests from a bank of test items. This component also includes a management system for generating reports.

▶ Test Preparation

Test Prep in the *Pupil Edition*

When faced with the challenge of taking standardized tests, students need to feel confident that the test will be an accurate reflection of what they know or need to learn. Learning to take standardized tests is essentially the same as being a good problem solver. The steps are the same: understand, plan, solve, and check.

To help students prepare for tests, the **Mixed Review and Test Prep** at the end of each skill lesson provides some items in standardized-test format. In addition, the **Cumulative Review** pages at the end of each chapter provide practice in solving problems in a standardized-test format. They include practical test-taking tips that give students ongoing strategies for analyzing problems and finding the best way to solve them.

Family Support

"In an effective mathematics program, materials are organized so that parents, siblings, and community members can provide extended learning experiences." (p. 16)

A strong partnership among home, school, and the community helps students succeed in mathematics. *Harcourt Math* encourages that partnership in a variety of ways.

Family Involvement Activities

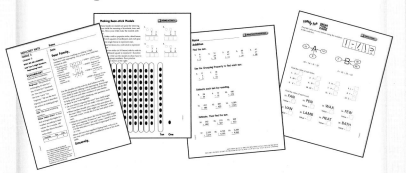

An informative, four-page family letter is provided for every chapter in *Harcourt Math*. Each letter contains:

- Information about the California Mathematics Content Standards.

- An explanation, in family-friendly terms, of the expectations for student learning.

- Models of the chapter skills and tips that enable family members to assist students.

- Homework practice.

- A math game that family members can enjoy together.

Activities and Games for Home or School

These colorful activity cards and game boards can be used in classroom centers or may be sent home with students to enjoy with family members.

THE LEARNING SITE

Harcourt's user-friendly Website provides a wealth of resources for family members. A clearly organized menu leads family members to interactive learning games. At the Multimedia Math glossary, families can see animated examples of *Harcourt Math* vocabulary terms and hear them pronounced. There is also a special page with tips and ideas for parents. www.harcourtschool.com

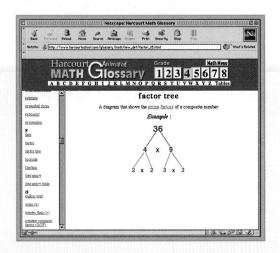

California Mathematics Standards

In the *Pupil Edition*, the California Math Standards are labeled for each lesson. An appendix at the back of the book also shows the Standards in their entirety. This enables family members to stay informed about the Standards their children are learning.

"When used appropriately, technology may help students develop the skills, knowledge, and insight necessary to meet rigorous content standards in mathematics and make a successful transition to the world beyond school." (p. 21)

Harcourt Math includes an array of technology products that can be used to promote mathematics learning.

Harcourt Math Newsroom Videos

Harcourt has joined forces with the leaders in news broadcasting — CNN and Turner Learning — to bring timely math-related news events to the classroom. A CNN broadcast personality introduces the news segment and then follows the segment with discussion questions and ideas. Students can view the video segment to explore how unit math concepts relate to news events and everyday life. (Grades 3–6)

Intervention Strategies and Activities CD-ROM

This electronic component provides independent learning for students who have difficulty with a particular math concept or skill. Each activity provides direct instruction, conceptual models, and scaffolded practice. Built-in assessment determines whether students are ready to move on to the next level in the chapter concepts. (Grades 1–6)

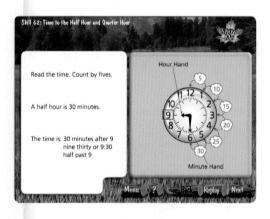

The Harcourt Electronic Assessment System — Math Practice and Assessment CD-ROM

This component provides you with the opportunity to make and grade chapter tests electronically. You can customize the tests to meet individual needs or create Standards-based tests from a bank of test items. The component includes a management system for generating reports. (Grades 1–6)

Stanley's Sticker Stories®

Children in the early grades can use this software to create animated number books that involve number sense, addition, and subtraction. Reading and language skills develop naturally from these experiences. (Grades K–2)

The Harcourt Learning Site

The Learning Site, a product of Harcourt, is a user-friendly Website that provides interactive learning for students, professional development for teachers, and school-home resources. Visit The Learning Site at any time for a wealth of math resources. (Grades K–6) **www.harcourtschool.com**

Mighty Math® Software

This software, codeveloped by Harcourt and Edmark, provides engaging practice activities designed to meet individual needs. For each activity, teachers use a Grow Slide to determine the appropriate level at which to begin. As children progress, the activities increase in difficulty. (Grades K–6)

E-Lab®

This Internet-based program builds conceptual understanding and provides reinforcement of math concepts. Students can explore and extend math concepts and check understanding with a printable worksheet. (Grades 3–6)

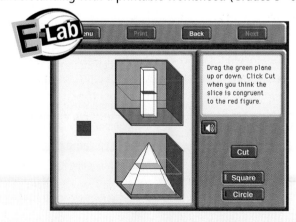

Components

HARCOURT MATH COMPONENTS	K	1	2	3	4	5	6
Daily Lesson Support							
Pupil Edition	■	■	■	■	■	■	■
Unit/Chapter Books	■	■	■				
Big Book	■						
Teacher's Edition	■	■	■	■	■	■	■
Reteach Workbook (Pupil and Teacher Editions)		■	■	■	■	■	■
Practice Workbook (Pupil and Teacher Editions)	■	■	■	■	■	■	■
Problem Solving and Reading Strategies Workbook (Pupil and Teacher Editions)		■	■	■	■	■	■
Challenge Workbook (Pupil and Teacher Editions)	■	■	■	■	■	■	■
Teacher's Resource Book	■	■	■	■	■	■	■
Daily Transparencies		■	■	■	■	■	■
Teaching Transparencies				■	■	■	■
Vocabulary Cards with Teacher's Activity Guide	■	■	■	■	■	■	■
Success for English Language Learners		■	■	■	■	■	■
Answer and Solution Key							■
Intervention							
Intervention Strategies and Activities—Kit with Cards		■	■	■	■	■	■
Intervention Strategies and Activities—Teacher's Guide with Copying Masters		■	■	■	■	■	■
Intervention Strategies and Activities—CD-ROM		■	■	■	■	■	■
Check What You Know: Enrichment Book (Pupil Edition and Answer Key)		■	■	■	■	■	■
Check What You Know: Intervention Practice Book (Pupil Edition and Answer Key)		■	■	■	■	■	■
Assessment Resources							
Assessment Guide	■	■	■	■	■	■	■
Performance Assessment		■	■	■	■	■	■
Math Practice and Assessment CD-ROM		■	■	■	■	■	■
Family Involvement							
Family Involvement Activities—English	■	■	■	■	■	■	■
Family Involvement Activities—in Other Languages	■	■	■	■	■	■	■
Activities and Games for Home or School	■	■	■	■	■	■	■
Literature and Music							
Math Readers	■	■	■				
Literature Big Books and Little Books	■						
Literature Books on Tape	■						
Math Jingles®	■	■	■	■	■	■	■
Math Jingles® Copying Masters	■	■	■	■	■	■	■
Technology Resources							
Harcourt Math Newsroom Videos (CNN)				■	■	■	■
Stanley's Sticker Stories® Software	■	■	■				
Mighty Math® Software	■	■	■	■	■	■	■
E-Lab® and E-Lab Recording Sheets				■	■	■	■
Math Practice and Assessment CD-ROM		■	■	■	■	■	■
Intervention Strategies and Activities—CD-ROM		■	■	■	■	■	■
Intervention Strategies and Activities Teaching Transparencies		■	■	■	■	■	■
Harcourt Math Lesson Planner and Resources CD-ROM	■	■	■	■	■	■	■
The Learning Site	■	■	■	■	■	■	■
Manipulative Options							
My Manipulatives and Workmats	■	■	■				
Core Manipulative Kit	■	■	■	■	■	■	■
Teacher Modeling Kit	■	■	■	■	■	■	■
Build-a-Kit® Manipulatives	■	■	■	■	■	■	■

HARCOURT
Math

CALIFORNIA EDITION

Harcourt School Publishers

Orlando • Boston • Dallas • Chicago • San Diego

www.harcourtschool.com

Mathematics Advisors

Jerome Dancis
Associate Professor of Mathematics
University of Maryland
College Park, Maryland

Tom Roby
Assistant Professor of Mathematics
California State University
Hayward, California

Senior Author

Evan M. Maletsky
Professor of Mathematics
Montclair State University
Upper Montclair, New Jersey

Authors

Angela Giglio Andrews
Math Teacher, Scott School
Naperville District #203
Naperville, Illinois

Grace M. Burton
Chair, Department of Curricular Studies
Professor, School of Education
University of North Carolina
  at Wilmington
Wilmington, North Carolina

Howard C. Johnson
Dean of the Graduate School
Associate Vice Chancellor
  for Academic Affairs
Professor, Mathematics and
  Mathematics Education
Syracuse University
Syracuse, New York

Lynda A. Luckie
Administrator/Math Specialist
Gwinnett County Public Schools
Lawrenceville, Georgia

Joyce C. McLeod
Visiting Professor
Rollins College
Winter Park, Florida

Vicki Newman
Classroom Teacher
McGaugh Elementary School
Los Alamitos Unified School District
Seal Beach, California

Janet K. Scheer
Executive Director
Create A Vision
Foster City, California

Karen A. Schultz
College of Education
Georgia State University
Atlanta, Georgia

Program Consultants and Specialists

Janet S. Abbott
Mathematics Consultant
California

Arax Miller
Curriculum Coordinator and English
  Department Chairperson
Chamlian School
Glendale, California

Lois Harrison-Jones
Education and Management
  Consultant
Dallas, Texas

Rebecca Valbuena
Language Development Specialist
Stanton Elementary School
Glendora, California

Chapter Features

Daily Review and Practice
  Quick Review
  Mixed Review and
    Test Prep
Intervention
  Troubleshooting,
    pp. H2–H5, H13, H15
Extra Practice
  pp. H32–H35

Technology Resources

Harcourt Math Newsroom Video:
Chapter 1, p. 18

E-Lab:
Chapter 2, p. 43
Chapter 4, p. 75

Mighty Math Calculating Crew:
Chapter 1, p. 24

Multimedia Glossary:
The Learning Site at
www.harcourtschool.com/ glossary/math

v

UNIT 2
CHAPTERS 5–6
Statistics and Graphing

Chapter Features

Daily Review and Practice
Quick Review
Mixed Review and
  Test Prep
Intervention
Troubleshooting,
  pp. H5-H7
Extra Practice
pp. H36-H37

Technology Resources

**Harcourt Math
Newsroom Video:**
Chapter 5, p. 95

E-Lab:
Chapter 6, p. 129

Multimedia Glossary:
The Learning Site at
**www.harcourtschool.com/
glossary/math**

Chapter 6
GRAPH DATA

UNIT 3
CHAPTERS 7–10

Fraction Concepts and Operations

Chapter Features

Daily Review and Practice
- Quick Review
- Mixed Review and Test Prep

Intervention
- Troubleshooting, pp. H3, H7-H11

Extra Practice
- pp. H38-H41

Technology Resources

Harcourt Math Newsroom Video:
Chapter 9, p. 178

E-Lab:
Chapter 8, pp. 162, 168
Chapter 9, pp. 181, 191
Chapter 10, p. 208

Mighty Math Calculating Crew:
Chapter 8, p. 171
Chapter 9, p. 188

Mighty Math Number Heroes:
Chapter 9, p. 183

Multimedia Glossary:
The Learning Site at
www.harcourtschool.com/glossary/math

UNIT 4
CHAPTERS 11–13
Algebra: Integers

Chapter Features

Daily Review and Practice
    Quick Review
    Mixed Review and
    Test Prep
Intervention
    Troubleshooting,
    pp. H12–H14
Extra Practice
    pp. H42–H44

Technology Resources

**Harcourt Math
Newsroom Video:**
Chapter 11, p. 234

E-Lab:
Chapter 12, p. 249

**Mighty Math Astro
Algebra:**
Chapter 13, pp. 258, 260

Multimedia Glossary:
The Learning Site at
**www.harcourtschool.com/
glossary/math**

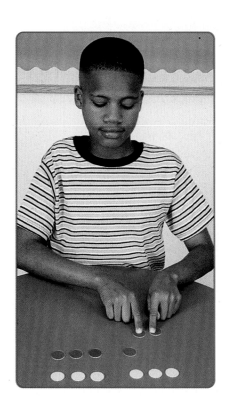

Chapter 13
MULTIPLY AND DIVIDE WITH INTEGERS . . **254**

UNIT WRAPUP

UNIT 5
CHAPTERS 14–16

Algebra: Expressions and Equations

Chapter Features

Daily Review and Practice
  Quick Review
  Mixed Review and
    Test Prep
Intervention
  Troubleshooting,
    pp. H8, H11, H15-H18
Extra Practice
  pp. H45-H47

Technology Resources

**Harcourt Math
Newsroom Video:**
Chapter 14, p. 277

E-Lab:
Chapter 14, p. 281
Chapter 15, p. 290
Chapter 16, pp. 300, 309

**Mighty Math Astro
Algebra:**
Chapter 16, p. 302

Multimedia Glossary:
The Learning Site at
**www.harcourtschool.com/
glossary/math**

Chapter 16
MULTIPLICATION AND DIVISION EQUATIONS

UNIT 6
CHAPTERS 17–19

Geometry and Spatial Reasoning

Chapter Features

Daily Review and Practice
   Quick Review
   Mixed Review and
      Test Prep
Intervention
   Troubleshooting,
      pp. H14, H18-H20
Extra Practice
   pp. H48-H50

Technology Resources

Harcourt Math Newsroom Video:
Chapter 18, p. 342

E-Lab:
Chapter 19, p. 357

Mighty Math Cosmic Geometry:
Chapter 17, p. 327
Chapter 18, pp. 338, 349

Multimedia Glossary:
The Learning Site at
**www.harcourtschool.com/
glossary/math**

Chapter 19

UNIT WRAPUP

UNIT WRAPUP

UNIT 9
CHAPTERS 28–30

Algebra: Patterns and Relationships

Chapter Features

Daily Review and Practice
Quick Review
Mixed Review and
Test Prep

Intervention
Troubleshooting,
pp. H18, H29–H31

Extra Practice
pp. H59–H61

Technology Resources

**Harcourt Math
Newsroom Video:**
Chapter 28, p. 529

E-Lab:
Chapter 28, p. 531
Chapter 30, p. 571

**Mighty Math Cosmic
Geometry:**
Chapter 29, p. 544

**Mighty Math Astro
Algebra:**
Chapter 30, p. 559

Multimedia Glossary:
The Learning Site at
**www.harcourtschool.com/
glossary/math**

WELCOME!

The authors of *Harcourt Math* want you to be a good mathematician, but most of all we want you to enjoy learning math and feel confident that you can do it. We invite you to share your math book with family members. Take them on a guided tour through your book!

THE GUIDED TOUR

Choose a chapter you are interested in. Show your family some of these things in the chapter that will help you learn.

☑ CHECK WHAT YOU KNOW

Do you need to review any skills before you begin the next chapter? If you do, you will find help in the Handbook in the back of your book.

•• THE MATH LESSONS

☑ **Quick Review** to check the skills you need for the lesson.

☑ **Learn section** to help you study problems, models, examples, and questions that give you different ways to learn.

☑ **Check for Understanding** to make sure you understood the lesson.

☑ **Practice and Problem Solving** to help you practice what you have just learned.

☑ **Mixed Review and Test Prep** to keep your skills sharp and prepare you for important tests. Look back at the pages shown by each problem to get help if you need it.

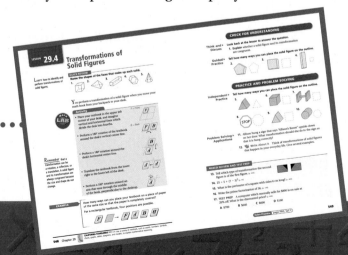

STUDENT HANDBOOK ·····················

Now show your family the **Student Handbook** in the back of your book. The sections will help you in many different ways.

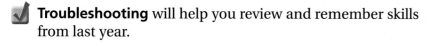

✓ **Troubleshooting** will help you review and remember skills from last year.

✓ **Extra Practice** will help you make sure that you are ready to move on to the next lesson.

✓ **Sharpen Your Test-Taking Skills** will help you feel confident that you can do well on a test.

✓ **Answers to Selected Exercises** will help you check your answers to part of an assignment.

California Standards tell you what you are expected to learn this year. Each lesson's standards are listed at the bottom of the lesson page.

Invite your family members to:

▶ talk with you about what you are learning.

▶ help you correct errors you have made on completed work.

▶ help you set a time and find a quiet place to do math homework.

▶ solve problems with you as you play, shop, and do household chores together.

▶ visit **The Learning Site** at www.harcourtschool.com

▶ have *FUN WITH MATH!*

Have a great year!

The Authors

FOCUS ON
PROBLEM SOLVING

Analyze
Choose
Solve
Check

Good problem solvers need to be good thinkers. They also need to know the strategies listed on page 1. This plan can help you learn how to think through a problem.

Analyze the problem.

What are you asked to find?	Restate the question in your own words.
What information is given?	Look for numbers. Find how they are related.
Is there information you will not use? If so, what?	Decide whether you need all the information you are given.

Choose a strategy to solve.

| What strategy will you use? | Think about some problem solving strategies you can use. Then choose one. |

Solve the problem.

| How can you use the strategy to solve the problem? | Follow your plan. Show your solution. |

Check your answer.

| Look back at the problem. Does the answer make sense? Explain. | Be sure you answered the question that is asked. |
| What other strategy could you use? | Solving the problem by another method is a good way to check your work. |

Try It

Here's how you can use the problem-solving steps to solve a problem.

Draw a Diagram

During summer vacation, Kayla will visit her cousin and then her grandmother. She will be gone for 5 weeks and 2 days and will spend 9 more days with her cousin than with her grandmother. How long will she stay with each?

PROBLEM SOLVING STRATEGIES

▶ **Draw a Diagram or Picture**
Make a Model
Predict and Test
Work Backward
Make an Organized List
Find a Pattern
Make a Table or Graph
Solve a Simpler Problem
Write an Equation
Use Logical Reasoning

Analyze

Kayla will visit her cousin and grandmother for 5 weeks and 2 days this summer. I need to find out how long she will stay with each if she spends 9 more days with her cousin than with her grandmother.

Choose

I can *draw a diagram* to show how long she will stay. I can use boxes for the length of each stay. The length of the boxes will represent the lengths of the stays.

Solve

5 weeks and 2 days is 37 days in all. So, my diagram looks like this:

Step 1

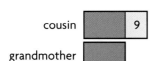

Sum of all parts (days) = 37.
37 − 9 = 28
28 ÷ 2 = 14

Step 2

= 23

= 14   So, each equal part = 14.

So, Kayla will stay with her cousin for 23 days and with her grandmother for 14 days.

Check

23 days is 9 days longer than 14 days. The total of the two stays is 23 + 14, or 37 days. This solution fits the description of Kayla's vacation trip.

Draw a Diagram

Eight basketball teams will play in a tournament. A team is out after it loses once. How many games does a team have to win in order to win the tournament?

Analyze

There are 8 teams. If a team loses, it is out of the tournament. If a team wins, it keeps playing.

Choose

You can *draw a diagram* to show which teams play in each game of the tournament. Use the diagram to show each pair of teams playing against each other.

Team 1

Team 2

Solve

Use the diagram to pair up the 8 teams. Make up a winner for each game. Then show the next games until the tournament has a winner.

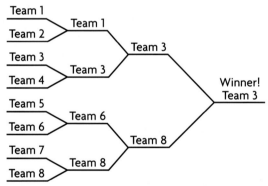

So, a team must win 3 games to win the tournament.

Check

Follow Team 3 through the tournament listing. Count the number of times it wins.

Problem Solving Practice

1. **What if** half as many teams play in the tournament? How many games will have to be played to determine the winner?
   2 games will determine the winner.
2. After the game, the teams have sandwiches at their coaches' houses. You can build your own sandwich with lettuce, tomato, and ham. How many different ways can you stack the 3 fillings to make a sandwich? 6 different ways

Analyze
Choose
Solve
Check

Make a Model

Alice has three pieces of ribbon. Their lengths are 7 in., 10 in., and 12 in. How can Alice use these ribbons to measure a length of 15 in.?

Analyze

Each of the three ribbons is a different length. No ribbon is 15 in. long, but you can combine the ribbon lengths to measure 15 in.

Choose

You can *make a model* of each piece of ribbon. Then you can organize the ribbons to show new lengths.

Solve

When you put two pieces together, you can form lengths of 17, 19, and 22 in. All of these are too long.

One Way
Alice can fold the 10-in. piece in half to model a 5-in. length. Then she can put the folded piece together with the 10-in. piece to make 15 in.

Another Way
Alice can place the 7-in. piece above the 12-in. piece to show that the 12-in. piece extends 5 in. beyond it. Then that 5 in. and the 10-in. piece together will make 15 in.

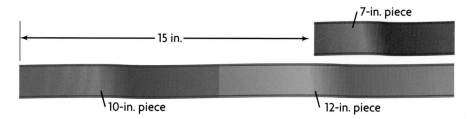

Check

Check that you used the correct lengths for the ribbon pieces. Then add the lengths of the two longer pieces and subtract the length of the short one. The result is 15 in.

Problem Solving Practice

1. Draw pictures of models you could make to measure other lengths with the three pieces of ribbon. Check students' drawings.

2. **What if** Andy is building a stand by using four cubes? He stacks the cubes, one on top of the other, and paints the outside of each cube (not the bottom). How many faces of the cubes are painted? 4 faces of bottom 3 cubes, 5 faces of top cube; 17 faces in all

Focus on Problem Solving 3

Analyze
Choose
Solve
Check

Predict and Test

Margaret sells tickets to a pizza dinner at her school. An adult ticket costs $3.50. A student ticket costs $2.50. Margaret sells 10 more adult tickets than student tickets. She collects $155 in ticket sales. A total of 450 people attend the pizza dinner. How many student tickets has Margaret sold?

Analyze

Student tickets cost $2.50 and adult tickets cost $3.50. Margaret sells 10 more adult tickets than student tickets. Her sales are $155. The number of people at the dinner is given, but this information is not needed.

Choose

You can use *predict and test* to solve. Use number sense and the needed information to predict how many student tickets Margaret has sold. Then test your prediction and revise it if needed.

Solve

Make a table to show each prediction and its result. Be sure you have 10 more adult tickets than student tickets each time.

PREDICTION		TEST	
Adult	Student	Sales	
20	10	$(20 \times \$3.50) + (10 \times \$2.50) = \$95$	too low, revise
40	30	$(40 \times \$3.50) + (30 \times \$2.50) = \$215$	too high, revise
30	20	$(30 \times \$3.50) + (20 \times \$2.50) = \$155$	✓ correct

So, Margaret has sold 20 student tickets.

Check

Check that each multiplication is correct: $30 \times \$3.50 = \$105$, and $20 \times \$2.50 = \$50$; $\$105 + \$50 = \$155$. The answer checks.

Problem Solving Practice

1. The sum of Margaret's and her younger brother's ages is 38. The difference between their ages is 8. How old is Margaret's brother? **15 years old**

2. Tables for the pizza dinner are set up in 3 rooms. One room has 11 tables to seat 98 people. Some tables are for 8 people, and others are for 10 people. How many tables for 8 people are set up in this room? **6 tables**

4 Focus on Problem Solving

Work Backward

Joe and his brother Tim go shopping. At the toy store, they use half of their money to buy a video game. Then they go to the pizza parlor and spend half of the money they have left on a pizza. Then they spend half of the remaining money to rent a video. After these stops, they have $4.50 left. How much money did they have at the start?

Analyze

You need to find how much money they had at the start. You know that they had $4.50 left and that they spent half of their money at each of three stops.

Choose

Start with the amount you know they have left—$4.50—and *work backward*. Knowing how much they have left will help you calculate first how much they spent to rent the video, then how much the pizza cost, then the price of the video game, and finally how much money they had at the start.

Solve

amount they had left → $4.50

$4.50 → twice that amount before a video → 2 × $4.50 = $9

$9 → twice that amount before a pizza → 2 × $9 = $18

$18 → twice that amount before a video game → 2 × $18 = $36

So, the amount they had at the start was $36.

Check

Put $36 in the original problem to check the amount they spent at each stop.

$36 ÷ 2 = $18, $18 ÷ 2 = $9, $9 ÷ 2 = $4.50

The amount they had left matches the amount given in the problem.

Problem Solving Practice

1. The Lauber family has 4 children. Joe is 5 years younger than his brother Mark. Tim is half as old as his brother Joe. Mary, who is 10, is 3 years older than Tim. How old is Mark?
Mark is 19 yr old.
2. If you divide this mystery number by 4, add 8, and multiply by 3, you get 42. What is the mystery number? **24**

Focus on Problem Solving 5

5

Make an Organized List

At Fun City Amusement Park you can throw 3 darts at a target to score points and win prizes. If each dart lands within the target area, how many different total scores are possible?

Analyze

If all 3 darts hit the center circle, you get 30 points. This is the highest score. If all 3 darts hit the outside circle, you get 6 points. This is the lowest score. If the 3 darts hit a different combination, other scores are possible.

Choose

Make an organized list to determine all possible hits and score totals. List the value of each dart and the total for all three darts.

Solve

First consider all 3 darts hitting the center circle. List the value of each dart and the total score. Then consider 2 darts hitting the center circle and the third dart hitting a different circle. List the value of each dart and the total scores. Do the same for 1 dart hitting the center circle and no darts hitting the center circle.

3 Darts Hit Center	2 Darts Hit Center	1 Dart Hits Center	0 Darts Hit Center
10 + 10 + 10 = 30	10 + 10 + 5 = 25	10 + 5 + 5 = 20	5 + 5 + 5 = 15
	10 + 10 + 2 = 22	10 + 5 + 2 = 17	5 + 5 + 2 = 12
		10 + 2 + 2 = 14	5 + 2 + 2 = 9
			2 + 2 + 2 = 6

So, there are 10 possible scores.

Check

Make sure that all possible combinations of scores are listed and that each set of scores in the list is different.

Problem Solving Practice

1. The Yogurt Store at Fun City sells 3 flavors of yogurt: chocolate, vanilla, and strawberry. You want to get a scoop of each flavor in a waffle cone. How many different ways can the scoops be arranged? **6 ways**

2. How many ways can you make change for a quarter by using dimes, nickels, and pennies? **12 ways**

6 Focus on Problem Solving

Find a Pattern

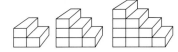

A contractor can build stairways to a deck or patio with any number of steps. She uses the pattern at the right to build them. How many blocks are needed to build a stairway with 7 steps?

Analyze

As the number of steps increases, so does the number of blocks. You must find the number of blocks needed for a stairway with 7 steps.

Choose

You can *find a pattern* for the number of blocks needed. For each stairway, count the number of blocks to make each step and then find the total number of blocks. Use the pattern to find the number of blocks for 7 steps.

Solve

The pattern shows that the number of the step in the stairway is the same as the number of blocks needed to make it. The 2nd step is made with 2 blocks, the 3rd step is made with 3 blocks, and so on.

Number of Step	Side View	Number of Blocks	Cumulative Total
2		2	$2 + 1 = 3$
3		3	$3 + 2 + 1 = 6$
4		4	$4 + 3 + 2 + 1 = 10$

So, a stairway with 7 steps has 7 blocks in the 7th step, 6 blocks in the 6th step, and so on. The total number of blocks is $7 + 6 + 5 + 4 + 3 + 2 + 1 = 28$ blocks.

Check

Sketch a stairway with 7 steps. Check the number of blocks needed. The number in the sketch matches the answer.

$7 + 6 + 5 + 4 + 3 + 2 + 1 = 28$

Problem Solving Practice

6 boxes; the pattern is add the next odd number to each sum: $3 + 3 = 6$, $6 + 5 = 11$, $11 + 7 = 18$, $18 + 9 = 27$, $27 + 11 = 38$.

1. A cereal company adds baseball cards to certain boxes of cereal. Cards are added to the 3rd box, the 6th box, the 11th box, and the 18th box of cereal. If this pattern continues, how many boxes will have baseball cards in them when a case of 40 is ready to be shipped? Explain.

Describe the pattern and find the missing numbers.

2. 1, 4, 16, 64, 256, ■ , ■ , 16,384 **multiply by 4; 1,024; 4,096**

Focus on Problem Solving 7

Make a Table

In math, Mrs. Laurence gave her class a 100-point test. Students who score 80 or above are eligible to join the Math Club. The test scores are in the box below. How many students scored 80 or above? How many students scored below 80?

90	83	80	77	78	91	92	73
62	83	79	88	72	85	93	84
75	68	82	75	94	70	98	82

Analyze

You have the test scores for the class. You need to find how many students scored below 80 and how many students scored 80 or above.

Choose

You can *make a table* and tally the test scores. This organizes the data and makes it easier to answer questions about the scores.

Solve

Make a two-column table for the range of scores. As you read each test score, place a tally mark across from the appropriate range. Be sure you end up with 24 tallies, one for each student.

SCORES	TALLIES
60–69	||
70–79	|||| |||
80–89	|||| |||
90–99	||||	

Now use the table to answer the questions.

SCORES OF 80 OR ABOVE	SCORES BELOW 80
8 students scored 80–89.	8 students scored 70–79.
6 students scored 90–99.	2 students scored 60–69.

So, 14 students scored 80 or above, and 10 students scored below 80.

Check

Recount the tallies in each row and check your addition.

Problem Solving Practice

1. Starting at 3:00, the director will give each student 5 minutes to try out for the talent show. The students, in order, are Ben, Tarek, Jan, Ed, and Frank. At what time does Frank start? **3:20**

2. Kelly reads stories to children at the library. There are three sessions, each lasting 45 minutes, with 30 minutes between sessions. If Kelly starts reading at 10:00 A.M., at what time does she finish? **1:15 P.M.**

Analyze
Choose
Solve
Check

Solve a Simpler Problem

Make a table of the first 2 odd numbers and their sum, the first 3 odd numbers and their sum, and so on. How does the table show a pattern? What is the sum of the first 20 odd numbers?

Analyze

You know how to begin finding sums for the first 2 odd numbers and the first 3 odd numbers. You need to find a pattern in the table to help you find the sum of the first 20 odd numbers.

Choose

You can begin by *solving a simpler problem*. Start with sums for the first 2 odd numbers, followed by sums for 3 odd numbers, 4 odd numbers, and 5 odd numbers.

Solve

Organize the data in a table and look for a pattern in the sums.

ODD NUMBERS	SUM	PATTERN
1 + 3	4	2^2
1 + 3 + 5	9	3^2
1 + 3 + 5 + 7	16	4^2
1 + 3 + 5 + 7 + 9	25	5^2

The table shows a pattern in the sums that relates to square numbers. Extend the pattern in the table to 20 odd numbers.

6 odd numbers → 36

7 odd numbers → 49

8 odd numbers → 64

20 odd numbers → 400

So, the sum of the first 20 odd numbers is 20^2, or 400.

Check

Extend the table a few more rows to check that there really is a pattern of square numbers. For example, find sums for the first 9, 10, 11, and 12 odd numbers. The answers check.

Problem Solving Practice

1. Martha has 5 pairs of slacks and 4 blouses for school. How many different outfits can she make with these items? **20 outfits**

2. What is the least 5-digit number that can be divided by 50 with a remainder of 17? **10,017**

Analyze
Choose
Solve
Check

Write an Equation

A school district can afford to build a gym with three basketball courts with an area of 18,700 square feet. The gym needs to be 110 feet wide to leave walking room around the courts. How long will the gym be?

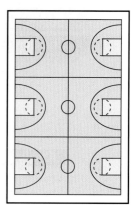

Analyze

The gym is rectangular. To find the area a rectangle covers, you multiply the length by the width. You know the area and the width of the gym and need to find its length.

Choose

You can *write an equation* for the area of the rectangle. Begin with the formula for the area of a rectangle. Use the numbers you know to find the missing number.

Solve

You find the area of a rectangle by multiplying its length by its width.

$A = l \times w$ Write the formula.
$18{,}700 = l \times 110$ Use the numbers you know.
$l = 18{,}700 \div 110$ Write a related division equation.
$l = 170$

So, the length of the gym should be 170 feet.

Check

Place your answer in the original equation.

$A = l \times w$
$A = 170 \times 110$
$A = 18{,}700$

The product matches the information in the problem.

Problem Solving Practice

1. A rectangular box of crackers has a volume of 128 cubic inches. The area of its base is 16 square inches. What is the height of the box?
   $128 = 16 \times h$, or $128 \div 16 = h$; $h = 8$ in.

2. The perimeter of an isosceles triangle is 70 cm. The sides of equal length each measure 28 cm. What is the length of the unknown side? **$70 = 28 + 28 + s$, or $70 - 56 = s$, $s = 14$ cm**

Use Logical Reasoning

Analyze
Choose
Solve
Check

Christine, Elizabeth, and Sharon like different sports. One girl likes to snow ski, one likes to run track, and the other likes to swim. Elizabeth is a good friend of the girl who likes track. Sharon is shorter than the girl who likes to ski. Elizabeth does not like cold weather. Which girl likes which sport?

Analyze

You know that there are three girls and that each one likes a different sport. Clues will help you determine which girl likes which sport.

Choose

You can *use logical reasoning* to solve this problem.

Solve

Make a table. List the sports and the names of the friends. Work with the clues one at a time. Write "yes" in a box if the clue applies to that girl. Write "no" in a box if the clue does not apply. Only one box in each row and column can have a "yes" in it.

a. Elizabeth is a good friend of the girl who likes track, so Elizabeth does not run track. Write "no" in the appropriate box.

	ski	track	swim
Christine	yes	no	no
Elizabeth	no	no	yes
Sharon	no	yes	no

b. Sharon is shorter than the girl who likes to ski, so Sharon does not ski. Write "no" in the appropriate box.

c. Elizabeth does not like cold weather. Write "no" in the appropriate box. With the other sports eliminated, Elizabeth must be the person who likes to swim. Write "yes" in the appropriate box. For Christine and Sharon, write "no" in each box under *swim*.

So, Christine likes to snow ski, Sharon likes track, and Elizabeth likes to swim.

Check

Compare your answers to the clues in the problem. Make sure none of your conclusions conflict with the clues.

Problem Solving Practice

Mike: 3-cheese;
Brent: sausage;
Tim: pepperoni

• Brent, Michael, and Tim always order their favorite pizzas: pepperoni, three-cheese, and sausage. Brent is allergic to pepperoni. Tim is going to see a movie with the boy who loves sausage. Mike does not like meat on his pizza. Which kind of pizza does each boy order?

Focus on Problem Solving 11

Analyze
Choose
Solve
Check

Compare Strategies

Mrs. Hagen is eager to plant her spring garden. She wants to plant 24 tomato plants in a rectangular array. For each plant, there will be a 1-foot square of space. How many different arrays can she make?

Analyze

There are 24 plants to be put into a rectangular array. You need to find how many arrays are possible.

Choose

Lexi and Jake use different strategies to solve this problem. Lexi chooses to *draw a diagram*, and Jake chooses to *write an equation*.

Solve

Lexi's Way: Draw a Diagram

Lexi uses graph paper to draw diagrams of rectangles to show all possible arrays. Each rectangle represents a garden that covers 24 square feet. The rectangles are 1 × 24, 2 × 12, 3 × 8, and 4 × 6.

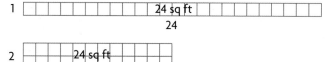
1   24 sq ft
24

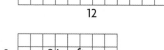
2   24 sq ft
12

3   24 sq ft
8

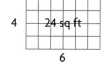
4   24 sq ft
6

Jake's Way: Write an Equation

Jake uses the equation $A = l \times w$ for finding the area of a rectangle to identify the different rectangles that could be formed. Each length and width needs to be a whole number.

$A = l \times w$ **Think:** What
$24 = 1 \times 24$ are the factors
$24 = 2 \times 12$ of 24?
$24 = 3 \times 8$
$24 = 4 \times 6$

So, Lexi and Jake both find that Mrs. Hagen can choose from four rectangular arrays.

Check

Lexi can do the problem Jake's way, and Jake can try it Lexi's way.

Problem Solving Practice

1. Mr. Sargent is buying math games for his class. One game costs $2.95, one costs $3.75, and one costs $6.00. He wants 6 of each game for his class. What is the total cost of these games? **$76.20**

2. How many triangles are in the figure at the right? **25**

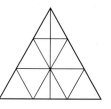

Analyze
Choose
Solve
Check

Multistep Problems

The Enrichment Program Committee at the Franklin School orders 500 T-shirts to sell at the school Field Day. Each T-shirt costs the school $4.20 and sells for $13.50. All 500 T-shirts are sold. After paying for the T-shirts, the school has reached its goal of raising $4,000. How much money has the school made?

Look at the facts in the problem. T-shirts cost $4.20 each and sell for $13.50. The committee orders and sells 500 T-shirts. You need to find how much money has been made after the costs are deducted. You know your answer should be at least $4,000.

One Way

First subtract to find how much the school has made on each T-shirt.

money earned on 1 T-shirt: $13.50 − $4.20 = $9.30

Then multiply to find the total earned.

money earned on 500 T-shirts: $9.30 × 500 = $4,650

Another Way

Find the total sales and subtract the total cost.

Total sales: 500 × $13.50 = $6,750

Total cost: 500 × $4.20 = $2,100

Total earned = $6,750 − $2,100 = $4,650

So, the school has made $4,650 on the sale of the T-shirts.

Problem Solving Practice

1. At the school Field Day, frozen yogurt cones sell for $2.25. Lin buys one for herself and one for each of her 4 friends. How much change does she get back from $20? **$8.75**

2. Fran is making a cabinet for her shell collection. She buys 3 boards at $2.75 each and 4 hinges at $0.99 each. What is the total cost of the supplies? **$12.21**

3. Mrs. Smith bought bread for $0.98, eggs for $1.17, ground turkey for $3.18, and 3 bunches of carrots for $0.65 each. She gave the clerk $10.03. How much change should Mrs. Smith receive? **$2.75**

Focus on Problem Solving 13

Teaching Notes

Additional Ideas:

Good Questions to Ask:

Additional Resources:

Notes for Next Time:

UNIT 1 Number Sense and Operations

UNIT AT A GLANCE

Assessment Options

What types of assessment are available?

Assessing Prior Knowledge

Determine whether students have the required prerequisite concepts and skills.

Check What You Know, PE pp. 15, 35, 51, 65

Test Preparation

Provide review and practice for chapter and standardized tests.

Cumulative Review, PE pp. 33, 49, 63, 85

Mixed Review and Test Prep
See the last page of each PE skill lesson.

Study Guide and Review, PE pp. 88–89

Formal Assessment

Assess students' mastery of chapter concepts and skills.

Chapter Review/Test
PE pp. 32, 48, 62, 84

Pretest and Posttest Options
Chapter Test, Form A
pp. AG9–10, 13–14, 17–18, 21–22
Chapter Test, Form B
pp. AG11–12, 15–16, 19–20, 23–24

Unit 1 Test • Chapters 1–4, pp. AG25–32

Harcourt Electronic Test System Math Practice and Assessment

Make and grade chapter tests electronically.

This software includes:

• **multiple-choice items**
• **free-response items**
• **customizable tests**
• **the means to make your own tests**

Daily Assessment

Obtain daily feedback on students' understanding of concepts.

Quick Review
See the first page of each PE lesson.

Mixed Review and Test Prep
See the last page of each PE skill lesson.

Number of the Day
See the first page of each TE skill lesson.

Problem of the Day
See the first page of each TE skill lesson.

Lesson Quiz
See the *Assess* section of each TE skill lesson.

Performance Assessment

Assess students' understanding of concepts applied to real-world situations.

Performance Assessment (Tasks A–B)
pp. PA3–4

Student Self-Assessment

Have students evaluate their own work.

How Did I Do?, p. AGxvii

A Guide to My Math Portfolio, p. AGxix

Math Journal
See **Write** in the *Assess* section of each TE skill lesson and TE pages 16B, 40B, 58B, 74.

Portfolio

Portfolio opportunities appear throughout the Pupil and Teacher's Editions.

Suggested work samples:

Problem Solving Project, TE pp. 14, 34, 50, 64

Write About It, PE pp. 19, 29, 39, 47, 61, 69

Chapter Review/Test, PE pp. 32, 48, 62, 84

KEY AG Assessment Guide   **TE** Teacher's Edition
PA Performance Assessment   **PE** Pupil Edition

How does the Unit 1 content correlate to standardized tests and California Mathematics Content Standards?

			STANDARDIZED TESTS					CALIFORNIA MATHEMATICS STANDARDS
LEARNING GOAL	**TAUGHT IN LESSONS**	**CAT**	**CTBS/ TERRA NOVA**	**ITBS**	**MAT**	**SAT**	
1A To write whole number estimates	1.1	●	●	●	●	●	
1B To write whole number sums, differences, products, and quotients	1.2, 1.3	●	●	●	●	●	NS 2.0 ⊙━ NS 2.3
1C To evaluate expressions, and to use mental math to solve equations involving addition, subtraction, multiplication, or division	1.5, 1.6	●	●	●	●	●	AF 1.0 AF 1.2
1D To solve problems by using an appropriate problem solving strategy such as *predict and test*	1.4				●		MR 2.0
2A To write whole number sums, differences, products, and quotients using number properties and mental math	2.1	●	●	●	●	●	
2B To evaluate expressions using exponents	2.2	●	●	●	●	●	
2C To evaluate expressions using order of operations	2.3, 2.4	●	●	●	●	●	AF 1.0
2D To solve problems by using an appropriate problem solving skill such as *sequence and prioritize information*	2.5	●	●	●	●	●	MR 1.1
3A To write, compare, and order decimals	3.1, 3.2	●	●	●	●	●	⊙━ NS 1.0 ⊙━ NS 1.1
3B To write estimates of decimal sums, differences, products, and quotients	3.3	●	●	●	●	●	⊙━ NS 2.0
3C To write decimals as percents and percents as decimals	3.4	●	●				⊙━ NS 1.4
3D To solve problems by using an appropriate problem solving strategy such as *make a table*	3.2		●				MR 2.0 MR 2.4
4A To write sums, differences, products, and quotients of decimals	4.1, 4.2, 4.3, 4.4	●	●	●	●	●	⊙━ NS 2.0
4B To evaluate expressions and use mental math to solve equations involving decimals	4.6		●			●	⊙━ NS 1.2
4C To solve problems by using an appropriate skill such as *interpret the remainder*	4.5	●	●	●	●	●	MR 2.0

Technology Links

🌐 The Harcourt Learning Site

Visit The Harcourt Learning Site for related links, activities, and resources:

- Exponents and order of operations activity *(Use with Chapter 2.)*
- *Animated Math Glossary*
- E-Lab interactive learning experiences
- current events stories that feature mathematics
- professional development and instructional resources

www.harcourtschool.com

Harcourt Math Newsroom Videos

These videos bring exciting news events to your classroom from the leaders in news broadcasting. For each unit, there is a **Harcourt Math Newsroom Video** that helps students see the relevance of math concepts to their lives. You may wish to use the data and concepts shown in the video for real-life problem solving or class projects.

TECHNOLOGY CORRELATION

Intervention Strategies and Activities This CD-ROM helps you assess students' knowledge of prerequisite concepts and skills.

Mighty Math CD-ROM Series includes *Calculating Crew, Number Heroes,* and *Astro Algebra.* These provide levels of difficulty that increase from A up to Z.

E-Lab is a collection of electronic learning activities.

The chart below correlates technology activities to specific lessons.

LESSON	ACTIVITY/LEVEL	SKILL
1.1	**Calculating Crew** • *Nautical Number Line,* Levels C, H **Harcourt Math Newsroom Video** • *Weather-Stacked Stadium*	Estimate with whole numbers
1.2	**Number Heroes** • *Quizzo,* Levels L, M	Use addition and subtraction
1.3	**Number Heroes** • *Quizzo,* Levels S, U, Y **Calculating Crew** • *Nick Knack,* Level V	Use multiplication and division
1.5	**Astro Algebra** • *Red,* Level J	Use expressions
1.6	**Astro Algebra** • *Red,* Level E	Use mental math and equations
2.2	**Astro Algebra** • *Red,* Level S	Use exponents
2.3	**E-Lab** • *Order of Operations* **Astro Algebra** • *Red,* Level B	Use order of operations
2.4	**Astro Algebra** • *Red,* Level B	Use order of operations
3.1	**Calculating Crew** • *Nautical Number Line,* Levels O, P	Represent, compare, and order decimals
4.1	**Calculating Crew** • *Nautical Number Line,* Level R	Add and subtract decimals
4.2	**Calculating Crew** • *Nautical Number Line,* Level U	Multiply decimals
4.3	**E-Lab** • *Exploring Division of Decimals*	Divide decimals
4.4	**Number Heroes** • *Quizzo,* Level W	Divide decimals

Intervention Strategies and Activities

Review and practice the prerequisite skills for Chapters 1–4.

E-LAB These interactive learning experiences reinforce and extend the skills taught in Chapters 1–4.

• Skill development   • Practice

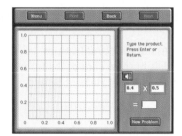

Mighty Math

The learning activities in this comprehensive math software series complement, enrich, and enhance the Pupil Edition lessons.

Calculating Crew

• *Nautical Number Line*
• *Nick Knack*

Number Heroes • *Quizzo*

Astro Algebra • *Red*

For the Teacher

Teacher Support Software

• **Intervention Strategies and Activities** Provide instruction, practice, and a check of the prerequisite skills for each chapter.

• **Electronic Lesson Planner** Quickly prepare daily and weekly lessons for all subject areas.

• **Harcourt Electronic Test System**
Math Practice and Assessment Edit and customize Chapter Tests or construct unique tests from large item banks.

For the Parent

The Harcourt Learning Site

• Encourage parents to visit The Harcourt Learning Site to help them reinforce mathematics vocabulary, concepts, and skills with their children.

• Have them click on *Math* for vocabulary, activities, real-life connections, and homework tips for Chapters 1–4.

www.harcourtschool.com

Internet

Teachers can find number sense and operations activities and resources.

Students can learn more about exponents and order of operations and reinforce the critical concepts and skills for Chapters 1–4.

Parents can use The Harcourt Learning Site's resources to help their children with the vocabulary, concepts, and skills needed for Chapters 1–4.

Visit The Harcourt Learning Site
www.harcourtschool.com

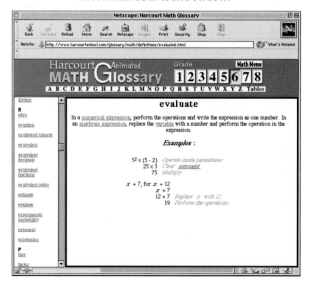

Reaching All Learners

ADVANCED LEARNERS

MATERIALS *For each pair* number lines, p. TR12

Challenge students to **compare and order decimals.** Display the following:

What hundredth is closest to 0.507? 0.51
What hundredth is closest to 0.528? 0.53
What hundredth is closest to 0.513? 0.51

Ask students to show where each decimal is placed on the number line. Then ask them to write the answer to each question. Challenge students to create a similar set of questions for a number line with decimals 0.74, 0.75, 0.76, 0.77. *Use with Lesson 3.1.*

VISUAL

SPECIAL NEEDS

MATERIALS *For each pair* decimal models (tenths), p. TR6; decimal models (hundredths), p. TR7; markers or colored pencils

To help students **understand decimal values,** ask them to shade a pair of decimal models to show each of the following statements. Then have them complete each statement by writing < or >.

0.23 ● 0.3 <   0.62 ● 0.08 >   0.5 ● 0.05 >

Have a volunteer read each statement aloud. Ask students to write and illustrate three more comparison statements. *Use with Lessons 3.1 or 3.4.*

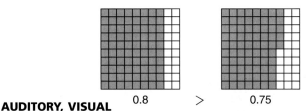

0.8   >   0.75

AUDITORY, VISUAL

BLOCK SCHEDULING

INTERDISCIPLINARY COURSES

- Astronomy—Relate writing large numbers, such as distance or volume, to scientific notation.

- Social Studies—Round large numbers to a reasonable place value in order to compare population data quickly.

- Physical Fitness—Use historical Olympic data to compare and order Olympic finish times for various events.

- Health Education—Explore the percents noted on the sides of common food packaging.

COMPLETE UNIT

Unit 1 may be presented in
- fourteen 90-minute blocks.
- seventeen 75-minute blocks.

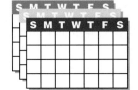

INTERDISCIPLINARY SUGGESTIONS

PURPOSE To connect *Number Sense and Operations* to other subjects with these activities

CHAPTER 1 — Social Studies

Students round numbers to compare data. First students find and round the area of each state in the United States to the nearest thousand. Then they sort the states into three categories by size.

CHAPTER 3 — Earth Science

Students research the largest earthquakes recorded in the twentieth century. They then make a table listing the earthquakes by magnitude from least to greatest based on the Richter Scale (for example: Japan—7.7, Peru—7.8, India—8.7).

7.2 Earthquake Does Major Damage

VISUAL

EARLY FINISHERS

Students who finish their work early can

- make visual aids for lessons that teach the concept of decimal numbers, for comparing decimal values, and for adding, subtracting, and multiplying decimals.

- assemble and play the Practice Game. See *Decimal Challenge.*

- solve the *Problem of the Day.*
  Use with TE Skill lessons 1.1–4.6.

ENGLISH LANGUAGE LEARNERS ELL•SDAIE

VOCABULARY PREVIEW Have students make a three-column chart for the new vocabulary. In the first column, have them write the word and in the second column, what they think the word means. Then in the third column, have them record the definition they learn. *Use with Lessons 1.1–3.4.*

Word	What I Think It Means	Definition

NUMERICAL EXPRESSION Numerical expressions are to equations as phrases are to sentences. Have students give examples of each.

Use with Lesson 1.5.

ORDER OF OPERATIONS Review the meaning of the word *order* by discussing phrases such as "keeping things in order." *Use with Lesson 2.3.*

AUDITORY, VISUAL

PRACTICE GAME

Decimal Challenge

PURPOSE To add, subtract, and multiply decimals

MATERIALS *For each group* game cards, pp. TR76–77; spinner, p. TR71 (prepared as below); calculator

ABOUT THE GAME Players in small groups stack the cards face down. A facilitator spins for an operation and turns up 2 cards. Other players race to perform the operation while the facilitator checks the answers. The first player to answer correctly earns 1 point. Another player becomes the facilitator and repeats the process. Play continues until all players have served as the facilitator. The player with the most points wins. *Use with Lesson 4.2.*

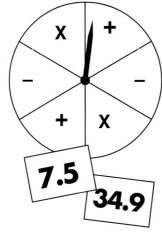

LITERATURE CONNECTIONS

These books provide students with additional ways to explore whole number and decimal applications and operations.

FROM THE MIXED-UP FILES OF MRS. BASIL E. FRANKWEILER by E. L. Konigsberg (Atheneum, 1987) tells of Claudia and James who run away from their "boring" home to the Museum of Natural History.

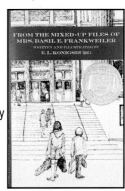

- Suppose Claudia and James stay away for a week and have $30. Have students devise a reasonable amount to spend per meal per person. Use with Lesson 1.3.

Not for a Billion, Gazillion Dollars by Paula Danziger (Delacorte Press, 1992) tells how Matthew learns about money management and friendship.

- Matthew saved $100 in coins. Have students decide if it is possible for him to have saved a total of 15,000, 1,000, or 800 coins. *Use with Lesson 4.6.*

Whole Number Applications

CHAPTER PLANNER

PACING OPTIONS	
Compacted	5 Days
Expanded	10 Days

Getting Ready for Chapter 1 • Assessing Prior Knowledge and INTERVENTION (See PE and TE page 15.)

LESSON	CALIFORNIA STANDARDS	PACING	VOCABULARY*	MATERIALS	RESOURCES AND TECHNOLOGY
1.1 Estimate with Whole Numbers pp. 16–19 **Objective** To use estimation strategies to find sums, differences, products, and quotients of whole numbers	NS 2.0 MR 2.0 (*Also* MR 2.4, MR 2.5)	2 Days	**clustering** **underestimate** **overestimate** compatible numbers		Reteach, Practice, Problem Solving, Challenge 1.1 Worksheets Extra Practice p. H32, Set A ▢ Transparency 1.1 ◉ **Calculating Crew** • *Nautical Number Line* ▭ **Harcourt Math Newsroom Video** • *Weather Stacked Stadium*
1.2 Use Addition and Subtraction pp. 20–21 **Objective** To use addition and subtraction of whole numbers to solve real-life problems	NS 2.0 MR 2.1 MR 3.1 (*Also* MR 2.7)	1 Day			Reteach, Practice, Problem Solving, Challenge 1.2 Worksheets Extra Practice p. H32, Set B ▢ Transparency 1.2 ◉ **Number Heroes** • *Quizzo*
1.3 Use Multiplication and Division pp. 22–25 **Objective** To use multiplication and division of whole numbers to solve real-life problems	NS 2.0 MR 2.1 MR 3.1 (*Also* MR 1.3, MR 2.7)	2 Days			Reteach, Practice, Problem Solving, Challenge 1.3 Worksheets Extra Practice p. H32, Set C ▢ Transparency 1.3 ◉ **Number Heroes** • *Quizzo* ◉ **Calculating Crew** • *Nick Knack* **Math Jingles™ CD 5-6** • *Track 4*
1.4 Problem Solving Strategy: *Predict and Test* pp. 26–27 **Objective** To use the strategy *predict and test* to solve addition, subtraction, multiplication, and division problems with whole numbers	NS 2.0 MR 3.2 (*Also* AF 3.1, MR 1.1, MR 1.3, MR 2.0, MR 2.7)	1 Day			Reteach, Practice, Reading Strategy, Challenge 1.4 Worksheets ▢ Transparency 1.4 Problem Solving Think Along, p. TR1
1.5 Algebra: Use Expressions pp. 28–29 **Objective** To identify, write, and evaluate numerical and algebraic expressions involving whole numbers	AF 1.0 (*Also* MR 2.4, MR 2.5)	1 Day	**numerical expression** **variable** **algebraic expression** **evaluate**		Reteach, Practice, Problem Solving, Challenge 1.5 Worksheets Extra Practice p. H32, Set D ▢ Transparency 1.5 ◉ **Astro Algebra** • *Red* **Math Jingles™ CD 5-6** • *Track 8*
1.6 Algebra: Mental Math and Equations pp. 30–31 **Objective** To solve equations with whole numbers by using mental math and substitution	NS 2.0, AF 1.0 AF 1.1 (*Also* NS 2.0, MR 2.5)	1 Day	**equation** **solution** variable		Reteach, Practice, Problem Solving, Challenge 1.6 Worksheets Extra Practice p. H32, Set E ▢ Transparency 1.6 ◉ **Astro Algebra** • *Red*

Ending Chapter 1 • Chapter 1 Review/Test, p. 32 • **Cumulative Review,** p. 33

*****Boldfaced** terms are new vocabulary. Other terms are review vocabulary.

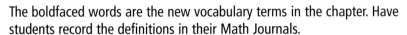

CHAPTER AT A GLANCE

Vocabulary Development

The boldfaced words are the new vocabulary terms in the chapter. Have students record the definitions in their Math Journals.

clustering, p. 16

underestimate, p. 17

overestimate, p. 17

numerical expression, p. 28

variable, p. 28

algebraic expression, p. 28

evaluate, p. 28

equation, p. 30

solution, p. 30

clustering

Vocabulary Cards
Have students use the Vocabulary Cards on *Teacher's Resource Book pp. 117–120* to make graphic organizers or word puzzles. The cards can also be added to a file of mathematics terms.

Writing Opportunities

PUPIL EDITION	TEACHER'S EDITION	ASSESSMENT GUIDE
• **Write About It,** pp. 19, 29	• **Write**—See the *Assess* section of each TE lesson.	• **How Did I Do?,** p. AGxvii
• **Write a Problem,** p. 21	• **Writing in Mathematics,** p. 16B	
• **What's the Error?,** p. 25		
• **What's the Question?,** pp. 27, 31		

Family Involvement Activities

These activities provide:

• Letter to the Family

• Information about California Standards

• Math Vocabulary

• Family Game

• Practice (Homework)

HARCOURT MATH	Name
GRADE 6	Date
Chapter I	
WHAT WE ARE LEARNING	**Dear Family,**
Whole Number Applications	Your child will be working on estimating, numerical and algebraic expressions, and solving equations. Discuss with your child how you use estimating and mental math on a day-to-day basis to solve problems.
VOCABULARY	Problem: You need gasoline, but you only have $10.00. Gasoline costs $1.25 per gallon. How many gallons can you buy?
Here are some of the vocabulary words we use in class:	Ask questions such as these as you work together:
Numerical expression A mathematical phrase that uses only numbers and operation symbols	• **What do you need to figure out?** Your child might say: How many gallons of gas can I buy with $10.00?
Variable A letter or symbol that stands for one or more numbers	• **What do you need to know to figure out the answer?** Your child might say: I need to know how much money I have and how much gasoline costs.
Algebraic expression An expression that includes at least one variable	• **What kind of mathematical operation can you use to solve it?** I can multiply the number of gallons I buy by $1.25 to get $10.00, the amount I will spend.
Evaluate The process of finding the value of a numerical expression or an algebraic expression	• **How can you write that idea as an algebraic equation?** Your child might answer: $1.25 × n = $10.00 where n is the number of gallons that I can purchase.
Equation A statement showing that two quantities are equal	• **How do you solve the equation using mental math?** Your child might say: I try values for the variable n until I find a value that makes the equation true. The solution is 8 because $1.25 × 8 = $10.00.
	Use this model and the exercises that follow this page to help your child practice estimating and computing with whole numbers, evaluating expressions, and using mental math to compute and to solve equations.
	Sincerely,
The California Math Standards Your child's **Harcourt Math** book lists the California Math Standards that are taught in every lesson. If you have questions about the standards, be sure to consult *California Standards for Grade 6* that was sent home at the beginning of the school year.	

Family Involvement Activities, p. FA1

California Mathematics Content Standards for Grade 6

Strands

Number Sense

Lesson 1.1: ⊶ NS 2.0

Lesson 1.2: ⊶ NS 2.0

Lesson 1.3: ⊶ NS 2.0

Lesson 1.4: ⊶ NS 2.0

Lesson 1.5: ⊶ NS 2.0

Lesson 1.6: ⊶ NS 2.0

Algebra and Functions

Lesson 1.4: AF 3.1

Lesson 1.5: AF 1.0

Lesson 1.6: AF 1.0, ⊶ 1.1

Measurement and Geometry

Statistics, Data Analysis, and Probability

Mathematical Reasoning

Lesson 1.1: MR 2.0, 2.4, 2.5

Lesson 1.2: MR 2.1, 2.7, 3.1

Lesson 1.3: MR 1.3, 2.1, 2.7, 3.1

Lesson 1.4: MR 1.1, 1.3, 2.0, 2.7, 3.2

Lesson 1.5: MR 2.4, 2.5

Lesson 1.6: MR 2.5

Whole Number Applications

MATHEMATICS ACROSS THE GRADES

SKILLS TRACE ACROSS THE GRADES

GRADE 5	GRADE 6	GRADE 7
Estimate sums, differences, products, and quotients; find sums and differences; multiply by 2-digit numbers; divide by 2-digit divisors; evaluate and write whole number expressions	Write whole number estimates, sums, differences, products, and quotients; evaluate expressions with whole numbers and use mental math to solve 1-step equations	Write and evaluate numerical and algebraic expressions; solve multiple step equations; solve inequalities

SKILLS TRACE FOR GRADE 6

LESSON	FIRST INTRODUCED	TAUGHT AND PRACTICED	TESTED	REVIEWED
1.1	Grade 4	PE pp. 16–19, H32, p. RW1, p. PW1, p. PS1	PE p. 32, pp. AG9–12	PE pp. 32, 33, 88–89
1.2	Grade 4	PE pp. 20–21, H32, p. RW2, p. PW2, p. PS2	PE p. 32, pp. AG9–12	PE pp. 32, 33, 88–89
1.3	Grade 4	PE pp. 22–25, H32, p. RW3, p. PW3, p. PS3	PE p. 32, pp. AG9–12	PE pp. 32, 33, 88–89
1.4	Grade 4	PE pp. 26–27, p. RW4, p. PW4, p. PS4	PE p. 32, pp. AG9–12	PE pp. 32, 33, 88–89
1.5	Grade 5	PE pp. 28–29, H32, p. RW5, p. PW5, p. PS5	PE p. 32, pp. AG9–12	PE pp. 32, 33, 88–89
1.6	Grade 5	PE pp. 30–31, H32, p. RW6, p. PW6, p. PS6	PE p. 32, pp. AG9–12	PE pp. 32, 33, 88–89

KEY   **PE**   Pupil Edition   **PS**   Problem Solving Workbook   **RW**   Reteach Workbook
       PW   Practice Workbook   **AG**   Assessment Guide

Looking Back Prerequisite Skills

To be ready for Chapter 1, students should have the following understandings and skills:

- **Vocabulary**—Factor, *product, divisor, dividend, sum, difference*

- **Place Value of Whole Numbers**—name place value to hundred billions

- **Round Whole Numbers**—round to nearest thousand or ten-thousand

Check What You Know

Use page 15 to determine students' knowledge of prerequisite concepts and skills.

Intervention

Help students prepare for the chapter by using the intervention resources described on TE page 15.

Looking at Chapter 1 Essential Skills

- develop skill and accuracy with whole number operations.
- use the strategy *predict and test* to solve problems.
- understand the function of variables in algebraic expressions.
- make the connection between word expressions and algebraic and numerical expressions.
- **develop skill in solving equations with one variable by using mental math.**

EXAMPLE

Solve. $n + 6 = 13$

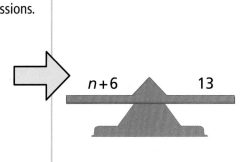

Think what number plus 6 is 13.

$7 + 6 = 13$

So, $n = 7$.

Looking Ahead Applications

Students will apply what they learn in Chapter 1 to the following new concepts:

- Operations with Decimals (Chapter 4)
- Writing Expressions (Chapter 14)
- Operations with Integers (Chapters 12 and 13)
- Solving Equations (Chapters 15 and 16)

Whole Number Applications

INTRODUCING THE CHAPTER

Tell students that operations with whole numbers and estimation are often used to compare data. Have students formulate a question about the photograph that can be answered by applying what they know about whole numbers. Possible answer: Using estimation, what is the total number of hours for the five shuttle missions shown on the graph? about 1,000 hr

USING DATA

To begin the study of this chapter, have students

* Write a number sentence to tell the total length of the three shortest missions to the nearest day. $1 + 5 + 8 = 14$ days

* Determine which missions had a combined length of time almost equal to the length of the 1996 mission. STS-1, STS-9 and STS-34

* Display the data in the graph in another way. Check students' work.

PROBLEM SOLVING PROJECT

Purpose To use whole numbers to solve a problem

Grouping pairs or small groups

Background The longest space shuttle flight (through 1/1/98) was STS-80, which lasted 423 hr, 53 min, 18 sec from Nov. 19–Dec. 7, 1996.

Analyze, Choose, Solve, and Check

Have students

* Research the five longest space shuttle flights.

* Make a table with the mission dates, the length of the missions rounded to the nearest day, and the total distance each traveled.

* Write a summary of the data by describing how the lengths and distances of the missions compare to each other.

Check students' work.

Suggest that students place the tables and summaries in their portfolios.

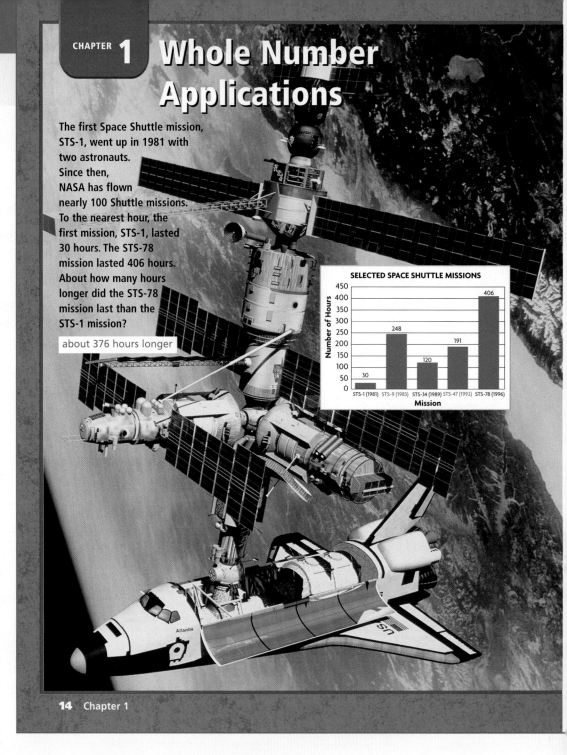

CHAPTER 1 **Whole Number Applications**

The first Space Shuttle mission, STS-1, went up in 1981 with two astronauts. Since then, NASA has flown nearly 100 Shuttle missions. To the nearest hour, the first mission, STS-1, lasted 30 hours. The STS-78 mission lasted 406 hours. About how many hours longer did the STS-78 mission last than the STS-1 mission?

about 376 hours longer

SELECTED SPACE SHUTTLE MISSIONS

(bar graph: Number of Hours vs Mission)
- STS-1 (1981): 30
- STS-9 (1983): 248
- STS-34 (1989): 120
- STS-47 (1992): 191
- STS-78 (1996): 406

14 Chapter 1

Why learn math? Explain that astronauts and support staff use whole number operations to determine all kinds of essential information they need to travel successfully through space. For example, they need to know how long their oxygen supply can last, how much the payload weighs, and how much food they will need to bring for specific missions. Ask: What other ways do you think astronauts use math? Possible answer: to determine how much fuel they will need for maneuvering in space; how long it will take to perform mission experiments; landing time adjustments in case of bad weather

Estimate with Whole Numbers

LESSON PLANNING

Objective To use estimation strategies to find sums, differences, products, and quotients of whole numbers

Intervention for Prerequisite Skills

Place Value of Whole Numbers, Round Whole Numbers (For intervention strategies, see page 15.)

 ### California Mathematics Content Standards

NS 2.0 Students calculate and solve problems involving addition, subtraction, multiplication, and division.

MR 2.0 Students use strategies, skills, and concepts in finding solutions.

(*Also* MR 2.4, MR 2.5)

Vocabulary

clustering a method used in estimation when all addends have about the same value

underestimate an estimate that is less than the exact answer

overestimate an estimate that is greater than the exact answer

Math Background

Estimation is a powerful tool that students can use to verify that answers are reasonable or to solve problems when exact answers are not needed. Students may choose from the following estimation techniques:

- rounding, used in addition, subtraction, and multiplication, where numbers are rounded to a specified place value before computation occurs.

- clustering, used when numbers in a group that are being added are near a single value, where numbers are rounded to the common value.

- compatible numbers, used in finding a quotient, where numbers are rounded to values that can be easily divided.

WARM-UP RESOURCES

 ### NUMBER OF THE DAY
 Transparency **1.1**

Take the number of the year you were born. Round it to the nearest 10, 100, and 1,000. 1990, 2000, 2000

 ### PROBLEM OF THE DAY
 Transparency **1.1**

Find the three-digit number that rounds to 440 and includes a digit that is the quotient of $24 \div 3$. Is there more than one possible answer? Explain. 438; No. The numbers that round to 440 are 435–444 and $24 \div 3 = 8$. Only one of those numbers has 8 as a digit.

Solution Problem of the Day tab, p. PD1A

 ### DAILY FACTS PRACTICE

Have students practice addition facts by completing Set A of *Teacher's Resource Book*, p. TR93.

Check What You Know

Use this page to help you review and remember important skills needed for Chapter 1.

 Vocabulary

Choose the best term from the box.

	factor
	difference
	dividend
	divisor
	product
	sum

1. In $8 \times 3 = 24$, the ___?___ is 24. **product**

2. In $48 \div 12 = 4$, the ___?___ is 12. **divisor**

3. In $40 - 30 = 10$, the ___?___ is 10. **difference**

4. In $4\overline{)412}$, the ___?___ is 412. **dividend**

5. In $3 + 8 + 5 = 16$, the ___?___ is 16. **sum**

Place Value of Whole Numbers (See p. H3.)

Name the place value of the digit 8.

6. 56,485,013
   ten thousands
7. 2,403,815
   hundreds
8. 4,568,137
   thousands
9. 423,859,100
   hundred thousands
10. 207,108,629
    thousands
11. 813,593,005
    hundred millions
12. 375,178,955,276
    millions
13. 351,480,994,133
    ten millions
14. 748,630,123,944
    billions

Give the value of the blue digit.

15. 321,497,580 90,000 or
    9 ten thousands
16. 321,497,580 500 or
    5 hundreds
17. 321,497,580 300,000,000
    or 3 hundred millions
18. 628,705,814,956
    5,000,000 or 5 millions
19. 628,705,814,956
    20,000,000,000 or
    2 ten billions
20. 628,705,814,956
    800,000 or 8 hundred
    thousands

Round Whole Numbers (See p. H4.)

Round to the nearest thousand.

21. 2,467 2,000
22. 5,609 6,000
23. 28,500 29,000
24. 299   0
25. 34,831 35,000
26. 19,089 19,000
27. 6,136 6,000
28. 43,712 44,000
29. 134,612 135,000
30. 217,501 218,000
31. 59,832 60,000
32. 539,513 540,000

Round to the nearest ten thousand.

33. 51,677 50,000
34. 228,260 230,000
35. 12,435 10,000
36. 78,562 80,000
37. 639,108 640,000
38. 40,500 40,000
39. 90,499 90,000
40. 381,810 380,000

> **LOOK AHEAD**
>
> **In Chapter 1 you will**
> - estimate and compute with whole numbers
> - evaluate expressions
> - use mental math to compute and to solve equations

Assessing Prior Knowledge

Use the **Check What You Know** page to determine whether your students have mastered the prerequisite skills critical for this chapter.

Intervention

- **Diagnose and Prescribe**

  Evaluate your students' performance on this page to determine whether intervention is necessary. **How to Help Options** that provide instruction, practice, and a check are listed in the chart below.

- **Review Prerequisite Skills**

  The following resources provide a review for the prerequisite vocabulary and skills.

  Option 1—Check What You Know, Pupil Edition p. 15

  Option 2—Troubleshooting, Pupil Edition pp. H3–4

TEACHER'S NOTES

Check What You Know
INTERVENTION • Diagnose and Prescribe

Prerequisite Skill	Items (Pupil Edition p. 15)	How to Help Options
☑ Place Value of Whole Numbers	6–20	• **Troubleshooting, Pupil Edition p. H3** • **Intervention Strategies and Activities** Card, Copying Master, or CD-ROM • **Skill 1**
☑ Round Whole Numbers	21–40	• **Troubleshooting, Pupil Edition p. H4** • **Intervention Strategies and Activities** Card, Copying Master, or CD-ROM • **Skill 2**

INTERVENTION AND EXTENSION RESOURCES

ALTERNATIVE TEACHING STRATEGY (ELL)

Ask students to **practice estimating with whole numbers.** Have students round to the nearest ten to estimate the total annual energy cost for the use of these appliances. $400 Then have them estimate the annual cost for all the families in the class. Estimates will vary.

Appliance	Average Annual Energy Cost
Washer/Dryer	$77
Color TV	$22
Range/Oven	$42
Refrigerator/Freezer	$239
Microwave oven	$7
Dishwasher	$12

See also page 18.

VISUAL

MIXED REVIEW AND TEST PREP

Cumulative Review Grade 5

Refer to the Grade 5 Pupil Edition pages for further review.

Mixed Review and Test Prep, p. 19

How to Help	
Item	Page
56	Grade 5
57	Grade 5
58	Grade 5
59	Grade 5
60	Grade 5

CAREER CONNECTION

Explain that a journalist is a writer or editor for a newspaper or magazine. Have students **write newspaper headlines that include exact numbers and estimates.** Two examples are given.

TEMPERATURES REACH A RECORD-BREAKING HIGH OF 102°F
exact

MORE THAN 2,000 TURN OUT FOR MEMORIAL DAY PARADE
estimate

Check students' work.

VISUAL

WRITING IN MATHEMATICS

Reinforce the concept of estimating whole numbers by having students complete the following activity. Ask students to work in pairs to write problems that use the populations per square mile of these cities. Then have students exchange papers and have their partners estimate the answers.

City	Population
Cairo	97,106
Hong Kong	237,501
New York City	24,089
Bangkok	58,379
Bombay	127,461

TECHNOLOGY LINK

 Intervention Strategies and Activities CD-ROM • *Skills 1, 2*

 Calculating Crew • *Nautical Number Line,* Levels C, H

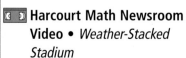 **Harcourt Math Newsroom Video •** *Weather-Stacked Stadium*

Objective To use estimation strategies to find sums, differences, products, and quotients of whole numbers

Vocabulary clustering, underestimate, overestimate *Review* compatible numbers

1 Introduce

provides review of prerequisite skills.

Why Learn This? You can use this skill to solve problems that do not need an exact answer, such as estimating the distance a flying disc is thrown. *Share the lesson objective with students.*

2 Teach

Guided Instruction

• *Discuss with students the accuracy of the estimate 460 ft at the top of page 16.*

If you rounded the addends to the nearest hundred, what would your estimate be? 400 ft

Find the exact answer. 465 ft

Which estimate is closer? 460 ft

• *Lead students to draw a conclusion about rounding and the accuracy of an estimate.*

How does the place you round to affect the accuracy of the estimate? Rounding to numbers with a lesser place value results in a more accurate estimate.

ADDITIONAL EXAMPLE

Example 1, p. 16

Use clustering to estimate the sum.

$$
\begin{array}{r}
5,889 \\
6,019 \\
+5,999 \\
\end{array}
$$

The sum is about 18,000.

See also page 17.

LESSON **1.1**

Estimate with Whole Numbers

Learn how to estimate sums, differences, products, and quotients of whole numbers.

1. 30 + 40 70
2. 25 + 60 85
3. 70 − 20 50
4. 100 − 45 55
5. 1,200 + 1,200 + 1,200 3,600

Vocabulary
clustering
underestimate
overestimate

Remember that when rounding, you look at the digit to the right of the place to which you are rounding.
• If that digit is 5 or greater, round up.
• If that digit is less than 5, round down.

The longest throw of a flying disc was 656 ft 2 in., made by Scott Stokely in 1995. Carmen, David, and Leona each threw a disc. Is the total distance of the three throws close to the record distance?

You don't need an exact sum to answer the question, so estimate.

$$
\begin{array}{rcl}
134 & \rightarrow & 130 \\
148 & \rightarrow & 150 \\
+183 & \rightarrow & +180 \\
\hline
& & 460 \\
\end{array}
$$

Round each number to the nearest ten.

NAME	DISTANCE
David	134 ft
Leona	148 ft
Carmen	183 ft

The estimate, 460, is not close to the record distance of 656 ft, so the total distance is not close either.

Use **clustering** to estimate a sum when the addends are about the same.

EXAMPLE 1

Estimate 1,802 + 2,182 + 1,999.

$$
\begin{array}{r}
1,802 \\
2,182 \\
+1,999 \\
\end{array}
$$

The three addends all cluster around 2,000, so use 2,000 for each number.

$3 \times 2,000 = 6,000$ *Multiply.*

So, the sum is about 6,000.

You can use rounding to estimate a difference.

EXAMPLE 2

Estimate 31,928 − 20,915.

Round to the nearest ten thousand.	*Round to the nearest thousand.*
$\begin{array}{r} 30,000 \\ -20,000 \\ \hline 10,000 \end{array}$	$\begin{array}{r} 32,000 \\ -21,000 \\ \hline 11,000 \end{array}$

So, both 10,000 and 11,000 are reasonable estimates.

16

RETEACH 1.1

Estimate with Whole Numbers

You can use compatible numbers to estimate a quotient. **Compatible numbers** are helpful to use because they divide without a remainder, are close to the actual numbers, and are easy to compute mentally.

Oakdale Middle School is collecting recycled cans. The school has set a goal of collecting 2,788 cans. There are 38 homerooms in the school. About how many cans should each homeroom collect for the school to reach its goal?

Because you are asked "about how many," an estimate is appropriate for the answer. Use compatible numbers to estimate.

Step 1: Look at the actual numbers that make up the problem. Think about numbers that are close to the real numbers that will divide without a remainder.

$2,788 \div 38$ → $2,800 \div 40$

Step 2: Divide.   → $2,800 \div 40 = 70$

So, each homeroom should collect about 70 cans.

Complete to show how compatible numbers are used to estimate the quotient.

1. $2,615 \div 47 \rightarrow 2,500 \div \underline{50} = \underline{50}$
2. $3,104 \div 62 \rightarrow 3,000 \div \underline{60} = \underline{50}$
3. $3,591 \div 88 \rightarrow \underline{3,600} \div 90 = \underline{40}$
4. $4,733 \div 74 \rightarrow 4,800 \div \underline{80} = \underline{60}$
5. $7,105 \div 77 \rightarrow \underline{7,200} \div 80 = \underline{90}$
6. $5,511 \div 62 \rightarrow 5,400 \div \underline{60} = \underline{90}$
7. $15,843 \div 381 \rightarrow 16,000 \div \underline{400} = \underline{40}$
8. $20,972 \div 287 \rightarrow 21,000 \div \underline{300} = \underline{70}$
9. $29,100 \div 307 \rightarrow \underline{30,000} \div 300 = \underline{100}$
10. $95,347 \div 795 \rightarrow 96,000 \div \underline{800} = \underline{120}$

Use compatible numbers to estimate the quotient. Possible estimates are given.

11. $434 \div 68$ __6__
12. $394 \div 5$ __80__
13. $448 \div 15$ __30__
14. $986 \div 102$ __10__
15. $627 \div 89$ __7__
16. $554 \div 63$ __9__
17. $293 \div 31$ __10__
18. $705 \div 97$ __7__
19. $1,246 \div 43$ __30__
20. $2,779 \div 28$ __100__
21. $3,896 \div 38$ __100__
22. $7,164 \div 78$ __90__

PRACTICE 1.1

Estimate with Whole Numbers

Vocabulary

1. When both factors in a multiplication problem are rounded up to estimate the product, the estimate is an __overestimate__.

2. When all addends are about the same, you can use __clustering__ to estimate their sum.

Estimate the sum or difference. Possible estimates are given.

3. $\begin{array}{r} 2,489 \\ 1,601 \\ +2,109 \\ \hline 6,000 \end{array}$
4. $\begin{array}{r} 398 \\ 415 \\ +368 \\ \hline 1,200 \end{array}$
5. $\begin{array}{r} 4,723 \\ +2,198 \\ \hline 6,900 \end{array}$
6. $\begin{array}{r} 7,132 \\ 6,594 \\ +7,301 \\ \hline 21,000 \end{array}$
7. $\begin{array}{r} 5,401 \\ +9,188 \\ \hline 14,600 \end{array}$

8. $\begin{array}{r} 478 \\ -26 \\ \hline 450 \end{array}$
9. $\begin{array}{r} 263 \\ -211 \\ \hline 50 \end{array}$
10. $\begin{array}{r} 5,877 \\ -5,318 \\ \hline 600 \end{array}$
11. $\begin{array}{r} 8,528 \\ -6,491 \\ \hline 2,000 \end{array}$
12. $\begin{array}{r} 8,903 \\ -4,575 \\ \hline 4,300 \end{array}$

Estimate the product or quotient. Possible estimates are given.

13. $\begin{array}{r} 53 \\ \times 8 \\ \hline 400 \end{array}$
14. $\begin{array}{r} 76 \\ \times 9 \\ \hline 720 \end{array}$
15. $\begin{array}{r} 72 \\ \times 28 \\ \hline 2,100 \end{array}$
16. $\begin{array}{r} 47 \\ \times 53 \\ \hline 2,500 \end{array}$
17. $\begin{array}{r} 660 \\ \times 42 \\ \hline 28,000 \end{array}$

18. $\begin{array}{r} 371 \\ \times 78 \\ \hline 32,000 \end{array}$
19. $\begin{array}{r} 68 \\ \times 37 \\ \hline 2,800 \end{array}$
20. $\begin{array}{r} 480 \\ \times 192 \\ \hline 100,000 \end{array}$
21. $\begin{array}{r} 375 \\ \times 591 \\ \hline 240,000 \end{array}$
22. $\begin{array}{r} 824 \\ \times 693 \\ \hline 560,000 \end{array}$

23. $331 \div 5$
24. $643 \div 7$
25. $1,827 \div 59$
26. $5,543 \div 77$
27. $9,165 \div 28$ __70__
28. $6,281 \div 875$ __70__
29. $7,118 \div 614$ __30__
30. $8,215 \div 897$ __70__
   __300__   __7__   __12__   __9__

Mixed Review

Round to the nearest 1,000.

31. $4,571$ __5,000__
32. $8,445$ __8,000__
33. $1,902$ __2,000__
34. $6,679$ __7,000__

Find the product.

35. $6 \times 6 \times 6$ __216__
36. $3 \times 3 \times 3 \times 3$ __81__
37. $4 \times 4 \times 4 \times 4$ __256__

You can show an estimate by using the "approximately equal to" symbol, ≈.

5,125 − 1,920 ≈ 3,000   *Read: 5,125 − 1,920 is approximately equal to 3,000.*

An estimate that is less than the exact answer is an **underestimate**.
An estimate that is greater than the exact answer is an **overestimate**.

366 +198 564 *Exact answer*	370 +200 *Round up.* 570 *Overestimate*
144 ×123 17,712 *Exact answer*	100 ×100 *Round down.* 10,000 *Underestimate*

EXAMPLE 3

Students set up 28 rows of 36 seats each for a talent show in the school cafeteria. About how many programs should the school print for the show?

Estimate 28 × 36. To make sure there are enough programs, find an overestimate.

Remember that compatible numbers are numbers that divide without a remainder, are close to the actual numbers, and are easy to compute with mentally.

$$\begin{array}{c}28 \\ \times 36\end{array} \rightarrow \begin{array}{c}30 \\ \times 40\end{array}$$ *Round each factor up to the nearest ten.*

$$\begin{array}{c}30 \\ \times 40 \\ \hline 1,200\end{array}$$ *Multiply. Because each factor is rounded up, the product is an overestimate.*

So, the school should print about 1,200 programs.

To estimate a quotient, use rounding or compatible numbers.

EXAMPLE 4

The employees of the Briar Creek office building have collected 1,545 lb of paper to be recycled. The building has 36 offices. About how many pounds of paper, on average, did the employees in each office collect?

Estimate 1,545 ÷ 36.

1,600 ÷ 40   *4 is compatible with 16, so use 1,600 ÷ 40.*
1,600 ÷ 40 = 40   *Divide.*

So, the employees in each office collected an average of about 40 lb.

- Is 1,488 ÷ 36 easier to estimate using rounding or compatible numbers? Explain. **Possible answer: Compatible numbers; 1,600 ÷ 40 is easier to compute than 1,500 ÷ 40.**

Math **I**dea ▶ Some of the strategies you can use to estimate are rounding, clustering, and compatible numbers.

17

17

LESSON **1.1**

3 Practice

Guided Practice

Do Check for Understanding Exercises 1–18 with your students. Identify those having difficulty and use lesson resources to help.

As students work through Exercises 3, 7, 12, and 16, have them rewrite the problems with the numbers they will use to make the estimates.

> ///// **COMMON ERROR ALERT** \\\\\\

When estimating products, students may make a place-value error in the product. Have students add the number of zeros in the rounded factors to any zeros in the basic fact product, and verify that the total number of zeros equals the number of zeros in the product.

Independent Practice

Assign Exercises 19–55.

CHECK FOR UNDERSTANDING

Think and Discuss Look back at the lesson to answer each question.

1. **Explain** why 6,000 + 1,500 is an overestimate or an underestimate of 6,108 + 1,524.
   underestimate since both addends are rounded down
2. **Describe** how to estimate a quotient by using compatible numbers. Give an example to illustrate your answer.
   Answers will vary.

Guided Practice Estimate the sum or difference. Possible estimates are given.

3. 723	4. 2,940	5. 4,480	6. 5,449
+819	3,140	4,100	4,869
1,500	+2,834	+3,967	+4,834
	9,000	**12,000**	**15,000**

7. 667	8. 8,855	9. 34,855	10. 67,184
−133	−2,268	−11,268	−49,650
600	**7,000**	**24,000**	**17,000**

Estimate the product or quotient. Possible estimates are given.

11. 36	12. 59	13. 48	14. 490
× 9	×33	×29	× 66
360	**1,800**	**1,500**	**35,000**

15. 321 ÷ 4   16. 1,544 ÷ 28   17. 4,156 ÷ 64   18. 8,429 ÷ 39
   80   **50**   **70**   **200**

PRACTICE AND PROBLEM SOLVING

Independent Practice Estimate the sum or difference. Possible estimates are given.

19. 1,700	20. 293	21. 5,765	22. 43,643
2,008	348	5,948	+84,211
+2,324	+343	+6,324	**128,000**
6,000	**900**	**18,000**	

23. 389	24. 3,556	25. 44,123	26. 667,184
− 43	−3,339	−29,512	−249,650
350	**300**	**14,000**	**420,000**

27. 17,809 − 2,145 **16,000**   28. 321,059 + 42,950 **364,000**

Estimate the product or quotient. Possible estimates are given.

29. 364	30. 53	31. 482	32. 1,874
× 12	×41	×299	× 582
4,000	**2,000**	**150,000**	**1,200,000**

33. 1,844 ÷ 22 34. 3,575 ÷ 56 35. 6,435 ÷ 529 36. 21,416 ÷ 521
   90   **60**   **12**   **40**
37. 4,135 × 784 **3,200,000**   38. 62,217 ÷ 4,889 **12**

Possible estimates are given. Tell whether the estimate is an *overestimate* or an *underestimate*. Then show how the estimate was determined.

39. 352 + 675 ≈ 1,100   40. 4,134 + 47 ≈ 4,100   41. 96 × 19 ≈ 2,000
   over; 400 + 700   under; 4,100 + 0   over; 100 × 20
42. 709 + 151 ≈ 850   43. 291 × 28 ≈ 9,000   44. 25 × 29 ≈ 900
   under; 700 + 150   over; 300 × 30   over; 30 × 30

> **TECHNOLOGY LINK**
> To learn more about estimation with whole numbers, watch the **Harcourt Math Newsroom Video** *Weather Stacked Stadium.*

18   Chapter 1

> ### Alternative Teaching Strategy
>
> **Purpose** Students use base-ten blocks and number lines to learn about estimation.
>
> **Materials** *For each group* base-ten blocks: 4 hundreds, 16 tens
>
> Display the following problem and ask students to estimate the sum to the nearest ten:
>
>   134
>   148
>   +183
>
> Then draw a number line and have students locate each of the addends on the number line.
>
>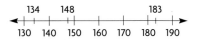
>
> Ask a volunteer to identify the tens between which 134 falls and to identify the ten closer to 134. 130 and 140; 130
>
> Have each group model the number 130 by using hundreds and tens. Repeat for the remaining two numbers, having groups model 150 and 180 by using hundreds and tens.
>
>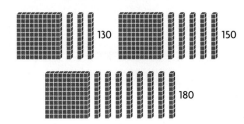
>
> Write the estimates next to the problem:
>
>   134   130
>   148   150
>   +183 +180
>
> Have groups model the sum of 130, 150, and 180, regrouping to show the final answer as 460.
>
>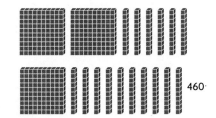

18   Chapter 1

Use estimation to compare. Write < or > for ●. Possible answers are given.

45. 614×41 ● $21{,}119 + 1{,}899$ > **46.** $18{,}391 \div 19$ ● 59×21 <

47. $4{,}012 - 3{,}508$ ● $3{,}624 \div 6$ < **48.** $12{,}283 + 19{,}971$ ● $209{,}910 \div 7$ >

49. 711×63 ● $28{,}520 + 16{,}990$ < **50.** 513×52 ● $29{,}190 - 1{,}986$ <

Problem Solving ▶ Applications

Use Data For 51–52, use the table. Possible estimates are given.

51. About how many more library books does Harvard have than the University of Illinois at Urbana? **about 4,500,000 books**

52. Estimate the total number of library books at Yale and the University of California at Berkeley. **about 17,000,000 books**

LARGEST UNIVERSITY LIBRARIES IN THE UNITED STATES (1999)	
Library	**Books**
Harvard University	12,877,360
Yale University	9,485,823
University of Illinois–Urbana	8,474,737
University of California–Berkeley	8,078,685
University of Texas	7,019,508

53. The theater of the Natural Science and History Museum was filled to capacity for 276 shows. The theater holds 36 people. How many people attended the shows? **9,936 people**

54. Possible answer: Compatible numbers; 750 ÷ 75 is easier to compute than 760 ÷ 70.

54. ✏️ **Write About It** Is it easier to use rounding or compatible numbers to estimate $756 \div 74$? Explain.

55. Two numbers, each rounded to the nearest hundred, have a product of 60,000. What are two possible numbers? **Possible answer: 235 and 345**

MIXED REVIEW AND TEST PREP

For 56–58, find the perimeter and area.

56.
12 ft
12 ft
48 ft; 144 ft²

57.
36 in.; 54 in.²
12 in. 15 in.
9 in.

58.
10 cm
3 cm
26 cm; 30 cm²

59. TEST PREP Ms. Cannon baked a total of 60 apple and blueberry pies. She baked a dozen more apple pies than blueberry pies. How many apple pies did she bake? **C**

A 18   **B** 24   **C** 36   **D** 48

60. TEST PREP Allen and Mei began working at the same time. It took Allen 50 minutes to mow the lawn, while Mei took $1\frac{1}{4}$ hr to paint the fence. How much longer did Mei work than Allen? **J**

F 85 min   **G** 65 min   **H** 35 min   **J** 25 min

Extra Practice page H32, Set A

19

For Exercises 51 and 52, have students round each of the numbers in the table to the nearest million. Then help them identify which parts of the table they will use for each problem.

MIXED REVIEW AND TEST PREP

Exercises 56–60 provide **cumulative review** (Grade 5).

4 Assess

Summarize the lesson by having students:

DISCUSS Would the exact answer to Exercise 30 be greater than or less than the estimated answer? Why? greater than; because both factors were rounded down

 WRITE A total of 367 students completed a 6-mile walk. Give two ways to estimate the total mileage walked by the students. Possible answer: Method 1: Round 367 to 400 and multiply. $400 \times 6 = 2{,}400$ miles; Method 2: Round 367 to 370 and multiply. $370 \times 6 = 2{,}220$ miles

Lesson Quiz

Transparency

1.1

Estimate the sum or difference. Possible estimates are given.

1. 756
   + 229
   ‾‾‾‾‾
   1,000

2. 3,214
   −1,570
   ‾‾‾‾‾
   1,600

3. 4,893
   6,275
   + 1,025
   ‾‾‾‾‾
   12,000

Estimate the quotient. Possible estimates are given.

4. $415 \div 7$ 60   **5.** $4{,}765 \div 5$ 900

Use Addition and Subtraction

LESSON PLANNING

Objective To use addition and subtraction of whole numbers to solve real-life problems

Intervention for Prerequisite Skills

Place Value of Whole Numbers, Round Whole Numbers (For intervention strategies, see page 15.)

California Mathematics Content Standards

⊶ NS 2.0 Students calculate and solve problems involving addition, subtraction, multiplication, and division.

MR 2.1 Use estimation to verify the reasonableness of calculated results.

MR 3.1 Evaluate the reasonableness of the solution in the context of the original situation.

(*Also* MR 2.7)

Math Background

Consider the following as you help students work successfully with the addition algorithm.

- Rounding is a useful tool for determining the reasonableness of an answer, but it does not provide a check that the answer is correct.
- Aligning the digits by place value is essential for finding the correct sum.
- Regrouping may occur from column to column; that is, 10 ones are regrouped as 1 ten; 10 tens are regrouped as 1 hundred, and so on.

Students may check addition by adding up instead of down and check subtraction by adding the difference to the number above.

WARM-UP RESOURCES

 NUMBER OF THE DAY   Transparency **1.2**

If you add 80 to me and subtract 3, you get 102. What number am I? 25

 PROBLEM OF THE DAY   Transparency **1.2**

Presidents George Washington, John Adams, and Thomas Jefferson lived a total of 240 years. Adams lived the longest, 23 years longer than Washington. Jefferson lived 16 years longer than Washington. How old was each President when he died? Washington, 67; Adams, 90; Jefferson, 83

Solution Problem of the Day tab, p. PD1A

 DAILY FACTS PRACTICE

Have students practice addition and subtraction facts by completing Set B of *Teacher's Resource Book,* p. TR93.

INTERVENTION AND EXTENSION RESOURCES

REACHING ALL LEARNERS

ALTERNATIVE TEACHING STRATEGY (ELL)

Materials *For each pair* base-ten blocks: 19 hundreds, 19 tens, and 19 ones

Have students **practice addition and subtraction.** Display two addition and two subtraction problems using 2- and 3-digit numbers. Have pairs of students work together to model the sums and differences using the hundreds, tens, and units models. After they have modeled all the problems, let each student use paper and pencil to find the answers.

Check students' work.

KINESTHETIC

MIXED REVIEW AND TEST PREP

Cumulative Review Grade 5 and Chapter 1

Refer to the Pupil Edition pages referenced in the exercises for further review. Have students go to the lesson page, review the lesson, and correct any problem they missed.

Mixed Review and Test Prep, p. 21

How to Help	
Item	Page
17	Grade 5
18	Grade 5
19	Grade 5
20	Grade 5
21	Grade 5

EARLY FINISHERS

Students can improve their ability to **add and subtract.** Have students use each of the digits 1–6 once in the following addition problem.

$$
\begin{array}{r}
\blacksquare\blacksquare\blacksquare \\
+\ \blacksquare\blacksquare\blacksquare \\
\hline
1{,}0\,4\,7
\end{array}
$$

$$632 + 415$$

Challenge students to make up a similar subtraction problem to share with others.

VISUAL

ADVANCED LEARNERS

Challenge students to **add a column of numbers** mentally using a zigzag pattern.

$$
\begin{array}{r}
84 \\
33 \\
+56 \\
\hline
\end{array}
$$

Think: **84 + 30** = 114

114 + 3 = 117
117 + 50 = 167
167 + 6 = 173

Use this method to find the following sums.

$$
\begin{array}{r}
59 \\
42 \\
+\ 36 \\
\hline
137
\end{array}
\qquad
\begin{array}{r}
46 \\
29 \\
+\ 65 \\
\hline
140
\end{array}
\qquad
\begin{array}{r}
47 \\
38 \\
93 \\
+\ 44 \\
\hline
222
\end{array}
$$

VISUAL

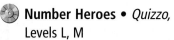

TECHNOLOGY LINK

- **Intervention Strategies and Activities CD-ROM** • *Skills 1, 2*
- **Number Heroes** • *Quizzo,* Levels L, M

LESSON **1.2** ORGANIZER

Objective To use addition and subtraction of whole numbers to solve real-life problems

1 Introduce

QUICK REVIEW provides review of prerequisite skills.

Why Learn This? You can use this skill to help you solve more complex word problems. *Share the lesson objective with students.*

2 Teach

Guided Instruction

- *As you discuss Examples 1 and 2, have students describe how to choose the correct operation to solve the problem.*

  How did you know whether to add or subtract in Example 1? In Example 2? You are joining amounts of time, so you add; You are comparing two numbers, so you subtract.

- *Help students evaluate the role of an estimate in checking their work.*

REASONING Does an estimate show that your answer is correct? Explain. Possible answer: No; it shows that your answer is reasonable. You still need to check to be sure it is correct.

- *Present this multi-step problem and guide students through the steps.*

  How many more hours were spent in space for the Apollo and Skylab programs than for the Mercury and Gemini programs? 17,864 hr

  What do you need to find out before you can solve this problem? the number of hours in space for both the Apollo and Skylab programs and the Mercury and Gemini programs

ADDITIONAL EXAMPLE

Example 1, p. 20

Captain Juarez is a pilot. He flew 256 miles during week 1 of January. Week 2 he flew 2,753 miles, week 3 he flew 8,809 miles, and week 4 he flew 14,174 miles. How many miles did Captain Juarez fly in January? estimate: 26,000; exact sum: 25,992 mi.

LESSON **1.2**

Use Addition and Subtraction

Learn how to add and subtract whole numbers.

Remember that you add when joining groups of different sizes and subtract when taking away or comparing groups.

QUICK REVIEW

Round to the nearest thousand.

1. 3,841 4,000   2. 2,490 2,000
3. 7,450 7,000   4. 8,500 9,000
5. Add. 4,256 + 1,725 5,981

PROGRAM	YEARS	TOTAL HOURS IN SPACE
Mercury	1961–1963	54
Gemini	1965–1966	1,940
Apollo	1968–1972	7,506
Skylab	1973–1974	12,352

During the early years of space flight, the total time United States astronauts spent in space increased with each program.

EXAMPLE 1

How many hours did U.S. astronauts spend in space?

Find 54 + 1,940 + 7,506 + 12,352.

Estimate to check for reasonableness.

Round to the nearest thousand. | Find the sum.

```
     54          0              54
  1,940      2,000           1,940     Compare your estimate.
  7,506  →   8,000           7,506     21,852 is close to 22,000, so
+12,352    +12,000         +12,352     the sum is reasonable.
           22,000          21,852
```

So, U.S. astronauts spent 21,852 hours in space.

EXAMPLE 2

How many more hours did U.S. astronauts spend in Skylab than on the Gemini missions?

Find 12,352 − 1,940.

Estimate to check for reasonableness. | Find the difference.

```
 12,352     12,000        12,352     Compare your estimate.
- 1,940  →  - 2,000       - 1,940    10,412 is close to 10,000, so
            10,000        10,412     the difference is reasonable.
```

So, U.S. astronauts spent 10,412 more hours in Skylab than on the Gemini missions.

20   **CALIFORNIA STANDARDS** O—n NS 2.0 Students calculate and solve problems involving addition, subtraction, multiplication, and division. MR 2.1 Use estimation to verify the reasonableness of calculated results. MR 3.1 Evaluate the reasonableness of the solution in the context of the original situation. *also,* MR 2.7

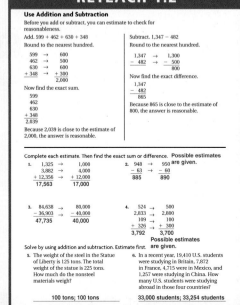

RETEACH 1.2

Use Addition and Subtraction

Before you add or subtract, you can estimate to check for reasonableness.

Add. 599 + 462 + 630 + 348
Round to the nearest hundred.

```
599  →    600
462  →    500
630  →    600
+348  →  + 300
         2,000
```

Now find the exact sum.

```
 599
 462
 630
+348
2,039
```

Because 2,039 is close to the estimate of 2,000, the answer is reasonable.

Subtract. 1,347 − 482
Round to the nearest hundred.

```
1,347  →   1,300
- 482  →  -  500
             800
```

Now find the exact difference.

```
1,347
- 482
  865
```

Because 865 is close to the estimate of 800, the answer is reasonable.

Complete each estimate. Then find the exact sum or difference. **Possible estimates are given.**

```
1.   1,325  →    1,000        2.    948  →  950
     3,882  →    4,000            -  63  →  - 60
   +12,356  →  + 12,000             885      890
    17,563      17,000
```

```
3.  84,638  →   80,000        4.    524  →   500
   -36,903  →  - 40,000            2,833  → 2,800
    47,735      40,000              109  →    100
                                  + 326  →  + 300
                                   3,792    3,700
```
Possible estimates are given.

Solve by using addition and subtraction. Estimate first. **are given.**

5. The weight of the steel in the Statue of Liberty is 125 tons. The total weight of the statue is 225 tons. How much do the nonsteel materials weigh?

   100 tons; 100 tons

6. In a recent year, 19,410 U.S. students were studying in Britain, 7,872 in France, 4,715 were in Mexico, and 1,257 were studying in China. How many U.S. students were studying abroad in those four countries?

   33,000 students; 33,254 students

PRACTICE 1.2

Use Addition and Subtraction

Find the sum or difference. Estimate to check. **Possible estimates are given.**

1. 504 + 343	2. 684 + 193 + 217	3. 3,991 − 953	4. 4,616 + 1,382
800; 847	1,100; 1,094	3,000; 3,038	6,000; 5,998

5. 4,183 − 2,851	6. 794 + 578 + 909	7. 17,079 − 8,805	8. 29,114 − 13,513
1,000; 1,332	2,300; 2,281	8,000; 8,274	15,000; 15,601

```
9.  12,379   10.  53,852   11.  60,118   12.  43,192   13.  72,583
   + 7,166       +15,098       -38,541       -10,476       +16,205
    19,000;       69,000;       20,000;       90,000;       90,000;
    19,545        68,950        21,577        32,716        88,788

14. 68,450   15. 154,022   16. 864,191   17. 571,042   18. 389,077
   -31,754      - 46,389      - 95,361      -462,790      +605,213
    40,000;      100,000;      800,000;      100,000;    1,000,000;
    36,696       107,633       768,830       108,252      944,290
```

Solve.

19. 158 + 2,876 − 586	20. 1,422 + 806 + 539	21. 4,950 − 674 + 1,805
2,448	2,767	2,471

22. 70,376 − 5,845 − 3,541	23. 8,026 + 11,061 + 3,824	24. 1,753 + 2,210 − 1,907
60,990	22,911	2,056

25. 5,951 + 4,676 − 1,050 + 47,320	26. 19,321 − 1,322 + 939 − 3,084
56,897	15,854

Mixed Review

Estimate the product or quotient. **Possible estimates are given.**

```
27.   57      28.   685     29.   173     30.   915     31.   718
    × 26          ×  51         ×  96        ×506         ×386
    1,800        35,000        20,000      450,000      280,000

32. 8,161 ÷ 87    33. 3,307 ÷ 47    34. 7,985 ÷ 432    35. 25,641 ÷ 197
      90                70                20                 130
```

CHECK FOR UNDERSTANDING

Think and ▶ Discuss

Look back at the lesson to answer each question.

1. **Explain** how you know whether to add or subtract when solving a word problem. **Answers will vary.**

2. **Explain** why it is a good idea to find an estimate before or after you find the exact answer.
   to determine if your exact answer is reasonable

Guided ▶ Practice

Find the sum or difference. Estimate to check.

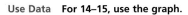

3. 835 + 604
   1,439

4. 6,901 + 342 + 67
   7,310

5. 40,190 − 13,982
   26,208

PRACTICE AND PROBLEM SOLVING

Independent ▶ Practice

Find the sum or difference. Estimate to check.

6. 9,500 − 289
   9,211

7. 21,670 + 14,704
   36,374

8. 31,227 + 56,995
   88,222

9.   999,999
   +111,385
   1,111,384

10.   987,654
   −456,789
   530,865

11.   50,000,000
   − 3,604,381
   46,395,619

Solve.

12. 1,485 + 2,019 + 1,310 + 3,665 + 798 **9,277**

13. 43,875 + 81,420 − 38,288 + 12,108 − 23,990 **75,125**

Problem Solving ▶ Applications

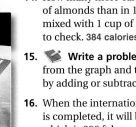

International space station

Use Data For 14–15, use the graph.

14. How many more calories are in 1 cup of almonds than in 1 cup of carrots mixed with 1 cup of raisins? Estimate to check. **384 calories**

15. ✎ **Write a problem** that uses data from the graph and that can be solved by adding or subtracting. **Problems will vary.**

16. When the international space station is completed, it will be 290 ft long, which is 206 ft longer than Skylab. Skylab was 41 ft longer than Mir, the Russian space station. How long is Mir? **43 ft**

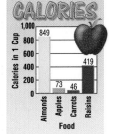

CALORIES

MIXED REVIEW AND TEST PREP

17. 6,785 + 4,521 **11,306**

18. Complete. 36 in. = ▉ ft **3**

19. List the factors of 24. **1, 2, 3, 4, 6, 8, 12, 24**

20. List the first six multiples of 9.
   9, 18, 27, 36, 45, 54

21. **TEST PREP** Which is a prime number? **C**

   A 15   **B** 27   **C** 31   **D** 50

(Extra Practice) page H32, Set B

21

---

3 Practice

Guided Practice

Do Check for Understanding Exercises 1–5 with your students. Identify those having difficulty and use lesson resources to help.

///// COMMON ERROR ALERT \\\\\

In an addition problem, if students' answers are off by 1 in any place, they may be neglecting to add regrouped ones, tens, hundreds, and so on. Make sure they are notating the regroupings as they work the problems.

```
                     11
   376              376
   224              224
 + 538            + 538
 1,028            1,138
```

Independent Practice

Assign Exercises 6–16.

MIXED REVIEW AND TEST PREP

Exercises 17–21 provide **cumulative review** (Grade 5 and Chapter 1).

4 Assess

Summarize the lesson by having students:

DISCUSS How do you decide if your answer is reasonable? Possible answer: Compare the answer to an estimate. If it is close to the estimate, it is reasonable.

 WRITE Describe the steps you used to find the exact answer in Example 1. Possible answer: Add the ones. Write 2 and regroup 10 ones as 1 ten. Add the tens. Write 5 and regroup 10 tens as 1 hundred. Add the hundreds. Write 8 and regroup 10 hundreds as 1 thousand. Add the thousands. Write 1 and regroup 10 thousands as 1 ten thousand. Add the ten thousands. Write 2.

Lesson Quiz

Estimate. Then find the solution.

Transparency
1.2

1.   32,421
   +14,085
   46,000; 46,506

2.   54,273
   −21,509
   32,000; 32,764

3. Randall earns $26,855 a year and his wife, Karyn, earns $32,425. How much do they earn together? $59,000; $59,280

21

PROBLEM SOLVING 1.2

Use Addition and Subtraction

Solve.

(Analyze Choose Solve Check)

1. In 1995, there were about 58,000 farms in North Carolina and about 22,000 farms in South Carolina. There were about 100,000 farms in Iowa in 1995. About how many more farms were there in Iowa than in North Carolina and South Carolina combined in 1995?

   about 20,000 more farms

2. Carrie participated in a bird census during three days last week. She counted 435 birds on Monday, 206 birds on Tuesday, and 359 birds on Wednesday. How many birds did she count in all during these three days?

   1,000 birds

3. Give the value represented by the digit 8 in the number 258,034,199.

   8 million

4. Use clustering to estimate the sum.
   65 + 57 + 62 + 54

   4 × 60 = 240

Choose the letter for the best answer.

5. In 1999, a world record for the largest gathering of twins was set in Taipei, Taiwan, with 3,961 pairs of twins in attendance. The number of twins shattered the previous record of 2,900 pairs set in Twinsburg, Ohio, in 1998. What is a reasonable estimate of the increase in the number of pairs of twins?
   A 60 pairs
   B 160 pairs
   C 900 pairs
   (D) 1,100 pairs

6. When a children's museum opened near Roberto's home, he was among 14,756 children who visited it during the first month it was open. The next month, 18,355 children visited, while 27,982 children visited during the third month. What is a reasonable estimate of the number of children who visited the museum during the first three months it was open?
   F 40,000 children (H) 60,000 children
   G 50,000 children J 70,000 children

7. What 2 numbers have a sum of 4,949 and a difference of 1,963?
   A 1,999 and 2,950
   (B) 1,493 and 3,456
   C 1,358 and 3,591
   D 1,078 and 3,871

8. Which is the greatest number of the four shown below?
   23,887; 32,109; 24,999; 32,190
   F 23,887
   G 32,109
   H 24,999
   (J) 32,190

9. **Write About It** Which operation would you use to solve a problem in which you are asked to find an amount of increase? Explain.

   Subtraction; an amount of increase or change implies a difference.

To find the difference between two numbers, you should subtract.

CHALLENGE 1.2

Shopping at the Airport

Airports across the nation are discovering a captive audience for shopping. Millions of people spend time—and money—in airports.

The table shows the number of passengers at five airports in 1998 and the annual sales concessions at the airports.

Airport	Number of Passengers	Annual Sales Concessions
Portland International	12,739,851	$45.2 million
Pittsburgh International	20,500,000	$87.1 million
Denver International	36,831,400	$89.0 million
Baltimore/Washington International	15,000,000	$35.0 million
Los Angeles International	59,730,530	$158.2 million

1. Estimate the total number of passengers who used the Los Angeles and Denver airports during 1998.

   Possible answer: about 100,000,000 passengers

2. Which airport had the fewest passengers?

   Portland

3. What was the total number of passengers who used these five airports during 1998?

   144,801,781 passengers

4. How many more passengers used the Denver airport than used the Portland airport?

   24,091,549 more passengers

5. Portland International had fewer passengers than Baltimore/Washington International. How did their annual sales compare?

   Portland had $10.2 million more in sales.

6. Find the difference between the greatest annual sales and the least annual sales.

   $123.2 million (or $123,200,000)

7. What was the total annual sales concessions for these five airports during 1998?

   $414.5 million (or $414,500,000)

21

Use Multiplication and Division

LESSON PLANNING

Objective To use multiplication and division of whole numbers to solve real-life problems

Intervention for Prerequisite Skills

Place Value of Whole Numbers, Round Whole Numbers (For intervention strategies, see page 15.)

 California Mathematics Content Standards

○━ NS 2.0 Students calculate and solve problems involving addition, subtraction, multiplication, and division.

MR 2.1 Use estimation to verify the reasonableness of calculated results.

MR 3.1 Evaluate the reasonableness of the solution in the context of the original situation.

(*Also* MR 1.3, MR 2.7)

Math Background

These ideas will help students understand the steps in the multiplication and division algorithms:

- When you find the product of multi-digit numbers, the partial products except for the first one must end with one, two, or more zeros, as appropriate, or be moved to the left the appropriate number of places. The sum of all partial products is then taken.

- Estimating helps you choose the place for the first digit in the quotient.

- The steps in the division algorithm—divide, multiply, subtract, and compare—are repeated for each digit in the quotient.

WARM-UP RESOURCES

 NUMBER OF THE DAY   Transparency 1.3

Begin with your age. Multiply by 4, add 20, divide by 2, and subtract 10. Describe the number you get as an answer. It is 2 times your age.

 PROBLEM OF THE DAY   Transparency 1.3

Find the product. Compare the product with the first factor. Write a rule for multiplying a 2-digit number by 11 and a rule for multiplying greater numbers by 11.

1. $13 \times 11 = $ __?__ 143

2. $72 \times 11 = $ __?__ 792

3. $326 \times 11 = $ __?__ 3,586

4. $6,045 \times 11$ __?__ 66,495

Solution Problem of the Day tab, p. PD1A

 DAILY FACTS PRACTICE

Have students practice multiplication and division facts by completing Set C of *Teacher's Resource Book,* p. TR93.

INTERVENTION AND EXTENSION RESOURCES

ALTERNATIVE TEACHING STRATEGY ⓔⓛⓛ

Have students **practice multiplication and division** by doing the following. Display the multiplication exercises. Have students tell to which place they would round each number to estimate the product and then name the greatest place they will have in the product.

82 × 31 tens, tens, thousands

437 × 129 hundreds, hundreds, ten-thousands

Display these division exercises. Have students tell which will be the greatest place in the quotient.

873 ÷ 9 tens

7,894 ÷ 32 hundreds

See also page 24.

VISUAL

SCIENCE CONNECTION

Increase students' ability to **apply multiplication and division to real-life problems**. Have students apply their knowledge of multiplication by using the following information.

The average amount of garbage generated by each person in the United States in one year includes 190 lb of plastic, 85 lb of glass, 72 lb of aluminum cans, and 24 lb of plastic containers.

• As a class, students can calculate how much garbage is generated by the entire class. Have students make a pictograph showing the results.

• Have students find the total amount of each type of garbage generated by the number of people in their homes.

Check students' work.

VISUAL

MIXED REVIEW AND TEST PREP

Cumulative Review Grade 5 and Chapter 1

Refer to the Pupil Edition pages referenced in the exercises for further review. Have students go to the lesson page, review the lesson, and correct any problem they missed.

Mixed Review and Test Prep, p. 25

How to Help	
Item	**Page**
46	20
47	Grade 5
48	Grade 5
49	Grade 5
50	Grade 5

ADVANCED LEARNERS

Challenge students to **use multiplication mentally.** Ask students to solve the following multiplication problem. Have them replace the boxes with the numbers 1–6. They can use each number only once.

$$
\begin{array}{r}
5\ 4 \\
\times\quad 3 \\
\hline
1\ 6\ 2
\end{array}
$$

VISUAL

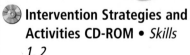

TECHNOLOGY LINK

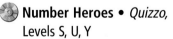

🔘 **Intervention Strategies and Activities CD-ROM** • *Skills 1, 2*

🔘 **Number Heroes** • *Quizzo,* Levels S, U, Y

🔘 **Mighty Math Calculating Crew** • *Captain Nick Knack,* Level V

LESSON **1.3** ORGANIZER

Objective To use multiplication and division of whole numbers to solve real-life problems

1 Introduce

QUICK REVIEW provides review of pre-requisite skills.

Why Learn This? You can use this skill to determine the total amount of money earned by selling car wash tickets for a school fundraiser, or to determine average test scores. *Share the lesson objective with students.*

2 Teach

Guided Instruction

• *As you work through Example 1, discuss with students how to tell if an answer is reasonable.*

In Example 1, is the estimate close enough to the actual product to be reasonable? Explain. Possible answer: Yes; both numbers are more than 2,000.

• *In Example 2, ask students to think about another way of rounding to estimate the product.*

How else could you have rounded the factors? Possible answer: to 10,000 and 100

ADDITIONAL EXAMPLES

Example 1, p. 22

A warehouse has 831 shelves. How many boxes are in the warehouse if there are 32 boxes on each shelf? estimate: 800 × 30 = 24,000; exact answer: 26,592 boxes

Example 2, p. 22

Monthly train tickets cost $132. How much will the transit company receive if it sells 13,316 monthly tickets? estimate: 130 × 13,000 = 1,690,000; exact answer: $1,757,712

LESSON **1.3**

Use Multiplication and Division

Learn how to multiply and divide whole numbers.

QUICK REVIEW

1. 7 × 3 21   **2.** 72 ÷ 9 8   **3.** 12 × 4 48   **4.** 300 ÷ 25 12

5. 800 × 40 32,000

*S*ometimes you can multiply to solve a word problem.

EXAMPLE 1

Remember that you multiply when joining equal-sized groups, and you divide when separating into equal-sized groups or when finding how many in each group.

Sixth-grade students sold 132 books of carnival ride coupons. How many ride coupons did they sell if there were 18 in each book?

Multiply. 132 × 18   Estimate. 130 × 20 = 2,600

```
    132
  ×  18        Compare the exact product to your estimate.
  1 056        Since 2,376 is close to the estimate of 2,600,
 +1 32         the exact product is reasonable.
  2,376
```

So, the students sold 2,376 coupons.

You can omit the zero placeholders when you multiply. Just be careful to line up the products correctly.

```
       Correct    Incorrect
        132          132
      ×  24        ×  24
        528          528
       +264         +264
```

EXAMPLE 2

Season tickets to an amusement park are on sale for $125 each. On the first day of the sale, the amusement park sold 12,383 tickets. How much money did the amusement park receive for season tickets that day?

Multiply. 12,383 × 125

Estimate. 12,000 × 130 = 1,560,000

```
    12,383      Compare the exact
  ×    125      product to your estimate.
    61 915      Since 1,547,875 is close
   247 66       to the estimate of
  +1 238 3      1,560,000, the exact
  1,547,875     product is reasonable.
```

So, the amusement park received $1,547,875.

22

CALIFORNIA STANDARDS O⎯ⁿ NS 2.0 Students calculate and solve problems involving addition, subtraction, multiplication, and division. **MR 2.1** Use estimation to verify the reasonableness of calculated results. **MR 3.1** Evaluate the reasonableness of the solution in the context of the original situation. *also,* MR 1.3, MR 2.7

RETEACH 1.3

Use Multiplication and Division

Mr. Rivera's class has collected 1,272 rocks. The students are using egg cartons to hold the rocks. If a dozen rocks fit in each carton, how many cartons are needed for the collection?

Paul did some calculations to solve this problem. This is what he did.

```
      106
  12)1,272    • Since 12 is greater than 1, the first digit appears in the
   −12    ← (1 × 12)    hundreds place. Paul divided the 12 hundreds.

     07
    − 0    ← (0 × 12)   • Paul brought down the 7 tens. Since 12 > 7, he wrote 0 in
                          the quotient.

      72
     −72    ← (6 × 12)   • Paul brought down the 2 ones. He divided the 72 ones.
       0
```

The class needs 106 egg cartons to hold the collection.

Multiply or divide.

```
  1.   399        2.   824        3.  1,440
     ×171           ×  32           ×   78
     68,229         26,368          112,320


        209            206             62
  4. 17)3,553     5. 35)7,210     6. 28)1,736


        307            110             503
  7. 38)11,666    8. 46)5,060     9. 68)34,204


         421            511             245
 10. 32)13,472   11. 43)21,973   12. 52)12,740
```

PRACTICE 1.3

Use Multiplication and Division

Multiply or divide. Estimate to check.

```
  1.   46        2.   230       3.  417      4.  2,515      5.   387
     × 12          ×  15          × 40          ×  52          × 66
     552           3,450         16,680        130,780       25,542
  6.  217        7. 6,903       8.  582       9.  6,148     10.  8,132
     ×154          ×  627         ×316          ×  744         × 915
     33,418        4,328,181     183,912       4,574,112     7,440,780
        24            47            19            108          14 r2
 11. 4)96      12. 9)423      13. 19)361     14. 7)756      15. 32)450

        145           48           246           156           345
 16. 12)1,740   17. 19)912    18. 22)5,412   19. 31)4,836   20. 17)5,865
```

Divide. Write the remainder as a fraction.

```
      7½             39²⁄₉          25¼           322⁸⁄₄₁         602³⁄₁₁
 21. 6)45      22. 14)550     23. 18)459     24. 41)13,210   25. 55)33,125
```

Mixed Review

Estimate the sum, difference, product, or quotient. Possible estimates are given.

```
 26.   1,087     27.  56,803    28.   347     29.  26,811 ÷ 885
       2,109        − 31,942         ×261
     + 4,837         30,000         90,000            30
       8,000
```

Solve by using addition and subtraction.

```
 30. 9,271 − 3,587 − 1,266 − 2,650                1,768

 31. 2,114 + 739 + 4,799 + 557 + 1,632            9,841
```

Sometimes you have to use division to solve word problems.

EXAMPLE 3

Remember that the procedure for dividing is divide, multiply, subtract, compare, and bring down.

Mrs. Lopez is redesigning the company cafeteria to seat 540 employees. Each table in her design seats 12 employees. How many tables will she need?

Divide. $540 \div 12$

Estimate. $480 \div 12 = 40$

$$
\begin{array}{r}
45 \\
12\overline{)540} \\
-48\downarrow \\
\hline
60 \\
-60 \\
\hline
0
\end{array}
$$

Compare the exact quotient to your estimate. Since 45 is close to the estimate of 40, the exact quotient is reasonable.

So, Mrs. Lopez will need 45 tables in her design.

• What if each table seats 10 employees? How many tables will Mrs. Lopez need? **54 tables**

Sometimes a division problem has a zero in the quotient.

EXAMPLE 4

A school collected 2,568 newspapers. The newspapers were bundled in packages of 25. How many packages of newspapers did the school bundle?

Divide. $2,568 \div 25$

Estimate. $2,500 \div 25 = 100$

$$
\begin{array}{r}
102 \text{ r}18 \\
25\overline{)2,568} \\
-25 \\
\hline
06 \\
-0 \\
\hline
68 \\
-50 \\
\hline
18
\end{array}
$$

Compare the exact answer to your estimate. Since 102 r18 is close to the estimate of 100, the exact quotient is reasonable.

So, the school bundled 102 packages of newspapers.

In Example 4 there is a remainder. Some calculators allow you to show a whole-number remainder.

2,568 ÷R 25 = | 102 R18 |

You can express a remainder with an *r*, or you can express it as a fractional part of the divisor or as a decimal. The quotient and remainder in Example 4 can also be expressed as $102\frac{18}{25}$ or as 102.72.

23

• *Discuss with students the choice of compatible numbers with which to estimate.*

In Example 3, what compatible numbers would you use to estimate the product to ensure you had enough tables? $600 \div 12 = 50$

• *Review with students how to interpret and use remainders.*

In Example 4, why do you drop the remainder? The question asks about bundles and each bundle must have 25 newspapers.

REASONING Interpreting remainders helps students develop reasoning skills.

• *Have students discuss the remainder in this situation.*

The instructions in a bow-making kit say to use 5 yd of ribbon to make each bow. How many bows could you make with 48 yd of ribbon? 9 bows

Did you drop the remainder or increase the quotient by 1? Explain. drop the remainder; You don't have enough ribbon to make another bow.

ADDITIONAL EXAMPLES

Example 3, p. 23

Each table can seat 15 people. There are 465 people. How many tables are needed? estimate: $450 \div 15 = 30$; exact answer: 31 tables

Example 4, p. 23

The Craft Club makes wooden houses out of craft sticks. It has 4,356 sticks. Each house takes 43 sticks to build. How many houses can the Craft Club build? estimate: $4,000 \div 40 = 100$; exact answer: 101 r13; 101 houses

---

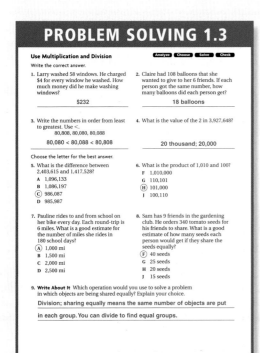

PROBLEM SOLVING 1.3

Use Multiplication and Division

Analyze Choose Solve Check

Write the correct answer.

1. Larry washed 58 windows. He charged $4 for every window he washed. How much money did he make washing windows?

$232

2. Claire had 108 balloons that she wanted to give to her 6 friends. If each person got the same number, how many balloons did each person get?

18 balloons

3. Write the numbers in order from least to greatest. Use <.
80,808, 80,080, 80,088

80,080 < 80,088 < 80,808

4. What is the value of the 2 in 3,927,648?

20 thousand; 20,000

Choose the letter for the best answer.

5. What is the difference between 2,403,615 and 1,417,528?
A 1,096,133
B 1,086,197
(C) 986,087
D 985,987

6. What is the product of 1,010 and 100?
F 1,010,000
G 110,101
(H) 101,000
J 100,110

7. Pauline rides to and from school on her bike every day. Each round-trip is 6 miles. What is a good estimate for the number of miles she rides in 180 school days?
(A) 1,000 mi
B 1,500 mi
C 2,000 mi
D 2,500 mi

8. Sam has 9 friends in the gardening club. He orders 340 tomato seeds for his friends to share. What is a good estimate of how many seeds each person would get if they share the seeds equally?
(F) 40 seeds
G 25 seeds
H 20 seeds
J 15 seeds

9. **Write About It** Which operation would you use to solve a problem in which objects are being shared equally? Explain your choice.

Division; sharing equally means the same number of objects are put in each group. You can divide to find equal groups.

CHALLENGE 1.3

Number Crossword

Solve each problem. Complete the puzzle with the answers.

Across		Down	
1. $1,685 \times 124 =$	208,940	1. $6,150 \div 3 =$	2,050
2. $65 \times 104 =$	6,760	4. $3,454 \div 22 =$	157
3. $2,549 \times 317 =$	808,033	5. $855 \div 19 =$	45
4. $596 \times 240 =$	143,040	9. $25,344 \div 36 =$	704
5. $99 \times 5 =$	495	10. $16,740 \div 54 =$	310
6. $6,058 \times 847 =$	5,131,126	11. $7,968 \div 16 =$	498
7. $351 \times 208 =$	73,008	12. $46,295 \div 47 =$	985
8. $872 \times 234 =$	204,048	13. $17,568 \div 36 =$	488
		14. $14,761 \div 29 =$	509
		15. $32,625 \div 87 =$	375
		16. $9,672 \div 93 =$	104
		17. $7,896 \div 12 =$	658

LESSON 1.3

3 | Practice

Guided Practice

Do Check for Understanding Exercises 1–13 with your students. Identify those having difficulty and use lesson resources to help.

//// **COMMON ERROR ALERT** \\\\

If students have difficulty lining up partial products correctly, they may want to continue to use zero as a place holder or do their work on grid paper.

Independent Practice

Assign Exercises 14–45.

CHECK FOR UNDERSTANDING

Think and ▸ Discuss Look back at the lesson to answer each question.

1. There were 102 full packages. The 18 newspapers left over were not enough to make a full package.

1. **Explain** why the school bundled 102 packages of newspapers instead of 103 packages of newspapers in Example 4.

2. **Tell** the different ways to express the remainder for the division problem $153 \div 6$. as a remainder, a decimal, and a fraction; 25 r3, 25.5, and $25\frac{1}{2}$

Guided ▸ Practice Multiply or divide. Estimate to check.

3. $1,113 \times 712$
792,456

4. $2,115 \div 72$
29.375

5. $16,225 \times 219$
3,553,275

Multiply or divide.

6. $13\ 182$
$\times 14$

7. $8\overline{)432}$ 54

8. $12\overline{)144}$ 12

9. $962\ 38,480$
$\times\ 40$

10. 159×340
54,060

11. $7,658 \times 111$
850,038

12. $7,044 \div 14$
503 r2

13. $1,068 \div 19$
56 r4

PRACTICE AND PROBLEM SOLVING

Independent ▸ Practice Multiply or divide. Estimate to check.

14. $2,250 \div 18$
125

15. $4,904 \times 196$
961,184

16. $193,200 \div 46$
4,200

17. $7,021 \times 498$
3,496,458

18. $249,900 \div 49$
5,100

19. $24,587 \times 71$
1,745,677

Multiply or divide.

TECHNOLOGY LINK
More Practice: Use **Mighty Math Calculating Crew**, *Captain Nick Knack*, Level V.

20. $16\overline{)1,664}$
104

21. 298
$\times\ 89$
26,522

22. $5,233$
$\times\ 238$
1,245,454

23. $52\overline{)728}$
14

24. $4\overline{)412}$
103

25. 380
$\times\ 55$
20,900

26. $2,382$
$\times\ 12$
28,584

27. $24\overline{)626}$
26 r2

28. 327
$\times 123$
40,221

29. $26\overline{)2,314}$
89

30. $68\overline{)24,820}$
365

31. $5,470$
$\times\ 240$
1,312,800

32. $29\overline{)13,253}$
457

33. $6,378$
$\times\ 291$
1,855,998

34. $2,009$
$\times\ 562$
1,129,058

35. $120\overline{)10,080}$
84

Divide. Write the remainder as a fraction.

36. $5\overline{)49}$
$9\frac{4}{5}$

37. $7,349 \div 20$
$367\frac{9}{20}$

38. $386 \div 15$
$25\frac{11}{15}$

39. $4\overline{)3,385}$
$846\frac{1}{4}$

40. **Algebra** What is the least whole number, n, for which it is true that $n \div 8 > 542 + 258$? 6,401

41. **Algebra** What is the least whole number, n, for which it is true that $70 \times n > 29,000$? 415

24 Chapter 1

Alternative Teaching Strategy

Purpose Students use an activity to help develop proficiency with the division algorithm.

Materials *For each pair* 1-inch graph paper, p. TR62; 1-inch by 1-inch squares of paper

Give each pair of students a piece of graph paper on which you have written a division problem that will have a zero in the quotient. The problem should be written with one digit to a graph square.

Then give each group 1-inch squares of paper with the digits of the quotient and remainder, written one to a square.

Each pair works together to decide where to place the first digit in the quotient and which digit to use. When they decide, they place the small square with that digit in the proper place on the graph paper and then multiply it by the divisor. The graph paper will help students align their digits properly.

They repeat the process with the second digit in the quotient, until the problem is complete. The square(s) for the remainder can then be placed beside the quotient.

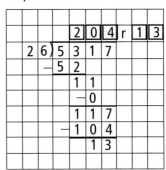

When each group is done, have students show and explain their division problem to the rest of the class.

24 Chapter 1

Problem Solving ▸ Applications

42. Yuji's parents bought an entertainment center for $1,176. They plan to pay for it with 14 equal monthly payments. How much will each payment be if a $3.50 service charge is added every month? **$87.50**

43. Lincoln Middle School had a car wash to raise money. The students charged $3.00 for every car and $5.00 for every van. If they washed 23 cars and 18 vans, how much did they earn? **$159**

44. ❓ **What's the Error?** Describe the error. Then solve the problem correctly. **forgot to write a zero in the quotient; 620 r15**

$$\begin{array}{r} 62\ r15 \\ 49\overline{)30,395} \end{array}$$

45. There are 5 children in Brenda's family. Brenda is 16 years old. Brenda's twin sisters are 6 years old, and her brothers are 10 and 12 years old. What is the mean of the 5 children's ages? **10**

MIXED REVIEW AND TEST PREP

46. How much more than 96,784 is 142,981? (p. 20) **46,197**

47. Complete. 4 lb = ■ oz **64**

48. Order 804, 824, 818, and 803 from least to greatest. **803, 804, 818, 824**

49. TEST PREP How many meters are in 1,800 millimeters? **B**

  A 0.18 m **B** 1.8 m **C** 18 m **D** 180 m

50. TEST PREP Teresa is buying perfume for her mother. The prices are $16.19, $15.89, $15.99, and $17.00. How much will she save by buying the least expensive instead of the most expensive? **J**

  F $0.01 **G** $0.11 **H** $0.81 **J** $1.11

LiNKuP to Reading

Strategy • Use Context Many word problems contain clues such as *more than, fewer than, twice as many,* and *total*. Be sure to interpret clue words within the context of the problem before you choose an operation.

Use Data For each problem, write the clue words and the operation. Then solve the problem.

1. How many more calories will you burn in 1 hr by skiing than by hiking? **clue words: more than; operation: subtraction; 135 calories**

2. On Saturday, Connie spent an hour in gymnastics class and then walked for 1 hr. How many total calories did she burn during these two activities? **clue word: total; operation: addition; 240 calories**

3. Clara burned half as many calories while raking the lawn for 1 hr than she did while jogging for 1 hr. How many calories did she burn while raking the lawn? **clue words: half as many; operation: division; 112 calories**

CALORIES BURNED PER HOUR	
Activity	**Calories**
Walking (at 2 mi per hr)	112
Gymnastics	128
Hiking	191
Jogging	224
Cross-country skiing	326

Extra Practice page H32, Set C

25

MIXED REVIEW AND TEST PREP
Exercises 46–50 provide **cumulative review** (Grade 5 and Chapter 1).

LiNKuP to READING

- *Have students look at the table. Ask:*

How are the activities in the table arranged? from the least amount of calories burned to greatest amount of calories burned

Do you think every person burns the same number of calories listed for each exercise? Explain. No; the number of calories burned would vary with the age and weight of the person.

REASONING If you burned twice as many calories walking 4 mi per hour as walking 2 mi per hour, what exercise would burn the same number of calories as walking 4 mi per hour? jogging

4 Assess

Summarize the lesson by having students:

DISCUSS What is the value of estimating solutions when solving word problems? Comparing estimates to exact answers helps you determine the reasonableness of your solution.

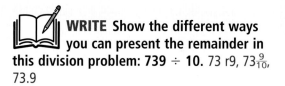

WRITE Show the different ways you can present the remainder in this division problem: 739 ÷ 10. 73 r9, $73\frac{9}{10}$, 73.9

Lesson Quiz

Transparency **1.3**

Find the product.

1. $\begin{array}{r} 34 \\ \times\ 8 \\ \hline 272 \end{array}$ **2.** $\begin{array}{r} 420 \\ \times\ 13 \\ \hline 5,460 \end{array}$ **3.** $\begin{array}{r} 4,216 \\ \times\ 51 \\ \hline 215,016 \end{array}$

Find the quotient.

4. $5\overline{)180}$ **36** **5.** $22\overline{)1,659}$ **75 r9** **6.** $37\overline{)8,475}$ **229 r2**

Problem Solving Strategy: *Predict and Test*

LESSON PLANNING

Objective To use the strategy *predict and test* to solve addition, subtraction, multiplication, and division problems with whole numbers

Intervention for Prerequisite Skills

Place Value of Whole Numbers (For intervention strategies, see page 15.)

Lesson Resources Problem Solving Think Along, p. TR1

 California Mathematics Content Standards

○━┓ NS 2.0 Students calculate and solve problems involving addition, subtraction, multiplication, and division.

MR 3.2 Note the method of deriving the solution and demonstrate a conceptual understanding of the derivation by solving similar problems.

(*Also* AF 3.1, MR 1.1, MR 1.3, MR 2.0, MR 2.7)

Math Background

The idea behind the *predict and test* strategy is that the student will:

- think about a reasonable or logical solution to the problem and give an answer based on that logic.
- test the predicted solution in the context of the problem to decide if it satisfies all the conditions.
- use the result of the test to change the predicted answer as needed.

The process is continued until the correct answer is obtained.

WARM-UP RESOURCES

 NUMBER OF THE DAY

The sum of a smaller number and a larger number is 20. Their product is 64. What is the larger number? 16

 PROBLEM OF THE DAY

At noon on Monday, Latisha sets her watch to the correct time. If her watch loses one minute each hour and she does not correct it, what time will her watch show at noon on Wednesday? 11:12 At noon on what day will her watch show 10:00? Saturday

Solution Problem of the Day tab, p. PD1A

 DAILY FACTS PRACTICE

Have students practice subtraction facts by completing Set D of *Teacher's Resource Book*, p. TR93.

INTERVENTION AND EXTENSION RESOURCES

ALTERNATIVE TEACHING STRATEGY (ELL)

Have students work in small groups to **practice the strategy** *predict and test.* Ask: How many students does it take to reach across the classroom with their arms out and fingertips touching?

First, ask students to come up with an estimate they feel is reasonable without using any measuring tools. Have them explain their estimate.

Once the estimates are made, have students determine how many students are needed to span the classroom. Make a table to compare their estimates with the actual number they determined. Check students' work.

KINESTHETIC

SOCIAL STUDIES CONNECTION

Students can **apply the strategy** *predict and test* **to everyday problems**. Have students work in small groups to predict the number of students in their class born in each month of the year. Then tabulate the class birthdays by month and compare totals with the predictions.

Regroup the students into 12 groups according to the months in which they were born. Have group members research historical events that occurred on their birthdays or during the month that they were born. Then have them make a poster describing and illustrating the events. Check students' work.

VISUAL

READING STRATEGY

Compare Have students use the reading strategy *compare* to help them understand the problem on page 26. Have students compare the information about correct answers with the information about incorrect answers. They should recognize that for each correct answer, 4 points are added to the score, and for each incorrect answer, 1 point is subtracted.

Direct students' attention to the Solve section on page 26. Ask: When you check, what are you comparing your prediction to? Tammy's score of 85 points

ADVANCED LEARNERS

Challenge students to **use the strategy** *predict and test* to complete the magic square. The oldest-known magic square is the *lo-shu*, which was discovered about 4,000 years ago in China. Some of the numbers from the *lo-shu* are shown below. Have students complete the square and find the sum. top left = 6; middle = 5; bottom left = 2; sum = 15

	1	8
7		3
	9	4

VISUAL

TECHNOLOGY LINK

Intervention Strategies and Activities CD-ROM • *Skill 1*

LESSON **1.4** ORGANIZER

Objective To use the strategy *predict and test* to solve addition, subtraction, multiplication, and division problems with whole numbers

Lesson Resources Problem Solving Think Along, p. TR1

1 Introduce

QUICK REVIEW provides review of pre-requisite skills.

Why Learn This? You can use this strategy to find the number of specific types of coins needed to make a given amount of money or to solve equations with two variables. *Share the lesson objective with students.*

2 Teach

Guided Instruction

• *As you work through the problem with students, be sure they understand the scoring process.*

How many points would be given for 10 right answers? 40 points

How many points would be subtracted for 3 wrong answers? 3 points

How would you find the total score for 10 right answers and 3 wrong answers? 40 – 3 = 37

• *Encourage students to consider another starting point for their prediction/test table.*

REASONING **What would be another logical starting point for your predictions of correct and incorrect answers?** Possible answer: Start just below a perfect score of 25 correct answers at 24 correct and 1 incorrect and work backward.

• *Discuss with students the reasoning for this scoring method.*

Why do you think a test might be scored this way? to discourage guessing

Algebraic Thinking The process of making a prediction and then testing it is much like substituting different values for a variable in an algebraic equation.

LESSON **1.4**

PROBLEM SOLVING STRATEGY
Predict and Test

Analyze
Choose
Solve
Check

Learn how to use the strategy *predict and test* to solve problems with whole numbers.

1.	2.	3.	4.	5.
22 +62 = 84	88 −47 = 41	16 ×20 = 320	40 9)360	150 − 72 = 78

You can solve some problems by using your number sense to predict a possible answer. You should then test your answer and revise your prediction if necessary.

There were 25 problems on a test. For each correct answer, 4 points were given. For each incorrect answer, 1 point was subtracted. Tania answered all 25 problems. Her score was 85. How many correct answers did she have?

Analyze

What are you asked to find? **number of correct answers**

What facts are given? **total number of problems; number of points for correct and incorrect; Tania's score**
Is there any numerical information you will not use? If so, what? **no**

Choose

What strategy will you use?

You can use the strategy *predict and test*. Use the given information and your number sense to predict about how many correct answers Tania had. Then test your prediction, and revise it if necessary.

Solve

How will you solve the problem?

Make a table to show your prediction, your test of it, and any revisions you need. Be sure that the total of correct and incorrect problems is 25.

PREDICTION		TEST	
Correct	**Incorrect**	**SCORE**	
20	5	(20 × 4) − 5 = 75	*too low, so revise*
21	4	(21 × 4) − 4 = 80	*too low, so revise*
22	3	(22 × 4) − 3 = 85	*← correct*

So, Tania had 22 correct answers.

Check

How can you check your answer? **Answers will vary.**

What if Tania's score were 65? How many incorrect answers would she have? **7 incorrect answers**

26 **CALIFORNIA STANDARDS** O━NS 2.0 Students evaluate and solve problems involving addition, subtraction, multiplication, and division. **MR 3.2** Note the method of deriving the solution and demonstrate a conceptual understanding of the derivation by solving similar problems. *also,* **AF 3.1, MR 1.1, MR 1.3, MR 2.0, MR 2.7**

RETEACH 1.4

Problem Solving Strategy

Predict and Test

Looking for clues in a problem can help you find its answer. You can use the clues to help you guess and check different answers until you find the right one.

Valley Middle School is holding a canned food drive. Sixth-grade students have collected 150 more cans than seventh-grade students. Together, the students in both grades have collected a total of 530 cans. How many cans did the sixth graders collect? How many cans did the seventh graders collect?

Step 1: Think about what you know.
• You are asked to find the number of cans collected by each grade.
• You know the total number of cans collected and how many more cans the sixth graders collected than the seventh graders.

Step 2: Plan a strategy to solve.
• Use the *predict and test* strategy.
• Use these clues: total cans collected is 530; the difference between amounts collected by sixth and seventh graders is 150.

Step 3: Solve.
• Use a table to record your predictions and tests. Try to predict in an organized way to help you get closer to the exact answer.

PREDICT		TEST		
Sixth Graders	**Seventh Graders**	**Clue 1:** The sum is 530.	**Clue 2:** The difference is 150.	
330	200	330 + 200 = 530 ✓	330 − 200 = 130 ⊗	← Difference is too low.
350	180	350 + 180 = 530 ✓	350 − 180 = 170 ⊗	← Difference is too high.
340	190	340 + 190 = 530 ✓	340 − 190 = 150 ✓	← Both clues are satisfied.

Use the strategy *predict and test* with a table to help you solve.

1. In the problem above, what if the sixth graders had collected 120 more cans than the seventh graders? How many cans would each grade have collected?

sixth grade: 325 cans; seventh grade: 205 cans

2. Tony collected 85 cans of either soup or fruit. He collected 15 more cans of soup than of fruit. How many cans of soup did he collect? How many cans of fruit did he collect?

50 soup; 35 fruit

PRACTICE 1.4

Problem-Solving Strategy: Predict and Test

Solve by predicting and testing.

1. Ryan bought a total of 40 juice boxes. He bought 8 more boxes of apple juice than of grape juice. How many of each kind did he buy?

24 apple juice, 16 grape juice

2. The perimeter of a rectangular garden is 56 ft. The length is 4 ft more than the width. What are the dimensions of the garden?

l = 16 ft; w = 12 ft

3. The Hawks soccer team played a total of 24 games. They won 6 more games than they lost, and they tied 2 games. How many games did they win?

14 games

4. Rico collected a total of 47 rocks. He gathered 5 more jagged rocks than smooth rocks. How many of each kind of rock did he collect?

26 jagged rocks, 21 smooth rocks

5. Matt has earned $75. To buy a bicycle, he needs twice that amount plus $30. How much does the bicycle cost?

$180

6. The perimeter of a rectangular lot is 190 ft. The width of the lot is 15 ft more than the length. What are the dimensions of the lot?

w = 55 ft; l = 40 ft

7. The Wolverines swimming team won a total of 15 first- and second-place medals at their last swim meet. If they won 7 more first-place medals than second-place medals, how many first-place medals did they win?

11 first-place medals

8. Valley High School's football team played a total of 16 games. They won twice as many games as they lost. If they tied one game, how many games did the team win?

10 games

Mixed Review

Find the product or quotient. Estimate to check. Possible estimates are given.

9. 306 × 582

180,000; 178,092

10. 8,246 ÷ 38

200; 217

11. 21,420 ÷ 51

400; 420

Tell whether the estimate is an *overestimate* or *underestimate*. Then show how the estimate was determined.

12. 1,872 + 4,774 ≈ 7,000

overestimate; 2,000 + 5,000

13. 321 × 82 ≈ 24,000

underestimate; 300 × 80

Solve by predicting and testing.

1. Rodney bought a total of 40 oranges and apples. He bought 14 fewer apples than oranges. How many of each fruit did he buy? **13 apples, 27 oranges**

2. The Mighty Tigers soccer team played a total of 25 games. They won 9 more games than they lost, and 2 games ended in ties. How many games did they win? **16 games**

3. The perimeter of a rectangular garden is 40 ft. If the length is 6 ft more than the width, what are the length and width of the garden? **B**

   A $l = 12$ ft, $w = 6$ ft

   B $l = 13$ ft, $w = 7$ ft

   C $l = 6$ ft, $w = 12$ ft

   D $l = 7$ ft, $w = 13$ ft

4. The perimeter of a rectangular lawn is 28 yd. If the length is 4 yd more than the width, what are the length and width of the lawn? **G**

   F $l = 10$ yd, $w = 4$ yd

   G $l = 9$ yd, $w = 5$ yd

   H $l = 5$ yd, $w = 9$ yd

   J $l = 4$ yd, $w = 10$ yd

PROBLEM SOLVING STRATEGIES

- Draw a Diagram or Picture
- Make a Model
- ▶ **Predict and Test**
- Work Backward
- Make an Organized List
- Find a Pattern
- Make a Table or Graph
- Solve a Simpler Problem
- Write an Equation
- Use Logical Reasoning

MIXED STRATEGY PRACTICE

5. Rosalia waters her tomato plants every other day. She waters her pepper plants every 3 days. If she waters both on April 20, what are the next three dates on which she will water both? **April 26, May 2, and May 8**

6. Stacy spent a total of $28.45. She bought a ticket for a basketball game for $8.50, food for $7.95, and some T-shirts for $6.00 each. How many T-shirts did she buy? **2 T-shirts**

7. Sam has 98 baseball cards. This is 2 more than twice as many as Paul has. How many cards does Paul have? **48 cards**

8. Use the table below. If the pattern continues, how many miles in all will four runners run on the fifth day? **72 mi**

9. Melina and her two sisters collect stamps. Melina has twice as many as her older sister, who has 33 stamps. Melina has three times as many as her younger sister. How many stamps do they have in all? **121 stamps**

Each Runner's Training Schedule

Day	1	2	3	4	5
Miles	2	6	10	14	▢

10. **? What's the Question?** The sum of the ages of Jeff, Elijah, and Stefan is 41. Jeff is 14 years old. Stefan is 3 years older than Elijah. The answer is 12 years old. **Possible question: How old is Elijah?**

11. The train that leaves at 11:45 A.M. usually arrives in New York City 34 minutes after that. Today it arrived at 12:24 P.M. How late was the train? **5 min**

---

3 Practice

Guided Practice

Do Problem Solving Practice Exercises 1–4 with your students. Identify those having difficulty and use lesson resources to help.

Independent Practice

Assign Exercises 5–11.

4 Assess

Summarize the lesson by having students:

DISCUSS How would you use *predict and test* to solve this problem: A poster costs $4 less than a banner. Together, the poster and banner cost $20. What is the price of the poster? Possible answer: Choose two numbers with a difference of 4 and check to see if the sum is 20. 10 + 14 = 24, so I would try two lesser numbers, 8 and 12. 8 + 12 = 20. So the poster costs $8 and the banner costs $12.

 WRITE Explain how you solved Exercise 2. Possible answer: I made a table to keep track of win/loss predictions and tests that total 23 due to 2 ties.

Lesson Quiz

Transparency
1.4

Predict and test to solve.

1. Juan paid $21 for two model airplanes. One airplane cost $7 more than the other. What was the cost of each airplane? **$7, $14**

2. The Lorenzos traveled 300 more miles during the first week of their camping trip than they did the second week. They traveled a total of 2,280 miles. How many miles did they travel each week? **first week, 1,290 mi; second week, 990 mi**

READING STRATEGY 1.4

Compare

Analyze Choose Solve Check

When you **compare** two or more things, you examine how they are alike. It can be helpful to compare information in a problem. Read the following problem.

VOCABULARY
compare

Ralph has some chickens and some pigs. Together, the animals have 38 legs. They have 15 heads. How many of each kind of animal does he have?

This is a problem for which you might want to use the *predict and test* strategy. When you use this strategy, you think of possible solutions. Then you compare to see whether your solution fits the information given in the problem. You can use a table to compare information.

1. Complete the table. Compare the information about heads and legs in the chart with the information given in the problem.

Predict		Test	
Number of Chickens	Number of Pigs	Number of Legs	Number of Heads
7	8	46	15
9	6	42	15
10	5	40	15
11	4	38	15

2. Solve the problem.

11 chickens and 4 pigs

Make a table to compare the facts. Solve.

3. The Ping-Pong Paddlers table-tennis team played 15 games. They lost 4 fewer games than they won. They tied 2 more games than they lost. What was the team's record?

7 wins, 3 losses, 5 ties

4. Janine bought 20 pieces of fruit. Ten can be eaten without peeling. Eight are yellow and 6 are orange. She has 2 more pears than bananas. She bought grapefruit, lemons, bananas, apples, yellow pears, and oranges. How many of each fruit did she buy?

4 pears, 1 grapefruit, 2 bananas, 1 lemon, 6 apples, 6 oranges

---

CHALLENGE 1.4

Patterns, Patterns

Draw the next three figures of the pattern. Then describe the rule used to form the pattern.

1. Rule: __Triangle, square, then repeat adding one__
   __triangle and one square, repeating__

2. Rule: __Circle, square, diamond, then reverse__

3. Rule: __Circle, diamond, circle, then replace circles with__
   __squares, then back to circle, diamond, circle, repeating__

4. Rule: __Square 1/4 shaded, square 1/2 shaded, square__
   __entirely shaded, then reverse__

Give the next three numbers in the pattern. Then describe the rule.

5. 1, 2, 4, 8, 16, 32, __64__, __128__, __256__, ...
   Rule: __Multiply by 2.__

6. 3, 2, 4, 3, 5, 4, __6__, __5__, __7__, ...
   Rule: __Subtract 1, add 2.__

7. 3, 6, 9, 15, 24, 39, __63__, __102__, __165__, ...
   Rule: __Add the two previous terms.__

Algebra: Use Expressions

LESSON PLANNING

Objective To identify, write, and evaluate numerical and algebraic expressions involving whole numbers

Intervention for Prerequisite Skills

Place Value of Whole Numbers (For intervention strategies, see page 15.)

California Mathematics Content Standards

NS 2.0 Students calculate and solve problems involving addition, subtraction, multiplication, and division.

AF 1.0 Students write verbal expressions and sentences as algebraic expressions and equations; they evaluate algebraic expressions, solve simple linear equations, and graph and interpret their results.

(*Also* MR 2.4, MR 2.5)

Vocabulary

numerical expression a mathematical phrase that includes only numbers and operation symbols

variable a letter or symbol that stands for one or more numbers

algebraic expression an expression that is written using one or more variables

evaluate to find the answer to an expression

Math Background

One of the first steps in using equations to solve problems is to learn to interpret and evaluate expressions. Consider the following as you help students understand how to work with expressions:

- A numerical expression uses numbers and operation symbols to express the ideas given in a word expression.

- An algebraic expression uses numbers, operation symbols, and variables to express a quantitative idea.

- Evaluating an expression means simplifying it or replacing the variable with a number and simplifying it.

It is important for students to understand that an expression is like a phrase, or part of a sentence. An expression does not contain an equal sign or an inequality sign.

WARM-UP RESOURCES

NUMBER OF THE DAY

Transparency **1.5**

I am a number. Add 5 to me and multiply the result by 8. Subtract 40 and you get 48. What number am I? 6

PROBLEM OF THE DAY

Transparency **1.5**

In a number game, when Tina says *three*, Jay says *ten*. When Tina says *five*, Jay says *sixteen*. When Tina says *nine*, Jay says *twenty-eight*. When Tina says *eight*, what does Jay say? twenty-five If Jay says *one*, what number has Tina said? zero

Solution Problem of the Day tab, p. PD1B

DAILY FACTS PRACTICE

Have students practice addition and subtraction facts by completing Set E of *Teacher's Resource Book,* p. TR93.

INTERVENTION AND EXTENSION RESOURCES

ALTERNATIVE TEACHING STRATEGY ELL

Materials 20 index cards

Have students **identify numerical and algebraic expressions.** Display 10 numerical and 10 algebraic expressions. Write the corresponding word expressions on cards, one to a card. Divide the class into small groups and give each group several cards. Then choose the expressions one at a time. Let the groups decide who has the corresponding word expression. Call on a volunteer from the group to read the word expression. Check students' work.

VISUAL

MIXED REVIEW AND TEST PREP

Cumulative Review Grade 5 and Chapter 1

Refer to the Pupil Edition pages referenced in the exercises for further review. Have students go to the lesson page, review the lesson, and correct any problem they missed.

Mixed Review and Test Prep, p. 29

How to Help	
Item	Page
24	22
25	22
26	20
27	20
28	Grade 5

CAREER CONNECTION

Encourage students to **apply their knowledge of numerical and algebraic expressions to real life.** Read the following to students:

Shari works as a plumber. When she comes to your home to fix a plumbing problem, she charges a basic service fee of $65. Then she charges $35 per hour for every hour or part of an hour she spends at your home. She uses the expression $65 + 35h$ to determine how much you owe her. Find out how much you would owe Shari if she spent the following amounts of time at your home.

a. 45 min $100

b. 1 hr 15 min $135

c. 6 hr 10 min $310

AUDITORY

EARLY FINISHERS

Materials *For each pair* 6 index cards

Have students work in pairs to **practice using expressions.** First have them write 6 simple algebraic expressions on cards, one to a card. Then one student names a number between 1 and 50. The other student draws a card and evaluates the algebraic expression for that number. They then check the work and trade roles. Answers will vary.

AUDITORY

TECHNOLOGY LINK

- **Intervention Strategies and Activities CD-ROM** • *Skill 1*

- **Astro Algebra** • *Red,* Level J

LESSON **1.5** ORGANIZER

Objective To identify, write, and evaluate numerical and algebraic expressions involving whole numbers

Vocabulary numerical expression, variable, algebraic expression, evaluate

1 Introduce

QUICK REVIEW provides review of prerequisite skills.

Why Learn This? You can apply this skill to solving equations and more challenging word problems. *Share the lesson objective with students.*

2 Teach

Guided Instruction

- Help students compare the phrases "numerical expression" and "algebraic expression."

  What does the word *numerical* make you think of? numbers

  How is an algebraic expression different from a numerical expression? The algebraic expression contains one or more variables.

- Direct students' attention to the other examples of algebraic expressions.

  What is another way to write $y \div 2$? $\frac{y}{2}$

REASONING Write the other examples of algebraic expressions in words. five more than n; seven times (or multiplied by) a; three less than k (or k minus 3); y divided by 2; six times five times b

ADDITIONAL EXAMPLES

Example 1, p. 28

Write a numerical or algebraic expression for the word expression.

A. the number of slices in 3 dozen oranges, each of which has 10 slices $3 \times 12 \times 10$, $3(12)(10)$, or $3 \cdot 12 \cdot 10$

B. the height of a 17-step stairway of which each step is y in. high $17 \times y$, $17(y)$ or $17y$, or $17 \cdot y$

Example 2, p. 28

Evaluate each expression.

A. $s - 16$, for $s = 125$ 109

B. $t \div 7 \times 2$, for $t = 140$ 40

28 Chapter 1

ALGEBRA
Use Expressions

Learn how to identify, write, and evaluate expressions involving whole numbers.

Vocabulary
numerical expression
variable
algebraic expression
evaluate

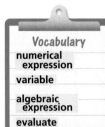

QUICK REVIEW

1. $23 + 14$ 2. $67 - 40$ 3. 15×6 4. $180 \div 30$ 5. 25×8
   37   27   90   6   200

In a basketball game, a team scored 27 points in the first half and 38 points in the second half. To represent the total points, you could use a numerical expression. A **numerical expression** is a mathematical phrase that includes only numbers and operation symbols.

$$27 + 38 \leftarrow \text{total points}$$

Here are other examples of numerical expressions.

$$60 + 25 \qquad 42 \div 7 \qquad 16 - 3 \qquad 51 \times 36 \qquad 30 + 12 + 41$$

If you didn't know how many points the team scored in the second half, you could use a variable to represent the points. A **variable** is a letter or symbol that can stand for one or more numbers. An expression that includes a variable is called an **algebraic expression**.

$$27 + p \leftarrow \textit{Use p to represent points scored in second half.}$$

Here are other examples of algebraic expressions.

$$5 + n \qquad 7 \times a \qquad k - 3 \qquad y \div 2 \qquad 6 \times 5 \times b$$

In an expression, there are several ways to show multiplication.

$$7 \times a \text{ can be written as } 7a, 7(a), \text{ or } 7 \cdot a.$$

Word expressions can be translated into numerical or algebraic expressions.

EXAMPLE 1

Write a numerical or algebraic expression for the word expression.

A. three dollars less than five dollars $5 - 3$

B. two times a distance, d $2 \times d$, $2(d)$, $2d$, or $2 \cdot d$

To **evaluate** a numerical expression, you find its value. To evaluate an algebraic expression, replace the variable with a number and then find the value.

EXAMPLE 2

Evaluate each expression.

A. $a + 150$, for $a = 18$ **B.** $b \div 10 \times 3$, for $b = 120$

$a + 150$	*Replace a*	$b \div 10 \times 3$	*Replace b with*
$18 + 150$	*with 18.*	$120 \div 10 \times 3$	*120.*
168	*Add.*	12×3	*Divide and*
		36	*then multiply.*

28

CALIFORNIA STANDARDS O→ NS 2.0 Students calculate and solve problems involving addition, subtraction, multiplication, and division. AF 1.0 Students write verbal expressions and sentences as algebraic expressions and equations; they evaluate algebraic expressions, solve simple linear equations, and graph and interpret their results. *also,* MR 2.4, MR 2.5

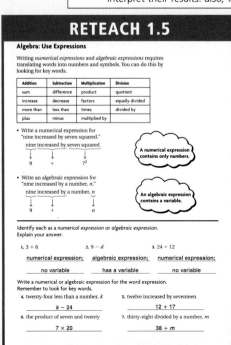

RETEACH 1.5

Algebra: Use Expressions

Writing *numerical expressions* and *algebraic expressions* requires translating words into numbers and symbols. You can do this by looking for key words.

Addition	Subtraction	Multiplication	Division
sum	difference	product	quotient
increase	decrease	factors	equally divided
more than	less than	times	divided by
plus	minus	multiplied by	

- Write a numerical expression for "nine increased by seven squared."

  nine increased by seven squared

  $9 \qquad + \qquad 7^2$

  A numerical expression contains only numbers.

- Write an algebraic expression for "nine increased by a number, n."

  nine increased by a number, n

  $9 \qquad + \qquad n$

  An algebraic expression contains a variable.

Identify each as a *numerical expression* or *algebraic expression*. Explain your answer.

1. $3 + 6$ 2. $9 - d$ 3. $24 \div 12$

numerical expression;   algebraic expression;   numerical expression;

no variable   has a variable   no variable

Write a numerical or algebraic expression for the word expression. Remember to look for key words.

4. twenty-four less than a number, k 5. twelve increased by seventeen

   $k - 24$ $12 + 17$

6. the product of seven and twenty   7. thirty-eight divided by a number, m

   7×20 $38 \div m$

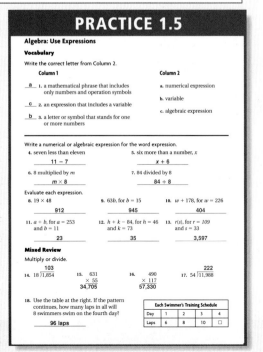

PRACTICE 1.5

Algebra: Use Expressions

Vocabulary

Write the correct letter from Column 2.

Column 1	Column 2
a 1. a mathematical phrase that includes only numbers and operation symbols	a. numerical expression
c 2. an expression that includes a variable	b. variable
b 3. a letter or symbol that stands for one or more numbers	c. algebraic expression

Write a numerical or algebraic expression for the word expression.

4. seven less than eleven   5. six more than a number, x

   $11 - 7$ $x + 6$

6. 8 multiplied by m 7. 84 divided by 8

   $m \times 8$ $84 \div 8$

Evaluate each expression.

8. 19×48 9. $63b$, for $b = 15$ 10. $w + 178$, for $w = 226$

   912   945   404

11. $a \div b$, for $a = 253$ 12. $h + k - 84$, for $h = 46$ 13. $r(s)$, for $r = 109$
    and $b = 11$ and $k = 73$ and $s = 33$

    23   35   3,597

Mixed Review

Multiply or divide.

14. $18\overline{)1,854}$ 15. $\begin{array}{r}631 \\ \times 55 \\ \hline 34,705\end{array}$ 16. $\begin{array}{r}490 \\ \times 117 \\ \hline 57,330\end{array}$ 17. $54\overline{)11,988}$
    103   222

18. Use the table at the right. If the pattern continues, how many laps in all will 8 swimmers swim on the fourth day?

    96 laps

Each Swimmer's Training Schedule				
Day	1	2	3	4
Laps	6	8	10	□

CHECK FOR UNDERSTANDING

Think and ▶
Discuss

Look back at the lesson to answer each question.

1. **Explain** the difference between a numerical expression and an algebraic expression. Give some examples of each. **An algebraic expression has one or more variables; examples will vary.**

2. **Show** four different ways to write an algebraic expression for the product of the number 10 and the variable g.
$10 \times g$, $10g$, $10(g)$, or $10 \cdot g$

Guided ▶
Practice

Write a numerical or algebraic expression for the word expression.

3. forty-six less than one hundred twenty-five
$125 - 46$

4. one hundred seven more than y
$y + 107$

5. y divided by fifteen
$y \div 15$, or $\frac{y}{15}$

Evaluate each expression.

6. 21×15
315

7. $100 - g$, for $g = 54$
46

8. $s \div 8$, for $s = 720$
90

PRACTICE AND PROBLEM SOLVING

Independent ▶
Practice

Write a numerical or algebraic expression for the word expression.

9. twenty-five $20 bills
25×20

10. q more than two hundred fifteen
$215 + q$

11. seventy-six decreased by k
$76 - k$

12. x divided by fourteen
$x \div 14$, or $\frac{x}{14}$

Evaluate each expression.

13. 15×31
465

14. $3,021 + 915$
3,936

15. $10,340 - 1,340$
9,000

16. $k - 65$, for $k = 95$ **30**

17. $\frac{d}{7} \times 2$, for $d = 490$
140

18. $100b$, for $b = 54$
5,400

19. $m \div n$, for $m = 1,230$ and $n = 410$ **3**

20. cd, for $c = 5$ and $d = 200$
1,000

Problem Solving ▶
Applications

21. Let n represent the number of free throws Nathan scored. Bryan scored 12 more free throws than Nathan. Write an algebraic expression to show how many free throws Bryan scored. **$n + 12$**

22. ✏️ **Write About It** Explain how to evaluate an algebraic expression when you know the value of each variable. Give an example. **Replace each variable with its value and perform each operation. Examples will vary.**

23. **REASONING** Tiffany, Deidre, Luisa, Kendall, and Ann Marie are runners. Kendall can outrun Luisa and Tiffany, but Deidre can outrun Kendall. Luisa can outrun Ann Marie, but Deidre can outrun Luisa. Which one of the girls is the fastest runner? **Deidre**

MIXED REVIEW AND TEST PREP

24. 530×42 (p. 22)
22,260

25. $3,870 \div 18$ (p. 22)
215

26. $1,234 + 453$ (p. 20)
1,687

27. $8,000 - 357$ (p. 20)
7,643

28. **TEST PREP** Christina bought 3 pens and 1 notebook for $5.85. A pen cost $1.20. How much did the notebook cost? **D**

A $1.20   B $1.25   C $1.85   D $2.25

Extra Practice page H32, Set D

29

---

3 Practice

Guided Practice

Do Check for Understanding Exercises 1–8 with your students. Identify those having difficulty and use lesson resources to help.

Independent Practice

Assign Exercises 9–23.

Algebraic Thinking The ability to translate words into symbols is fundamental to solving word problems and to all future work in algebra.

Before assigning Exercises 9–21 remind students that a variable holds the place of a number, much like the symbol ■ that they have seen in previous expressions.

MIXED REVIEW AND TEST PREP

Exercises 24–28 provide **cumulative review** (Grade 5 and Chapter 1).

4 Assess

Summarize the lesson by having students:

DISCUSS What can a variable represent? A variable can represent one or more numbers.

 WRITE Describe three algebraic and three numerical expressions. Then rewrite them as word expressions. Check students' work.

Lesson Quiz

Transparency **1.5**

Match the word expression with the numerical expression.

1. 7 times s c   a. $s - 7$
2. 7 less than s a   b. $q + 7$
3. q minus s e   c. $7 \times s$
4. twice q plus 7   f   d. $\frac{q}{s}$
5. 7 more than q b   e. $q - s$
6. q divided by s d   f. $2q + 7$

Evaluate the expression.

7. $5r - 6$, for $r = 9$ and $r = 12$ **39; 54**

PROBLEM SOLVING 1.5

Algebra: Use Expressions

Write the correct answer.

1. Write an algebraic expression for the word expression.

15 less than a number, a

$a - 15$

2. Write a numerical expression for the word expression.

24 times 8

24×8

3. Fred scored 8 points more than Dale during the game. If together they scored 32 points, determine the number of points Dale scored.

12 points

4. Patricia wants to share her package of 36 pretzels equally among her 5 friends and herself. How many pretzels will each person receive?

6 pretzels

Choose the letter for the best answer.

5. Which algebraic expression represents the word expression?

the sum of 9 and a number, a, squared

A $9 - a^2$ C $9 \div a^2$
B $9 + a^2$ D $9 \times a^2$

6. Which word expression represents the numerical expression?

$24 \div 6$

F 24 decreased by 6
G the sum of 24 and 6
H 24 increased by 6
J the quotient of 24 and 6

7. What 2 numbers have a product of 48 and a quotient of 48?

A 8 and 6
B 12 and 4
C 48 and 1
D 96 and 2

8. Joan bought 5 yards of fabric for $2.85 a yard, including tax. Which equation could be used to find the change loan received, a, if she gave the cashier $50?

F $a = 50 + (5 \times 2.85)$
G $a = 50 - (5 + 2.85)$
H $a = 50 - (5 \times 2.85)$
J $a = 50 + 5 + 2.85$

9. **Write About It** Give examples of phrases that can usually be translated into subtraction expressions.

Phrases such as *less than*, *difference*, and *decreased by* usually indicate subtraction.

CHALLENGE 1.5

Expression Match

Write an algebraic expression for "a number, n, less than seven, all divided by 2."

$(7 - n) \div 2$
- The 7 must come first, because n is less than 7.
- To show "all divided by 2," use parentheses.

Draw a line connecting the word expression in Column 1 to the correct algebraic expression in Column 2.

Column 1

1. twenty-two less than a number, a, all times three
2. twenty-two times a number, a, plus three
3. a number, a, increased by three, all times twenty-two
4. a number, a, decreased by twenty-two, all divided by three
5. twenty-two times a number, a, decreased by three
6. a number, a, divided by three, increased by twenty-two
7. the sum of three and twenty-two, all divided by a number, a
8. a number, a, less than twenty-two, all times three
9. the sum of a number, a, and three, all divided by twenty-two.
10. a number, a, decreased by three and then increased by twenty-two

Column 2

A. $a + 3 + 22$
B. $a - 3 + 22$
C. $22 \times a + 3$
D. $(a - 22) \times 3$
E. $(22 - a) \times 3$
F. $(a - 22) \div 3$
G. $(a + 3) \div 22$
H. $(a + 3) \times 22$
I. $22 \times a - 3$
J. $(3 + 22) \div a$

29

Algebra: Mental Math and Equations

LESSON PLANNING

Objective To solve equations with whole numbers by using mental math and substitution

Intervention for Prerequisite Skills

Place Value of Whole Numbers (For intervention strategies, see page 15.)

 California Mathematics Content Standards

AF 1.0 Students write verbal expressions and sentences as algebraic expressions and equations; they evaluate algebraic expressions, solve simple linear equations, and graph and interpret their results.

AF 1.1 Write and solve one-step linear equations in one variable.

(*Also* **NS 2.0, MR 2.5**)

Vocabulary

equation an algebraic or numerical sentence that shows two quantities are equal

solution a value that, when substituted for the variable, makes an equation true

Math Background

Before students learn to solve problems by using the properties of equality, it is important that students understand what a solution is. Accordingly, in this lesson students:

• test a possible solution by substituting it in the equation to see if the resulting statement is true.

• solve simple equations by using mental math.

To solve by using mental math, students rely on number facts. This process of using related number facts and then testing the solution strengthens the students' understanding of what constitutes a solution of an equation.

WARM-UP RESOURCES

 NUMBER OF THE DAY Transparency **1.6**

Take the number that represents the day of the month. Find the value for each of these expressions: $n + 8$, $n - 1$, $n \times 5$, and $n \div 2$. Check students' answers.

 PROBLEM OF THE DAY Transparency **1.6**

Martin saves n dollars each week. Kara saves twice as much as Martin. In 15 weeks their combined savings total $450. How much does Martin save each week? How can you use mental math to solve it? $10

Solution Problem of the Day tab, p. PD1B

 DAILY FACTS PRACTICE

Have students practice multiplication and division facts by completing Set F of *Teacher's Resource Book,* p. TR93.

INTERVENTION AND EXTENSION RESOURCES

ALTERNATIVE TEACHING STRATEGY

Materials *For each pair* number cube, p. TR75

Have students work in pairs to **write equations for each other to solve.** Display this formula:

variable + low roll = high roll

Have one student in each pair roll the number cube twice and use the formula to write an equation for his or her partner to solve. If the two rolls are equal, then the high roll and the low roll will be the same number. Have students record their equations and solutions. Answers will vary.

KINESTHETIC

MIXED REVIEW AND TEST PREP

Cumulative Review Grade 5 and Chapter 1

Refer to the Pupil Edition pages referenced in the exercises for further review. Have students go to the lesson page, review the lesson, and correct any problem they missed.

Mixed Review and Test Prep, p. 31

How to Help	
Item	Page
27	28
28	22
29	20
30	Grade 5
31	Grade 5

ENGLISH LANGUAGE LEARNER ELL•SDAIE

Explore the word *equation* with your students. Display the words *equal, equality,* and *equinox*. Have students suggest meanings of these words. Record their ideas. You may want to explain that the equinox occurs when day and night are of approximately equal length, the beginning of spring and fall. Then ask:

- What do these words have in common? all have *equ-* as part of the word
- What does *equation* mean? an algebraic sentence with parts that are equal on either side of the equal sign
- In what ways is the word *equation* similar to the other three words? They all deal with things being equal.

Have students illustrate each word for a class poster and add "equ"- words throughout the unit.

VISUAL

**ENG-LANG ARTS
Standards
R 1.0**

SPECIAL NEEDS

Provide additional **practice with variables and solutions.** Have each student write a number less than 15 on a sheet of paper. Then write this equation and read it to the students: $2n = 20$

Ask a volunteer to come to the board and place his or her number over the variable in the equation. Have other students decide if that student's number is a solution to the equation. Call on another volunteer to explain why it is a solution or why it is not.

Repeat with other equations, such as $a + 7 = 18$ and $b - 9 = 11$. Check students' work.

VISUAL

TECHNOLOGY LINK

- **Intervention Strategies and Activities CD-ROM** • *Skill 1*
- **Astro Algebra** • *Red,* Level E

LESSON **1.6** ORGANIZER

Objective To solve equations with whole numbers by using mental math and substitution

Vocabulary equation, solution
Review variable

1 Introduce

QUICK REVIEW provides review of pre-requisite skills.

Why Learn This? You can apply this skill to future math problems to determine unknown numbers in an equation. *Share the lesson objective with students.*

2 Teach

Guided Instruction

• *Ask students to describe an equation.*

What symbol differentiates an equation from an expression? an equal sign

• *After working through Example 1, ask:*

REASONING Are there any other numbers that are not solutions of $12p = 108$? yes, any number other than 9

Are there any other numbers that are solutions? Explain. No; When you replace p with any other number, the statement is no longer true.

• *Help students explore ways to use mental math to solve the equations.*

How did you use mental math to solve Example 2? Possible answer: I remembered that $8 + 8 = 16$.

How could you use subtraction to help you solve Example 2? Think that $16 - 8 = 8$, so $8 + 8 = 16$.

ADDITIONAL EXAMPLES

Example 1, p. 30

Which of the following numbers, 6, 7, or 8, is a solution of the equation $9n = 72$? 8

Example 2, p. 30

Solve the equation $15 = t + 9$ by using mental math. $t = 6$; The solution is 6.

ALGEBRA
Mental Math and Equations

Learn how to use mental math to solve equations.

Vocabulary

equation

solution

An **equation** is a statement showing that two quantities are equal. These are equations:

$$6 + 7 = 13 \qquad 24 \div 3 = 8 \qquad k - 3 = 1 \qquad 2d = 18 \qquad a + b = 11$$

If an equation contains a variable, you can solve the equation by finding the value of the variable that makes the equation true. That value is the **solution**.

EXAMPLE 1

Remember that a variable is a letter or symbol that stands for one or more numbers.

Which of the numbers 8, 9, and 10 is a solution of the equation $12p = 108$?

Replace p with 8.	*Replace p with 9.*	*Replace p with 10.*
$12(8) \overset{?}{=} 108$	$12(9) \overset{?}{=} 108$	$12(10) \overset{?}{=} 108$
$96 = 108$ *false*	$108 = 108$ *true*	$120 = 108$ *false*

The solution is 9 because $12(9) = 108$.

• Which of the numbers 4, 5, and 6 is a solution of the equation $222 \div n = 37$? 6

Some equations with variables can be solved by using mental math. Think of the value of the variable that makes the equation true. Then check your answer.

EXAMPLE 2

The Statue of Liberty's hand is about 16 ft long. The index finger is 8 ft long. What is the length of the palm of her hand? Solve the equation $16 = c + 8$ by using mental math.

| $16 = c + 8$ | *What number added to 8 gives 16?* |
| $8 = c$ | *The solution is 8.* |

Check:

| $16 = 8 + 8$ | *Replace c with 8.* |
| $16 = 16$ | *8 + 8 is equal to 16.* |

• Solve the equation $m \times 7 = 56$ by using mental math. $m = 8$

30

RETEACH 1.6

Algebra: Mental Math and Equations

You can use the number facts you know to help solve equations.
Remember, you can use fact families to find missing numbers.

• Solve the equation $8 + x = 12$ by using mental math.

Related fact: $12 - 8 = 4$
So, $8 + 4 = 12$.
$8 + x = 12$
$\quad x = 4$ *The solution is 4.*

Check to be sure your answer is correct.
$8 + 4 = 12$ *Replace x with 4.*
$12 = 12$ *8 + 4 is equal to 12.*

• Solve the equation $y \times 7 = 35$ by using mental math.

Related fact: $35 \div 7 = 5$
So, $5 \times 7 = 35$.
$y \times 7 = 35$
$\quad y = 5$ *The solution is 5.*

Check to be sure your answer is correct.
$5 \times 7 = 35$ *Replace y with 5.*
$35 = 35$ *5 × 7 is equal to 35.*

• Solve the equation $m - 9 = 8$ by using mental math.

Related fact: $9 + 8 = 17$.
So, $17 - 9 = 8$.
$m - 9 = 8$
$\quad m = 17$ *The solution is 17.*

Check to be sure your answer is correct.
$17 - 9 = 8$ *Replace m with 17.*
$8 = 8$ *17 − 9 is equal to 8.*

• Solve the equation $d + 6 = 8$ by using mental math.

Related fact: $8 \times 6 = 48$
So, $48 \div 6 = 8$.
$d \div 6 = 8$
$\quad d = 48$ *The solution is 48.*

Check to be sure your answer is correct.
$48 \div 6 = 8$ *Replace d with 48.*
$8 = 8$ *48 ÷ 6 is equal to 8.*

Solve each equation by using mental math.

1. $a - 5 = 9$
Related fact:
$9 + 5 =$ ___14___
The solution is ___14___

2. $\frac{k}{5} = 5$
Related fact:
$5 \times 5 =$ ___25___
The solution is ___25___

3. $3r = 18$
Related fact:
$18 \div 3 =$ ___6___
The solution is ___6___

4. $10 + f = 15$
$f = $ ___5___

5. $n + 12 = 3$
$n = $ ___36___

6. $8s = 64$
$s = $ ___8___

7. $w - 20 = 10$
$w = $ ___30___

8. $n \times 9 = 81$
$n = $ ___9___

9. $x + 9 = 16$
$x = $ ___7___

10. $\frac{m}{10} = 10$
$m = $ ___100___

11. $g - 30 = 6$
$g = $ ___36___

12. $16 = c + 100$
$c = $ ___1,600___

PRACTICE 1.6

Algebra: Mental Math and Equations

Determine which of the given values is a solution of the equation.

1. $4d = 28$;
$d = 7, 8,$ or 9
$d = $ ___7___

2. $50 - t = 28$;
$t = 20, 21,$ or 22
$t = $ ___22___

3. $42 \div n = 6$;
$n = 5, 6,$ or 7
$n = $ ___7___

4. $72 \div v = 85$;
$v = 12, 13,$ or 14
$v = $ ___13___

5. $m + 7 = 18$;
$m = 9, 10,$ or 11
$m = $ ___11___

6. $s - 17 = 10$;
$s = 26, 27,$ or 28
$s = $ ___27___

7. $c + 8 = 3$;
$c = 22, 23,$ or 24
$c = $ ___24___

8. $155 = 5k$;
$k = 30, 31,$ or 32
$k = $ ___31___

9. $8 = 25 - x$;
$x = 17, 18,$ or 19
$x = $ ___17___

Solve each equation by using mental math.

10. $e + 6 = 20$
$e = $ ___14___

11. $x \div 2 = 10$
$x = $ ___20___

12. $6 \times h = 300$
$h = $ ___50___

13. $s - 18 = 40$
$s = $ ___58___

14. $92 = b + 7$
$b = $ ___85___

15. $90 \div t = 15$
$t = $ ___6___

16. $m - 150 = 420$
$m = $ ___570___

17. $8 \times n = 72$
$n = $ ___9___

18. $f - 6 = 98$
$f = $ ___104___

19. $c \times 4 = 40$
$c = $ ___10___

20. $63 = d \times 7$
$d = $ ___9___

21. $k + 28 = 32$
$k = $ ___4___

22. $9x = 180$
$x = $ ___20___

23. $6 = v - 58$
$v = $ ___64___

24. $w \div 9 = 12$
$w = $ ___108___

25. $p + 62 = 100$
$p = $ ___38___

Mixed Review

Find the sum or difference. Estimate to check. Possible estimates are given.

26. 390
$+ 789$
___1,179___
1,200;

27. $9,056$
$- 1,732$
___7,324___
7,000;

28. $1,978$
$+ 693$
___2,671___
2,700;

29. $47,813$
$- 9,507$
___38,306___
40,000;

30. $73,681$
$+ 50,342$
___124,023___
120,000;

Evaluate each expression.

31. $n + 701$, for $n = 510$
___1,211___

32. $50p$, for $p = 53$
___2,650___

33. $r \times s$, for $r = 12$ and $s = 30$
___360___

34. $h + g$, for $h = 65$ and $g = 41$
___106___

CHECK FOR UNDERSTANDING

Think and Discuss ▶ Look back at the lesson to answer each question.

1. Tell whether 4 is a solution of the equation $x + 3 = 9$. If it is not, find the solution. **No; 6**

2. Give an example of an equation with a solution of 5.
Possible answer: $b \times 2 = 10$

Guided Practice ▶ Determine which of the given values is the solution of the equation.

3. $f \div 7 = 3$; $f = 19, 20,$ or 21
$f = 21$

4. $t + 9 = 20$; $t = 10, 11,$ or 12
$t = 11$

Solve each equation by using mental math.

5. $7 = x + 3$
$x = 4$

6. $\dfrac{h}{9} = 3$
$h = 27$

7. $4 \times k = 16$
$k = 4$

PRACTICE AND PROBLEM SOLVING

Independent Practice ▶ Determine which of the given values is the solution of the equation.

8. $3h = 39$; $h = 11, 12,$ or 13
$h = 13$

9. $17 - x = 12$; $x = 5, 6,$ or 7
$x = 5$

10. $48 + s = 57$; $s = 8, 9,$ or 10
$s = 9$

11. $3 = 54 \div k$; $k = 16, 17,$ or 18
$k = 18$

Solve each equation by using mental math.

12. $p - 7 = 7$
$p = 14$

13. $9m = 81$
$m = 9$

14. $13 + r = 30$
$r = 17$

15. $x - 16 = 4$
$x = 20$

16. $h \div 8 = 7$
$h = 56$

17. $14 = k - 15$
$k = 29$

18. $87 = e \div 10$
$e = 870$

19. $12 \times v = 240$
$v = 20$

20. $t \div 6 = 125$
$t = 750$

21. $12 + 4 + d = 25$
$d = 9$

22. $3 \times 4 = c - 8$
$c = 20$

23. $p + 14 = 32 - 12$
$p = 6$

Problem Solving Applications ▶

24. The equation $w + 12 = 40$ describes the number of men and women riding the bus to a convention. If w is the number of women riding the bus, how many men are riding the bus? **12 men**

25. Mr. Murakami teaches 5 classes of 25 students each. One hundred of his students are sixth graders. How many are not sixth graders?
25 students

26. **(?) What's the Question?** A roller coaster has 7 cars. Fifty-six people can ride the roller coaster at one time. The answer is 8.
Possible question: How many people can ride in each car?

MIXED REVIEW AND TEST PREP

27. Evaluate $a + 14$ for $a = 27$. (p. 28) **41**

28. $525 \div 25$ (p. 22) **21**

29. Find $4,310 - 1,900 + 3,450 - 870$. (p. 20)
4,990

30. Find the greatest common factor of 15 and 35. **5**

31. TEST PREP Andre left the house at 8:45 A.M. He arrived home $4\frac{1}{2}$ hours later. At what time did Andre arrive home? **D**

A 11:45 A.M. **B** 12:45 A.M. **C** 12:45 P.M. **D** 1:15 P.M.

Extra Practice page H32, Set E

31

---

3 Practice

Guided Practice

Do Check for Understanding Exercises 1–7 with your students. Identify those having difficulty and use lesson resources to help.

Independent Practice

Assign Exercises 8–26.

Algebraic Thinking Students are introduced to the concept of solving equations by testing solutions and using mental math. As they solve the exercises, ask them to explain their thought processes to lead into the idea of using inverse operations to solve equations.

MIXED REVIEW AND TEST PREP
Exercises 27–31 provide **cumulative review** (Grade 5 and Chapter 1).

4 Assess

Summarize the lesson by having students:

DISCUSS Once you have found the solution to an equation, how do you know if it is correct? You can substitute your value for the variable and see if the resulting statement is true.

WRITE Describe the steps you would use to solve the equation $6m = 54$ mentally. Think either that $6 \times 9 = 54$ or that $54 \div 6 = 9$, so the solution is 9. Check by substituting the solution for the variable: $6 \times 9 = 54$ is a true statement.

Lesson Quiz

Transparency **1.6**

Solve each equation by using mental math.

1. $v + 8 = 28$ 20
2. $5 \times m = 45$ 9
3. $65 = d + 22$ 43
4. $10 = n \div 3$ 30
5. $16 = t - 14$ 30
6. $17 \times s = 0$ 0

PROBLEM SOLVING 1.6

Algebra: Mental Math and Equations

Analyze Choose Solve Check

Write the correct answer.

1. Shania is saving $25 each week for a bicycle. When she began saving, she used the equation $25y = 200$ to find out how many weeks she needed to save the money for the bike. How many weeks will it take her to save enough for the bike?

8 weeks

2. An average of 2 million people visited a new encyclopedia web site each day during the first 5 days it was open. You can use the equation $n \div 2 = 5$ to determine how many millions of people visited the site during the 5 days. How many visitors were there?

10 million visitors

3. Write the number 86,003 in words.

eighty-six thousand, three

4. Write 40,610 in expanded form.

40,000 + 600 + 10

Choose the letter for the best answer.

5. Determine which of the values is a solution of the equation $5x = 55$.
A 5
B 10
Ⓒ 11
D 55

6. Which of the following numbers is divisible by 3, 4, and 9?
F 9,164
Ⓖ 6,372
H 4,581
J 3,762

7. It is 12 blocks from Hiro's house to the store. He uses the equation $12 + b = 24$ to find out how much farther he needs to walk to get to the library, which is 24 blocks from his house. How far does he have to walk?
A 2 blocks
Ⓑ 12 blocks
C 36 blocks
D 268 blocks

8. A video costs $16.48. Sondra has saved $7.95. Which equation could she use to find how much more money she needs to buy the video?
F $16.48 + n = $7.95
Ⓖ $7.95 + n = $16.48
H $7.95 + $16.48 = n
J $n + $16.48 = $7.95

9. Write About It How would you use mental math to solve the equation $z \div 8 = 9$?

Possible answer: Think about what number divided by 8 equals 9.
Use the related fact $8 \times 9 = 72$ to determine that the value of z is 72.

CHALLENGE 1.6

Solve the Clues!

Use mental math to solve each equation clue. Find the answer in the Tip Box below. Write the letter of that equation above it. When you have solved all the equations, you will have discovered a math tip that is especially important when solving equations.

Clues

A $12a = 96$	**8**	N $n + 4 = 100$ **400**
B $b - 10 = 1$	**11**	O $o - 8 = 16 + 12$ **36**
C $c \div 3 = 5$	**15**	P $p \times 2 = 700$ **350**
D $12 + d = 12$	**0**	R $7 \times 36 = r \times 14$ **18**
E $4e = 20$	**5**	S $s \div 10 = 41$ **410**
G $8g = 320$	**40**	T $t + 83 = 289$ **206**
H $7 + 9 + h = 80$	**64**	U $u \times 184 = 184$ **1**
I $28 \div i = 47$	**19**	W $9 \times 16 = w \times 12$ **12**
K $2k = 100$	**50**	X $x - 17 = 29$ **46**
L $300 = l - 75$	**375**	Y $5y = 1,000$ **200**

Tip Box

A	L		W	A	Y	S		C	H	E	C	K		Y	O	U	R
8	375		12	8	200	410		15	64	5	15	50		200	36	1	18

A	N	S	W	E	R		T	O	B	E		S	U	R	E
8	400	410	12	5	18		206	36	11	5		410	1	18	5

I	T		I	S		C	O	R	R	E	C	T
19	206		19	410		15	36	18	18	5	15	206

Use your answers to solve the riddle.

Riddle: Which football bowl game do flies like best?

T	H	E		S	U	G	A	R		B	O	W	L
206	64	5		410	1	40	8	18		11	36	12	375

31

CHAPTER 1

REVIEW/TEST

Purpose To check understanding of concepts, skills, and problem solving presented in Chapter 1

USING THE PAGE

The Chapter 1 Review/Test can be used as a **review** or a **test**.

- Items 1–3 check understanding of concepts and new vocabulary.
- Items 4–38 check skill proficiency.
- Items 39–40 check students' abilities to choose and apply problem solving strategies to real-life problems involving whole numbers.

 Suggest that students place the completed Chapter 1 Review/Test in their portfolios.

USING THE ASSESSMENT GUIDE

- Multiple-choice format of Chapter 1 Posttest—See *Assessment Guide*, pp. AG9–10.
- Free-response format of Chapter 1 Posttest—See *Assessment Guide*, pp. AG11–12.

USING STUDENT SELF-ASSESSMENT

The How Did I Do? survey helps students assess what they have learned and how they learned it. This survey is available as a copying master in *Assessment Guide*, p. AGxii.

---

1. **VOCABULARY** A way to estimate a sum when all of the addends are about the same is __?__. (p. 16)
   clustering

2. **VOCABULARY** A letter or symbol that can stand for one or more numbers is a(n) __?__. (p. 28)
   variable

3. **VOCABULARY** A statement showing that two quantities are equal is a(n) __?__. (p. 30)
   equation

Estimate. (pp. 16–19) Possible estimates are given.

4. 593
    $+724$
    1,300

5. $1,420$
    $+5,791$
    7,200

6. 935
    -549
    400

7. $2,371$
    $-1,456$
    900

8. $43,816$
    $-39,972$
    4,000

9. 48×6 **300**

10. 308×67 **21,000**

11. $374 \div 7$ **50**

12. $276 \div 42$ **7**

13. $3,764 \div 591$ **6**

Find the sum or difference. (pp. 20–21)

14. $4,762$
    $+39,038$
    43,800

15. $9,724 - 286$ **9,438**

16. $50,031$
    $- 9,352$
    40,679

17. 737
    $4,650$
    $+11,821$
    17,208

18. $678,040$
    $-329,193$
    348,847

Multiply or divide. (pp. 22–25)

19. 526
    $\times 42$
    22,092

20. 123×12 **1,476**

21. $2,250 \div 18$ **125**

22. 189
    $\times 108$
    20,412

23. $40\overline{)3,206}$ **80 r6**

Evaluate each expression for $a = 63$, $b = 150$, **and** $c = 7$. (pp. 28–29)

24. $a + 305$ **368**

25. $b - 36$ **114**

26. $300 \div b$ **2**

27. $3c$ **21**

28. $a \div 9$ **7**

29. $215 - b$ **65**

30. $112 \div c$ **16**

31. $a \times 5$ **315**

32. $2a + 4$ **130**

33. $a + b$ **213**

Solve each equation by using mental math. (pp. 30–31)

34. $3m = 27$
    $m = 9$

35. $14 = q + 6$
    $q = 8$

36. $20 = y - 9$
    $y = 29$

37. $w \div 50 = 5$
    $w = 250$

38. $74 + a = 85$
    $a = 11$

Solve. (pp. 26–27)

39. At school during spirit week, Ming sold a total of 36 red and blue ribbons. She sold 6 more red ribbons than blue ribbons. How many of each color did she sell? **15 blue and 21 red ribbons**

40. Colton worked two days on a project for school. He worked a total of 195 minutes. If he worked 45 minutes longer on the first day, how long did Colton work each day? **120 min, 75 min**

CHAPTER 1 TEST, page 1

Choose the best answer.

For 1–4, estimate.

1. 617
   -285
   A 900
   B 800
   C 400
   (D) 300

2. $2,391 \div 57$
   F 4
   (G) 40
   H 400
   J 4,000

3. $3,134$
   $2,876$
   $+2,945$
   (A) 9,000
   B 8,000
   C 7,000
   D 6,000

4. 863
   $\times 48$
   F 32,000
   G 36,000
   (H) 45,000
   J 50,000

For 5–8, find the sum or difference.

5. $132,534$
   $+389,145$
   A 511,479
   B 511,679
   C 521,411
   (D) 521,679

6. $876,611$
   $+454,686$
   F 421,925
   G 1,320,297
   H 1,321,297
   (J) 1,331,297

7. $998,355$
   $-366,541$
   A 632,214
   (B) 631,814
   C 621,814
   D 531,814

8. $782,561$
   $-485,192$
   F 279,369
   G 279,396
   (H) 297,369
   J 297,963

For 9–12, multiply or divide.

9. $4,267 \times 22$
   A 17,068
   B 83,874
   C 92,674
   (D) 93,874

10. $10,982 \div 19$
    (F) 578
    G 587
    H 600
    J 10,963

11. $7,884 \div 12$
    A 656
    (B) 657
    C 658
    D 3,942

12. $5,741 \times 489$
    F 2,831,449
    (G) 2,807,349
    H 2,381,448
    J 120,561

Go On

CHAPTER 1 TEST, page 2

13. Mrs. Morris has 84 dance students. If she has five times as many teenage students as adult students, how many adult students does she have?
    A 12
    B 13
    (C) 14
    D 70

14. José has played 152 baseball games in the last 3 years. If he has won 7 times as many games as he has lost, how many games has he won?
    (F) 133
    G 132
    H 22
    J 19

15. Delia has 115 science fiction and mystery books. If she has 4 times as many mystery books as she has science fiction books, how many mystery books does she have?
    A 4
    B 23
    (C) 92
    D 115

16. Steve can play 153 songs on the piano or the guitar. If he can play twice as many songs on the piano as on the guitar, how many songs can he play on the piano?
    F 104
    (G) 102
    H 98
    J 51

For 17–20, evaluate each expression for the given value.

17. $d - 21$, for $d = 35$
    (A) 14
    B 16
    C 54
    D 66

18. $g \div 8 \times 2$, for $g = 40$
    F 1
    G 7
    (H) 10
    J 80

19. $126 \div z$, for $z = 9$
    (A) 14
    B 15
    C 117
    D 123

20. $238 + f$, for $f = 872$
    F 634
    G 646
    (H) 1,110
    J 1,111

For 21–25, solve each equation by using mental math.

21. $35 - t = 27$
    A $t = 62$
    B $t = 52$
    C $t = 12$
    (D) $t = 8$

22. $9 \times 8 = c - 42$
    F $c = 30$
    G $c = 98$
    H $c = 106$
    (J) $c = 114$

23. $35 \div r = 7$
    A $r = 4$
    (B) $r = 5$
    C $r = 28$
    D $r = 245$

24. $30 \times 12 = 3g$
    F $g = 1,080$
    G $g = 360$
    (H) $g = 120$
    J $g = 14$

25. $49 \div k = 84$
    (A) $k = 35$
    B $k = 45$
    C $k = 123$
    D $k = 133$

Stop

TIP!

Understand the problem.
See item **7**.

The words describe an algebraic expression. *Less* describes the relationship of the given number to the unknown number.
Also see problem **1**, p. H62.

Choose the best answer.

1. Which is the best estimate for this sum?
   $6,204 + 5,893 + 6,028 + 5,991$ **B**

   A 22,000   C 28,000

   B 24,000   D 30,000

2. Which is the best estimate for this quotient?
   $4,923 \div 71$ **G**

   F 7

   G 70

   H 700

   J 7,000

3. A new jogging track at a recreation center is 580 feet longer than the old track. The new track is 1,320 feet long. How long was the old track? **A**

   A 740 ft   C 1,900 ft

   B 860 ft   D Not here

4. There are 9,800 beads to put in boxes. Each box holds 48 beads. How many boxes are needed to hold all of the beads? **H**

   F 48 boxes   H 205 boxes

   G 204 boxes   J Not here

5. Which is the best estimate for this product?
   81×409 **A**

   A 32,000

   B 28,000

   C 3,200

   D 2,800

6. What is the value of $35 + b$ for $b = 5$? **H**

   F 7   H 40

   G 30   J 175

7. Which algebraic expression represents the expression "28 less than a number, q"? **D**

   A $28 - q$

   B $q + 28$

   C $q \div 28$

   D $q - 28$

8. What is the value of n for $8 \times n = 24$? **F**

   F 3

   G 16

   H 32

   J 192

9. A bus can carry 16 people. There are 9 people on board and there is room for x more people. Which equation shows this relationship? **C**

   A $16 + x = 9$ C $9 + x = 16$

   B $x - 9 = 16$ D $x - 16 = 9$

10. Which algebraic expression represents the expression "7 more than a number, t"? **J**

    F $7 \times t$

    G $t - 7$

    H $7 - t$

    J $t + 7$

11. $1,225 \times 37$ **C**

    A 12,250   C 45,325

    B 34,225   D 48,390

12. $115,309 - 67,899$ **F**

    F 47,410   H 58,410

    G 57,410   J 58,510

33

CUMULATIVE REVIEW •
Chapter 1

USING THE PAGE

This page may be used to help students get ready for standardized tests. The test items are written in the same style and arranged in the same format as those on many state assessments. The page is cumulative. It covers math objectives and essential skills that have been taught up to this point in the text. Most of the items represent skills from the current chapter, and the remainder represent skills from earlier chapters.

This page can be assigned at the end of the chapter as classwork or as a homework assignment. You may want to have students use individual recording sheets presented in a multiple-choice (standardized) format. A Test Answer Sheet is available as a blackline master in *Assessment Guide* (p. AGxlii).

You may wish to have students describe how they solved each problem and share their solutions.

Operation Sense

CHAPTER PLANNER

PACING OPTIONS

Compacted	3 Days
Expanded	7 Days

Getting Ready for Chapter 2 • Assessing Prior Knowledge and INTERVENTION (See PE and TE page 35.)

LESSON	CALIFORNIA STANDARDS	PACING	VOCABULARY*	MATERIALS	RESOURCES AND TECHNOLOGY
2.1 Mental Math: Use the Properties pp. 36–39 Objective To use properties and mental math to find sums, differences, products, and quotients	AF 1.3 MR 2.0 (*Also* O—n NS 2.0, MR 1.3)	2 Days	**compensation** Commutative Property Associative Property Distributive Property		Reteach, Practice, Problem Solving, Challenge 2.1 Worksheets Extra Practice p. H33, Set A ▫ Transparency 2.1
2.2 Algebra: Exponents pp. 40–41 Objective To represent numbers by using exponents	O—n NS 2.0 (*Also* MR 2.4, MR 2.5)	1 Day	**exponent** **base** factor		Reteach, Practice, Problem Solving, Challenge 2.2 Worksheets Extra Practice p. H33, Set B ▫ Transparency 2.2 🔴 **Astro Algebra • ** *Red* **Math Jingles™ CD 5-6 • ** *Track 12*
2.3 Math Lab: Explore Order of Operations pp. 42–43 Objective To explore how to evaluate expressions by using order of operations	AF 1.3 AF 1.4 (*Also* O—n NS 2.0, MR 1.0, MR 2.4, MR 2.5, MR 3.2)		**order of operations** **algebraic operating system**	*For each student* calculator	🌐 **E-Lab • ** *Order of Operations;* E-Lab Recording Sheet 🔴 **Astro Algebra • ** *Red*
2.4 Algebra: Order of Operations pp. 44–45 Objective To use the order of operations	AF 1.3 AF 1.4 (*Also* MR 1.0, MR 3.2, O—n NS 2.0)	1 Day (For Lessons 2.3 and 2.4)			Reteach, Practice, Problem Solving, Challenge 2.4 Worksheets Extra Practice p. H33, Set C ▫ Transparency 2.4 🔴 **Astro Algebra • ** *Red* **Math Jingles™ CD 5-6 • ** *Track 11*
2.5 Problem Solving Skill: *Sequence and Prioritize Information* pp. 46–47 Objective To use the skill *sequence and prioritize information* to solve problems	MR 1.0 MR 1.1 (*Also* MR 2.0, MR 3.2)	1 Day			Reteach, Practice, Reading Strategy, Challenge 2.5 Worksheets ▫ Transparency 2.5 Problem Solving Think Along, p. TR1

Ending Chapter 2 • Chapter 2 Review/Test, p. 48 • **Cumulative Review,** p. 49

*****Boldfaced** terms are new vocabulary. Other terms are review vocabulary.

Vocabulary Development

The boldfaced words are the new vocabulary terms in the chapter. Have students record the definitions in their Math Journals.

compensation, p. 37

exponent, p. 40

base, p. 40

order of operations, p. 42

algebraic operating system, p. 43

compensation

Vocabulary Cards
Have students use the Vocabulary Cards on *Teacher's Resource Book* pp. TR119–120 to make graphic organizers or word puzzles. The cards can also be added to a file of mathematics terms.

Writing Opportunities

PUPIL EDITION
- **Write About It,** pp. 39, 47
- **What's the Question?,** p. 41
- **What's the Error?,** p. 45

TEACHER'S EDITION
- **Write**—See the *Assess* section of each TE lesson.
- **Writing in Mathematics,** p. 40B

ASSESSMENT GUIDE
- **How Did I Do?,** p. AGxvii

Family Involvement Activities

These activities provide:
- Letter to the Family
- Information about California Standards
- Math Vocabulary
- Family Game
- Practice (Homework)

HARCOURT MATH   Name

GRADE 6   Date

Chapter 2

WHAT WE ARE LEARNING
Operation Sense

Dear Family,

Your child is learning about using mental math strategies to find sums, differences, products, and quotients; using exponents to represent numbers; and using the order of operations.

VOCABULARY

Here are some of the vocabulary words we use in class:

This is how your child is learning to use properties and mental math to find sums.

Ask questions such as these as you work together:

Compensation A mental math strategy you can use for some addition and subtraction problems

- Use the Commutative Property.
$54 + 52 + 6 = 54 + 6 + 52$
$= 60 + 52$
$= 112$

Can you explain the Commutative Property and the Associative Property to me? Your child might say: With the Commutative Property I can change the order of the addends and get the same sum.

Exponent An exponent shows how many times a number is used as a factor

Base The base is the number that an exponent shows is used as a factor

- Use the Associative Property.
$(54 + 52) + 6 = 54 + (52 + 6)$
$= 54 + 58$
$= 112$

The Associative Property lets me group addends in any way and get the same sum.

Algebraic operating system Some calculators use an algebraic operating system so they automatically follow the order of operations.

- Use compensation.
$54 + 52 = (54 + 6) + (52 - 6)$
$= 60 + 46$
$= 106$

Can you explain the strategy of compensation? Your child might respond: When I'm adding, I can change one addend to a multiple of ten and then adjust the other addend by subtracting the same number to keep the balance. When I use compensation to subtract, I have to do the same thing to each number.

The California Math Standards Your child's **Harcourt Math** book lists the California Math Standards that are taught in every lesson. If you have questions about the standards, be sure to consult *California Standards for Grade 6* that was sent home at the beginning of the school year.

Why might you use these properties? Your child might reply: When I use mental math, the properties help me to find the answer more easily.

Family Involvement Activities, p. FA5

California Mathematics Content Standards for Grade 6

Strands

Number Sense

Lesson 2.1: O➔ NS 2.0

Lesson 2.2: O➔ NS 2.0

Lesson 2.3: O➔ NS 2.0

Lesson 2.4: O➔ NS 2.0

Algebra and Functions

Lesson 2.1: AF 1.3

Lesson 2.3: AF 1.3, 1.4

Lesson 2.4: AF 1.3, 1.4

Measurement and Geometry

Statistics, Data Analysis, and Probability

Mathematical Reasoning

Lesson 2.1: MR 1.3, 2.0

Lesson 2.2: MR 2.4, 2.5

Lesson 2.3: MR 1.0, 2.4, 2.5, 3.2

Lesson 2.4: MR 1.0, 3.2

Lesson 2.5: MR 1.0 1.1, 2.0, 3.2

Operation Sense

MATHEMATICS ACROSS THE GRADES

SKILLS TRACE ACROSS THE GRADES

GRADE 5	GRADE 6	GRADE 7
Understand the properties of addition and multiplication; use mental math and recognize patterns in multiplication	Use properties and mental math strategies with whole number operations; represent numbers by using exponents; use the order of operations to evaluate expressions with whole numbers	Use mental math strategies with whole number and decimal operations; apply the order of operations to expressions with whole numbers and decimals

SKILLS TRACE FOR GRADE 6

LESSON	FIRST INTRODUCED	TAUGHT AND PRACTICED	TESTED	REVIEWED
2.1	Grade 4	PE pp. 36–39, H33, p. RW7, p. PW7, p. PS7	PE p. 48, pp. AG13–16	PE pp. 48, 49, 88–89
2.2	Grade 5	PE pp. 40–41, H33, p. RW8, p. PW8, p. PS8	PE p. 48, pp. AG13–16	PE pp. 48, 49, 88–89
2.3	Grade 6	PE pp. 42–43	PE p. 48, pp. AG13–16	PE pp. 48, 49, 88–89
2.4	Grade 6	PE pp. 44–45, H33, p. RW9, p. PW9, p. PS9	PE p. 48, pp. AG13–16	PE pp. 48, 49, 88–89
2.5	Grade 5	PE pp. 46–47, p. RW10, p. PW10, p. PS10	PE p. 48, pp. AG13–16	PE pp. 48, 49, 88–89

KEY PE Pupil Edition   PS Problem Solving Workbook   RW Reteach Workbook
PW Practice Workbook   AG Assessment Guide

Looking Back Prerequisite Skills

To be ready for Chapter 2, students should have the following understandings and skills:

- **Repeated Multiplication**—find products of repeated factors

- **Properties**—Commutative and Associative of Addition and Multiplication, Distributive, Identity of Zero and One, and Property of Zero

- **Use of Parentheses**—solve equations; evaluate expressions

Check What You Know

Use page 35 to determine students' knowledge of prerequisite concepts and skills.

Intervention

Help students prepare for the chapter by using the intervention resources described on TE page 35.

Looking at Chapter 2 Essential Skills

Students will

- apply the properties and other mental math strategies with whole number operations.

- find the value of numbers written in exponent form.

- **use the order of operations to evaluate expressions involving whole numbers.**

- use the skill *sequence and prioritize information* to solve problems.

EXAMPLE

$$12 + (7 + 1) \div 2^2$$

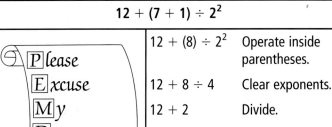

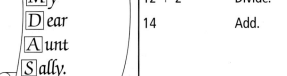

$12 + (8) \div 2^2$	Operate inside parentheses.
$12 + 8 \div 4$	Clear exponents.
$12 + 2$	Divide.
14	Add.

Please
Excuse
My
Dear
Aunt
Sally.

Looking Ahead Applications

Students will apply what they learn in Chapter 2 to the following new concepts:

- Decimal Expressions (Chapter 4)
- Expressions with Squares (Chapter 14)
- Operations with Integers (Chapters 12 and 13)
- Solve Equations (Chapters 15 and 16)

Operation Sense

INTRODUCING THE CHAPTER

Tell students that they can use operation sense to relate the structure of the human body to the body structure of a variety of animals. Have students focus on the photograph. Ask them to write another expression that tells how many cervical vertebrae flamingos have. Possible answer: $3^2 + 10$

USING DATA

To begin the study of this chapter, have students

- Write an expression for the total number of cervical vertebrae of 7 people. 7×7

- Which bird has $(36 - 16) + 5$ vertebrae? swan

- Which bird has twice as many cervical vertebrae as a human does? Owl

- Formulate and answer three questions about the data. Check students' work.

PROBLEM SOLVING PROJECT

Purpose To use operation sense to solve a problem.

Grouping pairs or small groups

Background The human backbone has a total of 24 vertebrae (7 cervical, 12 thoracic, 5 lumbar and two fused bones (sacrum and Coccyx).

Analyze, Choose, Solve, and Check

Have each group

- Research the number of vertebrae in the backbones of three other animals.

- Make number riddles by using exponents and parentheses in expressions for the number of vertebrae each animal has.

- Exchange and evaluate each other's expressions.

Check students' work.

 Suggest that students place the riddles and solutions in their portfolios.

CHAPTER **2** **Operation Sense**

A bird can reach almost any part of its body with its beak because it has an extremely flexible neck. The bones in the neck are called cervical vertebrae. Humans have 7 cervical vertebrae. Most birds have more cervical vertebrae than humans or other mammals. Flamingos have $4^2 + 8 \times 2 - 13$ cervical vertebrae. About how many times as many cervical vertebrae does a flamingo have than a human?

about 3 times as many

CERVICAL VERTEBRAE

Animal: Human, Owl, Pigeon, Swan, Calif. Condor

Number of Cervical Vertebrae (0 2 4 6 8 10 12 14 16 18 20 22 24 26)

34 Chapter 2

Why learn math? Explain that biologists study all aspects of animal life. They collect and use the data for a variety of purposes. For example, by studying the bones of an animal, biologists can tell the animal's height, weight, and often its diet. Ask: How could you use math to care for animals? Possible answer: To calculate the weekly cost of pet supplies; to measure appropriate daily food amounts

TECHNOLOGY LINK

To find out more about exponents and order of operations, visit The Harcourt Learning Site.

www.harcourtschool.com

Check What You Know

Use this page to help you review and remember important skills needed for Chapter 2.

☑ **Repeated Multiplication** (See p. H15.)

Find the product.

1. $3 \times 3 \times 3$ 27
2. $2 \times 2 \times 2 \times 2$ 16
3. $4 \times 4 \times 4$ 64
4. $5 \times 5 \times 5 \times 5$ 625
5. $10 \times 10 \times 10 \times 10$ 10,000
6. $9 \times 9 \times 9$ 729
7. $8 \times 8 \times 8$ 512
8. $6 \times 6 \times 6$ 216
9. $7 \times 7 \times 7$ 343
10. $10 \times 10 \times 10$ 1,000
11. $4 \times 4 \times 4 \times 4$ 256
12. $5 \times 5 \times 5$ 125

☑ **Properties** (See p. H2.)

Name the property illustrated.

13. $48 + 13 + 5 = 13 + 48 + 5$
    Commutative of Addition
14. $8 \times (3 + 1) = (8 \times 3) + (8 \times 1)$
    Distributive
15. $0 \times 999 = 0$
    Property of Zero
16. $15 \times 1 = 15$
    Identity of Multiplication
17. $(9 + 5) + 10 = 9 + (5 + 10)$
    Associative of Addition
18. $27 + 36 = 36 + 27$
    Commutative of Addition
19. $(4 + 2) \times 7 = (4 \times 7) + (2 \times 7)$
    Distributive
20. $7 \times 9 \times 2 = 2 \times 9 \times 7$
    Commutative of Multiplication
21. $1 \times 148 = 148$
    Identity of Multiplication
22. $(2 \times 9) \times 5 = 2 \times (9 \times 5)$
    Associative Property of
    Multiplication
23. $8 \times (20 + 8) = (8 \times 20) + (8 \times 8)$
    Distributive Property
24. $6 \times 3 = 3 \times 6$
    Commutative of Multiplication

☑ **Use of Parentheses** (See p. H15.)

Solve the equation.

25. $5 \times (4 + 3) = (a \times 4) + (a \times 3)$ $a = 5$
26. $7 + (3 + 9) = (7 + m) + 9$ $m = 3$
27. $4 + 6 + 3 = 4 + (6 + r)$ $r = 3$
28. $(9 \times 4) + (9 \times 2) = h \times (4 + 2)$ $h = 9$
29. $4 \times (8 - 4) = (4 \times t) - (4 \times 4)$ $t = 8$
30. $(5 + 6) + (4 + 7) = (5 + 4) + (r + 7)$ $r = 6$

Evaluate the expression.

31. $(4 + 7) + 9$ 20
32. $5 \times (6 + 2)$ 40
33. $(1 + 7) \times 4$ 32
34. $(7 + 8) + 3$ 18
35. $4 + (7 - 3)$ 8
36. $6 \times (9 - 3)$ 36
37. $2 \times (3 + 5 + 8)$ 32
38. $(8 + 5) + (3 + 1)$ 17
39. $4 + (5 + 7) + 2$ 18
40. $2 \times (3 \times 1)$ 6

> **LOOK AHEAD**
>
> **In Chapter 2 you will**
> - use properties and mental math to find sums, differences, products, and quotients
> - use exponents
> - use order of operations

Assessing Prior Knowledge

Use the **Check What You Know** page to determine whether your students have mastered the prerequisite skills critical for this chapter.

Intervention

- **Diagnose and Prescribe**

  Evaluate your students' performance on this page to determine whether intervention is necessary. **How to Help Options** that provide instruction, practice, and a check are listed in the chart below.

- **Review Prerequisite Skills**

  The following resources provide a review for the prerequisite vocabulary and skills.

  Option 1—Check What You Know, Pupil Edition p. 35

  Option 2—Troubleshooting, Pupil Edition pp. H2, H15

TEACHER'S NOTES

Check What You Know
INTERVENTION • Diagnose and Prescribe

Prerequisite Skill	Items (Pupil Edition p. 35)	How to Help Options
☑ Repeated Multiplication	1–12	• **Troubleshooting, Pupil Edition p. H15** • **Intervention Strategies and Activities** Card, Copying Master, or CD-ROM • **Skill 12**
☑ Properties	13–24	• **Troubleshooting, Pupil Edition p. H2** • **Intervention Strategies and Activities** Card, Copying Master, or CD-ROM • **Skills 13–14**
☑ Use of Parentheses	25–40	• **Troubleshooting, Pupil Edition p. H15** • **Intervention Strategies and Activities** Card, Copying Master, or CD-ROM • **Skill 40**

Mental Math: Use the Properties

LESSON PLANNING

Objective To use properties and mental math to find sums, differences, products, and quotients

Intervention for Prerequisite Skills

Use of Parentheses, Multiplication Properties (For intervention strategies, see page 35.)

 California Mathematics Content Standards

AF 1.3 Apply algebraic order of operations and the commutative, associative, and distributive properties to evaluate expressions; and justify each step in the process.

MR 2.0 Students use strategies, skills, and concepts in finding solutions.

(*Also* NS 2.0, MR 1.3)

Vocabulary

compensation an estimation strategy in which you change one addend to a multiple of ten and then adjust the other addend to keep the balance

Math Background

The properties of numbers serve as a basis for operating within our number system. Consider these ideas as you help students understand properties:

- Changing the order of numbers, based on the Commutative Property, or the grouping of numbers, based on the Associative Property, may result in numbers that are simpler to compute.

- Compensation is based on the Identity Property of Zero. Adding a number to a sum and then subtracting it is the same as adding zero to it.

- Thinking of one factor in a multiplication exercise as a sum or difference allows the use of the Distributive Property.

 NUMBER OF THE DAY Transparency 2.1

Calculate your age in number of months. Possible answer: for 11 years and 8 months—140 months

 PROBLEM OF THE DAY Transparency 2.1

Replace the ■ with the digits 0–9 to make correct number sentences. Use each digit only once.

■ × ■ = 18 2 × 9 = 18
■ × ■ = 24 3 × 8 = 24
■ × ■ = 0 5 × 0 = 0
■ × ■ = 28 4 × 7 = 28
■ × ■ = 6 6 × 1 = 6

Solution Problem of the Day tab, p. PD2

 DAILY FACTS PRACTICE

Have students practice addition facts by completing Set G of *Teacher's Resource Book*, p. TR93.

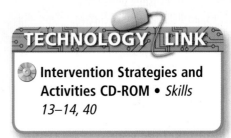
ALTERNATIVE TEACHING STRATEGY (ELL)

Materials *For each pair* index cards

Have students work in pairs to **practice using properties.**

- They prepare five index cards by writing the name of a multiplication property on each.

- One student draws a card, and both students write one multiplication sentence illustrating the property.

- After all the cards have been drawn, students combine their examples, mix them up, and exchange with another pair.

- They then identify the properties for the new set of problems. Check students' work.

See also page 38.

VISUAL

MIXED REVIEW AND TEST PREP

Cumulative Review Chapters 1–2

Refer to the Pupil Edition pages referenced in the exercises for further review. Have students go to the lesson page, review the lesson, and correct any problem they missed.

Mixed Review and Test Prep, p. 39

How to Help	
Item	**Page**
56	30
57	22
58	22
59	22
60	28

SPECIAL NEEDS

To encourage students to **apply properties to real-life problems**, present the following:

- Suppose you were to take 2 showers, brush your teeth 3 times, and wash dishes 2 times today. How much water would you use? 106 gal

Activity	Water Used
Washing dishes	20 gal
Taking shower	30 gal
Brushing teeth	2 gal

VISUAL

VOCABULARY STRATEGY

Present the **Associative and Distributive Properties** by discussing the meaning of the terms *associate* and *distribute*.

- To act out the term *associate,* have three students stand up in front of the class spaced evenly apart.

- Then have two of the students move closer together. Describe the action as associating.

- Now ask a volunteer to relate the action to the property.

- To illustrate the term *distribute,* have one student pass out a piece of paper to each student. Describe the action as distributing the paper.

- Now ask a volunteer to relate the action to the property.

- Have volunteers practice using the words *associate* and *distribute.*

TECHNOLOGY LINK

Intervention Strategies and Activities CD-ROM • *Skills 13–14, 40*

Objective To use properties and mental math to find sums, differences, products, and quotients

Vocabulary compensation *Review* Commutative Property, Associative Property, Distributive Property

1 Introduce

QUICK REVIEW provides review of prerequisite skills.

Why Learn This? You can use this skill to help you determine the number of favors needed for a party. *Share the lesson objective with students.*

2 Teach

Guided Instruction

• *Review the Distributive Property.*

How would you use the Distributive Property to multiply a number by 7? Break the 7 into addends, 5 + 2 or 3 + 4. Multiply the number by each addend and add the products.

REASONING **Ellen scheduled four 45-minute classes and four 10-minute breaks. How could you use the Distributive Property to find the number of minutes she scheduled in all?** Possible answer: $(4 \times 45) + (4 \times 10) = 4 \times (45 + 10) = 4 \times 55 = (4 \times 50) + (4 \times 5) = 200 + 20 = 220$

• *Refer students to Example 2.*

Modifying Instruction In the Commutative Property part of Example 2, the Associative Property is also used twice:
$(8 \times 6) \times 5 = 8 \times (6 \times 5)$ by Associative Property
$= 8 \times (5 \times 6)$ by Commutative Property
$= (8 \times 5) \times 6$ by Associative Property

What is the purpose of the parentheses in the Associative Property? to regroup factors that are easier to multiply

ADDITIONAL EXAMPLE

Example 1, p. 36

Use the Distributive Property to solve 9×43.

$9 \times 43 = 9 \times (40 + 3)$
$= (9 \times 40) + (9 \times 3)$
$= (360) + (27)$
$= 387$

36 Chapter 2

Use the Properties

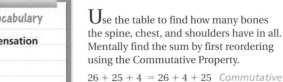

Learn how to use properties and mental math to find sums, differences, products, and quotients.
1. $d = 20$

Vocabulary

compensation

Remember these properties:
Commutative Property
$4 + 8 = 8 + 4$
$6 \times 7 = 7 \times 6$

Associative Property
$(6 + 8) + 5 = 6 + (8 + 5)$
$(2 \times 9) \times 5 = 2 \times (9 \times 5)$

Distributive Property
$12 \times 32 = 12 \times (30 + 2) = (12 \times 30) + (12 \times 2)$

QUICK REVIEW

Solve by using mental math.
1. $d + 13 = 33$ 2. $25 - g = 17$ $g = 8$
3. $6m = 54$ $m = 9$ 4. $9 = t \div 11$ $t = 99$
5. $340 + 34 + 3$ **377**

Use the table to find how many bones the spine, chest, and shoulders have in all. Mentally find the sum by first reordering using the Commutative Property.

$26 + 25 + 4 = 26 + 4 + 25$ *Commutative Property*
$= 30 + 25$ *Use mental math.*
$= 55$

Mentally find the sum by regrouping using the Associative Property.

$(26 + 25) + 4 = 26 + (25 + 4)$ *Associative Property*
$= 26 + 29$ *Use mental math.*
$= 55$

BONES IN THE HUMAN BODY	
Part	Number of Bones
Head	28
Spine	26
Throat	1
Chest	25
Shoulders	4
Arms	6
Hands	54
Legs	10
Feet	52

So, the spine, chest, and shoulders have a total of 55 bones.

You can use the Distributive Property to mentally solve a problem.

EXAMPLE 1

How many bones are in 5 models of the human spine?
$5 \times 26 = 5 \times (20 + 6)$ *Break 26 into parts.*
$= (5 \times 20) + (5 \times 6)$ *Use the Distributive Property. Multiply mentally.*
$= 100 + 30$ *Add the products.*
$= 130$

So, there are 130 bones in 5 models.

You can also use the Commutative and Associative Properties.

EXAMPLE 2

James has 8 storage boxes on each of 6 shelves. Each box contains 5 items. How many items are there altogether?

Commutative Property   **Associative Property**
$(8 \times 6) \times 5 = (8 \times 5) \times 6$ $(8 \times 6) \times 5 = 8 \times (6 \times 5)$
$= 40 \times 6$ $= 8 \times 30$
$= 240$ $= 240$

36

 CALIFORNIA STANDARDS **AF 1.3** Apply algebraic order of operations and the commutative, associative, and distributive properties to evaluate expressions; and justify each step in the process. **MR 2.0** Students use strategies, skills, and concepts in finding solutions. *also,* **O–n NS 2.0, MR 1.3**

RETEACH 2.1

Use the Properties

One way to find a sum or product mentally is to use a number property.

Commutative Property
Numbers can be added in any order without changing the sum.
$45 + 29 + 55 = 29 + 45 + 55$
Order has been changed.

Associative Property
Addends can be grouped differently. The sum is always the same.
$(45 + 29) + 55 = 29 + (45 + 55)$
Grouping has been changed.

Numbers can be multiplied in any order without changing the product.
$5 \times 13 \times 8 = 5 \times 8 \times 13$
Order has been changed.

Factors can be grouped differently. The product is always the same.
$(5 \times 13) \times 8 = 5 \times (8 \times 13)$
Grouping has been changed.

Distributive Property
$25 \times 23 = 25 \times (20 + 3) = (25 \times 20) + (25 \times 3)$
Product of a number and a sum   Sum of two products

1. Complete to show how to find the sum. Name the reason for each step.

$19 + 45 + 21 + 5 = 19 + \underline{21} + \underline{45} + 5$ → Commutative Property
$= (\underline{19 + 21}) + (\underline{45 + 5})$ → Associative Property
$= \underline{40} + \underline{50}$ → Use mental math.
$= \underline{90}$

Add. Use mental math.
2. $16 + 9 + 24$ 3. $33 + 26 + 17 + 44$ 4. $21 + 14 + 29 + 36$
    $\underline{49}$ $\underline{120}$ $\underline{100}$

Complete to show how to use the Distributive Property to find each product.
5. $8 \times 14 = 8 \times (\underline{10} + 4)$ 6. $9 \times 34 = 9 \times (30 + \underline{4})$
$= (8 \times \underline{10}) + (8 \times \underline{4})$ $= (9 \times \underline{30}) + (9 \times \underline{4})$
$= \underline{80} + \underline{32}$ $= \underline{270} + \underline{36}$
$= \underline{112}$ $= \underline{306}$

PRACTICE 2.1

Use the Properties

Vocabulary

Write the correct letter from Column 2.

Column 1		Column 2
_b_ 1. Associative Property	a.	$58 + 72 = (58 + 2) + (72 - 2)$
_c_ 2. Commutative Property	b.	$3 \times (2 \times 4) = (3 \times 2) \times 4$
_a_ 3. compensation	c.	$10 \times 23 = 23 \times 10$
_e_ 4. Distributive Property	d.	$18x = 18$
_d_ 5. Identity Property of One	e.	$6 \times 24 = 6 \times (20 + 4)$

Use mental math to find the value.

6. $37 + 14$ **51**   7. $65 - 23$ **42**   8. 18×6 **108**
9. $258 \div 3$ **86**   10. 18×22 **396**   11. $141 \div 3$ **47**
12. $78 - 45$ **33**   13. $49 + 14$ **63**   14. $41 + 18$ **59**
15. 19×11 **209**   16. $37 - 11$ **26**   17. $366 \div 6$ **61**
18. $320 \div 5$ **64**   19. $59 + 26$ **85**   20. $74 - 23$ **51**
21. 15×51 **765**   22. $88 - 54$ **34**   23. 43×21 **903**
24. $465 \div 15$ **31**   25. $56 + 15$ **71**   26. 15×48 **720**
27. $32 + 35$ **67**   28. $153 \div 9$ **17**   29. $96 - 25$ **71**
30. $37 + 14 + 43$ **94**   31. $(7 \times 12) + (7 \times 18)$ **210**   32. $5 \times 33 \times 6$ **990**

Mixed Review

Evaluate each expression for $a = 72$, $b = 28$, and $c = 8$.
33. $b \times 7$ 34. $a + b + 362$ 35. $a \div c$ 36. $225 - a$
   196   **462**   **9**   **153**

Solve each equation using mental math.
37. $n \times 8 = 56$ 38. $19 + w = 36$ 39. $h \div 20 = 35$ 40. $98 - x = 59$
   $n = 7$ $w = 17$ $h = 700$ $x = 39$

A strategy you can use for some addition and subtraction problems is **compensation**. For addition, change one number to a multiple of 10 and then adjust the other number to keep the balance.

EXAMPLE 3

Mr. Forge and his friends play basketball for an hour on Fridays and Saturdays. On Friday they scored a total of 44 points, and on Saturday they scored 57 points. Use compensation to find the total points scored for both days.

$44 + 57 = (44 + 6) + (57 - 6)$ *Add 6 to 44 and subtract 6 from 57.*

$\quad\quad\quad = 50 + 51$ *Use mental math to add.*

$\quad\quad\quad = 101$

So, the total points scored is 101.

When you use compensation to subtract, you have to do the same thing to each number.

EXAMPLE 4

Use compensation to find $128 - 56$.

$128 - 56 = (128 + 4) - (56 + 4)$ *Add 4 to 128 and to 56 before subtracting.*

$\quad\quad\quad = 132 - 60$

$\quad\quad\quad = 72$

So, the difference is 72.

You can sometimes divide mentally by breaking a number into smaller parts that are each divisible by the divisor.

EXAMPLE 5

Use mental math to find $396 \div 4$.

$396 = 360 + 36$ *Break 396 into parts.*

$360 \div 4 = 90$ and $36 \div 4 = 9$ *Divide each part by 4 mentally.*

$90 + 9 = 99$ *Add the parts of the quotient.*

So, $396 \div 4 = 99$.

• Tell another way to break 396 into two parts to divide by 4.
   Answers will vary. Possible answers: 320 and 76; 324 and 72; 200 and 196

Math Idea ▶ Using the number properties and other mental math strategies will help you add, subtract, multiply, and divide mentally.

CHECK FOR UNDERSTANDING

Think and ▶ **Discuss**   Look back at the lesson to answer each question.

1. **Tell** how using the Associative Property in Example 2 made the problem easier to solve. **Possible answer: It is easier to find 8×30 than 48×5.**

2. Possible answer: Add 1 to 349, subtract 1 from 138, add 350 and 137 to get 487; add 2 to 138, subtract 2 from 349, add 140 and 347 to get 487.

2. **Explain** two different ways to use compensation to find $349 + 138$ mentally.

37

ADDITIONAL EXAMPLES

Example 2, p. 36

The Office Supply Store has 4 boxes of binders on each of 6 shelves. There are 5 binders in each box. How many binders are there altogether?

Commutative Property

$(4 \times 6) \times 5 = (4 \times 5) \times 6$
$\quad\quad\quad = 20 \times 6$
$\quad\quad\quad = 120$

Associative Property

$(4 \times 6) \times 5 = 4 \times (6 \times 5)$
$\quad\quad\quad = 4 \times 30$
$\quad\quad\quad = 120$

So, there are 120 binders altogether.

Example 3, p. 37

Use compensation to find $46 + 97$.

$46 + 97 = (46 + 4) + (97 - 4)$
$\quad\quad\quad = \quad 50 \quad + \quad 93$
$\quad\quad\quad = 143$

So, the sum is 143.

Example 4, p. 37

Use compensation to find $147 - 98$.

$147 - 98 = (147 + 2) - (98 + 2)$
$\quad\quad\quad = \quad 149 \quad - \quad 100$
$\quad\quad\quad = 49$

So, the difference is 49.

Example 5, p. 37

Use mental math to find $450 \div 6$.

$450 = 420 + 30$
$420 \div 6 = 70$ and $30 \div 6 = 5$
$70 + 5 = 75$
So, $450 \div 6 = 75$.

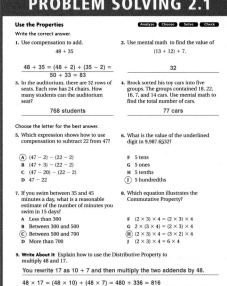

PROBLEM SOLVING 2.1

Use the Properties

Write the correct answer.

Analyze *Choose* *Solve* *Check*

1. Use compensation to add.
   $48 + 35$

   $48 + 35 = (48 + 2) + (35 - 2) =$
   $50 + 33 = 83$

2. Use mental math to find the value of
   $(13 + 12) + 7$.

   32

3. In the auditorium, there are 32 rows of seats. Each row has 24 chairs. How many students can the auditorium seat?

   768 students

4. Brock sorted his toy cars into five groups. The groups contained 18, 22, 16, 7, and 14 cars. Use mental math to find the total number of cars.

   77 cars

Choose the letter for the best answer.

5. Which expression shows how to use compensation to subtract 22 from 47?

   A $(47 - 2) - (22 - 2)$
   B $(47 + 3) - (22 - 2)$
   C $(47 - 20) - (22 - 2)$
   D $47 - 22$

6. What is the value of the underlined digit in 9,987.65_3_2?

   F 5 tens
   G 5 ones
   H 5 tenths
   J 5 hundredths

7. If you swim between 35 and 45 minutes a day, what is a reasonable estimate of the number of minutes you swim in 15 days?

   A Less than 300
   B Between 300 and 500
   C Between 500 and 700
   D More than 700

8. Which equation illustrates the Commutative Property?

   F $(2 \times 3) \times 4 = (2 \times 3) \times 4$
   G $2 \times (3 \times 4) = (2 \times 3) \times 4$
   H $(2 \times 3) \times 4 = (3 \times 2) \times 4$
   J $(2 \times 3) \times 4 = 6 \times 4$

9. **Write About It** Explain how to use the Distributive Property to multiply 48 and 17.

   You rewrite 17 as $10 + 7$ and then multiply the two addends by 48.

   $48 \times 17 = (48 \times 10) + (48 \times 7) = 480 + 336 = 816$

CHALLENGE 2.1

Solve It

Use mental math to solve each problem in the Decoder Box. Find the value in the Tip Box. Each time the value appears, write the letter of that problem above it. When you have solved all the problems, you will have discovered the math tip.

Decoder Box

A	$63 + 27 =$	90	N	$13 \times 6 =$	78
B	$112 - 14 =$	98	O	$4 \times 11 \times 3 =$	132
C	$480 \div 8 =$	60	P	$198 \div 9 =$	22
D	$6 \times 7 \times 10 =$	420	Q	$5 + 34 + 4 =$	43
E	$55 \times 3 =$	165	R	$15 \times 4 \times 2 =$	120
F	$397 - 158 =$	239	S	$16 \times 7 =$	112
H	$2 \times 13 \times 5 =$	130	T	$25 \times 6 =$	150
I	$7 \times 21 =$	147	U	$440 \div 5 =$	88
K	$803 - 571 =$	232	V	$25 + 19 + 4 =$	48
L	$9 \times 2 \times 6 =$	108	Y	$197 + 326 =$	523
M	$8 \times 5 \times 4 =$	160	Z	$1,135 - 797 =$	338

Tip Box

F	A	C	T	O	R	S		C	A	N	B	E
239	90	60	150	132	120	112		60	90	78	98	165

M	U	L	T	I	P	L	I	E	D	I	N
160	88	108	150	147	22	108	147	165	420	147	78

A	N	Y		O	R	D	E	R
90	78	523		132	120	420	165	120

Now use the Decoder Box to help you find the answer to a riddle. What is useful only when it's used up?

A	N		U	M	B	R	E	L	L	A
90	78		88	160	98	120	165	108	108	90

LESSON 2.1

3 Practice

Guided Practice

Do Check for Understanding Exercises 1–18 with your students. Identify those having difficulty and use lesson resources to help.

Independent Practice

Assign Exercises 19–55.

Before students begin to work independently, have them list the different mental math techniques they can use. Encourage them to identify an exercise where they can use each of the techniques.

Guided Practice ▶ Use mental math to find the value.

3. 12×17
204

4. $45 + 9 + 15$
69

5. $124 + 17 + 16$
157

6. 9×36
324

7. $(6 + 37) + 13$
56

8. $2 \times 9 \times 50$
900

9. 5×29
145

10. 11×43
473

11. $39 + 16$
55

12. $83 + 38$
121

13. $426 \div 3$
142

14. $16 + 35$
51

15. $279 \div 3$
93

16. $137 - 51$
86

17. $65 - 22$
43

18. $567 \div 7$
81

PRACTICE AND PROBLEM SOLVING

Independent ▶ Use mental math to find the value.
Practice

19. 24×7
168

20. $73 - 27$
46

21. 45×11
495

22. 12×35
420

23. $87 + 98$
185

24. $(12 + 23) + 8$
43

25. 4×27
108

26. $18 + 26$
44

27. 4×53
212

28. $64 - 29$
35

29. $24 + 32 + 16$
72

30. 19×14
266

31. $126 + 118$
244

32. $293 - 137$
156

33. $765 \div 9$
85

34. $32 + 36$
68

35. $19 + 26$
45

36. $4 \times 6 \times 50$
1,200

37. $25 \times 30 \times 2$
1,500

38. $172 \div 4$
43

39. $1,526 - 498$
1,028

40. $40 \times 15 \times 2$
1,200

41. $(4 \times 33) + (4 \times 7)$
160

42. $(6 \times 24) + (6 \times 6)$
180

43. $192 \div n$ for $n = 3$
64

44. $c \times 9 \times 5$ for $c = 8$
360

45. $p \div 12$ for $p = 624$
52

46. $a + 19 + 32$ for $a = 18$
69

Name each missing reason.

47. $80 \times 3 = (8 \times 10) \times 3$ 80 means 8×10.

$= 8 \times (10 \times 3)$ Associative Property of Multiplication

$= 8 \times (3 \times 10)$ __?__ Commutative Property of Multiplication

$= (8 \times 3) \times 10$ __?__ Associative Property of Multiplication

$= 24 \times 10$ __?__ $8 \times 3 = 24$

$= 240$ __?__ $24 \times 10 = 240$

48. What if the product of three whole numbers is 210? Without using 1 as a factor, what are the possible choices for the numbers? Possible answers: 3, 7, 10; 3, 5, 14; 5, 6, 7; 2, 3, 35; 2, 7, 15; 2, 5, 21

Problem Solving ▶ Use Data   For 49–51, use the data below.
Applications

49. Use mental math to find how many CDs were bought in all. Explain how you got your answer. 72 CDs; Explanations will vary.

50. If Nick and Selena each gave 12 CDs to Brenda, how many would Brenda have then? 36 CDs

51. How many CDs would Brenda, Selena, Ricardo, and Nick each have if they shared their CDs equally? 18 CDs each

CDs Bought
Brenda 12
Selena 17
Nick 25
Ricardo 18

Alternative Teaching Strategy

Purpose Students practice using compensation in a game of mental addition.

Materials For each group of 4 9-section spinner, p. TR73

Give each of several groups a spinner with 9 equal sections labeled as shown:

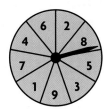

One student serves as Recorder. Each group uses the spinner to generate 2 two-digit numbers to add. The recorder writes the numbers on a sheet of paper. For example, 54 and 28.

The first student decides which number to adjust and states the adjusted number; for example, 30.

The second student decides how to compensate with the second number, thinking "2 has been added to 28, so I should subtract 2 from 54." That student should then state the second adjusted number; for example, 52.

The third student finds the sum mentally and states it; for example, 82.

The Recorder records each of the numbers as the students say them. The recording sheet might look like this:

$$\begin{array}{r} 54 \\ + 28 \\ \hline \end{array} \qquad \begin{array}{r} 30 \\ + 52 \\ \hline 82 \end{array}$$

The group members then find the sum of the two original numbers to check their mental math. If they are correct, they get a point.

Have students repeat the activity, with each student assuming a different role. The group with the most points at the end of a certain time is the winner.

52. A toy store has 7 boxes on each of 4 shelves. Each box has 25 items in it. How many items altogether are on the 4 shelves? **700 items**

53. Ann needs 250 signatures on a petition. On Monday she got 23 signatures, on Tuesday she got 3 times as many as on Monday, and on Wednesday and Thursday she got 45 each. How many more signatures does she need? **68 more signatures**

54. Jocelyn has $253.47. Her aunt gives her $87.95 more. Jocelyn buys a pair of shoes for $39.99, three T-shirts for $7.77 each, and two pairs of jeans for $60.22. Use estimation to find about how much money Jocelyn has left. **about $216**

55.  **Write About It** Explain how to use compensation to add two numbers. Give an appropriate example to support your explanation. **Change one addend to a multiple of 10, and adjust the other addend to keep the balance. Examples will vary.**

MIXED REVIEW AND TEST PREP

56. Use mental math to solve. $a \div 7 = 21$ (p. 30) **a = 147**

57. Multiply. 732×46 (p. 22) **33,672**

58. Divide. $64,270 \div 35$ (p. 22) **1,836 r10**

59. **TEST PREP** Rob changes 4 quarts of oil in his car every 3,000 miles. How many quarts of oil will Rob have used after driving 9,000 miles? (p. 22) **C**

   A 3   **B** 9   **C** 12   **D** 36

60. **TEST PREP** Joe bought 3 basketballs for $22.99 each and a net for $5.99. Which number sentence can be used to find the total cost of the basketballs and net? (p. 28) **G**

   F $3 \times (22.99 + 5.99)$ **H** $(3 \times 5.99) + 22.99$

   G $(3 \times 22.99) + 5.99$ **J** $(3 + 22.99) + 5.99$

Thinker's CORNER

Math Fun Practice using mental math strategies to solve this puzzle.

1. Copy the diagram. Place the values of the expressions below in the circles so that every sum of three numbers in a line is the same.

   $84 \div 2$ **42**
   $36 + 8$ **44**
   $28 + 16 + 2$ **46**
   $3 \times 8 \times 2$ **48** $8 + 14 + 32$ **54**
   $28 + 22$ **50** $448 \div 8$ **56**
   4×13 **52** $4 + 38 + 16$ **58**

2. Use mental math. What is the sum of each row of three numbers? **150**

42
52   44
54   50   46
56   48
58

Extra Practice page H33, Set A

39

MIXED REVIEW AND TEST PREP
Exercises 56–60 provide **cumulative review** (Chapters 1–2).

Thinker's Corner

• *If students have trouble solving the puzzle, you may wish to give a hint and guide their thinking.*

   Hint: The center value is the sum of 28 and 22. 50

   What do you notice about the other values? Possible answers: They are all even; there are four numbers in the forties and four in the fifties.

REASONING **What do you think the sum for each line of three circles might be? Explain.** 150; you can pair the remaining numbers so that the sum of each pair is 100: $100 + 50 = 150$

4 Assess

Summarize the lesson by having students:

DISCUSS How can the Commutative and Associative Properties help you find the product $5 \times 3 \times 8$? Possible answer: Reorder the factors: $5 \times 3 \times 8 = 5 \times 8 \times 3$. Group the factors in order to use mental math: $(5 \times 8) \times 3 = 40 \times 3 = 120$.

WRITE What property did you use to solve Exercise 42? Why? Possible answer: Distributive Property; it is easier to multiply 30 by 6 than it is to add the products of 6×24 and 6×6.

Lesson Quiz

Transparency **2.1**

Use mental math to find the value.

1. $7 \times 3 \times 3$ 63

2. $7 \times 7 \times 8$ 392

3. 220×3 660   **4.** 9×42 378

5. $56 + 49$ 105   **6.** $72 + 17$ 89

7. $76 - 41$ 35   **8.** $472 \div 8$ 59

Algebra: Exponents

LESSON PLANNING

Objective To represent numbers by using exponents

Intervention for Prerequisite Skills

Repeated Multiplication (For intervention strategies, see page 35.)

California Mathematics Content Standards

NS 2.0 Students calculate and solve problems involving addition, subtraction, multiplication, and division.

(*Also* MR 2.4, MR 2.5)

Vocabulary

exponent a number that tells how many times a base is to be used as a factor

base a number used as a repeated factor

Math Background

Exponential notation is a convenient way to write multiplication of repeated factors in compact form. Exponents are used in many situations in mathematics. In order for students to understand exponential notation, it is important that they understand these ideas:

- The base in an exponential expression is the number used as a factor.
- The exponent tells how many times the base is used as a factor.
- The value of a base raised to an exponent n is called the nth power of the base.

In order for the properties of exponents to be consistent, a nonzero number to the zero power is 1.

WARM-UP RESOURCES

NUMBER OF THE DAY

Transparency 2.2

Use today's calendar date. Square it. Identify the base and the exponent. Check students' answers. The base is the number of the day and the exponent is 2.

PROBLEM OF THE DAY

Transparency 2.2

Replace the letters a, b, and c with the numbers 3, 4, and 5 to make a true sentence.

$2^a + 2^a = b^c \quad 2^5 + 2^5 = 4^3$

Solution Problem of the Day tab, p. PD2

DAILY FACTS PRACTICE

Have students practice multiplication facts by completing Set A of *Teacher's Resource Book*, p. TR94.

ALTERNATIVE TEACHING STRATEGY

Materials *For each pair* 64 square tiles and 64 centimeter cubes

Ask pairs of students to **use area models to represent squares** and find their values.

1. 2^2 4   **2.** 1^2 1

3. 4^2 16   **4.** 5^2 25

Then have students use volume models to represent these cubed numbers and find their values.

5. 2^3 8   **6.** 1^3 1

7. 4^3 64   **8.** 3^3 27

KINESTHETIC

ENGLISH LANGUAGE LEARNERS   ELL•SDAIE

Help students acquiring English to **develop their understanding of base.** Have them relate the idea of base to the number on the bottom of an exponential expression, just as the base of some geometric solids is the foundation that the shape stands on. Have the whole class join in finding expressions in which the word *base* means "foundation." Possible answer: the base of a pyramid or basement of a building

Have groups of students illustrate the words they find and present them to the class.

AUDITORY

MIXED REVIEW AND TEST PREP

Cumulative Review Chapters 1–2

Refer to the Pupil Edition pages referenced in the exercises for further review. Have students go to the lesson page, review the lesson, and correct any problem they missed.

Mixed Review and Test Prep, p. 41

How to Help	
Item	Page
36	30
37	16
38	20
39	22
40	28

WRITING IN MATHEMATICS

Reinforce students' understanding of squaring numbers. Read the following question to students: Can you cover a square area with 10 square tiles or 12 square tiles?

Have them write a paragraph to explain their answer.

Possible answer: No; in order to cover a square area, you need the same number of tiles on each side, so you need a number of tiles that forms a square, such as 4 or 9. Neither 10 nor 12 tiles will cover a square area.

TECHNOLOGY LINK

- Intervention Strategies and Activities CD-ROM • *Skill 12*
- Astro Algebra • *Red,* Level S

LESSON **2.2** ORGANIZER

Objective To represent numbers by using exponents

Vocabulary **exponent, base** *Review* factor

1 | Introduce

QUICK REVIEW provides review of pre-requisite skills.

Why Learn This? In science, you can use this skill to write large numbers in a shortened form. *Share the lesson objective with students.*

2 | Teach

Guided Instruction

• *Help students verbalize the relationship between the exponent and the base.*

What does the exponent tell you? the number of times the base is used as a factor

• *Demonstrate to students a simple rule for evaluating base 10 exponents.*

$10^n = 1$ followed by n zeros. Write the exponent form of 1,000,000. 10^6

• *Call to students' attention a common error in evaluating exponents.*

Juan found the value of 2^3 by multiplying 2 by 3. What mistake did he make? He multiplied the base by the exponent rather than using the base 2 as a factor 3 times.

• *Guide students to apply what they know about exponents.*

REASONING **Numbers with the exponent 3 are called cubes or cubed numbers. Why do you think the name *cubed* is used?** The volume of a cube is equal to the length of one side of the cube raised to a power of 3.

ADDITIONAL EXAMPLES

Example 1, p. 40

Find the value of 3^3.

$3^3 = 3 \times 3 \times 3 = 27$

Example 2, p. 40

Express 16 by using an exponent and the base 2.

$16 = 2 \times 2 \times 2 \times 2 = 2^4$

LESSON **2.2**

ALGEBRA
Exponents

Learn how to represent numbers by using exponents.

QUICK REVIEW
1. 3×3 9
2. 6×6 36
3. $4 \times 4 \times 4$ 64
4. $2 \times 2 \times 2 \times 2$ 16
5. $9 \times 9 \times 9$ 729

Vocabulary

exponent

base

Remember that when you multiply two or more numbers to get a product, the numbers multiplied are called factors.
$8 \times 3 \times 4 = 96$
The numbers 8, 3, and 4 are factors of 96.

Some football stadiums can seat over 100,000 people. Large numbers can be hard to understand. On the right are four ways to write 100,000 using smaller numbers.

$10 \times 10,000$
$10 \times 10 \times 1,000$
$10 \times 10 \times 10 \times 100$
$10 \times 10 \times 10 \times 10 \times 10$

Another way to write 100,000 is by using exponents. An **exponent** shows how many times a number called the **base** is used as a factor.

$$10^5 = 10 \times 10 \times 10 \times 10 \times 10 = 100,000$$

exponent ↓ / base ↑ / equal factors

EXPONENT FORM	READ	VALUE
10^1	The first power of ten	10
$10^2 = 10 \times 10$	Ten squared, or the second power of ten	100
$10^3 = 10 \times 10 \times 10$	Ten cubed, or the third power of ten	1,000

EXAMPLE 1

Find the values of 2^4, 4^2, and 6^3.

$2^4 = 2 \times 2 \times 2 \times 2$
$= 16$
2 is a factor four times.

$4^2 = 4 \times 4$
$= 16$
4 is a factor two times.

$6^3 = 6 \times 6 \times 6$
$= 216$
6 is a factor three times.

Note: The first power of any number equals that number.

$6^1 = 6$ $\qquad 9^1 = 9$ $\qquad 10^1 = 10$

The zero power of any number, except zero, is defined to be 1.

$6^0 = 1$ $\qquad 19^0 = 1$ $\qquad 10^0 = 1$

EXAMPLE 2

Write 125 using an exponent and the base 5.

$125 = 5 \times 25 = 5 \times 5 \times 5$ *Find the equal factors.*
$= 5^3$ *Write the base and the exponent.*

So, $125 = 5^3.$

40

 CALIFORNIA STANDARDS O—⊓NS 2.0 Students calculate and solve problems involving addition, subtraction, multiplication, and division. *also,* MR 2.4 MR 2.5

RETEACH 2.2

Exponents

Powers of numbers can be written in exponent form. An *exponent* shows how many times a number called the *base* is used as a factor.

exponent
$10^5 = \underline{10 \times 10 \times 10 \times 10 \times 10} = 100,000$
base factors
10 used as a factor 5 times

exponent
$2^6 = \underline{2 \times 2 \times 2 \times 2 \times 2 \times 2} = 64$
base factors
2 used as a factor 6 times

Joan is asked to express 64 using an exponent and the base 4.

Step 1 The base is 4. So, Joan must find equal factors.
$8 \times 8 \qquad = 64$
$4 \times 2 \times 2 \times 4 = 64$
$4 \times 4 \times 4 = 64$

Step 2 Joan writes the base. Then she counts how many times it is used as a factor.
$4^3 \leftarrow$ used as a factor 3 times
↑
base
So, $64 = 4^3$.

Write in exponent form.

1. $4 \times 4 \times 4$ ___ 4^3
2. $3 \times 3 \times 3 \times 3 \times 3$ ___ 3^5
3. $10 \times 10 \times 10 \times 10 \times 10$ ___ 10^6
4. $30 \times 30 \times 30 \times 30$ ___ 30^4

Express with an exponent and the base given.

5. 36, base 6 ___ 6^2
6. 32, base 2 ___ 2^5
7. 81, base 3 ___ 3^4
8. 625, base 5 ___ 5^4
9. 343, base 7 ___ 7^3
10. 128, base 2 ___ 2^7
11. 512, base 8 ___ 8^3
12. 1,000,000, base 10 ___ 10^6
13. 121, base 11 ___ 11^2

PRACTICE 2.2

Exponents

Vocabulary

Complete using *exponent* or *base*.

1. A(n) ___ exponent ___ shows how many times a number called the ___ base ___ is used as a factor.

Write the equal factors. Then find the value.

2. 5^4 ___ $5 \times 5 \times 5 \times 5 = 625$
3. 10^5 ___ $10 \times 10 \times 10 \times 10 \times 10 = 100,000$
4. 18^2 ___ $18 \times 18 = 324$
5. 2^6 ___ $2 \times 2 \times 2 \times 2 \times 2 \times 2 = 64$
6. 15^1 ___ 15
7. 4^3 ___ $4 \times 4 \times 4 = 64$

Write in exponent form.

8. $1 \times 1 \times 1$ ___ 1^3
9. $n \times n \times n \times n$ ___ n^4
10. $6 \times 6 \times 6 \times 6 \times 6$ ___ 6^5
11. $10 \times 10 \times 10$ ___ 10^4
12. $y \times y$ ___ y^2
13. $4 \times 4 \times 4 \times 4 \times 4 \times 4$ ___ 4^6

Express with an exponent and the given base.

14. 125, base 5 ___ 5^3
15. 256, base 4 ___ 4^4
16. 729, base 9 ___ 9^3
17. 64, base 2 ___ 2^6
18. 81, base 3 ___ 3^4
19. 1,000,000, base 10 ___ 10^6

Mixed Review

Use mental math to find the value.

20. $65 + 27$ ___ 92
21. $20 \times 14 \times 5$ ___ 1,400
22. $(9 \times 4) + (9 \times 6)$ ___ 90
23. $84 - 45$ ___ 39
24. $3 \times 3 \times 3 \times 3$ ___ 81
25. 7^2 ___ 49

CHECK FOR UNDERSTANDING

Think and ▶ Discuss

Look back at the lesson to answer each question.

1. **Tell** how many zeros there are in the standard form of 10^7. **7**

2. **Explain** how to write $6 \times 6 \times 6 \times 6$ using exponents. **6 will be the base and 4 is the exponent; 6^4.**

Guided ▶ Practice

Write the equal factors. Then find the value.

3. 2^3 — $2 \times 2 \times 2$; 8 **4.** 5^2 — 5×5; 25 **5.** 3^4 — $3 \times 3 \times 3 \times 3$; 81 **6.** 9^3 — $9 \times 9 \times 9$; 729 **7.** 1^4 — $1 \times 1 \times 1 \times 1$; 1

PRACTICE AND PROBLEM SOLVING

For 10, 15, 17, and 20, see left.

Independent ▶ Practice

Write the equal factors. Then find the value.

8. 4^5 — $4 \times 4 \times 4 \times 4 \times 4$; 1,024 **9.** 7^3 — $7 \times 7 \times 7$; 343 **10.** 1^{12} **11.** 5^3 — $5 \times 5 \times 5$; 125 **12.** 2^5 — $2 \times 2 \times 2 \times 2 \times 2$; 32

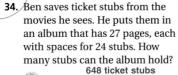

10. $1 \times 1 \times 1 \times 1 \times 1 \times 1 \times 1 \times 1 \times 1 \times 1 \times 1 \times 1$; 1

13. 34^2 — 34×34; 1,156 **14.** 13^2 — 13×13; 169 **15.** 10^8 **16.** 20^2 — 20×20; 400 **17.** 2^{10}

15. $10 \times 10 \times 10 \times 10 \times 10 \times 10 \times 10 \times 10$; 100,000,000

18. 10^4 — $10 \times 10 \times 10 \times 10$; 10,000 **19.** 3^0 1 **20.** 15^2 **21.** 25^1 — 25 **22.** 90^2 — 90×90; 8,100

17. $2 \times 2 \times 2 \times 2 \times 2 \times 2 \times 2 \times 2 \times 2 \times 2$; 1,024

20. 15×15; 225

Write in exponent form.

23. $12 \times 12 \times 12$ 12^3 **24.** $1 \times 1 \times 1 \times 1 \times 1$ 1^5 **25.** $4 \times 4 \times 4 \times 4$ 4^4

26. $2 \times 2 \times 2 \times 2 \times 2$ 2^5 **27.** $n \times n$ n^2 **28.** $y \times y \times y \times y$ y^4

Express with an exponent and the given base.

29. 64, base 8 8^2 **30.** 216, base 6 6^3 **31.** 10,000; base 10 10^4

32. Write 64 using a base of 8, a base of 4, and a base of 2. 8^2; 4^3; 2^6

Problem Solving ▶ Applications

33. Use Data When did California have a population less than 10^7? Explain. **See left.**

33. 1947; $10^7 = 10$ million; the value is less than 10 million

34. Ben saves ticket stubs from the movies he sees. He puts them in an album that has 27 pages, each with spaces for 24 stubs. How many stubs can the album hold? **648 ticket stubs**

35. Possible question: How many more games does Scott have than Aaron?

35. **?** What's the Question? Scott has 3^2 video games and Aaron has 2^3 games. The answer is 1. **See left.**

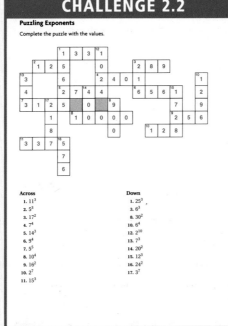

Population of California

POPULATION (in Millions)
Years: 1947 1948 1949 1950 1951 1952

MIXED REVIEW AND TEST PREP

36. Use mental math to find the value of $279 \div 3$. (p. 30) **93**

37. Round 45,621 to the nearest thousand. (p. 16) **46,000**

38. $943,012 - 57,806$ (p. 20) **885,206** **39.** $32,047 \div 43$ (p. 22) **745 r12**

40. TEST PREP Which expression is equivalent to $(3 + 5) \times 2$? (p. 28) **B**

   A $(7 - 3) + 10$ **B** $(4 \times 2) + 8$ **C** $(2 \times 3) + 5$ **D** $10 + (7 \times 10)$

Extra Practice page H33, Set B

41

---

3 Practice

Guided Practice

Do Check for Understanding Exercises 1–7 with your students. Identify those having difficulty and use lesson resources to help.

Independent Practice

Assign Exercises 8–35.

Algebraic Thinking Seeing the relationship between the base and the exponent is an important step in developing relationship thinking. To ensure that students understand this concept, check their answers to Exercises 23–32.

MIXED REVIEW AND TEST PREP
Exercises 36–40 provide **cumulative review** (Chapters 1–2).

4 Assess

Summarize the lesson by having students:

DISCUSS How do you solve Exercise 17? Possible answer: Write 2 as a factor 10 times and multiply.

WRITE Explain how to find the value of a number with an exponent. Possible answer: The exponent tells how many times to write the base as a factor. Then multiply to solve.

Lesson Quiz

Transparency 2.2

Write the equal factors. Then find the value.

1. 10^5 $10 \times 10 \times 10 \times 10 \times 10$; 100,000

2. 11^2 11×11; 121

3. 3^4 $3 \times 3 \times 3 \times 3$; 81

Express with an exponent and the given base.

4. 1,331; base 11 11^3 **5.** 625; base 5 5^4

6. 7,776; base 6 6^5

PROBLEM SOLVING 2.2

Exponents

Write the correct answer.

1. Write in exponent form.
   $5 \times 5 \times 5 \times 5 \times 5 \times 5$
   5^8

2. Compare the fractions $\frac{3}{4}$ and $\frac{7}{8}$. Use < or >.
   $\frac{3}{4} < \frac{7}{8}$ or $\frac{7}{8} > \frac{3}{4}$

3. Claire is working on her reading assignment for school. On Monday she read three pages. Then, on each day after the first day, she read triple the amount of the previous day. Using exponent form, write the number of pages she will read on the fifth day.
   3^5

4. Bill needs to know the decimal equivalent of $\frac{3}{16}$ to solve a problem in his math homework. He changes the fraction to a decimal by dividing the numerator by the denominator. What decimal does he get?
   0.1875

Choose the letter for the best answer.

5. Find the value of 7^3.
   A 73
   B 343
   C 21
   D 10

6. Which is the exponent form of $n \times n \times n \times n \times n$?
   F n^5 H $5n$
   G 5^n J $5n^5$

7. Which group of numbers is listed from greatest to least?
   A 3.045, 3.04, 3.05
   B 4.2, 4.013, 4.01
   C 2.7, 2.86, 2.68
   D 5.10, 5.010, 5.02

8. A salesman travels 517 miles a week to cover his territory. Which is a good estimate for the number of miles he travels in 4 weeks?
   F 500 mi
   G 1,000 mi
   H 1,500 mi
   J 2,000 mi

9. **Write About It** Explain how you can tell which is greater, 8^6 or 12^6, without finding their values.

   The one with the greater base is greater because they have the same exponent. 12^6

CHALLENGE 2.2

Puzzling Exponents

Complete the puzzle with the values.

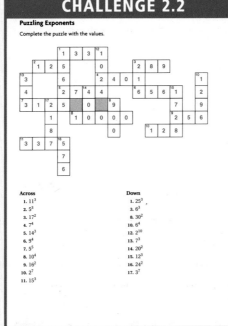

Across
1. 11^3
2. 5^3
3. 17^2
4. 7^4
5. 14^3
6. 9^4
7. 5^5
8. 10^4
9. 16^2
10. 2^7
11. 15^3

Down
1. 25^3
3. 6^3
8. 30^2
10. 6^4
12. 2^{10}
13. 7^3
14. 20^2
15. 12^3
16. 24^2
17. 3^7

41

ORGANIZER

Objective To explore how to evaluate expressions by using order of operations

Vocabulary order of operations, algebraic operating system

Materials *For each student* calculator

Lesson Resources E-Lab Recording Sheet • *Order of Operations*

Intervention for Prerequisite Skills Use of Parentheses (For intervention strategies, see page 35.)

Using the Pages

Point out to students that just as we construct models in a certain order, we must also perform expression operations in a certain order.

Activity 1

Some students will find the value for $23 + 12 \times (6 - 2)^2$ by performing the operations in the order they are presented. After they have reviewed the correct order of operations, have them find the value again.

Reinforce students' understanding that expressions which contain the same numbers and operation signs may have different solutions.

Evaluate the following expressions, and explain why the solutions are different.
$(23 + 12) \times (6 - 2)$ 140 $23 + (12 \times 6) - 2$ 93 $23 + 12 \times (6 - 2)$ 71 Possible answer: The parentheses dictate which operations are performed first on which numbers.

Think and Discuss

Ask students to evaluate this expression:
$13 + 5 - 3 \times (21 \div 7)$
Was this expression easier to evaluate than those you evaluated in Activity 1? Why?
Possible answer: Yes, because the mnemonic helped me remember the order of operations.

Practice

Ask students why they subtracted before clearing the exponents in Exercises 1, 4, and 5. You must perform the operation in parentheses first, which was subtraction in these 3 exercises.

Explore Order of Operations

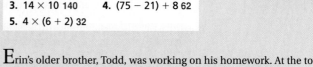

Explore how to evaluate expressions by using order of operations.

You need a calculator.

QUICK REVIEW
1. $16 + 24$ 40
2. $(24 \div 6) \div 2$ 2
3. 14×10 140
4. $(75 - 21) + 8$ 62
5. $4 \times (6 + 2)$ 32

Vocabulary

order of operations

algebraic operating system (AOS)

Erin's older brother, Todd, was working on his homework. At the top of the page, he wrote, "**P**lease **E**xcuse **M**y **D**ear **A**unt **S**ally." Erin didn't understand. She said, "We don't have an aunt named Sally."

Todd said, "You'll see why I wrote this on my paper."

Activity 1

• Use paper and pencil to find the value of $23 + 12 \times (6 - 2)^2$. 215
• How does your answer compare with the answer of a classmate? Answers may vary.

Math Idea ▶ When you find the value of an expression with more than one operation, you need to use the **order of operations**.

1. Perform operations in parentheses.
2. Clear exponents.
3. Multiply and divide from left to right.
4. Add and subtract from left to right.

• Use the order of operations to evaluate $(41 + 31) \div 2^2 - 8$. 10

Think and Discuss
• What do the underlined letters in "**P**lease **E**xcuse **M**y **D**ear **A**unt **S**ally" represent? parentheses, exponents, multiplication, division, addition, and subtraction
• List the order of operations you would use to find the value of $3^3 + 5 - 3 \times (21 \div 7)$. Explain why the order is important. parentheses, exponents, multiplication, addition, subtraction; **Practice** so that the value of an expression is always the same
Tell the order in which you would perform the operations in each expression. Then find the value of the expression.
1. $(120 - 14) + 4^2 \times 3$ parentheses, exponent, multiplication, addition; 154
2. $3 + 5^2 \times 2 \div 10 - 4$ exponent, multiplication, division, addition, subtraction; 4
3. $9 \times 1 + 12 \times 2 \div 8 + 4$ multiplication, division, addition; 16
4. $5 + (7 - 4)^2 - 8 \div 2$ parentheses, exponent, division, addition, subtraction; 10
5. $16 - 2^3 - (9 - 7) \times 4$ parentheses, exponent, multiplication, subtraction; 0

CALIFORNIA STANDARDS AF 1.3 Apply algebraic order of operations and the commutative, associative, and distributive properties to evaluate expressions; and justify each step in the process. AF 1.4 Solve problems manually by using the correct order of operations or by using a scientific calculator. *also*, NS 2.0, MR 2.4, MR 2.5, MR 3.2

42

MATH CONNECTION: ALGEBRA

Review with students the effect of **parentheses in expressions**. Point out that parentheses do not always change the value of an expression. Have students evaluate this expression with and without parentheses: $(2 \times 3) + (5 \times 6) - 4$ 32

They should find that, with or without the parentheses, the value is 32.

Have students write one expression in which the parentheses are essential and one in which they are not. Possible answer: $(4 + 5) \times 2 - 8$ and $(3 \times 5) + 8$

VISUAL

 Intervention and Extension Resources

WRITING IN MATHEMATICS

Have students compare and contrast using the order of operations and using a calculator that uses an AOS to solve an expression. Tell them to include examples of each. Check students' work.

You can use a calculator to evaluate expressions with more than one operation. Some calculators use an **algebraic operating system (AOS)** that automatically follows the order of operations.

Activity 2

- Use your calculator to find the value of $8 \div 2 + 6 \times 3 - 4$. **Answers may vary.**
- Following the order of operations, use paper and pencil to find the value of $8 \div 2 + 6 \times 3 - 4$. **18**
- Exchange papers with a classmate, and check each other's work.

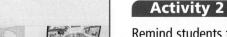

Think and Discuss

- How does the calculator value for $8 \div 2 + 6 \times 3 - 4$ compare with the value you got by using paper and pencil? Does your calculator use an AOS? **Answers may vary.**

To find the value of an expression with a calculator that does not use an AOS, follow the order of operations or use the memory keys.

Follow the order of operations to find the value of the expression $2 + 6 \times 3^2 - 4$.

Use the memory keys to find the value of the expression $9^2 + 6 \div 2 \times 4$.

- When you enter values into a calculator that does not have an AOS, how do you know which values to enter first? **Use the order of operations to identify order.**

> **TECHNOLOGY LINK**
> More Practice: Use E-Lab, *Order of Operations.*
> www.harcourtschool.com/elab2002

Practice

1. A calculator shows the display 9 as the value of $12 + 15 \div 3$. Does the calculator use an AOS? Explain. **No; 17 is the correct value, not 9.**

2. How could you use memory keys to evaluate the expression $12 + 15 \div 3$? **12 M+ 15 ÷ 3 M+ MR**

3. How could you use the order of operations to evaluate the expression $12 + 15 \div 3$? **15 ÷ 3 + 12**

Use a calculator to find the value.

4. $12 + 8 \times 4^2$ **140** 5. $9 + (6 - 2) \times 5$ **29** 6. $18 \div (6 - 4) + 5$ **14**

MIXED REVIEW AND TEST PREP

7. Find the value for 6^3. (p. 40) **216**

8. $34{,}056 + 2{,}207$ (p. 20) **36,263**

9. Evaluate $6p - q$ for $p = 7$ and $q = 11$. (p. 28) **31**

10. $807 \div 45$ (p. 22) **17 r42**

11. **TEST PREP** Write $5 \times 5 \times 5 \times 5$ in exponent form. (p. 40) **C**

   A 4^5 **B** 5^3 **C** 5^4 **D** 10^2

43

Activity 2

Remind students that whether they are using a calculator or pencil and paper, they need to follow the order of operations for the value of the expression to be correct.

Think and Discuss

Ask students which method of evaluating expressions on a calculator they prefer. Some may explain that they prefer memory keys because an operation may be used more than once in the expression. Others may prefer using the order of operations because there are fewer keys to remember.

Practice

After students work Exercise 4, ask:

How could you use memory keys to evaluate the expression?

MIXED REVIEW AND TEST PREP

Exercises 7–11 provide **cumulative review** (Chapters 1–2).

Oral Assessment

Find the value of the expression $17 + 8 - 2^3 \div 4$. Tell the order in which you performed the operations. 23; clear exponents, division, addition, subtraction

A calculator shows the display 13 as the value of $8 + 20 \div (12 - 8)$. Does the calculator use AOS? Explain. Yes; 13 is the correct answer when you follow the order of operations.

E-LAB RECORDING SHEET

USING E-LAB

Students use the order of operations to insert the correct operation in an expression in order to solve a problem.

The E-Lab Recording Sheets and activities are available on the E-Lab website.

www.harcourtschool.com/elab2002

> **TECHNOLOGY LINK**
> ⚙ **Intervention Strategies and Activities CD-ROM** • *Skill 40*
> 🌐 **E-Lab** • *Order of Operations*
> 💿 **Astro Algebra** • *Red*, Level B

Algebra: Order of Operations

LESSON PLANNING

Objective To use the order of operations

Intervention for Prerequisite Skills

Use of Parentheses (For intervention strategies, see page 35.)

 California Mathematics Content Standards

AF 1.3 Apply algebraic order of operations and the commutative, associative, and distributive properties to evaluate expressions; and justify each step in the process.

AF 1.4 Solve problems manually by using the correct order of operations or by using a scientific calculator.

(*Also* MR 1.0, MR 3.2, 🔑 NS 2.0)

Math Background

Without the order of operations it would be impossible to determine a single value for many expressions. Consider the following ideas as you help students understand order of operations:

- No matter what operations are involved within parentheses, these operations are done first.
- Before basic operations are completed, exponents must be cleared.
- If operations occur in the order divide, multiply, divide, they should be done in that order. In other words, multiplication should not always be done before division. Similarly, addition should not be done before subtraction unless they occur in that order.

WARM-UP RESOURCES

 NUMBER OF THE DAY   Transparency 2.4

Find the value of the expression (3 + your age) × 4 − 3^2. Possible answer: $(3 + 11) \times 4 - 3^2 = 47$

 PROBLEM OF THE DAY   Transparency 2.4

Complete the expression using the numbers 3, 4, and 5 so that it equals 19.

___ + ___ × ___

$4 + 5 \times 3$

Solution Problem of the Day tab, p. PD2

 DAILY FACTS PRACTICE

Have students practice multiplication and division facts by completing Set C of *Teacher's Resource Book*, p. TR94.

ALTERNATIVE TEACHING STRATEGY ELL

Some students may still have difficulty **understanding the need for the order of operations.** Ask them to act out the procedure for a common activity, such as making a telephone call, to stress the idea that order is important. Point out that it makes a difference whether you lift the receiver and then touch the numbers or touch the numbers and then lift the receiver. The results are not the same.

KINESTHETIC

MIXED REVIEW AND TEST PREP

Cumulative Review Chapters 1–2

Refer to the Pupil Edition pages referenced in the exercises for further review. Have students go to the lesson page, review the lesson, and correct any problem they missed.

Mixed Review and Test Prep, p. 45

How to Help	
Item	Page
24	40
25	36
26	20
27	22
28	26

SCIENCE CONNECTION

Encourage students to **write two word problems using the order of operations.** Have students use the following data about the five longest snakes in the world. The solution to each problem should require two operations. Have students exchange problems and solve.

AVERAGE LENGTH OF SNAKES	
Reticulated python	35 ft
Anaconda	28 ft
Indian python	25 ft
Diamond python	21 ft
King cobra	19 ft

Possible answer: How much longer are two reticulated pythons than one king cobra? 51 ft

VISUAL

ADVANCED LEARNERS

Challenge students to **use the order of operations** to write an expression that equals 100 by using the number 5 five times. The expression may include any number of $+$, $-$, $\times$, and $\div$ signs as well as parentheses.

Possible answers: $(5 \times 5 \times 5) - (5 \times 5)$ or $(5 + 5 + 5 + 5) \times 5$

VISUAL

TECHNOLOGY LINK

- Intervention Strategies and Activities CD-ROM • *Skill 40*
- Astro Algebra • *Red,* Level B

Objective To use the order of operations

1 Introduce

QUICK REVIEW provides review of pre-requisite skills.

Why Learn This? You can use the order of operations to solve problems that include more than one operation. *Share the lesson objective with students.*

2 Teach

Guided Instruction

• *Check students' understanding of the examples.*

Why do you start with exponents in Example 1? There are no parentheses.

In Example 2, what do you do first? Subtract within the parentheses.

REASONING **In Example 2, would you get a different answer if you did not use parentheses? Explain.** Yes; without the parentheses, you would divide 93 by 3 instead of by 1.

ADDITIONAL EXAMPLES

Example 1, p. 44

Tell the operations used to evaluate the expression.
$54 \div 6 + 4 \times 2^3$ clear exponents, divide, multiply, add; 41

Example 2, p. 44

Find the value of the expression.
$186 + 68 \div 2 - 2 \times (5 \times 2^2)$

$186 + 68 \div 2 - 2 \times (5 \times 2^2)$	Operate inside parentheses
$186 + 68 \div 2 - 2 \times (5 \times 4)$	Clear exponents
$186 + 68 \div 2 - 2 \times 20$	Divide
$186 + 34 - 2 \times 20$	Multiply
$186 + 34 - 40$	Add
$220 - 40$	Subtract
180	

LESSON 2.4

ALGEBRA
Order of Operations

$\mathcal{L}$earn how to use the order of operations.

To evaluate an expression that contains more than one operation, you use rules called the order of operations. The first letters of these words help you remember the order of operations.

Please Excuse My Dear Aunt Sally

Parentheses
Exponents
Multiplication or **D**ivision
Addition or **S**ubtraction

EXAMPLE 1 ▶ Tell the operations used to evaluate the expression.

$35 \div 7 + 5 \times 3^2$	*Clear exponents.*
$35 \div 7 + 5 \times 9$	*Divide.*
$5 + 5 \times 9$	*Multiply.*
$5 + 45$	*Add.*
50	

EXAMPLE 2 ▶ Find the value of the expression $285 + 93 \div (3 - 2) \times 3 \times 4^2$.

$285 + 93 \div (3 - 2) \times 3 \times 4^2$	*Operate inside parentheses.*
$285 + 93 \div 1 \times 3 \times 4^2$	*Clear exponents.*
$285 + 93 \div 1 \times 3 \times 16$	*Divide.*
$285 + 93 \times 3 \times 16$	*Multiply twice.*
$285 + 4,464$	*Add.*
$4,749$	

CHECK FOR UNDERSTANDING

Think and ▶ Discuss   Look back at the lesson to answer each question.

1. **Show** where to insert parentheses to make this equation true.
$420 - 100 \div 40 = 8$ $(420 - 100) \div 40 = 8$

2. **Tell** which operation you would do last to evaluate the expression $7 + 8 - 2^3 \div 4$. subtraction

Guided ▶ Practice   Evaluate the expression.
3. $30 - 15 \div 3$ 25   4. $5^2 - (40 \div 4) \div 2$ 20   5. $5^2 + 10^2 \div 25 - 1$ 28

44

 CALIFORNIA STANDARDS **AF 1.3** Apply algebraic order of operations and the commutative, associative, and distributive properties to evaluate expressions; and justify each step in the process. **AF 1.4** Solve problems manually by using the correct order of operations or by using a scientific calculator. *also,* ⊶ **NS 2.0,** **MR 1.0, MR 3.2**

RETEACH 2.4

Algebra: Order of Operations

When an expression involves more than one operation, you use the order of operations to evaluate it.

1. Operate inside parentheses.
2. Clear exponents.
3. Multiply and divide from left to right.
4. Add and subtract from left to right.

What is the value of $2 \times 3 + (6 - 2) \div 2$?

Step 1 Simplify inside parentheses.	$2 \times 3 + \underbrace{(6 - 2)}_{} \div 2$
Step 2 There are no exponents.	
Step 3 Multiply and divide in order from left to right.	$\underbrace{2 \times 3}_{} + \underbrace{4 \div 2}_{}$
	$\underbrace{6}_{} + \underbrace{2}_{}$
Step 4 Add and subtract in order from left to right.	8

Evaluate the expression.

1. $5 + 4 + 7 \times 3$ 2. $28 \div 4 - (4 + 3)$
$5 + 4 + \underline{21}$ $28 \div 4 - \underline{7}$
$\underline{9} + \underline{21}$ $\underline{7} - \underline{7}$
$\underline{30}$ $\underline{0}$

3. $2^2 + 16 - 8$ 4. $(6 + 4)^2 \times 8$
$\underline{4} + 16 - 8$ $(\underline{10})^2 \times 8$
$\underline{20} - 8$ $\underline{100} \times 8$
$\underline{12}$ $\underline{800}$

Find the value of each expression. From the box at the right, choose the letter that corresponds to the value.

5. $(5 \times 6) \div (4 + 2)$ __B__   6. $10 + 15 - 9 \times 2$ __C__
7. $3^2 + 1 - (18 - 9)$ __A__   8. $(4 + 8) \times 3 \div 6 + 10$ __E__
9. $2 + 5^2 - (4 + 3)$ __G__   10. $4 \div 2 \times 6 - 3 + 3^2$ __F__

A	1
B	5
C	7
D	10
E	16
F	18
G	20
H	32

PRACTICE 2.4

Order of Operations

Give the correct order of operations.

1. $100 + 6^2 - 9$ 2. $(52 - 49)^2 \div 9$
   _____Clear exponents._____   _____Operate inside parentheses._____
   _____Add. Subtract._____   _____Clear exponents. Divide._____
3. $(5^2 + 1) \div 2$ 4. $(9 + 2) \times (16 - 12)^2$
   _____Inside parentheses: Clear_____   _____Operate inside parentheses._____
   _____exponents and add. Divide._____   _____Clear exponents. Multiply._____

Evaluate the expression.

5. $27 \div 3 + 1$ 6. $(6 + 8) \times (9 - 8)$ 7. $(6 + 7^2) \div 5 \times 2$
   _____10_____   _____14_____   _____22_____
8. $(12 \div 2)^3 + (2^3 + 1^3)$ 9. $(15 - 5)^2 - (4 \times 3)$ 10. $(57 + 3) \times 2^4$
   _____225_____   _____88_____   _____960_____
11. $(19 + 9) \div (2^3 - 1) + 20$ 12. $(3 \times 7^2) - (5^3 - 9^2) + 10^2$ 13. $3 \times (10^2 - 65) + (5^2 \times 2)$
   _____24_____   _____203_____   _____155_____

Evaluate the expression for $s = 5$ and $t = 12$.

14. $50 \div s + 7$ 15. $s^2 + 150$ 16. $2 \times t - 18$
   _____17_____   _____175_____   _____6_____
17. $t^2 - 3 \times 8$ 18. $15 + t \div 6$ 19. $27 + 9 \times s$
   _____120_____   _____17_____   _____72_____

Mixed Review

Use mental math to find the value.

20. 12×7 21. $37 + 62$ 22. $434 \div 7$ 23. $1,731 - 605$
   _____84_____   _____99_____   _____62_____   _____1,126_____

Write in exponent form.

24. $8 \times 8 \times 8 \times 8$ 25. $6 \times 6 \times 6 \times 6 \times 6$ 26. $n \times n \times n \times n \times n$
   _____8^4_____   _____6^5_____   _____n^5_____

Independent ▶ Practice

Evaluate the expression.

6. $45 \div 15 + 2 \times 3$ **9**

7. $7 \times 2^2 + 6 - 9$ **25**

8. $3 + 4 \times 250$ **1,003**

9. $12 + (36 \div 4)^2 - 25$ **68**

10. $2^6 - (27 - 8) + (5^2 - 21)$ **49**

11. $(43 + 57) \times (9 - 6)^0$ **100**

12. $4^4 - (5^3 - 7^2) + (3^3 - 25)^3$ **188**

13. $(6^2 + 3^2)^2 \div 5 \times 3 + 3$ **1,218**

14. $(24 + 1^8) \times (7 - 5)^3$ **200**

15. $(7 \times 4)^2 - (34 + 1^8) \times 2^3$ **504**

Algebra **Evaluate the expression for $a = 4$ and $b = 7$.**

16. $21 \div b + 8$ **11**

17. $a \times 31 - 8^2$ **60**

18. $(8 - a) \div 2 + 7$ **9**

19. $b^2 \div 7 \times (6 + 5)$ **77**

Problem Solving ▶ Applications

For 20–21, write and evaluate an expression to solve.

20. Heather mailed 3 packages that cost $2.50 each and 2 packages that cost $1.50 each. How much did she spend on postage? $(3 \times \$2.50) + (2 \times \$1.50) = \$10.50$

21. Minh bought a watermelon for $3.25 and 3 cantaloupes for $1.29 each. He gave the clerk $20. How much change did he get in return? $\$20 - (\$3.25 + 3 \times \$1.29) = \$12.88$

22. **What's the Error?** Joe and Brett found the value of $2 + 6 \times 3^2 - 4$. Joe said the answer is 68 and Brett said the answer is 52. Decide who made the error and describe what the error is. **Joe; he did not follow the order of operations correctly.**

23. The Island Theater holds 236 people. It was filled to capacity for each of its 43 shows last week. This week 8,299 people attended shows at the theater. How many people attended shows at the Island Theater during these two weeks? **18,447 people**

MIXED REVIEW AND TEST PREP

24. What are the equal factors and the value for 7^3? (p. 40) **7 × 7 × 7; 343**

25. Use mental math to find the value. 34×6 (p. 36) **204**

26. Subtract. $2,500 - 1,646$ (p. 20) **854**

27. Divide. $163 \div 5$ (p. 22) **32 r3**

28. TEST PREP Ricky's math class collected a total of 1,364 pennies and quarters. They collected 234 more pennies than quarters. How much money did Ricky's class collect? (p. 26) **A**

A $149.24   **C** $229.40

B $158.34   **D** $237.12

Extra Practice ▶ page H33, Set C

PROBLEM SOLVING 2.4

Order of Operations

Analyze · Choose · Solve · Check

For Problems 1–2, write and evaluate an expression to solve each problem.

1. Rita and Ken worked as volunteers in a fund-raising effort for a candidate in the Georgia primary. Rita stuffed 132 envelopes per hour for 4 hours and Ken stuffed 116 envelopes per hour for 6 hours. How many envelopes did they get done?

$(132 \times 4) + (116 \times 6)$; **1,224 envelopes**

2. The Academy School District filled 21 buses to capacity when it announced it would transport students to the state championship football game. If each bus holds 52 students and 145 more students went by car, how many attended the championship game?

$(21 \times 52) + 145$; **1,237 students**

3. Use mental math to find the value of $234 \div w$, for $w = 6$. **39**

4. Give two numbers between 4.8 and 4.9. **Possible answers: 4.81 and 4.85**

Choose the letter for the best answer.

5. Maureen plans to walk 2 miles a day for the first week in her exercise plan and 3 miles a day for the next 12 days after that. Which of the following expressions shows how far she plans to walk?

(A) $(2 \times 7) + (3 \times 12)$
B $(2 \times 7) \times (3 \times 12)$
C $(2 + 3) \times (7 + 12)$
D $(2 + 3) \times 12$

6. Denzel bought 14 boxes of cups for a party. Each box of cups cost $1.99. He also bought 5 bottles of juice that cost $2.39 each and paid $1.99 in sales tax. How much did he spend in all?

F $6.37
G $31.69
H $39.81
(J) $41.80

7. Which of the following is the value of 5^4?
A 20
B 125
(C) 625
D 1,024

8. Evaluate the expression $4^2 + 7 \times 8 - (15 - 2)$.
F 51
(G) 59
H 85
J 167

9. Write About It Explain the steps you would use in finding the value of $8^2 - 3 \times 7 + 21 - (5 + 8)$.

First, work inside the parentheses, $5 + 8 = 13$. Then evaluate $8^2 = 64$.

Multiply $3 \times 7 = 21$. Then add and subtract: $64 - 21 + 21 - 13 = 51$.

CHALLENGE 2.4

Order Counts!

Parentheses can change the value of an expression, as can the order of operations within the expression.

$6 + 6 \times 6 - 6 = 36$ but $6 + 6 \times (6 - 6) = 6$

1. Simplify $(3 + 3) \times 3 + 3 + 3$. **19**

2. Use five 3s to write an expression whose value is 5.

Possible answer: $3 \div 3 + 3 \div 3 + 3$

3. Use five 3s to write an expression whose value is 3.

Possible answer: $3 \times 3 \div 3 + 3 - 3$

Use parentheses and exponents.

4. Use five 3s to write an expression whose value is 27.

Possible answer: $(3 + 3) \times 3 + 3 \times 3$

5. Use five 3s to write an expression whose value is 29.

Possible answer: $(3 + 3) \times 3 + 3^3$

6. Use five 3s to write an expression whose value is 0 or 1.

Possible answers: $3 \times 3 - (3 + 3 \times 3)$; $(3 - 3)^3 + 3 \div 3$

Place one or more sets of parentheses in the expression on the left side of each equation so that the resulting equation is true.

7. $5 - 2 \times 4 + 3 = 15$
$(5 - 2) \times 4 + 3 = 15$

8. $6 + 1^2 - 20 = 29$
$(6 + 1)^2 - 20 = 29$

9. $3 + 2 \times 7 - 5 = 10$
$(3 + 2) \times (7 - 5) = 10$

10. $4 + 1 \times 6 - 2 = 20$
$(4 + 1) \times (6 - 2) = 20$

11. $11 + 6 - 3^2 = 20$
$11 + (6 - 3)^2 = 20$

12. $64 \times 4 \times 4 - 1 + 1 = 2$
$64 \div (4 \times 4) - (1 + 1) = 2$

Use each of the numbers 4, 6, 8, and 10 once to make a true expression.

13. $(\underline{8} \times \underline{4}) + (\underline{6} \times \underline{10}) = 92$

14. $\underline{10} \div (\underline{8} - \underline{6}) + \underline{4} = 9$

15. $(\underline{10} + \underline{4}) - (\underline{6} + \underline{8}) = 0$

16. $(\underline{10} + \underline{8}) - (\underline{6} + \underline{4}) = 8$

---

3 Practice

COMMON ERROR ALERT

In an expression such as $12 \div 2 \times 3$, students may evaluate it as 2 because they feel they must do multiplication before division. Point out that division may come before multiplication (or subtraction before addition) if that operation appears before the other when reading from left to right.

Guided Practice

Do Check for Understanding Exercises 1–5 with your students. Identify those having difficulty and use lesson resources to help.

Have students make a table like this one to remember the order of operations.

Step 1	( )	Parentheses
Step 2	3^2	Exponents
Step 3	×, ÷	Multiply, Divide
Step 4	+, −	Add, Subtract

Independent Practice

Assign Exercises 6–23.

MIXED REVIEW AND TEST PREP

Exercises 24–28 provide **cumulative review** (Chapters 1–2).

4 Assess

Summarize the lesson by having students:

DISCUSS Mike evaluated the expression $6 - 2 \times 3 + 1$ as 13. What did he do wrong? He subtracted before he multiplied.

WRITE Explain the order of operations. The order of operations defines the order in which operations are performed in an expression. The order is (1) operate inside parentheses, (2) clear exponents, (3) multiply and divide from left to right, and (4) add and subtract from left to right.

Lesson Quiz

Transparency 2.4

Evaluate the expression.

1. $5 + 2^2 \times 4 - 6$ **15**

2. $24 \div (3 - 1)^2 + 2 \times 3$ **12**

3. $10 - (2 \times 3) - (4 \div 2)$ **2**

Problem Solving Skill: *Sequence and Prioritize Information*

LESSON PLANNING

Objective To use the skill *sequence and prioritize information* to solve problems

Intervention for Prerequisite Skills

Use of Parentheses (For intervention strategies, see page 35.)

Lesson Resources Problem Solving Think Along, p. TR1

 California Mathematics Content Standards

MR 1.0 Students make decisions about how to approach problems.

MR 1.1 Analyze problems by identifying relationships, distinguishing relevant from irrelevant information, identifying missing information, sequencing and prioritizing information, and observing patterns.

(*Also* MR 2.0, MR 3.2)

Math Background

The following experiences will help students *sequence and prioritize information:*

- Put data in numerical order.
- Put steps in logical order.
- Choose important steps or information and disregard less important steps or information.

This is a skill students will use often in solving real-life problems. Learning to put steps in logical order involves the ability to foresee what would happen if they were done out of order.

WARM-UP RESOURCES

 NUMBER OF THE DAY
Transparency **2.5**

Start with your favorite number. Write an expression that includes subtracting 6, multiplying by 2, adding 3, and subtracting the starting number to end up with your original number. Possible answer: $(n + 3) \times 2 - 6 - n$

 PROBLEM OF THE DAY
Transparency **2.5**

Look at the following figure. Start at point *A*. Write the sequence that allows you to go around the entire figure, covering each segment only once. Is there only one way? Can you do the same thing if you start at *B*? *AFDEACD*; no, there is more than one sequence; no.

Solution Problem of the Day tab, p. PD2

 DAILY FACTS PRACTICE

Have students practice division facts by completing Set D of *Teacher's Resource Book,* p. TR94.

ALTERNATIVE TEACHING STRATEGY ELL

Materials *For each student* nine $10 bills and two $5 bills of play money

Have students practice the skill *sequence and prioritize information* by giving each student $100 of play money. Then give students the following instructions:

• Save half of what is left.
• Pay bills of $60.
• Buy a bus ticket for $30.

Have them use their money to illustrate the correct order of the steps. Possible answer: Pay bills, buy a bus ticket, save.

KINESTHETIC

READING STRATEGY

Sequence Information is not always presented in the order that it is needed. Point out that it was necessary to reorder the information to solve the problem on page 46. Present the following situation and have students suggest an order and explain their reasoning.

Mrs. Brown wants to pay her gardener, withdraw cash from the bank, and shop for groceries. Possible answer: Withdraw cash, pay the gardener, buy groceries; the cash is needed to do the other activities. Pay the gardener first to be sure you don't spend so much on groceries that there is not enough left to pay the gardener.

TECHNOLOGY

Students can **apply the skill *sequence and prioritize information*** by working in small groups to research an important scientific discovery or technology. They might want to consider personal computers, compact discs, lasers, the Internet, or space travel. Have them research the development of the technology or discovery, highlighting important inventions, discoveries, or earlier technologies that led to it. Then ask them to prepare an oral presentation for the class that includes a poster or other visual representation of the information. Check students' work.

AUDITORY

EARLY FINISHERS

Have students make a time line of the following composers' lives to demonstrate the skill *sequence and prioritize information:*

Ludwig van Beethoven, Leonard Bernstein, Frederic Chopin, Nikolay Rimsky-Korsakov, Antonio Vivaldi

Suggest that students use an encyclopedia or other reference source to find the date of birth, death, or first major work for each composer.

Play a recording for the class of a piece of music composed by one or more of the composers.

Dates of birth: Vivaldi (1678), Beethoven (1770), Chopin (1810), Rimsky-Korsakov (1844), Bernstein (1918)

VISUAL

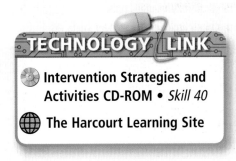

TECHNOLOGY LINK

Intervention Strategies and Activities CD-ROM • *Skill 40*

The Harcourt Learning Site

Objective To use the skill *sequence and prioritize information* to solve problems

Lesson Resources Problem Solving Think Along, p. TR1

1 Introduce

QUICK REVIEW provides review of pre-requisite skills.

Why Learn This? In the future, you can use this skill to plan a trip to an amusement park and visit a maximum number of attractions during the day. *Share the lesson objective with students.*

2 Teach

Guided Instruction

- *Point out that there are many activities in which order is important and in which some steps are more important than others.*

  What kinds of activities can you think of where you need to follow a series of steps? Students may suggest making lunch, playing games, or getting dressed.

  When you make a *Things to do* list, how do you prioritize the items on your list? Possible answer: by giving higher priority to items with a deadline or parental/teacher requests

- *As you study the example, ask:*

  How do you know you cannot pay bills as the first step? You cannot pay bills without having money.

Modifying Instruction Have students write the steps of the problem presented on page 46 on index cards, one to a card, and move the cards around to determine the most logical order.

LESSON **2.5**

PROBLEM SOLVING SKILL
Sequence and Prioritize Information

Analyze
Choose
Solve
Check

Learn how to solve problems by sequencing and prioritizing information.

QUICK REVIEW
1. $3 + (8 \times 2)$ 19
2. $6^2 + 18$ 54
3. $40 - (3 + 2)^2$ 15
4. $4 + 8 \div 2$ 8
5. $15 - 2 \times 3 + 7$ 16

Mrs. Rucki gets paid on the first workday of each month. She deposits her check in the bank and uses the money to pay her bills. Of the money that's left she uses part for spending money and puts the rest into savings.

On March 1, the following occurred:

- Mrs. Rucki had bills of $740, $85, $102, $33, and $52 to pay.
- She received her monthly paycheck for $1,570.
- She wanted to save at least $300 from her check.
- She needed at least $250 spending money.

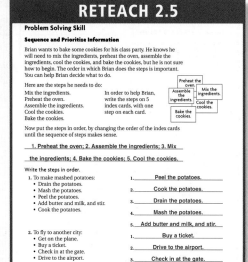

The sequence, or order, in which Mrs. Rucki does these things is important. For example, she cannot use the money until the bank gives her credit for her deposit. That may take three days.

Mrs. Rucki made the list at the left. The list shows the things to do and the order she planned to do them.

- Why does it make sense for Mrs. Rucki to write "Put the rest into my savings account" last? so that she pays all her bills and has enough money to spend

Suppose Mrs. Rucki follows the sequence above. How much will she have left to put into her savings account?

$740 + $85 + $102 + $33 + $52 = $1,012   *Find the total of her bills.*

$1,570 - $1,012 = $558   *Find the amount left after she pays her bills.*

$558 - $250 = $308   *Find what is left after she withdraws spending money.*

So, Mrs. Rucki could put $308 into her savings account.

Math Idea ▶ The order in which parts of an activity are carried out is often important to success. Some parts of an activity may be more important than others.

46

CALIFORNIA STANDARDS MR 1.0 Students make decisions about how to approach problems. **MR 1.1** Analyze problems by identifying relationships, distinguishing relevant from irrelevant information, identifying missing information, sequencing and prioritizing information, and observing patterns. *also,* **MR 2.0, MR 3.2**

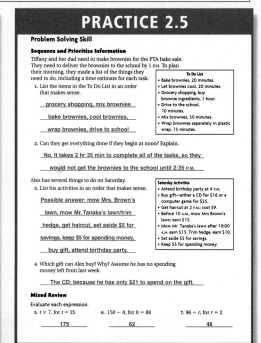

RETEACH 2.5

Problem Solving Skill

Sequence and Prioritize Information

Brian wants to bake some cookies for his class party. He knows he will need to mix the ingredients, preheat the oven, assemble the ingredients, cool the cookies, and bake the cookies, but he is not sure how to begin. The order in which Brian does the steps is important. You can help Brian decide what to do.

Here are the steps he needs to do:

Mix the ingredients.
Preheat the oven.
Assemble the ingredients.
Cool the cookies.
Bake the cookies.

In order to help Brian, write the steps on 5 index cards, with one step on each card.

[Preheat the oven. / Assemble the ingredients / Mix the ingredients. / Cool the cookies. / Bake the cookies.]

Now put the steps in order, by changing the order of the index cards until the sequence of steps makes sense.

1. Preheat the oven; 2. Assemble the ingredients; 3. Mix the ingredients; 4. Bake the cookies; 5. Cool the cookies.

Write the steps in order.

1. To make mashed potatoes:
   - Drain the potatoes.
   - Mash the potatoes.
   - Peel the potatoes.
   - Add butter and milk, and stir.
   - Cook the potatoes.

   1. Peel the potatoes.
   2. Cook the potatoes.
   3. Drain the potatoes.
   4. Mash the potatoes.
   5. Add butter and milk, and stir.

2. To fly to another city:
   - Get on the plane.
   - Buy a ticket.
   - Check in at the gate.
   - Drive to the airport.

   1. Buy a ticket.
   2. Drive to the airport.
   3. Check in at the gate.
   4. Get on the plane.

3. To find the value of $(3 \times 5) + 2 - 8$:
   - Subtract 8.
   - Multiply 3 by 5.
   - Add 2.
   - What is your answer? 9

   1. Multiply 3 by 5.
   2. Add 2.
   3. Subtract 8.

PRACTICE 2.5

Problem Solving Skill

Sequence and Prioritize Information

Tiffany and her dad need to make brownies for the PTA bake sale. They need to deliver the brownies to the school by 1 P.M. To plan their morning, they made a list of the things they need to do, including a time estimate for each task.

To Do List
- Bake brownies, 20 minutes.
- Let brownies cool, 20 minutes.
- Grocery shopping, buy brownie ingredients, 1 hour.
- Drive to the school, 10 minutes.
- Mix brownies, 30 minutes.
- Wrap brownies separately in plastic wrap, 15 minutes.

1. List the items in the To Do List in an order that makes sense.
   grocery shopping, mix brownies
   bake brownies, cool brownies,
   wrap brownies, drive to school

2. Can they get everything done if they begin at noon? Explain.
   No. It takes 2 hr 35 min to complete all of the tasks, so they
   would not get the brownies to the school until 2:35 P.M.

Alex has several things to do on Saturday.

3. List his activities in an order that makes sense.
   Possible answer: mow Mrs. Brown's
   lawn, mow Mr. Tanaka's lawn/trim
   hedge, get haircut, set aside $5 for
   savings, keep $5 for spending money,
   buy gift, attend birthday party.

Saturday Activities
- Attend birthday party at 4 P.M.
- Buy gift—either a CD for $16 or a computer game for $25.
- Get haircut at 2 P.M.; cost $9.
- Before 10 A.M., mow Mrs Brown's lawn; earn $15.
- Mow Mr. Tanaka's lawn after 10:00 A.M. earn $15. Trim hedge, earn $10.
- Set aside $5 for savings.
- Keep $5 for spending money.

4. Which gift can Alex buy? Why? Assume he has no spending money left from last week.
   The CD; because he has only $21 to spend on the gift.

Mixed Review

Evaluate each expression.

5. $t \times 7$, for $t = 25$ 6. $150 - h$, for $h = 88$ 7. $96 \div r$, for $r = 2$

     175   62   48

For 1–3, use the schedule at the right. Each show is 50 minutes long.

1. Jennifer and her family will visit Ocean World Park from 9:30 to 4:00. They want to see the Water Skiing show at 10:00. Name the order in which they can see all the other shows. **Aquarium Tour, Underwater Acrobats, Animal Acts, Whale Acts**

2. The Jackson family wants to see the Underwater Acrobats at 12:00 and then take 45 minutes to eat lunch. What other show could they see before leaving the park at 3:00? **B**

   A Aquarium Tour
   B Animal Acts
   C Whale Acts
   D Water Skiing

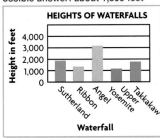

Ocean World Park Show Times

9:00, 12:00	Underwater Acrobats
9:00, 3:00	Whale Acts
10:00, 2:00	Animal Acts
10:00, 1:00	Water Skiing
11:00, 4:00	Aquarium Tour

3. Michele wants to go on the Aquarium Tour at 11:00. Before she leaves the park, she wants to see the Animal Acts show at 2:00. At which other time could she see a show after the Aquarium Tour? **H**

   F 9:00   H 1:00
   G 10:00   J 2:00

4. Ed wants to buy 3 boxes of cereal at $2.99 each, 2 melons at $1.29 each, and 5 cans of juice at $0.79 each. Ed has $12.80. How much more money does he need to buy all of the items? **$2.70**

5. At the Discount Book Barn, books cost $5.00 and magazines cost $1.50. José bought some books and magazines for $21. How many of each did he buy? **3 books, 4 magazines**

6. **Use Data** Use the graph below. The highest waterfall in the world is Angel Falls in Venezuela. About how much higher is Angel Falls than Ribbon Falls? **Possible answer: about 1,500 feet**

HEIGHTS OF WATERFALLS

Height in feet (y-axis: 0, 1,000, 2,000, 3,000, 4,000)

Waterfall (x-axis: Sutherland, Ribbon, Angel, Yosemite, Upper Yosemite, Takkakaw)

7. Tim has saved $1,475 to make a down payment on a new car. He wants to save a total of three times that amount plus $275. How much money does Tim want to save for a down payment? **$4,700**

8. Ron and his two cousins own videotapes. Ron has twice as many as his older cousin, who has 27 videos. Ron has three times as many as his younger cousin. How many videotapes do they have in all? **99 videotapes**

9. Harry hammered nails into a board to make a circular pegboard. The nails were the same distance apart, and the sixth nail was directly opposite the eighteenth nail. How many nails formed the circle? **24 nails**

10. **Write About It** Make a list of the steps you would follow to make a scrambled egg. **Possible answer: Crack an egg into a bowl. Stir the egg with a fork. Put butter in a pan. Heat the butter. Pour the egg into the pan. Let the egg cook.**

47

---

3 Practice

Guided Practice

Do Problem Solving Practice Exercises 1–3 with your students. Identify those having difficulty and use lesson resources to help.

When students approach Exercise 1, have them begin by listing the available hours and then fill in show names next to the times.

Independent Practice

Assign Exercises 4–10.

4 Assess

Summarize the lesson by having students:

DISCUSS Talk about the steps you might follow in crossing the street. Are any steps more important than others? Possible answer: go to a crosswalk, look for traffic, cross; it is very important to look for traffic.

WRITE Explain why it is important to use the skill *sequence information* when evaluating a numerical expression. If you do not use the correct sequence when you evaluate the expression, you may get a wrong answer.

Lesson Quiz

Transparency 2.5

1. Find a sequence of programming that allows Sean to finish each block on the half hour or hour of his radio show.

Programs	Min	Ads	Min
Country Music	28	Carpet Store	3
Golden Oldies	26	Restaurant	2
Rap	27	Grocery Store	4

Possible answer: country music, restaurant ad; rap, carpet store ad; golden oldies, grocery store ad

2. Write a sequence of steps for calling a store to get information. Possible answer: Look up the number, pick up the phone, listen for a dial tone, enter the number, ask for the appropriate department, ask the question.

READING STRATEGY 2.5

Sequence

Analyze • Choose • Solve • Check

Whether you are reading a story or a math problem, putting events in order, or in **sequence**, can help you understand it better. To put events in sequence, you prioritize the order of the events. You can use clues in the text and common sense. Read this problem.

VOCABULARY sequence

Albert gets home at 5:15 P.M. Dinner is at 5:30. Albert has four tasks to do tonight. In what order should he do them?

ALBERT'S EVENING SCHEDULE

Task	Time It Takes	Factors That Affect Sequence
Do homework	2 hr	not enough time before dinner
Pack up backpack for the next day	¾ hr	need to do last
Wash the dinner dishes	½ hr	do after dinner
Make a salad for the family dinner	¼ hr	do this first since dinner is at 5:30 P.M.

1. Next to each task in the chart above, write the factors that will help you sequence the events.

2. Using the information from the table and common sense, write a possible sequence for Albert's tasks.

   make salad, wash dishes, do homework, pack up backpack

Use the schedule below. Each event lasts 50 minutes. Sequence the events to solve.

CHITTENDEN COUNTY FAIR

Event	Times Offered
Pie Judging	10:00 A.M.
Dog Judging	11:00 A.M.
Pig Races	10:00 A.M., 10:00 A.M., 2:00 P.M.
Juggling Show	9:00 A.M., 10:00 A.M., 11:00 A.M., 12 noon
Tractor Pull	9:00 A.M., 11:00 A.M., 1:00 P.M.
Trained Bear Show	9:00 A.M., 1:00 P.M., 3:00 P.M.

3. Antoine and Penny get to the county fair at 9:45 A.M. They both want to go to as many activities as possible, with no breaks. What is the best schedule for Antoine and Penny?

   pie judging at 10 A.M.; dog judging at 11 A.M.; juggling at noon; tractor pull at 1 P.M.; pig races at 2 P.M.; bear show at 3 P.M.

4. Helen and Raoul want to see at least one judged event and they want to eat lunch at noon. They want to see the juggling show right after the tractor pull event. What is the best schedule for them?

   tractor pull at 9 A.M.; juggling at 10 A.M.; dog judging at 11 A.M.; lunch at noon; bear show at 1 P.M.; pig races at 2 P.M.

CHALLENGE 2.5

Problem Solving Skill:
Sequence and Prioritize Information

When you write a program for the computer, the first step is always to analyze the problem that you want to solve. Then you write a flowchart. A *flowchart* is a diagram that models a sequence of steps. The symbols shown below are used in flowcharts.

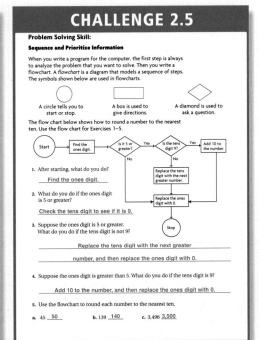

A circle tells you to start or stop.

A box is used to give directions.

A diamond is used to ask a question.

The flow chart below shows how to round a number to the nearest ten. Use the flow chart for Exercises 1–5.

1. After starting, what do you do?

   Find the ones digit.

2. What do you do if the ones digit is 5 or greater?

   Check the tens digit to see if it is 9.

3. Suppose the ones digit is 5 or greater. What do you do if the tens digit is not 9?

   Replace the tens digit with the next greater number, and then replace the ones digit with 0.

4. Suppose the ones digit is greater than 5. What do you do if the tens digit is 9?

   Add 10 to the number, and then replace the ones digit with 0.

5. Use the flowchart to round each number to the nearest ten.

   a. 45 50   b. 139 140   c. 3,496 3,500

47

REVIEW/TEST

Purpose To check understanding of concepts, skills, and problem solving presented in Chapter 2

USING THE PAGE

The Chapter 2 Review/Test can be used as a **review** or a **test**.

- Items 1–3 check understanding of concepts and new vocabulary.
- Items 4–29 check skill proficiency.
- Items 30–33 check students' abilities to choose and apply problem solving strategies to real-life problems involving operations.

 Suggest that students place the completed Chapter 2 Review/Test in their portfolios.

USING THE ASSESSMENT GUIDE

- Multiple-choice format of Chapter 2 Posttest—See *Assessment Guide*, pp. AG13–14.
- Free-response format of Chapter 2 Posttest— See *Assessment Guide*, pp. AG15–16.

USING STUDENT SELF-ASSESSMENT

The How Did I Do? survey helps students assess what they have learned and how they learned it. This survey is available as a copying master in *Assessment Guide*, p. AGxvii.

---

1. **VOCABULARY** In the expression 2^3, the number 2 is the __?__. (p. 40) **base**
2. **VOCABULARY** To find the value of an expression that has more than one operation, you need to use the __?__. (p. 42) **order of operations**
3. **VOCABULARY** In the expression 8^4, the number 4 is the __?__. (p. 40) **exponent**

Use mental math to find the value. (pp. 36–39)

4. $19 + 43$ **62**   5. $76 - 37$ **39**   6. $32 + (48 + 83)$ **163**
7. 26×12 **312**   8. $5,986 \times 1$ **5,986**   9. $4 \times 6 \times 25$ **600**

Write the equal factors. Then find the value. (pp. 40–41)

10. 6^2 **6 × 6; 36**   11. 9^2 **9 × 9; 81**   12. 3^5 **3 × 3 × 3 × 3 × 3; 243**   13. 5^4 **5 × 5 × 5 × 5; 625**   14. 2^0 **1**
15. 10^6 **10 × 10 × 10 × 10 × 10 × 10; 1,000,000**   16. 7^5 **7 × 7 × 7 × 7 × 7; 16,807**   17. 25^1 **25; 25**   18. 4^3 **4 × 4 × 4; 64**   19. 12^2 **12 × 12; 144**

Evaluate the expression. (pp. 44–45)

20. $4 \times 5 - 6 \times 3$ **2**   21. $(12 \times 7) + 9^2$ **165**
22. $13 + 4 \times (20 + 35)$ **233**   23. $4^3 - 4 \times 12$ **16**
24. $36 \div (24 - 18) + 9$ **15**   25. $45 - (12 \times 3) \div 6$ **39**
26. $16 \times 9 \div 2^3$ **18**   27. $(100 - 28) \div 3^2$ **8**
28. $43 + (6^2 - 3^3)^2$ **124**   29. $(19 + 9^2)^2 \div 5^2 + 94$ **494**

Use Data For 30–31, use the table at the right.

30. Michael wants to surprise his family by having dinner ready when they get home. The table shows the length of time each of the foods needs to cook. If Michael wants to have everything ready to eat at the same time, in what order should he start cooking the food? (pp. 46–47) **chicken, rice, stuffing, dinner rolls, peas**
31. Suppose Michael decides to cook baked potatoes instead of rice. The potatoes take 75 minutes to bake. In what order should he start cooking the food? (pp. 46–47) **potatoes, chicken, stuffing, dinner rolls, peas**
32. Doreen has $40.00. She wants to buy 3 pairs of socks for $2.75 each, gloves for $9.99, and 2 T-shirts for $8.79 each. How much money will she have left? (pp. 42–43) **$4.18**
33. Each of three pyramids of Egypt is made up of about 2.5 million large stones. Is the total number of stones greater than or less than 10^8? (pp. 40–41) **less than**

Cooking Times for Food

Type of Food	Cooking Time
Chicken	55 Minutes
Peas	5 Minutes
Rice	20 Minutes
Stuffing	15 Minutes
Dinner Rolls	12 Minutes

CHAPTER 2 TEST, page 1

Choose the best answer.

For 1–6, use mental math to find the value.

1. $19 + 254$
   A 263   C 273
   B 265   D 275

2. $2 \times 7 \times 40$
   F 280   H 560
   G 360   J 650

3. $395 - 87$
   A 318   C 306
   B 308   D 288

4. $225 \div 5$
   F 45   H 35
   G 41   J 31

5. $6,784 \times 1$
   A 6,785   C 1
   B 6,784   D 0

6. $20 \times 37 \times 5$
   F 137   H 925
   G 185   J 3,700

For 7–10, find the value.

7. 8^5
   A 390,625   C 32,768
   B 262,144   D 4,096

8. 5^6
   F 15,625   H 3,125
   G 5,600   J 25

9. 7^5
   A 49   C 7,500
   B 2,401   D 16,807

10. 6^4
    F 216   H 7,776
    G 1,296   J 46,656

For 11–15, evaluate the expression.

11. $3^3 + 4 \times 5$
    A 29   C 155
    B 47   D 180

12. $42 - (6 + 3) \times (5 + 3)$
    F 320   H 168
    G 312   J 26

13. $33 \times (4 - 2) - 4^2$
    A 50   C 82
    B 58   D 560

14. $(44 \div 4) \times (2 + 3^2)$
    F 39   H 110
    G 55   J 121

15. $(72 \div 9) + 13^2 - 8$
    A 22   C 169
    B 42   D 433

Go On →

CHAPTER 2 TEST, page 2

16. Ling has written 8 pages each day for the last 30 days. If she has to write a total of 400 pages in 46 days, how many pages will she have to write per day during the remaining time in order to meet her goal?
    F 10 pages   H 25 pages
    G 15 pages   J 50 pages

17. Robin baby-sits 5 hours a week for $6 per hour. He mows lawns for $10 each twice a week. How much will he make in 12 weeks?
    A $6,000   C $480
    B $600   D $380

For 18–21, evaluate the expression for $a = 8$ and $b = 3$.

18. $9 + a^2 \div (12 - 4)$
    F 64   H 11
    G 17   J 3

19. $b \times 5 \div 43$
    A 58   C 144
    B 88   D 645

20. $80 + a \times (28 - 23)$
    F 450   H 15
    G 50   J 2

21. $48 \div b - 7$
    A 23   C 10
    B 11   D 9

22. Deborah's train ride takes 8 hours. She reads 30 pages per hour. How many pages will she read if she sleeps for 2 hours and reads the rest of the time?
    F 300 pages   H 180 pages
    G 240 pages   J 38 pages

For 23–25, use the following chart.

GUIDED TOUR TIMES		
1	Expressionists	10 A.M., 4 P.M.
2	American Painters	10 A.M., 3 P.M.
3	Dutch Painters	12 P.M., 3 P.M.
4	Sculpture	1 P.M., 4 P.M.
5	Impressionists	2 P.M., 4 P.M.

Each tour lasts 50 minutes.

23. Miranda wants to take the Sculpture tour at 1 P.M. If she arrives at the museum at 10 A.M. and leaves at 4 P.M., in which order could she take all of the tours?
    A 1, 2, 3, 4, 5   C 2, 5, 4, 3, 1
    B 1, 3, 4, 5, 2   D 5, 4, 3, 2, 1

24. Ivan wants to take the 12 P.M. Dutch Painters tour. If he takes the tour and then eats for 45 minutes, what other tour could he take before he leaves the museum at 3:00 P.M.?
    F 1   H 4
    G 3   J 5

25. Susan wants to take the 10 A.M. Expressionists tour. If she plans to leave the museum by 2 P.M., which other tours could she take?
    A 3, 4   C 2, 3
    B 1, 2   D 5, 4

Stop

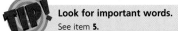

Look for important words.
See item **5**.

An important word is **not**. The words **not** true mean you need to find the one expression among the answer choices that is **not** an equality.

Also see problem **2**, p. H62.

Choose the best answer.

1. Which can be expressed as 3^5? **A**

 A $3 \times 3 \times 3 \times 3 \times 3$

 B $5 \times 5 \times 5$

 C 5×3

 D 3×3

2. Lori has 79 stickers. This is three more than twice as many as Beth has. How many stickers does Beth have? **H**

 F 34   **H** 38

 G 36   **J** 40

3. Calvin spent $43 on a video game and a CD. The video game cost $13 more than the CD. How much did the video game cost? **B**

 A $13   **C** $30

 B $28   **D** $56

4. Kim's class has been saving pennies to go on a field trip to the Gem and Mineral Museum. The class has collected 10,000 pennies. How is 10,000 written using an exponent with the base 10? **H**

 F 1^4 **H** 10^4

 G 10^2 **J** 10^5

5. Which number sentence is **not** true? **D**

 A $30 \times 12 \times 8 = 12 \times 30 \times 8$

 B $30 + 8 + 12 = 30 + 12 + 8$

 C $30 - 12 + 8 = 30 + 8 - 12$

 D $30 + 8 \times 12 = 30 \times 12 + 8$

6. Which expression is equivalent to $(51 + 32) + 71$? **G**

 F $(51 + 71) + (32 + 71)$

 G $51 + (32 + 71)$

 H $93 + 51$

 J $19 + 71$

7. Which expression is equivalent to $42 + 76$? **A**

 A $40 + 78$ **C** $42 + 72$

 B $40 + 79$ **D** $142 + 67$

8. Which expression is equivalent to $(3^2 + 7) \div (4 - 2)$? **G**

 F $(3 + 7)^2 - 2$

 G $(15 + 1) \div 2$

 H $(3 \times 5)^2 \div 15$

 J $100 - (4 \div 2)$

9. What is the value of $42 - d$ for $d = 6$? **B**

 A 7   **C** 48

 B 36   **D** Not here

10. Which algebraic expression represents the expression "13 less than a number, t"? **J**

 F $13 \times t$ **H** $13 - t$

 G $t + 13$ **J** $t - 13$

11. Which is the best estimate for this sum?
 $15,192 + 3,751 + 1,551$ **D**

 A 18,000   **C** 20,000

 B 19,000   **D** 21,000

12. Which is another way to write $y \times y \times y$? **H**

 F $3 \times y$ **H** y^3

 G $y \times 3y$ **J** y^4

49

CUMULATIVE REVIEW •
Chapters 1–2

USING THE PAGE

This page may be used to help students get ready for standardized tests. The test items are written in the same style and arranged in the same format as those on many state assessments. The page is cumulative. It covers math objectives and essential skills that have been taught up to this point in the text. Most of the items represent skills from the current chapter, and the remainder represent skills from earlier chapters.

This page can be assigned at the end of the chapter as classwork or as a homework assignment. You may want to have students use individual recording sheets presented in a multiple-choice (standardized) format. A Test Answer Sheet is available as a blackline master in *Assessment Guide* (p. AGxlii).

You may wish to have students describe how they solved each problem and share their solutions.

Decimal Concepts

CHAPTER PLANNER

PACING OPTIONS	
Compacted	4 Days
Expanded	7 Days

Getting Ready for Chapter 3 • Assessing Prior Knowledge and INTERVENTION (See PE and TE page 51.)

LESSON	CALIFORNIA STANDARDS	PACING	VOCABULARY*	MATERIALS	RESOURCES AND TECHNOLOGY
3.1 Represent, Compare, and Order Decimals pp. 52–55 Objective To use place value to express, compare, and order decimals	⊶ NS 1.0 ⊶ NS 1.1 (*Also* MR 2.5, MR 3.2)	2 Days		*For Thinker's Corner* 10-section spinner, place-value chart	Reteach, Practice, Problem Solving, Challenge 3.1 Worksheets Extra Practice p. H34, Set A ▭ Transparency 3.1 ⦿ **Calculating Crew** • *Nautical Number Line*
3.2 Problem Solving Strategy: *Make a Table* pp. 56–57 Objective To use the strategy *make a table* to solve problems	MR 2.0 MR 3.2 (*Also* ⊶ NS 1.0, MR 1.3)	1 Day			Reteach, Practice, Reading Strategy, Challenge 3.2 Worksheets ▭ Transparency 3.2 Problem Solving Think Along, p. TR1
3.3 Estimate with Decimals pp. 58–59 Objective To estimate decimal sums, differences, products, and quotients	⊶ NS 2.0 MR 2.0 (*Also* MR 2.4, MR 2.5)	1 Day			Reteach, Practice, Problem Solving, Challenge 3.3 Worksheets Extra Practice p. H34, Set B ▭ Transparency 3.3
3.4 Decimals and Percents pp. 60–61 Objective To write a decimal as a percent and a percent as a decimal	⊶ NS 1.0 (*Also* MR 1.1, MR 2.4)	1 Day	**percent**	*For each student* two 10×10 grids (decimal squares)	Reteach, Practice, Problem Solving, Challenge 3.4 Worksheets Extra Practice p. H34, Set C ▭ Transparency 3.4

Ending Chapter 3 • Chapter 3 Review/Test, p. 62 • **Cumulative Review,** p. 63

*****Boldfaced** terms are new vocabulary. Other terms are review vocabulary.

Vocabulary Development

The boldfaced word is the new vocabulary term in the chapter. Have students record the definition in their Math Journals.

percent, p. 60

percent

Vocabulary Cards
Have students use the Vocabulary Cards on *Teacher's Resource Book* pp. TR119–120 to make graphic organizers or word puzzles. The cards can also be added to a file of mathematics terms.

California Mathematics Content Standards for Grade 6

Strands

Number Sense

Lesson 3.1: ⊶ NS 1.0, ⊶ 1.1
Lesson 3.2: ⊶ NS 1.0
Lesson 3.3: ⊶ NS 2.0
Lesson 3.4: ⊶ NS 1.0

Algebra and Functions

Measurement and Geometry

Statistics, Data Analysis, and Probability

Mathematical Reasoning

Lesson 3.1: MR 2.5, 3.2
Lesson 3.2: MR 1.3, 2.0, 3.2
Lesson 3.3: MR 2.0, 2.4, 2.5
Lesson 3.4: MR 1.1, 2.4

Writing Opportunities

PUPIL EDITION
- **What's the Error?**, p. 55
- **What's the Question?**, p. 57
- **Write a Problem**, p. 59
- **Write About It**, p. 61

TEACHER'S EDITION
- **Write**—See the *Assess* section of each TE lesson.
- **Writing in Mathematics**, p. 58B

ASSESSMENT GUIDE
- **How Did I Do?**, p. AGxvii

Family Involvement Activities

These activities provide:
- Letters to the Family
- Information about California Standards
- Math Vocabulary
- Family Game
- Practice (Homework)

Family Involvement Activities, p. FA9

Decimal Concepts

MATHEMATICS ACROSS THE GRADES

SKILLS TRACE ACROSS THE GRADES

GRADE 5	GRADE 6	GRADE 7
Round decimals; estimate decimal sums and differences; add, subtract, multiply, and divide decimals; write fractions as decimals	**Write, compare, and order decimals; estimate decimal sums, differences, products, and quotients; write decimals as percents and percents as decimals**	Estimate and find decimal sums, differences, products, and quotients; write decimals with scientific notation; write fractions as repeating and terminating decimals

SKILLS TRACE FOR GRADE 6

LESSON	FIRST INTRODUCED	TAUGHT AND PRACTICED	TESTED	REVIEWED
3.1	Grade 5	PE pp. 52–55, H34, p. RW11, p. PW11, p. PS 11	PE p. 62, pp. AG17–20	PE pp. 62, 63, 88–89
3.2	Grade 4	PE pp. 56–57, p. RW12, p. PW12, p. PS 12	PE p. 62, pp. AG17–20	PE pp. 62, 63, 88–89
3.3	Grade 5	PE pp. 58–59, H34, p. RW13, p. PW13, p. PS 13	PE p. 62, pp. AG17–20	PE pp. 62, 63, 88–89
3.4	Grade 5	PE pp. 60–61, H34, p. RW14, p. PW14, p. PS 14	PE p. 62, pp. AG17–20	PE pp. 62, 63, 88–89

KEY **PE** Pupil Edition   **PS** Problem Solving Workbook   **RW** Reteach Workbook
PW Practice Workbook   **AG** Assessment Guide

To be ready for Chapter 3, students should have the following understandings and skills:

- **Represent Decimals**—write decimals for models
- **Write and Read Decimals**—decimals to hundredths
- **Compare Whole Numbers**—use <, > or =
- **Round Decimals**—round to nearest whole number

Check What You Know

Use page 51 to determine students' knowledge of prerequisite concepts and skills.

Intervention

Help students prepare for the chapter by using the Intervention resources described on TE page 51.

Looking at Chapter 3 Essential Skills

Students will

- develop skill in writing, comparing, and ordering decimals.
- use the strategy *make a table* to solve problems.
- develop skill estimating decimal sums, differences, products, and quotients.
- **make the connection between graphic representations of decimals and percents to write decimals as percents and percents as decimals.**

EXAMPLE

Write 0.2 as a percent.

Model Percents	Write Percents
	0.2 is 20 hundredths. So, 0.2 = 20%

Looking Ahead Applications

Students will apply what they learn in Chapter 3 to the following new concepts:

- Decimal Operations (Chapter 4)
- Representing Fractions as Decimals (Chapter 8)
- Solving Decimal Equations (Chapter 4)
- Equivalent Forms of Decimals, Fractions, and Percents (Chapter 21)

Decimal Concepts

INTRODUCING THE CHAPTER

Tell students that a decimal number includes numbers such as 44, 0.38, and 5.762. Have students focus on the Trail Mix chart and compare decimals to identify the cereal with the greater amount of fiber, the fruit with the greater amount of carbohydrates, and the nut or seed with the lesser amount of fat. bran flakes; raisins; sunflower seeds

USING DATA

To begin the study of this chapter, have students

• Write a new Daily Value label for toasted oat cereal if the portion size were doubled. Fat: 0.06, Fiber: 0.22, Carbohydrate: 0.18

• Write a new Daily Value label for sunflower seeds if the portion size were cut in half. Fat: 0.11, Fiber: 0.04, Carbohydrate: 0.04

• Decide which snack is best for a low-fat, high-fiber and high-carbohydrate diet. bran flakes

PROBLEM SOLVING PROJECT

Purpose To use decimals to solve problems

Grouping pairs or small groups

Background The U.S. Department of Agriculture (USDA) recommends a diet low in fat and high in complex carbohydrates such as fruit. Hikers and other athletes choose high-energy, healthful snacks that meet these standards.

Analyze, Choose, Solve, and Check

Have students

• Choose healthful foods, either from the chart or their own research, to make their own Trail Mix.

• Decide how many servings of each food choice they want to put in their Trail Mix.

• Make a chart of the foods in their Trail Mix and identify amounts, calories, and Daily Value for each.

 Students may want to display their Trail Mix charts in the classroom before placing them in their portfolios.

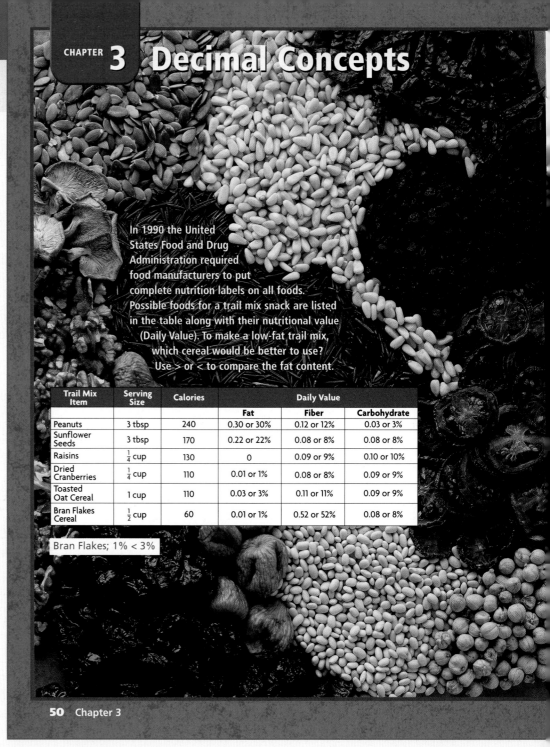

In 1990 the United States Food and Drug Administration required food manufacturers to put complete nutrition labels on all foods. Possible foods for a trail mix snack are listed in the table along with their nutritional value (Daily Value). To make a low-fat trail mix, which cereal would be better to use? Use > or < to compare the fat content.

Trail Mix Item	Serving Size	Calories	Daily Value		
			Fat	Fiber	Carbohydrate
Peanuts	3 tbsp	240	0.30 or 30%	0.12 or 12%	0.03 or 3%
Sunflower Seeds	3 tbsp	170	0.22 or 22%	0.08 or 8%	0.08 or 8%
Raisins	$\frac{1}{4}$ cup	130	0	0.09 or 9%	0.10 or 10%
Dried Cranberries	$\frac{1}{4}$ cup	110	0.01 or 1%	0.08 or 8%	0.09 or 9%
Toasted Oat Cereal	1 cup	110	0.03 or 3%	0.11 or 11%	0.09 or 9%
Bran Flakes Cereal	$\frac{1}{2}$ cup	60	0.01 or 1%	0.52 or 52%	0.08 or 8%

Bran Flakes; 1% < 3%

50 Chapter 3

Why learn math? Explain that knowing the Daily Value for different foods helps nutritionists customize diets to individual needs. For example, choosing frozen yogurt instead of ice cream decreases the fat content by 0.10 or 10%. Ask: What other professions might use decimals and percents? Possible answer: business people, pharmacists, teachers, accountants

Check What You Know

Use this page to help you review and remember important skills needed for Chapter 3.

 Represent Decimals (See p. H2.)

Write the decimal that is modeled.

1.
0.2

2.
0.18

3.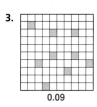
0.09

4.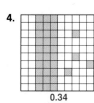
0.34

 Write and Read Decimals (See p. H3.)

Write the decimal.

5. 836 and 23 hundredths 836.23

6. 364 and 2 tenths 364.2

7. 93 thousand, 450 and 38 hundredths 93,450.38

8. 595 thousand, 821 and 9 tenths 595,821.9

9. 306 thousand, 7 and 6 hundredths 306,007.06

Complete to show how to read the numbers.

10. 1,463.05 1 thousand, 463 and __?__ 5 hundredths

11. 204.7 204 and __?__ tenths 7

12. 32,617.45 32 __?__, 617 and 45 __?__ thousand; hundredths

13. 4,382.1 4 thousand, 382 and __?__ 1 tenth

 Compare Whole Numbers (See p. H3.)

Compare the numbers. Write <, >, or = for ●.

14. 143 ● 140 >

15. 808 ● 880 <

16. 716 ● 716 =

17. 691 ● 961 <

18. 94 ● 49 >

19. 405 ● 305 >

20. 383 ● 383 =

21. 5,937 ● 397 >

22. 4,062 ● 4,206 <

23. 689 ● 648 >

24. 6,098 ● 6,908 <

25. 4,801 ● 4,108 >

Round Decimals (See p. H4.)

Round to the nearest whole number.

26. 3.64 4

27. 1.49 1

28. 6.938 7

29. 41.8 42

30. 18.70 19

31. 72.06 72

Round to the nearest tenth.

32. 69.64 69.6

33. 26.37 26.4

34. 52.489 52.5

35. 8.630 8.6

36. 9.479 9.5

37. 14.507 14.5

38. 90.63 90.6

39. 55.58 55.6

40. 26.397 26.4

> **LOOK AHEAD**
>
> **In Chapter 3 you will**
> • represent, compare, and order decimals
> • estimate with decimals
> • use decimals and percents

51

ASSESSING PRIOR KNOWLEDGE

Use the **Check What You Know** page to determine whether your students have mastered the prerequisite skills critical for this chapter.

INTERVENTION

• **Diagnose and Prescribe**

Evaluate your students' performance on this page to determine whether intervention is necessary. **How to Help Options** that provide instruction, practice, and a check are listed in the chart below.

• **Review Prerequisite Skills**

The following resources provide a review for the prerequisite vocabulary and skills.

Option 1—Check What You Know, Pupil Edition p. 51

Option 2—Troubleshooting, Pupil Edition pp. H2–4

TEACHER'S NOTES

Check What You Know
INTERVENTION • Diagnose and Prescribe

Prerequisite Skill	Items (Pupil Edition p. 51)	How to Help Options
☑ Represent Decimals	1–4	• **Troubleshooting, Pupil Edition p. H2** • **Intervention Strategies and Activities** Card, Copying Master, or CD-ROM • **Skill 32**
☑ Write and Read Decimals	5–13	• **Troubleshooting, Pupil Edition p. H3** • **Intervention Strategies and Activities** Card, Copying Master, or CD-ROM • **Skill 33**
☑ Compare Whole Numbers	14–25	• **Troubleshooting, Pupil Edition p. H3** • **Intervention Strategies and Activities** Card, Copying Master, or CD-ROM • **Skill 3**
☑ Round Decimals	26–40	• **Troubleshooting, Pupil Edition p. H4** • **Intervention Strategies and Activities** Card, Copying Master, or CD-ROM • **Skill 35**

TAFT MIDDLE SCHOOL
9191 GRAMERCY DRIVE
SAN DIEGO, CA 92123

Represent, Compare, and Order Decimals

LESSON PLANNING

Objective To use place value to express, compare, and order decimals

Intervention for Prerequisite Skills

Represent Decimals, Write and Read Decimals, Compare and Order Whole Numbers (For intervention strategies, see page 51.)

Materials *For Thinker's Corner* 10-section spinner, p. TR73; place-value chart

 California Mathematics Content Standards

○⌐ NS 1.0 Students compare and order positive and negative fractions, decimals, and mixed numbers. Students solve problems involving fractions, ratios, proportions, and percentages.

○⌐ NS 1.1 Compare and order positive and negative fractions, decimals, and mixed numbers and place them on a number line.

(*Also* MR 2.5, MR 3.2)

Math Background

Decimals can be compared and ordered using models such as place-value charts and number lines. Consider the following ideas as you help students understand the process of comparing and ordering decimals:

- The decimal with the greatest whole-number part is the greatest.

- Decimals can be compared, place by place, starting with the greatest place. The decimal that has a greater digit in a given place is greater.

- Adding zeros so that decimals have the same number of places helps to compare decimals.

- When comparing several decimals, it is helpful to compare two at a time until they are in order.

WARM-UP RESOURCES

 NUMBER OF THE DAY Transparency 3.1

Subtract your age from your age multiplied by 100. When you divide the result by 11 and then divide the quotient by 9, what number do you get? The answer will be the student's age.

 PROBLEM OF THE DAY Transparency 3.1

The money that Mrs. Frey deposited in her bank account was in $10 bills. The sum of the digits in the amount she deposited was 18. If she had deposited $10 more, the sum of the digits would have been 1. How much did Mrs. Frey deposit? $990

Solution Problem of the Day tab, p. PD3

 DAILY FACTS PRACTICE

Have students practice multiplication facts by completing Set E of *Teacher's Resource Book,* p. TR94.

ALTERNATIVE TEACHING STRATEGY

Have students **review ordering whole numbers** by making a time line from A.D. 1000 to 2000 with intervals of 100 years. Have them locate the year in which each of these items was invented and put the information on the time line. Students may wish to illustrate their work.

> telescope—1608
> printing press—1450
> computer—1943
> telephone—1876
> navigational compass—1086

Check students' work.

See also page 54.

VISUAL

MIXED REVIEW AND TEST PREP

Cumulative Review Chapters 1–3

Refer to the Pupil Edition pages referenced in the exercises for further review. Have students go to the lesson page, review the lesson, and correct any problem they missed.

Mixed Review and Test Prep, p. 55

How to Help	
Item	Page
43	42
44	22
45	28
46	40
47	16

SPECIAL NEEDS ⓔLL

Materials *For each student* index card

Engage students physically in **ordering decimals.** Write a different one- or two-place decimal on each index card, and distribute 1 card to each student. Have students form a line ordering the decimals from greatest to least. The first student in line holds the card with the greatest decimal; the last student holds the card with the least decimal.

Then have the students turn the cards over and write a different decimal. Have the students form a new line ordering the decimals they have written from least to greatest. Check students' work.

KINESTHETIC

TECHNOLOGY • *DATA TOOLKIT*

Show students how to **order data** from greatest to least or least to greatest by using a spreadsheet program, such as *Data ToolKit:*

- Insert the following data into the spreadsheet, and then highlight both columns. Bring down the Spreadsheet menu, select *Sort*, and click on the word *Descending* (greatest to least).

Energy Use (in quadrillion BTUs)

Canada	14.36
China	30.18
United States	66.68

Check students' work.

VISUAL

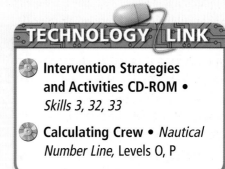

TECHNOLOGY LINK

- **Intervention Strategies and Activities CD-ROM •** *Skills 3, 32, 33*

- **Calculating Crew •** *Nautical Number Line,* Levels O, P

LESSON 3.1 ORGANIZER

Objective To use place value to express, compare, and order decimals

Materials *For Thinker's Corner* 10-section spinner, p. TR73; place-value chart

1 Introduce

QUICK REVIEW provides review of pre-requisite skills.

Why Learn This? Expressing, comparing, and ordering decimals helps you compare prices, measurements, and batting averages. *Share the lesson objective with students.*

2 Teach

Guided Instruction

• *Discuss with students how the value of the digit 3 changes depending on its position in the place-value chart on page 52.*

How does the value of the 3 in the second number compare with that of the 3 in the first number? It is 10,000 times as great.

How does the value of the 3 in the first number compare with that of the 3 in the third number? It is 10 times as great.

• *Draw students' attention to the different ways the numbers are expressed in Example 1.*

How can you remember the difference between *standard form* and *expanded form*? Possible answer: Standard form is the usual way to express a number. Expanded form is the longer way to express a number as addends.

Algebraic Thinking Understanding that the same number or value can be represented in more than one way is a fundamental concept needed for algebra. A decimal number can be written in standard form, in expanded form, in word form, as a fraction, or as a percent.

Represent, Compare, and Order Decimals

Learn how to use place value to express, compare, and order decimals.

Remember that when reading a number with a decimal point, read the decimal point as "and." Read 8.2 as "eight and two tenths."

Genna read that it costs $0.03 to use her hair dryer for 30 minutes, $0.08 to use her clock for a month, and $0.53 to wash and dry a load of laundry.

Place value helps you understand numbers. The digits and the position of each digit determine a number's value. Read each number on the place-value chart. These numbers are part of the decimal system. Notice that 3 has a value of 3 thousandths, 3 tens, or 3 ten-thousandths, depending on its position in the number.

PLACE VALUE	Ten Thousands	Thousands	Hundreds	Tens	Ones	Tenths	Hundredths	Thousandths	Ten-Thousandths
0.053					0	0	5	3	
32.4				3	2	4			
8.0023					8	0	0	2	3

When you read and write numbers, you are using place value.

EXAMPLE 1

A. Standard form: 0.053
Expanded form: 0.05 + 0.003
Word form: *fifty-three thousandths*

B. Standard form: 32.4
Expanded form: 30 + 2 + 0.4
Word form: *thirty-two and four tenths*

C. Standard form: 8.0023
Expanded form: 8 + 0.002 + 0.0003
Word form: *eight and twenty-three ten-thousandths*

Math **I**dea ▶ Knowing the place value of digits will help you read, write, and calculate numbers correctly, including decimal numbers.

52

RETEACH 3.1

Represent, Compare, and Order Decimals

The numbers you use every day are part of the decimal system. To find the value of a number, look at the digits and the position of each digit. A place-value chart can help you.

Knowing place values is useful when comparing decimal numbers. Mindy is asked to list 18.3, 17.8, and 24.1 in order from greatest to least.

Place Value	Millions	Hundred Thousands	Ten Thousands	Thousands	Hundreds	Tens	Ones	Tenths	Hundredths	Thousandths	Ten-Thousandths

decimal point

Step 1 Mindy compares the first two numbers.
• She starts at the left. Both numbers have the digit 1 in the tens place.   18.3 ←→ 17.8
• So, Mindy looks at the digits in the ones place. The first number has the digit 8 in the ones place, while the second number has the digit 7.   18.3 ←→ 17.8
• Since 8 > 7, 18.3 > 17.8.

Step 2 Mindy compares the third number to the greatest number so far, the first number.   24.1 ←→ 18.3
• The third number has the digit 2 in the tens place, while the first number has the digit 1 in the tens place.
• Since 2 > 1, 24.1 > 18.3.

Using what she has discovered, Mindy makes the list: 24.1; 18.3; 17.8.

Give the position and the value of each underlined digit.
1. 30.1̲94   2. 4,082,113.72̲3
  a. position ___tenths___   a. position ___thousandths___
  b. value ___1 tenth; 0.1___   b. value ___3 thousandths; 0.003___
Compare the numbers. Write <, >, or = in the ◯.
3. 9.03 > 0.93   4. 0.210 ◯ 0.012   5. 8.241 > 8.24
Write the numbers in order from least to greatest.
6. 42.05; 45.02; 40.52   7. 19.7; 19.007; 19.07   8. 0.59; 0.95; 0.6
  40.52; 42.05; 45.02   19.007; 19.07; 19.7   0.59; 0.6; 0.95

PRACTICE 3.1

Represent, Compare, and Order Decimals

Write the value of the underlined digit.
1. 485.03̲6   2. 16,005.84̲5   3. 8,492.7̲792
  6 thousandths   4 hundredths   7 tenths
Write the number in expanded form.
4. 5.71 ____5 + 0.7 + 0.01____
5. 85.083 ____80 + 5 + 0.08 + 0.003____
6. 0.4625 ____0.4 + 0.06 + 0.002 + 0.0005____
7. 17.00157 ____10 + 7 + 0.001 + 0.0005 + 0.00007____
Compare the numbers. Write <, >, or = for ◯.
8. 15.4 ◯ 14.5 >   9. 5.67 ◯ 5.76 <   10. 43.90 ◯ 43.9 =
11. 7.91 ◯ 9.17 <   12. 765.28 ◯ 762.58 >   13. 0.234 ◯ 2.304 <
Write the numbers in order from least to greatest.
14. 3,224; 2,432; 3,422   15. 88.5; 85.8; 58.8   16. 6.21; 6.02; 6.12
  2,432; 3,224; 3,422   58.8; 85.8; 88.5   6.02; 6.12; 6.21
Write the numbers in order from greatest to least
17. 0.005; 0.500; 0.050   18. 317.8; 318.7; 371.8   19. 16.04; 14.6; 16.4
  0.500; 0.050; 0.005   371.8; 318.7; 317.8   16.4; 16.04; 14.6

Mixed Review
Evaluate each expression.
20. $4 + 3^3 \times 2 - (6 - 1)$ 21. $(11 + 16) \div 3 + (4 - 2)^2$ 22. $45 + (6^2 - 11) \times 2$
  53   13   95
Solve each equation by using mental math.
23. $m - 7 = 36$ 24. $9x = 63$ 25. $a \div 6 = 14$
  $m = 43$ $x = 7$ $a = 84$
Evaluate each expression for $a = 6, b = 120$, and $c = 54$.
26. $b + 295$ 27. $93 - c$ 28. $b \div a$
  415   39   20

Mark notices that one jar of cinnamon contains 2.6 oz and another contains 2.3 oz. He wants to buy the jar with the greater amount of cinnamon.

You can use a number line to compare 2.6 and 2.3.

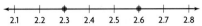

Since 2.6 is to the right of 2.3 on the number line, 2.6 is greater than 2.3.	Since 2.3 is to the left of 2.6 on the number line, 2.3 is less than 2.6.
2.6 > 2.3 ↓ greater than	2.3 < 2.6 ↓ less than

So, the 2.6-oz jar has more cinnamon.

You can also use place value to compare decimal numbers.

TECHNOLOGY LINK

More Practice: Use **Mighty Math Calculating Crew**, *Nautical Number Line*, Levels O and P.

EXAMPLE 2

Compare 7.28 and 7.2. Use < or >.

      Start at the left.

7.**28**   7.**2**   *Compare the ones digits. They are the same.*

7.**28**   7.**2**   *Compare the tenths digits. They are the same.*

7.2**8**   7.2**0**   *Add a zero so both numbers have the same number of places. Compare the hundredths digits. 8 is greater than 0.*

So, 7.28 > 7.2, and 7.2 < 7.28.

• Which is greater, 7.2 or 7.08? Explain. **7.2; compare the tenths, 2 > 0.**

$\underline{\text{Remember}}$ that you can add a zero to the right of a decimal without changing its value.

7.2 = 7.20

2 tenths is the same as 20 hundredths.

You can use place value to order two or more decimal numbers.

EXAMPLE 3

The prices for the same kind of CD player in four different stores are $132.95, $132.50, $130.25, and $135.25. Order the prices of the CD players from least to greatest.

Compare two numbers at a time.

$132.95 > $132.50	$132.95 > $130.25	$132.95 < $135.25
$132.50 > $130.25	$132.50 < $135.25	$130.25 < $135.25

So, the list of numbers in order from least to greatest is $130.25, $132.50, $132.95, $135.25.

• List 9.365, 9.271, 9.356, and 9.065 in order from greatest to least. **9.365, 9.356, 9.271, 9.065**

• *Engage students in a discussion of the greater than and less than symbols.*

Describe a method you use to differentiate between > and <. Possible answer: The symbol always opens to the greater number and narrows toward the lesser number.

ADDITIONAL EXAMPLES

Example 1, p. 52

Use place value to complete the following:

A. Standard form: 72.514

Expanded form: 70 + 2 + 0.5 + 0.01 + 0.004

Word form: seventy-two and five hundred fourteen thousandths

B. Standard form: 64.8

Expanded form: 60 + 4 + 0.8

Word form: sixty-four and eight tenths

C. Standard form: 0.0316

Expanded form: 0.03 + 0.001 + 0.0006

Word form: three hundred sixteen ten-thousandths

Example 2, p. 53

Compare 5.6 and 5.62. Use < or >.

5.6	5.62	*Compare the digits. Start at the left. Same number of ones.*
5.6	5.62	*Same number of tenths.*
5.60	5.62	*Add a zero so both numbers have the same number of places. Compare the hundredths.*

So, 5.6 < 5.62, and 5.62 > 5.6.

Example 3, p. 53

Philip Lewis priced three Internet services. The monthly rates were $19.95, $20.85, and $19.97. Order the rates from least to greatest. Which is the lowest rate? $19.95 < $19.97 < $20.85; $19.95 is the lowest rate.

PROBLEM SOLVING 3.1

Represent, Compare, and Order Decimals   Analyze   Choose   Solve   Check

Write the correct answer.

1. Write the numbers in order from least to greatest.

   6.2; 6.002; 6.02

   6.002; 6.02; 6.2

2. Write the value of the digit 3 in the number 145.36.

   3 tenths

3. Kirk ran 2.6 miles on Monday, 4.2 miles on Tuesday, 1.8 miles on Wednesday, and 5.1 miles on Thursday. Estimate how many miles he ran in the 4 days.

   about 14 mi

4. Morgan carries between 4 and 6 logs at a time. At this rate, what is a reasonable number of trips it will take her to move a pile of 118 logs?

   between 20 and 30 trips

Choose the letter for the best answer.

5. Which group of decimals is listed in order from least to greatest?

  A 1.010, 1.001, 1.100

  B 2.10, 2.200, 2.3

  C 1.400, 1.040, 1.44

  D 2.03, 2.33, 2.003

6. Jill went to the store with $20. She bought 6 cans of soup, 3 gallons of milk, and 2 packages of spaghetti. What else do you need to know to find how much change Jill received?

  F The brand of milk Jill bought

  G The size of a can of soup

  H The weight of a package of spaghetti

  J The cost of each item

7. What is the value of the underlined digit in 34.1̲7?

  A 1 ten

  B 1 one

  C 1 tenth

  D 1 hundredth

8. Simeon played the piano between 2 and 3 hours. What is a reasonable estimate of the number of minutes he played?

  F Less than 60 minutes

  G Between 60 and 120 minutes

  H Between 120 and 180 minutes

  J More than 180 minutes

9. **Write About It** Explain how you would compare 4.08 and 4.3.

You compare the digits starting at the left. Both numbers have 4 ones, so compare the tenths. Zero tenths is less than 3 tenths, so 4.08 < 4.3.

CHALLENGE 3.1

Comparing Scoring Leaders

SCORING LEADERS	
Player	Average
Elgin Baylor	27.4
Wilt Chamberlain	30.1
George Gervin	26.2
Bob Pettit	26.4
Oscar Robertson	25.7
Jerry West	27.0
Dominique Wilkins	24.8

The table above shows the scoring averages of some retired NBA scoring leaders. Use the table for 1–8.

1. Which of the players listed in the table has the greatest average?

   Wilt Chamberlain

2. Which of the players listed in the table has the least average?

   Dominique Wilkins

3. Use the symbol > to list the averages of Oscar Robertson, George Gervin, and Bob Pettit from greatest to least.

   26.4 > 26.2 > 25.7

4. Use the symbol < to list all of the averages shown in the table from least to greatest.

   24.8 < 25.7 < 26.2 < 26.4 < 27.0 < 27.4 < 30.1

5. Michael Jordan's scoring average was 31.5. Where would he be placed in the list you made for Exercise 4?

   after Wilt Chamberlain (30.1)

6. Through the 1998-1999 season, Karl Malone's scoring average was 26.1. Where would he be placed in the list you made for Exercise 4?

   after Oscar Robertson (25.7) but before George Gervin (26.2)

7. Which player in the table had an average greater than 25.5 but less than 26.0?

   Oscar Robertson

8. Which players in the table had an average greater than 26.0 but less than 28.0?

   Elgin Baylor, George Gervin, Bob Pettit, Jerry West

3 Practice

Guided Practice

Do Check for Understanding Exercises 1–14 with your students. Identify those having difficulty and use lesson resources to help.

//// COMMON ERROR ALERT \\\\

When ordering decimals, students sometimes assume that decimals with more decimal places must have a greater value. To avoid this error, have students add zeros to the decimal with fewer places in order to make a one-to-one comparison of each decimal place.

Error	Correction
$3.62 < 3.6\mid72$	$3.6200 > 3.6172$

Independent Practice

Assign Exercises 15–42.

For Exercises 22–27, if students have difficulty distinguishing many digits presented together, encourage them to use graph paper to help them compare the numbers. Have them write the first number, one digit to a square, giving the decimal point its own square. Then write the second number below the first one, lining up the decimal points. Ask them to circle the greater number.

CHECK FOR UNDERSTANDING

Think and ▶ Discuss   Look back at the lesson to answer each question.

1. **Name** the number that is 4 hundredths greater than 2.0369.
2.0769
2. **Tell** the place immediately to the right of hundred-thousandths.
millionths

Guided ▶ Practice   Read the number. Write the value of the blue digit.

3. 15,425.007   4. 2,654,000.25   5. 550.76
7 thousandths   2 tenths   6 hundredths

Write the number in expanded form.

6. 0.6 + 0.005
7. 0.001 + 0.00003
8. 10 + 2 + 0.008 + 0.0009
9. 300 + 40 + 2 + 0.04 + 0.006

6. 0.605   7. 0.00103   8. 12.0089   9. 342.046

Compare the numbers. Write <, >, or = for ●.

10. 1.15 ● 1.14 >   11. 92.3 ● 92.30 =   12. 0.82 ● 0.84 <

Write the numbers in order from least to greatest.

13. 1.361, 1.351, 1.363
1.351, 1.361, 1.363
14. 125.3, 124.32, 125.33
124.32, 125.3, 125.33

PRACTICE AND PROBLEM SOLVING

Independent ▶ Practice   Read the number. Write the value of the blue digit.

15. 5.0547   16. 827.142   17. 345.79456
7 ten-thousandths   4 hundredths   6 hundred-thousandths

Write the number in expanded form.

18. 40 + 6 + 0.001 + 0.00005
19. 0.03 + 0.006 + 0.0002
20. 1,000 + 500 + 0.1
21. 2 + 0.4 + 0.05 + 0.006

18. 46.00105   19. 0.0362   20. 1,500.1   21. 2.456

Compare the numbers. Write <, >, or = for ●.

22. 99.06 ● 99.6 <   23. 133.2 ● 133.32 <   24. 707.07 ● 707.07 =

25. 32.630 ● 32.63 =   26. 457.3685 ● 457.5683 <   27. 49.302 ● 49.203 >

28. 1 + 0.1 + 0.05 ● 1 + 0.1 + 0.04 >

29. 5 + 0.2 + 0.003 ● 5 + 0.3 + 0.02 <

Write the numbers in order from least to greatest.

30. 1.41, 1.21, 1.412, 1.12
1.12, 1.21, 1.41, 1.412
31. 1.45, 1.05, 0.405, 1.25, 1.125
0.405, 1.05, 1.125, 1.25, 1.45
32. 35.2, 35.72, 35.171, 35.7
35.171, 35.2, 35.7, 35.72
33. 9.82, 9.082, 8.91, 9.285, 9.85
8.91, 9.082, 9.285, 9.82, 9.85

Write the numbers in order from greatest to least.

34. 5.004, 5.040, 5.4
5.4, 5.040, 5.004
35. 125.33, 125.3, 125.35, 125.4
125.4, 125.35, 125.33, 125.3
36. $3\frac{1}{10}$, 3.001, $3\frac{1}{100}$, 3
$3\frac{1}{10}$, $3\frac{1}{100}$, 3.001, 3
37. 14.01, $14\frac{1}{10}$, 41.01, $14\frac{3}{100}$
41.01, $14\frac{1}{10}$, $14\frac{3}{100}$, 14.01

Alternative Teaching Strategy

Purpose Students use play money to compare decimals and order decimals.

Materials *For each group* play money—three $1-bills, 15 dimes, 15 pennies

Write: 3.07 ● 3.7

Relate dollars, dimes, and pennies to decimal numbers. Have students use play money to model each decimal. They then complete the number sentence with <, >, or = to make it true. 3.07 < 3.7

Ask: Which coin or bill do you use to model each place in a decimal? Why? Use pennies to model hundredths since there are 100 pennies in a dollar, dimes to model tenths since there are 10 dimes in a dollar, and dollars to model ones.

Demonstrate how to use play money to model and compare 3.07 and 3.7.

3.07   3.7

Count both money amounts. Ask: Which amount is less? $3.07

Point out that this model shows that 3.07 < 3.7.

Have students use play money to model and compare the following decimals: 2.17, 2.7, 2.65.

Ask:

• Which shows the least amount of money? $2.17

• Which shows the greatest amount? $2.70

• How would you order the decimals from least to greatest? Possible answer: The least amount represents 2.17, and the greatest amount represents 2.7. Thus, the decimals in order from least to greatest are 2.17, 2.65, 2.7.

Problem Solving ▶ Applications

38. The world's smallest cut diamond is 0.0009 inch in diameter and weighs 0.0012 carat. Write both numbers in words.
nine ten-thousandths; twelve ten-thousandths

39. A movie studio announced that the box office sales for its new release reached nine million, four hundred fifty-six thousand, three hundred two dollars in the first week. Write ten times that amount in standard and word forms. $94,563,020; 94 million, 563 thousand, twenty

40. ❓ **What's the Error?** Jon says 8.01 and 8.10 are equal because each number has the same digits. Explain his error. 0 and 1 have different place-value positions.

Use Data For 41–42, use the graph at the right.

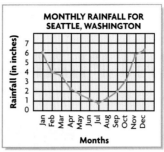

MONTHLY RAINFALL FOR SEATTLE, WASHINGTON

41. Estimate the total amount of rainfall during one year in Seattle. Possible answer: about 38 in.

42. Gene would like to visit Seattle to do some outdoor sightseeing. He would like to visit when the normal amount of rainfall is below 2 inches. When might be the best time for Gene to visit?
Possible answers: May, June, July, or August

43. $12 + 3^3 \times 8$ (p. 42) **228**

44. 234×38 (p. 22) **8,892**

45. Evaluate $406 \div c$ for $c = 14$. (p. 28) **29**

46. TEST PREP Which shows the value of 4^4? (p. 40) **C**

   A 16   **B** 124   **C** 256   **D** 2,414

47. TEST PREP If you do homework for 35 to 45 minutes a day, which is a reasonable estimate of the number of minutes you do homework for 8 days? (p. 16) **G**

   F less than 200 min   **H** between 500 and 700 min
   G between 300 and 500 min   **J** more than 700 min

Thinker's CORNER

Spin a Decimal Practice comparing and ordering decimals as you play this game.

Materials: a spinner numbered 0–9, a place-value chart

- In a small group, decide whether the player with the greatest decimal or least decimal will win. Taking turns, spin the pointer six times. After each spin, write the digit on your place-value chart. Once you have written it on your chart, the digit cannot be moved or erased.
- Take turns reading your six-digit numbers aloud. The player with the greatest or the least decimal wins the round and receives a point.
- Continue playing until a player has five points.

MIXED REVIEW AND TEST PREP
Exercises 43–47 provide **cumulative review** (Chapters 1–3).

Thinker's Corner

- *After the students have had a chance to play the Spin a Decimal game, encourage them to discuss any strategies they may have discovered.*

REASONING **How did you decide where to put in the place-value chart each digit that you spun?** Possible answer: We were playing for the greatest decimal, so if I spun a number greater than 5, I put it in the greatest place available. When a number was less than 5, I put it in the least place available.

4 Assess

Summarize the lesson by having students:

DISCUSS Explain how you would use a number line to compare 91.9 and 91.4. Locate the numbers on the number line. Since 91.4 is to the left of 91.9, $91.4 < 91.9$.

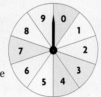 **WRITE Explain how you would determine the order of 4.5, 4, and 4.3 from greatest to least. Use >.** Add a decimal point and a zero to the 4. Compare 4.5 to 4.0: $4.5 > 4.0$. Compare 4.3 to 4.0: $4.3 > 4.0$. Compare 4.5 to 4.3: $4.5 > 4.3$. List the numbers in order: $4.5 > 4.3 > 4$.

Lesson Quiz

Transparency **3.1**

Compare the numbers. Write $>$, $<$, or $=$.

1. 742.3 ● 741.3 $>$ **2.** 8.047 ● 8.0473 $<$

3. 5.474 ● 6.474 $<$ **4.** 69.92 ● 69.920 $=$

Use $<$ to write the numbers in order from least to greatest.

5. 0.505, 0.5, 0.55 $0.5 < 0.505 < 0.55$

6. 27.6, 27.65, 27.62, 27
   $27 < 27.6 < 27.62 < 27.65$

Problem Solving Strategy: *Make a Table*

LESSON PLANNING

Objective To use the strategy *make a table* to solve problems

Intervention for Prerequisite Skills

Compare and Order Whole Numbers (For intervention strategies, see page 51.)

Lesson Resources Problem Solving Think Along, p. TR1

California Mathematics Content Standards

MR 2.0 Students calculate and solve problems involving addition, subtraction, multiplication, and division.

MR 3.2 Note the method of deriving the solution and demonstrate a conceptual understanding of the derivation by solving similar problems.

(*Also* ⊶ NS 1.0, MR 1.3)

Math Background

As you introduce this strategy, remind students of the following:

- It may be helpful to use the strategy *make a table* if there is a large amount of data.
- This strategy can be used to order data, summarize data, organize data, and to help show a pattern.
- When the data are arranged in the table, it is often easier to solve the stated problem.

WARM-UP RESOURCES

 NUMBER OF THE DAY

Transparency 3.2

Compare the number representing the month of the year to that representing the day of the month. Possible answer for Feb. 21: 2 < 21

 PROBLEM OF THE DAY

Transparency 3.2

Jake knows that Uranus is farther from Earth than Saturn but not as far as Neptune. Match each planet with its distance from Earth.

0.744 billion mi

2.7 billion mi

1.6 billion mi

Saturn, 0.744 billion mi
Uranus, 1.6 billion mi
Neptune, 2.7 billion mi

Solution Problem of the Day tab, p. PD3

 DAILY FACTS PRACTICE

Have students practice division facts by completing Set F of *Teacher's Resource Book,* p. TR94.

INTERVENTION AND EXTENSION RESOURCES

REACHING ALL LEARNERS

ALTERNATIVE TEACHING STRATEGY

Materials *For each student* 6 index cards

Help students **organize data for a table.** Provide them with 6 index cards. Have them write each skate model and price from page 56 on a card, one to a card.

Then have students compare pairs of cards and order the cards based on price. Once the cards are in order, have them write the information in a table. Check students' work.

KINESTHETIC

READING STRATEGY

Use Graphic Aids One way to solve the problem on page 56 is simply to list the numbers in order. However, the graphic aid of a table also points out to students the model number of the skates to which each price is attached, thus making it easier to determine which are the preferred models.

In solving Exercises 1 and 2 on page 57, what data will you put in your table? the name of each team and its standing, ordered from least to greatest or greatest to least

ENG-LANG ARTS
Standards
R 2.4

ENGLISH LANGUAGE LEARNERS [ELL•SDAIE]

Reinforce students' understanding of ordering data. Ask them to talk about another situation where different model numbers or names are used to describe items. Students may suggest cars, calculators, or computers.

Have them work in small groups to list several different models. Then have them decide which one would be most expensive, second most expensive, second least expensive, and least expensive. You may wish to assign reasonable whole number prices to the various cars or computers to help students decide. Have students share their lists with the class by using the words *least* and *most expensive.* Check students' work.

AUDITORY

EARLY FINISHERS

Encourage students to **practice making a table.** Ask them to look up the batting averages or other sports data for players or teams of their choice. Once they have collected the data, have them arrange the data in order in a table.

When students have completed their tables, have them write three statements about the people or teams, such as "Smith has the second-highest batting average." Check students' work.

AUDITORY

TECHNOLOGY LINK

Intervention Strategies and Activities CD-ROM • *Skill 3*

LESSON **3.2** ORGANIZER

Objective To use the strategy *make a table* to solve problems

Lesson Resources Problem Solving Think Along, p. TR1

1 Introduce

QUICK REVIEW provides review of pre-requisite skills.

Why Learn This? In the future you can use this strategy to solve problems involving patterns. *Share the lesson objective with students.*

2 Teach

Guided Instruction

- *Be sure students understand the difference between second least expensive and second most expensive models.*

If you arrange a list of prices in order with the least amount at the top, where would you place the second most expensive? second from the bottom

- *Have students examine the table used to solve the problem.*

Why is *make a table* a good strategy for solving this problem? A table helps you to organize the information in the problem in a visual manner that makes the solution more apparent.

How do you begin making the table? Possible answer: To order numbers, I must compare them. I see that 78 is less than the other numbers and 78.50 is less than 78.99, so I put 78.50 first.

REASONING **Describe another method of arranging the data in a table.** Arrange the prices in order from greatest to least and again select the price that is second from the top and the one that is second from the bottom.

LESSON **3.2**

PROBLEM SOLVING STRATEGY
Make a Table

Analyze
Choose
Solve
Check

Learn how to solve problems by organizing data in a table.

1. 276, 265, 263, 224
2. 375, 364, 356, 325
3. 8,903; 8,658; 8,586; 8,459
4. 2,961; 2,906; 2,609; 2,169
5. 3,765; 3,764; 3,456; 3,425

QUICK REVIEW

Order the numbers from greatest to least.

1. 263, 224, 276, 265   2. 364, 356, 375, 325
3. 8,658; 8,586; 8,459; 8,903   4. 2,961; 2,906; 2,609; 2,169
5. 3,764; 3,456; 3,765; 3,425

Andrew chooses new in-line skates from the models below.

RC-204 $99.95; PRX-100 $78.50; D-500 $99.99; OP-1000 $78.99; ZZ-2 $91.50; ZA-45 $99.25

Andrew wants to buy the second most expensive model. His parents want him to buy the second least expensive model. Which models are these? What is the difference in price of the two models?

Analyze — What are you asked to find? **the difference in price of the second most and second least expensive models of in-line skates**
What information is given? **the model numbers and prices of different styles of in-line skates**

Choose — What strategy will you use?
You can use the strategy *make a table* to show the prices of the in-line skates in order from least to greatest.

Solve — How will you solve the problem?
Compare the prices and order them in a table. Then find the second most expensive model, the second least expensive model, and the difference in their prices.

$78.50 < $78.99 < $91.50 < $99.25 < $99.95 < $99.99

MODEL	PRICE	
PRX-100	$78.50	
OP-1000	$78.99	← *second least expensive*
ZZ-2	$91.50	
ZA-45	$99.25	
RC-204	$99.95	← *second most expensive*
D-500	$99.99	

Subtract: $99.95 − $78.99 = $20.96

So, the difference in price of models RC-204 and OP-1000 is $20.96.

Check — How can you check your answer? **Read the prices from top to bottom; make sure that each is greater than the one above it.**
What if Andrew chose model ZZ-2? How much more would he spend than if he bought model OP-1000? **$12.51**

56

CALIFORNIA STANDARDS MR 2.0 Students calculate and solve problems involving addition, subtraction, multiplication, and division. MR 3.2 Note the method of deriving the solution and demonstrate a conceptual understanding of the derivation by solving similar problems. *also* ⊶ NS 1.0, MR 1.3

RETEACH 3.2

Problem Solving Strategy: Make a Table

Putting data in numerical order in a table can often help you determine the greatest or the least piece of data.

The areas of some sports fields are given below.

Basketball ....427 square yards   Ice hockey ....2,222 square yards
Football ....6,400 square yards   Tennis (doubles) .....312 square yards

The area of an Olympic swimming pool is 5,135 square yards less than the greatest area above and 953 square yards greater than the least area. What is the area of an Olympic swimming pool?

Step 1 Think about what you know and what you are asked to find.
- You know the sizes of different sports fields.
- You need to find the area of the pool.

Step 2 Plan a strategy to solve.
- Use the strategy *make a table* to order the data.
- Use the table entries to find the area of the pool.

Step 3 Carry out the strategy.
The greatest area is 6,400 square yards and the least area is 312 square yards. Use the greatest area to find the area of an Olympic swimming pool.

Tennis (doubles)	312 square yards
Basketball	427 square yards
Ice hockey	2,222 square yards
Football	6,400 square yards

6,400 − 5,135 = 1,265

So, the area of an Olympic pool is 1,265 square yards.

Now find the difference between the area of an Olympic swimming pool and the least area to check your answer.

1,265 − 312 = 953 The answer checks.

Solve the problem by making a table.

1. The areas of some other sports fields are boxing, 44 yd²; fencing, 33 yd²; judo, 306 yd²; karate, 75 yd²; and kendo, 132 yd². The area used for wrestling is 10 yd² greater than the least area above. How does the area for wrestling compare to the area for karate? **The area for karate is 32 yd² greater.**

2. Baseball fields are not a standard size. However, the bases on the field are the corners of a square whose area is 5,500 yd² less than the area of a football field and 867 yd² greater than the area for a fencing match. What is the area of this square? **900 yd²**

PRACTICE 3.2

Problem Solving Strategy: Make a Table

Solve the problem by making a table.

1. Earthquakes are measured using the Richter scale. The greater the number, the greater the magnitude (or strength). Some of the strongest earthquakes during the twentieth century had magnitudes of 7.2, 8.9, 8.4, 8.7, 8.3, 8.6, 7.7, and 8.1. The San Francisco earthquake of 1906 had the fifth highest magnitude of those given above. What was its magnitude on the Richter scale?
8.3

2. Late in 1999, one U.S. dollar was worth the following amounts in five other countries' money.

Australian dollar	1.5798
Brazilian real	1.8780
Canadian dollar	1.4796
German mark	1.9524
Swiss franc	1.5919

In which country could one U.S. dollar be exchanged for the greatest amount of that country's money?
Germany

3. Danny is doing library research on animals. He has spent 25 minutes reading about insects. He thinks he will need the same amount of time for each of 5 other types of animals. If he began at 9:45 A.M., at what time would he finish?
12:15 P.M.

4. A theater is showing two films. The starting times for the first film are every even hour, beginning at noon. The starting times for the second film are every odd hour, beginning at 1:00 P.M. If the last show begins at 10:00 P.M., how many times are both films shown?
11 times (1st: 6; 2nd: 5)

Use the table at the right for 5 and 6. The numbers are amounts of energy in quadrillion BTUs.

Country	Energy Produced	Energy Used
United States	66.68	82.19
Great Britain	9.23	9.68
China	30.18	29.22
Canada	14.36	10.97
India	6.94	8.51
Russia	45.66	32.72

5. In which country is the difference between amount of energy produced and amount used the greatest?
United States

6. In which country is the difference between amount of energy produced and amount used the least? **Great Britain**

Mixed Review

Use mental math to find the value.

7. 67 + 83 + 33   8. 449 − 398   9. 203 + 178 + 22
183   **51**   **403**

Write which operation you would do first.

10. 8 − 5 + 7   11. 16 + 4 ÷ 2   12. (10 + 4) × 2
subtraction   **division**   **addition**

PROBLEM SOLVING PRACTICE

Solve the problem by making a table.

Below are the fractions of games won by 8 baseball teams.

Hawks	0.650	Bulldogs	0.725
Tigers	0.750	Lions	0.490
Angels	0.675	Flames	0.700
Dolphins	0.550	Giants	0.695

1. Which team is in second place? **C**

   A Tigers **B** Flames **C** Bulldogs **D** Angels

2. How many teams are behind the Giants? **H**

   F 2   **G** 3   **H** 4   **J** 5

Use Data For 3–4, reorder the data in the table at the right from greatest to least.

3. Which appliance uses the greatest amount of electricity? **air conditioner**

4. Which appliance uses the least amount of electricity? **color TV**

PROBLEM SOLVING STRATEGIES

Draw a Diagram or Picture
Make a Model
Predict and Test
Work Backward
Make an Organized List
Find a Pattern
► **Make a Table or Graph**
Solve a Simpler Problem
Write an Equation
Use Logical Reasoning

Electricity Used By Appliances

Appliance	Electricity (In Kilowatts)
Refrigerator	0.6
Air conditioner	1.5
Color TV	0.33
Iron	1.2
Coffeepot	0.9
Toaster	1.2

MIXED STRATEGY PRACTICE

5. A calculator, pen, and notebook cost $14.00 altogether. The calculator costs $9.00 more than the pen and $8.50 more than the notebook. How much does each item cost? **calculator $10.50, pen $1.50, notebook $2.00**

7. Carlene makes greeting cards. It costs $0.20 to make each card. She then sells them for $0.75 each. How many cards does she need to sell in order to make a profit of $33.00? **60 cards**

9. In a survey, teens prefer the Boomer portable stereo over the Blaster, but not as much as the Soundmaster. The Tekesound was preferred above all the others. Which portable stereo was least preferred? **Blaster**

6. Kelly left the house with $16.00. She had $4.50 left after buying a movie ticket for $6.75, buying two snacks for $1.75 each, and paying for a bus ride. How much did she pay for the bus ride? **$1.25**

8. Frank walks 5 blocks to school for every 3 blocks Robert walks. They walk a total of 24 blocks. How many blocks from school does Robert live? **9 blocks**

10. ❓ **What's the Question?** Glen read 69 pages each day for 6 days. He then read 23 pages each day for 4 days. The answer is about 500.
Possible question: About how many pages did Glen read altogether?

57

---

3 Practice

Guided Practice

Do Problem Solving Practice Exercises 1–4 with your students. Identify those having difficulty and use lesson resources to help.

In the data for Exercises 1–2, point out that expressing fractions here as decimals does not change the fact that they are fractions. Demonstrate this point by showing that 0.725 represents $\frac{725}{1,000}$.

Independent Practice

Assign Exercises 5–10.

Encourage students to use the strategy *make a table* in Exercise 8 to show how many blocks Robert walks if Frank walks 5 blocks, 10 blocks, and so on. They should then record the total of each combination until their total is 24.

4 Assess

Summarize the lesson by having students:

DISCUSS **Talk about how you can make a table to find the best buy among six boxes of cereal.** Determine the unit price, or price per ounce, for each kind and select the one with the least cost per ounce.

WRITE **Compose a problem that can be solved by using a table. Ask another student to solve the problem, and then check your classmate's work.** Check students' work.

Lesson Quiz

Transparency 3.2

1. Clarice spent $3.45, $5.35, $2.55, $4.15, and $4.80 on lunches. Which lunch cost both more than and less than two of the other lunches? the mid-priced lunch of $4.15

2. Sean spent $39 on 10 pens and 8 note-books. The pens cost half as much as the notebooks. How much did he spend on each pen and on each notebook? $1.50 per pen and $3 per notebook

---

READING STRATEGY 3.2

Use Graphic Aids

Analyze Choose Solve Check

You have used **graphic aids** such as tables to find information. You can make a table to organize data with numbers to help you solve problems. Read the following problem.

VOCABULARY
graphic aids

Five friends have saved different amounts of money. Bob has $18.94; Dot, $25.37; Carol, $9.59; Ruth, $34.75; and Ann, $12.38. Who has saved the second greatest amount of money? the second least amount?

1. Order the data in the table below to make the problem easier to solve.

Name	Amount Saved
Ruth	$34.75
Dot	$25.37
Bob	$18.94
Ann	$12.38
Carol	$9.59

2. Solve the problem. Dot has saved the second greatest amount; Ann has saved the second least amount.

3. Explain the strategy you used to solve the problem. I ordered the data in a table. Then I could easily see who saved the second greatest and second least amounts of money.

Reorder the data in the table to solve.

MR. FRENCH'S OFFICE	
Equipment	Price
scanner	$299
copy machine	$1,769
printer	$995
phone system	$488
computer	$2,500
fax machine	$547

GIRLS' BASKETBALL	
Team	Games Won and Lost
Diamonds	1 win, 3 losses
Tigers	0 wins, 4 losses
Hawks	3 wins, 1 loss
Astros	2 wins, 2 losses
Rubies	1 win, 3 losses

4. Mr. French is buying new office equipment. The store requires him to pay for the least and most expensive items in advance. How much does he have to pay now? $2,799

5. There are five girls' basketball teams in the district. Which team is in second place? Astros

CHALLENGE 3.2

Come Fly with Me!

In 1995, about 47,000,000 visitors arrived in the United States by airplane. This was about 4,000,000 more than the number of Americans who traveled by airplane from the United States to other countries. Some of the countries from which the greatest number of visitors came were Canada (7,262,000), France (2,045,000), Germany (3,125,000), Japan (5,676,000), Mexico (4,884,000), and the United Kingdom (6,648,000). Complete the table below, ordering the countries from greatest number of visitors to the United States to the least number. Then use the table to do 2–6.

Airline Passenger Arrivals in the United States	
Country	Number of Visitors
Canada	7,262,000
United Kingdom	6,648,000
Japan	5,676,000
Mexico	4,884,000
Germany	3,125,000
France	2,045,000

1. Approximately how many Americans left the United States by airplane to visit other countries in 1995? **about 43,000,000 Americans**

2. From which two countries did the greatest number of visitors come?
Canada and the United Kingdom

3. About how many total visitors were there from these two countries?
about 14,000,000 visitors

4. About how many visitors flew to the United States from countries other than those included in the table?
Possible answer: about 17,000,000 visitors

5. In 1995, about 1,580,000 people flew to the United States from the Netherlands. About how many fewer people came from the Netherlands than from the last country listed in the table?
Possible answer: about 500,000 visitors

6. About three times as many visitors flew to the United States from France in 1995 as flew here in 1990. Approximately how many visitors flew to France in 1990?
Possible answer: about 700,000 visitors

57

Estimate with Decimals

LESSON PLANNING

Objective To estimate decimal sums, differences, products, and quotients

Intervention for Prerequisite Skills

Round Decimals (For intervention strategies, see page 51.)

California Mathematics Content Standards

NS 2.0 Students calculate and solve problems involving addition, subtraction, multiplication, and division.

MR 2.0 Students use strategies, skills, and concepts in finding solutions.

(*Also* MR 2.4, MR 2.5)

Math Background

Remind students of what they learned about estimating with whole numbers as they begin to estimate with decimals:

- Students may estimate by rounding, clustering, and by using compatible numbers.

- As students gain estimating experience, they will learn to determine the best strategy for different situations.

- Estimation with decimals helps to determine if an answer is a reasonable one. An estimate may also be used when it is not necessary to obtain an exact answer.

WARM-UP RESOURCES

NUMBER OF THE DAY

Transparency **3.3**

Estimate the product of your age in months and the number of days in a month. What does your answer represent? Possible answer: an estimate of your age in days

PROBLEM OF THE DAY

Transparency **3.3**

Randall, Kira, and Sean have 100 baseball cards in all. Randall has twice as many as Kira and 10 more than Sean. How many cards does each person have? Randall has 44 cards, Kira has 22 cards, and Sean has 34 cards.

Solution Problem of the Day tab, p. PD3

DAILY FACTS PRACTICE

Have students practice subtraction facts by completing Set G of *Teacher's Resource Book,* p. TR94.

INTERVENTION AND EXTENSION RESOURCES

REACHING ALL LEARNERS

ALTERNATIVE TEACHING STRATEGY [ELL]

Materials *For each group* 3 $10-bills, 6 $1-bills, 16 dimes, and 25 pennies in play money

Have students **model each decimal** in Example 1 on page 58 by using the play money. By looking at each model, students should be able to see more clearly that each amount is close to $2, and so using clustering is sensible. Then have them model amounts such as $11.35, $10.72, and $11.22 and estimate the sum by clustering. $3 \times \$11 = \$33$

KINESTHETIC

MIXED REVIEW AND TEST PREP

Cumulative Review Chapters 1–3

Refer to the Pupil Edition pages referenced in the exercises for further review. Have students go to the lesson page, review the lesson, and correct any problem they missed.

Mixed Review and Test Prep, p. 59

How to Help	
Item	Page
30	52
31	52
32	20
33	22
34	28

WRITING IN MATHEMATICS

Have each student **apply mental math strategies** by choosing one of the following: rounding, clustering, or compatible numbers. Then ask them to write a description of when they might use the strategy and how they would apply it. *Possible answer: clustering; I would apply it when there are several numbers very close in value. I would pick one number close to the given numbers and multiply by the number of values.*

EARLY FINISHERS

Materials *For each pair* spinner, labeled 0–9, p. TR73

To **reinforce estimation,** give each pair of students a spinner. The first student spins it four times, recording the digit spun each time. The second player makes two decimal numbers from the digits. Students take turns estimating the sum, difference, and product of the two numbers formed. Students then switch roles and repeat the activity. *Check students' work.*

VISUAL

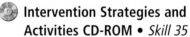

TECHNOLOGY LINK

Intervention Strategies and Activities CD-ROM • *Skill 35*

Objective To estimate decimal sums, differences, products, and quotients

1 Introduce

QUICK REVIEW provides review of pre-requisite skills.

Why Learn This? Decimal estimates will help you determine a car's gas mileage. *Share the lesson objective with students.*

2 Teach

Guided Instruction

• *Review the estimating strategies.*

Why would you use clustering in Example 1? All the numbers are close to 2.

Explain how you could use another estimation strategy in Example 1. Round each charge to the nearest dollar and add.

In Example 2B, why choose 160 as one of the compatible numbers? 8 divides evenly into 16 and 160 is close to 162.

ADDITIONAL EXAMPLES

Example 1, p. 58

Jasmine bought a small salad for $2.85, a chicken wrap for $3.29, and a fruit smoothie for $3.25. About how much did she pay for the meal? about $9.00

Example 2, p. 58

Estimate.

A. 57.6×13.21
Round to the nearest ten. $60 \times 10 = 600$
So, $57.6 \times 13.21 \approx 600$.

B. $249.8 \div 3.81$
Use compatible numbers. $240 \div 4 = 60$
So, $249.8 \div 3.81 \approx 60$.

LESSON 3.3

Estimate with Decimals

Learn how to estimate decimal sums, differences, products, and quotients.

QUICK REVIEW
Round each number to the nearest 100.
1. 346 300   2. 2,506 2,500   3. 54,067 54,100
4. 30,463 30,500   5. 156,556 156,600

You can estimate sums, differences, products, and quotients of decimals. To estimate with decimal numbers, use the same methods you used to estimate with whole numbers.

EXAMPLE 1

A long-distance phone company charges the rates shown at the right for calls from the United States. DeAnn made one-minute calls to India, Jordan, and Pakistan. About how much did the three calls cost?

Estimate $1.79 + $1.87 + $2.17.

  $1.79   *The three addends*
  $1.87   *cluster around $2.00.*
+$2.17   *So, multiply $2.00 by 3.*

$3 \times $2.00 = 6.00 *Multiply.*

So, the three calls cost about $6.00.

WIRED WORLD PHONE COMPANY	
Country	**Rate per Minute**
Argentina	$0.39
China	$0.49
France	$0.13
Germany	$0.09
India	$1.79
Ireland	$0.15
Jordan	$1.87
Pakistan	$2.17

EXAMPLE 2

Estimate.

A. 36.4×18.25
Round to the nearest ten.

Remember that the symbol $\approx$ means "is approximately equal to."

$$
\begin{array}{r}
36.4 \\
\times 18.25 \\
\end{array}
\rightarrow
\begin{array}{r}
40 \\
\times 20 \\
\hline
800 \\
\end{array}
$$

So, $36.4 \times 18.25 \approx 800$.

B. $162.8 \div 8.16$
Use compatible numbers.

$$8.16\overline{)162.8} \rightarrow 8\overline{)160}^{20}$$

So, $162.8 \div 8.16 \approx 20$.

CHECK FOR UNDERSTANDING

Think and ▶ Discuss

Look back at the lesson to answer each question.

1. Possible answer: Round each number to the nearest whole number and add.

1. **Tell** how you could estimate the sum of 4.79, 18.99, and 3.09.

2. **Explain** how to use compatible numbers to estimate $423.2 \div 2.7$.
Possible answer: Use 420 and 3; $420 \div 3 = 140$.

58

CALIFORNIA STANDARDS o—¬NS 2.0 Students calculate and solve problems involving addition, subtraction, multiplication, and division. **MR 2.0** Students use strategies, skills, and concepts in finding solutions. *also* **MR 2.4, MR 2.5**

RETEACH 3.3

Estimate with Decimals

When you estimate with decimals, you want to get an idea of the size of the result. Working with whole numbers can help you estimate quickly.

Estimate 19.7 + 40.13 + 100.4.	Estimate $78.31 − $49.47.
Step 1 Round each number to the nearest whole number.	**Step 1** Round to the nearest ten.
$19.7 \rightarrow 20$	$78.31 \rightarrow 80
$40.13 \rightarrow 40$	$49.47 \rightarrow 50
$100.4 \rightarrow 100$	**Step 2** Subtract the rounded numbers.
Step 2 Add the rounded numbers.	$80 − $50 = 30
$20 + 40 + 100 = 160$	So, a good estimate for the difference is $30.
So, a good estimate for the sum is 160.	

Estimate 62.88×28.97.	Estimate $54.67 \div 8.56$.
Step 1 Round to the nearest ten.	**Step 1** Find compatible numbers close to those given.
$62.88 \rightarrow 60$	$54.67 \rightarrow 54$
$28.97 \rightarrow 30$	$8.56 \rightarrow 9$
Step 2 Multiply the rounded numbers.	**Step 2** Divide the compatible numbers.
$60 \times 30 = 1,800$	$54 \div 9 = 6$
So, a good estimate for the product is 1,800.	So, a good estimate for the quotient is 6.

Estimate. Possible estimates are given.

1. $19.82 + 51.5$ __70__   2. $149.2 \div 23.8$ __6__   3. $784.49 − 610.88$ __200__
4. 39.66×6.75 __280__   5. $1003.2 − 796.1$ __200__   6. $7.86 + 10.03$ __18__
7. 98.15×8.23 __800__   8. 82.88×9.31 __9__   9. 38.8×9.12 __360__
10. $161.10 \div 7.84$ __20__   11. $108.46 + 392.54$ __500__   12. $80.55 − 67.86$ __10__
13. 57.93×21.5 __1,200__   14. $119.4 \div 42.3$ __3__   15. $53.3 + 39.2$ __90__
16. $48.28 \div 6.82$ __8__   17. 28.7×61.75 __1,800__   18. $982.3 − 498.7$ __500__
19. $411.9 + 298.34 + 128.6$ __800__   20. $49.28 + $32.61 + 18.95 __$100__

PRACTICE 3.3

Estimate with Decimals

Estimate. Possible estimates are given.

1. $3.8 + 7.9$ __12__   2. 7.1×6.2 __42__   3. $23.18 − 19.09$ __4__   4. $12.2 \div 5.9$ __2__
5. 4.09×6.18 __24__   6. $83.89 + 17.66$ __102__   7. $162.3 \div 15.7$ __10__   8. $31.6 − 8.82$ __23__
9. $7.7 + 118.2$ __126__   10. $101.2 − 34.9$ __66__   11. $35.99 − 6.02 __$30__   12. 19.8×21.3 __400__
13. 124.66×3 __$375__   14. $10.6 + 19.01$ __30__   15. 81.3×9.6 __800__   16. $810.1 − 69.9$ __740__
17. $602.5 + 87.3$ __690__   18. 397.9×21 __8,000__   19. $502.03 \div 4.9$ __100__   20. $88.20 + 79.10 __$170__
21. $1.8 + 2.9 + 11.8$ __17__   22. $203.99 \div 21$ __$10__   23. $199.50 − 53.99 __$145__
24. 8.8×7.1 __63__   25. $67.2 + 11.9 + 107.44$ __190__   26. $889.52 − 402.68$ __490__

Mixed Review

Write in exponent form.

27. $4 \times 4 \times 4$ __4^3__   28. $2 \times 2 \times 2 \times 2$ __2^4__   29. 6×6 __6^2__   30. $1 \times 1 \times 1 \times 1 \times 1$ __1^5__
31. $7 \times 7 \times 7 \times 7$ __7^4__   32. $8 \times 8 \times 8$ __8^3__   33. $9 \times 9 \times 9$ __9^3__   34. $3 \times 3 \times 3 \times 3$ __3^4__

Find the value.

35. 5^2 __25__   36. 2^5 __32__   37. 8^2 __64__   38. 1^4 __1__

Guided ▶ Practice

Estimate. Possible estimates are given.

3. 18.7 + 23.1
40

4. 123.76 ÷ 9
12

5. 185.32 − 101.99
90

6. 39.83 × 36
1,600

7. 67.8 + 66.1 + 71.7
210

8. 817.3 × 11
8,000

PRACTICE AND PROBLEM SOLVING

Independent ▶ Practice

Estimate. Possible estimates are given.

9. 6.7 + 9.4 + 15.82
32

10. 12.2 × 8.3
100

11. 82.5 ÷ 9.3
9

12. $266.08 − $97.30
$170

13. 9.8 + 38.2
50

14. 31.5 × 2.8
90

15. 6.8 × 18.2
140

16. 103.08 − 45.32
50

17. 56.20 × 30.7
1,800

18.   689.89
      − 98.5
      _____
         590

19.   1,038.54
      ×   26.12
      _____
        26,000

20. 234.91 ÷ 5.79
40

21. $7,805.90
      + 9,158.43
      _____
        $17,000

22. 81.5 × 23.1 ÷ 3.9
400

23. 18.2 × (7.2 −4.9)
36

Estimate to compare. Write < or > for each ●.

24. 4.32 × 8.56 ● 40
        <

25. 25 ● 81.27 ÷ 4.1
        >

26. 34.6 −12.4 ● 14
        >

Problem Solving ▶ Applications

Use Data For 27–29, the table shows the types of waste that make up a typical 100 pounds of garbage in the United States.

27. Possible answer: about 24 lb

27. About how many pounds of newspapers are included in every 300 pounds of garbage thrown away?

28. Possible answer: about 20 lb more

28. About how many more pounds of food waste than glass are thrown away for every 500 pounds of garbage?

What We Throw Away	
Type of Garbage	**Weight (in lb)**
Food Waste	8.6
Yard Waste	17.4
Newspapers	7.9
Other Paper	30.8
Metals	9.2
Glass	5.2
Other	20.9

29. ✎ **Write a problem** involving estimation. Use the data about yard waste, other paper, and metals, shown in the table.
Check students' problems.

MIXED REVIEW AND TEST PREP

30. Write the value of the digit 8 in the number 342.285. (p. 52) **8 hundredths**

31. Write 2.523, 2.325, 2.532, and 2.235 in order from least to greatest. (p. 52)
2.235, 2.325, 2.523, 2.532

32. 20,817 − 19,805 (p. 20) **1,012**

33. 25,801 ÷ 23 (p. 22) **1,121 r18**

34. TEST PREP Evaluate $a \times 32$ for $a = 426$. (p. 28) **D**

A 472   **B** 2,130   **C** 13,522   **D** 13,632

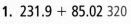

Extra Practice page H34, Set B

59

---

3 Practice

///// COMMON ERROR ALERT \\\\\

When students use compatible numbers in rounding, sometimes they forget to add enough zeros to their numbers. Thus, they might solve Example 2B by using the compatible numbers 8 and 16 instead of 8 and 160. Encourage students to write the compatible numbers and then compare them with the original numbers to be sure the numbers they have chosen are reasonable.

Guided Practice

Do Check for Understanding Exercises 1–8 with your students. Identify those having difficulty and use lesson resources to help.

Independent Practice

Assign Exercises 9–29.

For Exercises 27–29, remind students that the weights are given for every 100 lb of garbage. To find the amount of food waste in 1,000 lb of garbage, they should multiply 8.6 by 10.

MIXED REVIEW AND TEST PREP
Exercises 30–34 provide **cumulative review** (Chapters 1–3).

4 Assess

Summarize the lesson by having students:

DISCUSS How would you use the rounding strategy to estimate the solution to 48.92 + 103.7? Possible answer: Round each number to the nearest ten and then add.

📖✏ **WRITE Describe how you solved Exercise 28.** Possible answer: Use rounding to subtract 5 from 9. Then multiply the result by 5 because the question is for every 500 lb and the table gives data for every 100 lb.

Lesson Quiz

Transparency
3.3

Estimate. Possible estimates are given.

1. 231.9 + 85.02 **320**

2. 34.8 × 12 **350**

3. 522.4 − 176.91 **300**

4. 388.28 ÷ 6.2 **60**

5. 42.078 + 39.2 + 41.82 + 37.66 **160**

59

Decimals and Percents

LESSON PLANNING

Objective To write a decimal as a percent and a percent as a decimal

Intervention for Prerequisite Skills

Represent Decimals, Write and Read Decimals (For intervention strategies, see page 51.)

Materials *For each student* two 10 × 10 grids (decimal squares), p. TR7

 California Mathematics Content Standards

○━ NS 1.0 Students compare and order positive and negative fractions, decimals, and mixed numbers. Students solve problems involving fractions, ratios, proportions, and percentages.

(*Also* MR 1.1, MR 2.4)

Vocabulary

percent "per hundred"

Math Background

Most students are familiar with using percents to relay information. Percents are easy to use to compare information because they are based on a common number, 100. The word *percent* has a Latin origin meaning "per hundred." Based on this definition, percents can be:

• shown on a 10 × 10 grid (decimal square).

• written as decimals.

• written as fractions.

Students reinforce their understanding of place value when they write percents as decimals and one- or two-place decimals as percents. They will build on these skills to write percents as fractions and fractions as percents.

WARM-UP RESOURCES

 NUMBER OF THE DAY Transparency 3.4

Think of the school's grading system. At least what percent of a 100-point test must you answer correctly to make an A? Answers will vary.

 PROBLEM OF THE DAY Transparency 3.4

An estimate of the sum of two decimals is 27 and an estimate of the product is 140. Give two decimals that satisfy these requirements. Possible answer: 6.85 and 19.61

Solution Problem of the Day tab, p. PD3

 DAILY FACTS PRACTICE

Have students practice addition facts by completing Set A of *Teacher's Resource Book,* p. TR95.

INTERVENTION AND EXTENSION RESOURCES

ALTERNATIVE TEACHING STRATEGY

Materials *For each student* at least one 10 × 10 grid (decimal square), p. TR7

To **model the concept of decimals,** give each student one or more 10 × 10 grids. Ask students to make designs on the grids, using only whole squares. Suggest students make animals, letters, patterns, or other designs of their choosing. When they have finished, ask each person to determine what percent of the grid is taken up by the design. Ask them to write the number on the back of the design.

Students can then exchange designs, find the percent of the grid covered by the design, and compare his or her answer to the one written on the back. Check students' work.

VISUAL

MIXED REVIEW AND TEST PREP

Cumulative Review Chapters 1–3

Refer to the Pupil Edition pages referenced in the exercises for further review. Have students go to the lesson page, review the lesson, and correct any problem they missed.

Mixed Review and Test Prep, p. 61

How to Help	
Item	Page
25	52
26	44
27	22
28	22
29	20

ENGLISH LANGUAGE LEARNERS (ELL•SDAIE)

Materials *For each pair* 100 pennies and 1 $1-dollar bill of play money

Help students **model the concept of percent.** Give them play money (pennies and dollars) and talk about the fact that there are 100 pennies in a dollar. Then have students count out 18 pennies and write the money amount as a decimal and percent of a dollar. $0.18; 18%

Repeat the activity with other amounts, having students model the amounts and write the money amounts as decimals and as percents of a dollar. Check students' work.

Ask students to describe other monetary systems they may know about (such as peso, centavo, yen, or sen) that also have 100 smaller units in 1 larger unit.

KINESTHETIC

SOCIAL STUDIES CONNECTION

Encourage students to **relate percents and decimals.** According to a recent poll, teens want to be popular, but they really want to be remembered for their achievements. In response to the question *What title would you like to see under your yearbook picture?*, 54% said *most likely to succeed.* Of the rest, 18% would like to be *class valedictorian,* 11% would like to be *best athlete,* 8% would like to be *class clown,* and 5% would like to be *most popular.*

Have students write each percent as a decimal. 0.54, 0.18, 0.11, 0.08, 0.05

VISUAL

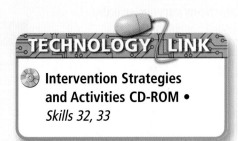

TECHNOLOGY LINK

Intervention Strategies and Activities CD-ROM • *Skills 32, 33*

Objective To write a decimal as a percent and a percent as a decimal

Vocabulary percent

Materials *For each student* two 10 × 10 grids (decimal squares), p. TR7

1 Introduce

QUICK REVIEW provides review of pre-requisite skills.

Why Learn This? Writing a decimal as a percent helps you convert the number of correct answers on a test to a letter grade. *Share the lesson objective with students.*

2 Teach

Guided Instruction

• *Discuss the circle graph showing the results of the survey.*

About what fraction of those surveyed eat cold cereal? How do you know? About $\frac{1}{4}$; about one-fourth of the circle is used to represent that category.

What percent represents about $\frac{1}{3}$ of the circle and therefore about $\frac{1}{3}$ of those surveyed? 34%

• *Reinforce students' understanding of the word percent.*

What is another example of using *cent* to mean "hundredth"? In our money system, 100 cents equal 1 dollar.

How are data from surveys usually reported? usually in percents

REASONING **Would you write 4% as 0.4 or 0.04? Explain.** 0.04; both 4% and 0.04 are the same as 4 hundredths, but 0.4 is 4 tenths.

ADDITIONAL EXAMPLES

Example A, p. 60

Write 0.02 as a percent.

0.02 is 2 hundredths. $0.02 = 2\%$

Example B, p. 60

Write 81% as a decimal.

81% is 81 hundredths. $81\% = 0.81$

Decimals and Percents

Learn how to write a decimal as a percent and a percent as a decimal.

QUICK REVIEW

1. 2,457 + 4,541 6,998   2. 3,470 − 350 3,120   3. 6 × 5 30

4. 50 ÷ 5 10   5. Write the decimal for $\frac{2}{100}$. 0.02

Vocabulary

percent

The graph at the right shows the responses to a question about what people in the United States like to eat for breakfast.

Percent means "per hundred" or "hundredths." The symbol used to write a percent is %.

40 percent: $40\% = \frac{40}{100}$

So, 40 out of 100 have toast or a roll.

26 percent: $26\% = \frac{26}{100}$

So, 26 out of 100 have cold cereal.

BREAKFAST FOODS

26%   40%

cold cereal

34%

toast, roll

eggs, meat

Activity

MATH LAB

You need: two 10 × 10 grids (decimal squares)

• On one grid, shade complete squares to make the first letter of your first name. On the other grid, shade complete squares to make the first letter of your last name. Make each letter as large as possible. Some examples are shown below.

Remember that when you read a decimal, you name the place with the least value. For 0.93, the place with the least value is hundredths. The number is read as "93 hundredths."

• Since 30 out of 100 squares are shaded for the letter Q, you can write 0.30 or 30%. What decimals and percents can be written for the squares shaded for X and Z? *X: 0.20, 20%; Z: 0.28, 28%*

• Count the number of complete squares you shaded on each of your grids. What percent of the squares are shaded? *Check students' grids.*

You can think about place value when you change decimals to percents or percents to decimals.

EXAMPLES

A. Write 0.08 as a percent.
0.08 is 8 hundredths.
So, 0.08 = 8%.

B. Write 32% as a decimal.
32% is 32 hundredths.
So, 32% = 0.32.

60

CALIFORNIA STANDARDS O—n NS 1.0 Students compare and order positive and negative fractions, decimals, and mixed numbers. Students solve problems involving fractions, ratios, proportions, and percentages. *also* MR 1.1, MR 2.4

RETEACH 3.4

Decimals and Percents

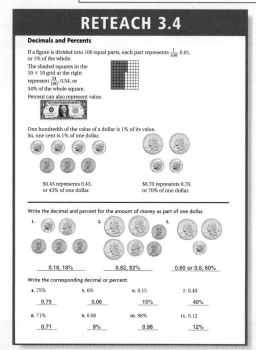

PRACTICE 3.4

Decimals and Percents

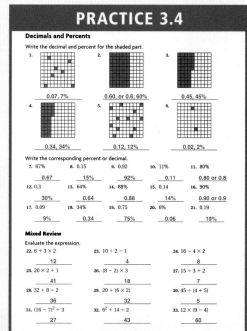

CHECK FOR UNDERSTANDING

Think and ▶ Discuss

Look back at the lesson to answer the question.

1. **Discuss** how you know that Sharon has 18 red cars if 18% of her 100 model cars are red. **18% means 18 per hundred, so 18 cars are red.**

Guided ▶ Practice

Write the decimal and percent for the shaded part.

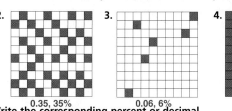

2. **0.35, 35%**   3. **0.06, 6%**   4. **0.82, 82%**

Write the corresponding percent or decimal.

5. 70% **0.7, or 0.70**   6. 0.20 **20%**   7. 0.03 **3%**   8. 84% **0.84**   9. 50% **0.5, or 0.50**

PRACTICE AND PROBLEM SOLVING

Independent ▶ Practice

Write the decimal and percent for the shaded part.

Favorite Types of Music

Alternative	21
Rhythm and Blues	14
Rap	21
Rock	20
Other or none	24

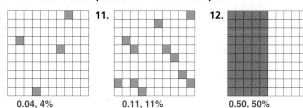

10. **0.04, 4%**   11. **0.11, 11%**   12. **0.50, 50%**

Write the corresponding percent or decimal.

13. 62% **0.62**   14. 0.05 **5%**   15. 28% **0.28**   16. 45% **0.45**   17. 53% **0.53**
18. 0.63 **63%**   19. 0.85 **85%**   20. 33% **0.33**   21. 0.4 **40%**   22. 7% **0.07**

Problem Solving ▶ Applications

23. **Use Data** The table shows how 100 teens responded to a survey. Write a decimal and a percent to show the number of teens who did not choose Alternative music. **0.79, 79%**

24. ✎ **Write About It** Explain how to write 0.6 as a percent. **Write 0.6 as 0.60 to show hundredths. Then write 60 hundredths as 60%.**

MIXED REVIEW AND TEST PREP

25. Order 27.8, 27.5, 27.82 from least to greatest. (p. 52) **27.5, 27.8, 27.82**

26. Evaluate. $35 + 17 \times 3^2 - 16$ (p. 44) **172**   27. 168×92 (p. 22) **15,456**   28. $3,470 \div 42$ (p. 22) **82 r26**

29. **TEST PREP** Which shows the sum $34,904 + 15,456 + 6,943$? (p. 20) **B**

   A 55,920   **B** 56,920   **C** 68,870   **D** 72,780

Extra Practice) page H34, Set C

61

PROBLEM SOLVING 3.4

Decimals and Percents

Write the correct answer.

1. Carl paid for a $0.25 box of crackers and a $0.55 drink with a one-dollar bill. What percent of the dollar did he receive in change?

   20%

2. There are 26 students in class 6-A, 24 in class 6-B, 23 in class 6-C, and 27 in class 6-D. What percent of the sixth graders are in classes 6-A and 6-B?

   50%

3. Rama's bus ride to or from school takes 9 minutes. How long is she on the bus in a 5-day school week?

   90 minutes

4. A rectangular array of dots has 6 rows. There are a total of 216 dots in the array. How many columns of dots are there?

   36 columns

Choose the letter for the best answer.

5. A computer in the school library has 100 web sites bookmarked. Of these, 68 are educational and 16 are travel-related. What percent of the sites are not related to either education or travel?
   Ⓐ 16%   C 52%
   B 18%   D 84%

6. Carlos is 7 years older than his sister. The sum of their ages is 13 less than their mother's age. If their mother is 30 years old, how old is Carlos?
   F 7 years old   Ⓗ 12 years old
   G 10 years old   J 17 years old

7. Using one possible route, the driving distance from New York City to Philadelphia is 100 miles. If you drive 1 hour at 50 miles per hour and one hour at 45 miles per hour, what percent of the trip will you still have left?
   A 95%
   B 50%
   C 10%
   Ⓓ 5%

8. During a sale on film, a store charges $4.99 for a roll of 36 exposures. You need enough film to take individual pictures of all 100 students in the sixth grade. If your budget for film is $25.00, how much extra money do you have?
   Ⓕ $10.03
   G $14.97
   H $15.02
   J $20.01

9. **Write About It** Explain how you would find an unknown percent if you know that a figure consists of two regions and you know the percent represented by one region.

   Possible answer: Subtract the known percent from 100, since the entire figure represents 100%.

CHALLENGE 3.4

Decimals and Percents

Shady Dealings

Shade each grid according to the given rule. Then answer the questions. For Exercises 1–4 and 6, sample shadings are given.

1. Shade the grid so there are 10 more shaded squares than unshaded squares. What percent of the grid is shaded and what percent of the grid is unshaded?
   55%; 45%

2. Shade the grid so there are 30 more unshaded squares than shaded squares. What percent of the grid is shaded and what percent of the grid is unshaded?
   35%; 65%

3. Shade the grid so that the unshaded part is one-fourth the size of the shaded part. What percent of the grid is shaded and what percent of the grid is unshaded?
   80%; 20%

4. Shade the grid so that the unshaded part is three times the size of the shaded part. What decimal names the part of the grid that is shaded? Unshaded?
   0.25; 0.75

5. Shade every square that touches the outside of the grid. What decimal names the part of the grid that is shaded?
   0.36
   What percent of the grid is unshaded?
   64%

6. Shade the grid so that if one more square is shaded, then the number of shaded squares would be 20 greater than the number of unshaded squares. What percent of the grid is shaded and what percent of the grid is unshaded?
   59%; 41%

---

3 Practice

Guided Practice

Do Check for Understanding Exercises 1–9 with your students. Identify those having difficulty and use lesson resources to help.

/////// **COMMON ERROR ALERT** \\\\\\\

For a number such as 6%, students often write 0.6 instead of 0.06. To reinforce their understanding of the relationship between decimals and percents, have them make graphic representations of 0.6 and 0.06 on 10 × 10 grids (decimal squares). They will then label the representations with *60% = 0.6* and *6% = 0.06*.

Independent Practice

Assign Exercises 10–24.

Have students use 10 × 10 grids (decimal squares) or place-value models, if necessary, as they work the exercises.

MIXED REVIEW AND TEST PREP

Exercises 25–29 provide **cumulative review** (Chapters 1–3).

4 Assess

Summarize the lesson by having students:

DISCUSS How do you know that 48% is equal to 0.48? Possible answer: Percent means "per hundred," so I think of the fraction $\frac{48}{100}$ which equals the decimal 0.48.

✎📖 **WRITE** Explain the steps in writing a decimal such as 0.07 as a percent. Possible answer: First, think of the number as 7 hundredths, and then replace the hundredths with the percent symbol %.

Lesson Quiz

Write the corresponding percent or decimal.

Transparency **3.4**

1. 0.34 **34%**   2. 3% **0.03**
3. 0.88 **88%**   4. 20% **0.20**   5. 0.09 **9%**

61

CHAPTER **3**

REVIEW/TEST

Purpose To check understanding of concepts, skills, and problem solving presented in Chapter 3

USING THE PAGE

The Chapter 3 Review/Test can be used as a **review** or a **test**.

- Item 1 checks understanding of concepts and new vocabulary.
- Items 2–28 check skill proficiency.
- Items 29–33 check students' abilities to choose and apply problem solving strategies to real-life decimal problems.

Portfolio Suggest that students place the completed Chapter 3 Review/Test in their portfolios.

USING THE ASSESSMENT GUIDE

- Multiple-choice format of Chapter 3 Posttest—See *Assessment Guide*, pp. AG17–18.
- Free-response format of Chapter 3 Posttest—See *Assessment Guide*, pp. AG19–20.

USING STUDENT SELF-ASSESSMENT

The How Did I Do? survey helps students assess what they have learned and how they learned it. This survey is available as a copying master in *Assessment Guide,* p. AGxvii.

---

1. **VOCABULARY** A word that means "per hundred" is ___?___. (p. 60) **percent**

Write the value of the blue digit. (pp. 52–55)

2. 3.2497 **nine thousandths**　　3. 14.5805 **five tenths**　　4. 0.09003 **nine hundredths**

5. 628.0402 **two ten-thousandths**　　6. 1.81738 **three ten-thousandths**　　7. 78.05124 **one thousandth**

Write the numbers in order from least to greatest. (pp. 52–55)

8. 2.365, 2.305, 2.3, 2.35, 2.035 **2.035; 2.3; 2.305; 2.35; 2.365**

9. 125.3, 124.32, 125.33, 12.245, 120.4 **12.245; 120.4; 124.32; 125.3; 125.33**

Estimate. (pp. 58–59) **Possible estimates are given.**

10. 27.6 + 135.2 **165**　　11. 4.8 × 2.3 **10**　　12. 30.7 − 6.25 **24**　　13. 89.75 ÷ 8 **11**

14. 8.45 + 8.99 + 9.2 **27**　　15. 219.48 − 107.43 **100**　　16. 416.2 × 31 **12,000**　　17. 40.02 ÷ 6.3 **7**

Write the decimal and percent for the shaded part. (pp. 60–61)

18. 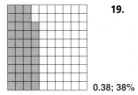 **0.38; 38%**

19. 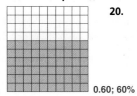 **0.60; 60%**

20. 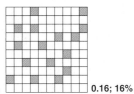 **0.16; 16%**

Write the corresponding percent or decimal. (pp. 60–61)

21. 74% **0.74**　　22. 0.07 **7%**　　23. 39% **0.39**　　24. 0.61 **61%**

25. 0.6 **60%**　　26. 3% **0.03**　　27. 0.04 **4%**　　28. 84% **0.84**

Solve.

29. The county library charges a fine of $0.10 a day for overdue books. The university library charges a fine of $0.50 for the first day and $0.05 for each additional day. On what day would overdue books have the same fine at both libraries? (pp. 56–57) **on the ninth day**

30. Planes leave Sacramento for San Francisco every 45 min. The first plane leaves at 5:45 A.M. What is the departure time closest to 4:30 P.M.? (pp. 56–57) **4:15 P.M.**

31. Donna is on the decoration committee. She spent $15.90 on streamers, $12.15 on balloons, $6.84 on tape, $19.98 on banner paper, and $13.22 on banner paint. What is a reasonable estimate of the amount she spent? (pp. 58–59) **Possible answer: about $68.00**

32. Frank earns $6.25 per hour. One week he worked 16 hours. About how much did Frank earn that week? (pp. 58–59) **Possible answer: about $96**

33. Kirk has to list 125.3, 124.32, 125.33, 12.345, 120.4 in order from greatest to least. Which number should he list third? (pp. 52–55) **124.32**

CHAPTER 3 TEST, page 1

Choose the best answer.

1. Compare the numbers in each pair. For which pair is > the correct symbol?

 (A) 43.27 ● 43.22
 B 43.77 ● 43.77
 C 3.22 ● 3.27
 D 43.22 ● 43.22

2. Compare the numbers in each pair. For which pair is < the correct symbol?

 F 188.3 ● 188.03
 (G) 188.03 ● 188.3
 H 188.03 ● 188.03
 J 88.3 ● 88.3

3. Which is equal to 0.834?

 (A) 0.8340　　C 0.84
 B 0.843　　D 8.8340

4. Which is greater than 92.05?

 F 1.0005
 G 92.005
 H 92.05
 (J) 92.5

For 5–8, order the numbers from least to greatest.

5. 5.22, 5.81, 5.27, 5.041

 A 5.81, 5.27, 5.22, 5.041
 B 5.81, 5.041, 5.27, 5.22
 C 5.041, 5.27, 5.22, 5.81
 (D) 5.041, 5.22, 5.27, 5.81

6. 22.1, 22.7, 22.09, 22.078

 F 22.7, 22.1, 22.09, 22.078
 G 22.09, 22.7, 22.078, 22.1
 (H) 22.078, 22.09, 22.1, 22.7
 J 22.09, 22.078, 22.7, 22.1

7. 18.87, 18.45, 18.03, 18.30

 A 18.87, 18.45, 18.30, 18.03
 B 18.03, 18.87, 18.45, 18.30
 C 18.30, 18.45, 18.87, 18.03
 (D) 18.03, 18.30, 18.45, 18.87

8. 25.05, 25.80, 25.40, 25.99

 F 25.99, 25.80, 25.40, 25.05
 (G) 25.05, 25.40, 25.80, 25.99
 H 25.80, 25.40, 25.99, 25.05
 J 25.40, 25.80, 25.99, 25.05

For 9–11, find the value of the underlined digit.

9. 5.2394

 A 3 ones
 B 3 tens
 (C) 3 hundredths
 D 3 thousandths

10. 37.66257

 (F) 2 thousandths
 G 2 hundredths
 H 2 tenths
 J 2 ones

11. 0.30809

 A 3 ones
 (B) 3 tenths
 C 3 hundredths
 D 3 thousandths

Go On →

CHAPTER 3 TEST, page 2

For 12–13, find the percent and the decimal for the shaded part.

12.

 F 0.66%, 66
 G 66%, 0.66
 (H) 34%, 0.34
 J 0.34%, 34

13.

 A 0.27%, 27
 (B) 27%, 0.27
 C 0.73%, 73
 D 73%, 0.73

For 14–16, find the corresponding percent or decimal.

14. 0.07

 F 700%　　(H) 7%
 G 70%　　J 0.7%

15. 5%

 A 5.0　　(C) 0.05
 B 0.5　　D 0.005

16. 0.9

 F 900%　　H 9%
 (G) 90%　　J 0.9%

For 17–20, use the data in the chart below. The greater the number, the stronger the earthquake.

STRENGTH OF RECENT EARTHQUAKES (MAGNITUDE ON THE RICHTER SCALE)	
Los Angeles	3.4
Tokyo	3.1
San Francisco	4.1
Mexico City	4.2
New Delhi	3.6
Hong Kong	3.9

17. Which of these cities had the weakest earthquake?

 A Hong Kong　　C San Francisco
 (B) Tokyo　　D New Delhi

18. Which of these cities had the strongest earthquake?

 (F) Mexico City　　H Hong Kong
 G San Francisco　　J New Delhi

19. Which of these cities had the second weakest earthquake?

 (A) Los Angeles　　C Mexico City
 B Tokyo　　D Hong Kong

20. Which city had the second strongest earthquake?

 F Tokyo　　H Mexico City
 G New Delhi　　(J) San Francisco

For 21–25, estimate.

21. 4.8 × 7.2

 A 28　　C 40
 (B) 35　　D 3,500

22. 64.3 ÷ 8.1

 F 0.7　　H 7
 G 0.8　　(J) 8

23. 38.9 + 162.3

 A 20　　C 150
 B 130　　(D) 200

24. 5.13 + 4.97 + 4.88 + 5.04

 F 21　　H 19
 (G) 20　　J 16

25. 80.7 − 2.5

 A 94　　(C) 78
 B 83　　D 75

Stop ■

Get the information you need.
See item **8**.
Recall that a percent is the ratio of a number to 100. Write the ratio as a decimal.
Also see problem **3**, p. H63.

Choose the best answer.

1. Which of these numbers rounds to 450 when rounded to the nearest ten and to 500 when rounded to the nearest hundred? **C**

   A 415   **C** 452

   B 428   **D** 478

2. Earth's orbit is more than 100,000,000 kilometers from the sun. How is this number written in exponential notation? **G**

   F 10^7 km   **H** 10^9 km

   G 10^8 km   **J** 10^{10} km

3. What is the value of $2 + 3 \times 4$? **B**

   A 11   **C** 20

   B 14   **D** Not here

4. Each of the 42 members of the band contributed $3.75 toward a gift for the band director. Which is a reasonable estimate of the total amount collected? **J**

   F Between $80 and $90

   G Between $90 and $110

   H About $120

   J About $160

5. Kate has 4 bags of birdseed that have masses of 2.5 kilograms, 1.25 kilograms, 1.9 kilograms, and 2.15 kilograms. Which shows the bags in order from least mass to greatest? **D**

   A 1.9 kg, 2.15 kg, 2.5 kg, 1.25 kg

   B 2.5 kg, 2.15 kg, 1.9 kg, 1.25 kg

   C 2.15 kg, 1.25 kg, 2.5 kg, 1.9 kg

   D 1.25 kg, 1.9 kg, 2.15 kg, 2.5 kg

6. A restaurant manager bought a total of 73 apples and oranges. She bought 11 more oranges than apples. How many of each kind of fruit did she buy? **F**

   F 31 apples and 42 oranges

   G 27 apples and 46 oranges

   H 36 apples and 37 oranges

   J 42 apples and 31 oranges

7. With tax, a CD player costs $77.75. Ken saves $4.85 each week. Which is a reasonable estimate of the number of weeks he must save for the CD player? **C**

   A More than 20 weeks

   B Between 18 and 20 weeks

   C Between 15 and 17 weeks

   D Less than 15 weeks

8. How is 6% written as a decimal? **H**

   F 6.0   **H** 0.06

   G 0.6   **J** 0.006

9. How is 0.36 written as a percent? **C**

   A 0.36%   **C** 36%

   B 3.6%   **D** 360%

10. Which is greater than 16.30? **F**

    F 16.45   **H** 16.03

    G 16.23   **J** 1.730

11. Which is the value of $(3 - 2) \times 5 + 6^2$? **C**

    A 29   **C** 41

    B 40   **D** 122

12. Which of these is in order from least to greatest? **F**

    F 0.0310, 0.301, 0.310

    G 0.310, 0.0310, 0.301

    H 0.301, 0.0310, 0.310

    J 0.0310, 0.310, 0.301

63

CUMULATIVE REVIEW •
Chapters 1–3

USING THE PAGE

This page may be used to help students get ready for standardized tests. The test items are written in the same style and arranged in the same format as those on many state assessments. The page is cumulative. It covers math objectives and essential skills that have been taught up to this point in the text. Most of the items represent skills from the current chapter and the remainder represent skills from earlier chapters.

This page can be assigned at the end of the chapter as classwork or as a homework assignment. You may want to have students use individual recording sheets presented in a multiple choice (standardized) format. A Test Answer Sheet is available as a blackline master in *Assessment Guide* (p. AGxlii).

You may wish to have students describe how they solved each problem and share their solutions.

Decimal Operations

CHAPTER PLANNER

PACING OPTIONS

Compacted	4 Days
Expanded	9 Days

Getting Ready for Chapter 4 • Assessing Prior Knowledge and INTERVENTION (See PE and TE page 65.)

LESSON	CALIFORNIA STANDARDS	PACING	VOCABULARY*	MATERIALS	RESOURCES AND TECHNOLOGY
4.1 Add and Subtract Decimals pp. 66–69 **Objective** To add and subtract decimals	NS 2.0 MR 2.1 (*Also* MR 2.4)	2 Days			Reteach, Practice, Problem Solving, Challenge 4.1 Worksheets Extra Practice p. H35, Set A □ Transparency 4.1 ⊙ **Calculating Crew** • *Nautical Number Line*
4.2 Multiply Decimals pp. 70–73 **Objective** To multiply decimals	NS 2.0 MR 2.1 (*Also* MR 1.3, 2.4, 2.5, 3.1)	1 Day		*For each student* decimal squares, colored pencils	Reteach, Practice, Problem Solving, Challenge 4.2 Worksheets Extra Practice p. H35, Set B □ Transparency 4.2 ⊙ **Calculating Crew** • *Nautical Number Line*
4.3 Math Lab: Explore Division of Decimals pp. 74–75 **Objective** To use a model to divide decimals	NS 2.0 MR 2.4			*For each student* decimal squares, colored pencils, scissors	⊕ **E-Lab** • *Exploring Division of Decimals;* E-Lab Recording Sheet **Math Jingles™ CD 5-6** • *Track 2*
4.4 Divide with Decimals pp. 76–79 **Objective** To divide a decimal by a whole number and a decimal by a decimal	NS 2.0 MR 2.1 (*Also* MG 1.1)	2 Days (For Lessons 4.3 and 4.4)		*For each student* calculator	Reteach, Practice, Problem Solving, Challenge 4.4 Worksheets Extra Practice p. H35, Set C □ Transparency 4.4 ⊙ **Number Heroes** • *Quizzo*
4.5 Problem Solving Skill: *Interpret the Remainder* pp. 80–81 **Objective** To solve problems by using the skill *interpret the remainder*	NS 2.0 MR 3.2 (*Also* MR 2.0, 3.1)	1 Day			Reteach, Practice, Reading Strategy, Challenge 4.5 Worksheets □ Transparency 4.5 Problem Solving Think Along, p. TR1 **Math Jingles™ CD 5-6** • *Track 6*
4.6 Algebra: Decimal Expressions and Equations pp. 82–83 **Objective** To evaluate expressions with decimals and to use mental math and substitution to solve equations with decimals	AF 1.0 AF 1.1 (*Also* NS 2.0)	1 Day			Reteach, Practice, Problem Solving, Challenge 4.6 Worksheets Extra Practice p. H35, Set D □ Transparency 4.6 **Math Jingles™ CD 5-6** • *Tracks 8-9*

Ending Chapter 4 • Chapter 4 Review/Test, p. 84 • **Cumulative Review,** p. 85

Ending Unit 1 • Math Detective, p. 86; **Challenge,** p. 87; **Study Guide and Review,** pp. 88–89; **California Connections,** pp. 90–91

*****Boldfaced** terms are new vocabulary. Other terms are review vocabulary.

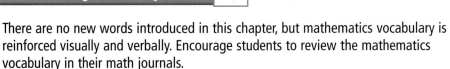

CHAPTER AT A GLANCE

Vocabulary Development

There are no new words introduced in this chapter, but mathematics vocabulary is reinforced visually and verbally. Encourage students to review the mathematics vocabulary in their math journals.

Writing Opportunities

PUPIL EDITION
- **Write a Problem,** p. 73
- **What's the Error?,** pp. 79, 83
- **Write About It,** p. 69
- **What's the Question?,** p. 81

TEACHER'S EDITION
- **Write**—See the *Assess* section of each TE lesson.
- **Writing in Mathematics,** p. 74

ASSESSMENT GUIDE
- **How Did I Do?,** p. AGxvii

California Mathematics Content Standards for Grade 6

Strands

Number Sense
Lesson 4.1: o—n NS 2.0
Lesson 4.2: o—n NS 2.0
Lesson 4.3: o—n NS 2.0
Lesson 4.4: o—n NS 2.0
Lesson 4.5: o—n NS 2.0
Lesson 4.6: o—n NS 2.0

Algebra and Functions
Lesson 4.6: AF 1.0, o—n 1.1

Measurement and Geometry
Lesson 4.4: o—n MG 1.1

Statistics, Data Analysis, and Probability

Mathematical Reasoning
Lesson 4.1: MR 2.1, 2.4
Lesson 4.2: MR 1.3, 2.1, 2.4, 2.5, 3.1
Lesson 4.3: MR 2.4
Lesson 4.4: MR 2.1
Lesson 4.5: MR 2.0, 3.1, 3.2

Family Involvement Activities

These activities provide:
- Letters to the Family
- Information about California Standards
- Math Vocabulary
- Family Game
- Practice (Homework)

HARCOURT MATH	Name
GRADE 6	Date
Chapter 4	
WHAT WE ARE LEARNING	**Dear Family,**
Decimal Operations	In this chapter, your child is adding, subtracting, multiplying, and dividing with decimals and evaluating expressions and equations with decimals.

VOCABULARY
Here are some of the vocabulary words we use in class:

This is how your child is learning to add and subtract with decimals.

Decimal A number that uses place value and a decimal point to show tenths, hundredths, thousandths, and so on

Expression A mathematical phrase that combines operations, numerals, and/or variables to name a number

	Add: 5.43 + 7 + 0.588	Subtract: 41.4 – 7.0388
Step 1 Estimate. • Round to the nearest whole number. • Find the estimated answer.	5.43 → 5 7 → 7 + 0.588 → + 1 13	41.4 → 41 – 7.0388 → – 7 34
Step 2 Compute. • Align the decimal points. • Use zeros as place holders. • Place the decimal point. • Compute.	5.430 7.000 + 0.588 13.018	41.4000 – 7.0388 34.3612
Step 3 Compare. • Compare the answer to your estimate. • Is your answer reasonable?	13.018 is close to 13. The answer is reasonable.	34.3612 is close to 34. The answer is reasonable.

The California Math Standards
Your child's **Harcourt Math** book lists the California Math Standards that are taught in every lesson. If you have questions about the standards, be sure to consult *California Standards for Grade 6* that was sent home at the beginning of the school year.

Family Involvement Activities, p. FA13

Decimal Operations

MATHEMATICS ACROSS THE GRADES

SKILLS TRACE ACROSS THE GRADES

GRADE 5	GRADE 6	GRADE 7
Add, subtract, multiply, and divide with decimals	Use addition, subtraction, multiplication, and division to solve problems involving decimals; evaluate expressions and solve one-step equations with decimals	Use addition, subtraction, multiplication, and division to solve problems involving decimals; write and evaluate expressions using decimals; solve equations using decimals

SKILLS TRACE FOR GRADE 6

LESSON	FIRST INTRODUCED	TAUGHT AND PRACTICED	TESTED	REVIEWED
4.1	Grade 4	PE pp. 66–69, H35, p. RW15, p. PW15, p. PS15	PE p. 84, pp. AG21–24	PE pp. 84, 85, 88–89
4.2	Grade 5	PE pp. 70–73, H35, p. RW16, p. PW16, p. PS16	PE p. 84, pp. AG21–24	PE pp. 84, 85, 88–89
4.3	Grade 5	PE pp. 74–75	PE p. 84, pp. AG21–24	PE pp. 84, 85, 88–89
4.4	Grade 5	PE pp. 76–79, H35, p. RW17, p. PW17, p. PS17	PE p. 84, pp. AG21–24	PE pp. 84, 85, 88–89
4.5	Grade 4	PE pp. 80–81, p. RW18, p. PW18, p. PS18	PE p. 84, pp. AG21–24	PE pp. 84, 85, 88–89
4.6	Grade 6	PE pp. 82–83, H35, p. RW19, p. PW19, p. PS19	PE p. 84, pp. AG21–24	PE pp. 84, 85, 88–89

KEY **PE** Pupil Edition   **PS** Problem Solving Workbook   **RW** Reteach Workbook
        PW Practice Workbook   **AG** Assessment Guide

Looking Back Prerequisite Skills

To be ready for Chapter 4, students should have the following understandings and skills:

Whole Number Operations—add, subtract, multiply, and divide whole numbers

Multiply Decimals by 10, 100, and 1,000—multiply one-, two-, and three-place decimals by 10, 100, and 1,000

Remainders—divide whole numbers and write remainders as decimals and as fractions

Check What You Know

Use page 65 to determine students' knowledge of prerequisite concepts and skills.

Intervention

Help students prepare for the chapter by using the intervention resources described on TE page 65.

Looking at Chapter 4 Essential Skills

Students will

- develop skill and accuracy adding, subtracting, multiplying, and dividing decimals.
- interpret remainders meaningfully in real-world division problems.
- **make the connections between models and the division algorithm for dividing decimals.**
- apply what they learned about whole number expressions and equations to decimal expressions and equations.

EXAMPLE

$$1.2 \div 0.4 \text{ or } 0.4\overline{)1.2}$$

Model	Algorithm
	$0.4\overline{)1.2}$ Make the divisor a whole number.
	$\begin{array}{r} 3.0 \\ 4\overline{)12.0} \\ \underline{12} \\ 0 \end{array}$ Place the decimal point. Divide.

0.4   0.4   0.4

Looking Ahead Applications

Students will apply what they learn in Chapter 4 to the following new concepts:

- Terminating and Repeating Decimals (Chapter 8)
- Solving Two-Step Equations (Chapter 16)
- Operations with Rational Numbers (Chapter 11)

Decimal Operations 64D

Decimal Operations

INTRODUCING THE CHAPTER

Tell students that they can apply the same operations to decimals as to whole numbers. Have students read the page and examine the graph. Ask them how many gigabytes a megabyte equals. 0.001 gigabytes

USING DATA

To begin the study of this chapter, have students

- Determine how many gigabytes of storage a computer with one Zip® disk and one Jaz® disk has. 1.1 GB

- Express the approximate number of gigabytes each type of disk listed on the graph holds. Zip® disk: 0.1; CD-ROM: 0.7; Jaz® disk: 1; DVD-RAM: 5.2

- Make a graph showing the storage capacity of each disk in megabytes. Check students' work.

PROBLEM SOLVING PROJECT

Purpose To use decimals to solve a problem

Grouping pairs or small groups

Background A 4.75-inch disk can hold a gigabyte of information which is encoded and stored on a spiral track that is more than 4.8 kilometers long.

Analyze, Choose, Solve, and Check

Have students

- Find the total amount of storage capacity possible for 3 Zip® disks, 5 CD-ROM disks, 2 Jaz® disks, and 1 DVD-RAM disk. 10.75 GB

- Make a graph to display the total storage capacity in gigabytes for the disks described above.

Check students' work.

Suggest that students place the graphs in their portfolios.

Today's computers use optical laser writing technology to store billions of bytes of information. A Jaz® disk holds 1 gigabyte of information. A gigabyte is about 1,000,000,000 (10^9) bytes. Sometimes capacity is given in megabytes. A megabyte is about 1,000,000 (10^6) bytes. A 3.5-inch floppy disk holds just 1.44 megabytes of information. About how many bytes is that?

STORAGE CAPACITY IN GIGABYTES

Type of Disk: Zip®, CD-ROM, Jaz®, DVD-RAM

Number of Gigabytes: 0 1 2 3 4 5 6

1,440,000 bytes

64 Chapter 4

Why learn math? Explain that computer applications programmers write commercial programs used in businesses, schools, and homes. Programmers need to calculate the amount of space their programs will need in order to be stored on both the internal and external memory devices. Ask: How do you use decimal operations when buying computer programs for your computer? Possible answer: to calculate the total cost of the computer program or supplies and the amount of change due

Check What You Know

Use this page to help you review and remember important skills needed for Chapter 4.

✅ Whole-Number Operations (See p. H4.)

Add or subtract.

1. 7 + 28 + 12 47
2. 45 − 15 30
3. 63 − 19 44
4. 19 + 41 + 27 + 23 110
5. 34 − 17 − 7 10
6. 27 + 56 + 100 183
7. 143 + 79 222
8. 213 − 88 125

Multiply.

9. 63 × 4 252
10. 49 × 9 441
11. 19 ×76 1,444
12. 88 ×32 2,816
13. 80 ×50 4,000
14. 75 ×11 825
15. 200 × 15 3,000
16. 340 × 20 6,800

Divide.

17. 4)96 24
18. 5)127 25 r2
19. 9)423 47
20. 7)760 108 r4
21. 32)448 14
22. 20)3,660 183
23. 37)1,073 29
24. 23)4,715 205

✅ Multiply Decimals by 10, 100, and 1,000 (See p. H13.)

Multiply.

25. 4.3 × 10 43
26. 9.61 × 1,000 9,610
27. 8.4 × 100 840
28. 25.397 × 1,000 25,397
29. 194.05 × 100 19,405
30. 408.08 × 10 4,080.8

✅ Remainders (See p. H5.)

Divide. Write the remainder as a decimal.

31. 4)35 8.75
32. 5)56 11.2
33. 8)100 12.5
34. 12)243 20.25
35. 15)2,412 160.8

Divide. Write the remainder as a fraction.

36. 6)45 $7\frac{1}{2}$
37. 8)77 $9\frac{5}{8}$
38. 12)134 $11\frac{1}{6}$
39. 14)550 $39\frac{2}{7}$
40. 18)459 $25\frac{1}{2}$

> **LOOK AHEAD**
>
> **In Chapter 4 you will**
> - add, subtract, multiply, and divide decimals
> - evaluate decimal expressions and solve equations

65

Assessing Prior Knowledge

Use the **Check What You Know** page to determine whether your students have mastered the prerequisite skills critical for this chapter.

Intervention

- **Diagnose and Prescribe**

  Evaluate your students' performance on this page to determine whether intervention is necessary. **How to Help Options** that provide instruction, practice, and a check are listed in the chart below.

- **Review Prerequisite Skills**

  The following resources provide a review for the prerequisite vocabulary and skills.

  Option 1—Check What You Know, Pupil Edition p. 65

  Option 2—Troubleshooting, Pupil Edition pp. H4–5, H13

TEACHER'S NOTES

Check What You Know
INTERVENTION • Diagnose and Prescribe

Prerequisite Skill	Items (Pupil Edition p. 65)	How to Help Options
✅ Whole-Number Operations	1–24	• **Troubleshooting, Pupil Edition p. H4** • **Intervention Strategies and Activities** Card, Copying Master, or CD-ROM • **Skill 4**
✅ Multiply Decimals by 10, 100, and 1,000	25–30	• **Troubleshooting, Pupil Edition p. H13** • **Intervention Strategies and Activities** Card, Copying Master, or CD-ROM • **Skill 36**
✅ Remainders	31–40	• **Troubleshooting, Pupil Edition p. H5** • **Intervention Strategies and Activities** Card, Copying Master, or CD-ROM • **Skill 18**

Add and Subtract Decimals

LESSON PLANNING

Objective To add and subtract decimals

Intervention for Prerequisite Skills

Whole Number Operations (For intervention strategies, see page 65.)

California Mathematics Content Standards

○━ NS 2.0 Students calculate and solve problems involving addition, subtraction, multiplication, and division.

MR 2.1 Use estimation to verify the reasonableness of calculated results.

(*Also* MR 2.4)

Math Background

The skills needed to add or subtract decimals are the same as those needed to add or subtract whole numbers.

Consider the following as you help students understand the procedures for adding and subtracting decimals.

- When adding or subtracting decimals in a column, align decimal points so the corresponding digits in each place are lined up properly.
- Before solving an addition or subtraction problem, place the decimal point for the answer below the decimal points in the problem.
- When decimals do not have the same number of places, add zeros as placeholders. These zeros do not change the value of the decimal.

It is important for students to estimate and to check the reasonableness of their answers.

WARM-UP RESOURCES

NUMBER OF THE DAY
Transparency 4.1

Suppose you are saving money and that each day you save d cents, where d is the number of the day of the month. What is the most you will save in one week of any month? $1.96

PROBLEM OF THE DAY

Transparency 4.1

Replace each [♥] with a different digit from 0–9 to make a true number sentence.

[♥].[♥] [♥] [♥] + [♥] [♥].[♥] [♥] + [♥].[♥] = 22.815
Possible answer: 0.725 + 13.69 + 8.4 = 22.815

Solution Problem of the Day tab, p. PD4

DAILY FACTS PRACTICE

Have students practice addition and subtraction facts by completing Set B of *Teacher's Resource Book,* p. TR95.

ALTERNATIVE TEACHING STRATEGY ELL

Materials *For each student* newspaper ads

Reinforce adding and subtracting decimals. Provide students with newspaper ads. Have them make lists of two or more items that they could buy for less than $20, not including any sales tax. Students should show their work, first estimating, then finding the total price of the items, and finally finding the change they would receive if they paid with a $20 bill.

Answers will vary.

See also page 68.

VISUAL

MIXED REVIEW AND TEST PREP

Cumulative Review Chapters 1–4

Refer to the Pupil Edition pages referenced in the exercises for further review. Have students go to the lesson page, review the lesson, and correct any problem they missed.

Mixed Review and Test Prep, p. 69

How to Help	
Item	**Page**
44	60
45	60
46	28
47	40
48	20

SOCIAL STUDIES CONNECTION

Have students **practice writing addition and subtraction word problems with decimals** by using the data below.

Form of Advertising	Money Spent
Newspaper	$31.0 billion
Television	$10.6 billion
Radio	$9.5 billion
Direct Mail	$27.3 billion
Yellow Pages	$9.5 billion
Other	$21.7 billion

Check students' work.

VISUAL

EARLY FINISHERS

Materials *For each pair* 10 index cards

Encourage students to **estimate decimal sums and differences.** Have each pair write a different decimal on each of the 10 cards. The decimals should be less than 100 and have from 1 to 3 places to the right of the decimal point.

The students then use the cards to generate addition and subtraction problems. One student selects two cards and computes either the exact sum or difference.

The other student rounds the numbers on the cards and estimates the sum or difference. Then they compare the exact answer with the estimate and discuss any adjustments that need to be made to either. Have students reverse roles and repeat the activity. Check students' work.

VISUAL

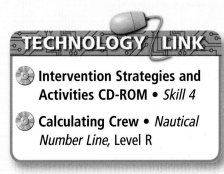

TECHNOLOGY LINK

- **Intervention Strategies and Activities CD-ROM** • *Skill 4*
- **Calculating Crew** • *Nautical Number Line*, Level R

LESSON **4.1** ORGANIZER

Objective To add and subtract decimals

1 Introduce

QUICK REVIEW provides review of pre-requisite skills.

Why Learn This? In the future, you will need to add and subtract decimals in order to verify your bank statement. *Share the lesson objective with students.*

2 Teach

Guided Instruction

• *Discuss with students the importance of aligning decimal points.*

Why is it important to align decimal points when you are adding or subtracting decimals? Possible answer: If you do not line up decimal points, it is difficult to perform operations on digits with the same place value.

If you have lined up the decimal points in all the numbers before you add or subtract, where should you place the decimal point in your answer? directly below the decimal point in the last number of the exercise

Modifying Instruction If students have difficulty aligning the numbers by the decimal points, you may want to have them work exercises on graph paper, placing each digit and decimal point in a separate square.

ADDITIONAL EXAMPLE

Example 1, p. 66

Mia has $75.88. She buys a new jacket for $58.50. How much money does she have left after buying the jacket? estimate: $17; answer: $17.38

LESSON **4.1**
Add and Subtract Decimals

Learn how to add and subtract decimals.

QUICK REVIEW

1.	2,526	2.	4,389	3.	43,026	4.	7,506
	+4,650		− 238		+ 3,507		−3,308
	7,176		4,151		46,533		4,198

5. 236 + 75 + 1,500 1,811

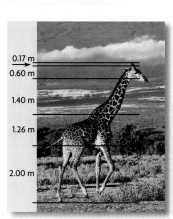

0.17 m
0.60 m
1.40 m
1.26 m
2.00 m

The tallest known mammal was a 6.1-m giraffe named George. Born in Kenya, George spent most of his life in the Chester Zoo in England.

To find the height of the giraffe shown, you must add five partial heights.

Math Idea ▶ When you add or subtract decimals, align the decimal points first and then add or subtact the digits, one place at a time.

2.00	*Align the decimal points.*
1.26	
1.40	
0.60	
+0.17	*Place the decimal point.*
5.43	*Then add.*

So, the total height is 5.43 m.

You can use estimation to check for reasonableness.

EXAMPLE 1

Jamie has $85.75. Running shoes cost $68.45. How much money will Jamie have left after buying the running shoes?

Estimate.

$85.75	→	$86	*Round to the nearest dollar.*
− 68.45		− 68	
		$18	

Find the answer.

$85.75	
− 68.45	*Align the decimal points.*
$17.30	*Place the decimal point. Then subtract.*

Use your estimate to check the reasonableness of the answer. Compare the two. Since $17.30 is close to the estimate of $18, the answer is reasonable.

So, Jamie will have $17.30 left.

66

CALIFORNIA STANDARDS O⌐NS 2.0 Students calculate and solve problems involving addition, subtraction, multiplication, and division. **MR 2.1** Use estimation to verify the reasonableness of calculated results. *also* **MR 2.4**

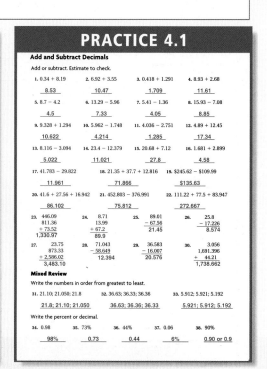

RETEACH 4.1

Add and Subtract Decimals

Ian is buying school supplies. Find the total cost.

Binder	$3.49	Paper	$2.79
Pen	$0.88	Highlighter	$0.98

Step 1: List the items in a column. Remember to align the decimal points.

$3.49
0.88
2.79
+ 0.98

Step 2: Write the decimal point for the answer. Place it directly under the other points.

Step 3: Add as you would whole numbers. Remember to regroup if needed.

$3.49
0.88
2.79
+ 0.98
$8.14

The total cost of Ian's school supplies is $8.14.

Now suppose Ian pays for his supplies with a $20 bill. Find the amount of change he should receive.

Step 1: Write the numbers in a column. Remember to align the decimal points.

$20.00
− 8.14

Step 2: Write the decimal point for the answer. Then subtract as you would with whole numbers, regrouping as necessary.

$20.00
− 8.14
$11.86

Ian should receive $11.86 in change.

Add or subtract.

1. $75.50 − $47.86	2. 347.9 − 69.38	3. 81.42 − 57.932
$27.64	278.52	23.488
4. 2.89 + 1.65 + 3.86	5. 4.62 + 7.89 + 9.17	6. 2.891 + 3.006 + 2.861
8.4	21.68	8.758
7. 18.21 + 6.85 + 2.77	8. 4.0689 − 1.0791	9. 2.478 + 6.811 + 7.222
27.83	2.9898	16.511
10. 6.42 + 5.1 + 0.28	11. 3.016 − 1.2173	12. 38.2 + 5 + 6.83
11.8	1.7987	50.03

PRACTICE 4.1

Add and Subtract Decimals

Add or subtract. Estimate to check.

1. 0.34 + 8.19	2. 6.92 + 3.55	3. 0.418 + 1.291	4. 8.93 + 2.68
8.53	10.47	1.709	11.61
5. 8.7 − 4.2	6. 13.29 − 5.96	7. 5.41 − 1.36	8. 15.93 − 7.08
4.5	7.33	4.05	8.85
9. 9.328 + 1.294	10. 5.962 − 1.748	11. 4.036 − 2.751	12. 4.89 + 12.45
10.622	4.214	1.285	17.34
13. 8.116 − 3.094	14. 23.4 − 12.379	15. 20.68 + 7.12	16. 1.681 + 2.899
5.022	11.021	27.8	4.58
17. 41.783 − 29.822	18. 21.35 + 37.7 + 12.816	19. $245.62 − $109.99	
11.961	71.866	$135.63	
20. 41.6 + 27.56 + 16.942	21. 452.803 − 376.991	22. 111.22 + 77.5 + 83.947	
86.102	75.812	272.667	

23. 446.09	24. 8.71	25. 89.01	26. 25.8
811.36	13.99	− 67.56	− 17.226
+ 73.52	+ 67.2	21.45	8.574
1,330.97	89.9		
27. 23.75	28. 71.043	29. 36.583	30. 3.056
873.33	− 58.649	− 16.007	1,691.396
+ 2,586.02	12.394	20.576	+ 44.21
3,483.10			1,738.662

Mixed Review

Write the numbers in order from greatest to least.

31. 21.10; 21.050; 21.8	32. 36.63; 36.33; 36.36	33. 5.912; 5.921; 5.192
21.8; 21.10; 21.050	36.63; 36.36; 36.33	5.921; 5.912; 5.192

Write the percent or decimal.

34. 0.98	35. 73%	36. 44%	37. 0.06	38. 90%
98%	0.73	0.44	6%	0.90 or 0.9

Some decimal numbers that you add or subtract do not have the same number of decimal places.

The samples below show how Courtney and Jamie found $17.06 + 5.493$. Think about which sum is reasonable.

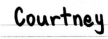

Courtney

$$\begin{array}{r} 17.06 \\ +5.493 \\ \hline 7.199 \end{array}$$

Jamie

$$\begin{array}{r} 17.06 \\ +5.493 \\ \hline 22.553 \end{array}$$

Use estimation to find which sum is reasonable.

$17.06 + 5.493 \rightarrow 17 + 5 = 22$ Jamie's sum is reasonable.

Remember that you can add zeros to the right of a decimal without changing its value. Use zeros to make all decimals have the same number of decimal places.

EXAMPLE 2

Add. $3.45 + 7 + 0.835$
Estimate.

$$\begin{array}{ll} 3.45 & \quad\;\; 3 \\ 7 & \rightarrow\;\; 7 \\ +0.835 & \underline{+1} \\ & \quad 11 \end{array}$$
          Round to the nearest whole number.

Find the answer.

$$\begin{array}{lll} 3.45 & & 3.450 \\ 7 & \text{or} & 7.000 \\ +0.835 & & +0.835 \\ \hline & & 11.285 \end{array}$$
          Align the decimal points.
          Use zeros as placeholders.
          Place the decimal point. Add.

Compare the answer to your estimate. 11.285 is close to the estimate of 11. The answer is reasonable.

So, $3.45 + 7 + 0.835 = 11.285$.

EXAMPLE 3

Find the difference. $351.4 - 65.25$
Estimate.

$$\begin{array}{ll} 351.4 & \rightarrow\quad 350 \\ -\;65.25 & \quad\;\; -\;70 \\ & \quad\;\;\; 280 \end{array}$$
          Round to the nearest ten.

Find the answer.

$$\begin{array}{lll} 351.4 & & 351.40 \\ -\;65.25 & \text{or} & -\;65.25 \\ \hline & & 286.15 \end{array}$$
          Align the decimal points.
          Use a zero as a placeholder.
          Place the decimal point. Subtract.

Compare the answer to your estimate. 286.15 is close to the estimate of 280. The answer is reasonable.

So, $351.4 - 65.25 = 286.15$.

67

- *Discuss with students how they might evaluate Courtney's work at the top of page 67.*

How can you tell, even before estimating, that Courtney's answer is not reasonable? Courtney's sum is less than the first addend 17.06. The sum should be greater than each of the addends.

- *As students look at Examples 2 and 3, discuss the use of zeros as placeholders.*

In Example 2, why were 3 zeros added to the right of 7 and only 1 zero added to the right of 3.45? The zeros were added so that each addend would have the same number of places to the right of the decimal point—in this case, 3.

In Example 3, how does using a zero as a placeholder help you avoid a careless error? The zero reminds you to subtract 5 from 10 and 2 from 3 rather than to bring the 5 down without regrouping and subtract 2 from 4.

ADDITIONAL EXAMPLES

Example 2, p. 67
Add. $4.32 + 9 + 0.673$
Estimate.

$$\begin{array}{ll} 4.32 & \quad 4 \\ 9 & \rightarrow\; 9 \\ +\,0.673 & \underline{+1} \\ & \quad 14 \end{array}$$
   Round to the nearest whole number.

Find the answer.

$$\begin{array}{lll} 4.32 & & 4.320 \\ 9 & \text{or} & 9.000 \\ +\,0.673 & & +\,0.673 \\ \hline & & 13.993 \end{array}$$

13.993 is close to the estimate of 14. The answer is reasonable.

Example 3, p. 67
Find the difference. $462.5 - 54.18$
Estimate.

$$\begin{array}{ll} 462.5 & \rightarrow\quad 460 \\ -\,54.18 & \quad\;\; -\,50 \\ & \quad\;\;\; 410 \end{array}$$

Find the answer.

$$\begin{array}{lll} 462.5 & \text{or} & 462.50 \\ -\,54.18 & & -\,54.18 \\ \hline & & 408.32 \end{array}$$

408.32 is close to the estimate of 410. The answer is reasonable.

PROBLEM SOLVING 4.1

Add and Subtract Decimals

Analyze Choose Solve Check

Write the correct answer.

1. Round 38.75 to the nearest whole number.

     39

2. Paul has a balance in his checkbook of $268.53. He writes a check to the store for $35.78. What is the new balance in his checkbook?

     $232.75

3. Michael bought a CD for $11.87 and a book for $8.76. How much money did he spend on the purchases?

     $20.63

4. The wall is covered with 27 rows of colorful tiles. If there are 43 tiles in each row, how many tiles are on the wall?

     1,161 tiles

Choose the letter for the best answer.

5. Which list of numbers is in order from greatest to least?
   A 0.034, 0.03, 0.8
   (B) 0.065, 0.05, 0.012
   C 0.008, 0.07, 0.3
   D 0.12, 0.21, 0.030

6. Which expression shows one way to use compensation to add 58 + 43?
   F (58 − 3) + (43 − 3)
   G (58 + 3) + (43 + 3)
   (H) (58 + 2) + (43 − 2)
   J (58 + 2) + (58 + 2)

7. Philip and George ran a race. Philip's time was 38.45 seconds and George's time was 34.76 seconds. Which expression can be used to find out how many seconds George finished before Philip?
   A 38.45 + 34.76
   B 38.45 × 34.76
   (C) 38.45 − 34.76
   D 38.45 ÷ 34.76

8. Daniel has ridden a total of 58 miles on his skateboard so far this month. He rides it about the same distance each day. What else do you need to know to find how many miles he rides each day?
   F The number of days in the month
   G The length of the skateboard
   H What time he starts riding each day
   (J) How many days this month he has ridden

9. **Write About It** Why is it important to align the decimal points when you add decimals?

   Aligning the decimal points helps you add the numbers in the same place values.

CHALLENGE 4.1

Pattern Practice

Identify the addition or subtraction rule that was used to create each pattern. Then name the next three decimals.

1. 94.8, 94.3, 92.8, 90.3, __86.8__ __82.3__ __76.8__ ...

   Rule: __Subtract 0.5, then 1.5, then 2.5, and so on.__

2. 54.95, 56.06, 58.28, 61.61, __66.05__ __71.6__ __78.26__ ...

   Rule: __Add 1.11, then 2.22, then 3.33, and so on.__

3. 52.3, 50.2, 48, 45.7, __43.3__ __40.8__ __38.2__ ...

   Rule: __Subtract 2.1, then 2.2, then 2.3, then 2.4, and so on.__

4. 27.5, 26, 23.5, 22, __19.5__ __18__ __15.5__ ...

   Rule: __Subtract 1.5, then 2.5, then 1.5, and so on.__

5. 64.23, 69.93, 74.73, 80.43, __85.23__ __90.93__ __95.73__ ...

   Rule: __Add 5.7, then 4.8, then 5.7, and so on.__

6. 12.72, 22.71, 31.59, 39.36, __46.02__ __51.57__ __56.01__ ...

   Rule: __Add 9.99, then 8.88, then 7.77, and so on.__

7. 815.634, 803.289, 748.968, 736.623, __682.302__ __669.957__ __615.636__ ...

   Rule: __Subtract 12.345, then 54.321, then 12.345, and so on.__

8. 28.003, 34.249, 42.448, 48.694, __56.893__ __63.139__ __71.338__ ...

   Rule: __Add 6.246, then 8.199, then 6.246, and so on.__

9. 38.15, 35.25, 40.65, 37.75, __43.15__ __40.25__ __45.65__ ...

   Rule: __Subtract 2.9, then add 5.4, then subtract 2.9, and so on.__

10. Make up two pattern problems of your own. Exchange papers with a classmate and solve. Check students' work.

67

3 Practice

Guided Practice

Do Check for Understanding Exercises 1–12 with your students. Identify those having difficulty and use lesson resources to help.

> //// **COMMON ERROR ALERT** \\\\\
>
> If students have difficulty subtracting decimals, emphasize the importance of using zeros to make equivalent decimals so that all the decimals have the same number of places and are aligned properly.

Independent Practice

Assign Exercises 13–43.

CHECK FOR UNDERSTANDING

Think and ▶ Discuss Look back at the lesson to answer each question.

1. **Tell** why it is important to align the decimal points when you add or subtract. Possible answer: If the decimal points are not aligned, like places will not be aligned correctly to add or subtract.

2. **Explain** the steps you would use to find $67 - 34.58$. Possible answer: Write 67 as 67.00. Align the decimal points, and subtract.

Guided ▶ Practice Add or subtract. Estimate to check.

3. $6.18
   $- 5.55$
   $0.63

4. 0.45
    0.5
   $+1.349$
   2.299

5. 6
    5.43
    1.4
   $+5.755$
   18.585

6. 10.72
   $- 1.3$
   9.42

7. $3.2 + 2.68 + 15.043$ 20.923

8. $142.108 - 63.8$ 78.308

Copy the problem. Place the decimal point correctly in the answer.

9. $37.5 - 0.19 = 3731$ 37.31

10. $0.431 + 1.549 + 2.017 = 3997$ 3.997

11. $6 + 118.59 + 0.35 = 12494$ 124.94

12. $9.7 - 3.01 = 669$ 6.69

PRACTICE AND PROBLEM SOLVING

Independent ▶ Practice Add or subtract. Estimate to check.

13. 50.28
    $+37.52$
    87.80

14. 153.95
    $+434.16$
    588.11

15. 805.41
    $+633.25$
    1,438.66

16. 31.62
    $- 5.8$
    25.82

17. $3.2 - 2.6$ 0.6

18. $735.1 + 37 + 105.73$ 877.83

19. $370.92 - 83.247$ 287.673

20. $275.2 - 86.05$ 189.15

21. $123.1 + 140 + 225.45$ 488.55

22. $\$8 + \$215.49 + \$0.75$ \$224.24

23. $620.87 - 91.386$ 529.484

24. $56.60 - 8.476$ 48.124

Copy the problem. Place the decimal point correctly in the answer.

25. $23.64 + 233.5 = 25714$ 257.14

26. $\$25.67 + \$7.16 + \$0.35 = \$3318$ \$33.18

27. $11.2 - 1.78 = 942$ 9.42

28. $4.98 - 3.235 = 1745$ 1.745

Estimate to determine if the given sum is reasonable. Write *yes* or *no*.

29. $14.78 + 122.4 = 137.18$ yes

30. $\$32.76 + \$8.09 + \$0.49 = \$41.34$ yes

31. $58.02 - 9.473 = 3.671$ no

32. $427.7 - 39.27 = 388.43$ yes

Algebra Evaluate each expression for $d = 4.3$.

33. $d - 3.05$ 1.25

34. $1 + d + 0.7$ 6

35. $8 + d$ 12.3

36. $37.60 - d$ 33.30

37. $d - 2.084$ 2.216

38. $(d + 16.05) - 4.5$ 15.85

Alternative Teaching Strategy

Purpose Students use decimal squares to learn about subtracting decimals.

Materials *For each group* 10 decimal squares, p. TR7; colored pencil

Have groups use their decimal squares to model 4.17.

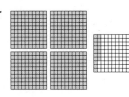

Display the following: $4.17 - 3.25$

Discuss with students and demonstrate how to use the decimal squares to show the subtraction of $4.17 - 3.25$. Students should realize that each small square within the decimal square stands for 1 hundredth.

Have students cross out decimal squares for 3.25. They can then use their models to copy and complete the subtraction sentence.

$$4.17 - 3.25 = 0.92$$

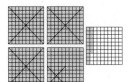

Have students then use decimal squares to find the difference $3.81 - 2.07$. 1.74

Ask volunteers to share their models and solutions.

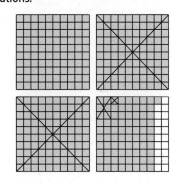

Check students' work.

Problem Solving ▶
Applications

39. Jake's batting average is 0.325. Last year it was 0.235. What is the difference between his average last year and this year? 0.090

40. Karen is saving $15.75 every week to buy a camera that costs $165.45. In how many weeks will Karen have enough money to buy the camera? 11 weeks

41. Estimate 30.53 + 95.7 + 75.12. Is the sum more than or less than your estimate? Explain how you know. Possible estimate: 210; more than; explanations will vary.

42.  Write About It   Why is it important to estimate the answer when you add and subtract decimals?

43. The computer club collected 3,905 lb of paper. Other clubs collected 3,950; 3,590; and 3,509 lb each. Write the weights of paper in order from greatest to least. 3,950 lb; 3,905 lb; 3,590 lb; 3,509 lb

42. You may have put the decimal point in the wrong place, so you want to make sure the answer is reasonable.

MIXED REVIEW AND TEST PREP

44. Write 0.05 as a percent. (p. 60) 5%   **45.** Write the decimal for 46%. (p. 60) 0.46

46. Evaluate $a \div c$ for a = 4,602 and c = 37. (p. 28) 124 r14

47. TEST PREP   Which shows the value of 7^4? (p. 40) D

   A 283   **B** 343   **C** 2,381   **D** 2,401

48. TEST PREP   Tanya bought milk for $2.09, two loaves of bread for $1.05 each, cheese for $4.50, and three bottles of juice for $3.00 each. How much did Tanya pay for the items? (p. 20) H

   F $12.04   **G** $12.64   **H** $17.69   **J** $23.04

LiNKUP to Science

Microbiologist   Microbiologists are scientists who specialize in the study of the tiny cells that make up every living thing. While cells vary widely in size, most plant and animal cells are so small that they can be seen only with a microscope. Microbiologists often must use decimals when measuring the sizes of cells and their structures, as in these examples:

Average plant cell	0.000035 meter
Small bacterium	0.0000002 meter
Cell wall or membrane	0.0000000075 meter

• Use your school library to find the sizes of blood cells, skin cells, and nerve cells in the human body. How much larger or smaller is each of these cell types than the average plant cell?

Extra Practice   page H35, Set A

69

READING STRATEGY

K-W-L Chart   Before having students read the Link Up, have them look at the photograph. Ask them to predict what the Link Up will be about. Then have students make a three-column chart headed What I Know, What I Want to Know, and What I Learned. Ask them to fill in the first two columns. Have them fill in the third column as they read the paragraph.

K-W-L Chart

What I Know	What I Want to Know	What I Learned

ENG-LANG ARTS Standards
R 2.4

MIXED REVIEW AND TEST PREP
Exercises 44–48 provide **cumulative review** (Chapters 1–4).

LiNKUP to SCIENCE

• As students read the Link Up to Science, have them identify the places in the numbers shown.

In the number that tells the size of the average plant cell, what place does the 3 name? hundred-thousandths

Read the number that describes the thickness of a cell wall or membrane. seventy-five ten-billionths

REASONING   A micron is 1 millionth of a meter. How many microns long are the average plant cell and the small bacteria? 35 microns; 0.2 micron

---

4 Assess

Summarize the lesson by having students:

DISCUSS   Gary says that 24.3 − 17.56 = 6.86. What might he have done wrong? Possible answer: He forgot to write a zero after the 3 before he subtracted and just brought the 6 down into the hundredths place.

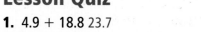

WRITE   What are some things you should be careful to do when you add and subtract decimals? Possible answer: Be sure decimal points are lined up correctly. If one of the numbers is a whole number, place a decimal point and zeros after the last digit. Estimate the answer so that you will have some way to know whether your computed answer is reasonable.

Lesson Quiz

Transparency 4.1

1. 4.9 + 18.8 23.7
2. 0.7 + 2.045 2.745
3. 8.5 − 7.8 0.7
4. 51.3 − 5.13 46.17
5. 145.89 − 65.036 80.854
6. 0.45 + 3.2 + 45.683 49.333

Multiply Decimals

LESSON PLANNING

Objective To multiply decimals

Intervention for Prerequisite Skills

Whole Number Operations, Multiply by 10, 100, and 1000 (For intervention strategies, see page 65.)

Materials *For each student* decimal squares, p. TR7; colored pencils

California Mathematics Content Standards

NS 2.0 Students calculate and solve problems involving addition, subtraction, multiplication, and division.

MR 2.1 Use estimation to verify reasonableness of calculated results.

(*Also* MR 1.3, MR 2.4, MR 2.5, MR 3.1)

Math Background

Students need the skills developed with whole number multiplication for multiplying decimals. To extend their skills in multiplying decimals, stress these points:

- Initially disregard the decimal points and multiply as if the numbers were whole numbers.
- The decimal point is placed in the product according to the sum of the number of places in the factors. That is, if you multiply tenths (1 place) by tenths (1 place), the answer will contain hundredths ($1 + 1 = 2$ places).
- An estimate is especially helpful because it shows if you have placed the decimal point correctly.

WARM-UP RESOURCES

 NUMBER OF THE DAY   Transparency **4.2**

I am a decimal less than 1. If you multiply a number by me, the number may gain or lose one zero, but all the other digits will still be there. What number am I? 0.1

 PROBLEM OF THE DAY   Transparency **4.2**

Rhonda is making an input/output table. When she sees 5, she writes 3.0. When she sees 10, she writes 6.0. When she sees 4, she writes 2.4. What will she write when she sees 12? 7.2 What did she see if she wrote 4.2? 7

Solution Problem of the Day tab, p. PD4

 DAILY FACTS PRACTICE

Have students practice multiplication facts by completing Set C of *Teacher's Resource Book,* p. TR95.

ALTERNATIVE TEACHING STRATEGY ELL

To help students better **understand the concept of multiplying decimals,** have them try this approach: Find 0.5×0.8. What fraction in simplest form is equal to 0.5? $\frac{1}{2}$ What is half of 0.8? 0.4 So, $0.5 \times 0.8 = 0.4$. Repeat this activity with 0.5×0.4 and with 0.5×0.6. 0.2; 0.3

See also page 72.

AUDITORY

MIXED REVIEW AND TEST PREP

Cumulative Review Chapters 1–4

Refer to the Pupil Edition pages referenced in the exercises for further review. Have students go to the lesson page, review the lesson, and correct any problem they missed.

Mixed Review and Test Prep, p. 73

How to Help	
Item	Page
47	66
48	66
49	28
50	36
51	16

CAREER CONNECTION

To **reinforce decimal multiplication,** display this ad. Ask students: Which job pays the most per week? How much does it pay? lawn mowing; $72.75

PART-TIME SUMMER JOBS		
Car Washing	Lawn Mowing	Bagging Groceries
$4.95/hr	$4.85/hr	$5.05/hr
14 hr a wk	15 hr a wk	13 hr a wk

VISUAL

ADVANCED LEARNERS

Materials *For each pair* a set of 8 cards, each with one of the following numbers: 0.2, 0.04, 0.008, 0.0016, 0.5, 0.25, 0.125, 0.0625

Challenge students to **extend their understanding of multiplying decimals.**

- Students should shuffle the cards and stack them face down.
- Students take turns turning over the top card.
- Each time a new card is turned over, both students try to find the least whole number by which the decimal can be multiplied to give a whole number product.
- The first student to find the answer earns a number of points equal to the number of decimal places in the number on the card.

0.2 (5), 0.04 (25), 0.008 (125), 0.0016 (625), 0.5 (2), 0.25 (4), 0.125 (8), 0.0625 (16)

VISUAL

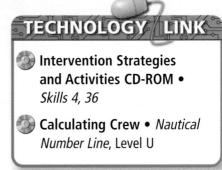

TECHNOLOGY LINK

- **Intervention Strategies and Activities CD-ROM** • *Skills 4, 36*

- **Calculating Crew** • *Nautical Number Line,* Level U

Objective To multiply decimals

Materials *For each student* decimal squares, p. TR7; colored pencils

1 Introduce

QUICK REVIEW provides review of prerequisite skills.

Why Learn This? Multiplying decimals will help you determine the total cost for several of the same item. *Share the lesson objective with students.*

2 Teach

Guided Instruction

- *Have students recall the relationship between addition and multiplication.*

  How would you write an addition expression for the activity exercise? 0.14 + 0.14 + 0.14

- *Remind students of the importance of estimating solutions.*

  In Example 1, why do you not place the decimal after the 1 or the second 0? The solution must be close to the estimated product of $9. It could not be $1.01 or $100.80.

ADDITIONAL EXAMPLE

Example 1, p. 70

Rick sold 8 comics for $1.35 each. How much did he get paid for the comics? estimate: $8; answer: $10.80

LESSON **4.2**

Multiply Decimals

Learn how to multiply decimals.

You need colored pencils and decimal squares.

You can use a model to find the product of a decimal number and a whole number.

Activity

- To find 3 × 0.14, shade 0.14, or 14 small squares, three times. Use a different color and shade a different group of 14 small squares each time.

- Count the number of shaded squares. What is 3 × 0.14? **0.42**

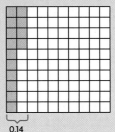 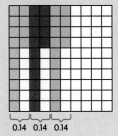

0.14   0.14 0.14 0.14

- Use a decimal square to find 5 × 0.18.

- Describe how you shaded your decimal square.   **Possible answer: I shaded groups of 18 small squares five times.**

- What is 5 × 0.18? **0.90**

Sometimes, when the factors are greater, as in 8 × 1.52, it is easier to compute the product by not using decimal squares.

EXAMPLE 1

Ed buys 9 sports cards at $1.12 each. How much does he spend?

Multiply. $1.12 × 9

Estimate. $1.12 × 9 → $1 × 9 = $9

Find the answer.

$1.12
× 9
$10.08

Multiply as with whole numbers. Since the estimate is $9, place the decimal point after the 10.

Since the estimate is $9, the answer is reasonable.

So, Ed pays $10.08 for sports cards.

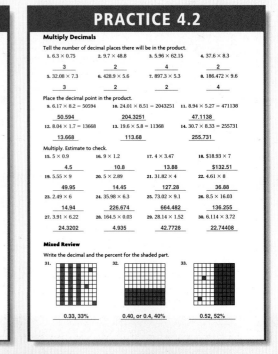

RETEACH 4.2 / PRACTICE 4.2

Multiply a Decimal by a Decimal

You can use a decimal square or paper and pencil to find the product of two decimals.

EXAMPLE 2

Multiply. 0.2×0.6

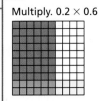

Shade 6 columns blue for 0.6.

Shade 2 rows yellow for 0.2.

The area in which the shading overlaps shows the product, or 0.2 of 0.6.

So, $0.2 \times 0.6 = 0.12$.

Place the decimal point in a product by estimating or by adding the number of decimal places in the factors.

$$
\begin{array}{r}
0.2 \quad \leftarrow \text{1 decimal place} \\
\times 0.6 \quad \leftarrow \text{1 decimal place} \\
\hline
0.12 \quad \leftarrow \textit{1 + 1, or 2, decimal places}
\end{array}
$$

EXAMPLE 3

Mr. Ponti works 37.5 hr per week. He earns $8.70 an hour. How much does he earn in a week?

Multiply. $\$8.70 \times 37.5$

Estimate. $\$8.70 \times 37.5 \rightarrow \$9 \times 38 = \$342$

Find the answer.

$$
\begin{array}{r}
\$8.70 \quad \leftarrow \text{2 decimal places} \\
\times\ 37.5 \quad \leftarrow \text{1 decimal place} \\
\hline
4350 \quad \textit{Multiply as with whole numbers.} \\
6090 \quad \textit{Place the decimal point in the} \\
+2610 \quad \textit{product.} \\
\hline
326.250 \quad \leftarrow \text{3 decimal places}
\end{array}
$$

Since the estimate is $342, the answer is reasonable.

So, Mr. Ponti earns $326.25.

When you multiply decimals, you sometimes have to insert zeros in the answer.

EXAMPLE 4

Multiply. 0.037×0.062

$$
\begin{array}{r}
0.037 \quad \leftarrow \text{3 decimal places} \\
\times 0.062 \quad \leftarrow \text{3 decimal places} \\
\hline
74 \quad \textit{Multiply as with whole numbers.} \\
+222 \quad \textit{Place the decimal point in the product.} \\
\hline
0.002294 \quad \textit{The answer must have 6 decimal places,} \\
\textit{so place 2 zeros to the left of 2.}
\end{array}
$$

So, $0.037 \times 0.062 = 0.002294$.

71

• *Remind students that Examples 2 and 4 show that the product of two factors less than 1 is always less than each of the factors.*

What part of the model in Example 2 shows the product? the part where the two colored sections overlap

How does this double shading show that the product is less than each of the factors? The overlapped portion is smaller than each of the individual sections representing the factors.

Modifying Instruction You may want to guide students in discovering for themselves the rules for proper decimal placement in products. Display exercises similar to those in Examples 2–4 and have students solve with calculators. Then ask them to compare the number of decimal places in the factors to the number of decimal places in the products.

ADDITIONAL EXAMPLES

Example 2, p. 71

Multiply. 0.4×0.7

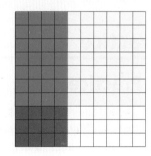

So, $0.4 \times 0.7 = 0.28$

Example 3, p. 71

Marshall bought 22.5 lb of meat from Grocery Warehouse. He paid $5.79 per lb. How much did he pay for the meat? estimate: $120; answer: $130.28

Example 4, p. 71

Multiply. 0.023×0.054

$$
\begin{array}{r}
0.023 \quad \text{3 decimal places} \\
\times 0.054 \quad \text{3 decimal places} \\
\hline
92 \quad \textit{Multiply as with whole} \\
+\ 115 \quad \textit{numbers.} \\
\hline
0.001242 \quad \textit{Place the decimal point. The} \\
\textit{answer must have 6 decimal} \\
\textit{places, so place 2 zeros to} \\
\textit{the left of 1.}
\end{array}
$$

So, $0.023 \times 0.054 = 0.001242$.

PROBLEM SOLVING 4.2

Multiply Decimals

Write the correct answer.

1. Which is greater, $\frac{3}{20}$ or $\frac{2}{5}$? Use > or <.

$$\frac{3}{20} < \frac{2}{5} \text{ or } \frac{2}{5} > \frac{3}{20}$$

2. Sonia wrote a check for $27.86. What is the number of dollars written in words?

twenty-seven and eighty-six hundredths

Choose the letter for the best answer.

3. Walter grew a pumpkin that weighed 38.73 pounds. Bill grew a pumpkin that weighed 42.1 pounds. How many more pounds did Bill's pumpkin weigh than Walter's pumpkin?
   - A 4.67 more pounds
   - B 4.63 more pounds
   - C 3.67 more pounds
   - (D) 3.37 more pounds

4. Ted wants to use a special wallpaper border in his living room. He has three pieces of border that are 11.7 meters, 6.05 meters, and 24.75 meters long. How many meters of border does he have in all?
   - F 24.75 meters
   - G 31.97 meters
   - (H) 42.5 meters
   - J 641.45 meters

5. A pencil costs $0.85 and a pen costs $1.76. Wayne buys 12 pencils and 8 pens. Which expression can be used to find the total cost of Wayne's purchases?
   - (A) $(12 \times 0.85) + (8 \times 1.76)$
   - B $(12 + 0.85) + (8 + 1.76)$
   - C $(12 \times 0.85) \times (8 \times 1.76)$
   - D $(12 + 0.85) \times (8 + 1.76)$

6. A grocery store needs to stock a new cereal on the shelf. There are 8 shelves that can hold 6 boxes in each row. What else do you need to know to find out how many boxes of the cereal the store can put out at once?
   - F The height of the box
   - (G) How many rows of boxes fit on a shelf
   - H How much a box of cereal costs
   - J The brand of cereal

7. **Write About It** Explain how you could use a decimal square to model the product 0.3 × 0.2.

Use a hundred square. Shade 2 columns one color for 0.2 and shade

3 rows another color for 0.3. The ___ in which the shading overlaps

shows the product, or 0.3 of 0.2.

CHALLENGE 4.2

Puzzling Problems

Find each product. Locate the product in the Tip Box. (Hint: Not all products are in the Tip Box.)
Each time the product appears, write the letter of that exercise above it. When you have solved all the problems, you will discover a math tip for multiplying decimals.

A $5.26 \times 7.5 =$	39.45		N $2.008 \times 1.2 =$	2.4096
B $0.12 \times 1.2 =$	0.144		O $6.1 \times 0.42 =$	2.562
C $3 \times 0.009 =$	0.027		P $0.54 \times 2.9 =$	1.566
D $2.9 \times 2.03 =$	5.887		R $0.3 \times 30 =$	9
E $8 \times 2.5 =$	20		S $1.8 \times 2.3 =$	4.14
G $0.15 \times 0.07 =$	0.0105		T $6 \times 1.7 =$	10.2
H $7.4 \times 6.8 =$	50.32		U $5.9 \times 0.04 =$	0.236
I $0.04 \times 40.5 =$	1.62		V $8.5 \times 6.3 =$	53.55
J $0.25 \times 3.8 =$	0.95		W $46.7 \times 2.3 =$	107.41
M $190 \times 0.03 =$	5.7			

Tip Box

R	E	M	E	M	B	E	R
9	20	5.7	20	5.7	0.144	20	9

T	O		E	S	T	I	M	A	T	E
10.2	2.562		20	4.14	10.2	1.62	5.7	39.45	10.2	20

T	H	E		P	R	O	D	U	C	T
10.2	50.32	20		1.566	9	2.562	5.887	0.236	0.027	10.2

LESSON 4.2

• After students work Example 5, ask:

REASONING Show how you could use the Distributive Property to multiply 4 and 11.08. $(4 \times 11) + (4 \times 0.08) = 44 + 0.32 = 44.32$

ADDITIONAL EXAMPLE

Example 5, p. 72

Multiply. 8×5.7
Estimate. $8 \times 5.7 \rightarrow 8 \times 6 = 48$

Find the answer.

$8 \times 5.7 = (8 \times 5) + (8 \times 0.7)$ *Use the Distributive Property.*

$\quad\quad = 40 + 5.6$
$\quad\quad = 45.6$ *Since the estimate is 48, place the decimal point after the 45.*

So, $8 \times 5.7 = 45.6$.

3 Practice

Guided Practice

Do Check for Understanding Exercises 1–13 with your students. Identify those having difficulty and use lesson resources to help.

Independent Practice

Assign Exercises 14–46.

EXAMPLE 5

You can also use the Distributive Property to multiply with decimals.

Multiply. 6×5.9

Use estimation to place the decimal point in the product.
Estimate. $6 \times 5.9 \rightarrow 6 \times 6 = 36$

Find the answer.

$6 \times 5.9 = (6 \times 5) + (6 \times 0.9)$ *Use the Distributive Property.*

$\quad\quad = 30 + 5.4$ *Since the estimate is 36, place the*
$\quad\quad = 35.4$ *decimal point after the 35.*

Since the estimate is 36, the answer is reasonable.

So, $6 \times 5.9 = 35.4$.

CHECK FOR UNDERSTANDING

Think and ▶ Discuss

Look back at the lesson to answer the question.

1. **Explain** how you would place the decimal point in the product 0.27×0.476. Count the decimal places in the factors. Then count that number of places from the right in the product.

Guided ▶ Practice

Use the decimal square shown to help you multiply.

2.   3.   4.

$4 \times 0.12 \ \mathbf{0.48}$ $0.7 \times 0.5 \ \mathbf{0.35}$ $0.6 \times 0.4 \ \mathbf{0.24}$

Tell the number of decimal places there will be in the product.

5. 3.62×7 **2**   6. 2.15×8.18 **4**   7. 4.04×5.2 **3**

Copy the problem. Place the decimal point in the product.

8. $9 \times 5.4 = 486$ 9. $0.7 \times 4.1 = 287$ 10. $2.2 \times 0.55 = 1210$
             48.6   **2.87**   **1.210**

Multiply. Estimate to check.

11. 0.42×2.9 **1.218**   12. 1.25×0.4 **0.500**   13. 3.23×8 **25.84**

PRACTICE AND PROBLEM SOLVING

Independent ▶ Practice

Use the decimal square shown to help you multiply.

14.   15.   16.

$5 \times 0.18 \ \mathbf{0.90}$ $0.3 \times 0.8 \ \mathbf{0.24}$ $0.7 \times 0.4 \ \mathbf{0.28}$

72   Chapter 4

Alternative Teaching Strategy

Purpose Students analyze errors involving misplaced decimal points in completed problems and correct them.

Display the following problem:

$$\begin{array}{r} 3.07 \\ \times \ 0.7 \\ \hline 0.02149 \end{array}$$

Have students work in pairs to find and correct the error.

Students should notice that the number of digits in the factors was counted to place the decimal point rather than the number of decimal places.

Have a volunteer show the correct solution and explain how to place the decimal point in the answer.

$$\begin{array}{rl} 3.07 & \text{2 places} \\ \times \ 0.7 & +\text{1 place} \\ \hline 2.149 & \text{3 places} \end{array}$$

Next have partners repeat the process with the following problem:

$$\begin{array}{r} 21.4 \\ \times \ 1.6 \\ \hline 1284 \\ +2140 \\ \hline 3.424 \end{array}$$

Guide students to realize that the number of places before the decimal point in each factor was counted instead of the number of places after the decimal point in each factor.

$$\begin{array}{rl} 21.4 & \text{1 place} \\ \times \ 1.6 & +\text{1 place} \\ \hline 1284 & \\ +2140 & \\ \hline 34.24 & \text{2 places} \end{array}$$

To help students avoid such errors, encourage them to circle each digit after the decimal point in each factor and then to count the circles. This total will be the number of decimal places they need in the answer.

Check students' work.

Tell the number of decimal places there will be in the product.

17. 3.79×8.2 **3**   **18.** 0.876×0.2 **4**   **19.** 1.3842×0.91 **6**

Copy the problem. Place the decimal point in the product.

20. $6.37 \times 2.91 = 185367$ **18.5367**   **21.** $20.4 \times 9.52 = 194208$ **194.208**

22. $7.32 \times 3 = 2196$ **23.** $0.82 \times 0.5 = 410$ **24.** $32.5 \times 0.06 = 1950$
21.96   **0.410**   **1.950**

Multiply. Estimate to check.

25. 3×4.6 **13.8**   **26.** 9×2.5 **22.5**   **27.** 7.3×5 **36.5**

28. 8.2×5 **41.0**   **29.** 1.2×4.1 **4.92**   **30.** 0.9×6.3 **5.67**

31. 0.2×0.4 **0.08**   **32.** 12.6×0.45 **5.67**   **33.** 0.21×2.1 **0.441**

34. 6.15×2.4 **14.760**   **35.** 4.08×1.35 **5.5080**   **36.** 6.21×0.95 **5.8995**

37. 24.63×1.09 **38.** 29.147×5.61 **39.** 0.189×2.09
26.8467   **163.51467**   **0.39501**
40. 118.001×0.37 **41.** 148.9×0.006 **42.** $1,200.5 \times 8.2$
43.66037   **0.8934**   **9,844.10**

Problem Solving ▶ Applications

43. The recipe for a pie calls for 2.25 lb of apples and 0.75 lb of walnuts. Apples are $1.60 per pound and walnuts are $4.95 per pound. How much will the apples and walnuts cost in all? **$7.31**

44. Keith has a wall that is 5.2 m wide. He has 3 bookcases that are each 1.9 m wide. Is there enough room for all of the bookcases to be placed against the wall? Explain. **No, $1.9 \times 3 = 5.7$; $5.7 > 5.2$**

45. Write a problem that uses multiplication of two decimals to find the answer. The product must have four decimal places.
Check students' problems.

46. Use Data   Look at the graph at the right. Rochelle had to earn 134 points in the first four rounds to advance in a competition. Rochelle says that she did advance. Is this a reasonable statement?
Explain. **yes; round each score to the nearest ten and add; 260 > 134**

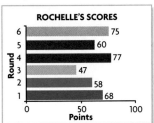

ROCHELLE'S SCORES

Round	Points
6	75
5	60
4	77
3	47
2	58
1	68

MIXED REVIEW AND TEST PREP

47. Add. $46.2 + 3.45 + 16$ (p. 66) **65.65**   **48.** Subtract. $604.5 - 76.38$ (p. 66) **528.12**

49. Evaluate the expression $a \div c$ for $a = 14,067$ and $c = 47$. (p. 28) **299 r14**

50. TEST PREP   Which shows the value of m when $8 = m \div 9$? (p. 36) **B**
   A 70   **B** 72   **C** 720   **D** 7,200

51. TEST PREP   Which is the best estimate for $21,563 \div 43$? (p. 16) **F**
   F 500   **G** 700   **H** 5,000   **J** 7,000

Extra Practice   page H35, Set B   73

Direct students' attention to Exercises 23–24, where the last digit in the products is a zero. Remind them that this digit must always be counted for correct placement of the decimal point in the product.

MIXED REVIEW AND TEST PREP
Exercises 47–51 provide spiral review (Chapters 1–4).

4 Asses

Summarize the lesson by having students:

DISCUSS How do you decide where to place the decimal point when multiplying two decimals? Possible answer: Find the sum of the number of places to the right of the decimal points in the factors. Place the decimal point so that there are the same number of places to the right of the decimal point in the product.

WRITE How does estimation help you multiply decimals? Possible answer: It shows you where to place the decimal point.

Lesson Quiz

Transparency **4.2**

Find the product.
1. 3×0.6 **1.8**
2. 5×3.3 **16.5**
3. 7.3×3.4 **24.82**
4. 2.18×5.6 **12.208**
5. 0.053×0.086 **0.004558**

ORGANIZER

Objective To use a model to divide decimals

Materials *For each student* decimal squares, p. TR7; colored pencils; scissors

Lesson Resources E-Lab Recording Sheet • *Exploring Division of Decimals*

Intervention for Prerequisite Skills Whole Number Operations (For intervention strategies, see page 65.)

Using the Pages

Discuss situations in which students may need to divide decimals, such as sharing money with other people.

Activity 1

In this activity students use decimal squares to model dividing decimals by whole numbers. This hands-on experience will help students visualize the concept of equal groups.

Think and Discuss

After discussing the questions, ask students to:

Summarize the relationship between the quotients of these identical digit dividends expressed as a whole number and then as hundredths. The quotient of the whole number dividends are 100 times as great as the quotient of the hundredths dividend.

Practice

Observe students as they model each exercise and ask:

In Exercise 2, how many shaded wholes did you put into each group? none **Why?** 3 is not great enough to be placed into 5 groups

How many hundredths did you put into each group? 65 hundredths

---

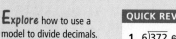

Explore Division of Decimals

Explore how to use a model to divide decimals.

You need decimal squares, colored pencils, scissors.

Remember
1 tenth (0.1) = 1 column

1 hundredth (0.01) = 1 small square

QUICK REVIEW

1. 6)$\overline{372}$ 62   2. 8)$\overline{427}$ 53 r3   3. 5)$\overline{524}$ 104 r4

4. 4)$\overline{123}$ 30 r3   5. 252 ÷ 6 42

You can shade and cut apart decimal squares to divide a decimal by a whole number.

Activity 1

Find 3.66 ÷ 3.

• Shade 3.66 decimal squares.

• Divide the shaded wholes into 3 equal groups. Divide the 66 hundredths into 3 equal groups.

• What decimal names each group? What is the quotient? **1.22; 1.22**

• Use decimal squares to find 1.32 ÷ 4. **Check students' models; 0.33.**

Think and Discuss

• Find 366 ÷ 3. How is the quotient the same as for 3.66 ÷ 3? How is it different? **122; it has the same digits; it is 100 times as great.**

• Find 132 ÷ 4. How is the quotient the same as for 1.32 ÷ 4? How is it different? **33; it has the same digits; it is 100 times as great.**

Practice

Use decimal squares to find the quotient.

1. 4.04 ÷ 4 **1.01**

2. 3.25 ÷ 5 **0.65**

3. 1.35 ÷ 3 **0.45**

74

SPECIAL NEEDS ELL

Materials *For each student* play money— 10 quarters, 10 dimes, 10 nickels

Display this **model for dividing decimals:**

$1.00 ÷ $0.25 = 4

$0.25 $0.25 $0.25 $0.25

Have students use play money to find quotients for the following: $0.30 ÷ $0.05 and $1.60 ÷ $0.80. 6; 2; Check students' models.

KINESTHETIC

REACHING ALL LEARNERS **Intervention and Extension Resources**

WRITING IN MATHEMATICS

Ask students to write a paragraph explaining the difference in how they would **use models to solve these decimal exercises:** 5.5 ÷ 5 and 5.5 ÷ 1.1. Possible answer: In the first case, you would divide 5.5 into 5 groups and count 1.1 in each group, showing that 5.5 ÷ 5 = 1.1. In the second case, you would divide 5.5 into equal groups of 1.1 and count the groups, showing 5.5 ÷ 1.1 = 5.

You can shade and cut apart decimal squares to divide a decimal by a decimal.

TECHNOLOGY LINK
More Practice:
Use E-Lab, *Exploring Division of Decimals.*
www.harcourtschool.com/elab2002

Activity 2

Find $3.6 \div 1.2$.

- Shade 3.6 decimal squares.

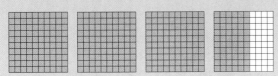

- Cut apart the 6 tenths.
- Divide the shaded squares and shaded tenths into equal groups of 1.2. How many groups of 1.2 are in 3.6? What is the quotient? **3; 3**

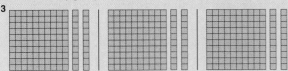

- Use decimal squares to find $3.2 \div 1.6$.
- How many groups of 1.6 are in 3.2? **2**

Think and Discuss

- Find $36 \div 12$. How is the quotient the same as for $3.6 \div 1.2$? How is the problem different from $3.6 \div 1.2$? **3; it is exactly the same; the divisor and dividend are each 10 times as great.**
- You know that $3.6 \div 12 = 0.3$ and $3.6 \div 1.2 = 3$. What do you think $3.6 \div 0.12$ equals? **30**

Practice

Use decimal squares to find the quotient.

1. $7.8 \div 1.3$ **6**
2. $5.6 \div 0.8$ **7**
3. $1.56 \div 0.52$ **3**
4. $5.5 \div 1.1$ **5**
5. $3.6 \div 0.9$ **4**
6. $1.8 \div 0.45$ **4**
7. $0.42 \div 0.14$ **3**
8. $10.8 \div 2.7$ **4**
9. $0.64 \div 0.08$ **8**

MIXED REVIEW AND TEST PREP

10. Multiply. 64.7×3.6 (p. 70) **232.92**
11. Write the decimal for 57%. (p. 60) **0.57**
12. Write the value of 3^4. (p. 40) **81**
13. Divide. $3,759 \div 42$ (p. 22) **89 r21**
14. **TEST PREP** Evaluate the expression. $12 \times 25 \div (12 + 18)$ (p. 44) **B**
   - **A** 8
   - **B** 10
   - **C** 43
   - **D** 300

75

Activity 2

Unlike Activity 1, in which the number of decimal squares that should go into each group was being determined, in this activity the number of groups is being determined.

Think and Discuss

REASONING **Explain how you know that $3.6 \div 0.12 = 30$.** Possible answer: by using a pattern: $3.6 \div 12 = 0.3$, $3.6 \div 1.2 = 3$, so $3.6 \div 0.12 = 30$. As the decimal in the divisor moves one place to the left, the decimal in the quotient moves one place to the right.

Practice

Before students begin the exercises, ask:

Which exercise could you solve by using mental math? Explain. Most students will say Exercise 2: $56 \div 8 = 7$, so $5.6 \div 0.8 = 7$ and Exercise 5: $36 \div 9 = 4$, so $3.6 \div 0.9 = 4$.

Have students model all six exercises even if they were able to find the answers by using mental math. The conceptual understanding they develop by modeling will help them solve more complex problems later.

MIXED REVIEW AND TEST PREP

Exercises 10–14 provide **cumulative review** (Chapters 1–4).

Oral Assessment

Have students explain how they would use decimal squares to model the equations.

1. $0.64 \div 2 = 0.32$ Possible answer: Shade 64 squares of a decimal square. Divide the 64 squares into 2 equal groups. Each group will have 32 squares, each of which represents a hundredth.

2. $0.9 \div 0.05 = 18$ Possible answer: Shade 9 tenths of a decimal square. Count the number of groups of 5 hundredths. There are 18 groups of 5 hundredths.

E-LAB RECORDING SHEET

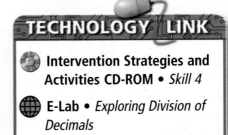

USING E-LAB

Students explore division of decimals by using computer models for decimal multiplication.

The E-Lab Recording Sheets and activities are available on the E-Lab website.

www.harcourtschool.com/elab2002

TECHNOLOGY LINK

- **Intervention Strategies and Activities CD-ROM** • *Skill 4*
- **E-Lab** • *Exploring Division of Decimals*

Divide with Decimals

LESSON PLANNING

Objective To divide a decimal by a whole number and a decimal by a decimal

Intervention for Prerequisite Skills

Whole Number Operations, Multiply Decimals by 10, 100 and 1,000; Remainders (For intervention strategies, see page 65.)

Materials *For each student* calculator

California Mathematics Content Standards

NS 2.0 Students calculate and solve problems involving addition, subtraction, multiplication, and division.

MR 2.1 Use estimation to verify the reasonableness of calculated results.

(*Also* **MG 1.1**)

Math Background

Emphasize these steps as you teach the division algorithm as applied to decimals.

- The division algorithm is defined for a whole number divisor. To divide one decimal by another, first multiply the divisor by a power of ten to make it a whole number. The dividend must be multiplied by the same power of ten. To do this, "move the decimal point to the right" in both divisor and dividend the same number of places. Add zeros to the dividend if needed.

- The decimal point in the quotient is then placed over the decimal point in the dividend. If the quotient is less than 1, insert zeros between the decimal point and first nonzero digit, if needed.

- Estimating the quotient helps locate the position of the first nonzero digit.

- Continue using the steps of whole number division.

WARM-UP RESOURCES

 NUMBER OF THE DAY Transparency 4.4

Write and solve 5 division problems using the number of inches in a yard. Possible answers: $36 \div 12 = 3$, $72 \div 36 = 2$, $108 \div 3 = 36$, $36 \div 2 = 18$, $36 \div 9 = 4$

 PROBLEM OF THE DAY Transparency 4.4

The sum of two decimal numbers is 9.3. Their difference is 4.3, and their product is 17.00. What are the numbers? 2.5 and 6.8

Solution Problem of the Day tab, p. PD4

 DAILY FACTS PRACTICE

Have students practice division facts by completing Set E of *Teacher's Resource Book,* p. TR95.

INTERVENTION AND EXTENSION RESOURCES

ALTERNATIVE TEACHING STRATEGY ELL

Remind students that they can **use repeated subtraction to find answers to division problems** that have whole number quotients. Have students use repeated subtraction to find each of the following quotients:

$0.18 \div 0.03$ 6

$2.4 \div 0.6$ 4

$6 \div 1.5$ 4

$0.72 \div 0.09$ 8

See also page 78.

VISUAL

MIXED REVIEW AND TEST PREP

Cumulative Review Chapters 1–4

Refer to the Pupil Edition pages referenced in the exercises for further review. Have students go to the lesson page, review the lesson, and correct any problem they missed.

Mixed Review and Test Prep, p. 79

How to Help	
Item	Page
42	70
43	52
44	36
45	30
46	22

EARLY FINISHERS

Remind students how to **check decimal division.** If a division calculation has been done correctly, the product of the quotient and the divisor should equal the dividend. Have students use this method to check their answers for six of the division exercises on page 79. Answers will vary.

VISUAL

ADVANCED LEARNERS

Challenge students to solve this **decimal division puzzle** by finding three different digits *A*, *B*, *C* such that:

$$C.BC \div A.A = C.C$$

There are three possibilities: $A = 1$, $B = 4$, $C = 2$; $A = 1$, $B = 6$, $C = 3$; $A = 1$, $B = 8$, $C = 4$.

If students need encouragement to get started, you may wish to offer one or both of these hints:

- In one possibility, all digits are less than 5.
- Let $A = 1$.

VISUAL

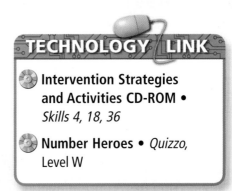

TECHNOLOGY LINK

- **Intervention Strategies and Activities CD-ROM •** *Skills 4, 18, 36*
- **Number Heroes •** *Quizzo,* Level W

LESSON 4.4 ORGANIZER

Objective To divide a decimal by a whole number and a decimal by a decimal

Materials *For each student* calculator

1 Introduce

QUICK REVIEW provides review of pre-requisite skills.

Why Learn This? Dividing a decimal by a decimal will enable you to determine the number of unit-priced items you can purchase with a given amount of money. *Share the lesson objective with students.*

2 Teach

Guided Instruction

• *Remind students of the importance of placing the decimal correctly in the quotient before applying the division algorithm.*

REASONING **In Example 1, why would estimating using compatible numbers not be enough to help you determine the reasonableness of your quotient?** Possible answer: The estimate would tell you that the digits in the quotient would be close to 90, but the decimal placement would depend on where the decimal is in the dividend.

Why would 0.90 be an incorrect quotient? The first non-zero digit in the decimal dividend is less than the divisor, making a zero to the right of the decimal in the quotient necessary.

ADDITIONAL EXAMPLE

Example 1, p. 76

Divide. 0.425 ÷ 5 0.085

LESSON 4.4

Divide with Decimals

Learn how to divide a decimal by a whole number and how to divide a decimal by a decimal.

QUICK REVIEW

1. $8\overline{)373}$ 46 r5   2. $6\overline{)205}$ 34 r1   3. $19\overline{)836}$ 44
4. $27\overline{)434}$ 16 r2   5. $294 ÷ 14$ 21

Remember that compatible numbers are numbers that divide without a remainder, are close to the actual numbers, and are easy to compute mentally.

Jacki wants to transfer photographs onto a CD to use with her computer. She bought a box of 5 blank CDs for $26.45. What was the cost of each CD?

Dividing a decimal by a whole number is like dividing whole numbers.

Divide. $26.45 ÷ 5$

Use compatible numbers to estimate.

$$26.45 ÷ 5 \rightarrow 25 ÷ 5 = 5$$

Find the answer.

```
    5.29
5)26.45
  −25↓
    14
   −10↓
     45
    −45
      0
```
Place a decimal point above the decimal point in the dividend.

Divide.

Since the estimate is $5, the answer is reasonable.
So, each CD cost $5.29.

Sometimes you have to place a zero in the quotient when the dividend is less than the divisor.

EXAMPLE 1

Divide. $0.285 ÷ 3$

```
  0.095
3)0.285
  −0↓
   28
  −27↓
    15
   −15
     0
```
Place a decimal point above the decimal point in the dividend.

Divide. Since 2 tenths is less than 3 ones, place a zero in the tenths place in the quotient.

So, $0.285 ÷ 3 = 0.095$.

76

CALIFORNIA STANDARDS O—n NS 2.0 Students calculate and solve problems involving addition, subtraction, multiplication, and division. MR 2.1 Use estimation to verify the reasonableness of calculated results. *also* O—n MG 1.1

RETEACH 4.4

Divide with Decimals

Mary has saved $0.35 each day. She now has a total of $9.10. How long has Mary been saving?

To solve, you need to divide 9.10 by 0.35.

Step 1: Make the divisor a whole number by multiplying the divisor by a multiple of 10. Multiply the dividend by the same multiple of 10.

$0.35\overline{)9.10}$ $\rightarrow$ $35\overline{)910}$
× 100 × 100

Step 2: Place the decimal point in the quotient directly above the decimal point in the dividend. Divide as you would with whole numbers.

```
      26.
35)910.
  −70
   210
  −210
     0
```

Since the remainder is 0, the answer is a whole number. You do not need to show the decimal point.

Mary has been saving for 26 days.

Complete to solve.

1. Dusty bought 7 movie tickets for his friends. The tickets cost a total of $34.65. How much does each friend owe him for the cost of one ticket?
   a. What division problem will you use to solve? $34.65 ÷ 7$
   b. Do you need to multiply to make the divisor a whole number? no
   c. How do you decide where to place the decimal point in the quotient? Place it directly above the decimal point in the dividend.
   d. How much does each friend owe? $4.95

Place the decimal point in the quotient.

2. 131.52 ÷ 6.4 = 2055   3. 50.085 ÷ 10.6 = 4725   4. 1936.95 ÷ 2.22 = 8725
   20.55   4.725   872.5

Find the quotient.

5. 16.88 ÷ 5   6. 81.9 ÷ 18   7. 332.8 ÷ 40
   3.376   4.55   8.32
8. 118 ÷ 12.5   9. 203.205 ÷ 5.7   10. 421.155 ÷ 14.7
   9.44   35.65   28.65

PRACTICE 4.4

Divide with Decimals

Rewrite the problem so that the divisor is a whole number.

1. 8.5 ÷ 2.3   2. 6.4 ÷ 1.3   3. 9.1 ÷ 0.15   4. 33.17 ÷ 6.8
   85 ÷ 23   64 ÷ 13   910 ÷ 15   331.7 ÷ 68

Place the decimal point in the quotient.

5. 7.48 ÷ 0.25 = 2992   6. 116.13 ÷ 4.2 = 2765   7. 56.68 ÷ 0.08 = 7085
   29.92   27.65   708.5

Divide. Estimate to check.

8. 36.9 ÷ 3   9. 22.4 ÷ 7   10. 37.5 ÷ 5   11. 89.6 ÷ 8
   12.3   3.2   7.5   11.2
12. 14)78.4 5.6   13. 40)6.8 0.17   14. 13)150.8 11.6   15. 70)23.8 0.34
16. 5.32 ÷ 0.7   17. 1.88 ÷ 0.4   18. 2.12 ÷ 0.2   19. 5.4 ÷ 0.08
    7.6   4.7   10.6   67.5
20. 7.54)24.882 3.3   21. 12.6)806.4 64   22. 0.91)6.734 7.4   23. 10.9)81.75 7.5
24. 2.9)0.3335 0.115   25. 0.18)64.296 357.2   26. 12.3)84.87 6.9   27. 8.7)53.244 6.12

Mixed Review

Add, subtract, or multiply.

28. 78.94   29. 1,083.75   30.   0.072
      9.66   − 706.9   × 0.48
   + 103.71   376.85   0.03456
     192.31
31. 215.6 + 49.87 + 8.351   32. 42.83 × 1.91   33. 65.85 − 39.478
    273.821   81.8053   26.372
34. 430.62 − 288.74   35. 192.6 + 847.56   36. 17.335 × 8.26
    141.88   1,040.16   143.1871

Activity

- Use a calculator to find the first three quotients in each set.
- Look for a pattern. Try to predict the last quotient in each set.

Set A	Set B
0.48 ÷ 0.03 = ■16	0.621 ÷ 0.023 = ■ 27
4.8 ÷ 0.3 = ■16	6.21 ÷ 0.23 = ■ 27
48 ÷ 3 = ■16	62.1 ÷ 2.3 = ■ 27
480 ÷ 30 = ■16	621 ÷ 23 = ■ 27

When the decimal point is moved the same number of places in the dividend and the divisor, the quotient remains unchanged.

- Describe the pattern that helped you predict the last quotient in each set.
- Look at 4.8 ÷ 0.3. Multiply both numbers by 10. How do the quotients for 4.8 ÷ 0.3 and 48 ÷ 3 compare? How does multiplying the divisor and the dividend by 10 affect the quotient? 4.8 × 10 = 48, 0.3 × 10 = 3; the same; does not affect it

To divide a decimal by a decimal, first multiply the divisor and the dividend by a power of 10 to change the divisor to a whole number.

$$0.7\overline{)62.44} \quad \rightarrow \quad 7\overline{)624.4}$$

THINK: $0.7 \times 10 = 7$

$62.44 \times 10 = 624.4$

EXAMPLE 2

Divide. 22.8 ÷ 0.8

$0.8\overline{)22.8}$

Make the divisor a whole number by multiplying the divisor and dividend by 10.

$0.8 \times 10 = 8 \qquad 22.8 \times 10 = 228$

Place the decimal point in the quotient. Divide.

$$\begin{array}{r} 28.5 \\ 8\overline{)228.0} \\ -16 \\ \hline 68 \\ -64 \\ \hline 40 \\ -40 \\ \hline 0 \end{array}$$

Since there is a remainder, place a zero in the tenths place in the dividend, and continue to divide.

So, 22.8 ÷ 0.8 = 28.5.

- Think about 63.7 ÷ 0.24. To change the divisor to a whole number, you multiply by 100. What does the dividend become? 6,370

77

- *After completing the Activity, emphasize that multiplying both the divisor and the dividend of a division problem by the same number does not change the value of the quotient.*

What is the quotient for 280 ÷ 70? 4

When you multiply both divisor and dividend by 100 to get 2,800 ÷ 700, does the quotient change? No, it is still 4.

- *Discuss the mathematical meaning of moving the decimal point in the divisor and dividend of a division problem.*

A quick way to multiply a decimal by 10 is to move the decimal point one place to the right. If you move the decimal point in 4.58 two places to the right, by what number are you multiplying? 100

If you move the decimal point in 0.674 three places to the right, by what number are you multiplying? 1,000

Example 2, p. 77

Divide. 39.8 ÷ 0.4 99.5

PROBLEM SOLVING 4.4

Divide with Decimals

Write the correct answer.

1. Find the quotient.

$7.4\overline{)153.92}$

20.8

2. Place the decimal point in the quotient.

$235.468 ÷ 8.6 = 2738$

27.38

3. Jacob bought a new computer for $2,124.00. He is paying $88.50 a month for the computer. For how many months will he have to make payments?

24 months

4. Selma needs a new notebook that costs $18.75 and a calculator that costs $23.64. How much money does she need to make the purchases?

$42.39

Choose the letter for the best answer.

5. Which expression is 211.68 ÷ 12.6 rewritten so that the divisor is a whole number?
   A) 2116.8 ÷ 126
   B) 21168 ÷ 126
   C) 211.68 ÷ 126
   D) 21168 ÷ 12.6

6. Which is the exponent form of the expression?

   24 × 24 × 24
   F 3 × 24   H 3²⁴
   G 3³   J) 24³

7. Loraine sleeps between 6 and 8 hours each night. What is a reasonable estimate of the number of minutes she sleeps in a week?
   A Less than 1,500
   B Between 1,500 and 2,500
   C) Between 2,500 and 3,500
   D Between 3,500 and 4,500

8. Hunter saves $3.50 each week to buy a CD boxed set that sells for $52.50. He has already saved $10.50. How many more weeks does he need to save money?
   F 11 weeks
   G) 12 weeks
   H 14 weeks
   J 15 weeks

9. **Write About It** Describe a pattern you see in the set of problems at the right.

   600 ÷ 10 = 60   6 ÷ 10 = 0.6
   60 ÷ 10 = 6   0.6 ÷ 10 = 0.06

   Possible answer: When dividing by 10, you move the decimal point one place to the left.

CHALLENGE 4.4

Decimal Solutions

Find each quotient. Locate the quotient in the Tip Box. (Hint: Not all quotients are in the Tip Box.)
Each time the quotient appears, write the letter of that exercise above it. When you have solved all the problems, you will discover a math tip for dividing decimals.

A 6.3 ÷ 0.05 =	126	N 9.3 ÷ 0.6 =	15.5	
B 50.2 ÷ 0.01 =	5,020	O 0.0024 ÷ 0.3 =	0.008	
C 33.6 ÷ 8 =	4.2	P 8.7 ÷ 17.4 =	0.5	
E 5.4 ÷ 0.02 =	270	Q 28.7 ÷ 8.2 =	3.5	
F 107.91 ÷ 5.5 =	19.62	R 400.98 ÷ 24.6 =	16.3	
G 4.077 ÷ 0.18 =	22.65	S 21.54 ÷ 0.6 =	35.9	
H 9 ÷ 0.3 =	30	T 0.4168 ÷ 8 =	0.0521	
I 1.6 ÷ 0.4 =	4	U 25 ÷ 0.005 =	5,000	
K 5.44 ÷ 1.7 =	3.2	W 0.568 ÷ 0.4 =	1.42	
L 0.192 ÷ 0.3 =	0.64	Y 4.48 ÷ 0.08 =	56	
M 8.05 ÷ 0.7 =	11.5	Z 6.3 ÷ 0.18 =	35	

Tip Box

M	U	L	T	I	P	L	Y		T	O
11.5	5,000	0.64	0.0521	4	0.5	0.64	56		0.0521	0.008

C	H	E	C	K		T	H	E
4.2	30	270	4.2	3.2		0.0521	30	270

A	N	S	W	E	R
126	15.5	35.9	1.42	270	16.3

• *Demonstrate the necessity of sometimes writing a zero in the dividend.*

In Example 3, what would the quotient have been if you had not written the zero in the dividend? 132

Example 3, p. 77

Divide. 663.5 ÷ 0.25 2,654

3 Practice

Guided Practice

Do Check for Understanding Exercises 1–11 with your students. Identify those having difficulty and use lesson resources to help.

COMMON ERROR ALERT

Students may mistakenly move the decimal point all the way to the right in both the divisor and the dividend. Remind them that they must move the decimal point the same number of places in both the divisor and dividend.

Error	Correction
42	4.2
$0.21\overline{)0.882}$	$0.21\overline{)0.882}$

Independent Practice

Assign Exercises 12–41.

Sometimes there aren't enough places in the dividend to move the decimal to the right.

EXAMPLE 3

Divide. 158.4 ÷ 0.12

$$0.\underset{\frown}{12}\overline{)158.\underset{\frown}{40}}$$

Multiply the divisor and dividend by 100.
0.12 × 100 = 12   158.4 × 100 = 15,840
Write a zero in the dividend.

$$\begin{array}{r} 1320 \\ 12\overline{)15840} \\ -12 \\ \hline 38 \\ -36 \\ \hline 24 \\ -24 \\ \hline 00 \end{array}$$

Divide.

Since the remainder is zero, the quotient is a whole number. You do not need to put the decimal point in the answer.

So, 158.4 ÷ 0.12 = 1,320.

CHECK FOR UNDERSTANDING

Think and ▶ Discuss

Look back at the lesson to answer each question.

1. **Explain** how to change the divisor and the dividend before you solve the problem 55.8 ÷ 0.18.   multiply both by 100

2. **Compare** the quotients 4.5 ÷ 1.5 and 45 ÷ 15.
The quotients are the same.

Guided ▶ Practice

Rewrite the problem so that the divisor is a whole number.

3. 9.6 ÷ 1.6
96 ÷ 16

4. 73.6 ÷ 0.5
736 ÷ 5

5. 48.24 ÷ 2.4
482.4 ÷ 24

Copy the problem. Place the decimal point in the quotient.

6. 28.50 ÷ 2.50 = 1140
11.40

7. 34.178 ÷ 2.3 = 1486
14.86

8. 62.44 ÷ 7 = 892
8.92

Divide. Estimate to check.

9. 7.88 ÷ 4 1.97

10. 33.66 ÷ 11 3.06

11. $0.55\overline{)2.42}$ 4.4

PRACTICE AND PROBLEM SOLVING

Independent ▶ Practice

Rewrite the problem so that the divisor is a whole number.

12. 48.4 ÷ 0.4
484 ÷ 4

13. 8.19 ÷ 0.09
819 ÷ 9

14. 3.7 ÷ 2.1
37 ÷ 21

15. 2.39 ÷ 0.05
239 ÷ 5

16. 45.218 ÷ 0.23
4,521.8 ÷ 23

17. 233.58 ÷ 10.2
2,335.8 ÷ 102

Copy the problem. Place the decimal point in the quotient.

18. 325.8 ÷ 3 = 1086
108.6

19. 53.07 ÷ 8.7 = 61
6.1

20. 10.2 ÷ 2 = 51
5.1

21. 84.87 ÷ 12.3 = 69
6.9

22. 274.89 ÷ 1.5 = 18326
183.26

Alternative Teaching Strategy

Purpose Students use play money to model dividing with decimals.

Materials *For each pair* 1 index card; play money—40 pennies

On index cards, write division exercises like the following, one to a card:

$$\begin{array}{r} 6 \\ 0.04\overline{)0.24} \end{array} \qquad \begin{array}{r} 4 \\ 0.06\overline{)0.24} \end{array} \qquad \begin{array}{r} 2 \\ 0.12\overline{)0.24} \end{array}$$

$$\begin{array}{r} 9 \\ 0.03\overline{)0.27} \end{array} \qquad \begin{array}{r} 5 \\ 0.06\overline{)0.30} \end{array} \qquad \begin{array}{r} 13 \\ 0.03\overline{)0.39} \end{array}$$

Display the following: $0.05\overline{)0.35}$

Discuss the meaning of the division with the students. They should realize that they are asked to find how many groups of 5 hundredths there are in 35 hundredths.

Direct the students to model the division using the pennies.

• Show 35 pennies.

• Separate pennies into groups of 5.

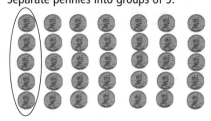

Review how each part of the division was modeled: the dividend was the total number of pennies, the divisor was the number of pennies in each group, and the quotient was the number of groups.

$$\begin{array}{r} 7 \\ 0.05\overline{)0.35} \end{array}$$

Give each pair one of the index cards with a division problem. Have them model the division and record their work. Have the pairs exchange index cards and repeat. Check students' work.

Divide. Estimate to check.

23. $11\overline{)109.01}$ **9.91**   24. $90\overline{)10.8}$ **0.12**   25. $60\overline{)12.6}$ **0.21**

26. $0.38\overline{)13.3}$ **35**   27. $6.41\overline{)135.892}$ **21.2**   28. $38.2\overline{)469.86}$ **12.3**

29. $44.28 \div 5.4$ **8.2**   30. $80.1 \div 9$ **8.9**   31. $90.3 \div 6$ **15.05**

32. $1.26 \div 0.2$ **6.3**   33. $13.2 \div 0.06$ **220**   34. $42.5 \div 0.05$ **850**

Evaluate each expression.

35. $3 - 1.6 \times 0.4$ **2.36**   36. $5 - 2.4 \div 8$ **4.7**   37. $0.09 \div 3 + 3$ **3.03**

Problem Solving ▶ Applications

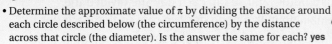

38. Emily rents 5 DVD movies for $28.75. Is the price for one movie closer to $5 or to $6? Explain. **$6; $28.75 ÷ 5 = $5.75**

39. Jonelle saves $4.95 every week to buy a video that costs $29.70. She has already saved $9. For how many more weeks does she need to save money to have enough to buy the video? **5 weeks**

40. **(?) What's the Error?** Michael divided 4.25 by 0.25 and got a quotient of 0.17. Explain the error. What is the correct quotient? **He did not multiply both the divisor and dividend by 100; 17.**

41. Andrew reads 22 pages the first day. He plans to increase the number of pages he reads by 4 a day until he finishes the book. How many pages will he be reading at the end of 3 days? **30 pages**

MIXED REVIEW AND TEST PREP

42. Multiply. 2.051×8.6 (p. 70) **17.6386**

43. Is 208.605 greater than or less than 206.605? (p. 52) **greater than**

44. Use mental math to find $210 \div 42$. (p. 36) **5**

45. **TEST PREP** Which shows the value of r when $18 + r = 52$? (p. 30) **A**

   A 34   **B** 30   **C** 24   **D** 14

46. **TEST PREP** Jocelyn works 12 hours per week. She earns $7.25 an hour. How much does she earn in 4 weeks? (p. 22) **J**

   F $87   **G** $174   **H** $290   **J** $348

Thinker's CORNER

REASONING The ancient Greeks discovered that there is one particular number that can be used to relate the dimensions of any circle. They called this particular number π (pi) and found that it is the same number regardless of the size of the circle.

• Determine the approximate value of π by dividing the distance around each circle described below (the circumference) by the distance across that circle (the diameter). Is the answer the same for each? **yes**

	Circumference	Diameter	
1. Circle 1	6.28 in.	2 in.	**3.14**
2. Circle 2	9.42 in.	3 in.	**3.14**

(Extra Practice) page H35, Set C

79

Algebraic Thinking Before students work on Exercises 35–37, you may want to remind them of the order of operations.

MIXED REVIEW AND TEST PREP
Exercises 42–46 provide **cumulative review** (Chapters 1–4).

Thinker's Corner

• Encourage students to use the table to write a formula for circumference.

Write a formula that the Greeks may have used to find π. $\pi = \dfrac{c}{d}$

Use this formula to write a different formula to show how to find the circumference of a circle. If $c \div d = \pi$, $\pi \times d = c$.

REASONING What number relates the length of a side of a square to the square's perimeter? 4

4 Assess

Summarize the lesson by having students:

DISCUSS Rita paid $1.44 for 3.2 lb of bananas. How much did she pay per pound? $0.45

WRITE Explain why you put a zero in the quotient in Exercise 31. Possible answer: 6 is greater than 3.

Lesson Quiz

Find the quotient.

1. $7.2 \div 12$ 0.6
2. $33.6 \div 7$ 4.8
3. $8.1 \div 0.90$ 9
4. $3.9 \div 0.15$ 26
5. $59.5 \div 2.38$ 25
6. $0.2835 \div 2.7$ 0.105

Transparency 4.4

Problem Solving Skill: *Interpret the Remainder*

LESSON PLANNING

Objective To solve problems by using the skill *interpret the remainder*

Intervention for Prerequisite Skills

Whole Number Operations, Remainders (For intervention strategies, see page 65.)

Lesson Resources Problem Solving Think Along, p. TR1

 California Mathematics Content Standards

○━ NS 2.0 Students calculate and solve problems involving addition, subtraction, multiplication, and division.

MR 3.2 Note the method of deriving the solution and demonstrate a conceptual understanding of the derivation by solving similar problems.

(*Also* MR 2.0, MR 3.1)

Math Background

The remainder can play different roles in division problems.

- Sometimes the remainder is disregarded, such as when you divide 42 pencils evenly among 12 students.

- Sometimes the remainder indicates that you must round up to the next whole number, such as if you want to know how many cars are needed to transport 22 children if 4 children can go in each car and all children must go.

- Sometimes the remainder is the answer, such as if you want to know how many apples will not be shipped if 203 apples are packed 48 to a box for shipping.

It may be helpful for students to draw a diagram of the division problem to help determine the role played by the remainder in each case.

 NUMBER OF THE DAY

Transparency
4.5

Divide your age in months by 12. What does the solution tell you? my age in years and months

 PROBLEM OF THE DAY

Transparency
4.5

Marge had five 32-oz bottles of milk. Monday she drank 6 oz from the first bottle, Tuesday she drank 12 oz from the second bottle, Wednesday she drank 18 oz from the third bottle, and so on. Each day she divided the remaining milk among her five cats so that each got a whole number of ounces. She saved the remainder. On the sixth day, she drank what was left. How much did she drink on Day 6? 10 oz

Solution Problem of the Day tab, p. PD4

 DAILY FACTS PRACTICE

Have students practice addition and subtraction facts by completing Set F of *Teacher's Resource Book*, p. TR95.

INTERVENTION AND EXTENSION RESOURCES

ALTERNATIVE TEACHING STRATEGY

Materials 6 index cards

Reinforce students' ability to **interpret remainders**. On each of 6 index cards, write a word problem such as this:

Mitch has $15. Batteries cost $2. How many can Mitch buy?
7 batteries

Call on a volunteer to read the problem and then ask students to solve. Ask: What is the remainder? What does the remainder represent? $1; the amount of money Mitch has left over

Repeat with other word problems in which the remainder might be the answer or might tell students that another bus or box, for instance, is needed. Check students' work.

AUDITORY

ENGLISH LANGUAGE LEARNERS (ELL•SDAIE)

To help students learn the **vocabulary of division,** bring a group of 10 students to the front of the class. Ask them to group themselves into 3 equal groups. Use word cards or sentence strips and have students identify the terms *dividend, divisor, quotient,* and *remainder*. 10 students, 3 groups, 3 students, 1 student

Ask:

- If you are riding a roller coaster in cars that hold 3 people, how many cars would you need? 4 cars
- How many would be in the fourth car? 1 student
- If the park attendant must fill each car, what does the remainder tell you? One person must ride with two other people to form a new group of three.

KINESTHETIC

READING STRATEGY

Use Context Tell students to look for words and phrases in a problem-solving situation to help them decide how to interpret the remainder. Have students identify the words or phrases in each of the three situations given on page 80 that give them information about how to interpret the remainder. How many packages will Ms. Gordon need to buy?; How many lengths will Ms. Gordon have?; How many (left-over) prizes were given?

ADVANCED LEARNERS

Challenge students to apply what they've learned about **interpreting remainders.** Have them work in pairs to write a division exercise with a remainder.

- Direct one of the students to select a number between 10 and 50 to use as a dividend and the other student to select a number between 1 and 10 to use as a divisor.
- Then, have students write two word problems based on their division exercise in which the remainder in each problem is interpreted differently. Check students' work.

VISUAL

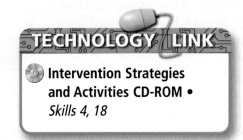

TECHNOLOGY LINK

Intervention Strategies and Activities CD-ROM • *Skills 4, 18*

LESSON 4.5 ORGANIZER

Objective To solve problems by using the skill *interpret the remainder*

Lesson Resources Problem Solving Think Along, p. TR1

1 Introduce

QUICK REVIEW provides review of pre-requisite skills.

Why Learn This? Interpreting remainders will help you know that you have a sufficient number of packaged party favors for a given number of guests. *Share the lesson objective with students.*

2 Teach

Guided Instruction

• *Call on a volunteer to read each problem on page 80, and discuss the solutions.*

How many drinks would Ms. Gordon have if she bought 27 packages? Is that enough? 162 drinks; no

How do you use the remainder 1? The remainder tells you that you will need to buy another package.

REASONING **How are the remainders different in the second and third problems?** In the second problem you do not need the remainder, but in the third problem it is the answer.

Does the remainder in the second problem refer to 6 ribbons or 6 feet of ribbon? 6 feet
What portion of an 8-foot length of ribbon would Ms. Gordon have left over? $\frac{3}{4}$

LESSON 4.5

PROBLEM SOLVING SKILL
Interpret the Remainder

Analyze
Choose
Solve
Check

Learn how to interpret the remainder in a division problem.

QUICK REVIEW

1. $6\overline{)480}$ 80   2. $8\overline{)656}$ 82   3. $7\overline{)1,047}$ 149 r4   4. $3\overline{)1,305}$ 435
5. 142 boxes ÷ 14 shelves = 10 shelves with ■ boxes left 2

The sixth-grade class at Hightown Middle School has an annual class picnic. With the help of some students, Ms. Gordon is planning for the picnic this year.

Ms. Gordon needs 163 boxed drinks for lunch. A package holds 6 boxes. How many packages of drinks will Ms. Gordon need to buy?	$\begin{array}{r} 27\ r1 \\ 6\overline{)163} \\ -12 \\ \hline 43 \\ -42 \\ \hline 1 \end{array}$	Since 27 packages hold only 162 total boxes, increase the quotient by 1. So, Ms. Gordon needs to buy 28 packages of drinks.
Ms. Gordon has 158 ft of ribbon to use for games. She will cut the ribbon into 8-ft lengths. How many 8-ft lengths of ribbon will Ms. Gordon have?	$\begin{array}{r} 19\ r6 \\ 8\overline{)158} \\ -8 \\ \hline 78 \\ -72 \\ \hline 6 \end{array}$	The remainder is not enough for another 8-ft length of ribbon. Drop the remainder. So, Ms. Gordon will have 19 pieces of ribbon.
Students collected 158 prizes. The prizes were put in packages of 5 each. The remaining prizes were given to another class in the school. How many prizes were given to the other class?	$\begin{array}{r} 31\ r3 \\ 5\overline{)158} \\ -15 \\ \hline 8 \\ -5 \\ \hline 3 \end{array}$	The remainder is your answer. So, 3 prizes were given to the other class.

Talk About It ▶
• What does the remainder in the first problem mean?
1 more boxed drink will be needed; 27 packages are not enough.
• **What if** Ms. Gordon buys 28 packages of boxed drinks? How many extra boxed drinks will Ms. Gordon buy?
5 extra boxed drinks
• **What if** Ms. Gordon has a total of 165 ft of ribbon? How many 8-ft lengths of ribbon will she have? How long is the ribbon that's too short? **20 lengths; 5 ft**

80

CALIFORNIA STANDARDS O—п**NS 2.0** Students calculate and solve problems involving addition, subtraction, multiplication, and division. **MR 3.2** Note the method of deriving the solution and demonstrate a conceptual understanding of the derivation by solving similar problems. *also* **MR 2.0, MR 3.1**

RETEACH 4.5

Problem Solving Skill: Interpret the Remainder

When you solve a problem using division, there is often a remainder. When there is a remainder, you must decide what it means for the problem. You need to determine whether the solution to the problem is

• the quotient without the remainder,
• the next whole number greater than the quotient,
• the next whole number less than the quotient, or
• the remainder.

A real-estate agent ordered 190 doughnuts for an open house. The Donut Shoppe packed the order in boxes of 12 doughnuts. How many boxes were needed?

Step 1: Think about what you know and what you are asked to find.
• You know the number of doughnuts ordered and the number that were put in each box.
• You are asked to find the number of boxes that were needed.

Step 2: Decide on a plan to solve.
• Since the same number of doughnuts were put into each box, use division to solve the problem.
• Examine the quotient and remainder and decide how they relate to the problem.

Step 3: Carry out the plan.
$$\begin{array}{r} 15\ r10 \\ 12\overline{)190} \end{array}$$
The quotient 15 means that 15 boxes were filled. The remainder 10 means that there were 10 doughnuts left after the last full box was packed.

So, the Donut Shoppe needed 15 + 1, or 16 boxes in all, to pack the agent's 190 doughnuts.

Interpret the remainder to solve.

1. A school received a shipment of 166 new social studies textbooks. The textbooks had been packed into cartons with 12 books in each full carton. How many cartons were delivered to the school?
14 cartons (13 full cartons, 1 with 10 books)

2. In the school science laboratory, students generally work in groups of 4. Extra students are divided among the groups to make some groups of 5. If there are 27 students in a class, how many groups will have 5 students?
3 groups (out of 6)

PRACTICE 4.5

Problem Solving Skill: Interpret the Remainder

Solve the problem by interpreting the remainder.

1. Thirty-seven people are attending a party at a restaurant. In the banquet room, the restaurant staff has set up tables that can each seat 8 people. What is the least number of tables that the group will use?
5 tables

2. There are 23 pancakes on the griddle at a restaurant. The chef places 4 pancakes on each order. How many orders can the chef fill, and how many pancakes must be added to those remaining to make another order?
5 orders; 1 pancake

3. A library reading room contains a number of tables that can seat 4 people. What is the least number of tables needed to seat 54 people?
14 tables

4. A group of 5 friends wants to buy snacks. If each snack costs $0.75 and they have a total of $4.80 to spend, how many snacks can they buy?
6 snacks

5. The chef at a restaurant uses 3 eggs to make each omelet. If the chef has 200 eggs, how many 3-egg omelets can he make?
66 omelets

6. A total of 125 hamburgers were sold at a fund-raiser at the last football game. If the hamburger patties came in packages of 8, how many packages were opened?
16 packages

Mixed Review

Estimate the sum or difference. Possible estimates are given.

7.	8.	9.	10.
$\begin{array}{r} 671 \\ +902 \\ \hline 1,600 \end{array}$	$\begin{array}{r} 478 \\ -310 \\ \hline 200 \end{array}$	$\begin{array}{r} 831 \\ -289 \\ \hline 500 \end{array}$	$\begin{array}{r} 1,226 \\ +533 \\ \hline 1,700 \end{array}$
11.	12.	13.	14.
$\begin{array}{r} 661 \\ +2,403 \\ \hline 3,100 \end{array}$	$\begin{array}{r} 1,729 \\ -494 \\ \hline 1,200 \end{array}$	$\begin{array}{r} 488 \\ -391 \\ \hline 100 \end{array}$	$\begin{array}{r} 2,994 \\ +1,258 \\ \hline 4,000 \end{array}$

Solve each equation by using mental math.

15. $m + 12 = 15$ 16. $5w = 20$ 17. $x - 7 = 8$ 18. $q + 4 = 10 + 6$
$m = 3$ **$w = 4$**   **$x = 15$**   **$q = 12$**
19. $6r = 24$ 20. $y - 9 = 10$ 21. $a - 2 = 8 + 6$ 22. $d + 3 = 21 - 7$
$r = 4$ **$y = 19$**   **$a = 16$**   **$d = 11$**

Solve the problem by interpreting the remainder.

A total of 39 students and adults tour the science museum to see an exhibit about the shaping of the Earth's surface. The tour director can take groups of up to 5 on each tour. All 39 students and adults need to see the exhibit.

1. How many complete groups of 5 people can the tour director take? **C**

   A 5 groups **B** 6 groups **C** 7 groups **D** 8 groups

2. What is the least number of tours the director will have to give to accommodate all 39 students? **H**

   F 6 groups **G** 7 groups **H** 8 groups **J** 9 groups

3. James has $4.39 to buy magnets at the science museum. Each magnet costs $0.95. He wants to buy as many magnets as he can. How many magnets can James buy? **4 magnets**

4. Sharon bought a package of 15 postcards at the museum. She gave the same number of postcards to each of her 4 teachers and kept the ones left over. How many postcards did Sharon keep? **Possible answers: 3, 7, 11, or 15 postcards**

MIXED APPLICATIONS

5. A train that is scheduled to arrive at 5:15 P.M. arrives 20 minutes late. If the train left at 9:30 A.M., how long was the trip? **8 hr 5 min**

6. A total of 51 students and teachers are using cars to go on a field trip. Six people ride in each car. How many cars are needed for the field trip? **9 cars**

7. Mark estimates that he needs 1 minute to solve a short homework problem and 5 minutes for each long problem. If he has 25 short and 8 long problems, how long should his homework take? **65 min, or 1 hr 5 min**

8. Tina makes bracelets for her friends. She uses 3 red beads for every 7 yellow beads to make a pattern. For one bracelet, she uses a total of 50 beads. How many of each color does she use? **15 red, 35 yellow**

9. A board game has 3 times as many red playing pieces as blue. It has 5 times as many green pieces as blue. There are 12 blue pieces. How many playing pieces are there in all? **108 pieces**

10. Edgar has twice as many library books as his brother. If Edgar has 10 books in all, how many library books must he return to have the same number as his brother? **5 library books**

11. **?** **What's the Question?** Use the table at the right. Each Presidential term in office is 4 years. The answer is that he served more than one term but less than two.
   Possible question: How many terms did Richard Nixon serve?

United States Presidents

President	Years in Office
Richard Nixon	1969-1974
Gerald Ford	1974-1977
Jimmy Carter	1977-1981
Ronald Reagan	1981-1989
George Bush	1989-1993

81

---

3 Practice

Guided Practice

Do Problem Solving Practice Exercises 1–4 with your students. Identify those having difficulty and use lesson resources to help.

Independent Practice

Assign Exercises 5–11.

For students who have limited reading skills, it may be helpful to have them draw pictures that show some of the information given in the problems as you read them aloud. For example, for Exercise 5 have students draw clocks showing the start and end times for the train. For Exercise 8 have them draw the beads.

4 Assess

Summarize the lesson by having students:

DISCUSS Describe how Exercises 3 and 4 are alike and how they are different.
Possible answer: They are alike because you divide to solve each; they are different in the role the remainder plays in the answer.

WRITE Describe three ways you can use a remainder. Possible answer: It can be the answer, it can be ignored, or it can help decide what the answer is.

Lesson Quiz

Transparency 4.5

1. Trent has invited 26 friends to a cookout. He wants 2 hot dogs for each friend, and hot dogs come in packages of 8. How many packages should he buy? 7 packages

2. Sharlene is making ribbon decorations for the party. Each one takes 18 inches of ribbon. How many decorations can she make from 100 inches of ribbon? 5 decorations

---

READING STRATEGY 4.5

Use Context

Analyze Choose Solve Check

If there is a word, phrase, or paragraph you do not understand, context can help you. **Context** means the words, phrases, pictures, or graphic aids that go along with what you are reading. Context can help you decide how to interpret the remainder.

VOCABULARY
context

Read the following problem.

Thirty-eight sixth graders are going to see a band from Puerto Rico that specializes in Caribbean music. Each driver can take 4 students. How many drivers are needed?

1. Use context to help you decide how to treat the remainder, if there is one. If there is a remainder, should you add 1 to the quotient, drop the remainder, or use it as the answer? Why?

   Whether or not the students fill every car, they still must be
   transported. Add 1 to the quotient.

2. Solve the problem.
   38 ÷ 4 = 9 R2; 10 drivers

Solve the problem. Use context to help you decide how to interpret the remainder.

3. The band needs 40 minutes of music to make 1 CD. The songs they know last for 2 hours and 42 minutes. How many CDs could they cut now?
   4 CDs

4. Alexis Rivera wants to take some friends to the concert. She has $135 and each ticket costs $30. How many tickets can she buy?
   4 tickets

5. The concert was attended by 1,000 people. If there were 36 seats in a row, how many rows could have been filled?
   27 rows

6. The band has 5,000 copies of their new CD. If 73 music stores each get the same number of copies of the CD, how many CDs will be left over?
   36 CDs

7. How many containers for 1 dozen eggs are needed for 2,000 eggs?
   167 containers

8. If 25 books fit on a shelf, how many shelves are needed for 465 books?
   19 shelves

CHALLENGE 4.5

Interpret the Remainder

In each problem, explain the mistake in reasoning that was made. Describe how the mistake might have been avoided. **Possible answers given.**

1. All 159 sixth grade students at McKinley Middle School and their 7 teachers are going on a trip. The principal ordered 5 buses that could each carry 31 passengers. He planned to use a school van that could carry 8 passengers as transportation for those people who would not have seats on the bus.

   The 5 buses could carry 155 of the 166 people, leaving 11 people, not 8.
   The principal could have planned for 6 buses.

2. A farmer is putting up a new fence that will measure 64 feet long. He wants to place fence posts 8 feet apart, beginning at one end, to support the fencing. He orders 8 fence posts.

   The farmer needs 9, not 8, posts. Instead of dividing 64 by 8, he could
   have drawn a diagram to find the number of posts needed.

3. Margo and her sister have $10.00 to spend on cards. The cards Margo has chosen cost $0.95 each. She tells her sister they can buy 11 cards with the money they have. They stand in line to pay for the 11 cards.

   Margo and her sister do not have enough money. $10.00 divided by
   $0.95 is 10 r50. The remainder means they only have $0.50 left. This
   is not enough to buy another card.

4. Eighty-five teenagers have come to register for a new baseball league. Each team will have 9 members. The organizers of the league tell the teens that as soon as 4 more people arrive, they will have exactly enough players for everyone to be assigned to a team.

   85 ÷ 9 = 9 r4; The organizers thought the remainder meant 4 more
   players were needed, but the remainder meant those not on a team, so,
   5 more players are needed.

Algebra: Decimal Expressions and Equations

LESSON PLANNING

Objective To evaluate expressions with decimals and to use mental math and substitution to solve equations with decimals

Intervention for Prerequisite Skills

Whole Number Operations (For intervention strategies, see page 65.)

California Mathematics Content Standards

AF 1.0 Students write verbal expressions and sentences as algebraic expressions and equations; they evaluate algebraic expressions, solve simple linear equations, and graph and interpret their results.

○ᴨ AF 1.1 Write and solve one-step linear equations in one variable.

(*Also* ○ᴨ NS 2.0)

Math Background

Students use the same skills to evaluate expressions involving decimals and solve decimal equations as they used with whole numbers. As you help students solve problems involving decimal expressions and equations, remind them of the following:

- An algebraic expression may have different values, depending on the number substituted for the variable.

- To evaluate an algebraic expression, replace the variable with a number and perform the indicated operation or operations.

- An equation has one solution. Determine if a number is a solution to an equation by substituting it into the equation. Then simplify. It is a solution if the resulting statement is true.

WARM-UP RESOURCES

 NUMBER OF THE DAY Transparency **4.6**

Write an expression that will give you the part of an hour that has passed so far this hour. $\frac{n}{60}$, where n is the number of minutes past the hour

 PROBLEM OF THE DAY Transparency **4.6**

Lashonda and Mark each have the same number of coins. Lashonda has $8.25 in quarters. Mark has all dimes. How much more money does Lashonda have than Mark? Lashonda has $4.95 more than Mark.

Solution Problem of the Day tab, p. PD4

 DAILY FACTS PRACTICE

Have students practice multiplication and division facts by completing Set G of *Teacher's Resource Book*, p. TR95.

INTERVENTION AND EXTENSION RESOURCES

ALTERNATIVE TEACHING STRATEGY

Display a list of equations on the left and a list of number sentences students can use to **solve the equations** on the right. For example:

$3 \times a = 0.9$ 0.3 $9.26 - 5.2 = 4.06$

$5.2 + c = 9.26$ 4.06 $1.5 \times 3 = 4.5$

$d \div 3 = 1.5$ 4.5 $10.4 + 5.2 = 15.6$

$l - 5.2 = 10.4$ 15.6 $0.9 \div 3 = 0.3$

Have students copy the equations on paper and then match the equation on the left with the number sentence on the right that helps solve the equation. Have volunteers explain their thinking and show that solutions check.

VISUAL

MIXED REVIEW AND TEST PREP

Cumulative Review Chapters 1–4

Refer to the Pupil Edition pages referenced in the exercises for further review. Have students go to the lesson page, review the lesson, and correct any problem they missed.

Mixed Review and Test Prep, p. 83

How to Help	
Item	Page
24	76
25	44
26	20
27	52
28	26

ENGLISH LANGUAGE LEARNERS ELL•SDAIE

Materials 9 index cards

Help students **understand how to evaluate an expression.** Write each number, operation, and variable on an index card: 3.2, +, x, 1.6, 4.8, 4.1, 7.3, 10.5, 13.7

Give three students the cards for +, 3.2, and x. Place them in the front of the room to form the expression $x + 3.2$. Then distribute the remaining cards to other students.

Ask students to evaluate the expression for $x = 1.6$. The student holding the card 1.6 should come to the front of the room and replace the student holding the x. Have students evaluate the expressions and then have the student with the 4.8 card show it.

Repeat the activity for these values of the variable 4.1 and 10.5. 7.3 and 13.7

KINESTHETIC

SCIENCE CONNECTION

Encourage students to **practice evaluating expressions.** Tell them that the distance a glacier flows in 52 weeks can be determined by substituting the rate of flow into the expression $52r$. Have students find the distance each of the following glaciers would flow in a year.

Alpine glacier

17.7 yd/wk   920.4 yd

Greenland glacier

54.9 yd/wk   2,854.8 yd

Antarctic glacier

84.6 yd/wk   4,399.2 yd

Extend the activity by having students write an expression to show each distance d as miles. HINT: 1 mi = 1,760 yd. To find the distance in miles, use the expression $\frac{d}{1,760}$.

VISUAL

Intervention Strategies and Activities CD-ROM • *Skill 4*

Objective To evaluate expressions with decimals and to use mental math and substitution to solve equations with decimals

1 Introduce

QUICK REVIEW provides review of pre-requisite skills.

Why Learn This? Solving decimal expressions and equations using mental math will prepare you for algebra and more complex problems. *Share the lesson objective with students.*

2 Teach

Guided Instruction

• *Review the meaning of the terms* numerical expression *and* algebraic expression.

Give an example of a numerical expression involving two decimals. Possible answer: $3.2 + 5.6$

Give an example of an algebraic expression containing a decimal. Possible answer: $4.5 \times s$

• *As students look at the first expression on page 82, ask:*

Why is the *a* replaced by the 7? 7 people ate lunch and we need to evaluate the expression for $a = 7$.

• *As students finish Example 1, ask:*

What operation will you use to find *t*? Explain. subtraction; you think what number added to $4.24 = 9.48$.

REASONING **What do you know about the relationship of *n* to 15.3 in the equation $n - 10.4 = 15.3$? Explain.** Possible answer: The variable n is greater than 15.3 because you subtract 10.4 to get 15.3.

Algebraic Thinking Substituting values for variables in expressions helps students become comfortable with the idea that variables stand for numbers. This will make the transition to solving for variables easier.

ADDITIONAL EXAMPLE

Example, p. 82

Solve the equation $n \div 5 = 0.3$ by using mental math. $n = 1.5$

Decimal Expressions and Equations

Learn how to evaluate expressions and solve equations with decimals.

Different groups of friends eat lunch together at a cafe. The cost of the lunch is $6.45 per person. Write an expression to find the total cost of a lunch for a group of friends.

Let a be the number of friends buying lunch.

$a \times 6.45$ or $6.45a$ *Write the expression.*

The number of friends varies. What is the total cost for 7 friends?

$a \times 6.45$ *Write the expression.*

7×6.45 *Replace a with 7.*

45.15 *Multiply.*

So, the total cost is $45.15.

• Evaluate the expression $w \div 3 + 9.3$ for $w = 4.8$. **10.9**

You solved equations with whole numbers by using mental math. You can use the same methods to solve some equations with decimals.

EXAMPLE

Solve the equation $h \div 6 = 0.6$ by using mental math.

$h \div 6 = 0.6$ *What number divided by 6 = 0.6?*

$h = 3.6$ THINK: $6 \times 0.6 = 3.6$.

$3.6 \div 6 = 0.6$ *Check your answer. Replace h with 3.6.*
$0.6 = 0.6$

So, $h = 3.6$.

• Solve. $t + 4.24 = 9.48$ $t = 5.24$

82

RETEACH 4.6

Algebra: Decimal Expressions and Equations

You speak and write using words, for example

  the number of days in a week times the number of weeks

Some words can be expressed as numbers or numerical expressions.

  days × weeks
    7×5

An algebraic expression uses a letter to represent a number. For example, if the number of weeks is written as the letter w, the algebraic expression is $7 \times w$.

It can also be written as $7w$.

To evaluate the expression $7w$ to find the number of days in 8 weeks, write $7 \times 8 = 56$.

Match the algebraic expression with the words.

1. number of inches in a foot times the number of feet   C
2. number of items in a dozen plus some more items   A
3. sum of money divided among several people   D
4. total amount of money less the amount spent   B

A	$12 + s$
B	$\$25 - d$
C	$12n$
D	$\$25 \div p$

Solve using mental math.

5. How much is $6y$ if $y = 3$? **18**   6. How much is $8 + r$ if $r = 9$? **17**
7. How much is $24 \div t$ if $t = 3$? **8**   8. How much is $35 - a$ if $a = 15$? **20**
9. How much is $4.5 - q$ if $q = 1.9$? **2.6**   10. How much is $5b$ if $b = 1.1$? **5.5**
11. How much is $3.6 \div z$ if $z = 3$? **1.2**   12. How much is $2.4 + c$ if $c = 4.2$? **6.6**

Evaluate each expression.

13. $5m$ for $m = 3.3$ 14. $w \div 2$ for $w = 8.4$ 15. $y + 12.4$ for $y = 5.2$
   16.5   **4.2**   **17.6**
16. $7.4 - b$ for $b = 1.3$ 17. $6x$ for $x = 2.5$ 18. $m - 4.6$ for $m = 8.9$
   6.1   **15**   **4.3**

PRACTICE 4.6

Algebra: Decimal Expressions and Equations

Evaluate each expression.

1. $t - 1.2$ for $t = 3$ 2. $y + 4.6$ for $y = 2.4$ 3. $8.2 - m$ for $m = 1.1$
   1.8   **7**   **7.1**
4. $2.4 \div a$ for $a = 6$ 5. $6g$ for $g = 1.5$ 6. $j - 6.3$ for $j = 9.6$
   0.4   **9**   **3.3**
7. $12.6 + r$ for $r = 4.4$ 8. $4.5 + p$ for $p = 9$ 9. $7.24 - q$ for $q = 1.04$
   17   **0.5**   **6.20 or 6.2**
10. $6.18 \div y$ for $y = 3$ 11. $t + 4.66$ for $t = 2.1$ 12. $5h$ for $h = 2.4$
   2.06   **6.76**   **12**

Solve each equation by using mental math.

13. $w + 4.5 = 8$ 14. $\frac{k}{3} = 2.5$ 15. $1.4 = \frac{t}{2}$
   w = 3.5   **k = 7.5**   **t = 2.8**
16. $m - 7.6 = 2.4$ 17. $3a = 6.9$ 18. $9c = 22.5$
   m = 10   **a = 2.3**   **c = 2.5**
19. $3b = 6.4 + 2.6$ 20. $w + 10.3 = 21.7$ 21. $13.7 = d - 3.4$
   b = 3   **w = 11.4**   **d = 17.1**
22. $4.8 = \frac{n}{4}$ 23. $\frac{x}{5} = 19.5$ 24. $7h = 15.4$
   n = 19.2   **x = 97.5**   **h = 2.2**

Mixed Review

Estimate. Possible estimates are given.

25. $6.9 + 7.8$ 26. 31.77×6 27. $63.85 \div 8$ 28. $17.04 - 9.8$
  15   **180**   **8**   **7**
29. $18.58 + 21.44$ 30. 91.92×4 31. $54.3 - 19.7$ 32. $80.8 \div 9.2$
  40   **360**   **34**   **9**

Find the quotient.

33. $88.8 \div 6$ 34. $59.4 \div 36$ 35. $38.88 \div 7.2$ 36. $31.108 \div 2.2$
  14.8   **1.65**   **5.4**   **14.14**

CHECK FOR UNDERSTANDING

Think and ▶ Discuss

Look back at the lesson to answer each question.

1. **What if** 12 friends went to lunch at the cafe? Show how you would find the total cost of the lunch. **$a \times 6.45$; 12×6.45; $77.40**

2. **Explain** how you would solve the equation $3.2 = a \div 2$.
   Possible answer: THINK: $6.4 \div 2 = 3.2$, so $a = 6.4$

Guided ▶ Practice

Evaluate each expression.

3. $a + 3.4$ **11.7**
   for $a = 8.3$

4. $1.6 \div b$ **4**
   for $b = 0.4$

5. $9.16 - a$ **5.08**
   for $a = 4.08$

Solve each equation by using mental math.

6. $\dfrac{4.8}{k} = 8$
   $k = 0.6$

7. $m - 12.7 = 6.3$
   $m = 19$

8. $3t = 21.9$
   $t = 7.3$

PRACTICE AND PROBLEM SOLVING

Independent ▶ Practice

Evaluate each expression.

9. $2h$ **4.6**
   for $h = 2.3$

10. $9.6 \div a$ **3.2**
    for $a = 3$

11. $j + 7.1$ **14**
    for $j = 6.9$

12. $4.17 - c$ **3.08**
    for $c = 1.09$

13. $m \div 6 + 3.6$ **3.9**
    for $m = 1.8$

14. $g + h - 3.2$
    for $g = 4.1$ and
    $h = 2.3$ **3.2**

Solve each equation by using mental math.

15. $r + 8.1 = 15.8$
    $r = 7.7$

16. $1.7 = \dfrac{d}{4}$
    $d = 6.8$

17. $4a = 32.8$
    $a = 8.2$

18. $x - 2.4 = 8.6$
    $x = 11$

19. $p + 11.1 = 28.7$
    $p = 17.6$

20. $3.2r = 7.1 + 5.7$
    $r = 4$

Problem Solving ▶ Applications

21. Let n represent the number of miles Jeremy rides his bicycle to attend 6 baseball practices. Write an expression to show how far he travels for one practice. Evaluate the expression for $n = 28.8$ mi.
    $n \div 6$; $n = 4.8$

22. **What's the Error?** Explain the error at the right. Give the correct solution. **24.8 should not be added to 30 to find the value of x; $x = 5.2$**

$24.8 + x = 30$
$x = 54.8$

23. David jogs 3 mi each weekday and 7 mi each Saturday. Ray jogs 18 mi each week. How much farther does David jog in a week? **4 mi**

MIXED REVIEW AND TEST PREP

24. $4.38 \div 7.5$ (p. 76)
    0.584

25. $18 \div 6 + (16 \times 3) - 14$ (p. 44)
    37

26. $6,045 - 973$ (p. 20)
    5,072

27. Order from least to greatest. 3.58, 3.08, 3.85, 3.508 (p. 52) **3.08, 3.508, 3.58, 3.85**

28. **TEST PREP** The sum of two numbers is 35. Their difference is less than 10. Which is not a possible pair? (p. 26) **C**

   A 15, 20   **B** 17, 18   **C** 10, 25   **D** 22, 13

Extra Practice page H35, Set D

83

---

3 Practice

Guided Practice

Do Check for Understanding Exercises 1–8 with your students. Identify those having difficulty and use lesson resources to help.

/// COMMON ERROR ALERT \\\

When using mental math to solve equations, students may use an incorrect operation to solve. That is, in solving $t + 4.24 = 9.48$, they may add 4.24 to 9.48 instead of subtracting it. The best way to catch these errors is to check. So, constantly encourage students to substitute each answer in its equation to verify the solution.

Independent Practice

Assign Exercises 9–23.

As students evaluate expressions, have them write the number for the variable on a small piece of paper and place it over the variable in the expression to see it as a numerical expression.

MIXED REVIEW AND TEST PREP

Exercises 24–28 provide **cumulative review** (Chapters 1–4).

4 Assess

Summarize the lesson by having students:

DISCUSS What operation did you use to solve Exercise 21? **Explain.** division; n is the total miles traveled for 6 practices.

WRITE Explain how to solve an equation such as $5 \times f = 30.5$.
Possible answer: I want a number that gives 30.5 when multiplied by 5, so I can use the related sentence $30.5 \div 5 = 6.1$. Then I check by writing 6.1 in the place of f and multiplying.

Lesson Quiz

Evaluate each expression for $n = 0.5$.

Transparency **4.6**

1. $n + 0.88$ **1.38**   2. $n - 0.02$ **0.48**

3. $3 \times n$ **1.5**   4. $n \div 0.25$ **2**

Solve for the variable.

5. $3 \times a = 4.8$ $a = 1.6$

6. $b - 1.1 = 12$ $b = 13.1$

7. $y + 4.2 = 5.8$ $y = 1.6$

PROBLEM SOLVING 4.6

Algebra: Decimal Expressions and Equations   Analyze Choose Solve Check

Write the correct answer.

1. Each child's meal at a fast-food restaurant costs $2.79. What is the greatest number of these meals that can be bought with $20.00?

   7 meals

2. Felipe is a teenager who is 10 years older than his sister Irene. In 6 years, Felipe will be twice as old as his sister. How old is Felipe now?

   14 years old

3. The winning car in a race had an average speed of 203.7 miles per hour. This was b miles per hour faster than the second-place car. Write an expression for the average speed of the second-place car.

   $203.7 - b$

4. The round-trip distance between Kaitlin's house and her school is 3.2 miles. Kaitlin rides her bike to school 3 days per week. Write an expression that can be used to find the number of miles Kaitlin rides in w weeks.

   $9.6w$

Choose the letter for the best answer.

5. At a self-service copy center, the cost of making copies is $0.08 per copy for the first 100 copies, $0.06 per copy for copies 101–200, and $0.05 per copy for any above 200. Stan needs to make 7 copies of a 30-page report. How much should he expect to pay?

   A $16.80   C $12.60
   B $14.50   D $10.50

6. Marla poured out g glasses of juice for a party she is hosting. If each glass contained 0.2 liter of juice, which expression describes the total amount of juice she poured?

   (F) $0.2g$ H $\dfrac{g}{0.2}$
   G $\dfrac{0.2}{g}$ J $0.2 + g$

7. After driving 159.7 miles, Rasheed had r miles left to travel. If the total distance he needed to travel was 201.3 miles, which equation can you use to find the value of r?

   A $r = 159.7 + 201.3$
   B $r + 201.3 = 159.7$
   C $159.7r = 201.3$
   (D) $201.3 - r = 159.7$

8. At a school cafeteria, 6 carrot sticks are served with each lunch order. Carrot sticks are purchased in bags of 120. If 310 lunches were served today, how many bags of carrots were opened?

   F 13 bags
   G 14 bags
   H 15 bags
   (J) 16 bags

9. **Write About It** Describe how you decided which operation was needed to find the total distance Kaitlin rides in w weeks in Problem 4.

   Possible answer: Since she rides the same distance each day, multiply to find the number of miles per week. Since she rides the same distance each week, multiply to find the total distance in w weeks.

CHALLENGE 4.6

Match Up

Match each description with its expression.

1. The cost of 3 shirts and 2 sweaters if each shirt costs s dollars and each sweater costs w dollars   **f**

2. The difference between the distances traveled on 3 days of driving and 2 days of walking if the distance driven each day is s miles, and the distance walked each day is w miles, and s is greater than w **d**

3. The total number of hours studied if you study s hours for 2 weeks and w hours for 3 weeks   **e**

4. The total distance run in training for a race if you run w miles per week for 3 weeks   **c**

5. The price paid for one apple if you pay w dollars for 3 apples   **a**

6. The difference between the greater amount you will earn in May if you work 3 weeks earning w dollars per week and the amount you will earn in June if you work 2 weeks earning s dollars per week   **j**

7. The total number of pages you study if you study 3 pages per hour for w hours and one page per hour for s hours   **h**

8. The price you pay for one container of juice and one container of milk if juice costs w dollars for 3 containers and milk costs s dollars per container   **b**

9. The number of miles you can drive on 3 tanks of gas if your car averages s miles per tankful   **g**

10. The cost of 2 entrees and 1 salad at a restaurant if each entree costs w dollars and salads cost s dollars for 3 salads   **k**

   a. $\dfrac{w}{3}$
   b. $\dfrac{w}{3} + s$
   c. $3w$
   d. $3s - 2w$
   e. $2s + 3w$
   f. $3s + 2w$
   g. $3s$
   h. $3w + s$
   j. $3w - 2s$
   k. $2w + \dfrac{s}{3}$

83

CHAPTER 4

REVIEW/TEST

Purpose To check understanding of concepts, skills, and problem solving presented in Chapter 4

USING THE PAGE

The Chapter 4 Review/Test can be used as a **review** or a **test**.

- Items 1–38 check skill proficiency.
- Items 39–40 check students' abilities to choose and apply problem solving strategies to real-life problems involving operations with decimals.

 Suggest that students place the completed Chapter 4 Review/Test in their portfolios.

USING THE ASSESSMENT GUIDE

- Multiple-choice format of Chapter 4 Posttest—See *Assessment Guide*, pp. AG21–22.
- Free-response format of Chapter 4 Posttest— See *Assessment Guide*, pp. AG23–24.

USING STUDENT SELF-ASSESSMENT

The How Did I Do? survey helps students assess what they have learned and how they learned it. This survey is available as a copying master in *Assessment Guide*, p. AGxvii.

Add or subtract. Estimate to check. (pp. 66–69)

1.
```
   3.9
   4
 +5.91
 ─────
 13.81
```

2.
```
   7.6
 −0.95
 ─────
  6.65
```

3.
```
   3.02
   0.17
 +4.338
 ──────
  7.528
```

4. $19.3 - 2.56$ 16.74   5. $0.126 + 5.3 + 3.04$ 8.466   6. $245 - 39.05$ 205.95

Tell the number of decimal places there will be in the product. Then multiply. (pp. 70–73)

7.
```
    8.3
  ×12.9
```
2; 107.07

8.
```
   7.82
 ×  4.5
```
3; 35.190

9.
```
   0.13
 ×2.07
```
4; 0.2691

10.
```
   53.6
 ×1.23
```
3; 65.928

11. 20.01×8.2 3; 164.082   12. 6.9×17.4 2; 120.06   13. 4.91×6.2 3; 30.442   14. 7.02×5.5 3; 38.610

Divide. Estimate to check. (pp. 76–79)

15. $1.4)\overline{35}$ 25   16. $3.7)\overline{5.92}$ 1.6   17. $0.45)\overline{1.08}$ 2.4   18. $0.25)\overline{85}$ 340

19. $22.8 \div 3$ 7.6   20. $9.72 \div 2.7$ 3.6   21. $33.33 \div 1.1$ 30.3   22. $6.9 \div 0.3$ 23

Evaluate each expression. (pp. 82–83)

23. $(2.3 + c) + 1.7$ for $c = 8$ 12

24. $3 \times d + b$ for $d = 1.7$ and $b = 5.4$ 10.5

25. $c \div 2 - a$ for $c = 8$ and $a = 2.3$ 1.7

26. $(5.4 - a) + d$ for $a = 2.3$ and $d = 1.7$ 4.8

27. $4 \times a - c$ for $a = 2.3$ and $c = 8$ 1.2

28. $(c - 5.4) \times c$ for $c = 8$ 20.8

29. $(d + c) - 5$ for $d = 1.7$ and $c = 8$ 4.7

30. $(a + d) \div 4$ for $a = 2.3$ and $d = 1.7$ 1

Solve each equation by using mental math. (pp. 82–83)

31. $c + 14.07 = 32.97$ $c = 18.9$

32. $6a = 24.78$ $a = 4.13$

33. $8d = 6.4$ $d = 0.8$

34. $7.14 - g = 3.24$ $g = 3.9$

35. $2.4 + f = 4.76$ $f = 2.36$

36. $4y = 29.6$ $y = 7.4$

37. $1.86 \div r = 6.2$ $r = 0.3$

38. $t + 3.6 = 4.5 + 3.3$ $t = 4.2$

Solve. (pp. 80–81)

39. There are 9 golf balls in a box. How many boxes does Hector need if he wants to give away 500 golf balls as souvenirs? 56 boxes

40. On Tuesday, Sabrina gets an invitation to a party that is in 20 days. She can go to the party if it does not fall on the weekend. Can she go to the party? Explain.
Yes; $20 \div 7 = 2$ r6, so the party will be on Monday.

CHAPTER 4 TEST, page 1

Choose the best answer.

1.
```
   75.9
 + 48.39
```
A 27.51
B 123.29
C 124.29
D 1,243.2

2.
```
  102.4
 − 89.72
```
F 12.68
G 12.72
H 13.38
J 192.12

3. $18.2 - 5.68$
A 12.52
B 12.68
C 13.48
D 23.88

4. $4.7 + 0.25 + 6.09$
F 35.79
G 13.29
H 11.04
J 9.14

5. 5.9×4.2
A 3.54
B 24.78
C 247.8
D 2,478

6. 8.03×3.22
F 2.6726
G 24.8566
H 25.8566
J 258.566

7. 77.32×6.8
A 52.5776
B 70.52
C 84.12
D 525.776

8. 34.52×4.8
F 165.696
G 65.696
H 39.32
J 29.72

9. $9.03 \div 3$
A 30.1
B 6.03
C 3.1
D 3.01

10. $15.75 \div 4.5$
F 35
G 11.25
H 5.3
J 3.5

11. $45.9 \div 7.5$
A 61.2
B 38.4
C 6.12
D 6.02

12. $59.52 \div 0.96$
F 62
G 49.2
H 9.2
J 6.2

Go On ▶

CHAPTER 4 TEST, page 2

13. Gordy has 187 CDs. He wants to put them on shelves. Each shelf holds 42 CDs. How many shelves will he be able to completely fill with CDs?
A 2
B 3
C 4
D 5

14. Sasha is making craft projects to sell at the fair. Each project will take 3 days to finish. If she can spend 35 days working on the projects, how many projects can she complete?
F 32
G 12
H 11
J 5

15. Lee is buying cupcakes for his class picnic. If each cupcake costs $0.50 and he has $12.35, how many cupcakes can he buy?
A 25
B 24
C 12
D 5

16. Carole is making flower baskets. Each basket takes 35 minutes to make. She works from 9:00 AM to 5:00 PM. How many flower baskets can she finish?
F 14
G 13
H 12
J 3

For 17–20, evaluate each expression for the given value.

17. $e \times 7$ for $e = 5.6$
A 0.8
B 12.6
C 35.2
D 39.2

18. $g \div 4.3 \times 7$ for $g = 13.76$
F 30.1
G 22.4
H 13.76
J 10.2

19. $6.8 + c - 5.2$ for $c = 7.4$
A 25
B 19.4
C 9.4
D 9

20. $5.9 \times f + r$ for $f = 4.2$ and $r = 7.8$
F 32.58
G 32.08
H 16.98
J 3.258

For 21–25, solve each equation using mental math.

21. $5.7t = 17.1$
A 12.2
B 9.2
C 9
D 3

22. $2.8 + c = 1.4$
F 38
G 18
H 2
J 1.876

23. $44.5 - d = 16.9$
A 2.76
B 16.9
C 27.6
D 61.4

24. $58.47 + y = 63.81$
F 122.28
G 55.34
H 5.34
J 0.534

25. $8.62 + k = 16.61$
A 7.99
B 8.62
C 16.61
D 25.13

Stop ■

Choose the answer.
See item **4**.

If your answer doesn't match one of the choices, check your computation and the placement of the decimal point. If your computation is correct, mark the letter for Not here.

Also see problem **6**, p. H64.

Choose the best answer.

1. Elise bought 4 balloons. Each balloon cost $0.98, including tax. Which is the total cost of the 4 balloons? B

   A $3.62   C $3.96

   B $3.92   D $4.00

2. At the end of a trip, the odometer of a car read 4,572.1 miles. The odometer read 2,998.7 miles at the beginning of the trip. How far did the car go? J

   F 7,570.8 mi

   G 7,460.8 mi

   H 2,684.4 mi

   J 1,573.4 mi

3. $0.27 + 1.098$ A

   A 1.368   C 1.125

   B 1.255   D Not here

4. $1.65 \div 0.5$ G

   F 0.33   H 33

   G 3.3   J Not here

5. Stu wants to buy a poster that costs $5.99, a desk lamp that costs $22.18, and bookends that cost $18.98. What is the cost of the 3 items he wants to buy, before tax is added? C

   A $46.15   C $47.15

   B $47.00   D $48.15

6. What is the value of $x + 16.714$ for $x = 20.3$? F

   F 37.014   H 3.614

   G 36.014   J 0.3614

7. A sweatshirt costs $9 more than a T-shirt. Together, the shirts cost $23. What is the cost of each type of shirt? D

   A T-shirt: $4, sweatshirt: $19

   B T-shirt: $16, sweatshirt: $7

   C T-shirt: $12, sweatshirt: $11

   D T-shirt: $7, sweatshirt: $16

8. What is the value of s for $s + 1.1 = 5.9$? G

   F 3.7   H 6.0

   G 4.8   J 7.0

9. In which pair of numbers is there a 5 in the hundredths place of both numbers? C

   A 553.621; 8,516.2

   B 87.35; 62,531.9

   C 36.157; 4,062.058

   D 513.26; 792.56

10. 7.8×0.3 F

    F 2.34   H 8.1

    G 3.24   J Not here

11. Which number sentence is true? D

    A $0.8 > 8.0$

    B $0.8 \geq 8.0$

    C $0.8 \leq 8.0$

    D $0.8 < 8.0$

12. $5^2 - 3 + 2 \times 8$ G

    F 15   H 40

    G 38   J 160

85

CUMULATIVE REVIEW •
Chapters 1 – 4

USING THE PAGE

This page may be used to help students get ready for standardized tests. The test items are written in the same style and arranged in the same format as those on many state assessments. The page is cumulative. It covers math objectives and essential skills that have been taught up to this point in the text. Most of the items represent skills from the current chapter, and the remainder represent skills from earlier chapters.

This page can be assigned at the end of the chapter as classwork or as a homework assignment. You may want to have students use individual recording sheets presented in a multiple-choice (standardized) format. A Test Answer Sheet is available as a blackline master in *Assessment Guide* (p. AGxlii).

You may wish to have students describe how they solved each problem and share their solutions.

UNIT 1

MATH DETECTIVE
Who Am I?

Purpose To use deductive reasoning to solve problems involving the division of whole numbers

USING THE PAGE

- *Direct students' attention to the Reasoning section and to Mystery Number 1.*

How did you use the clues in Mystery Number 1 to find the mystery number? Possible answer: by using the inverse operation of multiplication: $9 \times 5 = 45$ and $45 + 4 = 49$

- *Have students read the clues for Mystery Number 2.*

What is the first whole number that gives a remainder of 5 when divided by 9? the next whole number that gives a remainder of 5 when divided by 9? Explain. 14; 23; $23 \div 9 = 2 R5$

How would you find Mystery Number 2? Explain. Possible answer: Find the first multiple of 9 that is greater than 240 and then add 5 to that number: $27 \times 9 = 243$ and $243 + 5 = 248$.

- *After students find Mystery Number 4, have them explain their thinking.*

Reasoning Find the least whole number which when divided by 3, 6, or 8 gives a remainder of 3. Explain how finding this mystery number is different from finding Mystery Number 4. 50; Only multiply $6 \times 8 = 48$ and then add 2 because 6 is a multiple of 3. 4, 5, and 7 are not multiples of one another. So all three must be multiplied together to find mystery number 4.

Think It Over! After students complete the Write About It, have them work with a partner, exchange papers, and compare their methods for solving the cases.

Encourage a discussion of how to find the mystery number in Stretch Your Thinking. Have students explain how they can use the first mystery number to find the second mystery number in the problem.

MATH DETECTIVE

Who Am I?

REASONING Use the given information plus your knowledge of division to find the mystery number. Be prepared to explain how you solved the mystery.

Mystery Number 1

I'm the least whole number that gives a remainder of 4 when divided by 5 and when divided by 9. Who am I? 49

Mystery Number 2

I'm the first whole number greater than 240 that gives a remainder of 5 when divided by 9. Who am I? 248

Mystery Number 3

I'm the first whole number greater than 100 that gives a remainder of 3 when divided by 8 and when divided by 7. Who am I? 115

Mystery Number 4

I'm the least whole number that when divided by 4, by 5, and by 7 gives a remainder of 3. Who am I? 143

Think It Over! Possible Answers: #1: $9 \times 5 + 4 = 49$; #2: 243 is divisible by 9 and $243 + 5 = 248$; #3: 56 is divisible by 8 and 7, so $2 \times 56 = 112$, and $112 + 3 = 115$; #4: $4 \times 5 \times 7 + 3 = 143$

- **Write About It** Explain how you found each mystery number. See above.

- **Stretch Your Thinking** I'm the least number that when divided by 5 and when divided by 7 produces a remainder of 3. How much do you have to add to me to get a remainder of 0 when you divide by 5 and when you divide by 7? 38; 32

Intervention and Extension Resources

REACHING ALL LEARNERS

LITERATURE CONNECTION

Have students **use reasoning skills with whole number division.** In the book *From the Mixed Up Files of Mrs. Basil E. Frankweiler* by E. L. Konigsberg, Claudia and James run away to live in the Metropolitan Museum of Art. They stay for several days and while wandering around the museum they become interested in a beautiful statue of an angel and decide to find the name of the mysterious sculptor of the statue. The book describes their adventures as they attempt to solve the mystery.

Claudia and James must use their reasoning to solve the mystery of the sculptor's identity. Ask students to write clues that can be used to solve a mystery involving the division of whole numbers. Have them exchange with a partner and solve. Check students' work.

VISUAL

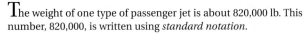

Challenge — Scientific Notation

Learn how to write numbers by using scientific notation.

820,000 pounds lifting off!

The weight of one type of passenger jet is about 820,000 lb. This number, 820,000, is written using *standard notation*.

You can also write the weight using **scientific notation**. Scientific notation is a shorthand method for writing large numbers.

A number written in scientific notation has two parts separated by a multiplication symbol.

$$8.2 \times 10^5$$

The first part is a number that is at least 1 but less than 10.

The second part is a power of 10.

To write the number 820,000 in scientific notation:

Count the number of places the decimal point must be moved to the left to form a number that is at least 1 but less than 10.

$$820,000 \;\rightarrow\; 8.2$$

5 places

Since the decimal point moved 5 places, the power of 10 is 5.

$$820,000 = 8.2 \times 10^5$$

The airplane's weight written in scientific notation is 8.2×10^5 lb.

EXAMPLE

About 32,500,000 passengers used Newark International Airport in 1998. Write the number of passengers in scientific notation.

$$32,500,000 \;\rightarrow\; 3.25 \times 10^7$$

7 places

The number of passengers was about 3.25×10^7.

TALK ABOUT IT

- Is 1.2×10^9 greater than 9.98×10^8? Explain.
  Yes. The exponent is greater.
- Show how to correctly write 782.5×10^8. **7.825×10^{10}**

TRY IT

Write the number in scientific notation.

1. 602,000 6.02×10^5
2. 199 1.99×10^2
3. 3,400,000 3.4×10^6
4. 8,540 8.54×10^3
5. 5,010,000 5.01×10^6
6. 113,000 1.13×10^5
7. 72 7.2×10^1
8. 48,900 4.89×10^4
9. 26,200,000 2.62×10^7

87

CHALLENGE
Scientific Notation

Objective To extend the concepts and skills of Chapters 1–4

USING THE PAGE

- *Have a volunteer read the caption under the photo. Have the student explain how to read the number in standard notation. Then direct students' attention to the term scientific notation.*

  Is 68×10^6 written in scientific notation? Explain. No; 68 is greater than 10.

  Is 0.3×10^4 written in scientific notation? Explain. No; 0.3 is less than 1.

  Reasoning Is 10^5 written in scientific notation? Explain. Yes; $10^5 = 1 \times 10^5$.

  How can you check that you have written a number correctly in scientific notation? Convert the number in scientific notation back into standard form.

- *Have students complete the Talk About It and then extend their thinking.*

  Reasoning How would you compare two numbers written in scientific notation? Explain. If the exponents are different, the number with the greater exponent is the greater number. If the exponents are the same, then compare the decimal numbers to find the greater number.

Try It Before assigning Try It Exercises 1–9, have students describe how to write a number in scientific notation.

 Intervention and Extension Resources

ALTERNATIVE TEACHING STRATEGY

Reinforce students' understanding of scientific notation. Explain that a number in scientific notation is a product of two factors: (a decimal that is at least 1 but less than 10) $\times$ (a power of 10).

Introduce scientific notation with 6,000:

$$6,000 \;=\; 6 \;\times\; 10^3$$

| Move the decimal 3 places left. | 6 is greater than 1 and less than 10. | Use 3 as the exponent, since the decimal moved 3 places. |

Remind students that a number in scientific notation has the same value as the number in standard form. Have students write 90,000,000 in scientific notation. 9×10^7

Then ask students to write 5.05×10^6 in standard form. 5,050,000

VISUAL

Number Sense and Operations 87

STUDY GUIDE AND REVIEW

Purpose To help students review concepts and skills presented in Chapters 1–4

USING THE PAGES

✅ Assessment Checkpoint

The Study Guide and Review includes content from Chapters 1–4.

Chapter 1

1.1 Estimate with Whole Numbers
1.2 Use Addition and Subtraction
1.3 Use Multiplication and Division
1.4 Problem Solving Strategy: *Predict and Test*
1.5 Algebra: Use Expressions
1.6 Algebra: Mental Math and Equations

Chapter 2

2.1 Mental Math: Use the Properties
2.2 Algebra: Exponents
2.3 Math Lab: Explore Order of Operations
2.4 Algebra: Order of Operations
2.5 Problem Solving Skill: *Sequence and Prioritize Information*

Chapter 3

3.1 Represent, Compare, and Order Decimals
3.2 Problem Solving Strategy: *Make a Table*
3.3 Estimate with Decimals
3.4 Decimals and Percents

Chapter 4

4.1 Add and Subtract Decimals
4.2 Multiply Decimals
4.3 Math Lab: Explore Division of Decimals
4.4 Divide with Decimals
4.5 Problem Solving Skill: *Interpret the Remainder*
4.6 Algebra: Decimal Expressions and Equations

The blue page numbers in parentheses provided with each group of exercises indicate the pages on which the concept or skill was presented. The red number given with each group of exercises identifies the Learning Goal for the concept or skill.

VOCABULARY

1. An expression that includes a variable is a(n) __?__ expression. (p. 28) **algebraic**

2. When you __?__ a decimal by a power of 10, the decimal point moves one place to the right for each factor of 10. (p. 87) **multiply**

EXAMPLES

EXERCISES

Chapter 1

• Add and subtract whole numbers.
(pp. 20–21) **1B**

```
  3,921        3,000
     68       −1,650
+   205        1,350
  4,194
```

Find the sum or difference.

3. $756 + 902$ 1,658
4. $4,293 + 256 + 19$ 4,568
5. $3,511 − 1,345$ 2,166
6. $729 + 8 + 3,996$ 4,733
7. $16,092 − 5,618$ 10,474
8. $25,080 − 19,387$ 5,693

• Multiply and divide whole numbers.
(pp. 22–25) **1B**

```
    273              203 r16
  × 86          41)8,339
  1 638            −8 2
+21 84              13
 23,478            − 0
                   139
                  −123
                    16
```

Find the product or quotient.

9. 57×38 2,166
10. 430×17 7,310
11. 276×809 223,284
12. $489 \div 26$ 18 r21
13. $9,671 \div 42$ 230 r11
14. $9,538 \div 19$ 502

• Use mental math to solve equations.
(pp. 30–31) **1C**

Solve. $w \div 6 = 7$ THINK: *What number divided by 6 equals 7?*

$w = 42$ *42 ÷ 6 = 7*

Solve each equation by using mental math.

15. $b + 5 = 12$ b = 7
16. $a − 3 = 5$ a = 8
17. $3y = 18$ y = 6
18. $k \div 5 = 4$ k = 20

Chapter 2

• Use the order of operations to evaluate expressions. (pp. 44–45) **2C**

Evaluate. $25 \div 5 + (8 − 4)^2 \times 3$

$25 \div 5 + (4)^2 \times 3$ *Operate in parentheses.*
$25 \div 5 + 16 \times 3$ *Clear exponents.*
$5 + 16 \times 3$ *Divide.*
$5 + 48$ *Multiply.*
53 *Add.*

Evaluate the expression.

19. $3 \times 6 + 7^2 − 9$ 58
20. $(8 + 7) \div 3 + (5 − 3)^3$ 13
21. $(15 − 3 \times 4) + 8 \div 2$ 7
22. $9^2 − 20 \times 2 + 5$ 46
23. $32 + (8^2 − 50) \times 2$ 60
24. $16 \div 2^3 + 4 \times 3$ 14

88 Chapters 1–4

Chapter 3

- **Compare and order decimals.** (pp. 52–55) **3A**

  Compare 2.8 and 2.83.

2.8	2.83	*Start at the left.*
2.8	2.83	*← same number of ones*
2.8	2.83	*← same number of tenths*
2.80	2.83	*Add a zero to compare.*

  2.8 < 2.83, or 2.83 > 2.8

Compare the numbers. Write <, > or = for ●.

25. 3.72 ● 3.7 >

26. 5.02 ● 5.021 <

Write the numbers in order from least to greatest. Use <.

27. 1.67, 1.76, 1.607, 1.706, 1.076
1.076 < 1.607 < 1.67 < 1.706 < 1.76

28. 0.0014, 0.4001, 0.0401, 0.0041, 0.014
0.0014 < 0.0041 < 0.014 < 0.0401 < 0.4001

- **Write decimals as percents and percents as decimals.** (pp. 60–61) **3C**

  Write 0.05 as a percent.
  0.05 is 5 hundredths.
  So, 0.05 is 5%.

Write the percent or decimal.

29. 0.28 28%

30. 7% 0.07

31. 47% 0.47

32. 0.6 60%

Chapter 4

- **Add and subtract decimals.** (pp. 66–69) **4A**

  Find the difference. 8.2 − 6.391

8.200	*Align the decimal points.*
−6.391	*Use zeros as placeholders.*
1.809	*Place the decimal point. Subtract.*

Find the sum or difference.

33. 29.6 + 0.935
30.535

34. 26.53 + 5.238
31.768

35. 76.03 − 58.94
17.09

36. 347.31 − 48.896
298.414

- **Multiply and divide decimals.** (pp. 70–79) **4A**

  Find the quotient. 2.46 ÷ 0.6

  ```
       4.1
  0.6)2.46    Make the divisor a
     −2 4     whole number.
       06     0.6 × 10 = 6
      −6      2.46 × 10 = 24.6
       0      Divide.
  ```

Find the product or quotient.

37. 75.8 × 6
454.8

38. 4.83 × 0.9
4.347

39. 3.92 × 0.58
2.2736

40. 68.49 × 3.6
246.564

41. 36.48 ÷ 12
3.04

42. 43.5 ÷ 0.3
145

43. 59.04 ÷ 4.8
12.3

44. 8.094 ÷ 0.95
8.52

- **Evaluate expressions with decimals.** (pp. 82–83) **4B**

  Evaluate $r + s + 3$ for $r = 6.9$ and $s = 4.8$.
  $r + s + 3$ *Replace r with 6.9 and s with 4.8.*
  $6.9 + 4.8 + 3 = 14.7$

Evaluate each expression for $c = 2.5$, $d = 3.2$, and $f = 4.1$.

45. $(c \times 3) + d$ 10.7

46. $(10 − d) + f$ 10.9

47. $\dfrac{d}{8}$ 0.4

48. $f − c + d$ 4.8

PROBLEM SOLVING APPLICATIONS

49. Jake has half as many pennies as his sister has. Together their pennies are worth 72 cents. How many pennies does Jake have? (p. 26) **1D** 24 pennies

50. Movie tickets cost $3.75 each for the matinee. How many tickets can Ms. Hamil buy with $20? How much money will she have left over? (p. 76) **4C**
5 tickets; $1.25

89

STUDY GUIDE AND REVIEW INTERVENTION

How to Help Options

Learning Goal	Items	Text Pages	Reteach and Practice Resources
1B *See page 14C for Chapter 1 learning goals*	3–8, 9–14	20–21, 22–25	Worksheets for Lessons 1.2, 1.3
1C *See page 14C for Chapter 1 learning goals*	15–18	30–31	Worksheets for Lesson 1.6
1D *See page 14C for Chapter 1 learning goals*	49	26	Worksheets for Lesson 1.4
2C *See page 14C for Chapter 2 learning goals*	19–24	44–45	Worksheets for Lesson 2.4
3A *See page 14C for Chapter 3 learning goals*	25–28	52–55	Worksheets for Lesson 3.1
3C *See page 14C for Chapter 3 learning goals*	29–32	60–61	Worksheets for Lesson 3.4
4A *See page 14C for Chapter 4 learning goals*	33–36, 37–44	66–69, 70–73, 74–75, 76–79	Worksheets for Lessons 4.1, 4.2, 4.3, 4.4
4B *See page 14C for Chapter 4 learning goals*	45–48	82–83	Worksheets for Lesson 4.6
4C *See page 14C for Chapter 4 learning goals*	50	76	Worksheets for Lesson 4.4

UNIT 1

CALIFORNIA CONNECTIONS

Purpose To provide additional practice for concepts and skills in Chapters 1–4

USING THE PAGE

Wind Energy

- *After Exercise 4, have students consider other forms of comparisons.*

  How many turbines are there in California and in Denmark? 18,600

  About what percent of the total number of turbines in the world is this?
  about 34%

- *After Exercise 6, invite students to apply their knowledge to another problem.*

  Suppose each wind turbine in California generates the same average amount of electricity. About how many total kilowatt-hours would be generated daily in "other CA areas"? Explain. 2,500,000 kWh; Multiply the number of turbines by the average amount of electricity produced.

  Extension Discuss other ways to compare the numbers in the table, such as using fractions or percents of the total number of wind turbines in California or in the the world. Have students find the corresponding percents and discuss the advantages of these comparisons. Check students' work. Possible answer: percents of wind turbines in California: Altamont Pass, 40%; San Gorgonio Pass, 23%; Tehachapi Pass, 33%; and Other CA areas, 3%

Wind Energy

Wind energy has been used for centuries to pump water, grind grain, and power sailboats. Today, windmills called wind turbines are used to generate electricity. There are more wind turbines in California than anywhere else in the world.

SCIENCE Standards LS 6.a

These wind turbines are located at California's San Gorgonio Pass. When the blades spin, they drive generators, which in turn produce electricity.

Use Data For 1–7, use the table.

1. Order the locations from greatest number of turbines to least.
   Altamont Pass, Tehachapi Pass, San Gorgonio Pass, Other CA areas

WIND TURBINES IN CALIFORNIA	
Location	Number of Turbines
Altamont Pass	6,000
San Gorgonio Pass	3,500
Tehachapi Pass	5,000
Other CA areas	500

The total number of wind turbines in the world is about 8.5 times the number at Altamont Pass.

2. About how many wind turbines are there in the world? **about 51,000**

3. About how many more wind turbines are there outside of California than there are inside California? **about 36,000**

Denmark has 3,600 wind turbines. This is the second greatest total in the world.

4. How many times as many wind turbines are there in California as there are in Denmark? Write the answer as a fraction and as a mixed number. $\frac{25}{6}$; $4\frac{1}{6}$

5. How many more turbines are there in California than there are in Denmark? **11,400 more**

Electricity is measured in kilowatt-hours (kWh). The wind turbines at Tehachapi Pass together generate 25 million kWh of electricity every day.

6. It costs about $0.035 to produce 1 kWh of wind turbine energy. How much does it cost to produce the wind turbine energy at Tehachapi Pass each day? **$875,000**

7. On average, how many kWh are generated daily by each turbine at Tehachapi Pass? **5,000 kWh**

90 Chapters 1–4

Solar Energy

Each day, huge amounts of free energy strike the Earth in the form of radiation from the sun. This *solar* energy can be converted to heat and electricity for human use. California is one of the world's largest producers and users of solar energy.

1. In 1997, solar power cells produced about 126 million watts of electricity throughout the world. Cells made in California produced about 0.3 of the world total. How much electricity was produced by cells made in California?
37.8 million watts

2. It costs $0.045 to produce 1 kilowatt of electricity by natural gas. Leah's clothes dryer uses 4 kilowatts of electricity per hour. How much does it cost her to run her dryer for 2 hours? **$0.36**

Use Data For 3–5, use the table.

3. About how many times as much electricity is generated weekly in California by natural gas as by wind and solar power combined?
about 24 times

4. Write an equation you can use to find how much more electricity is generated each week in California by coal power than is generated by solar power. Then solve the equation. $1,030 - 16 = n$; $n = 1,014$; **1,014 gWh**

5. The total amount of electricity generated each week in California is 5,156 gWh. How much of the total comes from sources that are not listed in the table? **2,385 gWh**

Solar panels produce energy without polluting the environment.

ELECTRICITY GENERATED WEEKLY IN CALIFORNIA	
Energy Source	**Energy (gWh)***
Natural Gas	1,672
Coal	1,030
Wind	53
Solar	16
*One gigawatt-hour (gWh) equals one billion kilowatt-hours.	

SCIENCE Standards
LS 6.a

91

CALIFORNIA CONNECTIONS

Purpose To provide additional practice for concepts and skills in Chapters 1–4

USING THE PAGE

Solar Energy

• *After Exercise 3, have students compare the energy amounts listed in the table.*

If you round the gigawatt-hours for each energy source to the nearest hundred, how would the entries for wind and solar power change? to the nearest thousand? Possible answer: The entry for solar power would be zero, for wind power it would be 100; the entries for both solar and wind would be zero.

What does this suggest about wind and solar power as energy sources? Possible answer: They are not very common sources of energy today.

• *After Exercise 5, have students extend their thinking beyond the problem.*

Suppose you are interested in information about energy sources in California. Why would the total from Exercise 5 be important? Possible answer: almost half of the total energy comes from other sources

What other sources of electricity can you name? Possible answer: dams, nuclear power plants

Extension Challenge students to use the data in the table to write a problem that can be solved by writing an equation. Have students exchange problems and solve. Check students' work.

Teaching Notes

Additional Ideas:

Good Questions to Ask:

Additional Resources:

Notes for Next Time:

UNIT 2 Statistics and Graphing

UNIT AT A GLANCE

Assessment Options

What types of assessment are available?

Assessing Prior Knowledge

Determine whether students have the required prerequisite concepts and skills.

Check What You Know PE pp. 93, 119

Test Preparation

Provide review and practice for chapter and standardized tests.

Cumulative Review, PE pp. 117, 137

Mixed Review and Test Prep
See the last page of each PE skill lesson.

Study Guide and Review, PE pp. 140–141

Formal Assessment

Assess students' mastery of chapter concepts and skills.

Chapter Review/Test
PE pp. 116, 136

Pretest and Posttest Options
Chapter Test, Form A
pp. AG33–34, 37–38
Chapter Test, Form B
pp. AG35–36, 39–40

Unit 2 Test • Chapters 5–6, pp. AG41–48

 Harcourt Electronic Test System Math Practice and Assessment

Make and grade chapter tests electronically.

This software includes:
• **multiple-choice items**
• **free-response items**
• **customizable tests**
• **the means to make your own tests**

Daily Assessment

Obtain daily feedback on students' understanding of concepts.

Quick Review
See the first page of each PE lesson.

Mixed Review and Test Prep
See the last page of each PE skill lesson.

Number of the Day
See the first page of each TE skill lesson.

Problem of the Day
See the first page of each TE skill lesson.

Lesson Quiz
See the *Assess* section of each TE skill lesson.

Performance Assessment

Assess students' understanding of concepts applied to real-world situations.

Performance Assessment (Tasks A–B)
pp. PA12–13

Student Self-Assessment

Have students evaluate their own work.

How Did I Do?, p. AGxvii

A Guide to My Math Portfolio, p. AGxix

Math Journal
See *Write* in the *Assess* section of each TE lesson and TE pages 106B, 112B, 124B, 126B, 132B.

Portfolio

Portfolio opportunities appear throughout the Pupil and Teacher's Editions.

Suggested work samples:

Problem Solving Project
TE pp. 92, 118

Write About It, PE pp. 97, 99, 128

Chapter Review/Test
PE pp. 116, 136

KEY **AG** Assessment Guide   **TE** Teacher's Edition
         PA Performance Assessment   **PE** Pupil Edition

How does the Unit 2 content correlate to standardized tests and California Mathematics Content Standards?

| | LEARNING GOAL | TAUGHT IN LESSONS | STANDARDIZED TESTS | | | | | CALIFORNIA MATHEMATICS STANDARDS |
			CAT	CTBS/ TERRA NOVA	ITBS	MAT	SAT	
5A	To identify types of samples and to determine if they are representative of a given population or biased, and to draw conclusions about a set of data	5.1, 5.2, 5.7						SDAP 2.0, 2.1 O—n SDAP 2.2 O—n SDAP 2.3 O—n SDAP 2.4 O—n SDAP 2.5
5B	To organize, read, interpret, and analyze data in frequency tables and line plots	5.4		•	•	•		SDAP 1.0
5C	To calculate and compare measures of central tendency with and without outliers	5.5, 5.6	•			•		SDAP 1.2 SDAP 1.3
5D	To solve problems by using appropriate strategies such as *make a table*	5.3		•				MR 2.0 MR 2.4
6A	To make and analyze different kinds of graphs and visual displays including circle graphs, bar graphs, stem-and-leaf plots, histograms, and box-and-whisker graphs	6.1, 6.3, 6.4, 6.5	•	•	•	•	•	SDAP 1.0 O—n SDAP 3.1
6B	To estimate and solve for unknown values by using a graph, arithmetic, logical reasoning, and algebraic techniques	6.2	•	•	•	•	•	AF 1.0 O—n AF 1.1 AF 1.2
6C	To compare different types of graphs to determine if they are appropriate or misleading	6.6		•		•		O—n SDAP 2.3

Technology Links

 The Harcourt Learning Site

Visit The Harcourt Learning Site for related links, activities, and resources:

• Graphs and Graphing activity *(Use with Chapter 6.)*
• *Animated Math Glossary*
• E-Lab interactive learning experiences
• current events stories that feature mathematics
• professional development and instructional resources

www.harcourtschool.com

Harcourt Math Newsroom Videos

These videos bring exciting news events to your classroom from the leaders in news broadcasting. For each unit, there is a **Harcourt Math Newsroom Video** that helps students see the relevance of math concepts to their lives. You may wish to use the data and concepts shown in the video for real-life problem solving or class projects.

TECHNOLOGY CORRELATION

Intervention Strategies and Activities This CD-ROM helps you assess students' knowledge of prerequisite concepts and skills.

Data ToolKit allows students to enter data into a spreadsheet and display it on as many as four different graphs.

E-Lab is a collection of electronic learning activities.

The chart below correlates technology activities to specific lessons.

LESSON	ACTIVITY/LEVEL	SKILL
5.1	**Harcourt Math Newsroom Video** • *What is in a Poll?*	Explore random sampling
5.3	**Data ToolKit** • *Make a Table*	Organize survey results
5.4	**Data ToolKit** • *Make a Frequency Table* **Data ToolKit** • *Make a Line Plot*	Make a frequency table; make a line plot
6.1	**Data ToolKit** • *Make a Table* **Data ToolKit** • *Make a Bar Graph* **Data ToolKit** • *Make a Line Graph* **Data ToolKit** • *Make a Circle Graph*	Make a table; make a bar graph; make a line graph; make a circle graph
6.3	**Data ToolKit** • *Make a Stem-and-Leaf Plot* **Data ToolKit** • *Make a Histogram*	Make a stem-and-leaf plot; make a histogram
6.4	**E-Lab** • *Exploring Box-and-Whisker Graphs*	Explore box-and-whisker graphs
6.5	**Data ToolKit** • *Make a Table* **Data ToolKit** • *Make a Box-and-Whisker Graph*	Make a table; make a box-and-whisker graph

For the Student

 Intervention Strategies and Activities

Review and practice the prerequisite skills for Chapters 5–6.

 E-LAB These interactive learning experiences reinforce and extend the skills taught in Chapters 5–6.

- Skill development
- Practice

 Data ToolKit

This is a full-functioning graphing and spreadsheet program.

- *Make a Table*
- *Make a Frequency Table*
- *Make a Line Plot*
- *Make a Bar Graph*
- *Make a Line Graph*
- *Make a Circle Graph*
- *Make a Stem-and-Leaf Plot*
- *Make a Histogram*
- *Make a Box-and-Whisker Graph*

For the Teacher

Teacher Support Software

- **Intervention Strategies and Activities**

    Provide instruction, practice, and a check of the prerequisite skills for each chapter.

- **Electronic Lesson Planner**

    Quickly prepare daily and weekly lessons for all subject areas.

- **Harcourt Electronic Test System**
    Math Practice and Assessment

    Edit and customize Chapter Tests or construct unique tests from large item banks.

For the Parent

The Harcourt Learning Site

- Encourage parents to visit The Harcourt Learning Site to help them reinforce mathematics vocabulary, concepts, and skills with their children.

- Have them click on *Math* for vocabulary, activities, real-life connections, and homework tips for Chapters 5–6.

    www.harcourtschool.com

Internet

Teachers can find statistics and graphing activities and resources.

Students can learn more about graphs and graphing and reinforce the critical concepts and skills for Chapters 5–6.

Parents can use The Harcourt Learning Site's resources to help their children with the vocabulary, concepts, and skills needed for Chapters 5–6.

Visit The Harcourt Learning Site
www.harcourtschool.com

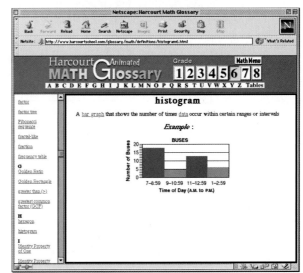

Reaching All Learners

ADVANCED LEARNERS

MATERIALS *For each pair* graph paper, p. TR64; watch with a second hand

Challenge pairs of students to perform this experiment and then **make a box-and-whisker graph using the group data:**

Have one student in each pair estimate when one minute of time has passed, while the other student watches a clock and records the actual time in seconds. Ask each pair to record and display their results.

Direct each pair to use the group data to make a box-and-whisker graph.

After students make their graphs, ask them to write a paragraph analyzing the data. *Use with Lessons 6.4–6.5.*

VISUAL

SPECIAL NEEDS

MATERIALS *For each group* 15 counters, a sheet of paper with four circles drawn on it

Have students **find the mean of a data set**. Tell them that a survey was taken in which four people were asked "How many pets do you own?" Display the results of the survey.

Person A – 0 pets   Person B – 2 pets

Person C – 5 pets   Person D – 1 pet

Ask students to place counters in each circle to represent each person's response to the survey question.

To find the mean, have students evenly distribute the counters in the circles. Then have them count to find the average. Connect this activity to the arithmetic method. *Use with Lesson 5.5.*

KINESTHETIC, AUDITORY

BLOCK SCHEDULING

INTERDISCIPLINARY COURSES
- Social Studies—Use a line plot to record the number of representatives per state in the U.S. House of Representatives.
- Statistics—Look at data trends and patterns in graphs.
- Physical Fitness—Use a stem-and-leaf plot to order the finish times for a 5-kilometer race.
- Geography—Compare weather data in a double-line graph of two cities that are equidistant from the equator—one in the Northern Hemisphere, one in the Southern Hemisphere.

COMPLETE UNIT

Unit 2 may be presented in
- ten 90-minute blocks.
- twelve 75-minute blocks.

INTERDISCIPLINARY SUGGESTIONS

PURPOSE To connect *Statistics and Graphing* to other subjects with these activities

CHAPTER 5—Social Studies

Students research changes in the United States workplace. Ask students to make a double-bar graph to compare the number of women who worked outside the home in 1965 to those who worked outside the home in 1995.

CHAPTER 6—Biology

Students research the approximate pH values for the following items: vinegar, apple juice, carrot juice, drinking water, milk, sea water, milk of magnesia, and household ammonia. Then they make a bar graph comparing the items' levels of acidity.

VISUAL

EARLY FINISHERS

Students who finish their work early can
- make a bar graph comparing the median income of individuals in relation to their level of education by using the information provided below. When they finish, have students write a paragraph explaining the data in the graph.

EDUCATION	INCOME
No diploma	$5,904
High school diploma	$12,924
Some college, no degree	$15,360
Associate degree	$20,064
Bachelor's degree	$25,392
Master's degree	$33,864

- assemble and play the Practice Game. See *Oranges for Sale*.
- solve the *Problem of the Day*. Use with TE Lessons 5.1–6.6.

ENGLISH LANGUAGE LEARNERS ELL•SDAIE

Vocabulary Preview Have students make a math dictionary for the vocabulary in the unit. The dictionary will provide students with an easy review tool for tests and will help them build toward independence when answering word problems. Have students make a three-column chart and label the columns. As students learn about each new term, they can fill in their dictionary. *Use with Lessons 5.1–6.4.*

Term	Example	Explanation

Survey Explain that the word *survey* is both a verb and a noun. Have students practice using the word both ways. *Use with Lesson 5.1.*

Outlier To illustrate the term *outlier*, show objects in a cluster and one object set apart. Have students draw an example to illustrate the term. *Use with Lesson 5.6.*

KINESTHETIC, AUDITORY

PRACTICE GAME

Oranges for Sale

PURPOSE To practice displaying data on a line graph and interpreting the results

MATERIALS *For each group* gameboard, p. TR78; game directions and scoring guide, p. TR79; 24 index cards; colored pencils

About the Game Partners graph earnings for orange sales over a period of 1 year. Players interpret the results, make comparisons, and use the scoring guide to determine who has the most points. *Use with Lesson 6.1.*

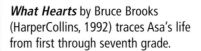

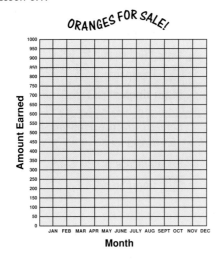

VISUAL

LITERATURE CONNECTIONS

These books provide students with additional ways to explore the gathering and reporting of data.

***Exploring the** Titanic* by Robert D. Ballard (Scholastic, Inc., 1988) gives a true account of the author's expedition to find the wreck of the *Titanic*.

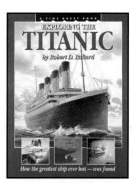

- The depth of the ocean at the *Titanic* wreck site is 12,460 ft. Have students research other shipwrecks or oceanic features to compare their depths to that of *Titanic*. Then have students graph their findings. *Use with Lesson 6.1.*

What Hearts by Bruce Brooks (HarperCollins, 1992) traces Asa's life from first through seventh grade.

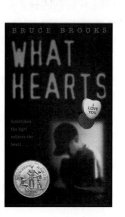

- Asa often had to ride his bike 5 to 6 miles to reach his friends' houses. Have students survey their classmates about the longest bike ride each has ever taken and make a box-and-whisker graph to show the results. *Use with Lessons 6.4–6.5*

Collect and Organize Data

CHAPTER PLANNER

PACING OPTIONS	
Compacted	7 Days
Expanded	13 Days

Getting Ready for Chapter 5 • Assessing Prior Knowledge and INTERVENTION (See PE and TE page 93.)

LESSON	CALIFORNIA STANDARDS	PACING	VOCABULARY*	MATERIALS	RESOURCES AND TECHNOLOGY
5.1 Samples pp. 94–97 **Objective** To identify different types of samples and to determine if a sample is representative of the population	SDAP 2.0 SDAP 2.1 O—n SDAP 2.2 (*Also* O—n SDAP 2.4)	2 Days	**survey** **population** **sample** **convenience sample** **random sample** **systematic sample**		Reteach, Practice, Problem Solving, Challenge 5.1 Worksheets Extra Practice p. H36, Set A ⬜ Transparency 5.1 📼 **Harcourt Math Newsroom Video •** *What Is in a Poll?*
5.2 Bias in Surveys pp. 98–99 **Objective** To determine whether a sample or a question in a survey is biased	O—n SDAP 2.3 O—n SDAP 2.4 (*Also* MR 2.0, MR 2.5)	1 Day	**unbiased sample** **biased sample** **biased question**		Reteach, Practice, Problem Solving, Challenge 5.2 Worksheets Extra Practice p. H36, Set B ⬜ Transparency 5.2
5.3 Problem Solving Strategy: *Make a Table* pp. 100–101 **Objective** To use the strategy *make a table* to organize data	MR 2.0 MR 3.2 (*Also* MR 3.3)	1 Day			Reteach, Practice, Reading Strategy, Challenge 5.3 Worksheets ⬜ Transparency 5.3 Problem Solving Think Along, p. TR1 💿 **Data ToolKit •** *Make a Table*
5.4 Frequency Tables and Line Plots pp. 102–105 **Objective** To record and organize data by using a frequency table or a line plot	SDAP 1.1 (*Also* SDAP 1.0, MR 2.4)	2 Days	**frequency table** **cumulative frequency** range		Reteach, Practice, Problem Solving, Challenge 5.4 Worksheets Extra Practice p. H36, Set C ⬜ Transparency 5.4 💿 **Data ToolKit •** *Make a Frequency Table, Make a Line Plot*
5.5 Measures of Central Tendency pp. 106–108 **Objective** To calculate the mean, median, and mode and to determine their meanings for a set of data	SDAP 1.1 SDAP 1.4 (*Also* NS 2.0, SDAP 1.0, MR 2.4)	1 Day	mean median mode	*For Thinker's Corner* 10-section spinner	Reteach, Practice, Problem Solving, Challenge 5.5 Worksheets Extra Practice p. H36, Set D ⬜ Transparency 5.5 **Math Jingles™ CD 5-6 •** *Track 7*
5.6 Outliers and Additional Data pp. 109–111 **Objective** To determine how outliers and additional data affect the mean, median, and mode	SDAP 1.2 SDAP 1.3 (*Also* SDAP 1.0, SDAP 1.1, MR 2.0)	1 Day	**outlier**		Reteach, Practice, Problem Solving, Challenge 5.6 Worksheets Extra Practice p. H36, Set E ⬜ Transparency 5.6
5.7 Data and Conclusions pp. 112–115 **Objective** To draw conclusions about a set of data	O—n SDAP 2.5 (*Also* MR 1.0, MR 2.4)	2 Days			Reteach, Practice, Problem Solving, Challenge 5.7 Worksheets Extra Practice p. H36, Set F ⬜ Transparency 5.7

Ending Chapter 5 • Chapter 5 Review/Test, p. 116 • Cumulative Review, p. 117

*Boldfaced terms are new vocabulary. Other terms are review vocabulary.

Vocabulary Development

The boldfaced words are the new vocabulary terms in the chapter. Have students record the definitions in their Math Journals.

survey, p. 94

population, p. 94

sample, p. 94

convenience sample, p. 95

random sample, p. 95

systematic sample, p. 95

biased sample, p. 98

unbiased sample, p. 98

biased question, p. 98

frequency table, p. 103

cumulative frequency, p. 103

outlier, p. 110

survey

Vocabulary Cards
Have students use the Vocabulary Cards on *Teacher's Resource Book* **pp. TR119–122** to make graphic organizers or word puzzles. The cards can also be added to a file of mathematics terms.

California Mathematics Content Standards for Grade 6

Strands

Number Sense

Lesson 5.5: NS 2.0

Algebra and Functions

Measurement and Geometry

Statistics, Data Analysis, and Probability

Lesson 5.1: SDAP 2.0, 2.1, ⊶ 2.2, ⊶ 2.4

Lesson 5.2: ⊶ SDAP 2.3, ⊶ 2.4

Lesson 5.4: SDAP 1.0, 1.1

Lesson 5.5: SDAP 1.0, 1.1, 1.4

Lesson 5.6: SDAP 1.0, 1.1, 1.2, 1.3

Lesson 5.7: ⊶ SDAP 2.5

Mathematical Reasoning

Lesson 5.2: MR 2.0, 2.5

Lesson 5.3: MR 2.0, 3.2, 3.3

Lesson 5.4: MR 2.4

Lesson 5.5: MR 2.4

Lesson 5.6: MR 2.0

Lesson 5.7: MR 1.0, 2.4

Writing Opportunities

PUPIL EDITION	TEACHER'S EDITION	ASSESSMENT GUIDE
• **Write About It,** pp. 97, 99 • **Write a Problem,** p. 101 • **What's the Question?,** p. 105 • **What's the Error?,** pp. 108, 115	• **Write**—See the *Assess* section of each TE lesson. • **Writing in Mathematics,** pp. 106B, 112B	**How Did I Do?,** p. AGxvii

Family Involvement Activities

These activities provide:

• Letters to the Family

• Information about California Standards

• Math Vocabulary

• Family Game

• Practice (Homework)

HARCOURT MATH   Name

GRADE 6   Date

Chapter 5

WHAT WE ARE LEARNING

Collecting and Organizing Data

Dear Family,

Your child is learning to identify different kinds of samples and to determine if surveys are biased.
This is how to recognize bias in the sample or in the survey questions.

VOCABULARY

Here are some of the vocabulary words we use in class:

Survey A method of gathering information about a group

Population The entire group of individuals or objects that could be a part of a survey

Sample A part of the population selected for a survey

Random sample A survey in which every individual or object in the population has an equal chance of being selected. This produces the most representative sample of the population.

The local boys and girls club is conducting a survey about teens' favorite vacation locations.

Biased	Unbiased
Randomly survey 15 out of 100 girls	Randomly survey 15 out of 100 teenagers
"Do you agree with the members of the Pep squad that the beach is the best spot for a vacation?"	"What is your favorite place to go on vacation?"

This is how your child is learning to work with and analyze measures of central tendency.
Compute mean, median, and mode for 25, 38, 43, 27, and 38.

Mean: $(25 + 38 + 43 + 27 + 38) \div 5 = 34.2$
Median: 25   27   [38]   38   43; 38
Mode: 38

Ask questions such as these as you work together:
Explain how you compute the mean, median, and mode.
Your child might respond: I find the mean by adding a group of numbers and dividing by the number of addends. The median is the number in the middle. The mode is the number that occurs most often.
How do you know which of the three measures of central tendency to use?
Your child might explain: I look for the central tendency that is closest to the data. Often it is the mean, but sometimes it is the median or the mode.
Determine which measure of central tendency is most useful to describe the data above.
The mean would be the most useful central tendency.

The California Math Standards
Your child's Harcourt Math book lists the California Math Standards that are taught in every lesson. If you have questions about the standards, be sure to consult *California Standards for Grade 6* that was sent home at the beginning of the school year.

Family Involvement Activities, p. FA17

Collect and Organize Data

MATHEMATICS ACROSS THE GRADES

SKILLS TRACE ACROSS THE GRADES

GRADE 5

Organize data in tables and line plots; interpret data using measures of central tendency; analyze data in graphs

GRADE 6

Determine if samples are representative of the population or biased and draw conclusions about a set of data; organize and analyze data in frequency tables and line plots; calculate and compare measures of central tendency

GRADE 7

Analyze samples and surveys for bias; collect, organize, and display data in graphs, frequency distributions, line plots, and histograms; draw conclusions about a set of data; determine which measure of central tendency best represents a set of data

SKILLS TRACE FOR GRADE 6

LESSON	FIRST INTRODUCED	TAUGHT AND PRACTICED	TESTED	REVIEWED
5.1	Grade 6	PE pp. 94–97, H36, p. RW20, p PW20, p. PS20	PE p. 116, pp. AG33–36	PE pp. 116, 117, 140–141
5.2	Grade 6	PE pp. 98–99, H36, p. RW21, p. PW21, p. PS21	PE p. 116, pp. AG33–36	PE pp. 116, 117, 140–141
5.3	Grade 4	PE pp. 100–101, p. RW22, p. PW22, p. PS22	PE p. 116, pp. AG33–36	PE pp. 116, 117, 140–141
5.4	Grade 4	PE pp. 102–105, H36, p. RW23, p. PW23, p. PS23	PE p. 116, pp. AG33–36	PE pp. 116, 117, 140–141
5.5	Grade 5	PE pp. 106–108, p. H36, p. RW24, p. PW24, p. PS24	PE p. 116, pp. AG33–36	PE pp. 116, 117, 140–141
5.6	Grade 6	PE pp. 109–111, H36, p. RW25, p. PW25, p. PS25	PE p. 116, pp. AG33–36	PE pp. 116, 117, 140–141
5.7	Grade 6	PE pp. 112–115, H36, p. RW26, p. PW26, p. PS26	PE p. 116, pp. AG33–36	PE pp. 116, 117, 140–141

KEY **PE** Pupil Edition   **PS** Problem Solving Workbook   **RW** Reteach Workbook
PW Practice Workbook   **AG** Assessment Guide

Looking Back Prerequisite Skills

To be ready for Chapter 5, students should have the following understandings and skills:

- **Vocabulary**—*mean, median, mode, range*
- **Reading a Table**—use data in a table to answer questions
- **Mean, Median, and Mode**—find mean, median, and mode for a set of data
- **Range**—find range for a set of data

Check What You Know

Use page 93 to determine students' knowledge of prerequisite concepts and skills.

Intervention

Help students prepare for the chapter by using the intervention resources described on TE page 93.

Looking at Chapter 5 Essential Skills

Students will

- identify different types of samples and determine whether a sample is representative of the population or biased and draw conclusions about a set of data.
- **understand the process of organizing and analyzing data in a frequency table or a line plot.**
- develop skill in calculating the mean, median, and mode and determining how outliers affect them.

EXAMPLE

Use the data to make a line plot.

Number of Migrating Whales Observed				
3	7	4	9	5
7	2	5	7	3
1	5	2	3	7

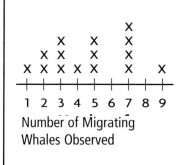

Looking Ahead Applications

Students will apply what they learn in Chapter 5 to the following new concepts:

- Make, Analyze, and Compare Graphs (Chapter 6)
- Circle Graphs (Chapter 21)
- Find Unknown Values (Chapter 6)
- Make Predictions (Chapter 23)

Collect and Organize Data

INTRODUCING THE CHAPTER

Tell students that people collect and organize numerical information, or data, to help them understand the world, identify patterns and trends, and make predictions. After students read the paragraph, explain that the 100 pails of water represent all of the water on Earth. Ask them to determine how many of the 100 pails are salt water. 97 Ask students to write 97 parts out of 100 as a decimal. 0.97

USING DATA

To begin the study of this chapter, have students

- Write a decimal for the part of Earth's total water that is liquid fresh water. 0.01
- Write decimals to compare the amount of salt water to the amount of fresh water. 0.97 > 0.03
- Write a decimal to show the part of Earth's fresh water that is ice. 0.67

PROBLEM SOLVING PROJECT

Purpose To collect and organize data

Grouping pairs

Background Malaspina Glacier in Alaska is the largest glacier in the United States. Yet, at 2,176 km², it is significantly smaller than Antarctica's glaciers, which account for about 70% of Earth's fresh water.

Analyze, Choose, Solve, and Check

Have students

- Research the areas of five large glaciers on Earth.
- Organize the data in a logical order and then sort the data using two different sets of criteria, such as area or location.
- Analyze each other's data and determine the criteria used for sorting.

Check students' work.

 Suggest that students place their data lists in their portfolios.

CHAPTER **5** Collect and Organize Data

Hubbard Glacier in Alaska

If you could look at Earth from space, you would see that most of its surface is covered with water. However, most of that water is salt water which is unusable for drinking, watering crops, or manufacturing. What information about Earth's water supply can you find in the graph?

Possible answer: there is 97 times as much salt water as fresh water; there is twice as much ice as fresh water.

WATER ON THE EARTH

Fresh Water

Ice

Salt Water

If you could put all the water on Earth into 100 buckets, 97 buckets would hold the salt water of the oceans and seas, and 2 buckets would hold the frozen fresh water of glaciers and icecaps. Only 1 bucket would hold liquid fresh water.

Why learn math? Explain that geologists collect data from core samples of ice taken from deep within a glacier. When these data from long ago are compared with more recent data, patterns emerge and predictions can be made. For example, one computer model shows a trend of glacial shrinkage that some scientists predict will cause a continued rise in sea level. Ask: What other jobs might require the collection and organization of data? Possible answer: book publishers, newspaper journalists, sports statisticians

Check What You Know

Use this page to help you review and remember important skills needed for Chapter 5.

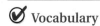 **Vocabulary**

Choose the best term from the box.

1. The middle number in a group of numbers arranged in numerical order is the __?__ . **median**

2. The sum of a group of numbers divided by the number of addends is the __?__ . **mean**

3. The difference between the greatest number and the least number in a set of data is the __?__ . **range**

> mean
> median
> mode
> range

 **Reading a Table** (See p. H5.)

STUDENTS' FAVORITE SPORTS				
	Gymnastics	Basketball	Baseball	Football
Boys	4	29	16	13
Girls	17	14	9	12

Use the data in the table above to answer the questions.

4. How many boys like baseball the best? **16 boys**

5. How many more girls than boys like gymnastics the best? **13 more girls**

6. Which sport was selected by more boys than any other? **basketball**

7. How many girls like gymnastics or football the best? **29 girls**

8. How many students were surveyed? **114 students**

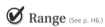 **Mean, Median, and Mode** (See p. H6.)

Find the mean for each set of data.

9. 7, 6, 11, 7, 9 **8**   10. 84, 73, 92, 77, 90 **83.2**

11. 8.9, 8.8, 7.9, 8.3 **8.475**   12. 4.6, 5.1, 6.2, 5.4, 4.8, 5.7 **5.3**

Find the median and the mode for each set of data.

13. 16, 32, 24, 10, 48, 32, 28 **28; 32**   14. 10, 15, 7, 8, 12, 13, 13, 19, 21 **13; 13**

15. 12.1, 10.8, 11.6, 10.8, 11 **11; 10.8**   16. 1.4, 0.9, 3.6, 2.5, 0.9, 6.2, 2.4 **2.4; 0.9**

Range (See p. H6.)

Find the range for each set of data.

17. 6, 3, 7, 5, 9 **6**   18. 105, 102, 116, 103, 96 **20**

> **LOOK AHEAD**
>
> **In Chapter 5 you will**
> - identify different kinds of samples and determine if surveys are biased
> - organize data in frequency tables and line plots
> - work with and analyze measures of central tendency

Assessing Prior Knowledge

Use the **Check What You Know** page to determine whether your students have mastered the prerequisite skills critical for this chapter.

Intervention

- **Diagnose and Prescribe**

  Evaluate your students' performance on this page to determine whether intervention is necessary. **How to Help Options** that provide instruction, practice, and a check are listed in the chart below.

- **Review Prerequisite Skills**

  The following resources provide a review for the prerequisite vocabulary and skills.

  Option 1—Check What You Know, Pupil Edition p. 93

  Option 2—Troubleshooting, Pupil Edition pp. H5–6

TEACHER'S NOTES

Check What You Know
INTERVENTION • Diagnose and Prescribe

Prerequisite Skill	Items (Pupil Edition p. 93)	How to Help Options
☑ Reading a Table	4–8	• **Troubleshooting, Pupil Edition p. H5** • **Intervention Strategies and Activities** Card copying Master, or CD-ROM • **Skill 75**
☑ Mean, Median, and Mode	9–16	• **Troubleshooting, Pupil Edition pp. H5–H6** • **Intervention Strategies and Activities** Card, copying Master, or CD-ROM • **Skills 77–78**
☑ Range	17–18	• **Troubleshooting, Pupil Edition p. H6** • **Intervention Strategies and Activities** Card, copying Master, or CD-ROM • **Skill 76**

Samples

LESSON PLANNING

Objective To identify different types of samples and to determine if a sample is representative of the population

Intervention for Prerequisite Skills

Read a Table (For intervention strategies, see page 93.)

California Mathematics Content Standards

SDAP 2.0 Students use data samples of a population and describe the characteristics and limitations of the samples.

SDAP 2.1 Compare different samples of a population with the data from the entire population and identify a situation in which it makes sense to use a sample.

○━ SDAP 2.2 Identify different ways of selecting a sample and which method makes a sample more representative for a population.

(*Also* **○━ SDAP 2.4**)

Vocabulary

survey a method of gathering information about a group

population the entire group of individuals or objects

sample a group of people or objects chosen from a larger group to provide data to make predictions about a larger group

convenience sample a sample for which the most available individuals or objects in the population were selected

random sample a sample for which every individual or item in the population had an equal chance of being selected

systematic sample a sample for which a pattern was used to select the individuals or items except for the randomly-selected first one

Math Background

Surveys are a common part of our culture. Since it is often difficult to survey an entire population, a sample can be chosen and queried. These ideas will help students understand the process of choosing a sample.

- A random sample is a sample whose individuals were selected from a population in such a way that any member of the population had an equal chance of being chosen.
- A systematic sample is a sample for which individuals were chosen by using a pattern.
- A convenience sample contains people or objects that are at hand or convenient.

It is essential for students to understand that the type of sample used can influence the validity of the results.

WARM-UP RESOURCES

NUMBER OF THE DAY
Transparency 5.1

In every year of 365 days, there are just as many days before me as after me. What date am I? July 2

PROBLEM OF THE DAY
Transparency 5.1

Dana's survey showed that 3 out of 8 students preferred pepperoni pizza and 1 out of 8 students preferred cheese pizza. How many more of the 72 students surveyed by Dana liked pepperoni pizza than liked cheese pizza? 18 more students like pepperoni pizza.

Solution Problem of the Day tab, p. PD5

DAILY FACTS PRACTICE

Have students practice addition facts by completing Set A of *Teacher's Resource Book,* p. TR96.

INTERVENTION AND EXTENSION RESOURCES

REACHING ALL LEARNERS

ALTERNATIVE TEACHING STRATEGY

Materials calculator

Discuss with students the words *population* and *sample* and relate them to the class. Ask for a show of hands of all left-handed students. Record that number and the total number of students in the class. Use a calculator to find the percent who are left-handed and record the percent.

Have students consider the class as a sample of a larger population, such as all sixth graders in the school, all people in the school including adults, all people in the town or city, and so on.

Discuss problems that arise when one is collecting data for very large populations and the difficulty of getting a representative sample.

See also page 96.

AUDITORY

MIXED REVIEW AND TEST PREP

Cumulative Review Chapters 1–5

Refer to the Pupil Edition pages referenced in the exercises for further review. Have students go to the lesson page, review the lesson, and correct any problem they missed.

Mixed Review and Test Prep, p. 97

How to Help	
Item	Page
21	82
22	82
23	82
24	70
25	66

VOCABULARY STRATEGY ELL

Before starting the lesson, **emphasize the vocabulary.** Display all terms on a three-column chart. Have volunteers suggest definitions and record one or two possible definitions for each word or phrase. As each word or phrase is covered in the lesson, ask volunteers to modify the definitions as needed.

VISUAL

ENG-LANG ARTS
Standards
R 1.0

ADVANCED LEARNERS

Challenge students to **apply their knowledge of samples.** Ask students to mention as many reasons as they can why the following survey uses a sample that is not representative.

A company wants to survey people about their favorite radio station. The company picks 200 phone numbers at random from the phone book, calls at about 10 A.M., and asks the person who answers what radio station they like the most.

Possible answer: The sample does not include people without phones, people with unlisted numbers, working people who are not at home at 10 A.M., or students who may be in school.

VISUAL

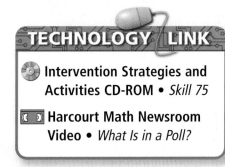

TECHNOLOGY LINK

- Intervention Strategies and Activities CD-ROM • *Skill 75*

- Harcourt Math Newsroom Video • *What Is in a Poll?*

94B

LESSON 5.1 ORGANIZER

Objective To identify different types of samples and to determine if a sample is representative of the population

Vocabulary survey, population, sample, convenience sample, random sample, systematic sample

1 Introduce

QUICK REVIEW provides review of prerequisite skills.

Why Learn This? You will know how to choose a sample to conduct a survey of your classmates. *Share the lesson objective with students.*

2 Teach

Guided Instruction

- *Discuss the meaning of the word population in the context of surveys.*

  If the population for a survey about favorite breakfast foods is all sixth graders in your school, would you want to include answers from teachers? from a seventh grader? from a sixth grader who does not like sports? no; no; yes

REASONING **What problems are presented by surveys such as the U.S. census or surveying people in your neighborhood?** Possible answer: It's impossible to reach the entire population or even to find everyone at home during a certain time.

Modifying Instruction If students have difficulty understanding a random sample, show them a spinner with 10 equal sections numbered 0–9. Explain that when you spin the spinner, there is an equal chance of landing on each number. Relate that to each member of a population having the same chance of being chosen for a sample.

ADDITIONAL EXAMPLE

Example 1, p. 94

Suppose Walter wants to find out the favorite sports team of the people in his hometown. Describe the population. Should Walter survey the population or use a sample? Explain. The population is all of the people in the town. He should survey a sample because it may not be possible to survey every person in town.

See also page 95.

LESSON 5.1

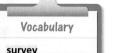

Samples

Learn how to identify different types of samples and to determine if a sample is representative of the population.

Vocabulary
- survey
- population
- sample
- convenience sample
- random sample
- systematic sample

QUICK REVIEW

1. $240 + 360$ 600
2. $94 - 60$ 34
3. 60×20 1,200
4. $270 \div 30$ 9
5. $850 \div 10$ 85

A **survey** is a method of gathering information about a group. Surveys are usually made up of questions or other items that require responses.

You can survey the **population**, the entire group of individuals or objects, such as all teenagers. Or, if the population is large, you can survey a part of the group, called a **sample**.

EXAMPLE 1

Suppose Jenna wants to find out the favorite game among students in her math class. Describe the population. Should Jenna survey the population or use a sample? Explain.

The population consists of all the students in Jenna's math class. Jenna should survey the population since it is small.

- **What if** the population is changed to all of the 1,800 students in Jenna's school? **Jenna could survey a sample.**

Surveying the population is not always possible, so samples are used.

EXAMPLE 2

Renee asked students at Roosevelt Middle School to indicate their favorite sport. She surveyed two samples and then the entire population of 600 students. How do the results from the two samples compare with the results from the population?

SAMPLE SIZE	NUMBER CHOOSING BASKETBALL	PERCENT OF SAMPLE
50	18	36%
100	33	33%

POPULATION	NUMBER CHOOSING BASKETBALL	PERCENT OF POPULATION
600	192	32%

The results from the samples are different from, but close to, the results from the population.

CALIFORNIA STANDARDS **SDAP 2.0** Students use data samples of a population and describe the characteristics and limitations of the samples. **SDAP 2.1** Compare different samples of a population with the data *(continued)*

RETEACH 5.1

Samples

A sample is a part of a population. Samples are used when it would be too time-consuming or too expensive to survey an entire population.

A population may be people, such as all the people in a city, or it may be objects, such as all the books in a bookstore.

A sample is chosen using one of several methods. Three such methods are:

- **Random sample:** Each person or object in a population has the same chance of being chosen.
- **Convenience sample:** Those people or objects that are most readily available are chosen.
- **Systematic sample:** A person or object is chosen randomly and then a pattern is used, such as every fifth person, to choose others.

In general, it is best to use a random sample, since it is most representative of an entire population. It is also important to use the largest sample possible, since the larger the sample, the closer the results will represent the entire population.

1. Carole is surveying members of her community asking them to name their favorite restaurant. Determine the type of sample. Write *convenience, random,* or *systematic.*
   a. She stands outside a local mall and asks people leaving the mall to name their favorite restaurant. convenience
   b. She opens the telephone book, randomly chooses a name, and then chooses every tenth name that begins with the same letter. systematic
   c. She knows that every family in her community is listed in the telephone book. She calls 5 people randomly chosen from each page of the book. random
2. Evan is on a committee to determine if the players in the Tri-Town Soccer League want to extend the season. Tell whether he should survey *all the players* or use *a sample* in each situation.
   a. There are 40 players in the league. all the players
   b. The players are difficult to reach since they live in many areas. a sample
   c. There are 650 players in the league. a sample

PRACTICE 5.1

Samples

Determine the type of sample. Write *convenience, random,* or *systematic.*

1. An assembly-line worker randomly selected one microwave oven and then checked every fifteenth oven to see whether it worked. systematic
2. Carl selected students to complete a survey by assigning each student's name a number from 1 to 6, rolling a cube numbered 1 to 6, and choosing each student whose name had the number he rolled. random
3. A store manager asked the first 50 shoppers to enter her store on Saturday to complete a survey about changes they would like to see made at the store. convenience

Tell whether you would survey the population or use a sample. Explain.

4. You want to know the type of computer, if any, that each student in your class has at home. population; There are not too many class members to survey them all.
5. You want to know the average number of siblings of all sixth grade students in your school district. Possible answer: sample; There are too many sixth graders to survey them all.
6. You want to know your friends' favorite television program. Possible answer: population; Your group of friends is not too large to survey them all.

Mixed Review

Evaluate each expression.

7. $9.03 \div x$ for $x = 3$ 3.01
8. $7m$ for $m = 2.2$ 15.4
9. $4.5 - w$ for $w = 1.9$ 2.6
10. $17.4 + h$ for $h = 5.9$ 23.3
11. $k \div 2$ for $k = 6.4$ 3.2
12. $6.58 + a$ for $a = 0.45$ 7.03

Types of Samples

There are many types of sampling methods. The table below shows three different sampling methods.

TECHNOLOGY LINK

To learn more about samples, watch the **Harcourt Math Newsroom Video** *What is in a Poll?*

Teacher Note:
You may want to tell students that even random samples may come out non-randomly over a finite number of samples.

TYPE	DEFINITION	EXAMPLE
convenience sample	The most available individuals or objects in the population are selected to obtain results quickly.	Choose a specific location, such as the cafeteria or the library, and survey students as they walk by you.
random sample	Every individual or object in the population has an equal chance of being selected. This produces the sample that is most representative of the population.	Assign a number to each student and then choose students by randomly selecting numbers with a computer.
systematic sample	An individual or object is randomly selected and then others are selected using a pattern.	Randomly choose a student from a list of students, and then choose every fourth student.

EXAMPLE 3

Identify each type of sample.

A. A bicycle shop owner randomly surveys a customer and then surveys every tenth customer after that to determine when customers expect to buy their next new bike.

This is a systematic sample since individuals are selected according to a pattern.

B. A sixth-grade middle school math teacher randomly selects 50 students in her math classes and asks them if they have a home computer.

This is a random sample since everyone has an equal chance of being selected.

C. The owner of a movie rental shop asks customers in the shop on a given day to fill out a card naming their favorite movie.

This is a convenience sample since the most available individuals are selected.

Math Idea ▶ The results from a sample can depend on how the sample is chosen. It is important to select a sample that is representative of the population. For example, if the population includes men and women, then the sample must include both men and women.

from the entire population and identify a situation in which it makes sense to use a sample. **SDAP 2.2** Identify different ways of selecting a sample and which method makes a sample more representative for a population.. also **SDAP 2.4**

95

• As students consider the three sampling methods, discuss difficulties that might arise with obtaining different kinds of samples.

Why might it be hard to obtain a random sample from a large population? Possible answer: You would need to insure that all members of the population have an equal chance of being included in the sample.

Which sampling method would you not use if you wanted to be sure of getting a representative sample? Why? Convenience sampling; it is likely that not every member of the population has an equal chance of being selected due to the time or place used to select the sample.

REASONING **Is a systematic sample always representative? Explain.** Possible answer: No; suppose you had a list of student names that alternate boy, girl, boy, girl. If you chose every fourth name on the list, the sample would be all girls, which would not represent the population.

ADDITIONAL EXAMPLES

Example 2, p. 94

The audience at the last school concert filled out surveys on their favorite concert song. First, two samples of the surveys were checked. Then the chorus instructor checked all 120 of them. How do the results from the two samples compare with the results from the population?

Sample Size	Number Choosing the National Anthem	Percent of Sample
30	10	33%
50	20	40%

Population	Number Choosing the National Anthem	Percent of Population
120	42	35%

The results from the samples are different from, but close to, the results from the population.

Example 3, p. 95

Identify the type of sample.

The cafeteria aide asks students to name their favorite food for lunch as they walk by. This is a convenience sample, since the most available individuals are selected.

PROBLEM SOLVING 5.1

Samples

Write the correct answer.

Analyze Choose Solve Check

1. Find the product.

   65.35 × 80.6

   5,267.21

2. Evaluate the expression.

   $(7^2 \times (5-3) + 22) \div 40$

   3

3. Fred wanted to find out the favorite color of all the students in his middle school. He surveyed all the students in his class. Is this a random sample? Explain.

   Yes. Students are not assigned on the basis of favorite color.

4. Cecily is ordering sodas for the class party. She asks a student in the lunch line for her favorite soda and then asks every tenth student. What kind of sample is she using?

   a systematic sample

Choose the letter for the best answer.

5. Thad conducted a survey on hair color at his school. His results were 23 students had blonde hair, 38 students had black hair, 7 students had red hair, and 19 students had brown hair. If he sampled 1 out of every 10 students at his school, how many people attend the school?

   A 900 people
   (B) 870 people
   C 820 people
   D 750 people

6. Jill surveyed students about their choice for a new school color. The results were that 45 people liked red, 33 liked green, 16 liked orange, and 8 liked blue. If she chose a student at random from the school's enrollment list and then asked every tenth student on the list, which describes the school's enrollment and her sample?

   F 1,020 students; random sample
   G 1,002 students; systematic sample
   (H) 1,020 students; systematic sample
   J 1,002 students; convenience sample

7. The owner of a grocery store ordered 56 cases of cups. Each case holds 16 packages. How many packages of cups did the store owner order?

   (A) 896 packages   C 1,026 packages
   B 1,006 packages D 1,128 packages

8. Paul has 1,716 eggs to put into cartons. Each carton holds one dozen eggs. How many cartons does Paul need to store all the eggs?

   F 163 cartons   (H) 143 cartons
   G 153 cartons   J 133 cartons

9. **Write About It** Why does a large sample generally give better results than a small sample?

   Possible answer: The larger the sample, the closer you come to surveying the entire population and the more representative the sample becomes.

CHALLENGE 5.1

My, How You've Aged!

The graph shows changes in the median age of the United States population from 1800 to 1990. Use the graph to answer the questions.

1. What was the median age of the population in 1900?

   about 23 years old

2. What was the median age of the population in 1840?

   about 18 years old

3. For which two years was the median age the same?

   1950 and 1980

4. By about how many years did the median age increase between the first and last dates shown on the graph?

   by about 17 years

5. What does the graph indicate about median age of the population between 1800 and 1920?

   It increased at a steady rate.

6. What does the graph indicate about the median age of the population between 1950 and 1970?

   It declined at a steady rate.

7. During which 10-year span did the median age remain almost constant?

   between 1800 and 1810

8. During which two 10-year spans did the median age change the most?

   from 1930 to 1940 and from 1980 to 1990

9. What might have caused the change that occurred between 1950 and 1970?

   a disproportionate number of births

10. Based on the data from 1970 to 1990, predict the median age for 2000.

   It is likely the median age will be greater than 35.

MEDIAN AGE OF
UNITED STATES POPULATION:
1800–1990

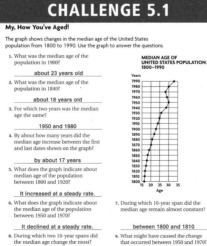

LESSON 5.1

3 Practice

Guided Practice

Do Check for Understanding Exercises 1–9 with your students. Identify those having difficulty and use lesson resources to help.

Independent Practice

Assign Exercises 10–20.

CHECK FOR UNDERSTANDING

Think and ▸ Discuss

Look back at the lesson to answer each question.

1. **Explain** why a sample is often used rather than a population when conducting a survey. Possible answer: There may be too many people in the population so it could take too much time and money.
2. **Tell** when you might survey a population rather than a sample. when the population is small
3. **Discuss** why a random sample is more likely to represent a population than a convenience sample. Possible answer: A random sample gives everyone an equal chance of being selected.

Guided ▸ Practice

Describe the population.

4. Suppose a random sample of 1,250 women in a city was taken in order to determine the favorite type of music of all women in the city. all women in the city

Tell whether you would survey the population or use a sample. Explain.

5. You want to find out where the students in your class want to go for a field trip. population, because there are not too many students and they are easily available
6. You want to know the favorite mountain bike of teenagers in your state. sample; because there are too many teenagers to survey all of them

For 7–9 determine the type of sample. Write *convenience, random*, or *systematic*.

7. A camp director was asked to conduct a survey to find which team game the campers liked best. She randomly selected one camper and then surveyed every fifth person on her list of campers. systematic
8. The names of one hundred high school students are drawn from a box containing all student names. random
9. The owners of a sports store ask shoppers in the store a question about the kind of running shoes they like. convenience

PRACTICE AND PROBLEM SOLVING

Independent ▸ Practice

Describe the population.

10. To find out the average salary of female architects, a researcher randomly selected 100 female architects. all female architects

Tell whether you would survey the population or use a sample. Explain.

11. You want to find out the daily exercise habits of the varsity basketball team. population; There are not too many basketball team members.
12. You want to know the favorite kinds of food of all teens in a large city. sample; There are too many teenagers to survey all of them.

96 Chapter 5

For 13–15, determine the type of sample. Write *convenience,* *random,* **or** *systematic.*

13. A cafeteria worker randomly selected a student and then asked every tenth student who entered the cafeteria a question.
systematic

14. When conducting a survey, Rachel selected 50 people by drawing names out of a hat without looking. random

15. To find out the favorite movie of students at her school, a teacher asked students in her math class to complete a survey.
convenience

Problem Solving ▶
Applications

16. The results from the smaller sample are different while the results from the larger sample are about the same.

16. Jim asked Lake Middle School students to indicate their favorite pet. The results are in the tables at the right. He surveyed two samples and then the population of 202 students. How do the results from the two samples compare with the results from the population?

SAMPLE SIZE	NUMBER CHOOSING DOGS	PERCENT OF SAMPLE
10	2	20%
50	24	48%

POPULATION	NUMBER CHOOSING DOGS	PERCENT OF POPULATION
320	160	50%

Dalton wants to conduct a survey to find out which computer game is most popular among the students in his school.

17. How can Dalton get a random sample? Possible answer: He can randomly select names from a list of students in his school.

18. How can Dalton get a convenience sample? Possible answer: He can survey 10 friends he eats lunch with.

19. Write About It Choose a topic you could find out about by conducting a survey. Then tell how you would choose a random sample. Possible answer: randomly choose names from a list of the population.

20. A target has three circles, one inside of the other. The bull's-eye is 10 points, the middle circle is 6 points, and the outer circle is 4 points. If 3 darts are thrown and only 2 hit the target, what are the possible scores? 20 pts, 16 pts, 14 pts, 12 pts, 10 pts, or 8 pts

MIXED REVIEW AND TEST PREP

Evaluate for $a = 3.1$ and $b = 6.2$. (p. 82)

21. $a + b$ 9.3

22. $a \times b$ 19.22

23. $b \div a$ 2

24. TEST PREP Which is the product of 5.25 and 1.9? (p. 70) **A**

A 9.975   **B** 99.75   **C** 997.5   **D** 9,975

25. TEST PREP Martha saved $0.50 one week. Then she saved $0.50 more each week than she had the week before. How many weeks did it take to save a total of $10.50? (p. 66) **G**

F 5 weeks   **G** 6 weeks   **H** 7 weeks   **J** 8 weeks

Extra Practice page H36, Set A

97

MIXED REVIEW AND TEST PREP
Exercises 21–25 provide **cumulative review** (Chapters 1–5).

4 Assess

Summarize the lesson by having students:

DISCUSS Give an example of each type of sample. Possible answer: convenience sample—the first 30 people who walk into a store; systematic sample—every tenth person who walks into the store all day long; random sample—30 people chosen at random from a list of the store's customers

WRITE Explain the difference between the three sampling methods presented in this lesson. For a convenience sample, individuals are selected based on their availability. For a random sample, every individual in a given population has an equal chance of being selected. For a systematic sample, an individual is randomly selected, and then other individuals are selected according to a pattern.

Lesson Quiz

Transparency
5.1

Determine the type of sample. Write *convenience, random,* or *systematic.*

1. Every tenth person to enter the movie theater was asked how many movies he or she attends in a month. systematic

2. The owner of the Ice Parlor asked customers in the store today about their favorite yogurt flavors. convenience

3. When conducting a survey of the student population, the teacher selected 100 students by assigning a number to each student in the school and then having a computer randomly select 100 of the numbers. random

4. Every fifth person leaving the hospital is asked about health care. systematic

97

Bias in Surveys

LESSON PLANNING

Objective To determine whether a sample or a question in a survey is biased

Intervention for Prerequisite Skills

Read a Table (For intervention strategies, see page 93.)

California Mathematics Content Standards

SDAP 2.3 Analyze data displays and explain why the way in which the question was asked might have influenced the results obtained and why the way in which the results were displayed might have influenced the conclusions reached.

SDAP 2.4 Identify data that represent sampling errors and explain why the sample (and the display) might be biased.

(*Also* MR 2.0, MR 2.5)

Vocabulary

unbiased sample a sample that is representative of the population

biased sample a sample that is not representative of the population

biased question a question that leads to a specific response or excludes a certain group

Math Background

Statistics are used to inform us or to persuade us to change our opinions. Since governments use statistics in making decisions that affect our lives, it is important that data are gathered in an unbiased manner.

Consider the following as you help students understand how to gather data in an unbiased manner:

- For an unbiased sample, everyone in the population has an equal chance of being chosen. Thus it is important not to choose just one subgroup of the population to interview.

- The questions asked must not lead the respondent to reply in any particular way.

WARM-UP RESOURCES

NUMBER OF THE DAY

Transparency 5.2

Draw squares around the numbers of 4 adjacent days on the calendar for this month. Add all the numbers in the squares, and subtract 4 times the first number. What number do you get? 6

PROBLEM OF THE DAY

Transparency 5.2

In a survey of students about a field trip to a nearby factory, 12 students were undecided, 5 times that many were in favor of the field trip, and half as many were against it as were in favor of it. How many students participated in the survey? 102 students

Solution Problem of the Day tab, p. PD5

DAILY FACTS PRACTICE

Have students practice subtraction facts by completing Set B of *Teacher's Resource Book*, p. TR96.

INTERVENTION AND EXTENSION RESOURCES

ALTERNATIVE TEACHING STRATEGY

Discuss with students the idea that a **question is biased** if it suggests a preferred answer. Display the following biased questions:

- Do you agree with me that dogs are the best pet?
- Do you like hot dogs the best?
- Do you agree that it is more fun to go out to dinner than to eat at home?

Have students rewrite the questions so that they are not biased.

Possible answers: What animal would you choose for a pet?; What is your favorite food?; Where do you prefer to eat, at home or in a restaurant?

VISUAL

MIXED REVIEW AND TEST PREP

Cumulative Review Chapters 1–5

Refer to the Pupil Edition pages referenced in the exercises for further review. Have students go to the lesson page, review the lesson, and correct any problem they missed.

Mixed Review and Test Prep, p. 99

How to Help	
Item	Page
14	98
15	76
16	76
17	76
18	44

ENGLISH LANGUAGE LEARNERS ELL•SDAIE

To help students **understand the meaning of** *biased* and *unbiased,* display the two words. Then write a behavior under *biased,* such as: *I did not choose Maria to be on my team because she is a girl.*

Have students work with partners and talk about why the behavior is biased. Possible answer: It assumes that a girl would not be as good a player as a boy.

Then ask each group to discuss what kind of action would not be biased and record that under *unbiased* on the chart. Possible answer: drawing numbers to determine teams

Finally suggest that students draw a visual for each term.

AUDITORY

ENG-LANG ARTS
Standards
R 1.0

SOCIAL STUDIES CONNECTION

Have students **demonstrate their knowledge of biased surveys.** Polls can play a very large part in influencing our decisions. Have students find examples of polls and bring them to class to share.

Give these and similar questions to small groups of students to discuss:

- How do you think it might affect you if you heard a poll on Election Day stating that Candidate A is winning in several states? Possible answer: You might not vote if you thought it would not make a difference.
- How do you think it might affect you if you saw a poll stating that 7 out of 10 college graduates favor a constitutional amendment? Possible answer: You might assume that college educated voters better understand the issue and adjust your vote to theirs.

AUDITORY

TECHNOLOGY LINK

Intervention Strategies and Activities CD-ROM • *Skill 75*

LESSON 5.2 ORGANIZER

Objective To determine whether a sample or a question in a survey is biased

Vocabulary unbiased sample, biased sample, biased question

1 Introduce

QUICK REVIEW provides review of pre-requisite skills.

Why Learn This? You can use this skill to help you detect biased samples and survey questions in consumer product studies. *Share the lesson objective with students.*

2 Teach

Guided Instruction

• *Discuss the two main sources of bias in surveys and what to look for to detect bias.*

What do you need to look for to detect bias in a survey? how the sample is selected and how the questions are worded

REASONING **In a survey of 500 Orange County teachers, would a sample of 50 middle school teachers be biased or unbiased? Explain.** biased; the sampling method does not include elementary and high school teachers

ADDITIONAL EXAMPLE

Example 1, p. 98

Keisha surveys students who take karate lessons at a local gym about the number of days per week they jog. There are 150 students in the school. Which samples will be biased? Explain.

A. Randomly survey 30 students over the age of 18.

B. Randomly survey 30 students.

C. Randomly survey 30 male students.

D. Randomly survey 30 new students.

Choices A, C, and D are biased. Choice A excludes students younger than 18, choice C excludes females, and choice D includes only new students.

LESSON 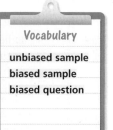 **5.2**

Bias in Surveys

Learn how to determine whether a sample or question in a survey is unbiased.

QUICK REVIEW

1. 0.25 1	**2.** 19.5 1.5	**3.** 30 15	**4.** $0.35 \div 0.5$ 0.7
$+0.75$	-18.0	$\times 0.5$	

5. $2.5 + 1.5 - 1.75$ 2.25

Vocabulary
- unbiased sample
- biased sample
- biased question

Does the earth revolve around the sun or does the sun revolve around the earth? In a recent survey of over 1,000 adults, 79% knew the correct answer.

When you collect data from a survey, your sample should represent the whole population. Every individual in that population should have an equal chance of being selected. Then the sample is an **unbiased sample**.

If individuals or groups from the population are not represented in the sample, then the sample is a **biased sample**. If the sample for the survey above included males only, it would be biased since the survey was for all adults.

EXAMPLE 1

Latosha wants to find out how many hours Polk Middle School students spend on the Internet. If she surveys students from this school, which samples below will be biased? Explain.

A. 200 girls

B. 200 athletes

C. 200 randomly selected students

D. Students who ride their bikes to school

Choices A, B, and D are biased. Choice A excludes boys, choice B only includes athletes, and choice D excludes students who don't ride their bikes to school.

Sometimes, questions are biased. A **biased question** leads to a specific response or excludes a certain group.

EXAMPLE 2

Is the following question biased?

Do you agree with a well-known movie critic that movies longer than two hours are boring?

This question is biased since it leads you to agree with the movie critic.

 CALIFORNIA STANDARDS SDAP 2.3 Analyze data displays and explain why the way in which the question was asked might have influenced the results obtained and why the way in which the results were displayed might have influenced the conclusions reached. **SDAP 2.4** Identify data that represent sampling errors and explain why the sample (and the display) might be biased. *also* **MR 2.0, MR 2.5**

RETEACH 5.2

Bias in Surveys

A sample is **biased** if individuals or groups from the population are not represented in the sample.

Linda wanted to survey the 125 sixth-grade students at her school to find out the number of hours they spent reading each week. She made a list of four sampling methods she could use.

- randomly survey 5 students
- randomly survey 15 sixth-grade boys
- randomly survey 13 students at her school
- randomly survey 15 sixth-grade students

She decided that the first method would not include a large-enough sample. The second method would not include sixth-grade girls. The third method was biased because it would not be exclusively for sixth graders. Linda decided to use the last method. It would contain a large-enough sample, and every member of the sixth grade would have an equal chance of being selected.

1. Marian wants to survey the 58 sixth-grade teachers at Oak Park School to find out the average number of hours they spend grading papers. She makes a list of four sampling methods she could use. Circle the sampling method that is not biased. Then explain how the other three methods are biased.
   a. randomly survey all teachers who have taught for more than 10 years
   b. randomly survey 10 male teachers at the school
   c. *(randomly survey 8 sixth-grade teachers)*
   d. randomly survey 8 math teachers at the school

   Method a excludes teachers who have taught less than 10 years. Method b excludes

   female teachers. Method d excludes teachers who teach subjects other than math.

2. Dan wants to survey the 230 members of a golf club to find out the average number of hours they play golf each week. He makes a list of four sampling methods he could use. Circle the sampling method that is not biased. Then explain how the other three methods are biased.
   a. randomly survey all club members who have won tournaments
   b. *(randomly survey 30 club members)*
   c. randomly survey all members who have ever shot a hole-in-one
   d. randomly survey 25 members under the age of 30

   Method a excludes members who have not won tournaments. Method c excludes

   members who never shot a hole-in-one. Method d excludes members over the age of 30.

PRACTICE 5.2

Bias in Surveys

Vocabulary

Complete.

1. A sample is ___biased___ if individuals in the population are not represented in the sample.

Tell whether the sampling method is *biased* or *unbiased*. Explain.

The Tri-State Soccer League is conducting a survey to determine if the players want to change the style of soccer shirt.

2. Randomly survey all players who wear size large shirts.

   biased; excludes players

   who wear other sizes

3. Randomly survey all members of championship teams.

   biased; excludes members of

   non-championship teams

4. Randomly survey 80 players.

   unbiased; all players in the

   league have an equal chance of

   being selected

5. Randomly survey all league coaches.

   biased; excludes all players

Determine whether the question is biased. Write *biased* or *unbiased*.

6. Do you feel that country music is better than all other types of music?

   biased

7. What type of team sport do you enjoy playing?

   unbiased

Mixed Review

Solve each equation by using mental math.

8. $w - 7.5 = 12.3$

   $w = 19.8$

9. $5x = 16.5$

   $x = 3.3$

10. $a + 6.9 = 14.3$

    $a = 7.4$

Find the quotient.

11. $22.78 \div 6.7$

    3.4

12. $49.6 \div 8$

    6.2

13. $20.37 \div 3.5$

    5.82

Solve.

14. Kyle rode his bicycle a total of 48 kilometers at a rate of 8 kilometers per hour. How long did he ride?

    6 hr

15. Joanne earns $24.50 per hour as a construction worker. How much does she earn if she works 7.5 hours?

    $183.75

98 Chapter 5

CHECK FOR UNDERSTANDING

Think and ▶ Discuss

Look back at the lesson to answer the question.

1. Write the question in Example 2 so that it is not biased. **Possible question: Do you enjoy movies that are longer than two hours?**

Guided ▶ Practice

Tell whether the sample is *biased* or *unbiased*. Explain.

The local gym wants to find out how its members feel about the new exercise equipment.

2. Female members **biased; excludes males**

3. Members under age 20 **biased; excludes members 20 and older**

4. Members who used the gym in August **biased; excludes members who did not use the gym in August**

5. 50 randomly selected members **unbiased; all members have equal chance**

PRACTICE AND PROBLEM SOLVING

Independent ▶ Practice

Tell whether the sample is *biased* or *unbiased*. Explain.

The Middletown Mall is conducting a survey of its shoppers to find out which days they prefer to shop.

6. 400 teenage shoppers **biased; excludes people who are not teenagers**

7. 400 randomly selected shoppers **unbiased; all have equal chance**

8. 400 female shoppers **biased; excludes males**

9. Shoppers who enter the record store **biased; does not include people who shop in other stores**

Determine whether the question is biased. Write *biased* or *unbiased*.

10. Is basketball your favorite sport? **unbiased**

11. Do you agree with the fruit industry president that green apples taste better than red apples? **biased**

Problem Solving ▶ Applications

12. REASONING Students at Memorial Middle School are being surveyed to find out their choice of a new school mascot. If 300 students are randomly selected, do equal numbers of boys and girls have to be chosen? Explain. **No; boys and girls are randomly selected.**

13. Write About It   Is this question biased? Explain.
I think pizza is the best choice for lunch, don't you? **yes; the question leads you to agree with the person asking the question.**

MIXED REVIEW AND TEST PREP

14. A store owner randomly selects a customer and then surveys every tenth customer. What type of sample is this? (p. 98) **systematic**

Find the quotient. (p. 76)

15. $3.6 \div 0.9$ **4**

16. $1.44 \div 0.12$ **12**

17. $270 \div 0.03$ **9,000**

18. TEST PREP Find the value of $3^2 \times (6 + 4)$. (p. 44) **D**

A 22   **B** 30   **C** 58   **D** 90

Extra Practice page H36, Set B

99

---

3 Practice

Guided Practice

Do Check for Understanding Exercises 1–5 with your students. Identify those having difficulty and use lesson resources to help.

Independent Practice

Assign Exercises 6–13.

MIXED REVIEW AND TEST PREP

Exercises 14–18 provide **cumulative review** (Chapters 1–5).

4 Assess

Summarize the lesson by having students:

DISCUSS Why would you probably not use a convenience sample to get an unbiased sample for a survey? Not everyone in the population would have an equal chance of being selected.

WRITE What is a biased question? Possible answer: a question that leads to a specific response

Lesson Quiz

Transparency 5.2

Tell whether the sample is biased or unbiased. Explain.

Sarah is doing a survey of 75 chess players to find out their favorite game strategy.

1. Randomly survey 8 members of the Chess Club. Biased; it excludes chess players who are not members of the Chess Club.

2. Randomly survey 8 chess players. Not biased; all players had an equal chance of being selected.

PROBLEM SOLVING 5.2

Bias in Surveys

Write the correct answer.

1. Bruce surveyed everyone in his math class to find out the favorite subject of the students in his school. Is his sample biased? Explain.

Yes, it is biased. He should have randomly selected students from the whole school.

2. Lisa randomly surveyed 1 out of every 10 people in her school to find out their favorite item in the cafeteria. Is her sample biased? Explain.

No, she surveyed a random sample of the people in her school.

3. Tell how many people you would survey out of a group of 970, if you survey 1 out of every 10 people.

97 people

4. Tell how many people you would survey out of a group of 320, if you survey 1 out of every 10 people.

32 people

Choose the letter for the best answer.

5. A supermarket wants to know the favorite brand of juice of its customers. Which group of customers should the store randomly survey to get results that are not biased?
A 1 out of every 50 child customers
B 1 out of every 100 adult customers
C 10 out of every 100 customers as they leave the store
D 2 out of every 5 female customers

6. Rachel sold tickets for the local charity. On Monday she sold 245 tickets, on Tuesday she sold 188 tickets, and on Thursday she sold 96 tickets. Which is the best estimate of how many tickets Rachel sold?
F 300 tickets
G 400 tickets
H 450 tickets
J 500 tickets

7. Larry needs to buy 60 cookies for his party. A dozen cookies cost $3.50, including tax. Which expression can be used to find the total cost of the cookies that Larry wants to buy?
A $60 \div 12 + 3.50$
B $60 \div 12 \times 3.50$
C $60 \div 12 + 3.50$
D $60 \div 12 - 3.50$

8. The head cook at a school wants to know the favorite meal of the 870 students who attend the school. Which sample of students in the lunchroom would not be biased?
F 1 out of every 100 male students
G 1 out of every 10 female students
H Every eighth student passing through the lunch line
J Every student seated at one table

9. Write About It Why is it important to base your survey on a random sample that is not biased?

A biased sample can lead to making wrong decisions about the results of the survey.

CHALLENGE 5.2

Bias in Advertising

Most advertisements try to persuade consumers to buy certain products. Some advertisements use biased surveys to make their products seem better than any others. Look carefully at advertisements shown in magazines and newspapers. Find an ad that includes either a biased question or a biased survey to promote a product. Answer these questions about the ad. Answers will vary.

1. What product does the advertisement feature? _____

2. How is the question or survey biased? _____

3. How does the bias make the product seem appealing? _____

4. Describe two ways that the question or survey could be changed to eliminate the bias. _____

5. Explain why recognizing bias in advertisements will help you become a smart shopper. _____

99

Problem Solving Strategy: *Make a Table*

LESSON PLANNING

Objective To use the strategy *make a table* to organize data

Intervention for Prerequisite Skills

Read a Table (For intervention strategies, see page 93.)

Lesson Resources Problem Solving Think Along, p. TR1

 California Mathematics Content Standards

MR 2.0 Students use strategies, skills, and concepts in finding solutions.

MR 3.2 Note the method of deriving the solution and demonstrate a conceptual understanding of the derivation by solving similar problems.

(*Also* MR 3.3)

Math Background

The strategy *make a table* can be used to:

• Order data

• Summarize data

• Organize data

• Help show a pattern

In statistics, the data collected must be organized or displayed in an enlightening fashion. Organizing data in a table allows students to more quickly answer questions about the data or to use it to make graphs or plots that illustrate the data.

WARM-UP RESOURCES

 NUMBER OF THE DAY Transparency 5.3

How many half-dollars are needed to equal $5.00? How many of each of the other kinds of coins? 10 half-dollars, 20 quarters, 50 dimes, 100 nickels, 500 pennies

 PROBLEM OF THE DAY Transparency 5.3

It takes 4 yd of material and 3 yd of trim to make 2 pumpkin decorations. Rhonda needs to make 10 decorations. How many yards of material and trim will she need? 20 yd of material and 15 yd of trim

Solution Problem of the Day tab, p. PD5

 DAILY FACTS PRACTICE

Have students practice subtraction facts by completing Set C of *Teacher's Resource Book,* p. TR96.

ALTERNATIVE TEACHING STRATEGY

Materials *For each student* 1-inch paper square

Have students **practice the strategy** *make a table* by displaying a vertical number line labeled *0, 1, 2, 3, 4, 5,* and *more than 5*. Above the number line write *Number of Brothers*.

- Give each student a small paper square.
- Ask them to tape their square to the right of the number naming the number of brothers they have.
- Then ask students how many have no brothers, 1 brother, and so on.
- Use tally marks to show the data, making tallies as you point to the squares.
- Point out how the slash indicates a total of 5 and thus helps organize the tallies.

KINESTHETIC

READING STRATEGY

Use Graphic Aids Remind students that making a table is not the only method to visually convey information. Extend your lesson discussion of other ways to solve the problem on page 100.

- Ask students to make a list of advantages of using a table, such as making the data more readable and usable, helping to avoid mistakes, and so on.
- Ask students how their strategy would change if 100 students had been interviewed. Possible answer: I would use a bar graph to display a greater number of responses rather than count so many tally marks.

**ENG-LANG ARTS
Standards
R 2.4**

ENGLISH LANGUAGE LEARNERS ELL•SDAIE

Materials 1 small twig

Reinforce the vocabulary associated with surveys and tables by pointing out to students that the word *tally* comes from a Latin word meaning *twig*. Show a twig and ask students to give the word in their language that has the same meaning. Discuss with students how the twig visually resembles a tally mark.

Have each student choose three colors and write them down in a list. Have students survey each other as to which of the three colors they like best. Ask them to record the responses with tally marks and display their tables for the class. Check students' work.

VISUAL

**ENG-LANG ARTS
Standards
R 1.0**

EARLY FINISHERS

Encourage students to **apply the strategy** *make a table*. Divide the class into small groups.

- Ask each group to decide on a question they want to have answered by their classmates, such as *What is your favorite ice cream?* or *How many pets do you have?*
- Students then collect data either by interviewing classmates or asking the class to write their answers on slips of paper.
- Then have each group make a table and tally the results.
- Finally, have groups write at least two summarizing statements about the data, such as *14 people like chocolate best*, or *more people like vanilla than the other two flavors combined*. Check students' work.

AUDITORY

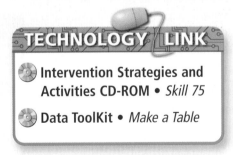

TECHNOLOGY LINK

Intervention Strategies and Activities CD-ROM • *Skill 75*

Data ToolKit • *Make a Table*

Objective To use the strategy *make a table* to organize data

Lesson Resources Problem Solving Think Along, p. TR1

---

1 Introduce

QUICK REVIEW provides review of pre-requisite skills.

Why Learn This? After conducting a survey, you can organize your data into a table to solve a problem. *Share the lesson objective with students.*

2 Teach

Guided Instruction

• *Begin by discussing the data shown at the top of the page.*

Are the numbers recorded in a meaningful list? Explain. No; the numbers are listed in the order students responded.

What does the number *2* mean? It means that one student saw 2 movies.

• *Consider the table shown in the Solve section.*

Why does the table make it easier to determine the number of students who saw either 3 or 4 movies? It's quicker to total tally marks grouped by 5 for a given category than to scan an entire list while counting specific numbers.

Would students who saw 3 movies be counted in both groups described in the problem? Explain. No; students who saw 3 movies would not be counted in the group that saw fewer than 3 movies.

REASONING **Describe another way to find the answers to the questions that does not involve making a table.** Possible answer: You could count all the numbers 3 and greater. That total would tell you the number of students that saw at least 3 movies. Then subtract that number from the total number of students in the class to find the number that saw fewer than 3 movies.

PROBLEM SOLVING STRATEGY
Make a Table

Analyze
Choose
Solve
Check

Learn how to solve problems by displaying information in a table.

QUICK REVIEW
Find the value.
1. 6^2 2. 3^3 3. 2^3 4. 2^4 5. 2^5
   36   27   8   16   32

Mrs. Donovan asked the students in her class to tell the number of movies they had seen since the start of the school year. The results are shown at the right.

Number of Movies Seen
1 5 3 2 1 6 1 2 3 3 4 5
1 1 6 3 4 2 2 2 4 3 2 1
2 2 4 5 1 3 2 1

How many students saw at least 3 movies? How many students saw fewer than 3 movies?

Analyze What are you asked to find? how many students saw at least 3 movies and how many saw fewer than 3 movies
What information is given? the number of movies each student has seen
Is there information you will not use? If so, what? **No.**

Choose What strategy will you use?

You can make a tally table to organize the data. Then you can use the table to answer the questions.

Solve How can you organize the tally table?

Make a row for each of the numbers of movies the students have seen. Then read the data and make a tally mark for each piece of information next to the appropriate number.

Next, use the table to answer the questions.

There are $6 + 4 + 3 + 2$, or 15, students who saw at least 3 movies and $8 + 9$, or 17, students who saw fewer than 3 movies.

NUMBER OF MOVIES SEEN	
1	丗 III
2	丗 IIII
3	丗 I
4	IIII
5	III
6	II

Check How can you check your answer?
Recount the totals in the tally table.

What if two students were absent that day and they each had seen 5 movies? How many students would have seen at least 3 movies? fewer than 3 movies? **17 students; 17 students**

100

 CALIFORNIA STANDARDS **MR 2.0** Students use strategies, skills, and concepts in finding solutions. **MR 3.2** Note the method of deriving the solution and demonstrate a conceptual understanding of the derivations by solving similar problems. *also* **MR 3.3**

RETEACH 5.3

Problem Solving Strategy: Make a Table

Sometimes, when you have a lot of data, you do not need to know about each value. It may be enough to know how many values fit into a particular category. When this is the case, a tally table can help you solve problems.

Mr. Franks corrected the test papers of the 29 students in his 3rd period class. The scores (out of 100) are given below. How many more students had a score below 90 than had a score of 90 or above?

73, 83, 85, 92, 93, 85, 89, 91, 99, 80, 80, 84, 76, 78, 80, 93, 90, 88, 98, 82, 100, 78, 67, 88, 98, 94, 90, 76, 73

Step 1: Think about what you know and what you are asked to find.
• You know all the grades that the students in the 3rd period class received. You do not know who received each grade, but that information is not needed in this situation.
• You are asked to find the difference between the number of students who scored less than 90 and the number who scored 90 or above.

Step 2: Plan a strategy to solve.
• Use the strategy *make a table*
• Organize the data into a tally table. Make only as many rows as you need to solve the problem. For this problem, you need 2 rows: *less than 90* and *90 or above*.

Step 3: Solve.
• Carry out the strategy.

Test Scores	
Less than 90	丗 丗 丗 III
90 or above	丗 丗 I

Count the tallies and find the difference. $18 - 11 = 7$
So, 7 more students had a score below 90 than had a score of 90 or above.

Use the data below and the strategy *make a table* to help you solve 1–2.
The students in a sixth-grade class were surveyed about the number of minutes they spend on the Internet on a typical day. The results of the survey are given below.
15, 0, 20, 15, 30, 0, 0, 0, 15, 20, 60, 45, 20, 10, 0, 30, 0, 0, 90, 45, 0, 10, 0, 20

1. How many more students said they spend some time on the Internet each day than said they do not spend any time on the Internet?
6 more students

2. Of those students who use the Internet, how many more of them spend less than 30 minutes online than spend at least 30 minutes online?
3 more students

PRACTICE 5.3

Problem Solving Strategy: Make a Table

For 1–6, use the data below. Display the data in the table at the right using intervals of 31–40, 41–50, 51–60, and 61–70.

During the basketball season, the Falcons scored the following numbers of points in their games: 63, 52, 47, 51, 60, 49, 48, 54, 61, 52, 40, 38, 57, 46, 44, 63, 70

Number of Points Scored	
31–40	II
41–50	丗
51–60	丗 I
61–70	IIII

1. How many rows of data are in your table?
4 rows

2. How many scores are greater than 40 but less than 61?
11 scores

3. The Falcons won every game in which they scored more than 60 points. How many games did they play in which they scored more than 60 points?
4 games

4. The team lost every game in which they did not score more than 40 points. How many games did they play in which they did not score more than 40 points?
2 games

5. The Falcons' record for the season was 10 wins and 7 losses. How many games did they win in which they scored 60 points or fewer?
6 games

6. With a record of 10 wins and 7 losses, how many games did the Falcons lose when they scored more than 40 points?
5 games

Solve.

7. Dennis has 5 friends and wants to invite 2 of them to go to a baseball game with him and his family. How many different choices of 2 friends can Dennis make?
10 different choices

8. Latifah has a project that is due on May 15. She expects the project to take her 3 weeks to complete. What is the latest date on which she could begin her project in order to be done on time?
April 24

Mixed Review
Write the percent or decimal.
9. 16% 10. 5% 11. 0.55 12. 0.83 13. 0.07
0.16   0.05   55%   83%   7%

Solve the problem by displaying the data in a table.

Members of the math club took a survey to find out how each person gets to school. These are the results.

skateboard	bike	in-line skates	bike
walk	bus	bike	walk
skateboard	bike	bike	bus
walk	skateboard	in-line skates	bike
bus	walk	bus	walk
skateboard	bike	bus	walk

PROBLEM SOLVING STRATEGIES
Draw a Diagram or Picture
Make a Model
Predict and Test
Work Backward
Make an Organized List
Find a Pattern
▶ Make a Table or Graph
Solve a Simpler Problem
Write an Equation
Use Logical Reasoning

1. Make a table using the data above. How many categories of data are in your table?

   A 2   **B** 3   **C** 4   **D** 5   D

2. How many of the math club members walk or ride a skateboard to school? **H**

   F 8   **G** 9   **H** 10   **J** 11

3. How many of the math club members ride a bike or the bus to school?
   12 members

4. How many more math club members walk to school than ride in-line skates to school? **4 more**

5. Julia receives a $50.00 gift certificate to a music store. If she wants to buy three $13.99 CDs and two $7.99 cassettes, how much of her own money will Julia have to add to the $50.00 gift certificate? **$7.95**

6. A basketball team scores 23 points, including six 1-point foul shots. How many 2-point and 3-point baskets could they have made? Make a list of all the possibilities. **1 3-point, 7 2-point; 3 3-point, 4 2-point; 5 3-point, 1 2-point**

7. An automobile club sells books of 10 movie tickets for $45.00. If tickets usually cost $8.75 each, how much do you save on 10 tickets by buying the book? **$42.50**

8. A fence separating two gardens is 24 ft long. If there is a post in the ground every 3 ft, how many posts are in the fence? **9 posts**

9. On a wildlife outing, Enrique spots 3 more seagulls than egrets and 5 more egrets than geese. If he spots 8 geese, how many birds does he spot in all?
   37 birds

10. If today is Tuesday, what day of the week will it be 200 days from today?
    Saturday

11. 📖 **Write a problem** using the data from the math club survey at the top of the page. **Check students' problems.**

101

---

3 Practice

Guided Practice

Do Problem Solving Practice Exercises 1–4 with your students. Identify those having difficulty and use lesson resources to help.

Independent Practice

Assign Exercises 5–11.

In Exercise 6, you may want to suggest students use the strategy *work backward* so that their 2-point and 3-point shot combinations don't incorrectly total 23 points.

4 Assess

Summarize the lesson by having students:

DISCUSS How did you make the table you used to solve Problem 1 on page 101?
Possible answer: I listed each way to get to school. Then I placed a tally for each time the way appeared in the survey results.

 WRITE Explain why *make a table* is a good strategy to use to solve Problem 1 on page 101. Possible answer: It organizes the information by substituting grouped symbols for words. These symbols are easier to total and help you answer more quickly.

Lesson Quiz

Transparency **5.3**

Solve the problem by displaying the data in a table.

Kara counted the number of birds at her feeder every 5 minutes for an hour. She wrote down 3, 5, 1, 3, 7, 3, 5, 2, 7, 6, 4, 4.

1. How many rows of data are in your table?
   7 rows

2. How many times did she see 2 or fewer birds? 2 times

3. How many times did she see 4 or more birds? 7 times

READING STRATEGY 5.3

Use Graphic Aids

Analyze | Choose | Solve | Check

Often you must look for relationships between data. You may have to compare two or more numbers and add amounts. This is easier to do if you use a **graphic aid** such as a tally table.

VOCABULARY
graphic aid

Read the following problem.

Mr. Quang asked his students to name their favorite animal. The results are shown below. Which animal do most students like best? Which animal was third in rank?

monkey	squirrel	dog	squirrel	cat
cat	cat	monkey	dog	monkey
rabbit	dog	cat	cat	monkey
dog	cat	mouse	snake	dog

1. Make a tally table to organize the data. Read the data. Make one tally mark for each animal below its name.

Monkey	Cat	Rabbit	Squirrel	Dog	Mouse	Snake
IIII	ЖII	I	II	ЖII	I	I

2. Solve the problem.

Cat is the favorite. Monkey is ranked third.

Make a table to organize the data; Solve.

3. The Belle School Student Council sold bags of nuts to raise money. These are their results.

peanuts	walnuts	peanuts
brazil nuts	almonds	almonds
brazil nuts	peanuts	almonds
walnuts	pecans	pecans
pecans	almonds	walnuts
walnuts	walnuts	peanuts

How many bags of pecans or almonds were sold in all? Which type of nut sold best?

7 bags; walnuts

4. The principal of a middle school needed to know how students travel to school. She randomly surveyed 20 students.

bike	bike	car	bus
bus	walk	bike	bike
walk	bus	bus	bike
bike	bike	bus	walk
walk	bike	bike	bike

What fraction of students bike to school? What fraction of students travel by car or bus?

$\frac{1}{2}$; $\frac{3}{10}$

CHALLENGE 5.3

Take a Survey

The table below shows the results of a survey in which sixth graders were asked how many televisions were in their homes.

Number of Televisions in Your Home	Number of Students
0	
1	ЖII
2	ЖI
3	Ж Ж
4	ЖI

1. How many students have televisions at home? **30 students**

2. Do more students have at least 3 televisions or fewer than 3 televisions? How many more students?
   at least 3 televisions; 3 more students

3. How many televisions do the students have? **78 televisions**

4. What is the median number of televisions? **3 televisions**

Use the data in the table below for 5–9. If no answer can be determined, write *cannot be determined*.

Number of Telephones in Your Home	Number of Students
0 or 1	ЖI
2 or 3	Ж Ж II
4 or 5	II

5. How many students have more than 3 telephones at home? **4 students**

6. How many students have fewer than 3 telephones at home?
   cannot be determined

7. How many students have telephones? **cannot be determined**

8. How many students have at least 2 telephones? **23 students**

9. How many students have no more than 4 telephones? **cannot be determined**

101

Frequency Tables and Line Plots

LESSON PLANNING

Objective To record and organize data by using a frequency table or a line plot

Intervention for Prerequisite Skills

Read a Table, Range (For intervention strategies, see page 93.)

 California Mathematics Content Standards

SDAP 1.1 Compute the range, mean, median, and mode of data sets.

(*Also* SDAP 1.0, MR 2.4)

Vocabulary

frequency table a table that organizes the total for each category or group

cumulative frequency a running total of frequencies, shown in a column of a frequency table

Math Background

Unorganized data do not provide much information. They are difficult to interpret. Data can be organized in line plots or frequency tables. The following ideas will help students understand and use frequency tables and line plots:

- In a line plot, the categories are placed horizontally along a line and X marks are placed above the numbers.

- The first step in making a frequency table is to tally the data. Once tallied, the total number for each category is entered in the frequency table.

- The running totals, or cumulative frequencies, give information about two or more categories.

WARM-UP RESOURCES

 NUMBER OF THE DAY

Looking at the calendar for one full year, you will see one digit for days more often than any other. What is it and how many times does it appear? 1; 163

 PROBLEM OF THE DAY

Anne's line plot of ages of students has a range of 4. Each age has twice as many x's as the previous one. If the last age has 16 x's, how many students did Anne include in her data? 31 students

Solution Problem of the Day tab, p. PD5

 DAILY FACTS PRACTICE

Have students practice addition facts by completing Set D of *Teacher's Resource Book,* p. TR96.

ALTERNATIVE TEACHING STRATEGY

Ask students to **make a tally table for the data** in the table for Example 1 on page 102. Discuss how the tally table and line plot show the same information in different forms. Then add a column labeled *Frequency* to the tally table. Explain that the frequency of a data item tells how many times the data item occurs. Show how to fill in the frequency column of the table.

During discussion, point out that the numbers in the frequency column provide the same information as the tally table and line plot. Use the discussion as a transition to the situation in Example 2 on page 103.

See also page 104.

VISUAL

MIXED REVIEW AND TEST PREP

Cumulative Review Chapters 1–5

Refer to the Pupil Edition pages referenced in the exercises for further review. Have students go to the lesson page, review the lesson, and correct any problem they missed.

Mixed Review and Test Prep, p. 105

How to Help	
Item	Page
18	98
19	98
20	28
21	40
22	22

ENGLISH LANGUAGE LEARNERS ELL•SDAIE

Materials dictionary

Have students talk about the **meaning of the words *frequency* and *frequently*.**

- Model the words by showing real-life connections such as a menu with multiple pizza entries or a monthly rainfall table for several cities.
- Ask them to look up the words in a dictionary, read the definitions aloud, and identify the meanings that match the way the words are used in this lesson.
- Encourage students to use the words in their own sentences. Possible answer: Pizza is frequently on the menu. The frequency of rain increases in the spring.

VISUAL

ENG-LANG ARTS Standards R 1.0

EARLY FINISHERS

Materials *For each group* 2 number cubes numbered 1–6, p. TR75

Encourage students to **practice making frequency tables.** Ask them to work in small groups to see what sums are rolled most often when the 2 cubes are rolled 30 times. Have groups prepare a cumulative frequency table that lists the possible sums in increasing order.

After they have completed their tables, have groups compare and discuss their results. Check students' work.

VISUAL

TECHNOLOGY LINK

- **Intervention Strategies and Activities CD-ROM** • *Skills 75, 76*
- **Data ToolKit** • *Make a Frequency Table, Make a Line Plot*

Objective To record and organize data by using a frequency table or a line plot

Vocabulary frequency table, cumulative frequency *Review* range

1 Introduce

QUICK REVIEW provides review of pre-requisite skills.

Why Learn This? Making a frequency table or line plot allows you to quickly analyze and draw conclusions from raw data. *Share the lesson objective with students.*

2 Teach

Guided Instruction

• *Discuss with students the meaning of the line plot in Example 1.*

Which numbers on the line plot represent data from the original table? the numbers with X's above them

If you made a tally table for the data, how would the number of tally marks after an entry compare with the number of X's for that same number? The number of tally marks would equal the number of X's.

ADDITIONAL EXAMPLE

Example 1, p. 102

TEST SCORES							
100	98	97	96	98	97	99	99
97	96	98	100	100	100	98	98

Use the data above to make a line plot.

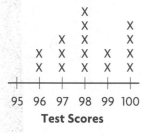

95 96 97 98 99 100
Test Scores

Frequency Tables and Line Plots

Learn how to record and organize data collected in a survey.

1. 70 90 $+20$	**2.** 35 75 $+40$	**3.** 67 37 -30	**4.** 50 35 -15	**5.** 240 ÷ 6 40

Vocabulary

frequency table
cumulative frequency

In 2000, the largest iceberg on record contained enough ice to provide everyone on earth with 4 gallons of water per day for 40 years! Most of an iceberg is below the surface of the water. The data in the table below show the number of icebergs a scientist observed every day for 20 days.

NUMBER OF ICEBERGS OBSERVED				
12	15	11	16	15
16	16	15	13	16
16	14	12	14	16
15	13	15	14	15

You can use a line plot to record data.

EXAMPLE 1

Use the data above to make a line plot.

Step 1: Draw a horizontal line.

Step 2: On your line, write the numerical values for the number of icebergs, using vertical tick marks.

TECHNOLOGY LINK

More Practice: Use *Data ToolKit* to make frequency tables and line plots.

Step 3: Plot the data.

Each X represents the number of icebergs the scientist observed during one day.

```
                        X  X
                        X  X
                        X  X
                  X     X  X
            X  X  X  X  X  X
            X  X  X  X  X  X
        +--+--+--+--+--+--+--+--
        10 11 12 13 14 15 16 17
```
Number of Icebergs Observed

A line plot helps you see if there are any gaps or extremes in the data. You can also see where data cluster. The line plot in Example 1 shows that the scientist observed 15–16 icebergs per day more often than she observed 11–14 icebergs per day.

102

RETEACH 5.4

Frequency Tables and Line Plots

A local fitness center wants to survey 50 adults to find out if they exercise daily. The age of each person who said *yes* was recorded. Use the data below to make a line plot.

Ages of Adults Who Said Yes					
28	33	45	25	50	42	33
25	48	31	37	28	25	50
42	29	45	50	38	31	29
38	52	40	33	25	37	52

Step 1: Draw a horizontal line.
Step 2: On the line, write numerical values for the ages, using vertical tick marks.
Step 3: Plot the data by drawing an x on the line plot for each value, or person's age, in the table.

```
x                       x
x           x       x x         x         x
x x x   x   x   x x x x x   x       x   x x
+--+--+--+--+--+--+--+--+--+--+--+--+--+--+--+--+--+--+--+--+--+--+--+--+--+--+--+--
25 26 27 28 29 30 31 32 33 34 35 36 37 38 39 40 41 42 43 44 45 46 47 48 49 50 51 52
```

For Exercises 1–2, use the data in the tables to make a line plot.
1. A local bookstore wants to survey 50 students to find out if they buy at least one book a month. The surveyor recorded the age of each student who said yes.

Ages of Students Who Said Yes					
13	12	16	15	11	14	15
11	16	14	14	13	15	11
14	15	11	12	16	11	13

```
x                   x   x  x x
x     x     x       x   x  x x
x x x x x   x     x x   x  x x
+--+--+--+--+--+
11 12 13 14 15 16
```

2. The 20 students in science class take a test. Here are their results.

Science Test Scores				
76	82	85	95	98
92	78	76	90	85
88	95	74	78	76
74	85	92	82	88

```
                x
x x x       x       x       x
x x x   x   x   x x x   x   x x
+--+--+--+--+--+--+--+--+--+--+--+--+--+--+--+--+--+--+--+--+--+--+--+--
74 75 76 77 78 79 80 81 82 83 84 85 86 87 88 89 90 91 92 93 94 95 96 97 98
```

PRACTICE 5.4

Frequency Tables and Line Plots

Vocabulary

1. A running total of the number of people surveyed is called
cumulative frequency

2. A ___frequency table___ shows the total for each category or group in a set of data.

For 3–4, use the data in the chart at the right.

Students' Heights (cm)					
160	137	158	155	136	154
154	159	142	147	148	144
152	133	135	136	162	158
139	160	154	139	159	144
155	147	136	148	162	133

3. Find the range. ___29___
4. Make a line plot

```
    x                       x
x   x   x       x       x x     x x   x x x   x
x x x x x   x   x   x   x x x   x x   x x x   x x x
+--+--+--+--+--+--+--+--+--+--+--+--+--+--+--+--+
133 135 137 139 141 143 145 147 149 151 153 155 157 159 161 162
```
Students' Heights (cm)

For 5–6, use the chart at the right.

Reading Test Scores				
98	100	81	92	78
75	96	78	84	100
82	100	100	86	78

5. Find the range. ___25___
6. Make a line plot

```
                                      x
x                                     x
x       x x     x       x     x       x
+--+--+--+--+--+--+--+--+--+--+--+--+--
74 76 78 80 82 84 86 88 90 92 94 96 98 100
```
Reading Test Scores

Mixed Review

Compare the numbers. Write >, <, or = for ●.

7. 31.7 ● 37.1 ___<___   8. 72.67 ● 72.670 ___=___   9. 66.61 ● 66.16 ___>___

Solve. Use the information in the table.

10. Estimate the combined population of the four cities. ___230,000___

11. How many more people lived in Billings than in Missoula? ___39,991___

Population of the Four Largest Cities in Montana in 1999	
City	Population
Billings	91,195
Great Falls	57,758
Missoula	51,204
Butte-Silver Bow	34,051

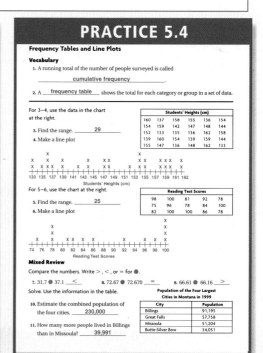

Frequency Tables

A **frequency table** shows the total for each category or group. You can add a cumulative frequency column to the table. **Cumulative frequency** is a running total of the frequencies.

EXAMPLE 2

The local mall surveyed 75 teens regarding the overall quality of food at the mall's food court. Use the data from the survey to make a frequency table. Do you think most teens like the quality of food at the food court?

Quality of Food at Food Court	
Quality	Tally
Very Good	IIII IIII IIII IIII
Good	IIII IIII IIII IIII IIII IIII
Fair	IIII IIII IIII
Poor	IIII IIII

List the categories of quality in one column. Record the total for each category in the frequency column. Record the running total in the cumulative frequency column.

QUALITY OF FOOD AT FOOD COURT		
Quality	Frequency	Cumulative Frequency
Very Good	20	20
Good	30	50	← 20 + 30 = 50
Fair	15	65	← 50 + 15 = 65
Poor	10	75	← 65 + 10 = 75

So, most teens liked the quality of food at the food court: 50 out of 75 teens surveyed rated the food as good or very good.

A local mall took a survey to find the number of times people go to the mall in one year. The survey results are shown below.

NUMBER OF TRIPS TO THE MALL									
12	20	5	7	13	11	3	9	19	16
8	17	17	16	1	6	8	5	14	9

EXAMPLE 3

Remember that the range of a set of data is the difference between the greatest number and the least number in the set of data.

Use the data about the number of trips to the mall to make a cumulative frequency table with intervals.

$20 - 1 = 19$ *Find the range.*

Since $4 \times 5 = 20$, which is close to 19, make 4 intervals that include 5 consecutive numbers.   *Use the range to determine intervals.*

TRIPS TO THE MALL		
Number of Trips	Frequency	Cumulative Frequency
1-5	4	4
6-10	6	10
11-15	4	14
16-20	6	20

Complete the cumulative frequency table.

103

- *Use Example 2 to help students understand how to find the frequency of a data item.*

  Use the tally table. Which quality rating occurred most often? Explain. *Good*; it occurred 30 times.

  Describe a survey situation in which the cumulative frequency column would not be meaningful. Possible answer: a survey concerning favorite pets or Internet sites when there is no natural way to order the categories

- *Discuss when intervals are useful in tables that show frequency and cumulative frequency.*

  Why is it helpful to group the number of trips by intervals in Example 3? Possible answer: Intervals give you a quick idea how many of those surveyed visited the mall *very often, often, from time to time,* or *seldom.*

REASONING **In what situation might you be unable to use intervals in a frequency table?** when the range for data is small

Algebraic Thinking Displaying data in a frequency table or line plot helps students develop representational thinking skills. Have students explain which method of organizing data they prefer and why.

ADDITIONAL EXAMPLES

Example 2, p. 103

The principal surveyed 35 sixth graders regarding their enjoyment of the school play. Use this data to make a frequency table. Do you think that most sixth graders liked the play? Responses are as follows: Very Good—15; Good—10; Fair—6; Poor—4. Check students' work; most students liked the play since 25 out of 35 students surveyed thought it was good or very good.

Example 3, p. 103

Number of Trips to the Grocery Store							
6	10	15	12	8	8	7	2
9	15	11	1	12	3	10	

Use the data above to make a cumulative frequency table with intervals.

Find the range: $15 - 1 = 14$

Since $3 \times 5 = 15$, which is close to 14, make 3 intervals that include 5 consecutive numbers. Check students' work.

PROBLEM SOLVING 5.4

Frequency Tables and Line Plots

Write the correct answer.

1. The scores on the last quiz are given below. What is the range of the data?

Scores				
15	11	8	19	20
16	14	18	20	19
16	14	11	19	20

12

2. The line plot shows the average length of a student's stride in centimeters. How many students participated in the survey?

24 students

Choose the letter for the best answer.

3. The recorded temperatures of selected cities were: 67°, 54°, 98°, 77°, 92°, 85°, 83°, 90°, 63°, 74°, and 96°. What is the range of the temperatures?
   A 29°
   B 31°
   C 35°
   D 44°

4. Sara likes to swim between 20 and 30 laps in her pool each day for exercise. What is a reasonable estimate for the number of laps she would swim in 35 days?
   F Less than 300
   G Between 300 and 500
   H Between 500 and 700
   I More than 700

5. George helped his father plant 4,836 trees last month. This month they planted 6,981 trees. Which is the best estimate of how many more trees George and his father planted this month than last month?
   A 2,000 trees
   B 2,500 trees
   C 3,000 trees
   D 3,500 trees

6. The results of the last test were: 67, 84, 98, 70, 72, 66, 78, 74, 90, 92, 77, 93, 95, 79, 91, 87, 88, 86, 68, 71, 62, and 78. If the data were grouped by 60s, 70s, 80s, and 90s, what would the frequency be for the 90s?
   F 3
   G 4
   H 6
   J 8

7. **Write About It** If the results of a survey are displayed on a line plot, how can you tell which answer was the most popular?

   The answer with the most Xs is the most popular.

CHALLENGE 5.4

Video Game Survey

Marla surveyed sixth-grade students about the number of hours per week they spend playing video games. She organized her data in the frequency table and line plot below. Use the table and line plot to answer the questions.

Hours Sixth Graders Spent Playing Video Games Each Week		
Number of Hours	Frequency	Cumulative Frequency
0	14	14
1	6	20
2	9	29
3	7	36
4	5	41
5	6	47
6	3	50

1. How many students did Marla survey?

   50 students

2. What is the range of her data?

   6

3. What fraction of the students surveyed spend 4 hours a week playing video games?

   $\frac{1}{10}$ of the students

4. What fraction of the students surveyed spend less than 2 hours a week playing video games?

   $\frac{2}{5}$ of the students

5. What fraction of the students surveyed spend more than 3 hours a week playing video games?

   $\frac{7}{25}$ of the students

6. For every 1 student who responded "6 hours," there are 2 students who responded "5 hours." What other pair of responses has a similar relationship?

   (1:2 ratio) 3 hr:0 hr; 6 hr:1 hr

7. Suppose Marla continued the survey and polled 100 additional classmates. Based on her first survey, how many students would likely respond "0 hours"?

   42 students

8. Suppose Marla wanted to expand her survey and ask another question about video game play. What are two possible questions she might ask? Possible answers: What is your favorite game? What type of system do you have?

LESSON 5.4

REASONING In Example 4, there are 30 responses. Why would 3 intervals of 10 consecutive numbers not be enough? The responses are not consecutive numbers but are spread over a range of 37, requiring more intervals.

Example 4, p. 104

AGES OF BICYCLISTS						
24	15	32	36	44	41	18
17	25	28	31	23	29	32

Use the data above to make a cumulative frequency table with intervals.

Find the range: $44 - 15 = 29$

Since $3 \times 10 = 30$, make 3 intervals that include 10 consecutive numbers. Check students' work.

3 Practice

Guided Practice

Do Check for Understanding Exercises 1–5 with your students. Identify those having difficulty and use lesson resources to help.

Independent Practice

Assign Exercises 6–17.

Cumulative frequency tables with intervals can also be used to organize data about different age groups. The data in the table below show the ages of joggers at the Get Fit exercise trail.

AGES OF JOGGERS									
27	31	11	22	25	42	44	36	33	24
19	34	48	17	28	33	32	30	40	31
38	18	22	23	24	27	36	19	26	32

EXAMPLE 4

Use the data about the ages of joggers at the Get Fit exercise trail to make a cumulative frequency table with intervals.

$48 - 11 = 37$ *Find the range.*

Since $4 \times 10 = 40$, which is close to 37, make 4 intervals that include 10 consecutive numbers. *Use the range to determine intervals.*

Complete the cumulative frequency table.

AGES OF JOGGERS		
Age	Frequency	Cumulative Frequency
10–19	5	5
20–29	10	15
30–39	11	26
40–49	4	30

CHECK FOR UNDERSTANDING

Think and Discuss ▶ Look back at the lesson to answer each question.

1. *REASONING* Name the intervals you could have in Example 3 if you made 2 intervals. Explain. 1–10, 11–20; Since $2 \times 10 = 20$, you would have 2 intervals that each include 10 numbers.
2. **Explain** how to find the size of the survey sample by using the frequency table in Example 4. Look at the last number in the cumulative frequency column.

Guided Practice ▶ For 3–5, use the data in the table.

3. Make a line plot. See Additional Answers, p. 117A.
4. Make a cumulative frequency table. See Additional Answers, p. 117A.
5. Find the range. 16

AGES OF POP MUSIC LISTENERS						
12	13	17	16	15	13	25
28	27	18	15	12	14	23
13	15	17	13	22	18	15

PRACTICE AND PROBLEM SOLVING

Independent Practice ▶ For 6–8, use the data in the table.

6. Make a line plot. See Additional Answers, p. 117A.
7. Make a cumulative frequency table. See Additional Answers, p. 117A.
8. Find the range. 12

NUMBER OF KILOMETERS BIKED						
6	11	7	8	8	5	15
14	12	10	11	6	7	9
15	15	8	9	12	17	10

Alternative Teaching Strategy

Purpose Students collect data, use data in a frequency table, and draw conclusions based on the data.

As a class, brainstorm a list of possible survey questions students can ask 50 students throughout the school. For example:

• How many brothers and sisters do you have?
• Do you rate the school lunch as Very Good, Good, Fair, or Poor?
• How many minutes of television do you watch each day?

Have students work in small groups to choose one of the questions to use for their survey. Then have each group survey 50 students from other classes in the school and record the results in a tally chart. A sample of a tally table is shown.

NUMBER OF BROTHERS AND SISTERS	
Number	Tally
0–2	⍫⍫ ⍫⍫ ⍫⍫ ⍫⍫ ⍫⍫ ⍫⍫
3–5	⍫⍫ ⍫⍫ ⍫⍫
More than 5	⍫⍫

The groups can then make a frequency table with appropriate headings. Have groups share their tally tables and frequency tables with the class. A sample of a frequency table is shown.

NUMBER OF BROTHERS AND SISTERS		
Number	Frequency	Cumulative Frequency
0–2	30	30
3–5	15	45
More than 5	5	50

Check students' work.

Kim asked people in her neighborhood about their favorite type of movie. Use the data for 9–10.

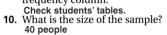

FAVORITE MOVIES	
Movies	**Tally**
Drama	卌 卌
Action	卌 III
Comedy	卌 卌 III
Mystery	卌 IIII

9. Organize the data into a frequency table. Include a cumulative frequency column.
   Check students' tables.

10. What is the size of the sample?
   40 people

For 11–14, use the data in the box at the right.

11. Make a line plot.
   See Additional Answers, p. 117A.

12. Find the range. 36

13. How many numbers would be in each interval if you used the range to make 4 intervals? 9 weights

WEIGHTS OF STUDENTS' PET DOGS (LB)					
40	10	22	33	44	40
41	42	12	35	20	10
30	25	20	18	46	35
34	35	40	40	35	38

14. Make a cumulative frequency table using 4 intervals for the weights.
   See Additional Answers, p. 117A.

Problem Solving ▶ Applications

15. *REASONING*   Survey your classmates about their favorite hobbies. Organize the data in a tally table and a frequency table. Can you make a line plot of the data? Explain. Tables will vary.
   No, the data are categories and are not numerical.

16. Decide on appropriate intervals and make a cumulative frequency table using intervals for the data in the table below.
   See Additional Answers, p. 117A.

POUNDS OF VEGETABLES CONSUMED YEARLY											
12	16	18	12	9	21	14	17	18	5	23	25	32
17	16	8	9	22	21	14	18	7	23	24	19	13

17. **?** What's the Question?   In a set of data, the greatest value is 54 and the least value is 30. If the answer is 24, what's the question? What is the range?

MIXED REVIEW AND TEST PREP

Tell whether the question is *biased* or *unbiased*. (p. 98)

18. Do you feel that sixth graders should do two hours of homework each night instead of watching TV? biased

19. Whom do you intend to vote for in the upcoming Student Government election? unbiased

20. Tell if the expression is numerical or algebraic. $a + 3.9$ (p. 28) algebraic

21. **TEST PREP**   Which is the value of 4^5? (p. 40) D

   A 9   **B** 20   **C** 625   **D** 1,024

22. **TEST PREP**   Sharon rode her bike a total of 36 km at a rate of 9 km per hr. How long did she ride? (p. 22) G

   F 2 hr   **G** 4 hr   **H** 6 hr   **J** 9 hr

Extra Practice   page H36, Set C

105

Exercises 18–22 provide **cumulative review** (Chapters 1–5).

4 Assess

Summarize the lesson by having students:

DISCUSS What does the greatest number in the cumulative frequency column of a table tell you about the original set of data? the number of responses in the original set of data

WRITE Which is closer to the original data for a survey, a tally table or a frequency table with intervals? Why?
Possible answer: A tally table is more like the original data because it gives information about how often each data item occurs. A frequency table with intervals reports only on groups of data items.

Lesson Quiz

Transparency **5.4**

A survey asked people how many pieces of fruit they eat in a week.

Pieces of Fruit Eaten in a Week						
3	1	5	5	2	4	5
9	4	1	2	6	7	4
9	2	7	5	4	3	5

1. Make a line plot for the data.

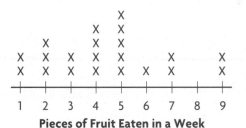

Pieces of Fruit Eaten in a Week

2. Use the data to make a cumulative frequency table with 3 intervals.

PIECES OF FRUIT EATEN IN A WEEK		
Pieces of Fruit	**Frequency**	**Cumulative Frequency**
1–3	7	7
4–6	10	17
7–9	4	21

105

Measures of Central Tendency
LESSON PLANNING

Objective To calculate the mean, median, and mode and to determine their meanings for a set of data

Intervention for Prerequisite Skills

Mean, Median, Mode (For intervention strategies, see page 93.)

Materials *For Thinker's Corner* 10-section spinner, p. TR73

 California Mathematics Content Standards

SDAP 1.1 Compute the range, mean, median, and mode of data sets.

SDAP 1.4 Know why a specific measure of central tendency (mean, median, mode) provides the most useful information in a given context.

(*Also* NS 2.0, SDAP 1.0, MR 2.4)

Math Background

One way to characterize a set of data is to use measures of central tendency, which are single numbers that help describe the set as a whole and are used to compare different sets of data. Consider these ideas when helping students understand the mean, median, and mode.

• The mean of the numbers in a set is the sum of the numbers divided by the number of members in the set.

• The median is the middle number in a set of ordered numbers.

• The mode is the most frequently occurring member of the set.

Of the three measures, only the mode is guaranteed to be a member of the data set.

WARM-UP RESOURCES

 NUMBER OF THE DAY Transparency 5.5

Find the range for the number of days of this month.
Answers will vary.

 PROBLEM OF THE DAY Transparency 5.5

A set of 9 numbers has a mean of 7. When one more number is added to the set, the mean is doubled. What number was added to the data set? 77

Solution Problem of the Day tab, p. PD5

 DAILY FACTS PRACTICE

Have students practice addition and subtraction facts by completing Set E of *Teacher's Resource Book,* p. TR96.

INTERVENTION AND EXTENSION RESOURCES

ALTERNATIVE TEACHING STRATEGY ELL

Materials *For each student* 1 index card

Engage students in **finding the mean, median, and mode.** Provide each student with an index card and ask each to write a number from 1 to 10 on it.

Draw a large line plot on a piece of paper and place it on the floor or hang it on a wall.

- Have each student attach his or her number over the appropriate number on the line plot.
- Summarize by stating, for example, "Five people chose 10."
- Then have students use the line plot to find the median of the numbers chosen.
- Also have them find the mode and mean of the numbers. Check students' work.

KINESTHETIC

MIXED REVIEW AND TEST PREP

Cumulative Review Chapters 1–5

Refer to the Pupil Edition pages referenced in the exercises for further review. Have students go to the lesson page, review the lesson, and correct any problem they missed.

Mixed Review and Test Prep, p. 108

How to Help	
Item	**Page**
16	102
17	102
18	60
19	60
20	70

WRITING IN MATHEMATICS

Have students **describe situations that represent mean, mode, or median** and have their classmates determine which measure of central tendency each situation represents.

Provide this example:

- Most of the cereal brands tested contained 6 grams of sugar per serving. mode

ADVANCED LEARNERS

Challenge students to **use the measures of central tendency** shown to find possible values for a data set containing the given number of data items.

	Mean	Mode	Median	# of items
1.	4	4	4	4

Possible answer: 3, 4, 4, 5

	Mean	Mode	Median	# of items
2.	31	37	37	5

Possible answer: 13, 25, 37, 37, 43

3.	47	42	42	5

Possible answer: 38, 42, 42, 56, 57

4.	79	77	78	6

Possible answer: 77, 77, 77, 79, 81, 83

VISUAL

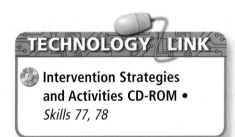

TECHNOLOGY LINK

Intervention Strategies and Activities CD-ROM •
Skills 77, 78

LESSON **5.5** ORGANIZER

Objective To calculate the mean, median, and mode and to determine their meanings for a set of data

Vocabulary *Review* mean, median, mode

Materials 10-section spinner, p. TR73

1 Introduce

QUICK REVIEW provides review of pre-requisite skills.

Why Learn This? You can use this skill to summarize data, such as test scores or sports statistics. *Share the lesson objective with students.*

2 Teach

Guided Instruction

• *As you discuss the three measures of central tendency, ask:*

To find the median of a set of data, when do you need to find the average of the two middle numbers? when there is an even number of data items

REASONING **How can you visually locate the mean, median, and mode on a line plot without looking at the numbers?** The tallest point represents the mode. The point where half the X's represent a lesser value and half the X's represent a greater value would be the median. If the plot were thought of as a seesaw or scale, the balance point represents the mean.

• *As students look at Example 2, ask:*

Would it be helpful to make a line plot? Explain. Possible answer: Probably not; there are only 5 data items, so a line plot is not necessary to find the mode or median.

ADDITIONAL EXAMPLE

Example 1, p. 106

Use the data to make a line plot. Find the mode and the median.

NUMBER OF BOOKS READ								
3	7	8	1	6	4	3	3	5
8	7	2	6	1	2	2	3	4

Check students' plots. mode: 3, median: 3.5

Measures of Central Tendency

L**earn** how to find the mean, median, and mode of a set of data and which best describes the set of data.

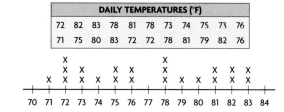

T**hree** measures of central tendency are mean, median, and mode. Measures of central tendency can help you to describe a set of data.

In April 1998, amateur rocket builder Gib Reynolds set an American record for 7- to 13-year-olds. His model rocket soared to a height of 47 meters. Data for heights some model rockets traveled, including Gib's, are shown at the right. Find the mean, median, and mode for the data.

ROCKET HEIGHTS (M)				
47	28	33	35	28

Mean: $(47 + 28 + 33 + 35 + 28) ÷ 5 = 171 ÷ 5 = $ 34.2 m

Median: 28 28 33 35 47; 33 m   **Mode:** 28 m

Sometimes a line plot can help you to find the mode and the median.

EXAMPLE 1

R**emember** that the mean is the sum of a group of numbers divided by the number of addends.

The median is the middle number in a group of numbers arranged in numerical order.

The mode is the number that occurs most often.

Use the data to make a line plot. Find the mode and the median.

DAILY TEMPERATURES (°F)										
72	82	83	78	81	78	73	74	75	73	76
71	75	80	83	72	72	78	81	79	82	76

```
         X                   X
 X   X       X   X       X           X   X   X
 X   X   X   X   X   X       X   X   X   X   X   X
 +---+---+---+---+---+---+---+---+---+---+---+---+---+---+
 70  71  72  73  74  75  76  77  78  79  80  81  82  83  84
```

Mode: The modes are 72 and 78 since each occurs three times.

Median: Since there are 22 temperatures, the median is the mean of the 11th and 12th temperatures. $(76 + 78) ÷ 2 = 77$

M**ath Idea** ▶ When you want to summarize a set of data as one value, you can use one of the three measures of central tendency.

EXAMPLE 2

Pedro jogged 6 mi, 5 mi, 2 mi, 2 mi, and 4 mi over 5 days. Which measure of central tendency is most useful to describe the data?

Mean: $(6 + 5 + 2 + 2 + 4) ÷ 5 = 19 ÷ 5 = 3.8$

Median: 2 2 4 5 6; 4   **Mode:** 2

The mean, or 3.8, and the median, 4, are close to most of the data while the mode, or 2, is closer to the lower end of the data. So, the mean or median is most useful to describe the data.

106

RETEACH 5.5

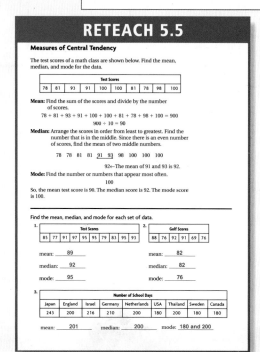

Measures of Central Tendency

The test scores of a math class are shown below. Find the mean, median, and mode for the data.

Test Scores									
78	81	93	91	100	100	81	78	98	100

Mean: Find the sum of the scores and divide by the number of scores.

78 + 81 + 93 + 91 + 100 + 100 + 81 + 78 + 98 + 100 = 900
900 ÷ 10 = 90

Median: Arrange the scores in order from least to greatest. Find the number that is in the middle. Since there is an even number of scores, find the mean of two middle numbers.

78 78 81 81 93 98 100 100 100
92←The mean of 91 and 93 is 92.

Mode: Find the number or numbers that appear most often.
100

So, the mean test score is 90. The median score is 92. The mode score is 100.

Find the mean, median, and mode for each set of data.

1.
Test Scores									
85	77	91	97	95	95	79	83	95	93

mean: 89
median: 92
mode: 95

2.
Golf Scores					
88	76	92	91	69	76

mean: 82
median: 82
mode: 76

3.
Number of School Days									
Japan	England	Israel	Germany	Netherlands	USA	Thailand	Sweden	Canada	
243	200	216	210	200	180	200	180	180	

mean: 201   median: 200   mode: 180 and 200

PRACTICE 5.5

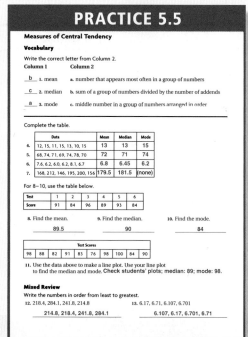

Measures of Central Tendency

Vocabulary

Write the correct letter from Column 2.

Column 1		Column 2
b	1. mean	a. number that appears most often in a group of numbers
c	2. median	b. sum of a group of numbers divided by the number of addends
a	3. mode	c. middle number in a group of numbers arranged in order

Complete the table.

	Data	Mean	Median	Mode
4.	12, 15, 11, 15, 13, 10, 15	13	13	15
5.	68, 74, 71, 69, 74, 78, 70	72	71	74
6.	7.6, 6.2, 6.0, 6.2, 8.1, 6.7	6.8	6.45	6.2
7.	168, 212, 146, 195, 200, 156	179.5	181.5	(none)

For 8–10, use the table below.

Test	1	2	3	4	5	6
Score	91	84	96	89	93	84

8. Find the mean.   9. Find the median.   10. Find the mode.
89.5   90   84

Test Scores									
98	88	82	91	83	76	98	100	84	90

11. Use the data above to make a line plot. Use your line plot to find the median and mode. Check students' plots; median: 89; mode: 98.

Mixed Review

Write the numbers in order from least to greatest.
12. 218.4, 284.1, 241.8, 214.8   13. 6.17, 6.71, 6.107, 6.701
214.8, 218.4, 241.8, 284.1   6.107, 6.17, 6.701, 6.71

Sometimes the mean is not the best measure of central tendency to describe a set of data.

EXAMPLE 3

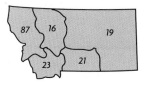

The bald eagle, America's national bird, was once a greatly endangered species. In recent decades, the species has made a dramatic recovery. The map at the right shows the number of nests in five zones of Montana. Which measure of central tendency is most useful to describe the data?

Numbers of nests: 87, 16, 19, 21, 23

Mean: $(87 + 16 + 19 + 21 + 23) \div 5 = 166 \div 5 = 33.2$

Median: 16 19 21 23 87 → 21

Mode: No value occurs more than any other, so there is no mode.

The median, 21, is close to most of the data. The high value of 87 makes the mean greater than any of the four other values. So, the median is most useful to describe the data.

CHECK FOR UNDERSTANDING

Think and Discuss ▶ Look back at the lesson to answer the question.

1. **What if,** in Example 3, the region with 87 nests had only 27 nests? Which of the measures would change? Which measure would be most useful to describe the data? The mean would become 21.2. The mean or median would be most useful to describe the data.

Guided Practice ▶ For 2–4, use the table below.

Day	Sun	Mon	Tue	Wed	Thu	Fri	Sat
Hours of Sleep	8	6	7	7	4	10	7

2. Find the mean. 7 hours
3. Find the median. 7 hours
4. Find the mode. 7 hours

Find the mean, median, and mode.

5. 22, 24, 22, 29, 33, 14
   24; 23; 22
6. 124, 120, 132, 133, 119, 90, 87
   115; 120; no mode

PRACTICE AND PROBLEM SOLVING

Independent Practice ▶ For 7–9, use the table below.

Game	1	2	3	4	5	6	7	8
Points Scored	10	12	10	17	18	12	20	24

7. Find the mean. 15.375 points
8. Find the median. 14.5 points
9. Find the mode. 10 and 12

Find the mean, median, and mode.

10. 76, 63, 40, 52, 52, 40, 6, 15
    43; 46; 40 and 52
11. 365, 180, 360, 720, 59
    336.8; 360; no mode

107

PROBLEM SOLVING 5.5

Measures of Central Tendency
Write the correct answer.

1. Find the mean of the numbers.
   23, 86, 97, 45, 12
   52.6

2. Evaluate the expression below.
   a + b − 12.7 for a = 4.9 and b = 28.6
   20.8

3. Find the median of the numbers.
   13, 8, 9, 16, 18
   13

4. If you survey 1 out of every 10 people, how many would you survey out of a group of 23,800 people?
   2,380 people

Choose the letter for the best answer.

5. Yolanda has received scores of 98, 76, 87, 98, and 80 so far this year on her math tests. What is the mean of her test scores?
   A 98
   B 87.8
   C 87.5
   D 87

6. Fred conducted a survey regarding hair color. Which measure of central tendency should he use to report the hair color that occurs most often?
   F range
   G mean
   H median
   J mode

7. A pilot logged 87,984 miles of flight time in one month. If he flew the same route every day for 20 days, what is a good estimate for the length of his route?
   A 3,500 mi
   B 4,000 mi
   C 4,500 mi
   D 5,000 mi

8. Mr. Jacob works between 9 and 12 hours each day, 5 days a week. What is a reasonable estimate of the number of hours he works in 50 weeks?
   F Less than 400 hr
   G Between 400 and 1,000 hr
   H Between 1,000 and 2,000 hr
   J More than 2,000 hr

9. **Write About It** Explain why the mean of a set of data is sometimes a number that is not in the set of data.
   The mean is the sum of a group of numbers divided by the number
   of addends. This average may or may not be one of the numbers
   in the group.

CHALLENGE 5.5

Number Puzzles
Use the information to find the numbers in the group. The first one is done for you. Possible answers are given.

1. There are 7 whole numbers in a group. The least number in the group is 6. The greatest number in the group is 16. The mode of the group is 15. The median is 10 and the mean is 11.
   6, 7, 8, 10, 15, 15, 16

2. There are 5 whole numbers in a group. The least number is 7 and the greatest is 14. The mode is 9 and the median is 9. The mean is 10.
   7, 9, 9, 11, 14

3. There are 7 whole numbers in a group. The greatest number is 20 and the least is 8. The median is 12 and the mode is 12. The mean is 13.
   8, 10, 12, 12, 14, 15, 20

4. There are 7 whole numbers in a group. The least number is 5 and the greatest is 15. The mean and the median are 11. The mode is 15.
   5, 7, 9, 11, 15, 15, 15

5. There are 7 whole numbers in a group. The least number is 11 and the greatest is 17. The mean and the median are 14. There is no mode.
   11, 12, 13, 14, 15, 16, 17

6. There are 7 whole numbers in a group. The least number is 15 and the greatest is 33. The mean is 23. The median is 22. The mode is 19.
   15, 19, 19, 22, 25, 28, 33

7. There are 7 whole numbers in a group. The greatest number is 37 and the least is 21. The median is 29. The mean is 28. The mode is 31.
   21, 23, 24, 29, 31, 31, 37

REASONING **What is a quick way to tell whether the mean will be a useful measure of central tendency?** Examine the data for items that are considerably greater or less than the others.

ADDITIONAL EXAMPLES

Example 2, p. 106

A CD producer recorded the following number of songs on her most recent CDs: 15, 10, 18, 17, 10, 16, 12. Find the mean, median, and mode of the data. Then tell which measure of central tendency best represents the data. Mean—14; Median—15; Mode—10; either the mean or the median represents the data best.

Example 3, p. 107

Which measure of central tendency is most useful to describe the data?

Math test scores: 34, 99, 94, 100, 93, 96

The median, or 95, is close to most of the data. The low value of 34 makes the mean less than any of the five other test scores. So, the median is most useful to describe this data.

3 Practice

Guided Practice

Do Check for Understanding Exercises 1–6 with your students. Identify students having difficulty and use lesson resources to help.

///// **COMMON ERROR ALERT** \\\\\

Some students may try to find the median by finding the middle number in an unordered set of data. Remind them to arrange the data from least to greatest before finding the measures of central tendency. This will also help them find the mode.

Error	Correction
9 3 ⑤ 7 7	3 5 ⑦ 7 9
Median = 5	Median = 7

Independent Practice

Assign Exercises 7–15.

107

Exercises 16–20 provide **cumulative review** (Chapters 1–5).

Thinker's Corner

• *After reading through the directions, emphasize that each round has 3 points at stake and ask:*

Which player is likely to be awarded 2 points? the player with the greatest mean and median

• *As students begin to play the rounds with 8 and 12 spins, ask:*

REASONING **How can you organize the numbers to find the mean, median, and mode most quickly?** Possible answer: a frequency table

4 Assess

Summarize the lesson by having students:

DISCUSS Can the mean, median, and mode of a set of data all be the same number? Give an example of such a set. Yes; Possible answer: 10, 11, 11, 12, 12, 12, 13, 13, 14; the mean, median, and mode are 12.

WRITE Describe how to find the mode of a set of data using a line plot. Possible answer: It is the number with the greatest number of X's above it.

Lesson Quiz

Transparency
5.5

The table below shows the number of hours Jenny's cat, Sylvester, slept every day for two weeks. Use the table to complete Exercises 1–3.

NUMBER OF HOURS SYLVESTER SLEPT EACH DAY							
Week 1	17	18	20	17	18	19	20
Week 2	12	12	22	18	21	18	19

1. What is the mode? 18

2. What is the mean number of hours Sylvester slept? about 17.9 hr

3. What is the median number of hours Sylvester slept? 18 hr

Problem Solving ▶ Applications

12. Check students' line plots. median: 14.5; mode: 13; mean: 17.6. The median is most useful to describe the data since it is near most of the data.

13. The mean, $8.75, or the median, $8.50, are most useful since they are near most of the data.

12. Use the data below to make a line plot. Use your line plot to find the median and the mode. Then use the data to find the mean. Which measure of central tendency would be most useful to describe the data? **See answer at left.**

YEARLY RAINFALL (IN.)									
47	11	8	14	15	16	13	13	17	22

13. Over the past 8 days, Fernando spent $5, $6, $9, $8, $10, $15, $15, and $2. Which measure of central tendency would be most useful to describe the data? **See answer at left.**

14. Algebra Reggie's average score on five math tests is 92. On his first four tests, Reggie's scores were 88, 97, 93, and 82. What was Reggie's score on his fifth test? 100

15. ❓ **What's the Error?** Tim wrote $(7 + 3 + 10 + 4) \div 3 = 8$ to find the mean of 7, 3, 10, and 4. What is his error? What is the correct mean? **Tim should divide by 4, not 3; mean is 6.**

Use the table for 16–17. (p. 102)

16. How many named blue or red as their favorite color? **49**

17. What is the size of the sample? **71 people**

Write the decimal as a percent. (p. 60)

18. 0.65 **65%**   **19.** 0.9 **90%**

FAVORITE COLOR	FREQUENCY	CUMULATIVE FREQUENCY
Blue	32	32
Red	17	49
Green	22	71

20. TEST PREP Which is the product of 0.56 and 2.5? (p. 70) **B**

   A 0.14   **B** 1.4   **C** 14   **D** 140

Thinker's CORNER

Spinnermeania Play the game below to practice finding the mean, median, and mode of a set of data.

Materials: spinner showing 0–9 for each player

• Each player spins four times, recording the results.

• Each player determines the mean, median, and mode of the numbers he or she spun. The player with the greatest number in each category gets a point. If there is a tie, each player with that number gets a point.

• Repeat for four more rounds, increasing the number of spins in each round to five, eight, ten, and twelve. The player with the greatest total points at the end of the five rounds wins.

Extra Practice page H36, Set D

Outliers and Additional Data

LESSON PLANNING

Objective To determine how outliers and additional data affect the mean, median, and mode

Intervention for Prerequisite Skills

Mean, Median, Mode (For intervention strategies, see page 93.)

California Mathematics Content Standards

SDAP 1.2 Understand how additional data added to data sets may affect these computations of measures of central tendency.

SDAP 1.3 Understand how the inclusion or exclusion of outliers affects measures of central tendency.

(*Also* SDAP 1.0, SDAP 1.1, MR 2.0)

Vocabulary

outlier a data value that stands out from other data values in a set and can significantly affect measures of central tendency

Math Background

The following points will help students understand how additional data—especially outliers—affect measures of central tendency:

- If a large outlier is added to a data set, the mode may not be affected. The median may change slightly, and the mean will increase.

- If a very small outlier is added to a data set, the mode may not be affected. The median may change slightly, and the mean will decrease.

A line plot showing the new data or the outliers is helpful in illustrating these concepts.

WARM-UP RESOURCES

NUMBER OF THE DAY

Transparency **5.6**

In a class of 23 sixth graders, all but one are 11 years old. Which two measures of central tendency will be the same, and what are they? the median and the mode; 11 years

PROBLEM OF THE DAY

Transparency **5.6**

Rita has 1 brother and 3 sisters. If the mean age of all the children is 5 years, what will their mean age be 7 years from now? 12 years

Solution Problem of the Day tab, p. PD5

DAILY FACTS PRACTICE

Have students practice multiplication facts by completing Set F of *Teacher's Resource Book,* p. TR96.

INTERVENTION AND EXTENSION RESOURCES

ALTERNATIVE TEACHING STRATEGY (ELL)

Materials *For each pair* 2 number cubes labeled 1–6, p. TR75

Ask students to work in pairs to **demonstrate how additional data affect measures of central tendency.**

• One student tosses 2 number cubes and the partner records the sum.

• They do this 8 times and find the mean, median, and mode for the 8 sums.

• Have them toss the cubes 2 more times and find the mean, median, and mode for all 10 sums.

• Have them explain how the 2 additional sums affected the mean, median, and mode for the 8 original sums. Check students' work.

KINESTHETIC

MIXED REVIEW AND TEST PREP

Cumulative Review Chapters 1–5

Refer to the Pupil Edition pages referenced in the exercises for further review. Have students go to the lesson page, review the lesson, and correct any problem they missed.

Mixed Review and Test Prep, p. 111

How to Help	
Item	Page
9	106
10	106
11	106
12	22
13	22

SPECIAL NEEDS

Materials *For each group* 1 index card

To further **explore the effect of outliers on the mean,** have students work in small groups of 4 or 5. For each group, prepare an index card with a different number. On most of the index cards, the numbers should be greater than 30 but less than 100. On the rest of the cards, write a number less than 5. Give each group one of the cards.

• Have students find the mean age of the students in the group.

• Then have them include the age written on the card and find the mean again.

• Have students compare the two means.

• Ask groups to present the two different means that they found and discuss the effect of including the outlier. Check students' work.

VISUAL

ADVANCED LEARNERS

Challenge students to **describe data sets that have specific measures of central tendency.** Display the following directions. Have students compare their answers.

• List six different numbers with a median of 30. Possible answer: 10, 20, 25, 35, 40, 50

• List six different numbers with a mean of 20. Possible answer: 5, 10, 22, 24, 26, 33

• List six numbers with a mode and median of 40. Possible answer: 10, 20, 40, 40, 60, 70

Have students formulate similar directions and exchange them with classmates to solve. Check students' work.

VISUAL

TECHNOLOGY LINK

Intervention Strategies and Activities CD-ROM • *Skills 77, 78*

Outliers and Additional Data

Learn how outliers and additional data affect the mean, median, and mode.

QUICK REVIEW

Find the mean.

1. 6, 8, 10 8   **2.** 20, 32, 41 31   **3.** 15, 17, 19, 41 23

4. 25, 25, 25, 25 25   **5.** 100, 200, 300, 400 250

When you add data to a data set, some measures of central tendency for the set change. How they change depends on how the new data are related to the original data.

EXAMPLE 1

Gina saved dimes for 8 weeks. She recorded the number of dimes in a table. In the ninth week, her parents gave her 25 dimes. In the tenth week, her grandparents gave her 52 dimes. Find the mean, median, and mode for Gina's data, using the values for the 8 weeks of her savings. Then find the measures for all 10 weeks.

DIMES GINA SAVED								
Week	1	2	3	4	5	6	7	8
Dimes	17	18	30	15	1	6	19	6

Data for 8 Weeks
Mean: $(17 + 18 + \ldots + 19 + 6) \div 8 = 14$ **Mode:** 6
Median: 1 6 6 15 17 18 19 30; $(15 + 17) \div 2 = 16$

Data for 10 Weeks
Mean: $(17 + 18 + \ldots + 25 + 52) \div 10 = 18.9$ **Mode:** 6
Median: 1 6 6 15 17 18 19 25 30 52; $(17 + 18) \div 2 = 17.5$

EXAMPLE 2

At age 61, Lev Sarkisov climbed Mount Everest. Suppose he climbed with a group whose ages were 30, 31, 33, 30, 29, 35, 33, 30, and 28. Which measure of central tendency is most affected by adding Sarkisov's age to the group?

Data without Sarkisov's Age

Mean: $(30 + 31 + \ldots + 30 + 28) \div 9 = 31$ **Mode:** 30

Median: 28 29 30 30 30 31 33 33 35; 30

Data with Sarkisov's age

Mean: $(30 + 31 + \ldots + 61) \div 10 = 34$ **Mode:** 30

Median: 28 29 30 30 30 31 33 33 35 61; $(30 + 31) \div 2 = 30.5$

The mean increases by 3, the median increases by 0.5, and the mode remains the same. So, the mean is the measure most affected by adding Sarkisov's age.

On May 12, 1999, Armenian Lev Sarkisov became the oldest person to climb Mount Everest.

CALIFORNIA STANDARDS SDAP 1.2 Understand how additional data added to data sets may affect these computations of measures of central tendency. **SDAP 1.3** Understand how the inclusion or exclusion of outliers affects measures of central tendency. *also* **SDAP 1.0, SDAP 1.1, MR 2.0**

109

RETEACH 5.6

Outliers and Additional Data

The measures of central tendency help you describe a set of data using only one number. Three measures of central tendency are the *mean*, the *median*, and the *mode*. When additional data values are added to a set, one or more of these measures may change.

Jenna has the five items shown below in her shopping cart.

She can describe the average amount in the containers using each of the measures of central tendency.

Mean: $(8 + 6 + 16 + 12 + 12) \div 5 = 54 \div 5 = 10.8$ ounces
Median: 6 8 **12** 12 16 → 12 ounces
Mode: 12 ounces

When Jenna adds the container of juice at the right to her cart, one or more of the measures of central tendency may change

Mean: $(8 + 6 + 16 + 12 + 12 + 64) \div 6 = 118 \div 6 \approx 19.7$ ounces
Median: 6 8 **12** 12 16 64 → $(12 + 12) \div 2 = 12$ ounces
Mode: 12 ounces

When the large container was added to the others in the cart, only the mean changed. The median and mode remained the same as before.

When new data values are added to a set, often the mean changes the most because the mean is found by adding all the data values.

The median and mode usually are not affected as greatly by the addition of an *outlier*, a data value very different from the other data values in a set.

The table below shows how much money Garrett spent buying house plants. Use the data for 1–2.

Date	March 1	March 7	March 15	March 24
Amount Spent	$10.00	$20.00	$15.00	$15.00

1. Find the mean, median, and mode of the amounts.

     mean: $15; median: $15; mode: $15

2. On April 3, Garrett bought a large plant that cost $60. What are the new mean, median, and mode for the costs of the five plants?

     mean: $24; median: $15; mode: $15

PRACTICE 5.6

Outliers and Additional Data

Use the following data for 1–2.

The first 6 packages that were checked in at an airline ticket counter when it opened for business weighed 15 pounds, 21 pounds, 19 pounds, 14 pounds, 18 pounds, and 15 pounds.

1. Find the mean, median, and mode of the weights of the first 6 packages that were checked in at the counter.

     17 lb; 16.5 lb; 15 lb

2. The next package checked in weighed 66 pounds. Find the mean, median, and mode of the weights of the 7 packages.

     24 lb; 18 lb; 15 lb

3. Some friends in the school chorus compared the number of siblings they had. Two had 3 siblings, three had 2 siblings, 6 had one sibling, and 1 had no siblings. What were the mean, median, and mode number of siblings for the group of friends?

     1.5 siblings, 1 sibling, 1 sibling

4. Refer to Exercise 3. Suppose another student who has 9 siblings joins the discussion. Of the three measures of central tendency (mean, median, and mode), which measure is affected the most by including the new data value of 9 siblings?

     the mean

Use the following data for 5–6.

A survey of stores found the following prices for a popular type of backpack: $17, $19, $21, $21, $20, $18, and $24.

5. What were the mean, median, and mode of the prices for the backpack that were found during the survey?

     $20; $20; $21

6. One of the stores charging $21 reduced its price to $14 for one day. What are the new mean, median, and mode?

     $19; $19; no mode

Mixed Review

Add or subtract.

7. 6.8
   + 7.9
   14.7

8. 7.03
   + 3.89
   10.92

9. 15.4
   − 6.7
   8.7

10. 45.04
   − 27.5
   17.54

11. 12.4
   64.8
   + 15.7
   92.9

12. 83.04
   − 59.23
   23.81

13. 102.5
   8.7
   + 76.04
   187.24

14. 234.19
   − 56.97
   177.22

Estimate. Possible estimates are given.

15. 19.8×6.3 120

16. $51.2 - 19.9$ 30

17. $8.9 + 24.2 + 16.7$ 50

LESSON **5.6** ORGANIZER

Objective To determine how outliers and additional data affect the mean, median, and mode

Vocabulary outlier

1 Introduce

QUICK REVIEW provides review of pre-requisite skills.

Why Learn This? This skill is useful in analyzing data and mentally adjusting measures of central tendency. *Share the lesson objective with students.*

2 Teach

Guided Instruction

• As you discuss Example 1, ask:

How do the methods of finding the mean, median, and mode of the data for 10 weeks differ from those for 8 weeks?

Possible answer: To find the mean of the 8-week data, divide by 8; for the 10-week data, divide by 10. To find the median of the 10-week data, insert the additional data items into the original order of the 8-week data and recalculate. The method of finding the mode for each set of data is the same.

REASONING **What number can be added to the following data so that all the measures of central tendency remain the same: 21, 22, 23, 25, 25, 29, 30?** 25

ADDITIONAL EXAMPLE

Example 1, p. 109

Tim recorded in a table the number of dimes he saved each week for 5 weeks. He saved 3 dimes in the sixth week and 1 dime in the seventh week. Find the mean, median, and mode for Tim's data by using the values for the 5 weeks and then for all 7 weeks.

DIMES TIM SAVED					
Week	1	2	3	4	5
Dimes	6	16	24	17	17

16, 17, 17; 12, 16, 17

See also page 110.

- *Remind students that the line plot can be viewed as a balance scale and the mean as its balance point. Ask:*

REASONING **Ignoring the data values, where would you place this balance point on the line plot?** at or to the right of the cluster of 3 X's

How are the values of the outliers related to the other data if the mean increases when the outliers are added to the other data? The values of the outliers are greater than the values of the other data.

ADDITIONAL EXAMPLES

Example 2, p. 109

Melanie has 3 brothers and 3 sisters. Her youngest sister, Tara, is 4 years old. Which measure of central tendency is most affected by adding Tara's age to the group?

Ages of Melanie and Her Siblings

| 18 | 21 | 16 | 15 | 19 | 19 | 4 |

The mean decreases by 2; the median decreases by 0.5; the mode remains the same. The mean is most affected.

Example 3, p. 110

Kelly recorded on this line plot the number of magazine subscriptions she and her classmates sold each day during the first 10 days of the school fundraiser.

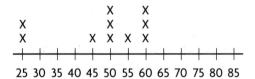

A. Find the measures of central tendency for the 8 data values in the line plot if the outliers are not included. mean, 53.75; median, 52.5; modes, 50 and 60

B. Find the measures of central tendency for all 10 data values with the outliers included. mean, 48; median, 50; modes, 50 and 60

3 Practice

Guided Practice

Do Check for Understanding Exercises 1–4 with your students. Identify those having difficulty and use lesson resources to help.

After Exercise 4, point out that some mathematicians initially consider outliers to be "suspect" and could be possible errors.

Bethany used a line plot to record the number of concert tickets she sold on 10 different days. Most of the data are between 11 and 16. The data values at 32 and 34 are outliers, or extreme values. An **outlier** is a data value that stands out from other data values in a set. Outliers can significantly affect measures of central tendency.

EXAMPLE 3

A. Find the measures of central tendency for the 8 data values in the line plot if the outliers are not included.

Mean: $(11 + 11 + 12 + 12 + 12 + 15 + 15 + 16) \div 8 = 104 \div 8 = 13$
Median: 11 11 12 12 12 15 15 16; 12   **Mode:** 12

B. Find the measures of central tendency for all the data values with the outliers included.

Mean: $(104 + 32 + 34) \div 10 = 170 \div 10 = 17$
Median: 11 11 12 12 12 15 15 16 32 34; $(12 + 15) \div 2 = 13.5$
Mode: 12

C. Suppose Bethany sold 1 ticket the next day and 0 tickets the final day. Include these data values with the data in the line plot and find the measures of central tendency for all 12 data values.

Mean: $(170 + 1 + 0) \div 12 = 171 \div 12 = 14.25$
Median: 0 1 11 11 12 12 12 15 15 16 32 34; 12   **Mode:** 12

- How do the outliers in part B affect the mean, median, and mode? The mean and median increase; the mode does not change.

CHECK FOR UNDERSTANDING

Think and Discuss
1. The median and mode would not change. The mean would not increase as much.

Guided Practice

Look back at the lesson to answer the question.

1. **What if** Gina's grandparents had given her 32 dimes in Example 1? How would the measures of central tendency be affected? See answers at left.

2. Find the mean, median, and mode for the ages in the table. 14.5; 13.5; 12

AGES OF MEMBERS OF MODEL AIRPLANE CLUB			
15	12	9	13
22	19	12	14

3. Find the mean, median, and mode if a 28-year-old joins the club. 16; 14; 12

Jeff received these scores on his science quizzes: 75, 70, 70, 45, 100, 70, 70, 80, 75, 80.

4. **a.** Use the scores to make a line plot. Circle the outliers. See Additional Answers, p. 117A.
   b. Find the mean, median, and mode with and without the outliers. with: 73.5; 72.5; 70; without: 73.75; 72.5; 70
   c. Why did these outliers have so little effect on the mean, median, and mode? Possible answer: They were both about 30 points from the mean, median, and mode.

PROBLEM SOLVING 5.6

Outliers and Additional Data

Write the correct answer.

Analyze Choose Solve Check

1. Brittany had test scores of 80, 85, 85, 92, and 90. If her score on the next test is 65, which measures of central tendency change?

   Only the mean changes.

2. While shopping, Debra estimated the sum of $48.99 and $78.85 as $130. How did she know that the result was an overestimate?

   She rounded both numbers up.

3. Robert's scores on six math tests are 90, 80, 80, 85, 88, and 45. How much higher is the mean of his scores without the outlier than when the outlier is included?

   6.6 points higher (84.6 − 78)

4. In Grades 6 through 8 at Adams Middle School, 45% of the members of the computer club are eighth graders and 19% are seventh graders. What percent are sixth graders?

   36%

Choose the letter for the best answer.

5. John wants to pay for a book that costs $28. He has 3 ten-dollar bills, 4 five-dollar bills, and 5 one-dollar bills. In how many different ways can John pay exactly $28 for the book using his money?
   - A 1 way
   - (B) 2 ways
   - C 3 ways
   - D 4 ways

6. A custodian is changing all the lightbulbs in an auditorium. The bulbs come in packages of 4. There are 17 light fixtures in the auditorium and each has 5 bulbs in it. How many packages of bulbs must the custodian open?
   - F 20 packages
   - G 21 packages
   - (H) 22 packages
   - J 23 packages

7. Danielle's first 3 test scores were 86, 87, and 91. If a perfect score is 100, what is the highest mean score she can have after 4 tests?
   - A 89
   - B 90
   - (C) 91
   - D 92

8. The five linemen on the football team weigh 240 pounds, 228 pounds, 230 pounds, 256 pounds, and 266 pounds. The quarterback weighs 172 pounds. How much greater is the mean weight of the five linemen than the mean weight of the six players?
   - F 244 pounds
   - G 232 pounds
   - H 20 pounds
   - (J) 12 pounds

9. **Write About It** In Exercise 3, what is the effect on the median and the mode of Robert's scores if the outlier is removed from his scores?

   The median becomes 85 rather than 82.5.

   The mode remains the same, 80.

CHALLENGE 5.6

Describe the Data

For each set of data, tell whether you think the mean, median, or mode gives the best description of the data. Give a reason for your choice. For some sets, you may wish to choose more than one of the measures of central tendency. Possible answers are given.

1. Salaries: $50,000; $52,000; $51,000; $400,000; $46,000.

   median; Most of the salaries are clustered around $50,000, while the mean is much higher than most of the salaries and there is no mode

2. Ages of club members in years: 17, 16, 18, 17, 16, 19, 16, 19, 18, 20

   median or mean; The data values are all close together but the mode (16) is the least age and could give the impression that the club members are younger than is the case.

3. Weights of packages in pounds: 3, 5, 3, 3, 3, 3, 3, 3

   mode or median; Only one item is different, but close enough not to have much of an effect.

4. Test scores: 82, 81, 85, 86, 90, 40, 40

   median; Most of the scores are in the range of 80—90, but the mean (72) is too low to be truly representative and the mode gives a completely false impression of the scores

5. Points scored: 23, 24, 26, 25, 24, 22, 21

   mean, median, or mode: All of the data values are close to one another, so the mean, median, and mode are all nearly the same.

6. TV sizes (inches) sold at a store this week: 27, 27, 32, 25, 32, 27, 20, 20

   mode; The mode shows the most-popular TV size, while the mean is not the size of an actual television. (In some situations, the median might not be a TV size either.)

Independent ▶ Practice

a. Abe: mean 7.5, median 6, mode 7; Bart: mean 7.5, median 8.5, mode 0

b. Abe: mean 9.3, median 7, modes 7 and 20; Bart: mean 6.4, median 5, mode 0

c. Abe's: all increase; Bart's: mean/median decrease; mode doesn't change

Problem Solving ▶ Applications

The table shows the points scored by two basketball players in the first six games of the season.

POINTS SCORED		
Game	Abe	Bart
1	7	15
2	5	0
3	4	0
4	20	12
5	7	13
6	2	5

5. **a.** Find the mean, median, and mode of each player's points for six games.

b. In the seventh game, Abe scored 20 points and Bart scored 0 points. Find the mean, median, and mode of each player's points for seven games.

c. How are the measures of central tendency for Abe's and Bart's scores affected by the points scored in the seventh game?

The table shows the number of pets owned by children in a pet club.

6. **a.** Draw a line plot for the data about the number of pets children own. Circle the outliers.
See Additional Answers, p. 117A.

NUMBER OF PETS OWNED			
1	1	2	1
3	12	4	4
3	3	10	1

b. Find the mean, the median, and the mode for the data with and without the outliers. with: 3.75; 3; 1; without: 2.3; 2.5; 1

c. How does including the outliers affect the mean? the median? the mode? **It increases the mean, increases the median a little, and does not change the mode.**

7. **a.** Emily scored 75, 85, 35, 85, 70, 10 on her first 6 math quizzes. What score does Emily need on her seventh quiz so that after 7 quizzes she will have a median score of 75? **75**

b. *REASONING* The greatest score Emily can make on a math quiz is 100. Explain whether it is possible for her to have a mean score of 70 after taking the seventh quiz. **No. With a perfect score of 100, the mean would be 65.7.**

8. *REASONING* The high temperatures in °F over 7 days in town were 72°, 73°, 70°, 68°, 70°, 71°, and 39°. Explain why the mean would not be a good measure to describe the temperatures.
The 39° temperature is an outlier and significantly decreases the mean.

Find the mean, median, and mode of the data. (p. 106)

9. 5, 6, 8, 6, 5, 7, 5, 4
5.75, 5.5, 5

10. 42, 56, 44, 38, 10
38, 42, no mode

11. 10, 12, 12, 10, 8, 5
9.5, 10, 10 and 12

12. A company claims that its 8-year warranty lasts 4 times as long as any other warranty. What is the longest of the other warranties? (p. 22) **2 years**

13. **TEST PREP** There are 180 players in a baseball league. Each team has 12 players. How many teams are in the league? (p. 22) **B**

A 12 teams   **B** 15 teams   **C** 16 teams   **D** 18 teams

Extra Practice page H36, Set E

111

LESSON 5.6

Independent Practice

Assign Exercises 5–8.

Exercises 9–13 provide **cumulative review** (Chapters 1–5).

4 Assess

Summarize the lesson by having students:

DISCUSS Can data added to a data set affect the mean, median, and mode? **Explain.** Possible answer: Yes; if most of the data added have a greater value than the original data, the mean and the median will be greater. If most of the data added have a lesser value than the data in the set, the mean and the median will be less. The mode will change only if a new value occurs more often than the original mode.

WRITE When will the mean, median, and mode of a data set remain about the same after additional data are added to the data set? Possible answer: when the added data values do not differ much from the values in the original set or when outliers added to both sides of the data set "balance out" each other

Lesson Quiz

Transparency
5.6

The ages of adults attending a community planning meeting are shown below.

48, 32, 27, 89, 48, 77, 23, 56

1. Find the mean, median, and mode for the data. 50; 48; 48

2. One 5-year-old child also attended the meeting. Find the mean, median, and mode for the ages if the child's age is also included. 45; 48; 48

3. How are the measures of central tendency affected by including this outlier? The mean is decreased by 5. The median and mode are not affected.

111

Data and Conclusions

LESSON PLANNING

Objective To draw conclusions about a set of data

Intervention for Prerequisite Skills

Read a Table (For intervention strategies, see page 93.)

 California Mathematics Content Standards

⊶ SDAP 2.5 Identify claims based on statistical data and, in simple cases, evaluate the validity of the claims.

(*Also* MR 1.0, MR 2.4)

Math Background

This lesson ties together the ideas presented in the chapter by showing students how to draw reasonable conclusions from data collected through samples. Remind students of the following points:

• The population to be surveyed must be defined accurately and clearly.

• To avoid a biased sample, everyone in the population must have an equal chance of being chosen. It is important to sample all segments of the population.

• The questions asked must not lead the respondent to reply in any particular way.

WARM-UP RESOURCES

 NUMBER OF THE DAY Transparency 5.7

A task takes $3\frac{1}{2}$ hr. If you start now, will you finish by 4:30 P.M.? If the current time is 1 P.M. or earlier, students should answer yes.

 PROBLEM OF THE DAY Transparency 5.7

The mean of these numbers is 14. The greatest number is 21 more than the least. The mode is 18. What are the missing numbers? 3 6 9 ♦ ♦ ♦ ♦

18, 18, 20, 24

Solution Problem of the Day tab, p. PD5

 DAILY FACTS PRACTICE

Have students practice division facts by completing Set G of *Teacher's Resource Book*, p. TR96.

INTERVENTION AND EXTENSION RESOURCES

ALTERNATIVE TEACHING STRATEGY ELL

Ask students to apply their knowledge of **collecting and analyzing data.**

- Divide the class into small groups and ask each group to pick a topic on which they would like to gather information, write questions about the topics, and then collect data from a random sample.

- Refer students to the questions on page 112 as they prepare their project to remind them of the importance of a random sample and unbiased questions.

- Then have each group write several conclusions based on their data.

- Ask groups to exchange questions and conclusions and evaluate each other's projects. Check students' work.

See also page 114.

AUDITORY

MIXED REVIEW AND TEST PREP

Cumulative Review Chapters 1–5

Refer to the Pupil Edition pages referenced in the exercises for further review. Have students go to the lesson page, review the lesson, and correct any problem they missed.

Mixed Review and Test Prep, p. 115

How to Help	
Item	Page
19	106
20	106
21	106
22	30
23	30

WRITING IN MATHEMATICS

Materials *For each student* newspaper or magazine

Ask students to **demonstrate what they've learned about collecting data and drawing conclusions.** Find the results of a survey in a newspaper or magazine. Have students write a paragraph discussing what the population is or might be, what kind of a sample might have been used, what questions might have been asked, and what conclusions you can draw from the results. Answers will vary.

CAREER CONNECTION

Have students apply their knowledge of **collecting data** to real life by sharing the following information.

Every 10 years the United States conducts a census of its population. Although questionnaires are mailed to all households, some households get more detailed questionnaires than others. Thus, some of the data collected by census workers is based on samples of the population. The answers to the questions are tabulated and reports are written by Census Bureau staff.

If an area's population is less than 2,500, one out of every two people will be given the detailed questionnaire. Colfax, California, has a population of 1,306. Ask: How many people in Colfax will be sent the detailed questionnaire? 653 people

AUDITORY

TECHNOLOGY LINK

Intervention Strategies and Activities CD-ROM • *Skill 75*

Objective To draw conclusions about a set of data

1 Introduce

QUICK REVIEW provides review of prerequisite skills.

Why Learn This? You can use this skill to compare data for a decision, such as choosing a pair of in-line skates. *Share the lesson objective with students.*

2 Teach

Guided Instruction

• *Read the opening question on page 112 to the class and record the class response.*

Raise your hand if you would say "yes" to this question.

• *Help students compare the number in your class to the result given. Discuss how Kendra might select students for her sample.*

Would it be a random sample if she asked 60 people who ride the bus to school? Explain. Possible answer: No; students who ride the bus might not be typical of everyone in the school.

• *Read the four questions in the box.*

What was the population when I asked our class this question? our class

Did we survey the population or a sample? the population

How could we sample our class for a survey? Possible answer: Place all the names in a hat and draw 10 or 15 names.

ADDITIONAL EXAMPLE

Example 1, p. 112

There are 32 students in Martin's class. He randomly selected 12 students and asked them what their favorite month of the year was. He found that 75% of students surveyed chose July. Martin concluded that July is the favorite month of 75% of his classmates. Is Martin's conclusion valid? The population he was interested in was his class. He surveyed 12 students from his class. The question used was unbiased. The sample was randomly selected. So, Martin's conclusion is valid.

LESSON **5.7**

Data and Conclusions

Learn how to decide whether conclusions based on data are valid.

QUICK REVIEW

Write each decimal as a percent.
1. 0.75 **75%** 2. 0.02 **2%** 3. 0.2 **20%** 4. 0.185 **18.5%** 5. 0.085 **8.5%**

Would you take $1,000 to give up watching television for three months? In a recent survey of adults, 87% answered "Yes!"

Kendra used the same question to survey students at her middle school. She randomly selected 60 of these students to participate in the survey. She found that 90% of the students she surveyed answered "Yes." So, Kendra concluded that about 90% of all students at her middle school would take $1,000 to give up watching television for three months.

EXAMPLE 1

Is Kendra's conclusion valid?

To determine if Kendra's conclusion is valid, use the checklist below.

Remember that when you want to collect data by asking a question, how you state the question is very important. The question must be unbiased.

• Who are the people you are interested in studying (the population)?	✓ The population Kendra is interested in is the students at her middle school.
• Was the sample selected from the correct population?	✓ Yes. Kendra surveyed students from her middle school.
• Was the sample randomly selected?	✓ Yes. The sample was randomly selected.
• Was the question unbiased?	✓ Yes. The question was unbiased.

So, Kendra's conclusion is valid.

• **What if** Kendra had surveyed 60 students who participate in school athletics? Would her conclusion be valid? Explain. **No. The sample was not randomly selected.**

Math Idea ▶ In order to draw a valid conclusion from a set of data, you must select a random sample from the correct population and ask an unbiased question.

112

CALIFORNIA STANDARDS ⊶ SDAP 2.5 Identify claims based on statistical data and, in simple cases, evaluate the validity of the claims. *also* MR 1.0, MR 2.4

RETEACH 5.7

Data and Conclusions

You must consider many things when you are deciding whether a conclusion based on a set of data is valid. Here are four considerations.

• You must know the population that you are interested in. A population may be people, such as the students in your school or class, or it may be objects, such as the cars produced by a factory in one week.
• You must know whether that population was surveyed. For example, if you are interested in adults between the ages of 25 and 40, how do you know that only people of this age were surveyed?
• You must know whether each survey question was unbiased. Were people led to believe that you wanted one answer rather than another?
• Were the people or objects selected randomly so that every member of the population had an equal chance of being chosen?

Diana's school has 986 students attending it. She asked 80 randomly selected students in the school the question "What kind of pet or pets do you have?" The results of her survey were as follows:

   26% said they had a cat.
   23% said they had a dog.
   12% said they had a pet other than a cat or dog.

She concluded that percentages close to these would apply to all the students in her school. Her conclusion was valid because:

• She wanted to find out data about the entire population of her school.
• She surveyed the population she was interested in.
• She asked the question in a fair and unbiased way.
• The sample was large enough to be representative of the students in her school and the students sampled were selected randomly.

Write *yes* or *no* to tell whether Diana's conclusions would have been valid if she had used each of these surveying methods. Explain your answer.

1. Diana asked some students who attend her school, as well as some students who attend another middle school.

   No. the students at the other school would not be

   representative of the students at her school.

2. Diana asked the first 80 students on the daily attendance sheet, which has students' names listed alphabetically.

   Yes. Students' last names are not related to their having pets,

   so her conclusions would still be valid.

PRACTICE 5.7

Data and Conclusions

Write *yes* or *no* to tell whether the conclusion is valid. Explain your answer.

1. A random sample of 100 middle school students were asked whether they think speed limits should be increased. Almost all of them believed that they should be. You conclude that drivers in general want higher speed limits.

   No. The sample is not representative of all drivers; in fact,

   the students are not members of the population of drivers.

2. At the music store where you buy CDs, the most popular type of music is rhythm and blues. You tell your friends that rhythm and blues must be the most popular type of music in the country.

   No. The store in which you shop may not be typical of stores

   around the country.

3. Your teacher tells you that in your class of 24 students, there are 2 student birthdays each month. You decide that in the entire school, student birthdays are distributed evenly throughout the year.

   Yes. Your class may or may not be a representative sample of

   the school population, but birthdays would probably be fairly

   evenly distributed for any random population.

4. You ask the first 60 students in line at the student cafeteria how they come to school. All but 15 students say they ride a school bus. You conclude that most students come to school by bus.

   Yes. The students in line probably represent a random sample

   of the students in the school.

Mixed Review

Find the value.

5. 5 + 5 × 4 __25__   6. 6 + (4 × 3) __18__   7. 20 ÷ 2 + 8 __18__

8. (14 − 6) × 2 __16__   9. 35 ÷ (15 − 8) __5__   10. 10 + (8 × 3) __34__

Find the mean, median, and mode.

11. 412, 387, 297, 343   12. 11, 14, 19, 14, 17, 16, 7   13. 6.7, 6.7, 7.6, 4.2, 7.6

   359.75; 365; no mode   14; 14; 14   6.56; 6.7; 6.7 and 7.6

Barry read the results of a survey conducted ten years ago at his school. A random sampling of sixth graders produced the results displayed in the circle graph at the right.

Barry wanted to see if a survey of sixth graders at his school today would produce the same results. He randomly selected 200 sixth graders from his school and asked them the same question.

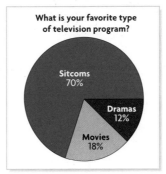

What is your favorite type of television program?

- Sitcoms 70%
- Dramas 12%
- Movies 18%

EXAMPLE 2

What conclusions can Barry draw from the results of his survey shown in the circle graph below?

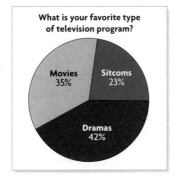

What is your favorite type of television program?

- Movies 35%
- Sitcoms 23%
- Dramas 42%

Barry can conclude the following:

Type of Show	Conclusion
Sitcoms	Interest in sitcoms decreased.
Movies	Interest in movies increased.
Dramas	Interest in dramas increased.

• How do you know Barry's conclusions are valid? **He selected a random sample from the correct population and asked an unbiased question and the differences are more than a few percent.**

CHECK FOR UNDERSTANDING

Think and ▶ Discuss

Look back at the lesson to answer each question.

1. **Tell** if Kendra's conclusions in Example 1 would still be valid if she had surveyed students from her first two classes of the day. Explain. **No. The sample would be a convenience sample and not a random sample.**

2. **What if,** in Example 2, Barry had asked, "Do you agree with me that a drama is the best kind of television show to watch?" Would he be able to make the same conclusions? Explain. **No. His question is biased since it leads people to agree with him.**

113

• *Discuss Example 2 on page 113.*

Reword the question to make it a biased question. Possible answer: Would you agree with eighth graders that dramas are the preferred type of television show?

Modifying Instruction Point out to students that running a survey several times can lead one to answers that vary by a few percentage points, resulting in negligible changes. For example, if sitcoms had changed from 70% to 66%, the difference would not have been enough to conclude necessarily that they had dropped in popularity.

ADDITIONAL EXAMPLE

Example 2, p. 113

What conclusions can you draw from the results of the surveys shown in the circle graphs below?

What is your favorite free-time activity?

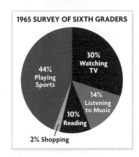

1965 SURVEY OF SIXTH GRADERS
- 44% Playing Sports
- 30% Watching TV
- 14% Listening to Music
- 10% Reading
- 2% Shopping

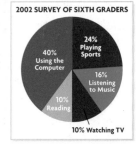

2002 SURVEY OF SIXTH GRADERS
- 24% Playing Sports
- 40% Using the Computer
- 16% Listening to Music
- 10% Reading
- 10% Watching TV

Conclusions:
Interest in playing sports decreased.
Interest in reading stayed the same.
Interest in watching TV decreased.
Shopping is no longer a favorite activity.
The new favorite activity is using the computer.
Interest in listening to music stayed about the same.

PROBLEM SOLVING 5.7

Data and Conclusions

Write the correct answer. Use the table at the right for 1–2.

PERCENT OF GLASS RECYCLED

Britain	17%
Japan	55%
Netherlands	57%
United States	20%

1. Karin concludes from the table that the percent of glass recycled in Japan is more than twice that recycled in the United States. Is she correct?

yes

2. Stefon concludes that the percent of glass recycled in the Netherlands is 4 times that in Britain. Is he correct?

no

Use the table below for 3–4.

Watches at Sea

Starting Time	Noon	4 P.M.	8 P.M.	Midnight	4 A.M.	8 A.M.	10 A.M.
Length of Watch	4 hr	4 hr	4 hr	4 hr	4 hr	2 hr	2 hr

3. If 15 sailors stand watch one at a time in order, what is the greatest number of hours a sailor must stand watch in any 48-hour period?

4 hr

4. If each watch is taken by a different sailor, how many sailors will stand a watch during one week at sea?

49 sailors

Choose the letter for the best answer. Use the survey results given in the chart below for 5–7.

WHAT DID YOU HAVE FOR BREAKFAST?

Toast	17 students
Cereal	39 students
Waffles	12 students
Nothing	14 students

6. Angela correctly concludes that the percent of students who had cereal is about ___?___.
   F 25%
   G 50%
   H 75%
   J 90%

8. **Write About It** For Exercise 6, how did you estimate the percent of students who had cereal?
   Possible answer: Round each data value to the nearest 10; so, cereal was eaten by about 40 out of 80 students, or 50%.

5. Mark correctly concludes that the least common breakfast was ___?___.
   A Toast   C Waffles
   B Cereal   D Nothing

7. How many more students had something for breakfast than had nothing for breakfast?
   A 14 more students
   B 54 more students
   C 68 more students
   D 82 more students

CHALLENGE 5.7

Important Inventions of the Twentieth Century

While reading a recent magazine article, Derek saw an interesting circle graph. It showed what students thoughts were the most important inventions of the twentieth century. The graph showed the following:

• Only 5% of students thought the car was the most important invention.
• Twice as many students named the airplane as named the car.
• The television was named by 3 times as many students as the car.
• The computer and the Internet were each named by the same number of students.

1. Use the circle at the right to sketch a circle graph displaying the results of the survey that Derek saw. Assume that car, airplane, television, computer, and Internet were the only responses. **car: 5%; airplane: 10%; television: 15%; computer: 35%; Internet: 35%**

Derek conducted a similar survey of members of the school computer club. These were his results:
• The same percent voted for the car as in the magazine article.
• An equal number of students voted for the television and airplane. The two inventions together received 20% of the votes cast by those surveyed.
• Twice as many students voted for the computer as for the Internet.

2. Sketch a circle graph to show the results of the survey that Derek conducted. First determine the percent for each of the five responses. Then sketch the sections of the circle graph. **car: 5%; television: 10%; airplane: 10%; computer: 50%; Internet: 25%**

3. Was Derek's survey a valid representation of the views of the students who attend his school? Explain your answer.
   No. Surveying the students in the computer club gave a biased view of
   what students thought were important inventions. The computer club
   members are probably not representative of the students who attend
   the school.

3 | Practice

Guided Practice

Do Check for Understanding Exercises 1–5 with your students. Identify those having difficulty and use lesson resources to help.

You may wish to do Exercises 3–5 orally with your students to generate discussion. In Exercise 3, encourage students to describe what would be a representative sample.

Independent Practice

Assign Exercises 6–18.

Before assigning Exercise 9, you may want to discuss the *Other* category on the graph. Students may conclude that broccoli is the least favorite vegetable, but each vegetable included in *Other* might have received fewer votes than broccoli.

Guided ▶ Practice

3. Yes. The sample is random and from the correct population and the question is unbiased.

4. Yes. The sample is random and representative; the question is unbiased.

Independent ▶ Practice

7. No. The sample is not representative of the population.

8. No. The data is for teenagers from California, not New York.

9. Yes. An unbiased question was asked of a random sample from the correct population.

Guided Practice For 3, write *yes* or *no* to tell whether the conclusion is valid. Explain your answer.

3. Five hundred randomly selected teenagers from Fresno are asked to name their favorite subject. Eighty percent of these teenagers respond that their favorite subject is math. You conclude that math is the most popular subject among teenagers in Fresno.

Use Data For 4–5, use the data in the graph.

4. The graph at the right shows the results of a survey of 600 randomly selected middle school students. Jen concludes that more middle school students are interested in football than in any other sport. Is her conclusion valid? Explain.

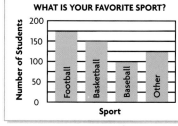

5. Robert concludes that more high school students are interested in football than in any other sport. Is his conclusion valid? Explain.
No. The data is for middle school students.

PRACTICE AND PROBLEM SOLVING

For 6–7, write *yes* or *no* to tell whether the conclusion is valid. Explain your answer.

6. All the members of the science club were asked if they wanted to take more science classes. Each of them answered yes. You decide that science is becoming more popular among all students. No. The sample is not representative of the student population.

7. A sample of your friends shows that their favorite color is green. You decide that the same is probably true for the entire school.

Use Data For 8–9, use the data in the graph.

8. The graph at the right shows the results of a survey of 1,000 randomly selected teenagers from California. José concludes that corn is the favorite vegetable of teenagers from New York. Is his conclusion valid? Explain.

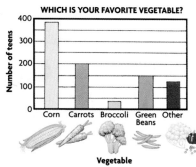

9. Jerome concludes that carrots are the second favorite vegetable among California teenagers. Is his conclusion valid? Explain.

Alternative Teaching Strategy

Purpose Students survey two diverse groups to collect data and draw conclusions.

Have students work in small groups. Instruct each group to survey 2 diverse groups such as 20 first graders and 20 teenagers or 20 boys and 20 girls. Surveys should use questions with choices, such as these:

Of the following, which is your favorite after-school activity?

- Bike riding
- Watching television
- Reading
- Using the computer
- Going to the playground

Have each group record the results in a table such as the one at the right.

FAVORITE AFTER-SCHOOL ACTIVITIES		
Activity	**First Graders**	**Teenagers**
Bike riding	6	2
Watching TV	4	5
Reading	1	7
Using the computer	3	6
Going to the playground	6	0

Direct groups to make a list of conclusions about each activity, based on the results of their survey. Ask them to share their conclusions with the class.

Sample list of conclusions:

Activity	Conclusions
Bike riding	First graders like to ride bikes more than teenagers do.
Watching TV	Teenagers and children both enjoy watching TV.
Reading	Teenagers like reading after school much more than first graders do.
Computer	Teenagers like to use the computer about twice as much as first graders do.
Playground	Teenagers do not like going to the playground after school, but first graders do.

Check students' work.

For a survey completed five years ago, middle school students from San Diego were asked, "What is your favorite hobby?"

A research company randomly selected 750 current middle school students from San Diego and asked them the same question. The results are in the table.

FAVORITE HOBBIES	
Reading	36%
Crafts	7%
Coin Collecting	2%
Stamp Collecting	2%
Building Models	12%
Trading Cards	39%
Other	2%

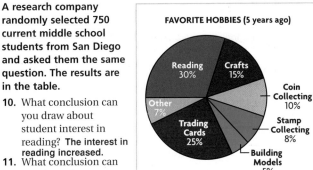

FAVORITE HOBBIES (5 years ago)

Reading 30%
Crafts 15%
Coin Collecting 10%
Stamp Collecting 8%
Building Models 5%
Trading Cards 25%
Other 7%

10. What conclusion can you draw about student interest in reading? **The interest in reading increased.**

11. What conclusion can you draw about student interest in crafts? **The interest in crafts decreased.**

12. What conclusion can you draw about student interest in coin collecting? **The interest in coin collecting decreased.**

13. What conclusion can you draw about student interest in trading cards? **The interest in trading cards increased.**

14. What conclusion can you draw about student interest in models? **The interest in building models increased slightly.**

15. How can you tell that your conclusions are valid? **A random sample was selected from the correct population and the question was unbiased.**

16. For which of the hobbies did interest increase the most? decrease the most? **increase: trading cards; decrease: coin collecting**

17. **?** **What's the Error?** A survey of middle school athletes showed that their favorite exercise is jogging. Cathy looked at the survey results and concluded that all students prefer jogging. Explain Cathy's error. **The sample is biased since it only includes middle school athletes.**

18. Robert spent $60 at the sports equipment store. He bought a glove for $35 and 5 baseballs. What was the price for each baseball? **$5**

Find the mean, median, and mode of the data. (p. 106)

19. 2, 4, 4, 3, 6, 8, 1, 6
4.25, 4, 4 and 6

20. 22, 44, 31, 46, 22
33, 31, 22

21. 6, 8, 11, 10, 2, 5
7, 7, no mode

22. **TEST PREP** Which is the solution of $x + 3 = 10$? (p. 30) **B**

   A $x = 3$ **B** $x = 7$ **C** $x = 10$ **D** $x = 13$

23. **TEST PREP** Which is the solution of $x \div 3 = 6$? (p. 30) **J**

   F $x = 2$ **G** $x = 3$ **H** $x = 9$ **J** $x = 18$

Extra Practice page H36, Set F   **115**

Exercises 19–23 provide **cumulative review** (Chapters 1–5).

4 Assess

Summarize the lesson by having students:

DISCUSS Why do you think someone might use a sample that was not randomly selected or a biased question in a survey? Possible answer: That person might have a personal stake or interest in the results or might want results that will support a certain position.

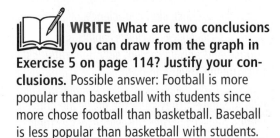

WRITE What are two conclusions you can draw from the graph in Exercise 5 on page 114? Justify your conclusions. Possible answer: Football is more popular than basketball with students since more chose football than basketball. Baseball is less popular than basketball with students.

Lesson Quiz

Transparency 5.7

1. Forty people shopping at Tabco Grocers stated that Tabco is their favorite grocery store. Is it valid to conclude that most people prefer to shop at Tabco? Explain. No; the sample is not representative.

2. Helena asks a random sample of 45 students at her school of 400 students to name their favorite food. Forty students name pizza. She concludes that most students in the school like pizza best. Is her conclusion justified? Explain. Yes; the sample is random, and 40 out of 45 is most of the students.

3. A random sample of people in a small city shows that 90 people think City Park should be left as it is, 240 people think it should be improved, and 30 people have no opinion. What conclusion can you draw from the survey? Possible answer: Most people feel the park should be improved.

CHAPTER 5

REVIEW/TEST

Purpose To check understanding of concepts, skills, and problem solving presented in Chapter 5

USING THE PAGE

The Chapter 5 Review/Test can be used as a **review** or a **test**.

- Items 1–3 check understanding of concepts and new vocabulary.
- Items 4–12 check skill proficiency.
- Items 13–15 check students' abilities to choose and apply problem solving strategies to problems involving data.

 Suggest that students place the completed Chapter 5 Review/Test in their portfolios.

USING THE ASSESSMENT GUIDE

- Multiple-choice format of Chapter 5 Posttest—See *Assessment Guide*, pp. AG33–34.
- Free-response format of Chapter 5 Posttest— See *Assessment Guide*, pp. AG35–36.

USING STUDENT SELF-ASSESSMENT

The How Did I Do? survey helps students assess what they have learned and how they learned it. This survey is available as a copying master in *Assessment Guide*, p. AGxvii.

CHAPTER 5 REVIEW/TEST

For 1–2, determine the type of sample. Write *convenience, random,* **or** *systematic.* (pp. 94-97)

1. A cereal company surveys a person in every third apartment in an apartment building. **systematic**

2. Alicia wants to find out what snack foods students in her school prefer. She randomly surveys 100 students. **random**

3. **VOCABULARY** In a survey, if individuals or groups in the population are not represented by the sample, the sample is __?__ . (p. 98) **biased**

Tell whether the sample is biased or unbiased. (pp. 98-99)

4. A store randomly surveys 10 out of every 100 customers about the quality of its service. **unbiased**

5. A teacher surveys girls about the best day to give a test. **biased**

For 6–9, use the table at the right. (pp. 102-105)

6. What is the sample size? **20**

7. Find the range. **12**

8. Make a line plot. See Additional Answers, p. 117A.

9. Make a frequency table. See Additional Answers, p. 117A.

STUDENTS' HEIGHTS (in inches)									
62	72	63	62	69	70	60	64	66	63
71	62	65	68	63	70	64	62	67	70

Find the mean, median, and mode. (pp. 106-109)

10. 17, 12, 23, 19, 23 **18.8; 19; 23**

11. 6.2, 5.5, 8.4, 5.5 **6.4; 5.85; 5.5**

12. 265, 235, 171, 253 **231; 244; no mode**

13. Ten people in Ana's neighborhood formed a bike club. The table shows the ages of the members. (pp. 106-109)

AGES OF MEMBERS OF BIKE CLUB				
13	14	10	11	13
12	13	9	11	10

   a. Find the mean, median, and mode for the ages of the ten members. **11.6, 11.5, 13**

   b. Find the mean, median, and mode if the adult advisor for the club is 27 years old and is a club member. Compare with part *a*. **13, 12, 13; mean and median increase, mode is unchanged**

14. Janyce wanted to find out where visitors to the local mall come from. She surveyed visitors, tallied her results, and came up with the following percents: California—34%; Idaho—14%; Nevada— 11%; Oregon—16%; Montana—8%; Washington—11%; other states—6%. Make a table to organize the information from greatest to least percent. (pp. 100-101)

14. Check students' tables. Order should be California, Oregon, Idaho, Washington or Nevada, Montana, other states.

15. If 50% of the people who visit the mall in Exercise 14 come from within 20 miles of the mall, which is a reasonable conclusion? Why? (pp. 100-101)

   A The mall where Janyce took her survey is in southern California.

   B The mall where Janyce took her survey is in eastern Nevada.

   C The mall where Janyce took her survey is in southern Washington.

   D The mall where Janyce took her survey is in northern California.

15. D; 50% of the people come from California and Oregon—that suggests a northern California location.

116 Chapter 5

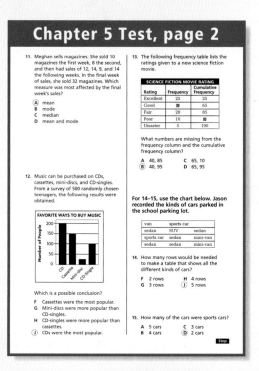

TIP!

Eliminate choices.

See item **5.**

Keep the question in mind as you read each answer choice. Look for the most important characteristic of a survey sample to decide what was wrong with the survey.

Also see problem **5,** p. H64.

Choose the best answer.

1. Which symbol makes this true? **A**

   8.34 ● 8.342

   A < **C** =

   B > **D** ÷

2. Which of the following is equivalent to 27 + 43? **G**

   F 25 + 50

   G 30 + 40

   H 27 + 40 + 12

   J 20 + 60

3. Which of the following numbers is between 8.07 and 8.3? **C**

   A 8.06

   B 8.017

   C 8.29

   D 8.312

4. The student council wants to conduct a survey to get an idea of what other students think about changing the school colors. Which group would be the best sample? **J**

   F 25 friends

   G 25 football players

   H 25 teachers

   J 25 students selected at random

5. Before Warren ran for class president, he surveyed 20 of his friends, asking "Would you vote for me for class president?" Of those surveyed, 100% answered "yes." Warren was very surprised when he lost the election. What was wrong with his survey? **B**

   A Nothing; his friends changed their minds and didn't vote for him.

   B His survey sample did not represent the student body.

   C He should have included teachers in his survey.

   D His survey did not ask the right question.

For 6–7, use the information below.

Jon had the following scores for 5 rounds of golf: 78, 80, 69, 75, 73.

6. What is the mean of the scores? **J**

   F 50 **H** 74

   G 71 **J** 75

7. What is the range of the scores? **A**

   A 11 **C** 80

   B 75 **D** Not here

8. The ages of students in the Hiking Club are 13, 11, 15, 14, 12, 13, 13. What is the mode of this set of data? **H**

   F 11 **H** 13

   G 12 **J** 14

9. What is $2 \times 2 \times 2 \times 2 \times 2 \times 2 \times 2$ expressed in exponential notation? **C**

   A 2^2 **C** 2^7

   B 7^2 **D** 2^6

10. $883.03 \div 22.7$ **G**

   F 389 **H** 3.89

   G 38.9 **J** Not here

117

CUMULATIVE REVIEW •
Chapters 1–5

USING THE PAGE

This page may be used to help students get ready for standardized tests. The test items are written in the same style and arranged in the same format as those on many state assessments. The page is cumulative. It covers math objectives and essential skills that have been taught up to this point in the text. Most of the items represent skills from the current chapter, and the remainder represent skills from earlier chapters.

This page can be assigned at the end of the chapter as classwork or as a homework assignment. You may want to have students use individual recording sheets presented in a multiple-choice (standardized) format. A Test Answer Sheet is available as a blackline master in *Assessment Guide* (p. AGxlii).

You may wish to have students describe how they solved each problem and share their solutions.

Lesson 5.4, page 104

3.

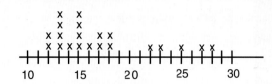

Lesson 5.4, page 105

11.

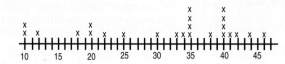

4. Possible table is given.

Age	Frequency	Cumulative Frequency
11-15	11	11
16-20	5	16
21-25	3	19
26-30	2	21

14. Possible table is given.

Weights	Frequency	Cumulative Frequency
10-19	4	4
20-29	4	8
30-39	8	16
40-49	8	24

Lesson 5.4, page 104

6.

7. Possible table is given.

Number of km	Frequency	Cumulative Frequency
1-5	1	1
6-10	11	12
11-15	8	20
16-20	1	21

16. Possible table is given.

Weights	Frequency	Cumulative Frequency
0-9	5	5
10-19	13	18
20-29	7	25
30-39	1	26

Lesson 5.6, page 110

4.

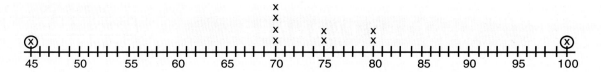

Lesson 5.6, page 111

6.

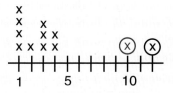

Chapter 5 Review/Test, page 116

8.

```
      x
    x x           x
    x x x         x
x   x x x x x x x x x x x
+-+-+-+-+-+-+-+-+-+-+-+-+-+-
60        65        70
```

9. Possible table is given.

Heights (in inches)	Frequency	Cumulative Frequency
60-64	10	10
65-69	5	15
70-74	5	20

Graph Data

PACING OPTIONS	
Compacted	5 Days
Expanded	10 Days

Getting Ready for Chapter 6 • Assessing Prior Knowledge and INTERVENTION (See PE and TE page 119.)

LESSON	CALIFORNIA STANDARDS	PACING	VOCABULARY*	MATERIALS	RESOURCES AND TECHNOLOGY
6.1 Make and Analyze Graphs pp. 120–123 **Objective** To display and analyze data in bar graphs, line graphs, and circle graphs	MR 1.1 (*Also* MR 2.2, MR 2.4)	2 Days	**multiple-bar graph** **multiple-line graph**		Reteach, Practice, Problem Solving, Challenge 6.1 Worksheets Extra Practice p. H37, Set A ▢ Transparency 6.1 ⊙ **Data ToolKit** • *Make a Table, Make a Bar Graph, Make a Line Graph, Make a Circle Graph*
6.2 Find Unknown Values pp. 124–125 **Objective** To estimate unknown values from a graph and to solve for the values by using arithmetic, logic, and algebra	MR 2.3 (*Also* AF 2.3, MR 3.2)	1 Day			Reteach, Practice, Problem Solving, Challenge 6.2 Worksheets Extra Practice p. H37, Set B ▢ Transparency 6.2
6.3 Stem-and-Leaf Plots and Histograms pp. 126–128 **Objective** To display and analyze data in stem-and-leaf plots and histograms	MR 2.4 (*Also* SDAP 1.0, SDAP 1.1)	2 Days	**stem-and-leaf plot** **histogram**		Reteach, Practice, Problem Solving, Challenge 6.3 Worksheets Extra Practice p. H37, Set C ▢ Transparency 6.3 ⊙ **Data Tool Kit** • *Make a Stem-and-Leaf Plot*
6.4 Math Lab: Explore Box-and-Whisker Graphs p. 129 **Objective** To make a box-and-whisker graph and understand its parts	SDAP 1.0 SDAP 1.1		**box-and-whisker graph** **lower extreme** **upper extreme** **lower quartile** **upper quartile**	*For each pair* at least eleven 3- × 5-in. index cards, marker	🌐 **E-Lab** • *Exploring Box-and-Whisker Graphs*; E-Lab Recording Sheet
6.5 Box-and-Whisker Graphs pp. 130–131 **Objective** To analyze a box-and-whisker graph	SDAP 1.0 SDAP 1.1 (*Also* MR 2.5)	1 Day (For Lessons 6.4 and 6.5)			Reteach, Practice, Problem Solving, Challenge 6.5 Worksheets Extra Practice p. H37, Set D ▢ Transparency 6.5 ⊙ **Data ToolKit** • *Make a Table, Make a Box-and-Whisker Graph*
6.6 Analyze Graphs pp. 132–135 **Objective** To analyze data displays and determine how results and conclusions may have been influenced	⊶ SDAP 2.3 (*Also* MR 1.0, MR 1.1, MR 2.4)	2 Days			Reteach, Practice, Problem Solving, Challenge 6.6 Worksheets Extra Practice p. H37, Set E ▢ Transparency 6.6

Ending Chapter 6 • Chapter 6 Review/Test, p. 136 **• Cumulative Review,** p. 137

Ending Unit 2 • Math Detective, p. 138; **Challenge,** p. 139 **• Study Guide and Review,** pp. 140–141; **California Connections,** pp. 142–143

*****Boldfaced** terms are new vocabulary. Other terms are review vocabulary.

CHAPTER AT A GLANCE

Vocabulary Development

The boldfaced words are the new vocabulary terms in the chapter. Have students record the definitions in their Math Journals.

multiple-bar graph, p. 120

multiple-line graph, p. 121

stem-and-leaf plot, p. 126

histogram, p. 127

box-and-whisker graph, p. 129

lower extreme, p. 129

upper extreme, p. 129

lower quartile, p. 129

upper quartile, p. 129

multiple-bar graph

Vocabulary Cards
Have students use the Vocabulary Cards on *Teacher's Resource Book* **pp. TR123–126** to make graphic organizers or word puzzles. The cards can also be added to a file of mathematics terms.

California Mathematics Content Standards for Grade 6

Strands

Number Sense

Algebra and Functions
Lesson 6.2: AF 2.3

Measurement and Geometry

Statistics, Data Analysis, and Probability
Lesson 6.3: SDAP 1.0, 1.1
Lesson 6.4: SDAP 1.0, 1.1
Lesson 6.5: SDAP 1.0, 1.1
Lesson 6.6: ⊶ SDAP 2.3

Mathematical Reasoning
Lesson 6.1: MR 1.1, 2.2, 2.4
Lesson 6.2: MR 2.3, 3.2
Lesson 6.3: MR 2.4
Lesson 6.5: MR 2.5
Lesson 6.6: MR 1.0, 1.1, 2.4

Writing Opportunities

PUPIL EDITION	TEACHER'S EDITION	ASSESSMENT GUIDE
• Write a Problem, p. 125	• Write—See the *Assess* section of each TE lesson.	How Did I Do?, p. AGxvii
• What's the Error?, p. 123	• Writing in Mathematics, pp. 124B, 126B, 132B	
• Write About It, p. 128		
• What's the Question?, p. 131		

Family Involvement Activities

These activities provide:
- Letter to the Family
- Information about California Standards
- Math Vocabulary
- Family Game
- Practice (Homework)

HARCOURT MATH	Name
GRADE 6	Date
Chapter 6	

WHAT WE ARE LEARNING
Graphing Data

Dear Family,
Your child is analyzing graphs and making stem-and-leaf plots and box-and-whisker graphs.
This is how to make a stem-and-leaf plot of the data.

Population Density of Selected South American Countries per Square Mile
30, 25, 17, 46, 45, 72, 68, 9, 77, 61, 27, 44, 56

VOCABULARY
Here are some of the vocabulary words we use in class:

Multiple-bar graph A bar graph that shows two or more sets of data on the same graph

Multiple-line graph A line graph that shows two or more sets of data on the same graph

Stem-and-leaf plot A way to organize data when you want to see each item in the data

Histogram A bar graph that shows the frequency, or number of times, data occur within intervals

Box-and-whisker graph A graph that shows how far apart and how evenly data are distributed

Step 1
First, group data by tens digits. Then, order data from least to greatest.

Step 2
Use ten digits as stems. Use ones digits as leaves. Write leaves in increasing order.

	Stem	Leaves
09	0	9
17	1	7
25, 27	2	5, 7
30	3	0
44, 45, 46	4	4, 5, 6
56	5	6
61, 68	6	1, 8
72, 77	7	2, 7

Ask questions such as these as you work together.
What reason might a person have for organizing data in a stem-and-leaf plot? Your child might reply: A stem-and-leaf plot shows each item of the data.
How would you organize data that has items in the hundreds? Your child might reason: I could make the stems 10, 11, 12, and so forth and the leaves would be single digits.

The California Math Standards
Your child's **Harcourt Math** book lists the California Math Standards that are taught in every lesson. If you have questions about the standards, be sure to consult *California Standards for Grade 6* that was sent home at the beginning of the school year.

Family Involvement Activities, p. FA21

Graph Data

MATHEMATICS ACROSS THE GRADES

SKILLS TRACE ACROSS THE GRADES

GRADE 5	GRADE 6	GRADE 7
Display, read, interpret, and analyze data in tables, graphs, and histograms	**Make, analyze, and compare different kinds of graphs and visual displays and determine if they are misleading; estimate and solve for unknown values by using a graph, arithmetic, logical reasoning, and algebraic techniques**	Make, analyze, and compare different kinds of graphs and visual displays, including scatterplots, and determine if they are misleading

SKILLS TRACE FOR GRADE 6

LESSON	FIRST INTRODUCED	TAUGHT AND PRACTICED	TESTED	REVIEWED
6.1	Grade 4	PE pp. 120–123, H37, p. RW27, p. PW27, p. PS27	PE p. 136, pp. AG37–40	PE pp. 136, 137, 140–141
6.2	Grade 6	PE pp. 124–125, H37, p. RW28, p. PW28, p. PS28	PE p. 136, pp. AG37–40	PE pp. 136, 137, 140–141
6.3	Grade 5	PE pp. 126–128, H37, p. RW29, p. PW29, p. PS29	PE p. 136, pp. AG37–40	PE pp. 136, 137, 140–141
6.4	Grade 6	PE p. 129	PE p. 136, pp. AG37–40	PE pp. 136, 137, 140–141
6.5	Grade 6	PE pp. 130–131, H37, p. RW30, p. PW30, p. PS30	PE p. 136, pp. AG37–40	PE pp. 136, 137, 140–141
6.6	Grade 4	PE pp. 132–135, H37, p. RW31, p. PW31, p. PS31	PE p. 136, pp. AG37–40	PE pp. 136, 137, 140–141

KEY **PE** Pupil Edition   **PS** Problem Solving Workbook   **RW** Reteach Workbook
       PW Practice Workbook   **AG** Assessment Guide

Looking Back Prerequisite Skills

To be ready for Chapter 6, students should have the following understandings and skills:

• **Read Bar Graphs**—use bar graphs to answer questions

• **Read Stem-and-Leaf Plots**—use stem-and-leaf plots to answer questions

Check What You Know

Use page 119 to determine students' knowledge of prerequisite concepts and skills.

Intervention

Help students prepare for the chapter by using the intervention resources described on TE page 119.

Looking at Chapter 6 Essential Skills

Students will

• **display and analyze data in bar graphs, line graphs, circle graphs, stem-and-leaf plots, histograms, and box-and-whisker graphs.**

• use graphs, logical reasoning, and arithmetic to estimate and solve for unknown values.

• compare different types of graphs and identify misleading graphs.

EXAMPLE

Make a stem-and-leaf plot of the data.

Ages of Piano Students

18	25	13	46	32
11	12	41	19	36

Ages of Piano Students

Stem	Leaves				
1	1	2	3	8	9
2	5				
3	2	6			
4	1	6			

Looking Ahead Applications

Students will apply what they learn in Chapter 6 to the following new concepts:

• Make a Circle Graph (Chapter 21)

• Display and Analyze Data (Grade 7)

• Collect and Summarize Data (Grade 7)

Graph Data

INTRODUCING THE CHAPTER

Tell students they can use graphs to represent data visually. Graphs make comparisons, trends, and patterns easier to see. After students read the paragraph, explain that graphs need scales to standardize the data. Ask students to explain how to set up a scale to represent the data in the table. Possible answer: One way is have 1 cm of the graph paper represent 200 km.

USING DATA

To begin the study of this chapter, have students

• Write the diameter of a model of the Popigri crater if 1 cm = 100 km. 0.97 cm

• Write the diameter of a model of the Manicouagan crater if the model of Aitken basin is 10 cm long. 0.4 cm

• Make a bar graph of the data in the chart. Check students' work.

PROBLEM SOLVING PROJECT

Purpose To represent data graphically

Materials *For each pair* centimeter rulers, p. TR22; compass

Background When the Shoemaker-Levy Comet hit Jupiter, one 3-km fragment left an impact site about 13,000 km in diameter. Only about 160 impact craters have been discovered so far on Earth.

Analyze, Choose, Solve, and Check

Have students

• Represent the relative sizes of the craters listed in the table with a graph that shows the craters as concentric circles.

• Determine a scale that will allow a model of the largest crater to fit on a single sheet of paper.

• Use the same scale and calculate the diameter of the model needed to show the 13,000-km impact site on Jupiter.

Check students' work.

Suggest that students place their calculations and graphs in their portfolios.

CHAPTER **6** **Graph Data**

In July 1994, fragments of Comet Shoemaker-Levy bombarded Jupiter. One impact left a crater about the same diameter as Earth, which is approximately 12,756 km wide. Evidence of past impacts of meteors, asteroids, or comets also appears on Earth and the Moon. One newly discovered crater on the floor of Chesapeake Bay has a diameter of about 80 km. On a bar graph, about how many times as long would the bar for the Jupiter crater be than the bar for the Chesapeake Bay crater?

EARTH'S AND MOON'S LARGEST CRATERS	
Location	Approximate Diameter (km)
Popigri, Siberia	97
Manicouagan, Canada	100
Chicxulub, Mexico	180
Orientale basin, Moon	1,300
Ibrium basin, Moon	1,800
Aitken basin, Moon	2,500

about 150 times as long

118 Chapter 6

Why learn math? Explain that newspaper reporters often use graphs to make their stories more informative and visually appealing. Graphs concisely show data that would take many paragraphs to explain. Ask: In what other jobs might people use graphs to make data easier to understand? Possible answer: bankers, scientists, sales managers

TECHNOLOGY LINK

To find out more about graphs and graphing, visit The Harcourt Learning Site.

www.harcourtschool.com

Check What You Know

Use this page to help you review and remember important skills needed for Chapter 6.

 **Read Bar Graphs** (See p. H6.)

For 1–4, use the bar graph at the right.

HEIGHTS OF LAUNCH VEHICLES

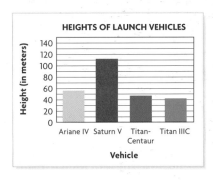

1. List the four launch vehicles in order of size from tallest to shortest. **Saturn V, Ariane IV, Titan-Centaur, Titan IIIC**
2. About how tall is the Saturn V? **about 110 m**
3. About how much taller is the Saturn V than the Ariane IV? **about 55 m**
4. About how much taller is the tallest launch vehicle than the shortest? **about 70 m**

For 5–8, use the bar graph at the left.

AREAS OF THE GREAT LAKES

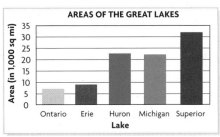

5. Name two Great Lakes whose combined area is less than the area of Lake Superior. **Possible answer: Ontario and Erie**
6. What is the area of the third-largest Great Lake? **about 22,000 sq mi**
7. How much larger is the area of Lake Michigan than the area of Lake Ontario? **about 15,000 sq mi**
8. Which Great Lake has an area of about 22,000 sq mi more than the area of Lake Erie? **Lake Superior**

 **Read Stem-and-Leaf Plots** (See p. H7.)

For 9–15, use the stem-and-leaf plot at the right.

9. What is the score shown by the third stem and fourth leaf? **92**
10. What is the median of Michael's golf scores? **85**
11. What is the range of Michael's golf scores? **22**
12. What is the mode of Michael's golf scores? **79, 85, and 90**
13. How many scores of 90 will Michael need in order to have a mode of 90 for all of his rounds? **3 or more**
14. How many rounds of golf did Michael play? **19**
15. If Michael plays two more rounds and has scores of 86 and 81, what would be the median of the scores? **85**

MICHAEL'S GOLF SCORES

Stems	Leaves
7	6 7 8 9 9
8	0 2 3 5 5 6 8 9
9	0 0 1 2 3 8

> **LOOK AHEAD**

In Chapter 6 you will
- make and analyze stem-and-leaf plots, box-and-whisker graphs, histograms, and line plots
- find unknown values
- analyze graphs

119

Make and Analyze Graphs

LESSON PLANNING

Objective To display and analyze data in bar graphs, line graphs, and circle graphs

Intervention for Prerequisite Skills

Read Bar Graphs (For intervention strategies, see page 119.)

 California Mathematics Content Standards

MR 1.1 Analyze problems by identifying relationships, distinguishing relevant from irrelevant information, identifying missing information, sequencing and prioritizing information, and observing patterns.

(*Also* MR 2.2, MR 2.4)

Vocabulary

multiple-bar graph a bar graph showing two or more sets of data at once

multiple-line graph a line graph showing two or more sets of data at once

Math Background

Graphs are a highly visual way of presenting data.

- Bar graphs are used to show and compare data in discrete categories that often are not ordered. For example, a bar graph may be used to show speeds or weights of different animals.

- Line graphs are used to show patterns of ordered data, such as changes in temperature or population over time.

- Circle graphs are used to show parts of a whole, such as the amounts for different items in a budget.

WARM-UP RESOURCES

 NUMBER OF THE DAY Transparency 6.1

If you triple this number and add 8, you get 23. What number is it? 5

 PROBLEM OF THE DAY Transparency 6.1

Maurie is the second-youngest of 4 teenagers, all 2 years apart in age. His mother is 3 times as old as he is and 24 years younger than her father. How old is Maurie's grandfather? His grandfather is 69 years old.

Solution Problem of the Day tab, p. PD6

 DAILY FACTS PRACTICE

Have students practice multiplication and division facts by completing Set A of *Teacher's Resource Book*, p. TR97.

Reaching All Learners

ALTERNATIVE TEACHING STRATEGY

Ask students to **practice using bar graphs and line graphs.** Have groups of students gather data on one of the following topics:

- city or state populations
- sizes of the Great Lakes
- heights of the six tallest mountains in the world
- lengths of the five longest tunnels or bridges in the world

Then have them decide what scale is appropriate and round the numbers as needed. They should then make a bar graph or line graph, as appropriate, to show their data. Check students' work.

See also page 122.

VISUAL

MIXED REVIEW AND TEST PREP

Cumulative Review Chapters 1–6

Refer to the Pupil Edition pages referenced in the exercises for further review. Have students go to the lesson page, review the lesson, and correct any problem they missed.

Mixed Review and Test Prep, p. 123

How to Help	
Item	Page
17	112
18	70
19	70
20	70
21	40

ENGLISH LANGUAGE LEARNERS (ELL·SDAIE)

Reinforce the **concepts of the words** *single, double,* and *multiple* with students. Show pictures of a single bed, double numbers on 2 number cubes, and twins or triplets and let students tell words in their native languages that have those meanings. Ask them to give examples, such as *double-dip ice cream cones* or *multiple events at a track meet.* Then have students make drawings to illustrate each of the words. Check students' work.

VISUAL

SPECIAL NEEDS

Materials magazines, newspapers

Have students work in small groups to **find an example of a line or bar graph** in current magazines and newspapers. Have each group discuss the graph and prepare answers to these questions:

- What does the graph show?
- What does the horizontal scale show?
- What does the vertical scale show?

Then have each group tell the rest of the class about the graph. Check students' work.

AUDITORY

TECHNOLOGY LINK

Intervention Strategies and Activities CD-ROM • *Skill 79*

Data ToolKit • *Make a Bar Graph, Make a Line Graph, Make a Circle Graph*

Objective To display and analyze data in bar graphs, line graphs, and circle graphs

Vocabulary multiple-bar graph, multiple-line graph

1 Introduce

QUICK REVIEW provides review of mental math skills.

Why Learn This? You can use graphing skills to show the results of a science project, such as how rapidly plants grow under different conditions. *Share the lesson objective with students.*

2 Teach

Guided Instruction

• *Conduct a discussion of the opening bar graph.*

Which whale weighs the most? How can you tell? Blue whale; it has the tallest bar.

How does the weight of the blue whale compare with that of the fin whale? Its weight is more than 2 times as great.

• *For Example 1, help students see that the data contrast in the graph is more quickly discerned than in the table.*

Which mammal has the largest weight difference between male and female? gorilla

Did you use the table or the graph to answer that question? Why? Possible answer: the bar graph; It was easier to see the difference.

Why does this graph need a key? You need to be able to tell the difference in the 2 sets of data.

Algebraic Thinking Comparing data in graphs helps students develop their understanding of equivalent and nonequivalent relationships. Have students look for other greater-than and less-than relationships in both graphs.

LESSON 6.1

Make and Analyze Graphs

Learn how to display and analyze data in bar graphs, line graphs, and circle graphs.

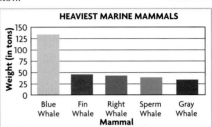

Vocabulary

multiple-bar graph

multiple-line graph

When data are grouped in categories, a bar graph is a good way to display the data. Look at the bar graph below.

HEAVIEST MARINE MAMMALS

(Weight in tons: 150, 125, 100, 75, 50, 25, 0)
Blue Whale, Fin Whale, Right Whale, Sperm Whale, Gray Whale — Mammal

The data in the table below show the weights of other mammals.

WEIGHTS OF SOME MAMMALS				
Mammal	**Lion**	**Gorilla**	**Tiger**	**Grizzly Bear**
Male (lb)	400	450	420	500
Female (lb)	300	200	300	400

A **multiple-bar graph** shows two or more sets of data.

EXAMPLE 1

Use the data in the table above to make a double-bar graph. How do the weights of males compare to the weights of females?

WEIGHTS OF SOME MAMMALS

(Male / Female)
Weight (in lb): 500, 400, 300, 200, 0
Lion, Gorilla, Tiger, Grizzly Bear — Mammal
 This means there is a break in the scale.

Determine an appropriate scale.

Use bars of equal width. Use the data to determine the heights of the bars.

Title the graph and both axes. Include a key.

For each of the mammals in the graph above, the males weigh more than the females.

120

CALIFORNIA STANDARDS MR 1.1 Analyze problems by identifying relationships, distinguishing relevant from irrelevant information, identifying missing information, sequencing and prioritizing information, and observing patterns. *also* MR 2.2, MR 2.4

RETEACH 6.1

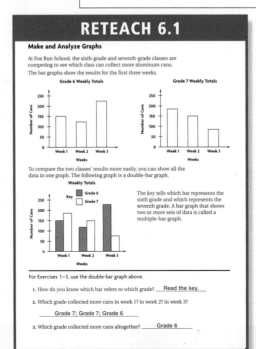

Make and Analyze Graphs

At Fox Run School, the sixth-grade and seventh-grade classes are competing to see which class can collect more aluminum cans. The bar graphs show the results for the first three weeks.

Grade 6 Weekly Totals   Grade 7 Weekly Totals

To compare the two classes' results more easily, you can show all the data in one graph. The following graph is a double-bar graph.

Weekly Totals

Key: Grade 6 / Grade 7

The key tells which bar represents the sixth grade and which represents the seventh grade. A bar graph that shows two or more sets of data is called a multiple-bar graph.

For Exercises 1–3, use the double-bar graph above.

1. How do you know which bar refers to which grade?   Read the key.

2. Which grade collected more cans in week 1? in week 2? in week 3?
   Grade 7; Grade 7; Grade 6

3. Which grade collected more cans altogether?   Grade 6

PRACTICE 6.1

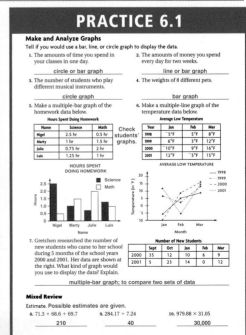

Make and Analyze Graphs

Tell if you would use a bar, line, or circle graph to display the data.

1. The amounts of time you spend in your classes in one day.
   circle or bar graph

2. The amounts of money you spend every day for two weeks.
   line or bar graph

3. The number of students who play different musical instruments.
   circle graph

4. The weights of 8 different pets.
   bar graph

5. Make a multiple-bar graph of the homework data below.

6. Make a multiple-line graph of the temperature data below.

Hours Spent Doing Homework

Name	Science	Math
Nigel	2.5 hr	0.5 hr
Marty	1 hr	1.5 hr
Julie	0.75 hr	2 hr
Luis	1.25 hr	1 hr

Check students' graphs.

Average Low Temperature

Year	Jan	Feb	Mar
1998	⁻5°F	5°F	8°F
1999	6°F	3°F	12°F
2000	⁻10°F	9°F	16°F
2001	12°F	⁻5°F	15°F

7. Gretchen researched the number of new students who came to her school during 5 months of the school years 2000 and 2001. Her data are shown at the right. What kind of graph would you use to display the data? Explain.

Number of New Students					
	Sept	Oct	Jan	Feb	Mar
2000	35	12	10	6	9
2001	5	23	14	0	12

multiple-bar graph; to compare two sets of data

Mixed Review

Estimate. Possible estimates are given.

8. 71.3 + 68.6 + 69.7   9. 284.17 ÷ 7.24   10. 979.88 × 31.05
   210   40   30,000

Line Graphs

A bar graph and a line graph are often used to display the same data. However, a line graph is the better choice when the data show change over time. The line graph below shows the change in the price of a stock every five years from 1970 to 2000.

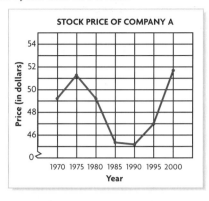

Like a multiple-bar graph, a **multiple-line graph** can show two or more different sets of data on one graph.

MONEY IN SAVINGS ACCOUNTS					
	March	**April**	**May**	**June**	**July**
Bob	$163	$172	$151	$138	$102
Jan	$43	$55	$76	$79	$96

EXAMPLE 2

Use the data in the table above to make a double-line graph. If the trends continue, how would you describe the amount of money that Bob is saving? that Jan is saving?

Determine an appropriate scale.

Mark a point for each amount saved for Bob and connect the points.

Mark a point for each amount saved for Jan and connect the points.

Title the graph and both axes. Include a key.

The money in Bob's savings account is decreasing. The money in Jan's savings account is increasing.

• Use the graph to predict what will happen to each savings account in August. **Possible answer: If the trends continue, Jan will have more money in her savings account than Bob will have in his savings account.**

121

• *Draw students' attention to the single line graph.*

Why doesn't this graph have a key? There is only 1 set of data.

• *After students work through Example 2 and predict what will happen to each savings account, ask:*

REASONING **What amount do you predict will be in each savings account in August?**
Possible answer: Jan's account: about $110; Bob's account: about $70

ADDITIONAL EXAMPLES

Example 1, p. 120

Use the data in the table to make a multiple-bar graph. Compare the amounts raised by the sixth and seventh grades.

MONEY RAISED IN PTA FUND-RAISERS				
Grade	**Holiday Treats**	**Pizza Party**	**Family Fun Night**	**Wrapping Paper**
Sixth	$125	$225	$475	$360
Seventh	$75	$190	$290	$225

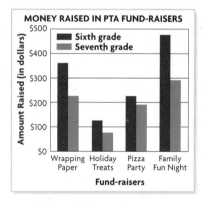

The sixth grade raised more money at each of the fund-raisers.

Example 2, p. 121

Use the data in the table below to make a double-line graph. How would you describe the sales of the two products?

NUMBER OF ITEMS SOLD					
Product	**January**	**February**	**March**	**April**	**May**
A	27	53	75	109	158
B	127	103	95	83	71

The sales of Product A are increasing. The sales of Product B are decreasing.

121

* *Tell students that sometimes more than one type of graph is appropriate.*

What other type of graph could you use to display the data in Example 3? a bar graph

ADDITIONAL EXAMPLE

Example 3, p. 122

The graph shows the sales of school apparel at Pace Middle School. About how many T-shirts were sold for each cap sold? about 4 T-shirts

PACE MIDDLE SCHOOL APPAREL SALES

Sweatshirts 31%
T-shirts 43%
Caps 11%
Jackets 15%

3 Practice

Guided Practice

Do Check for Understanding Exercises 1–4 with your students. Identify those who are having difficulty and use lesson resources to help.

Independent Practice

Assign Exercises 5–16.

Graphs show pictures of data. Bar graphs and line graphs use axes to help you analyze data. A circle graph helps you compare parts to the whole or to other parts.

EXAMPLE 3

In 1987, compact discs (CDs) were new. The circle graph shows the way recorded music was sold in the United States in 1987. About how many cassettes were sold for every CD sold that year?

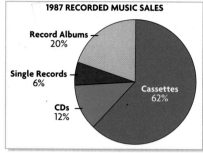

1987 RECORDED MUSIC SALES

Record Albums 20%
Single Records 6%
CDs 12%
Cassettes 62%

Find the parts that represent cassettes and CDs.

Compare the percent of recorded music sold on cassettes to the percent sold on CDs.

Cassettes made up 62% of recorded music sales, while CDs made up 12%. $62 \div 12 \approx 60 \div 12$, or 5.

So, about 5 cassettes were sold for every CD sold.

* By 1997, the percent of recorded music sold in the form of CDs was about 6 times as great as it had been in 1987. About what percent of recorded music was sold on CDs in 1997? **about 72%**

TECHNOLOGY LINK

More Practice: Use *Data Toolkit* to make bar graphs, line graphs, and circle graphs.

2. bar graph: data grouped in categories. line graph: data that show change over time. circle graph: data that compare parts to the whole or to other parts.

CHECK FOR UNDERSTANDING

Look back at the lesson to answer each question.

Think and ▶ Discuss

1. **Explain** why the graphs in Example 1 and Example 2 have a key. so you can tell the difference between the sets of data
2. **Describe** the kind of data you would display in a bar graph, a line graph, and a circle graph. See above left.

Guided ▶ Practice

Tell if you would use a bar, line, or circle graph to display the data.

3. The average monthly rainfall in your city over two years line graph

4. A family budget divided into types of expenses circle graph

PRACTICE AND PROBLEM SOLVING

Independent ▶ Practice

Tell if you would use a bar, line, or circle graph to display the data.

5. The heights of five different students bar graph

6. The price of a stock over a period of several months line graph

7. The way you spend your weekly allowance circle graph

8. The population of six different cities in your state bar graph

Alternative Teaching Strategy

Purpose Students make a double-bar graph and a double-line graph for temperature data to learn about multiple-bar and multiple-line graphs.

Materials bar graph paper, p. TR61 and 1-cm graph paper, p. TR64 or two colors of construction paper, stapler or glue stick, pushpins, string

Set up two graphs on a bulletin board, a bar graph and a line graph, for displaying temperature data. As a class, record the local daily high and low temperatures in your area for a week.

Have volunteers plot points or glue or staple construction paper bars to represent the temperatures in the bar graph.

For the line graph, ask volunteers to plot points or place pushpins for each temperature. Use string to connect the pushpins and make the double-line graph.

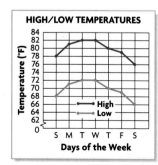

HIGH/LOW TEMPERATURES

Temperature (°F)
84 82 80 78 76 74 72 70 68 66 64 62 0
S M T W T F S
Days of the Week
High
Low

When the graphs are completed discuss the difference between the two graphs. Ask students which graph shows the changes in temperature more clearly.

Encourage students to discuss any trends they notice in the double-line graph. For example, does there seem to be a warming trend? Check students' work.

9. Make a multiple-bar graph using the data in the table at the right.
See Additional Answers, p. 137A.

NUMBER OF RAINY DAYS				
	April	May	June	July
1999	12	3	13	5
2000	6	7	9	11

10. Make a multiple-line graph using the data in the table at the right.
See Additional Answers, p. 137A.

AVERAGE STOCK PRICES				
	Sep	Oct	Nov	Dec
Stock A	$26	$29	$32	$27
Stock B	$14	$10	$8	$19

Problem Solving ▶
Applications

Use Data For 11-13, use the double-line graph below.

11. Each month, more comedies were rented.

11. How do the comedy video rentals compare to the action video rentals?

12. Between which two months did the number of action video rentals decrease the most?
February and March

Video Rentals

13. *REASONING* If the trends continue, what will happen to the number of comedy and action video rentals in July?
Comedy video rentals will increase and action video rentals will decrease.

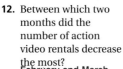
U.S. POPULATION BY AGE (1997)

Use Data For 14-16, use the circle graph at left.

14. The number of people aged 19-64 is about how many times the number who are 65 or older? about 4 to 5 times as many

15. *REASONING* Which of the three age groups do you think spends the most money? Explain. Possible answer: 19–64, since the group has the most people and is of working age.

16. What's the Error? Jay looked at the circle graph at the left and said that 61% of the U.S. population is aged 19 or older. What is his error? He forgot the 13% that are 65 or older.

MIXED REVIEW AND TEST PREP

17. Fifteen students in the gym are asked what their favorite sport is. All of them say "basketball." Ron concludes that the favorite sport of all students is basketball. Is Ron's conclusion valid? Explain. (p. 112)
No. The sample is not representative of the student population.

Find the product. (p. 70)

18. 6×0.4 2.4

19. 0.8×0.7 0.56

20. TEST PREP Which is 0.27×0.4? (p. 70) **A**

A 0.108 **B** 0.675 **C** 1.08 **D** 10.8

21. TEST PREP Find the value of 21^2. (p. 40) **J**

F 21 **G** 2^3 **H** 42 **J** 441

(Extra Practice) page H37, Set A   **123**

MIXED REVIEW AND TEST PREP

Exercises 17–21 provide **cumulative review** (Chapters 1–6).

4 Assess

Summarize the lesson by having students:

DISCUSS **Why does a multiple-bar graph need a key?** Possible answer: to indicate which bar shows which set of data

WRITE **Make up a word problem using the graph you made for Exercise 9.** Possible answer: Which months had more rainy days in 2000 than in 1999?

Lesson Quiz

Transparency **6.1**

What type of graph would you use to show the data?

1. the number of VCRs in American and Japanese homes over 5 yr multiple-line graph

2. the teachers' and students' favorite holidays multiple-bar graph

For 3–4, use the circle graph at the right.

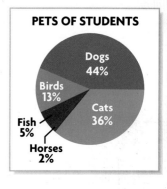
PETS OF STUDENTS

3. About how many students named cats as pets for every student who named fish?
about 6 or 7 students

4. For every student who has birds for pets, about how many students have dogs?
about 3 or 4 students

Find Unknown Values

LESSON PLANNING

Objective To estimate unknown values from a graph and to solve for the values by using arithmetic, logic, and algebra

Intervention for Prerequisite Skills

Read Bar Graphs (For intervention strategies, see page 119.)

California Mathematics Content Standards

MR 2.3 Estimate unknown quantities graphically and solve for them by using logical reasoning and arithmetic and algebraic techniques.

(*Also* AF 2.3, MR 3.2)

Math Background

These ideas will help students understand methods of estimating and solving for unknown values.

* On a line graph, if the data continue to change with the same pattern, you can use that idea to predict future values.

* You can use a formula to find an unknown value when given the other values in the formula. For example, given any two values of distance, rate, and time, you can solve for the third value.

WARM-UP RESOURCES

NUMBER OF THE DAY

Transparency 6.2

The number of the day is the number representing the day of the month. Use this number to find how many hours you have practiced this month if you practice from 4 P.M. to 6 P.M. each day. Possible answer for 21: $21 \times 2 = 42$ hr

PROBLEM OF THE DAY

Transparency 6.2

A line graph shows that the temperature at 6 A.M. was 4° warmer than at 4 A.M. In the hours between midnight and 4 A.M., the temperature had fallen an average of 3° per hour. If the temperature at 6 A.M. was 10°F, what was the temperature at midnight? 18°F

Solution Problem of the Day tab, p. PD6

DAILY FACTS PRACTICE

Have students practice addition facts by completing Set B of *Teacher's Resource Book,* p. TR97.

INTERVENTION AND EXTENSION RESOURCES

REACHING ALL LEARNERS

ALTERNATIVE TEACHING STRATEGY (ELL)

Materials *For each student* 1-cm graph paper, p. TR64

Have students **use graphing to find unknown values.** Display a large graph on a grid with the numbers 1 through 24 vertically (for miles) and 1 through 6 across the bottom (for hours).

Call on volunteers to fill in the appropriate number of blocks over each hour to show the total number of miles Karen walks in 1 hr, 2 hr, and so on, up to 5 hr.

As you work, ask students to copy the pattern on graph paper at their desks. Ask students to describe the pattern and then extend it to find the number of hours it takes Karen to walk 24 mi. Add 4 blocks each time; 6 hr

VISUAL

MIXED REVIEW AND TEST PREP

Cumulative Review Chapters 1–6

Refer to the Pupil Edition pages referenced in the exercises for further review. Have students go to the lesson page, review the lesson, and correct any problem they missed.

Mixed Review and Test Prep, p. 125

How to Help	
Item	Page
11	106
12	106
13	106
14	52
15	44

WRITING IN MATHEMATICS

Have students **practice finding unknown values.** Prepare a graph showing the following data:

Pounds	1	2	3	4	5
Cost	$3	$6	$9	$12	$15

Ask students to write a paragraph describing which of the methods introduced in Examples 1–3 on page 124 they would use to answer the following question and how they would go about using the method:

How much will 6 lb cost?

Possible answers: For the graph: the extended line appears to intersect the 6 lb vertical line at a point across from the $18 cost on the vertical scale. For logical reasoning: the cost increases by $3 when the weight increases by 1 lb.

SOCIAL STUDIES CONNECTION

Have students **practice graphing.** Share this information with students: According to a recent estimate, the world population reached 1 billion in 1804, 2 billion in 1927, 3 billion in 1960, 4 billion in 1974, 5 billion in 1987, and 6 billion on October 12, 1999.

Have students make a line graph to show the increase in population over the years and then predict what the population will be in 2050. Have volunteers give their predictions and explain their reasoning. Check students' work.

VISUAL

TECHNOLOGY LINK

Intervention Strategies and Activities CD-ROM • *Skill 79*

Objective To estimate unknown values from a graph and to solve for the values by using arithmetic, logic, and algebra

1 Introduce

QUICK REVIEW provides review of mental math skills.

Why Learn This? You can use this skill to predict how long it will take you to drive between two cities. *Share the lesson objective with students.*

2 Teach

Guided Instruction

- *Before exploring each example further, point out to students that the times listed are exclusive of any stops or breaks Karen takes while training.*

  In Example 1, what pattern do you see in the graph? The graph goes up the same number of units for each unit it goes across.

  Using the same logic and arithmetic used in Example 2, find how long it will take Karen to walk 22 miles. $5\frac{1}{2}$ hr

REASONING Rewrite the formula in Example 3, with only *t* on the left side of the equal sign. $t = \frac{d}{r}$

ADDITIONAL EXAMPLES

Example 1, p. 124

A bicyclist travels an average of 9 mi per hr. Make a line graph with the data in the table. Estimate how far the bicyclist will travel in 5 hr.

TIME (hr)	1	2	3	4
DISTANCE (mi)	9	18	27	36

Check students' graphs. about 45 mi in 5 hr

Example 3, p. 124

Use the distance formula to find how far the bicyclist will travel in 8 hr if he or she travels at a rate of 9 mi per hr. 72 mi in 8 hr

---

Find Unknown Values

Learn how to estimate unknown values from a graph and solve for the values by using logic, arithmetic, and algebra.

QUICK REVIEW

1. 90×4 2. 18×3 3. 20×5 4. 25×5 5. 50×4
   360   54   100   125   200

For fitness training this week, Karen wants to walk a total of 24 mi. She likes to walk at a rate of 4 mi per hr. The table above shows how long it will take her to walk certain distances.

Time (hr)	1	2	3	4	5
Distance (mi)	4	8	12	16	20

EXAMPLE 1

Make a line graph with the data in the table and use it to estimate how long it will take Karen to walk 24 mi.

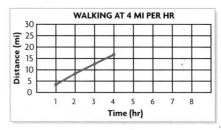

WALKING AT 4 MI PER HR

Look at the graph. If the pattern continues, it looks as if it will take Karen 6 hr to walk 24 mi.

EXAMPLE 2

Use logical reasoning and arithmetic to find how long it will take Karen to walk 24 mi.

Look at the data in the table. Notice that whenever the time increases by 1, the distance increases by 4 mi.

$5 + 1 = 6$, or 6 hr   *Add 1 to the last time in the table.*

$20 + 4 = 24$, or 24 mi   *Add 4 to the last distance in the table.*

So, it will take Karen 6 hr to walk 24 mi.

You can also use the formula $d = rt$ to solve problems about distance (*d*), rate (*r*), and time (*t*). The distance traveled is a product of the rate of speed and the amount of time.

EXAMPLE 3

Use the formula $d = rt$ to find how long it will take Karen to walk 32 mi if she walks at a rate of 4 mi per hr.

$d = rt$ *Write the formula.*

$32 = 4 \times t$ *Replace d with 32 and r with 4. What number multiplied by 4 gives 32?*

$8 = t$ *The solution is t = 8.*

So, it will take Karen 8 hr to walk 32 mi.

124

 CALIFORNIA STANDARDS MR 2.3 Estimate unknown quantities graphically and solve for them by using logical reasoning and arithmetic and algebraic techniques. *also* AF 2.3, MR 3.2

RETEACH 6.2

Find Unknown Values

Line graphs often show a pattern. You can use a line graph to estimate unknown values by extending the graph.

Shauna swims laps in a pool to train for a race. She swims at a rate of 25 m per min. The table below shows how far she swims.

Time (min)	1	2	3	4	5
Distance (m)	25	50	75	100	125

Make a line graph from the data in the table. Use the graph to estimate how many minutes it will take Shauna to swim 150 m.

Step 1 Use the data to draw the graph.

Step 2 Extend the graph until it crosses the 150 m line. Look directly down to the horizontal axis and estimate the value along that axis. If Shauna continues to swim at this rate, it will take her about 6 min to swim 150 m.

Shauna's Race Training

You can also use logical reasoning and arithmetic.
Since 150 m = 100 m + 50 m, add the number of minutes she takes to swim those two distances: 4 min + 2 min = 6 min.

The formula $d = rt$, where *d* is the distance, *r* is the rate, and *t* is the time, can also be used to find the time Shauna needs to swim 150 m.

$d = rt$ Write the formula.
$150 = 25t$ Substitute the values you know into the formula.
$6 = t$ Solve to find the value of *t*.

So, it will take Shauna 6 min to swim 150 m.

A bicycle racer has averaged 20 mi per hr during the first 4 hr of a race.

Time (hr)	1	2	3	4
Distance (mi)	20	40	60	80

1. Make a line graph. Use the graph to estimate how long it will take the racer to ride 100 mi. Check students' graphs; about 5 hr.

2. Use logical reasoning and arithmetic to find how long it will take the racer to ride 100 mi. ____5 hr____

3. Use the formula $d = rt$ to find how long it will take the racer to ride 140 mi.
____7 hr____

PRACTICE 6.2

Find Unknown Values

Sarina kept a record of her after-school earnings.

Number of Weeks Worked	1	2	3	4
Total Saved	$16	$30	$44	$58

Sarina's Earnings

1. Use the data in the table to make a line graph. Use the line graph to estimate how much Sarina will have saved after working for 5 weeks. __$70__
   Check students' graphs; about $70.

2. Use logical reasoning and arithmetic to find how much Sarina will have saved after working for 5 weeks. __$70__

3. Use the line graph to estimate how many weeks Sarina will need to work in order to save $98. __about 7 weeks__

4. Use logical reasoning and arithmetic to find how many weeks Sarina will have to work to save $98. __7 weeks__

A train averages 60 mi per hr while traveling between New York City and Chicago.

Time (hr)	1	2	3	4
Distance (mi)	60	120	180	240

Train Between New York City and Chicago

5. Use the data in the table to make a line graph. Use the line graph to estimate how long it will take the train to travel 360 mi.
   Check students' graphs; about 6 hr.

6. Use logical reasoning and arithmetic to find how long it will take the train to travel 360 mi. __6 hr__

7. Use the formula $d = rt$ to find how long it will take the train to travel 480 mi. __8 hr__

Mixed Review

Use mental math to find the value.

8. $59 + 16$ __75__   9. $63 - 21$ __42__   10. $89 - 54$ __35__

Compare the numbers. Write <, >, or = for each ●.

11. 0.547 ● 0.574 __<__   12. 3.61 ● 3.16 __>__   13. 68.90 ● 68.9 __=__

CHECK FOR UNDERSTANDING

Think and ▶ Discuss

Look back at the lesson to answer the question.

1. **Explain** how you used the graph in Example 1 to predict how long it would take Karen to walk 24 mi. **extended the graph until it intersected with 24 mi and found the corresponding time**

Guided ▶ Practice

Ty averaged 50 mi per hr on his car trip. Use the table for 2–4.

2. Make a line graph. Use the line graph to find how long it will take Ty to drive 250 mi.
See Additional Answers, p. 137A. About 5 hr.

Time (hr)	1	2	3	4
Distance (mi)	50	100	150	200

3. Use logical reasoning and arithmetic to find how long it will take Ty to drive 250 mi. **5 hr**

4. Use the formula $d = rt$ to find how long it will take Ty to drive 350 mi. **7 hr**

PRACTICE AND PROBLEM SOLVING

Independent ▶ Practice

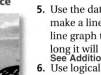

Juan averaged 8 mi per hr while biking. Use the table for 5–7.

5. Use the data in the table to make a line graph. Use the line graph to estimate how long it will take Juan to bike 48 mi.
See Additional Answers, p. 137A. About 6 hr.

Time (hr)	1	2	3	4
Distance (mi)	8	16	24	32

6. Use logical reasoning and arithmetic to find how long it will take Juan to bike 48 mi. **6 hr**

7. Use the formula $d = rt$ to find how long it will take Juan to bike 64 mi. **8 hr**

Problem Solving ▶ Applications

Calvin is training for a marathon. The total distance he has run each week is shown in the table.

8. Make a line graph using the data in the table. **See Additional Answers, p. 137A.**

9. If the trend in Calvin's training continues, about how far will he run in the sixth week of training? **about 45 mi**

Distance Run

Week	1	2	3	4	5
Miles	14	20	26	33	39

10. **Write a problem** using Calvin's training data. Explain your solution. **Check students' problems and solutions.**

MIXED REVIEW AND TEST PREP

Find the mean, median, and mode. (p. 106)

11. 9, 6, 4, 4, 5 **5.6, 5, 4**   12. 12, 14, 32, 28 **21.5, 21, none** 13. 2, 9, 9, 9, 6, 5, 8, 4 **6.5, 7, 9**

14. Order 0.76, 0.765, and 0.076 from least to greatest. (p. 52)
0.076, 0.76, 0.765

15. **TEST PREP** Find the value of $56 - 32 \div (4 \times 2)$. (p. 44) **C**

   A 3   **B** 12   **C** 52   **D** 96

Extra Practice page H37, Set B

125

Guided Practice

Do Check for Understanding Exercises 1–4 with your students. Identify those having difficulty and use lesson resources to help.

//// COMMON ERROR ALERT \\\\

When interpreting a graph, students may confuse the horizontal change with the vertical change. To help avoid this problem, have them mark the horizontal and vertical changes on the graph and label each with the size of the change.

Independent Practice

Assign Exercises 5–10.

MIXED REVIEW AND TEST PREP

Exercises 11–15 provide **cumulative review** (Chapters 1–6).

4 Assess

Summarize the lesson by having students:

DISCUSS When you use the distance formula and the rate is given in feet traveled per second, in what unit should time be given? **seconds**

 WRITE Describe how you solved Exercise 9. Possible answer: I extended the line to intersect with the vertical line extending from 6 on the horizontal axis.

Lesson Quiz

Transparency **6.2**

The following table shows how far a giant tortoise can travel.

TIME (min)	1	2	3	4	5
DISTANCE (m)	5	10	15	20	25

1. Make a line graph using the data in the table. Check students' graphs.

2. Estimate how far the tortoise will travel in 6 min. about 30 m

3. Use the distance formula to find how long it will take the tortoise to travel 100 m.
20 min

PROBLEM SOLVING 6.2

Find Unknown Values

Write the correct answer.

1. While driving from Cincinnati to Toledo, Ohio, a distance of 200 mi, Jamie averages 40 mi per hr. If she left at 10:30 A.M., at what time should she expect to arrive in Toledo?

   3:30 P.M.

2. In the 1990 Census, the population of Los Angeles was 3,485,557. About how many more people would it take for the population to reach 4,000,000?

   about 500,000 people

3. Kiona kept a record of how much she saved by using an on-line grocery shopping service. Over the first 6 weeks she used this service, she saved $102. If her savings continue at the same rate, about how much can she expect to save during the seventh week she uses the shopping service?

   about $17

4. Carmen pays $5.95 per month for a long-distance calling plan that charges her $0.07 per min for her long-distance calls. She averages about 2 hr of long distance calls per month. About how much does she save each month over a plan that charges $0.15 per min for her calls, with no monthly fee?

   about $3.65

Write the letter of the best answer.

5. Ty mows lawns after school for $45 per week. He wants to use the money to pay for a trip that will cost $350. If he spends $20 each week and saves the rest, what is the least number of weeks he must work to pay for the trip?

   A 12 weeks   C 14 weeks
   B 13 weeks   D 15 weeks

6. For an art project, you need to cut squares that measure 4 in. on each side from a rectangular sheet of paper that measures 8 in. by 12 in. What is the greatest number of squares that you can cut?

   F 4 squares   H 8 squares
   G 6 squares   J 10 squares

7. An airplane is climbing at a steady rate of 600 ft per min. From the time it reaches an altitude of 3,600 ft, how many more minutes will it take to reach an altitude of 9,000 ft?

   A 6 min   C 8 min
   B 7 min   D 9 min

8. Brady counted 240 words on the first page of a reading assignment. If the reading assignment is 6 pages long, about how many words should he expect to read?

   F 1,200 words   H 1,440 words
   G 1,340 words   J 1,500 words

9. **Write About It** In Exercise 1, what formula could you use to find the time Jamie would arrive in Toledo?

Possible answer: Use $d = rt$ to find the number of hours needed;

then add the number of hours to 10:30 A.M.

CHALLENGE 6.2

Decisions, Decisions

For each situation, pick the choice that would reach the goal first. Then explain your reasoning.

1. Two planes are heading to the same airport. Plane A is 2,000 mi from the airport, and will average 400 mi per hr for the rest of the trip. Plane B is 1,600 mi from the airport and will average 350 mi per hr for the rest of its trip. Which plane will arrive at the airport first?

Plane B will reach the airport first. Possible answer: Plane B will arrive

in about 4.5 hr, while plane A will arrive in 5 hr.

2. Michael and Wade are reading the same chapter of a book for homework. The chapter begins on page 216 and ends on page 230. Michael has just finished page 222 and is reading at a rate of 1 page every 5 min. Wade is about to begin page 224 and is reading at the rate of 1 page every 6 min. Who will finish reading first?

Michael will finish first. Possible answer: Michael has 8 pages to read,

and reading at 1 page every 5 min, he will finish in 40 min; Wade has 7

pages to read, and reading at 1 page every 6 min, he will finish in 42 min.

3. Two trains leave from the same station. The Express leaves at 1:00 P.M., heading for a city that is 180 mi away. The Express averages 60 mi per hr. The Clipper leaves at 1:30 P.M., averaging 70 mi per hr, heading for a city that is 120 mi away. Which train reaches its destination first?

The Clipper arrives first. Possible answer: The Express needs 3 hr to

make the trip and arrive at 4:00 P.M. The Clipper needs less than 2 hr

to make the trip and will arrive before 3:30 P.M.

4. Breanna and Luz work in the school library, where a major remodeling project has just been completed. All of the books that were packed away must now be unpacked. They begin unpacking books from cartons at the same time. Breanna unpacks 12 books per min and has 200 books to unpack. Luz unpacks 10 books per min and has 180 books to unpack. Who will finish unpacking first?

Breanna will finish first. Possible answer: Breanna needs less than 17

min to unpack the cartons (200 ÷ 12 ≈ 16.7 min), while Luz needs 18

min (180 ÷ 10 = 18 min).

Stem-and-Leaf Plots and Histograms

LESSON PLANNING

Objective To display and analyze data in stem-and-leaf plots and histograms

Intervention for Prerequisite Skills

Read Stem-and-Leaf Plots (For intervention strategies, see page 119.)

California Mathematics Content Standards

MR 2.4 Use a variety of methods, such as words, numbers, symbols, charts, graphs, tables, diagrams, and models, to explain mathematical reasoning.

(*Also* SDAP 1.0, SDAP 1.1)

Math Background

Stem-and-leaf plots and histograms present a more graphic picture of organized data than does a table.

- Stem-and-leaf plots show individual data items organized by stem, which may be the first one, two, or more digits of the number. The leaves display the items' ones digits.

- If a stem-and-leaf plot is turned counterclockwise one quarter turn, its information resembles that of a histogram.

- Histograms show the frequency of data in bars for a range or interval. The vertical axis always shows the frequency and the horizontal axis shows the intervals.

Vocabulary

stem-and-leaf plot a method of organizing data that displays each data item's digits in a stem (vertical) and leaf (horizontal) design

histogram a bar graph that shows the frequency, or the number of times, data occur within intervals

WARM-UP RESOURCES

 NUMBER OF THE DAY Transparency 6.3

Multiply the number of minutes in this class period by 60. Give the product and tell its significance. Possible answer for 48 minutes: 2,880; the number of seconds in this class period

 PROBLEM OF THE DAY Transparency 6.3

What is the least number that can be divided evenly by each of the numbers 1 through 12? 27,720

Solution Problem of the Day tab, p. PD6

 DAILY FACTS PRACTICE

Have students practice addition facts by completing Set C of *Teacher's Resource Book*, p. TR97.

INTERVENTION AND EXTENSION RESOURCES

ALTERNATIVE TEACHING STRATEGY ELL

Display a place-value chart and the **outline for a stem-and-leaf plot.**

Stem	Leaves

Ask volunteers to write the digits for each number from the Card-Tower Competition on page 126 in the place-value chart.

Then have students write them one by one in the stem-and-leaf plot, discussing where to place the tens digit and the ones digit for each number. Check students' work.

VISUAL

MIXED REVIEW AND TEST PREP

Cumulative Review Chapters 1–6

Refer to the Pupil Edition pages referenced in the exercises for further review. Have students go to the lesson page, review the lesson, and correct any problem they missed.

Mixed Review and Test Prep, p. 128

How to Help	
Item	Page
12	112
13	94
14	82
15	60
16	20

WRITING IN MATHEMATICS

Ask students to **write a paragraph that describes how to make a stem-and-leaf plot** from a given set of data.

Students should include information on how to choose the stem and the leaves and then how to make the plot itself. Possible answer: Examine the numbers. If they are two-digit numbers, choose the tens digits as the stems and the ones digits as leaves. Draw a T and list the stems along the left. Then write each ones digit in the same row as its stem. Finally, arrange the leaves in numerical order.

ADVANCED LEARNERS

Materials reference books, almanacs

Challenge groups of students to make **histograms.** Have each group make a histogram of the populations of all 50 states. Have groups present their graphs and explain how they chose their population intervals.

Check students' work.

VISUAL

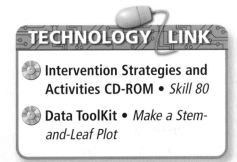

TECHNOLOGY LINK

- **Intervention Strategies and Activities CD-ROM** • *Skill 80*
- **Data ToolKit** • *Make a Stem-and-Leaf Plot*

Objective To display and analyze data in stem-and-leaf plots and histograms

Vocabulary stem-and-leaf plot, histogram

1 Introduce

QUICK REVIEW provides review of mental math skills.

Why Learn This? You can use a stem-and-leaf plot to organize test scores for your class. *Share the lesson objective with students.*

2 Teach

Guided Instruction

• *Review the parts of a stem-and-leaf plot.*

If you have 10 pieces of data to put in a stem-and-leaf plot, how many leaves will you need? 10

How is a leaf related to its stem? Possible answer: The stem is the tens digit which might be 0, and the leaf is the ones digit of a piece of data.

• *Ask the students to look at Example 1.*

Why are there 3 ones next to the 2 stem? There are three 21's in the data.

ADDITIONAL EXAMPLE

Example 2, p. 126

Use the data for the number of prize tickets collected by students at the Fun Center to make a stem-and-leaf plot. Use the stem-and-leaf plot to help find the mode and the median.

NUMBER OF PRIZE TICKETS COLLECTED						
30	65	53	42	45	66	35
35	49	43	50	72	65	42
66	55	37	47	42	71	34

Number of Prize Tickets Collected

Stem	Leaves
3	0 4 5 5 7
4	2 2 2 3 5 7 9
5	0 3 5
6	5 5 6 6
7	1 2

Mode: 42; Median: 47

LESSON 6.3

Stem-and-Leaf Plots and Histograms

Learn how to display and analyze data in stem-and-leaf plots and histograms.

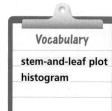

Vocabulary

stem-and-leaf plot
histogram

QUICK REVIEW

1. 8.5 + 4.2 12.7	2 125.80 + 11.20 137.0	3. 10.8 − 8.6 2.2
4. 225.65 − 5.60 220.05	5. 10.2 + 2.4 + 3.1 15.7	

$\mathbf{Y}$ou can use a **stem-and-leaf plot** to organize data when you want to see each item in the data. For a stem-and-leaf plot, choose the stems first and then write the leaves.

The table shows the number of levels reached, without cards falling, at a card-tower building competition. Use the data to make a stem-and-leaf plot.

CARD-TOWER COMPETITION					
21	18	32	47	50	33
19	21	11	54	31	18
33	42	21	29	16	12

EXAMPLE 1

Bryan Berg built a 19 ft 16½ in. high card tower with 102 levels.

11	12	16	18	18	19
21	21	21	29		
31	32	33	33		
42	47				
50	54				

First, group the data by tens digits. Then, order the data from least to greatest.

Card Tower Competition

Stems	Leaves
1	1 2 6 8 8 9
2	1 1 1 9
3	1 2 3 3
4	2 7
5	0 4

Use the tens digits as stems. Use the ones digits as leaves. Write the leaves in increasing order.

The line 4 | 2 7 means 42 and 47.

Use the data from a domino stacking competition to make a stem-and-leaf plot. Then use the stem-and-leaf plot to help find the mode and the median.

EXAMPLE 2

NUMBER OF DOMINOES STACKED									
97	88	74	96	98	58	68	90	80	90
72	86	69	78	93	84	99	92	85	

Stems	Leaves
5	8
6	8 9
7	2 4 8
8	0 4 5 6 8
9	0 0 2 3 6 7 8 9

90 occurs more than any other number.

There are 19 scores. The median is the 10th score.

Mode: 90   Median: 86

CALIFORNIA STANDARDS MR 2.4 Use a variety of methods, such as words, numbers, symbols, charts, graphs, tables, diagrams, and models, to explain mathematical reasoning. *also* SDAP 1.0, SDAP 1.1

126

RETEACH 6.3

Stem-and-Leaf Plots and Histograms

A histogram is a type of bar graph. Histograms are different from bar graphs in two ways.
• The bars are side by side, not spaced apart.
• Each bar refers to an interval, not a single item.

All of the students in Mr. Higgins' physical education class ran the 100-yard dash. This histogram shows the students' times to the nearest second.

100-Yard Dash Times

Complete.

1. The number of runners with times of 17–19 sec was ____6____.

2. ___3___ students had times of 11–13 sec.

There were 18 students who recorded how many baskets they made in 30 sec. Their results are in the following tables.

Student	1	2	3	4	5	6	7	8	9
Baskets made	5	8	17	13	15	5	19	7	7

Student	10	11	12	13	14	15	16	17	18
Baskets made	8	9	6	14	7	16	12	12	10

3. Use the data above to complete the histogram.

4. Complete the stem-and-leaf plot of the *Baskets Made* data.

Stem	Leaves
0	5 5 6 7 7 8 8 9
1	0 2 2 3 4 5 6 7 9

Key: 0 | 5 = 5

Baskets Made in 30 Sec

PRACTICE 6.3

Stem-and-Leaf Plots and Histograms

Tell whether a bar graph or a histogram is more appropriate.

1. number of fish caught at different times of day

   histogram

2. average monthly phone bill for every month of one year

   bar graph

3. number of shoppers in a store during 3 different time intervals

   histogram

Make a stem-and-leaf plot of each set of data.

4. Janet's math test scores:
95, 83, 78, 91, 75, 85, 91, 98, 80

Janet's Math Test Scores

7	5 8
8	0 3 5 Key: 8	3 = 83
9	1 1 5 8

5. Raoul's golf scores:
79, 85, 82, 86, 90, 94, 83, 85, 79, 91

Raoul's Golf Scores

7	9 9
8	2 3 5 5 6 Key: 9	0 = 90
9	0 1 4

For 6–7, use the table below.

Campers at Day Camp				
Age	5–7	8–10	11–13	14–16
Number	6	11	18	9

6. Make a histogram. Check students' graphs.

7. How would the number of campers in each group change if you used 5 groups instead of 4 groups?

   The number of campers per group would decrease.

Campers at Day Camp

For 8–9, use the histogram at the right.

8. During which time period did the most flights arrive?

   9:00–10:59

9. How many flights arrived after 11:00?

   7 flights

Flight Arrivals

Mixed Review

10. Bill has 180 baseball cards. He has 3 times as many infielders as outfielders. How many of each does he have?

   135 infielders; 45 outfielders

11. Tim gave a clerk $20.00 for a book and received $3.85 in change. How much did the book cost?

   $16.15

A **histogram** is a bar graph that shows the frequency, or the number of times, data occur within intervals. The bars in a histogram are connected, rather than separated.

BAR GRAPH

HISTOGRAM

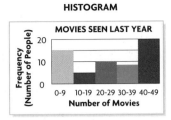

Remember that you can use the range of a set of data to help determine intervals.

This bar graph is used to show information about individual movie customers. The histogram is used to show information about groups of movie customers.

EXAMPLE 3

The table below shows the number of sit-ups students in gym class did in one minute. Make a histogram for the data.

NUMBER OF SIT-UPS									
28	19	32	45	44	12	24	32	35	47
55	59	24	25	37	36	38	36	42	41

First, make a frequency table with intervals of 10. Start with 10.

Interval	10-19	20-29	30-39	40-49	50-59
Frequency	2	4	7	5	2

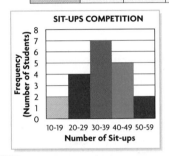

Title the graph and label the scales and axes.

Graph the number of students who did sit-ups within each interval.

1. Possible answer: It helps you compare how many towers were of different heights, such as 10–19 and 40–49.

CHECK FOR UNDERSTANDING

Think and ▶ Discuss

Look back at the lesson to answer each question.

1. **Tell** how the stem-and-leaf plot in Example 1 is useful in showing how well people did in the competition. See above left.

2. **Explain** how data displayed in a histogram are different from data displayed in a bar graph. The data in a histogram occur in intervals while data in a bar graph occur in categories.

127

• _Draw students' attention to the bar graph and the histogram._

How is the bar graph similar to the histogram? Possible answer: Both give customer information on the x-axis and the number of movies on the y-axis.

How is the bar graph different from the histogram? Possible answer: The bar graph shows information for only 4 customers. The histogram shows data for more customers and the bars are connected.

ADDITIONAL EXAMPLE

Example 3, p. 127

Make a histogram for the data.

BOOKS READ BY CLUB MEMBERS									
13	53	59	36	75	50	44	64	12	57
19	39	8	61	66	17	48	42	79	

Possible answer:

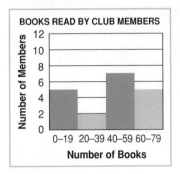

3 Practice

Guided Practice

Do Check for Understanding Exercises 1–5 with your students. Identify those having difficulty and use lesson resources to help.

In discussing Exercise 2, point out that the horizontal axis of a histogram is always numerical while that of a bar graph may be categorical.

PROBLEM SOLVING 6.3

Stem-and-Leaf Plots and Histograms

Write the correct answer.

Analyze Choose Solve Check

1. Harry wants to make a graph to show the number of cars that go down his street during 1-hour intervals during the day. Would a bar graph or a histogram be more appropriate?

histogram

2. A contest to see who could jump the farthest was conducted. The shortest jump was 87 centimeters and the longest jump was 162 centimeters. What is the range for the data?

75 cm

3. If you survey 1 out of every 10 people, how many would you survey out of a group of 930 girls?

93 girls

4. Gregg wants to compare the population in five states. Would a bar graph or a histogram be more appropriate?

bar graph

Write the letter of the best answer.

5. A set of data ranges from 12 to 86. What intervals would you use to display this data in a histogram with 4 intervals?

A 10–39, 40–49, 50–69, 70–89
B 10–19, 20–39, 40–59, 60–89
C 10–29, 30–49, 50–69, 70–89
D 10–29, 30–39, 40–49, 50–89

6. This year Mary has scored 87, 89, 93, 94, 78, 76, 99, and 100 on her math tests. Which could be the stems for a stem-and-leaf plot of the data?

F 7, 8, 9, 10
G 1, 7, 8, 9
H 70, 80, 90, 100
J 7, 8, 9

7. Dolly and her three friends pool their baby-sitting money. Last month they earned a total of $90. If they share the money equally, how much would each girl receive?

A $21.50   C $23.50
B $22.50   D $30.00

8. Rick has a book with 48 pages of stickers. Each page has between 12 and 23 stickers. What is a reasonable estimate of the total number of stickers in Rick's book?

F Fewer than 550
G Between 550 and 1,100
H Between 1,100 and 1,600
J More than 1,600

9. **Write About It** Why are the bars in a histogram connected rather than separated?

In a histogram the bars represent adjoining intervals.

CHALLENGE 6.3

Play Ball!

The Ted Williams Middle School just finished its baseball season. The team played 20 games. Here are the results.

Game	1	2	3	4	5	6	7	8	9	10
Runs Scored by Williams	4	5	0	1	9	11	10	17	0	2
Runs Scored by Opponents	0	6	6	9	7	2	1	3	8	4

Game	11	12	13	14	15	16	17	18	19	20
Runs Scored by Williams	3	5	5	9	1	3	4	2	12	6
Runs Scored by Opponents	1	3	11	10	5	6	2	3	8	5

According to the table, Williams won its first game 4 to 0 and lost game 13 by a score of 11 to 5.

You are the team's statistician. Answer each question.

1. What was the final record of the Ted Williams Middle School baseball team for the season?

10 wins, 10 losses

2. In a shutout, a team scores no runs in the game. How many times did Williams get shut out? How many times did Williams shut out its opponent?

2 times; 1 time

3. Complete the histogram showing runs scored by Williams.

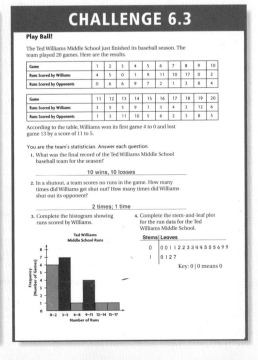

4. Complete the stem-and-leaf plot for the run data for the Ted Williams Middle School.

Stems	Leaves
0	0 0 1 1 2 2 3 3 4 4 5 5 5 6 9 9
1	0 1 2 7

Key: 0 | 0 means 0

127

Independent Practice

Assign Exercises 6–11.

MIXED REVIEW AND TEST PREP
Exercises 12–16 provide **cumulative review** (Chapters 1–6).

 **Assess**

Summarize the lesson by having students:

DISCUSS How would you label the axes of the histogram for Exercise 8? *x*-axis = Ice-Skaters' Ages; *y*-axis = Number of Ice-Skaters

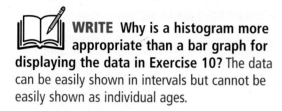 **WRITE** Why is a histogram more appropriate than a bar graph for displaying the data in Exercise 10? The data can be easily shown in intervals but cannot be easily shown as individual ages.

Lesson Quiz

Transparency 6.3

1. Make a stem-and-leaf plot of the data: 33, 47, 68, 36, 34, 59, 37, 52, 65, 75, 78, 78

Stem	Leaves
3	3 4 6 7
4	7
5	2 9
6	5 8
7	5 8 8

Tell whether a bar graph or a histogram is more appropriate.

2. the number of teenagers in each of the four largest cities in Japan bar graph

3. the 100 distances in a long-jump competition histogram

4. the number of candy bars sold by students in a school fund-raiser histogram

---

Guided Practice

3. Make a stem-and-leaf plot of the data 32, 24, 44, 57, 31, 25, 41, 26. See at left.

3.
Stem	Leaves
2	4 5 6
3	1 2
4	1 4
5	7

Tell whether a bar graph or a histogram is more appropriate.

4. number of customers at different intervals of time histogram

5. populations of five different states bar graph

PRACTICE AND PROBLEM SOLVING

Independent Practice

6. Make a stem-and-leaf plot of the data 89, 74, 63, 65, 68, 74, 71, 80. See at left.

6.
Stem	Leaves
6	3 5 8
7	1 4 4
8	0 9

Tell whether a bar graph or a histogram is more appropriate.

7. heights of the tallest mountains in the United States bar graph

8. ages of 75 ice-skating competitors at a competition histogram

Problem Solving Applications

Use the data in the table for 9.

9. a. Make a stem-and-leaf plot of the data.

b. Use the stem-and-leaf plot to help find the median and mode. 24.5 in., 28 in.

9.
Stem	Leaves
1	2 5 8 9
2	0 4 5 6 8 8
3	2 6

PLANT HEIGHTS IN INCHES					
28	36	25	24	20	32
15	18	28	12	19	26

c. *REASONING* Can you tell what the mean is for this set of data by looking at the stem-and-leaf plot? Explain. No. You must still compute the mean.

AGES OF MARIA'S MUSIC CUSTOMERS									
10	25	33	14	54	62	29	44	41	40
11	31	41	24	65	16	39	50	51	55
19	22	17	26	31	42	17	18	42	37

10. Use the data in the table above to make a histogram. See Additional Answers, p. 137A.

11. **Write About It** Write a question that can be answered using the data from Exercise 10. Explain your answer. Check students' questions and answers.

MIXED REVIEW AND TEST PREP

12. Thirty students in the gym are asked their favorite sport. They all respond by saying "basketball." Is this valid for all students? (p. 112) no

13. What type of sample does Ron get if he randomly surveys 175 out of 500 students? (p. 94) random

14. Evaluate 3*k* for *k* = 6.5. (p. 82) 19.5   15. Write 0.73 as a percent. (p. 60) 73%

16. **TEST PREP** Mt. McKinley has a height of 20,320 ft. Mt. Whitney has a height of 14,494 ft. How much higher is Mt. McKinley than Mt. Whitney? (p. 20) B

A 34,814 ft   B 5,826 ft   C 5,800 ft   D 3,286 ft

Extra Practice page H37, Set C

Explore Box-and-Whisker Graphs

MATH LAB

Explore how to make a box-and-whisker graph and understand its parts.

You need at least eleven 3 in. × 5 in. cards, marker.

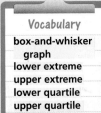

Vocabulary

box-and-whisker graph
lower extreme
upper extreme
lower quartile
upper quartile

TECHNOLOGY LINK
More Practice: Use E-Lab, *Exploring Box-and-Whisker Graphs.*
www.harcourtschool.com/elab2002

A **box-and-whisker graph** shows how far apart and how evenly data are distributed.

Activity

- Write each of the data in the table on a separate card.

NUMBER OF TROPHIES WON									
35	21	24	32	36	20	24	29	27	30

- Order the data from least to greatest. Draw a star on the card with the least value, or **lower extreme**, and the card with the greatest value, or **upper extreme**. 20; 36

- Find the median of the data. If the median is not one of the numbers already written, write it on a card, put it in the middle of the data, and circle it. 28

- Find the median of the lower half of the data. This median is called the **lower quartile**. Circle it. Separate the data to the left of the lower quartile from the rest of the data. 24

- Find the median of the upper half of the data. This median is the **upper quartile**. Circle it. Separate the data to the right of the upper quartile from the rest of the data. 32

Think and Discuss

- Look at your cards. Into how many parts do the lower quartile, the median, and the upper quartile separate the data? 4 parts

- What fraction of the data are to the left of the lower quartile? to the right of the upper quartile? What fraction of the data are between the lower quartile and the upper quartile? $\frac{1}{4}, \frac{1}{4}, \frac{1}{2}$

You have found all you need to make this box-and-whisker graph.

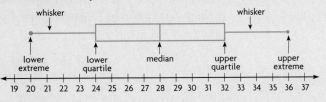

Practice

- Make a box-and-whisker graph of the data.

POINTS SCORED									
10	12	9	22	17	7	14	8	11	19

See Additional Answers, p. 137A.

129

CALIFORNIA STANDARDS SDAP 1.0 Students compute and analyze statistical measurement for data sets. **SDAP 1.1** Compute the range, mean, median, and mode of data sets.

ORGANIZER

Objective To make a box-and-whisker graph and understand its parts

Vocabulary box-and-whisker graph, lower extreme, upper extreme, lower quartile, upper quartile

Materials *For each pair* at least eleven 3 in. × 5 in. index cards, marker

Lesson Resources E-Lab Recording Sheet • *Exploring Box-and-Whisker Graphs*

Intervention for Prerequisite Skills Read Bar Graphs (For intervention strategies, see page 119.)

Activity

If necessary, assist students as they organize data into the parts that make up a box-and-whisker graph. Record each step as students work with their partners.

Think and Discuss

Have students check to be sure their data are separated into the parts described in the first question and associate them with the graph numbers.

Practice

Have students share their graphs with the class. Ask:

What are the names for certain numbers on the graph? lower extreme, lower quartile, median, upper quartile, upper extreme

Oral Assessment

What are the lower and upper quartiles? lower quartile: the median of the data to the left of the overall median; upper quartile: the median of the data to the right of the overall median

What are the lower and upper extremes? the least number and the greatest number, respectively, in a data set

---

E-LAB RECORDING SHEET

Name _____

Exploring Box-and-Whisker Graphs

The boxes show balances for two student-run businesses. One student works a paper route, while the other sells greeting cards.

STUDENT A	
ACCOUNT BALANCE ON 9 FRIDAYS	
-43 -30 20 25 35 40 52 60 70	

STUDENT B	
ACCOUNT BALANCE ON 9 FRIDAYS	
-70 -28 -5 8 15 30 45 60 64	

Use the computer.

1. Click **New Problem**. Enter the weekly balances for student A. Copy the box-and-whisker graph.

2. Click **New Problem** and enter the weekly balances for student B. Copy the box-and-whisker graph.

Box-and-whisker graphs provide an easy way to compare two data sets.

3. How do the graphs show that student B had a wider range of balances than those of student A?
   The whiskers on graph B extend farther.

4. How can you tell from the box-and-whisker graphs that student A generally had a higher weekly balance than the typical weekly balance of student B?
   The median value is higher in graph A than in graph B.

Suppose that the account record of student B had an error. Instead of a balance of 64 at the end of the ninth week, the record should have shown a balance of 68.

5. Replace the incorrect balance of 64 with 68. Explain how this change affects the following.
   a. median _The median value is not affected._
   b. range _The range increases by 4._

Box-and-whisker graphs provide an easy way to compare the medians and ranges of data sets.

E-Lab Recording Sheet   23

USING E-LAB

Students use a computer tool to make box-and-whisker graphs that they then interpret.

The E-Lab Recording Sheets and activities are available on the E-Lab website.

www.harcourtschool.com/elab2002

TECHNOLOGY LINK

- **Intervention Strategies and Activities CD-ROM** • *Skill 79*

- **E-Lab** • *Exploring Box-and-Whisker Graphs*

Box-and-Whisker Graphs

LESSON PLANNING

Objective To analyze a box-and-whisker graph

Intervention for Prerequisite Skills

Read Bar Graphs (For intervention strategies, see page 119.)

California Mathematics Content Standards

SDAP 1.0 Students compute and analyze statistical measurements for data sets.

SDAP 1.1 Compute the range, mean, median, and mode of data sets.

(*Also* MR 2.5)

Math Background

A box-and-whisker graph provides different information from a histogram or a stem-and-leaf plot about the center, spread, and symmetry of the data.

- The box-and-whisker graph uses the median because it is not as affected by outliers as the mean is.

- You can read the median of the data from the box-and-whisker graph as well as the middle points of the upper and lower halves of the data, called the quartiles.

- Because the median may not be in the data set, the only values you can read that you know must be in the set are the extremes.

WARM-UP RESOURCES

NUMBER OF THE DAY

Transparency 6.5

How much money would you have if you had the same number of quarters as the number for the last day of the month? Possible answer: 31 days—$7.75

PROBLEM OF THE DAY

Transparency 6.5

Jason made a stem-and-leaf plot of the ages of all the adults at a family reunion. His father's age was the median age. Jason is 1 year younger than $\frac{1}{3}$ his father's age. How old is Jason?

Ages of the Adults

Stem	Leaves
2	2 6
3	0 3 7
4	2 3 3
5	5 8
6	8

13 years old

Solution Problem of the Day tab, p. PD6

DAILY FACTS PRACTICE

Have students practice subtraction facts by completing Set E of *Teacher's Resource Book*, p. TR97.

INTERVENTION AND EXTENSION RESOURCES

REACHING ALL LEARNERS

ALTERNATIVE TEACHING STRATEGY (ELL)

Help students **make a box-and-whisker graph.** They should draw a number line and plot these data points: 20, 37, 42, 30, 31, 33, 50, 22, 25, 35. Then from the number line, have them draw dotted vertical lines to points above the least and greatest values, the median, and the medians of the upper and lower halves, or quartiles. Direct students to complete the box-and-whisker graph by connecting the extremes to the quartiles with a line and by making a box from the quartiles to include a median line.

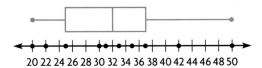

20 22 24 26 28 30 32 34 36 38 40 42 44 46 48 50

Ask volunteers to relate the whiskers and the box to the data distribution. Check students' work.

VISUAL

MIXED REVIEW AND TEST PREP

Cumulative Review Chapters 1–6

Refer to the Pupil Edition pages referenced in the exercises for further review. Have students go to the lesson page, review the lesson, and correct any problem they missed.

Mixed Review and Test Prep, p. 131

How to Help	
Item	**Page**
12	126
13	98
14	52
15	52
16	40

CAREER CONNECTION

Have students **research the career of statistician.** Tell them that the box-and-whisker graph was invented by statistician John Tukey in the 1960s. Another of his creations is the stem-and-leaf plot, a method of organizing data in order to make comparisons.

Have students find the different types of jobs statisticians might have, and what the employment prospects are for statisticians in government, industry, and education. Then have them make a poster advertising the career of statistician. Check students' work.

VISUAL

ADVANCED LEARNERS

Challenge students to **make a box-and-whisker graph.** Have them work in pairs to research the high temperatures for several cities in your state over a period of 10 days.

Ask the pairs to make box-and-whisker graphs showing the data for one of the cities researched. Then ask them to exchange graphs with another pair.

Have students write several statements similar to those in Example 2 on page 130 about the graph they have. Then have them compare their conclusions with the actual data. Check students' work.

VISUAL

TECHNOLOGY LINK

- **Intervention Strategies and Activities CD-ROM** • *Skill 79*

- **Data ToolKit** • *Make a Table, Make a Box-and-Whisker Graph*

LESSON **6.5** ORGANIZER

Objective To analyze a box-and-whisker graph

1 Introduce

provides review of mental math skills.

Why Learn This? You can use this skill to compare how your class does on two different tests. *Share the lesson objective with students.*

2 Teach

Guided Instruction

- *As students look at Example 1, have them review the parts of the graph.*

  What value is the lower quartile? the upper quartile? 5; 9

  What does the vertical line in the box indicate? the median

- *Direct students' attention to Example 2.*

  Why is the box part of the graph in Example 2 divided in half, but the box in Example 1 is not? Possible answer: The median lines fall in different places because the data are distributed differently.

ADDITIONAL EXAMPLES

Example 1, p. 130

The data in the graph show the results of a survey of 20 restaurants for the price of a pizza with 2 toppings. What are the most expensive and the least expensive pizzas? $15; $8

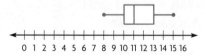

0 1 2 3 4 5 6 7 8 9 10 11 12 13 14 15 16

Example 2, p. 130

The graph shows data about the number of CDs sold each day during a sale at The Music Box. What does the graph show about how the data are distributed?

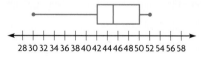

28 30 32 34 36 38 40 42 44 46 48 50 52 54 56 58

Possible answer: The data in the lowest $\frac{1}{4}$ are spread out. The data in the middle $\frac{1}{2}$ are closer together. On at least one day 30 CDs were sold. On at least one day 52 CDs were sold.

Box-and-Whisker Graphs

Learn how to analyze a box-and-whisker graph.

Find each for the data 4, 0, 4, 6, 5, 3, 3, 3, 5, and 9.
1. mean 4.2 2. median 4 3. mode 3 4. range 9 5. outliers
0 and 9

The only actual data you can identify from the data set in a box-and-whisker graph are the extremes.

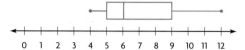 **EXAMPLE 1**

The data in the box-and-whisker graph represent the diameters in kilometers of some asteroids observed by a scientist. What was the diameter of the largest asteroid? of the smallest asteroid?

0 1 2 3 4 5 6 7 8 9 10 11 12

The upper extreme is 12 and the lower extreme is 4. So, the diameter of the largest asteroid was 12 km, and the diameter of the smallest asteroid was 4 km.

- Look again at the graph. Which of the following can you determine—mean, median, mode, range? **median and range**

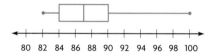 **EXAMPLE 2**

Data about the number of meteors seen during a particular hour at different locations during the 1999 Leonids meteor shower are shown in the box-and-whisker graph. What does the graph show about how the data are distributed?

80 82 84 86 88 90 92 94 96 98 100

The data in the lowest $\frac{1}{4}$ of the data set are very close together. The data in each part of the middle $\frac{1}{2}$ are farther apart. They are closer to the lower extreme than to the upper extreme. The data in the highest $\frac{1}{4}$ are farther apart than those in the middle. At least one person saw 82 meteors, and at least one person saw 100 meteors.

CHECK FOR UNDERSTANDING

Think and ▶ Discuss

Look back at the lesson to answer the question.

1. **Explain** why you can't find the mean and the mode when looking at a box-and-whisker graph. **A box-and-whisker graph shows the distribution of data, not all of the data.**

130

RETEACH 6.5

Box-and-Whisker Graphs

The owner of a gift shop made a box-and-whisker graph to represent the number of customers who came into the shop each day.

lower
quartile median quartile upper
lower
extreme upper
extreme

12 14 16 18 20 22 24 26 28 30

The least number in a box-and-whisker graph is called the **lower extreme**. It is the black dot at the end of the left whisker. In this graph, the lower extreme represents the least number of customers to enter the shop in a single day. The lower extreme is 17.

The greatest number in a box-and-whisker graph is called the **upper extreme**. It is the black dot at the end of the right whisker. In this graph, the upper extreme represents the greatest number of customers to enter the shop in one day. The upper extreme is 28.

The range is the difference between the upper and lower extremes. The range of this set of data is 11.

The median of a set of data is the middle number when all numbers are arranged in numerical order. The median of this set is 21.

Another store owner also made a box-and-whisker graph of the customers who entered her store daily.

26 30 34 38 42 46 50 54 58 62

1. What is the lower extreme? __30__
2. What is the upper extreme? __54__
3. What is the lower quartile? __40__
4. What is the upper quartile? __50__
5. What is the range of this set of data? __24__
6. What is the median for this set of data? __44__

PRACTICE 6.5

Box-and-Whisker Graphs

For 1–3, use the box-and-whisker graph below.

16 18 20 22 24 26 28 30 32 34

1. What is the median? __23__
2. What are the lower and upper quartiles? __21; 29__
3. What are the lower and upper extremes and the range? __18; 30; 12__

For 4–8, use the data in the chart below.

Lengths of Phone Calls (in min)

17	21	16	22	24	26	18	28	25	29
21	18	14	23	25	18	26	24	22	23

4. What is the median? __22.5__
5. What are the lower and upper quartiles? __18; 25__
6. What are the lower and upper extremes and the range? __14; 29; 15__
7. Make a box-and-whisker graph. **Check students' graphs.**
8. What fractional part of the data is less than 25 minutes? __$\frac{7}{10}$__

Mixed Review

For 9–10, use the data in the chart above for 4–8.

9. Complete the cumulative frequency table below for the data.

Lengths of Phone Calls

Minutes	Frequency	Cumulative Frequency
11–15	1	1
16–20	5	6
21–25	10	16
26–30	4	20

10. Make a line plot for the data. **Check students' graphs.**

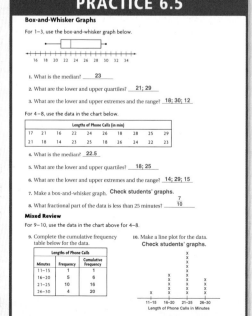

11–15 16–20 21–25 26–30
Length of Phone Calls in Minutes

Guided Practice

For 2–3, use the box-and-whisker graph.

2. What are the median, lower quartile, and upper quartile?
   18; 16; 21

3. What are the lower and upper extremes and the range? **11; 22; 11**

PRACTICE AND PROBLEM SOLVING

Independent Practice

For 4–5, use the box-and-whisker graph.

4. What are the median, lower quartile, and upper quartile?
   61; 60; 63

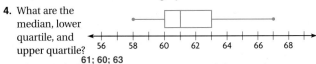

5. What are the lower and upper extremes and the range? **58; 67; 9**

For 6–8, use the data in the table below.

6. What are the median, lower quartile, and upper quartile?
   95; 90; 101

WEIGHTS OF PANTHERS FOOTBALL PLAYERS					
85	102	89	86	104	92
103	97	91	100	100	93

7. What are the lower and upper extremes and the range? **85; 104; 19**

8. Make a box-and-whisker graph and a histogram. Compare them.
   See Additional Answers, p. 137A.

Problem Solving Applications

The box-and-whisker graph shows data about the numbers of points scored by the basketball team each game.

9. What are the least and greatest numbers of points? **72 points, 97 points**

10. **The data in the middle $\frac{1}{2}$ and upper $\frac{1}{4}$ are close together; the data in the lower $\frac{1}{4}$ are more spread out.**

10. What does the graph show about how the data are distributed?

11. **?** What's the Question? Use the box-and-whisker graph for 9–10. The answers are 88 and 94. **What are the lower and upper quartiles of the data?**

MIXED REVIEW AND TEST PREP

12. If you are displaying data about the number of cars that cross an intersection during different intervals of time, is a bar graph or a histogram more appropriate? (p. 126) **histogram**

13. A grocer wants to know if customers like the new store hours. She surveys 50 male customers. Is the sample biased? (p. 98) **yes**

Write the value of the blue digit. (p. 52)

14. 9.64 **0.6, or six tenths**

15. 124.024 **0.02, or two hundredths**

16. **TEST PREP** Which is $3 \times 3 \times 3 \times 3$ in exponent form? (p. 40) **D**

   A 3×4 **B** 3^2 **C** 3^3 **D** 3^4

(Extra Practice) page H37, Set D)   **131**

---

3 Practice

Guided Practice

Do Check for Understanding Exercises 1–3 with your students. Identify those having difficulty and use lesson resources to help.

Independent Practice

Assign Exercises 4–11.

Students may need to be reminded that a box-and-whisker graph divides a set of data into four parts. If necessary, help them identify the numbers that do this.

MIXED REVIEW AND TEST PREP

Exercises 12–16 provide **cumulative review** (Chapters 1–6).

4 Assess

Summarize the lesson by having students:

DISCUSS What three medians divide the box-and-whisker graph at the top of page 131? 16; 18; 21

WRITE Why can't you use a box-and-whisker graph to find the **mean?** Possible answer: A box-and-whisker graph does not show every data item.

Lesson Quiz

Transparency **6.5**

For each exercise, use the box-and-whisker graph below.

1. What is the median? 2.5

2. What are the lower and upper quartiles? 2; 4

3. What are the lower and upper extremes? 1; 7

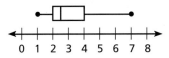

PROBLEM SOLVING 6.5

Box-and-Whisker Graphs

Write the correct answer.

1. What is the lower quartile of the data?
   24, 26, 28, 29, 30, 32, 34, 36, 37
   27

2. What is the upper quartile of the data?
   56, 58, 58, 59, 60, 62, 64, 64, 90
   64

3. George is 145 centimeters tall and his brother is 167 centimeters tall. What is the mean of their heights?
   156 cm

4. If you survey 1 out of every 10 people, how many would you survey out of a group of 145,910 people?
   14,591 people

Write the letter of the best answer.

5. Ashley dusts the house for her mother every 5 days. How many times in a year does Ashley dust the house for her mother?
   A 52   **C** 73
   B 63   **D** 75

6. Peter wants to use a box-and-whisker graph to display his test scores. If his scores are 100, 79, 64, 89, 80, 86, and 89, what is the median?
   F 89   **H** 81
   G 86   **J** 25

7. Kate took 131 pictures of her classmates during the year. She gave each of the 31 students in the class 2 pictures. Which number sentence could be used to find p, the number of pictures Kate has left after giving some to her classmates?
   A $p = 131 + (31 \times 2)$
   B $p = 131 - (31 \times 2)$
   C $p = 131 - (31 \div 2)$
   D $p = 131 + (31 \div 2)$

8. On the last test, nine students scored 64, 68, 68, 70, 72, 78, 82, 84, and 100 points. What is the upper quartile of the data?
   F 78, 82, 84, and 100
   G 68
   H 72
   J 83

9. **Write About It** Into how many equal parts does the lower quartile divide the lower half of the data? Explain.
   The lower quartile divides the lower half of the data into 2 equal parts.
   From the lower extreme to the lower quartile is one part and from
   the lower quartile to the median is the other part.

CHALLENGE 6.5

Name the Amount!

Write your answer.

1. Sue received scores of 79, 83, 76, and 100 on her first four math tests. What score must she get on her fifth test to have an average of 85 for all five tests?
   87

2. Kyle bowled scores of 112, 126, 98, and 118 in his first four games. What score must he bowl in his fifth game to have an average of 120 for all five games?
   146

3. In his first five rounds of golf, Jon scored 84, 71, 77, 68, 74. What score must Jon achieve in his sixth round in order to have an average of 75 for all six rounds?
   76

4. Matt scored 89, 93, 100, 77, and 81 on his first five science tests. What score must he earn on his sixth test in order to have an average of 90 for all six tests?
   100

5. In her first five games, Betty bowled 128, 116, 104, 112, and 134. What must she bowl in her sixth game in order to have an average of 120 for all six games?
   126

6. The following numbers of moviegoers saw the first six showings of a recently released movie: 213, 322, 278, 309, 258, 296. How many movie fans must attend the seventh showing in order to have an average of 280 people per showing?
   284 people

7. The following number of students went to the first five basketball games: 180, 200, 175, 200, 205. How many students must attend the sixth game in order to have an average of 200 students per game?
   240 students

131

Analyze Graphs

LESSON PLANNING

Objective To analyze data displays and determine how results and conclusions may have been influenced

Intervention for Prerequisite Skills

Read Bar Graphs (For intervention strategies, see page 119.)

California Mathematics Content Standards

SDAP 2.3 Analyze data displays and explain why the way in which the question was asked might have influenced the results obtained and why the way in which the results were displayed might have influenced the conclusion reached.

(*Also* MR 1.0, MR 1.1, MR 2.4)

Math Background

Graphs sometimes show data based on biased questions. They also may show the data in such a way as to give an erroneous impression that is not warranted.

- Students probably cannot tell from a graph if a question was fairly stated. However, they should be aware of this problem as they collect data of their own.

- When looking at a graph, students should learn to examine the scales on the graph to see if they are distorted or abbreviated, which could result in a biased impression of the data.

Because graphs may be distorted intentionally and can influence feelings and opinions, it is important for students to read all graphs very carefully.

WARM-UP RESOURCES

NUMBER OF THE DAY

Transparency **6.6**

Start with your age. Multiply by 5 and add any number on a number cube, 1 to 6. Multiply by 2 and subtract the same number on the number cube. What do the digits in your answer tell you? your age and the number on the number cube

PROBLEM OF THE DAY

Transparency **6.6**

A circle graph shows that half of the 120 ancestors of the students surveyed came to the U.S. from Europe or South America, a quarter came from Africa, and the rest from Asia and Australia. Five times as many came from Europe as from South America. How many of the students' ancestors came from South America? 10 ancestors

Solution Problem of the Day tab, p. PD6

DAILY FACTS PRACTICE

Have students practice addition and subtraction facts by completing Set F of *Teacher's Resource Book,* p. TR97.

INTERVENTION AND EXTENSION RESOURCES

ALTERNATIVE TEACHING STRATEGY (ELL)

Materials index cards

Strengthen students' understanding of biased questions.
Write several biased survey questions, one to a card. Then, on other cards, write unbiased questions that can be paired with each of the biased questions. Examples:

Do you prefer the yummy taste of chocolate ice cream, or do you like vanilla, strawberry, or some other flavor?

What is your favorite ice cream: vanilla, chocolate, strawberry, or some other flavor?

Call on volunteers to read each pair of questions and to explain why one of each pair should elicit fairer responses than the other. Have students highlight the phrases that lead to a biased response, and discuss why they created bias. Check students' answers.

See also page 134.

AUDITORY

MIXED REVIEW AND TEST PREP

Cumulative Review Chapters 1–6

Refer to the Pupil Edition pages referenced in the exercises for further review. Have students go to the lesson page, review the lesson, and correct any problem they missed.

Mixed Review and Test Prep, p. 135

How to Help	
Item	Page
14	129
15	129
16	106
17	82
18	44

WRITING IN MATHEMATICS

Materials *For each student* graph from a magazine or a newspaper

Find several bar graphs and line graphs in newspapers or magazines. Ask each student to choose a graph and write a few lines to describe what the graph shows.

Then have the student write a paragraph about the graph, describing why and how someone might want to change the graph so the appearance would be distorted. For example, break the scale to make it appear as though sales figures increased more than they did, or that the fat content in Product A is greater than in Product B.

Check students' answers.

EARLY FINISHERS

Combine pairs of students into groups of 4 to **explore the effect of biased questions on graphs.** Give each group a topic, such as their classmates' favorite classes. Assign one pair in each group to write a fair question and the other pair to write a question they feel is biased.

Each pair is assigned half the class to poll with their question.

Ask each group of students to display their data in two graphs. Post the graphs. Then have students compare and contrast the graphs to conclude whether the type of question asked affected the outcome. Check students' work.

VISUAL

TECHNOLOGY LINK

Intervention Strategies and Activities CD-ROM • *Skill 79*

The Harcourt Learning Site
www.harcourtschool.com

Objective To analyze data displays and determine how results and conclusions may have been influenced

1 Introduce

QUICK REVIEW provides review of mental math skills.

Why Learn This? You can examine a graph in a newspaper and decide whether it presents data fairly. *Share the lesson objective with students.*

2 Teach

Guided Instruction

• *Examine the graph in Example 1.*

About how many people did Rita interview? about 120 people

How could you reword the question so it would be less biased? Possible answer: Whom would you choose as the greatest U.S. President—Washington, Lincoln, or Jefferson?

• *As you discuss the second example, ask:*

REASONING **Can you be positive that Graph A goes with Question 2? Explain.** No; it is possible that the biased question results in Graph B.

> **ADDITIONAL EXAMPLE**

Example 2, p. 132

Match each graph with one of the questions. Explain your reasoning.

Question 1: After school would you rather do something fun like skateboard or would you rather bike or read?

Question 2: After school would you rather skateboard, bike, or read?

AFTER SCHOOL ACTIVITIES
Read 29% Bike 31% 40% Skateboard
Graph A

AFTER SCHOOL ACTIVITIES
Read 25% Skateboard 59% Bike 16%
Graph B

The more evenly divided Graph A probably goes with Question 2. The results in Graph B probably reflect the biased Question 1.

LESSON 6.6

Analyze Graphs

Learn how to analyze data displays and determine how results and conclusions may have been influenced.

QUICK REVIEW
Write the corresponding decimal or percent.
1. 75%   2. 3%   3. 4.6%   4. 0.36   5. 0.07
   0.75   0.03   0.046   36%   7%

Data can be displayed in many different ways. Sometimes, the way a question is asked can influence the results that are displayed.

Rita took a survey asking the following question: Do you agree with me that George Washington was the greatest U.S. President, or would you choose Thomas Jefferson or Abraham Lincoln?

> **EXAMPLE 1**

The results of Rita's survey are displayed in the bar graph shown at the right. Could the way the question was asked have influenced the results? Explain.

GREATEST U.S. PRESIDENT
Number of People: 100, 80, 60, 40, 20
Washington Jefferson Lincoln
Presidents

Yes. Rita's question is biased, since it leads people to agree with her that George Washington was the greatest U.S. President. As a result, the graph is misleading.

> **EXAMPLE 2**

The results of two other surveys are shown below. Which graph is more likely to come from which question? Explain your reasoning.

Question 1:   Would you rather visit the Grand Canyon, Mount Rushmore, or the Statue of Liberty?

Question 2:   Would you rather visit the spectacular Grand Canyon, or would you rather visit Mount Rushmore or the Statue of Liberty?

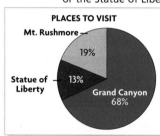
PLACES TO VISIT
Mt. Rushmore 19%
Statue of Liberty 13%
Grand Canyon 68%
Graph A

PLACES TO VISIT
Mt. Rushmore 31%
Grand Canyon 38%
Statue of Liberty 31%
Graph B

Graph A probably goes with Question 2, since the question is biased and leads people to choose the Grand Canyon. Graph B probably goes with Question 1, since that question is not biased.

132 **CALIFORNIA STANDARDS** ⊶ **SDAP 2.3** Analyze data displays and explain why the way in which the question was asked might have influenced the results obtained and why the way in which the results were displayed might have influenced the conclusions. *also* **MR 1.0, MR 1.1, MR 2.4**

RETEACH 6.6

Analyze Graphs

Graphs are sometimes drawn in order to mislead the reader. In order for a graph to provide information honestly, it must meet several requirements. One requirement is that the scale must be accurate.

Stereo City placed an advertisement for a stereo system in a newspaper. The advertisement included the graph at the right, which compares its price for the system to the price of the system at Speaker Town.

Compare Prices!
System Price (in dollars): 380, 360, 340, 320, 300
Stereo City, Speaker Town

In the graph, the bar for Speaker Town appears to be twice the height of the bar for Stereo City. Some readers might think this means Speaker Town's price is twice that of Stereo City's. The scale, however, shows that Speaker Town's price for the stereo system is not twice the price at Stereo City. The actual difference between the two prices is only $380 − $340, or $40.

In order to give a true representation of a set of data, any scale used on a graph should follow these rules:
• The scale should begin with zero.
• An interval that makes sense for the data that is shown in the graph should be chosen.
• Every interval on the scale must be the same size.

A consumer research company conducted a survey at both Stereo City and Speaker Town. At each store, customers who had just purchased an item were asked if they would return to the store for their next electronics purchase. The results of the survey are shown in the graph.

Customer Loyalty
Percent Answering "Yes": 100, 95, 90, 85, 80, 75
Stereo City, Speaker Town

1. What percent of Stereo City's customers said they would make their next electronics purchase there? __95%__

2. What percent of Speaker Town's customers said they would make their next electronics purchase there? __80%__

3. About how many times as high is the bar for Stereo City as the bar for Speaker Town? __about 4 times as high__

4. How can you change the graph so that it is not misleading?
__Start the scale at zero and have equal intervals.__

PRACTICE 6.6

Analyze Graphs

Renee asked each student in her math class the following question: "Would you rather have some great vanilla ice cream or would you prefer chocolate or strawberry?"

For 1–2, use the graph at the right, which shows the results of her survey.

Strawberry 10%
Chocolate 25%
Vanilla 65%

1. Could the way Renee asked the question have influenced her classmates' answers? Explain.
__Yes. The question is biased and could__
__lead people to choose vanilla ice cream.__

2. Tell how you could rewrite the question so it would not influence the results of the survey.
__Possible answer: "Which ice cream flavor do you__
__prefer, chocolate, strawberry, or vanilla?"__

A television network used the graph at the right. The network wanted to convince viewers that one of its shows, Show A, was far more popular than one of its competitors' shows, Show B, which airs at the same time.

Television Shows
Percent of Viewers: 40, 35, 30, 25, 20, 15, 10
A, B
Shows

3. The bar for Show A is about how many times as high as the bar for Show B?
__about twice as high__

4. Does twice the percent of the viewing audience watch Show A as watches Show B? __no__

5. How can you change the graph so that it is not misleading?
__Adjust the scale to start at zero and have equal intervals.__

Mixed Review

During one day at an airport, an airline experienced flight delays of the following numbers of minutes: 5, 7, 5, 10, 15, 15, 20, 91.

6. Find the mean length of all the flight delays. __21 min__

7. Find the mean of the delays if the outlier is not included. __11 min__

Evaluate each expression.

8. $g + 1.7$ for $g = 3.3$ 9. $5y$ for $y = 1.8$ 10. $p - 4.9$ for $p = 11$
   __5__   __9__   __6.1__

Graphs can communicate information quickly. That's why they are used by advertisers on television and in magazines and newspapers. Some graphs can be misleading and influence conclusions that are drawn.

EXAMPLE 3

Jon looked at the bar graph below and concluded that the Mississippi River is twice as long as the Missouri River. Explain Jon's mistake and tell why his conclusion is wrong.

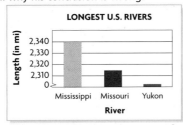

LONGEST U.S. RIVERS

The bar for the Mississippi is twice as long as the bar for the Missouri. However, if you look at the scale, you see that the rivers are about the same length. Because the lower part of the scale is missing, the differences are exaggerated.

When two graphs with different scales show two similar sets of data, comparing the graphs can sometimes be misleading.

EXAMPLE 4

The weekly ticket sales for the Mississippi River tour boat cruise are shown in the graphs below. Deb looked at the graphs and concluded that more tickets were sold in April than in March. Explain Deb's mistake.

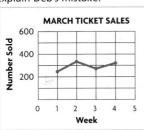

It appears that the April ticket sales were greater than in March since the line for April is higher than the line for March. However, if you look at the scale for each graph, you can see that ticket sales were much greater in March than in April.

1. Possible answer: Do you think George Washington, Thomas Jefferson, or Abraham Lincoln was the greatest U.S. President?

CHECK FOR UNDERSTANDING

Think and ▶ Discuss

Look back at the lesson to answer each question.

1. **Tell** how you could rewrite the question in Example 1 so it would not influence the results of the survey. **See above left.**

133

- *The visual picture of the data can be misleading with a break (zigzag) in the scale, as in Example 3, or to vary the scales, as in Example 4. Ask:*

What is the actual difference in length of the Mississippi and Missouri Rivers? a little more than 20 mi out of 2,300 mi

Where would the April ticket sales appear if graphed with the March sales? All April values would be below the March values.

ADDITIONAL EXAMPLES

Example 3, p. 133

Emily looked at the bar graph and concluded that only half as many seventh-grade students participated in the book fair as sixth-grade students. What part of the graph's construction influenced Emily's conclusion?

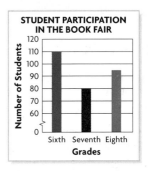

The scale in the number of students exaggerates the difference in student participation.

Example 4, p. 133

These bar graphs show the prices of bicycles sold at two different stores. How are these graphs misleading?

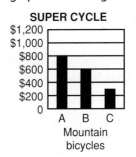

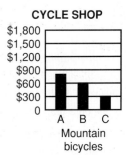

The graphs make it appear that the bicycle prices at Super Cycle are greater than those at Cycle Shop. However, the bicycle prices are actually the same at both stores.

PROBLEM SOLVING 6.6

Analyze Graphs

Write the correct answer.
Use the graph below for 1–3.

LAND AREAS

2. Explain how the graph could be fixed so that Casey would not have made the mistake he did.

Start the vertical scale at zero

and make every interval the

same size.

Write the letter of the best answer.
Use the graph below for 4–6.

DOMINIQUE'S DOG

5. If the scale started at 0 and ended at 60, with intervals of 2, how would the appearance of the graph change?
A The line would be steeper.
B The line would be flatter.
C The line would look the same as it does now.
D The line would be a straight line.

7. **Write About It** Why does increasing the size of the interval used in the vertical scale of a line graph make the line seem flatter?

Possible answer: As the interval increases, the range appears to be

more compact.

Analyze Choose Solve Check

1. After looking at the graph, Casey decided that the area of Argentina was about three times the area of Mexico. Explain why Casey's conclusion is wrong.

The scale does not begin

at zero.

3. Use the graph to estimate the total combined area of Mexico and Argentina.

Possible answer: approximately

1.8 million square miles

4. During which of these times did Dominique's dog gain the least amount of weight?
F from January to February
G from February to March
H from March to April
I from April to May

6. If the scale began at 0, which interval would make Dominique's dog's weight gain seem the greatest?
F an interval of 2 lb
G an interval of 5 lb
H an interval of 10 lb
I an interval of 15 lb

CHALLENGE 6.6

Scale the Heights

For each set of data, assume that you are going to draw a bar graph. Describe the scale you would use for the vertical axis. Include the minimum value, the maximum value, and the size of each interval. **Possible answers are given.**

1. Maximum animal speeds: zebra, 40 mi per hr; lion, 50 mi per hr; grizzly bear, 30 mi per hr; elephant, 25 mi per hr

   minimum: 0; maximum: 50; interval size: 10

2. Average animal life spans: horse, 20 years; leopard, 12 years; Asian elephant, 40 years; rabbit, 5 years

   minimum: 0; maximum: 50; interval size: 5

3. Countries with the fewest people: Nauru, 10,605; Palau, 18,467; San Marino, 25,061; Tuvalu, 10,588

   minimum: 0; maximum: 30,000; interval size: 5,000

4. Professional basketball games won during the 1998–1999 season: Miami Heat, 33; New Jersey Nets, 16; Orlando Magic, 33; Philadelphia 76ers, 28; Washington Wizards, 18

   minimum: 0; maximum: 35; interval size: 5

5. Miles of border shared with the United States: Mexico, 1,933 mi; Pacific Ocean, 7,623 mi; Atlantic Ocean, 2,069 mi; Gulf of Mexico, 1,631 mi

   minimum: 0; maximum: 8,000; interval size: 1,000

6. Number of members of the U.S. House of Representatives: New York, 31; California, 52; Rhode Island, 2; Florida, 23

   minimum: 0; maximum: 60; interval size: 4

7. Warmest temperatures ever recorded, by continent: Africa, 136°F; Asia, 129°F; North America, 134°F; Antarctica, 59°F

   minimum: 0; maximum: 140; interval size: 10

8. Highest point on the continent: North America, 20,320 ft; Australia, 7,310 ft; Asia, 29,035 ft; Europe, 18,510 ft; South America, 22,834 ft

   minimum: 0; maximum: 30,000; interval size: 2,000

9. Most widely used languages in the world (in millions of speakers): Mandarin, 1,075; English, 514; Hindi, 496

   minimum: 0; maximum: 1,200; interval size: 100

3 Practice

Guided Practice

Do Check for Understanding Exercises 1–6 with your students. Identify those having difficulty and use lesson resources to help.

Independent Practice

Assign Exercises 7–13.

3. Yes. The question is biased and could lead people to choose the Mustangs as the best baseball team.

5. No. Angel Falls is about 3,200 ft high, while Tugela Falls is about 3,000 ft high.

6. Adjust the scale to start at zero and have equal intervals.

Independent ▸ Practice

7. Yes. The question is biased and could lead people to choose oranges.

2. **Explain** how you could change the graph in Example 3 so it is not misleading. Adjust the scale to include numbers between 0 and 2,300.

Guided ▸ Practice

Rosa took a survey, asking the following question: Don't you think that the Mustangs are the best baseball team, or would you choose the Wildcats or Cougars? The results of her survey are displayed in the bar graph at the right.

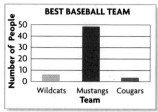

3. Could the way the question was asked have influenced the results? Explain. See above left.

For 4–6, use the graph at the right. The graph is misleading.

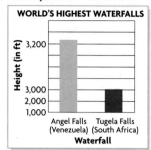

4. About how many times as high is the bar for Angel Falls than for Tugela Falls? about 3 times as high
5. Is Angel Falls 3 times as high as Tugela Falls? Explain. See above left.
6. How could you change the graph so it is not misleading? See below left.

PRACTICE AND PROBLEM SOLVING

Miguel took a survey, asking the following question: What is your favorite fruit—apples, bananas, or delicious, juicy Florida navel oranges? The results of Miguel's survey are displayed in the circle graph.

7. Could the way the question was asked have influenced the results? Explain.

For 8–10, use the graph at the right. The graph is misleading.

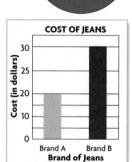

8. About how many times as high is the bar for Brand B than for Brand A? about 2 times as high
9. Does Brand B cost twice as much as Brand A? Explain. No. Brand B costs $30 and Brand A costs $20.
10. How can you change the graph so it is not misleading? Adjust the scale so the intervals are equal.

134 Chapter 6

Alternative Teaching Strategy

Purpose Students explore how changing the scale on a graph affects its appearance.

Materials *For each group* 1-in. graph paper, p. TR62

Present these data for lengths of the rivers given in Example 3: Mississippi—2,340 mi; Missouri—2,315 mi; Yukon—1,979 mi.

Divide the class into small groups. Have each group draw two different graphs presenting the same information. The first graph uses a scale with intervals of 500 from zero to 2,500.

For the second graph, have them use a scale with intervals of 100 from 1,900 to 2,400, so that part of the scale is missing.

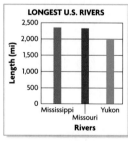

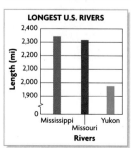

Have each group write a statement comparing the two graphs. Then as a class discuss the different impression each graph gives about the lengths of the rivers. Possible answer: The 1st graph with the scale beginning at zero gives a truer picture of the actual data than the 2nd graph with the scale break. The 1st graph shows that the Mississippi and Missouri Rivers are much closer in length than they appear in the 2nd graph. In the 2nd graph, the Yukon River appears to be much shorter in comparison to the other two rivers than it does in the 1st graph.

Problem Solving ▶ Applications

11. Jeff compared the bars but did not look at the scale.

13. Lin looked only at the lines and did not look at the scales.

11. Jeff looked at the bar graph at the right and concluded that Los Angeles has three times the population of Chicago. Explain Jeff's mistake and tell why his conclusion is wrong.

CITY POPULATIONS

12. How could you fix the graph so Jeff would not make a mistake? **Adjust the scale to include zero and have equal intervals.**

13. Lin looked at the graphs below and concluded that from July to October, the temperatures in San Francisco are about the same as the temperatures in San Diego. Explain Lin's mistake. **See above left.**

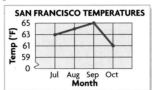

SAN DIEGO TEMPERATURES   **SAN FRANCISCO TEMPERATURES**

MIXED REVIEW AND TEST PREP

For 14–15, use the box-and-whisker graph. (p. 129)

14. What is the median? **50**

15. What are the least and greatest values? **43 and 55**

16. Find the mean of the data set 18, 12, 10, 8, 9, 14, and 6. (p. 106) **11**

17. **TEST PREP** Which is the value of $2n + 3.7$ for $n = 2.9$? (p. 82) **B**

   A 8.6   **B** 9.5   **C** 10.4   **D** 21.46

18. **TEST PREP** Choose the correct value. $(3 + 24) \div 3 \times 2 - 1$ (p. 44) **G**

   F 14   **G** 17   **H** 18   **J** 21

 **to Reading**

Strategy • Classify and Categorize
To classify information means to group together similar information. To categorize the information, label the groups.

Shape	Color
rectangular	red, blue, white, or green
circular	red, blue, white, or green
oval	red, blue, white, or green

Paige wants to make a tablecloth. She has rectangular, circular, and oval patterns. She can choose from red, blue, white, or green fabric. By classifying and categorizing the data, you can see that there are 12 ways to make the tablecloth.

• The soccer coach is choosing new uniforms. The shorts are blue, black, or gray. The jerseys are white, yellow, green, blue, or turquoise. How many different uniforms are possible? **15 different uniforms**

Extra Practice page H37, Set E   135

Exercises 14–18 provide **cumulative review** (Chapters 1–6).

 to READING

• *After the students read the definitions, ask:*

How do you determine that 12 is the answer? Possible answer: There are 3 shapes and 4 colors, so $3 \times 4 = 12$.

REASONING Mitch keeps a running list of all his test scores. He notes the subject by putting S for science, M for math, and H for humanities. Here is his list: M92, S89, S80, M100, H95, H73, M90. Find the mean score for each of his subjects. math 94; science 84.5; humanities 84

4 Assess

Summarize the lesson by having students:

DISCUSS Why might someone use some of the techniques illustrated in this lesson to display data? Possible answer: in order to sell a product, sway an audience, or make a point

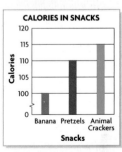 **WRITE Explain how you would examine a graph for bias.** Possible answer: Check the scale to see if part is missing or if the intervals are uneven; if available, see if the survey question is biased.

Lesson Quiz   Transparency **6.6**

1. Martin asked, "What is your favorite 60's group, the Beatles, the Drifters, or the fabulous Beach Boys?" Do you think his graph will be fair or biased? Explain. Possibly biased; his question favors one group.

Use the graph at the right for 2–3.

CALORIES IN SNACKS

2. Sheri looked at the graph and concluded that a serving of animal crackers has four times as many calories as a banana. Explain her mistake. The break in the scale exaggerates the difference in calories per serving.

3. How many more calories are in a serving of animal crackers than in a banana? only 15

REVIEW/TEST

Purpose To check understanding of concepts, skills, and problem solving presented in Chapter 6

USING THE PAGE

The Chapter 6 Review/Test can be used as a **review** or a **test**.

- Items 1–2 check understanding of concepts and new vocabulary.
- Items 3–20 check skill proficiency.

 Suggest that students place the completed Chapter 6 Review/Test in their portfolios.

USING THE ASSESSMENT GUIDE

- Multiple-choice format of Chapter 6 Posttest—See *Assessment Guide*, pp. AG37–38.
- Free-response format of Chapter 6 Posttest—See *Assessment Guide*, pp. AG39–40.

USING STUDENT SELF-ASSESSMENT

The How Did I Do? survey helps students assess what they have learned and how they learned it. This survey is available as a copying master in *Assessment Guide*, p. AGxvii.

---

1. **VOCABULARY** A bar graph that shows frequencies within intervals is a(n) __?__. (p. 127) **histogram**

2. **VOCABULARY** A graph that shows how far apart and how evenly data are distributed is a(n) __?__. (p. 129) **box-and-whisker graph**

3. What type of graph would best show the highest and lowest temperatures for each of the last four years? (pp. 120–123) **multiple-bar graph**

4. What type of graph would best show high and low temperatures for a week? (pp. 120–123) **multiple-line graph**

5. Make a double-line graph with the data at the right. (pp. 120–123)
   See Additional Answers, p. 137A.

6. Make a double-bar graph with the data at the right. (pp. 120–123)
   See Additional Answers, p. 137A.

END-OF-MONTH STOCK PRICES					
	Sep	Oct	Nov	Dec	Jan
Stock A	$80	$74	$45	$50	$52
Stock B	$50	$52	$52	$50	$45

For 7–9, use the graph at the right. (pp. 124–125)

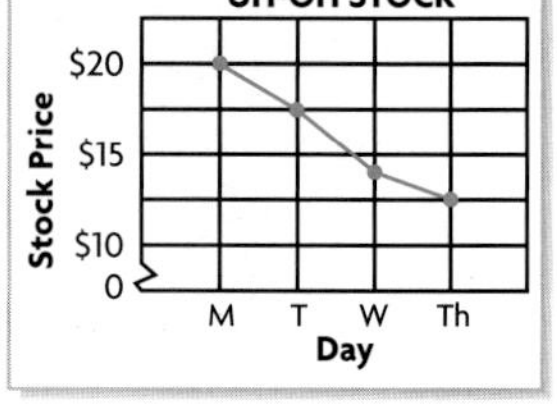

7. About how much did the stock price decrease from Monday to Tuesday? **about $2.50**

8. Describe the pattern in the graph. **Stock prices are falling.**

9. If the trend continues, what do you think the stock price will be on Friday? **Possible answer: about $10**

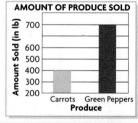

10. Make a stem-and-leaf plot for the data. (pp. 126–128) **See Additional Answers, p. 137A.**

11. Make a histogram for the data. (pp. 126–128) **See Additional Answers, p. 137A.**

POINTS SCORED					
33	52	45	47	34	52
34	58	48	52	46	59

HEIGHTS OF BUILDINGS (IN FT)						
20	50	80	20	40	45	85
25	30	80	60	70	75	55

For 12–17, use the following data: 14, 16, 9, 21, 35, 2, 26, 8, 17. (pp.130–131)

12. Find the upper extreme. **35**

13. Find the lower extreme. **2**

14. Find the upper quartile. **23.5**

15. Find the lower quartile. **8.5**

16. Find the median. **16**

17. Make a box-and-whisker graph. **See Additional Answers, p. 137A.**

For 18–20, use the graph at the right. (pp. 132–135)

18. About how many times as high is the bar for green peppers as the bar for carrots? **about 3 times as high**

19. Were three times as many pounds of carrots sold as pounds of green peppers? Explain. **No. 700 pounds of carrots and 400 pounds of green peppers were sold.**

20. How could you change the graph so that it is not misleading? **Adjust the scale to start at zero and to include equal intervals.**

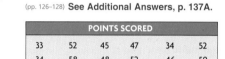

CHAPTER 6 TEST, page 1

Choose the best answer.

For 1–8, choose the best type of graph to show the given situation.

1. a stock price changing over time
   - A histogram
   - **B line graph**
   - C bar graph
   - D circle graph

2. the lengths of five different rivers
   - F box-and-whisker
   - G line graph
   - **H bar graph**
   - J circle graph

3. the number of visitors to a museum grouped by intervals
   - **A histogram**
   - B box-and-whisker
   - C bar graph
   - D circle graph

4. favorite music choices by percent
   - F histogram
   - G line graph
   - H stem-and-leaf
   - **J circle graph**

5. the season scores of a basketball team
   - A histogram
   - B line graph
   - **C stem-and-leaf**
   - D circle graph

6. how the extreme numbers are related to the median numbers
   - F stem-and-leaf
   - **G box-and-whisker**
   - H bar graph
   - J circle graph

7. to compare parts to the whole or to other parts
   - A histogram
   - B box-and-whisker
   - C bar graph
   - **D circle graph**

8. to show how data change over time
   - **F line graph**
   - G histogram
   - H circle graph
   - J bar graph

For 9–13, use the graph below.

TOURISTS SINCE HOTEL OPENED

9. Which month had the most tourists?
   - **A January**
   - B February
   - C March
   - D April

10. How many tourists would be a good prediction for July, if the trend continues?
    - F 17,000
    - G 16,000
    - **H 15,000**
    - J 14,000

11. How many tourists came in April?
    - A 17
    - B 18
    - C 17,000
    - **D 18,000**

12. Which other type of graph could be used to show the same data?
    - F circle
    - G multiple-line
    - **H bar**
    - J stem-and-leaf

13. Which of these changes could cause the graph to be misleading?
    - A Use larger numbers.
    - **B Make the intervals unequal.**
    - C Double the intervals.
    - D Start the scale at zero.

Go On

CHAPTER 6 TEST, page 2

14. Choose the least biased question.
    - F Do you think that vanilla is the favorite flavor, or is it chocolate?
    - G Do you think chocolate is the favorite flavor, or is it vanilla?
    - **H Which do you think is the favorite flavor, chocolate or vanilla?**
    - J Isn't vanilla the favorite flavor, or is it chocolate?

15. Choose the least biased question.
    - **A Who is correct, Karen, Lars, or David?**
    - B Is Lars correct, or is it Karen or David?
    - C Karen is correct, isn't she? Or is it Lars or David?
    - D Do you think that David is correct, or is it Lars or Karen?

For 16–19, use the graph below.

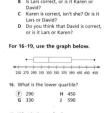

16. What is the lower quartile?
    - **F 290**
    - G 330
    - H 450
    - J 590

17. What is the median?
    - A 33
    - B 270
    - **C 290**
    - D 330

18. What is the lower extreme?
    - F 170
    - **G 270**
    - H 390
    - J 450

19. What is the upper quartile?
    - **A 390**
    - B 330
    - C 290
    - D 120

For 20–23, make a stem-and-leaf plot of the following scores.

87, 88, 94, 77, 98, 68, 72, 96, 80, 90, 79, 81, 69, 93, 92, 85, 99, 92, 83, 74

20. Which list shows the leaves for the stem 6?
    - F 9, 8, 0
    - G 0, 1, 3, 5, 7, 8
    - H 2, 4, 7, 9
    - **J 8, 9**

21. Which list shows the leaves for the stem 7?
    - A 8, 9
    - **B 2, 4, 7, 9**
    - C 0, 1, 3, 5, 7, 8
    - D 9, 7, 4, 2, 0

22. Which list shows the leaves for the stem 8?
    - F 2, 4, 7, 9
    - **G 0, 1, 3, 5, 7, 8**
    - H 8, 9
    - J 1, 3, 5, 7, 8

23. Which list shows the leaves for the stem 9?
    - **A 0, 2, 3, 4, 6,** C 8, 9
      8, 9
    - B 0, 1, 3, 5, 7, 8
    - D 2, 4, 7, 9

For 24–25, use the table below.

DISTANCE ALLIE BICYCLED					
Week	1	2	3	4	5
Miles	65	80	95	115	135

24. If Allie continues her trend, estimate how far she will bike in week 6.
    - F 95 miles
    - G 130 miles
    - **H 160 miles**
    - J 240 miles

25. If the trend continues, in which week will Allie bike more than 200 miles?
    - A week 8
    - B week 9
    - **C week 10**
    - D week 11

Stop

Check your work.

See item **6.**

Think about the different kinds of graphs and the most appropriate data for them. Check that your answer choice could be made into a bar graph.

Also see problem **7**, p. H65.

Choose the best answer.

1. Which type of graph would be the best to show the favorite sports of a sample of teenagers? **D**

   A Stem-and-leaf plot   C Line graph

   B Histogram   D Bar graph

2. The owner of a music shop made a line graph to show the number of CDs sold during a 4-week period. Which trend does the graph show? **H**

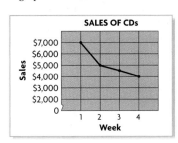

   F Sales are increasing.

   G Sales are even.

   H Sales are decreasing.

   J No trend is shown.

3. What is the value of $\frac{12 - 2^3}{4}$? **B**

   A $^-5$ C 11

   B 1   D Not here

4. Which of the following is best suited for display in a multiple-bar graph? **H**

   F Average temperatures a town recorded during a 1-year period

   G Number of CDs owned by sixth-grade students

   H Number of hours sixth- and seventh-grade students spend reading each week

   J Changes in water temperature over a 24-hour period

5. Which kind of graph is shown? **B**

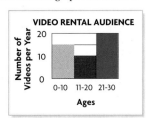

   A Circle graph

   B Histogram

   C Line graph

   D Stem-and-leaf plot

6. A bar graph would be best to display which data? **F**

   F Heights of the tallest buildings in a city

   G Frequency of cars stopping at a tollbooth

   H Changes in a person's weight over a year

   J Part of a day a person spends reading

7. $22.8 - 3.11$ **B**

   A 18.79   C 19.79

   B 19.69   D Not here

137

CUMULATIVE REVIEW •
Chapters 1–6

USING THE PAGE

This page may be used to help students get ready for standardized tests. The test items are written in the same style and arranged in the same format as those on many state assessments. The page is cumulative. It covers math objectives and essential skills that have been taught up to this point in the text. Most of the items represent skills from the current chapter, and the remainder represent skills from earlier chapters.

This page can be assigned at the end of the chapter as classwork or as a homework assignment. You may want to have students use individual recording sheets presented in a multiple-choice (standardized) format. A Test Answer Sheet is available as a blackline master in *Assessment Guide* (p. AGxlii).

You may wish to have students describe how they solved each problem and share their solutions.

Lesson 6.1, page 123

9.

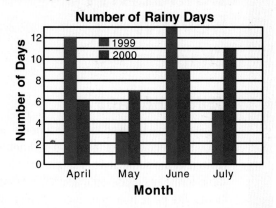

Lesson 6.2, page 125

8.

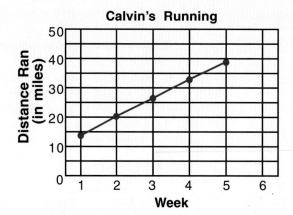

Lesson 6.3, page 128

10.

Lesson 6.2, page 125

10.

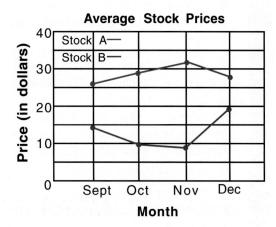

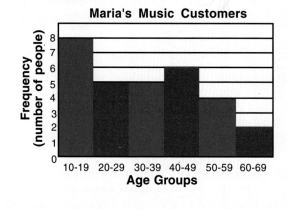

Lesson 6.2, page 125

2.

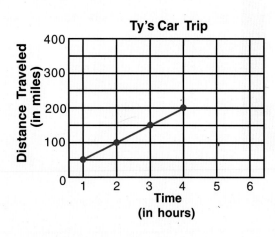

Lesson 6.4, page 129

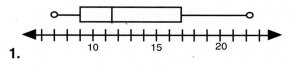

1.

Lesson 6.2, page 125

5.

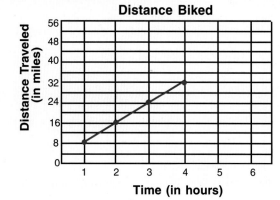

Lesson 6.5, page 131

8.

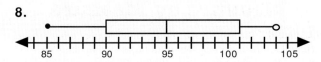

Possible Histogram:

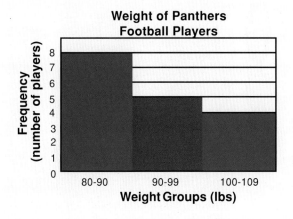

11.

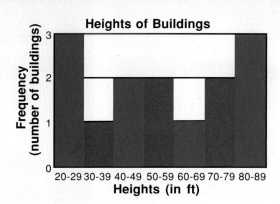

Chapter 6 Review/Test, page 136

5.

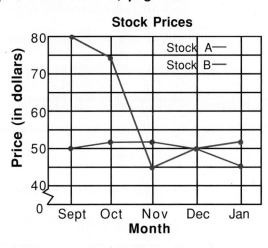

17.

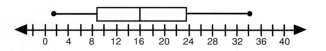

6.

10.

Stem	Leaves
3	3 4 4
4	5 6 7 8
5	2 2 2 8 9

MATH DETECTIVE
Measure by Measure

Purpose To use deductive reasoning to solve problems involving measures of central tendency

USING THE PAGE

- *Direct students' attention to the Reasoning section and Mystery Number 1.*

  What two numbers can you immediately identify from the clues? Explain. Since the mode is 8 and there are only three numbers in the set with a mean that is not 8, two of the numbers must be 8.

  How would you find the third missing number in the set? Possible answer: Write and solve an equation or predict and test until you find a third number in the set that will yield a mean of 10.

- *Have students read the clues for Mystery Number 2.*

  How do you know that the median must be one of the numbers in the set? There is an odd number (3) of numbers in the set.

  How can you use the range to find the third number in the set? Explain. Add, 16 + 5 = 21. Five must be the least number in the set since the median is 9 and there are only three numbers.

- *After students solve Mystery Number 3, have them explain their thinking.*

  How do you know that the median is not one of the numbers in the set? There are an even number (4) of numbers in the set, so the median must be the average of the middle two numbers in the set.

  Think It Over! After students complete the Write About It, have them explain how they used the clues to find each of the Mystery Number sets. Encourage students to compare and contrast their solution methods.

Measure by Measure

REASONING Use the clues and your knowledge of the measures of central tendency to find the set of numbers described. Be prepared to explain how you solved the mystery.

Mystery Number 1

Clues:
1. There are three numbers in the set.
2. The mean is 10.
3. The mode is 8.
What is the set of numbers? 8, 8, 14

Mystery Number 2

Clues:
1. There are three numbers in the set.
2. One number in the set is 5.
3. The median is 9.
4. The range is 16.
What is the set of numbers? 5, 9, 21

Mystery Number 3

Clues:
1. There are four numbers in the set.
2. The median is 12.
3. Two numbers in the set are 3 and 10.
4. The range is 15.
What is the set of numbers? 3, 10, 14, 18

Think It Over! You can find the mean by dividing 150 ÷ 6 = 25. To find the median, mode, or range, you need more information.

- **Write About It** If you know that the sum of a set of six numbers is 150, which of the following measures could you find: mean, median, mode, range? Explain. See above.

- **Stretch Your Thinking** A set of numbers forms the pattern 1, 3, 5, 7, ... If the median of the set is 15, what is the range? 28

Intervention and Extension Resources

LANGUAGE ARTS CONNECTION

Ask students to **construct sets of numbers with two given measures of central tendency: mean, median, mode, and range.**

For example, have students construct a set of 5 numbers with a median of 5 and a mean of 6. Possible answer: 2, 4, 5, 9, 10

Then have them write clues about their number sets. Ask them to exchange with a partner and solve. Check students' work.

VISUAL

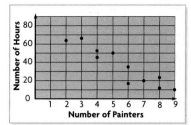

Challenge

Explore Scatterplots

Learn how to read and interpret a scatterplot.

Do you think there is any relationship between the number of people who paint a large building and the number of hours it takes them to finish the job?

The *scatterplot* displays data for 11 large buildings that were painted. It shows that as the number of painters increased, the time it took them to finish the job tended to decrease.

A scatterplot shows the relationship between two variables.

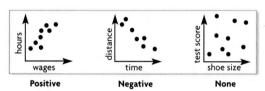

Positive | **Negative** | **None**

When the values of the two variables increase or decrease together, there is a **positive correlation**.

When the values of one variable increase while the others decrease, there is a **negative correlation**.

When the data points show no pattern of increase or decrease, there is **no correlation**.

TALK ABOUT IT

• Tell if the relationship between the speed of a car and the number of hours needed to drive 500 miles has a positive correlation, a negative correlation, or no correlation. **negative correlation**

TRY IT

Sketch a scatterplot that could represent the situation. Then identify the type of correlation between the variables.
Check students' scatterplots.

1. positive
2. none

1. amount of time walking *and* total distance that you walk

2. number of rooms in house *and* street address of house

Write *positive correlation*, *negative correlation*, or *no correlation* to describe the relationship shown in the scatterplot.

3.  negative correlation

4.  positive correlation

139

Intervention and Extension Resources

REACHING ALL LEARNERS

PHYSICAL EDUCATION/HEALTH CONNECTION

MATERIALS *For each student* graph paper, p. TR64

Have students **apply their knowledge of scatterplots.** Ask them to keep a training log for a week recording physical activities in which they participate. Or, if necessary, encourage them to start something new, such as total number of pushups they can do, or a timed run or walk. For each activity or exercise, have students record the data in a table.

At the end of the week, have them make scatterplots to relate the data. Then ask them to analyze the scatterplots to describe any relationships they recognize. Check students' work.

VISUAL, KINESTHETIC

CHALLENGE
Explore Scatterplots

Objective To extend the concepts and skills of Chapters 5–6

USING THE PAGE

• *Direct students' attention to the scatterplot at the top of the page. Show them that the points on the scatterplot are plotted as ordered pairs: (number of painters, number of hours).*

How does the scatterplot suggest that as the number of painters increases, the length of time it takes them to finish the job decreases? Possible answer: The data resemble a straight line that angles downward from upper left to lower right.

• *Discuss each of the scatterplots showing positive correlation, negative correlation, and no correlation.*

How does each scatterplot show the correlation associated with it? Possible answer: Positive correlation looks like a straight line angling from lower left to upper right; negative correlation looks like a straight line angling from upper left to lower right; and no correlation looks like points scattered throughout the plane.

What type of correlation does the scatterplot showing the number of hours and the number of painters show? negative correlation

• *Have students complete the Talk About It and then extend their thinking.*

What are some relationships that you think would have a positive correlation, a negative correlation, and no correlation? Possible answer: positive—study time and grade on a test; negative—age of cars and resale value; no correlation—age and number of miles run each week

Try It Before assigning Try It Exercises 1–2, suggest that students use the first variable for the *x*-axis, or horizontal axis, and the second variable for the *y*-axis, or vertical axis. Have students compare their scatterplots for Exercises 1–2. After completing Exercises 3–4, have students use words to explain the relationships shown in the scatterplots.

UNIT 2   CHAPTERS 5–6

STUDY GUIDE AND REVIEW

Purpose To help students review concepts and skills presented in Chapters 5–6

USING THE PAGES

☑ Assessment Checkpoint

The Study Guide and Review includes content from Chapters 5–6.

Chapter 5
5.1   Samples
5.2   Bias in Surveys
5.3   Problem Solving Strategy: *Make a Table*
5.4   Frequency Tables and Line Plots
5.5   Measures of Central Tendency
5.6   Outliers and Additional Data
5.7   Data and Conclusions

Chapter 6
6.1   Make and Analyze Graphs
6.2   Find Unknown Values
6.3   Stem-and-Leaf Plots and Histograms
6.4   Math Lab: Explore Box-and-Whisker Graphs
6.5   Box-and-Whisker Graphs
6.6   Analyze Graphs

The blue page numbers in parentheses provided with each group of exercises indicate the pages on which the concept or skill was presented. The red number given with each group of exercises identifies the Learning Goal for the concept or skill.

VOCABULARY

1. Everyone in the population has the same chance of being selected in a(n) __?__. (p. 95) **random sample**

2. A bar graph that shows the frequency at which data occur within intervals is a(n) __?__. (p. 127) **histogram**

3. Individuals in the population are not represented in the sample if the sample is __?__. (p. 98) **biased**

EXAMPLES

Chapter 5

• **Identify the type of sample.** (pp. 94–97) **5A**

Determine the sampling method used if workers on an assembly line check every tenth tire.

This is a systematic sample.

• **Record and organize data.** (pp. 102–105) **5B**

What is the size of the sample?

SCORES ON MATH TEST		
Score Interval	Frequency	Cumulative Frequency
91–100	5	5
81–90	8	13
71–80	6	19
Below 71	5	24

There are 24 people in the sample.

• **Find the mean, median, and mode.** (pp. 106–111) **5C**

24, 20, 24, 21, 26
Mean: 24 + 20 + 24 + 21 + 26 = 115;
    115 ÷ 5 = 23

Median: 24

Mode: 24

EXERCISES

Determine the type of sample. Write *convenience*, *random*, or *systematic*.

4. From a computer list of students, each with an equal chance of being selected, 100 students are chosen. **random**

5. Every tenth person walking down the street is surveyed about the President. **systematic**

For 6–7, use the following data.

NUMBER OF MOVIES SEEN IN ONE YEAR			
8	12	16	12
9	10	9	8
9	15	20	14
12	7	9	15

6. Make a line plot. **Check students' plots.**
7. Make a cumulative frequency table with intervals. **Check students' table.**

Find the mean, median, and mode.

8. 2, 7, 9, 4, 6, 8, 6   **6; 6; 6**
9. 5.3, 8.8, 4.7, 6.5, 4.7   **6; 5.3; 4.7**
10. 79, 87, 90, 100, 96, 89, 92, 87   **90; 89.5; 87**
11. Suppose you added the number 10.6 to the data in Exercise 9. Which measure(s) of central tendency would change? **mean and median**

140 Chapters 5–6

Additional Answers, page 141

15.
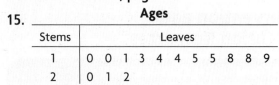

Stems	Leaves
1	0 0 1 3 4 4 5 5 8 8 9
2	0 1 2

Ages

20.
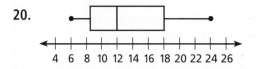

Chapter 6

- **Display data in graphs.** (pp. 120–123) **6A**

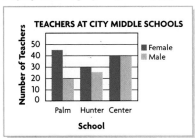

For 12, use the graph at the left.

12. Which schools have more female teachers than male teachers? **Palm and Hunter**
13. Would you use a bar graph, line graph, or circle graph to display a city's temperature readings for 1 month? Explain. **line; shows change over time**
14. Make a multiple-line graph with the data below. **Check students' graphs.**

HIGH AND LOW TEMPERATURES					
	Mon	**Tues**	**Wed**	**Thurs**	**Fri**
Highs	45°	53°	41°	48°	50°
Lows	34°	39°	35°	40°	41°

- **Use stem-and-leaf plots and histograms.** (pp. 126–128) **6A**

In a stem-and-leaf plot, the tens digits of the data are stems, and the ones digits are leaves.

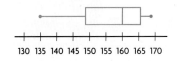

Ages

Stem	Leaves
1	1 3 3
2	0 3 5 5
3	7 7 8

Some students are participating in a jump-rope benefit. Their ages are 10, 15, 18, 20, 15, 11, 13, 10, 14, 14, 18, 19, 22, and 21.

15. Use the data to make a stem-and-leaf plot. **See Additional Answers, page 140.**
16. Use the data to make a histogram. **Check students' graphs.**

- **Make a box-and-whisker graph.** (pp. 129–131) **6A**

Heights of Students (in cm)
135 168 148 160 159 148 163 165 167

Draw a box-and-whisker graph.

For 17–20, use the table below.

HEIGHTS OF TREES (in ft)								
8	12	6	9	15	9	16	20	24

17. What is the median? **12 ft**
18. What are the lower and upper quartiles? **8.5 ft, 18 ft**
19. What are the lower and upper extremes? **6 ft, 24 ft**
20. Make a box-and-whisker graph. **See Additional Answers, page 140.**

PROBLEM SOLVING APPLICATIONS

21. Roberto has to pay $27 for his CDs at the record store. In how many ways can he pay, using only bills of $10, $5, and $1? (pp. 100–101) **12 ways**
23. The machines in the exact change lane of a tollway accept any combination of coins that total exactly 75¢, but they do not accept pennies or half dollars. In how many different ways can a driver pay the toll in an exact change lane? (pp. 100–101) **18 ways**

22. The sixth-grade students are having a car wash. They charge $4 for cars and $6 for SUVs. In how many ways can they earn $100? (pp. 100–101) **9 ways**
24. The debate club has 10 members. Each member will debate each of the other members only once. How many debates will they have? (pp. 100–101) **45 debates**

141

✅ Assessment Checkpoint

Portfolio Suggestions The portfolio represents the growth, talents, achievements, and reflections of the mathematics learner. Students might spend a short time selecting work samples for their portfolios and completing A Guide to My Math Portfolio from *Assessment Guide*, page AGxix.

You may want to have students respond to the following questions:

- **What new understanding of math have I developed in the past several weeks?**
- **What growth in understanding or skills can I see in my work?**
- **What can I do to improve my understanding of math ideas?**
- **What would I like to learn more about?**

For information about how to organize, share, and evaluate portfolios, see *Assessment Guide*, page AGxviii.

Use the item analysis in the **Intervention** chart to diagnose students' errors. You may wish to reinforce content or remediate misunderstandings by using the text pages or lesson resources.

STUDY GUIDE AND REVIEW INTERVENTION

How to Help Options

Learning Goal	Items	Text Pages	Reteach and Practice Resources
5A *See page 92C for Chapter 5 learning goals*	4–5	98–99	Worksheets for Lesson 5.2
5B *See page 92C for Chapter 5 learning goals*	6–7	102–105	Worksheets for Lesson 5.4
5C *See page 92C for Chapter 5 learning goals*	8–11	106–108, 109–111	Worksheets for Lessons 5.5, 5.6
5D *See page 92C for Chapter 5 learning goals*	21–24	100–101	Worksheets for Lesson 5.3
6A *See page 92C for Chapter 6 learning goals*	12–14, 15–16, 17–20	120–123, 126–128, 129–131	Worksheets for Lessons 6.1, 6.3, 6.4, 6.5

CALIFORNIA CONNECTIONS

Purpose To provide additional practice for concepts and skills in Chapters 5–6

USING THE PAGE

Water Resources

• *Direct students' attention to the circle graph.*

About how many times as much water is used by environment as is used by "other"? about 25 times as much water

Suppose 100,000 gallons of runoff are used by agriculture. About how many gallons of runoff would be used by the environment? by cities? in all? about 100,000 gal; about 25,000 gal; about 240,000 gal

• *After Exercise 4, discuss how students made their graphs.*

How did you choose the scale for your graph? Answers will vary.

Extension Have students use the data for Exercise 5 to find the measures of central tendency. Then encourage them to use any of the data on the page about water resources to write at least two problems. Have groups of four students exchange problems and solve. Check students' work.

Water Resources

Water is a critical natural resource in California. Densely populated Southern California is relatively dry. More sparsely populated Northern California has more water.

Water is stored in reservoirs and carried along aqueducts to the places where it is needed most.

SCIENCE Standards LS 6.b

Rainwater that flows into lakes, rivers, and streams is called *runoff.*

Use Data For 1–3, use the circle graph.

1. About how many times as much runoff water is used by agriculture as is used by cities? **about 4 times**

2. Which category uses about the same amount of runoff as agriculture? **environment**

3. Would you say that agriculture and "other" use a little less than half or a little more than half of the runoff water? **a little less than half**

Use Data For 4, use the table at the right.

4. The California Department of Water Resources has predicted the supply and demand for water in the year 2020 for both average conditions and drought conditions. Make and label a double-bar graph of the data. **Check students' graphs.**

Use Data For 5, use the table below.

5. The United States Geological Survey measures the flow of hundreds of California streams. Make a line plot of the data. **Check students' plots.**

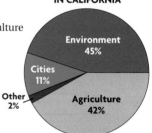

WATER RUNOFF USE IN CALIFORNIA

Environment 45%
Cities 11%
Other 2%
Agriculture 42%

WATER SUPPLY AND DEMAND IN 2020

	Millions of Acre-feet*
Average Conditions	
Supply	63
Demand	71
Drought Conditions	
Supply	50
Demand	60

*One acre-foot equals the amount of water needed to cover 1 acre of land to a depth of 1 foot.

STREAMFLOW OF 18 CALIFORNIA STREAMS (cubic ft per second)

5	7	8	5	7	4
6	7	6	9	6	5
5	7	4	6	7	7

142 Chapters 5–6

Dams

Dams, reservoirs, and aqueducts help to collect, store, and transport water in California. The state has about 1,400 dams of all types and sizes. Some of California's water comes from dams and reservoirs outside the state.

California's 230-ft-tall Oroville Dam (above) is the tallest dam in the United States. Hoover Dam, on the Arizona-Nevada border, also supplies some of California's water needs.

SCIENCE Standards LS 6.b

4. No. Because of the huge range in values, from 1,000 to 28,500,000, the mean is not close to any of the values.

Use Data For 1–3, find the measure of central tendency for the dams listed in the table.

1. mean storage capacity
6,920,200 acre-ft

2. median length 3,475 ft

3. range of storage capacities
28,499,000 acre-ft

4. Is the mean a good measure for comparing the storage capacities of the dams? Explain.
See above.

5. Make and label a bar graph showing the storage capacities of Parker, Oroville, San Luis, and Hoover Dams. Why would it be difficult to include Imperial Dam on your graph? See below.

7. *REASONING* Nora said that the longer a dam is, the greater is its storage capacity. Do you agree? Explain, using examples from the table to illustrate your answer.
No; Possible answer: San Luis is the longest dam, yet its storage capacity is less than both Oroville's and Hoover's.

DAMS IMPORTANT TO CALIFORNIA			
Name	**Location**	**Storage Capacity**	**Length**
Parker Dam	California	600,000 acre-ft	856 ft
Imperial Dam	California	1,000 acre-ft	3,475 ft
Oroville Dam	California	3,500,000 acre-ft	6,920 ft
San Luis Dam	California	2,000,000 acre-ft	18,600 ft
Hoover Dam	Arizona/Nevada	28,500,000 acre-ft	1,244 ft

6. Mental Math One acre-foot is equivalent to 43,560 cubic feet of water. Mentally calculate the storage capacity of Imperial Dam in cubic feet. 43,560,000 cu ft

8. Make and label a bar graph showing the lengths of the five dams in the table.
Check students' graphs.

5. Check students' graphs; Imperial Dam's capacity is extremely small compared to the others.

143

CALIFORNIA CONNECTIONS

Purpose To provide additional practice for concepts and skills in Chapters 5–6

USING THE PAGE

Dams

- *After Exercise 8, have students look back at the graphs they made for Exercises 5 and 8.*

How did you choose the scale for the graphs in Exercises 5 and 8? Answers will vary.

How do your bar graphs make it easier to compare the data? Possible answer: It is easier to see differences in capacities and lengths.

How can you use the bar graphs to help solve Exercise 7? Possible answer: It is easy to see on the graphs that the longest dam does not have the greatest storage capacity.

Reasoning Why do you think length does not mean the greatest storage capacity? Possible answer: Length is only one dimension, and storage capacity would also depend on width and depth.

Extension Challenge students to use the data in the table to write riddles that can be solved by comparing the data. Have students exchange riddles and solve. Check students' work.

Teaching Notes

Additional Ideas:

Good Questions to Ask:

Additional Resources:

Notes for Next Time:

UNIT 3 Fraction Concepts and Operations

UNIT AT A GLANCE

Assessment Options

What types of assessment are available?

Assessing Prior Knowledge

Determine whether students have the required prerequisite concepts and skills.

Check What You Know, PE pp. 145, 159, 175, 199

Test Preparation

Provide review and practice for chapter and standardized tests.

Cumulative Review, PE pp. 157, 173, 197, 219

Mixed Review and Test Prep
See the last page of each PE skill lesson.

Study Guide and Review, PE pp. 222–223

Formal Assessment

Assess students' mastery of chapter concepts and skills.

Chapter Review/Test, PE pp. 156, 172, 196, 218

Pretest and Posttest Options
   Chapter Test, Form A
      pp. AG49–50, 53–54, 57–58, 61–62
   Chapter Test, Form B
      pp. AG51–52, 55–56, 59–60, 63–64

Unit 3 Test • Chapters 7–10, pp. AG65–72

Harcourt Electronic Test System Math Practice and Assessment

Make and grade chapter tests electronically.

This software includes:

- **multiple-choice items**
- **free-response items**
- **customizable tests**
- **the means to make your own tests**

Daily Assessment

Obtain daily feedback on students' understanding of concepts.

Quick Review
See the first page of each PE lesson.

Mixed Review and Test Prep
See the last page of each PE skill lesson.

Number of the Day
See the first page of each TE skill lesson.

Problem of the Day
See the first page of each TE skill lesson.

Lesson Quiz
See the *Assess* section of each TE skill lesson.

Performance Assessment

Assess students' understanding of concepts applied to real-world situations.

Performance Assessment (Tasks A–B)
pp. PA21–22

Student Self-Assessment

Have students evaluate their own work.

How Did I Do?, p. AGxvii

A Guide to My Math Portfolio, p. AGxix

Math Journal
See *Write* in the *Assess* section of each TE skill lesson and TE pages 148B, 164B, 176B, 180, 186B, 202B, 208, 216B.

Portfolio

Portfolio opportunities appear throughout the Pupil and Teacher's Editions.

Suggested work samples:

Problem Solving Project, TE pp. 144, 158, 174, 198

Write About It, PE pp. 149, 165, 171, 193, 201, 207, 215

Chapter Review/Test, PE pp. 156, 172, 196, 218

KEY **AG** Assessment Guide   **TE** Teacher's Edition
       PA Performance Assessment **PE** Pupil Edition

How does the Unit 3 content correlate to standardized tests and California Mathematics Content Standards?

LEARNING GOAL	TAUGHT IN LESSONS	CAT	CTBS/ TERRA NOVA	ITBS	MAT	SAT	CALIFORNIA MATHEMATICS STANDARDS
7A To write and apply divisibility rules	7.1	●		●	●	●	
7B To write and apply prime factorization in exponent form	7.2						
7C To write and apply greatest common factors and least common multiples	7.3	●	●	●	●	●	⊙ NS 2.4
7D To solve problems by using an appropriate strategy such as *make an organized list*	7.4						MR 2.0
8A To write fractions in equivalent and simplest form	8.1	●	●		●		⊙ NS 2.4
8B To convert between, compare, and order fractions and mixed numbers	8.2, 8.3	●	●	●	●	●	⊙ NS 1.0 ⊙ NS 1.1
8C To represent and use equivalent representations for fractions; decimals, including terminating and repeating; and friendly percents	8.4, 8.5	●		●	●	●	
9A To write estimates of sums and differences of fractions and mixed numbers	9.1			●	●	●	NS 2.1
9B To write fraction and mixed number sums and differences	9.2, 9.3, 9.4, 9.5, 9.6	●	●	●	●	●	⊙ NS 2.0 NS 2.1
9C To solve problems by using an appropriate strategy such as *draw a diagram*	9.7		●				MR 2.4
10A To estimate products and quotients of fractions and mixed numbers	10.1				●	●	⊙ NS 2.0
10B To write products and quotients of fractions and mixed numbers	10.2, 10.3, 10.4, 10.5	●		●	●	●	NS 2.1 NS 2.2
10C To evaluate expressions and to use mental math to solve equations involving addition, subtraction, multiplication, or division of fractions	10.7	●		●	●	●	NS 2.1 NS 2.2
10D To solve problems by using an appropriate skill such as *choose the operation*	10.6	●	●	●	●	●	MR 2.0

Technology Links

🌐 The Harcourt Learning Site

Visit The Harcourt Learning Site for related links, activities, and resources:

- Number theory activity *(Use with Chapter 7.)*
- *Animated Math Glossary*
- E-Lab interactive learning experiences
- current events stories that feature mathematics
- professional development and instructional resources

www.harcourtschool.com

Harcourt Math Newsroom Videos

These videos bring exciting news events to your classroom from the leaders in news broadcasting. For each unit, there is a **Harcourt Math Newsroom Video** that helps students see the relevance of math concepts to their lives. You may wish to use the data and concepts shown in the video for real-life problem solving or class projects.

TECHNOLOGY CORRELATION

Intervention Strategies and Activities This CD-ROM helps you assess knowledge of prerequisite concepts and skills.

Mighty Math CD-ROM Series includes *Calculating Crew, Number Heroes,* and *Astro Algebra.* These provide levels of difficulty that increase from A up to Z.

E-Lab is a collection of electronic learning activities.

The chart below correlates technology activities to specific lessons.

LESSON	ACTIVITY/LEVEL	SKILL
8.1	**E-Lab** • *Equivalent Fractions* **Number Heroes** • *Fraction Fireworks,* Levels D, K, P	Write equivalent fractions
8.2	**Calculating Crew** • *Nautical Number Line,* Level K	Write mixed numbers and fractions
8.4	**E-Lab** • *Equivalent Fractions, Decimals, and Mixed Numbers* **Astro Algebra** • *Red,* Level C **Number Heroes** • *Fraction Fireworks,* Levels Q, Y	Write fractions as decimals
8.5	**Astro Algebra** • *Red,* Level D **Calculating Crew** • *Nautical Number Line,* Level Q	Write fractions, decimals, and percents
9.1	**Harcourt Math Newsroom Video** • *Portable Planetarium*	*Estimate with fractions and mixed numbers*
9.2	**E-Lab** • *Addition and Subtraction of Unlike Fractions*	Add and subtract unlike fractions
9.3	**Number Heroes** • *Fraction Fireworks,* Levels T, U, W **Calculating Crew** • *Nautical Number Line,* Level M	Add and subtract fractions
9.4	**Calculating Crew** • *Nautical Number Line,* Level N	Add and subtract mixed numbers
9.5	**E-Lab** • *Subtraction of Mixed Numbers*	Subtract mixed numbers
9.6	**Calculating Crew** • *Nautical Number Line,* Level N	Subtract mixed numbers
10.2	**Calculating Crew** • *Nautical Number Line,* Level T **Number Heroes** • *Fraction Fireworks,* Level X	Multiply fractions
10.4	**E-Lab** • *Exploring Division of Fractions*	Divide fractions

For the Student

🔵 Intervention Strategies and Activities

Review and practice the prerequisite skills for Chapters 7–10.

🌐 **E-LAB** These interactive learning experiences reinforce and extend the skills taught in Chapters 7–10.

- Skill development
- Practice

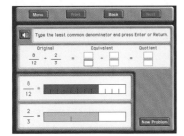

🔵 Mighty Math

The learning activities in this comprehensive math software series complement, enrich, and enhance the Pupil Edition lessons.

🔵 Calculating Crew • *Nautical Number Line*

🔵 Number Heroes • *Fraction Fireworks*

🔵 Astro Algebra • *Red*

For the Teacher

🔵 Teacher Support Software

- **Intervention Strategies and Activities**
  Provide instruction, practice, and a check of the prerequisite skills for each chapter.
- **Electronic Lesson Planner**
  Quickly prepare daily and weekly lessons for all subject areas.
- **Harcourt Electronic Test System**
  Math Practice and Assessment
  Edit and customize Chapter Tests or construct unique tests from large item banks.

For the Parent

🌐 The Harcourt Learning Site

- Encourage parents to visit The Harcourt Learning Site to help them reinforce mathematics vocabulary, concepts, and skills with their children.
- Have them click on *Math* for vocabulary, activities, real-life connections, and homework tips for Chapters 7–10.

  www.harcourtschool.com

Internet

Teachers can find fraction concepts and operations activities and resources.

Students can learn more about number theory and reinforce the critical concepts and skills for Chapters 7–10.

Parents can use The Harcourt Learning Site's resources to help their children with the vocabulary, concepts, and skills needed for Chapters 7–10.

Visit The Harcourt Learning Site
www.harcourtschool.com

Reaching All Learners

ADVANCED LEARNERS

MATERIALS *For each pair* graph paper, p. TR62; calculator

Challenge students to **explore patterns in equivalent decimals.** Display the following table.

Thirds	$\frac{1}{3} =$ 0.3333	$\frac{2}{3} =$ 0.6666	$\frac{3}{3} =$ 1.0		
Fourths	$\frac{1}{4} = ?$	$\frac{2}{4} = ?$	$\frac{3}{4} = ?$	$\frac{4}{4} = ?$	
Fifths	$\frac{1}{5} = ?$	$\frac{2}{5} = ?$	$\frac{3}{5} = ?$	$\frac{4}{5} = ?$	$\frac{5}{5} = ?$

Ask students to copy and extend the chart to include sixths, sevenths, eighths, ninths, tenths, and elevenths. Then ask them to find decimal equivalents by dividing the numerator by the denominator. Have students discuss the patterns they see and offer suggestions for remembering the decimal equivalents for commonly used fractions. *Use with Lessons 8.5 and 10.1.*

VISUAL, AUDITORY

SPECIAL NEEDS

MATERIALS *For each pair* 3 decimal squares (hundredths), p. TR7; scissors; tape

Have students **convert among decimals, fractions, and percents.** Display the following equivalent expressions statements:

"Eighteen hundredths written in simplest form is nine-fiftieths. Eighteen hundredths also equals eighteen percent. Eighteen percent equals the decimal eighteen hundredths." Have volunteers read the statements aloud.

For each decimal, percent, and fraction shown below, ask students to make a decimal square.

$$0.15 \qquad 79\% \qquad \frac{3}{5}$$

Have them cut out each square and tape it to a sheet of paper. Tell them to write on the bottom of the paper the equivalent fraction, decimal, or percent in numbers and in words. Ask them to read the equivalent expressions statements aloud. *Use with Lesson 8.5.*

AUDITORY, VISUAL

BLOCK SCHEDULING

INTERDISCIPLINARY COURSES

- Art—Describe geometric designs and fractional parts used in works of art.
- Life Science — Make a chart of the average weight of various animals at birth, written to the nearest $\frac{1}{4}$ pound.
- Ecology — Make a chart with diagrams that illustrate how the fractional width requirements for birdhouse doors vary depending upon species.

COMPLETE UNIT

Unit 3 may be presented in
- fourteen 90-minute blocks.
- seventeen 75-minute blocks.

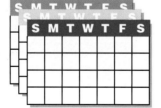

INTERDISCIPLINARY SUGGESTIONS

PURPOSE To connect *Fraction Concepts and Operations* to other subjects with these activities

Chapter 8 — Social Studies

Students research why and how the metal composition of the penny was changed by the 1981 Coinage Act.

Chapter 10 — Music

Students explore *time* in music as it relates to fractions by comparing the rhythms of two unlike compositions—one traditional and one contemporary.

KINESTHETIC, VISUAL

EARLY FINISHERS

Students who finish their work early can

- make visual aids for lessons that teach the fraction concepts and for lessons that teach adding, subtracting, multiplying, and dividing fractions and mixed numbers.

- assemble and play the Practice Game. See *Spin It*.

- solve the *Problem of the Day*.
  Use with TE Lessons 7.1-10.7.

ENGLISH LANGUAGE LEARNERS (ELL•SDAIE)

Vocabulary Preview Ask students to make a math dictionary for the vocabulary in the unit. Have them make a three-column chart and label the columns. As students learn about each new term, they can fill their dictionary. *Use with Lessons 7.2–10.4.*

Term	Example	Explanation

Mixed Number The term *mixed* is an adjective describing the word *number*. Just as a can of mixed nuts has several kinds of nuts, a mixed number is made up of two different types of numbers, a fraction and a whole number. *Use with Lesson 8.2.*

Terminating decimal Help students understand the word *terminating* to mean "having an end." Relate it to the phrase bus *terminal* which is the end of the bus line. *Use with Lesson 8.5.*

VISUAL

PRACTICE GAME

Spin It

PURPOSE To convert data in a table to fractions, decimals, and percents and to show the data in a circle graph

MATERIALS tally tables, p. TR80; fraction circles (tenths), p. TR20; 3-section spinner, p. TR70, colored red, blue, and yellow

About the Game This game is played in groups of three. Each player chooses a color on the spinner. Players take turns spinning and tallying data for ten spins in the Round One tally table. They complete the table by showing data as a fraction, a decimal, and a percent. They then use the same 3 spinner colors and show the data in a circle graph. The player with the greatest fraction scores one point for the round. The player with the most points after five rounds wins the game. *Use with Lesson 8.5.*

Round One

Spinner	Tally	Fraction	Decimal	Percent
Red	III	$\frac{3}{10}$	0.3	30%
Blue	IIII	$\frac{5}{10}$	0.5	50%
Yellow	II	$\frac{2}{10}$	0.2	20%

VISUAL

LITERATURE CONNECTIONS

These books provide students with additional ways to explore fractions.

Funny and Fabulous Fraction Stories by Dan Greenberg (Scholastic, 1996) consists of 30 fun math tales and problems that reinforce important concepts related to fractions.

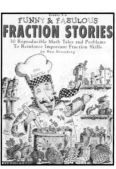

- Read "Enid the Magnificent, Part 1 and Part 2" for additional help with equivalent fractions and decimals. *Use with Lessons 8.4–8.5.*

Island of the Blue Dolphins by Scott O'Dell (Houghton Mifflin, 1990) tells of an American Indian girl who is left behind when her tribe leaves for a better place.

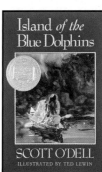

- The island that Karana lives on measures 1 league by 2 leagues. One league is about $4\frac{4}{5}$ kilometers long. Assuming the island is roughly rectangular, have students estimate the perimeter of the island. *Use with Lessons 9.4 and 10.3.*

Number Theory

CHAPTER PLANNER

PACING OPTIONS	
Compacted	4 Days
Expanded	7 Days

Getting Ready for Chapter 7 • Assessing Prior Knowledge and INTERVENTION (See PE and TE page 145.)

LESSON	CALIFORNIA STANDARDS	PACING	VOCABULARY*	MATERIALS	RESOURCES AND TECHNOLOGY
7.1 Divisibility pp. 146–147 **Objective** To use divisibility rules	NS 2.0 MR 1.1 (*Also* MR 2.2, MR 3.0)	1 Day	divisible	hundred chart	Reteach, Practice, Problem Solving, Challenge 7.1 Worksheets Extra Practice p. H38, Set A Transparency 7.1 **Math Jingles™ CD 5-6•** *Track 7*
7.2 Prime Factorization pp. 148–149 **Objective** To write a composite number as the product of prime factors	NS 2.0 (*Also* MR 1.0, MR 2.2, MR 2.5)	1 Day	**prime factorization**		Reteach, Practice, Problem Solving, Challenge 7.2 Worksheets Extra Practice p. H38, Set B Transparency 7.2
7.3 Least Common Multiple and Greatest Common Factor pp. 150–153 **Objective** To find the least common multiple and greatest common factor of numbers and use them to solve problems	NS 2.4 (*Also* MR 2.7, MR 3.2, MR 3.3)	2 Days	**least common multiple (LCM)** **greatest common factor (GCF)**		Reteach, Practice, Problem Solving, Challenge 7.3 Worksheets Extra Practice p. H38, Set C Transparency 7.3
7.4 Problem Solving Strategy: *Make an Organized List* pp. 154–155 **Objective** To solve problems by using the strategy *make an organized list*	NS 2.4 MR 3.2 (*Also* MR 2.0)	1 Day			Reteach, Practice, Reading Strategy, Challenge 7.4 Worksheets Transparency 7.4 Problem Solving Think Along, p. TR1

Ending Chapter 7 • Chapter 7 Review/Test, p. 156 • **Cumulative Review,** p. 157

*****Boldfaced** terms are new vocabulary. Other terms are review vocabulary.

CHAPTER AT A GLANCE

Vocabulary Development

The boldfaced words are the new vocabulary terms in the chapter. Have students record the definitions in their Math Journals.

prime factorization, p. 148

least common multiple (LCM), p. 150

greatest common factor (GCF), p. 151

Vocabulary Cards
Have students use the Vocabulary Cards on *Teacher's Resource Book* pp. TR125–126 to make graphic organizers or word puzzles. The cards can also be added to a file of mathematics terms.

Writing Opportunities

PUPIL EDITION
- **Write About It**, p. 149
- **What's the Question?**, p. 155
- **What's the Error?**, p. 153

TEACHER'S EDITION
- **Write**—See the *Assess* section of each TE lesson.
- **Writing in Mathematics**, p. 148B

ASSESSMENT GUIDE
- **How Did I Do?**, p. AGxvii

California Mathematics Content Standards for Grade 6

Strands

Number Sense

Lesson 7.1: ⊶ NS 2.0

Lesson 7.2: ⊶ NS 2.0

Lesson 7.3: ⊶ NS 2.4

Lesson 7.4: ⊶ NS 2.4

Algebra and Functions

Measurement and Geometry

Statistics, Data Analysis, and Probability

Mathematical Reasoning

Lesson 7.1: MR 1.1, 2.2, 3.0

Lesson 7.2: MR 1.0, 2.2, 2.5

Lesson 7.3: MR 3.2, 3.3

Lesson 7.4: MR 2.0, 3.2

Family Involvement Activities

These activities provide:
- Letter to the Family
- Information about California Standards
- Math Vocabulary
- Family Game
- Practice (Homework)

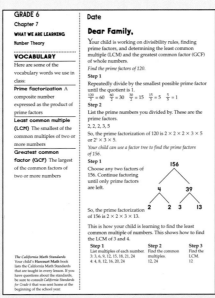

Family Involvement Activities, p. FA25

144I

Number Theory

MATHEMATICS ACROSS THE GRADES

SKILLS TRACE ACROSS THE GRADES

GRADE 5	GRADE 6	GRADE 7
Find least common multiple and greatest common factor of two whole numbers; determine if a number is prime or composite	**Use divisibility rules; write prime factorization in exponent form; write and apply greatest common factors and least common multiples**	Use and write divisibility rules; write prime factorization in exponent form; write and apply greatest common factors and least common multiples

SKILLS TRACE FOR GRADE 6

LESSON	FIRST INTRODUCED	TAUGHT AND PRACTICED	TESTED	REVIEWED
7.1	Grade 5	PE pp. 146–147, H38, p. RW32, p. PW32, p. PS32	PE p. 156, pp. AG49–52	PE pp. 156, 157, 222–223
7.2	Grade 6	PE pp. 148–149, H38, p. RW33, p. PW33, p. PS33	PE p. 156, pp. AG49–52	PE pp. 156, 157, 222–223
7.3	Grade 5	PE pp. 150–153, H38, p. RW34, p. PW34, p. PS34	PE p. 156, pp. AG49–52	PE pp. 156, 157, 222–223
7.4	Grade 4	PE pp. 154–155, p. RW35, p. PW35, p. PS35	PE p. 156, pp. AG49–52	PE pp. 156, 157, 222–223

KEY   **PE**   Pupil Edition   **PS**   Problem Solving Workbook   **RW**   Reteach Workbook
       PW   Practice Workbook   **AG**   Assessment Guide

Looking Back Prerequisite Skills

To be ready for Chapter 7, students should have the following understandings and skills:

• **Vocabulary**—*composite number, multiple, prime number*

• **Prime Numbers**—decide whether a number is prime

• **Composite Numbers**—decide whether a number is composite

• **Multiples**—write multiples of a number

• **Factors**—write all factors of a number

Check What You Know

Use page 145 to determine students' knowledge of prerequisite concepts and skills.

Intervention

Help students prepare for the chapter by using the intervention resources described on TE page 145.

Looking at Chapter 7 Essential Skills

Students will

• understand how to apply and write divisibility rules.

• **develop skill in writing a composite number as the product of prime factors in exponent form.**

• develop skill writing and applying the least common multiple and greatest common factor of two whole numbers.

EXAMPLE

Write the prime factorization of 225.

Factor Tree	Exponent Form
225 5×45 45 is not prime. 5×9 9 is not prime. 3×3 So, the prime factorization of 225 is $5 \times 5 \times 3 \times 3$.	$225 = 3 \times 3 \times 5 \times 5$ $225 = 3^2 \times 5^2$ So, the prime factorization of 225 expressed in exponent form is $3^2 \times 5^2$.

Looking Ahead Applications

Students will apply what they learn in Chapter 7 to the following new concepts:

• Equivalent Fractions and Simplest Form (Chapter 8)

• Adding and Subtracting Fractions (Chapter 9)

• Adding and Subtracting Mixed Numbers (Chapter 9)

Number Theory

INTRODUCING THE CHAPTER

Tell students that number theory is the study of relationships between numbers. Have students focus on the chart to see that relationships between numbers affect how marbles can be packaged. Ask them to explain whether or not the marbles can be packaged 11 to a pack with no leftovers. No; $1{,}200 \div 11 = 109$ r1.

USING DATA

To begin the study of this chapter, have students

- Determine if there will be leftover marbles when 1,200 marbles are divided into packages of 8. No; $1{,}200 \div 8 = 150$.

- Determine if 60 marbles could be packaged with a number of marbles in an equivalent number of packages and no leftovers. No; 60 is not the square of a whole number: $7 \times 7 = 49$ and $8 \times 8 = 64$.

- Use the data in the chart to determine if 1,200 marbles can be divided into packages of 24 with no leftovers. Yes, since $1{,}200 \div 5 = 240$, then $1{,}200 \div 24 = 50$.

PROBLEM SOLVING PROJECT

Purpose To use number theory to solve problems

Grouping pairs or small groups

Background Bakeries package baked goods in varied amounts. For example, a baker's dozen of cookies is a package of 13 cookies instead of 12.

Analyze, Choose, Solve, and Check

Have students

- Determine if there will be leftovers when packages of 13 are made from 144 baked cookies. Yes; $144 \div 13 = 11$ r1.

- Find out what size packages can be made, without leftovers, from 144 cookies. packages with 2, 3, 4, 6, 8, 9, 12, 16, 18, 24, 36, 48, or 72 cookies

- Make a chart to show their findings. Check students' work.

 Suggest that students display their charts in the classroom and later add them to their portfolios.

Thousands of years ago, marbles were made of flint, stone, or baked clay. Today, marbles are made of different types of materials, and glass is the most popular. The glass is melted in a furnace and poured out. It is cut into cylinders, and these cylinders are rounded off by rollers and then cooled. Suppose 1,200 cooled marbles are put into packages of 10. How many packages could be made? Would there be any left over?

120 packages; no

PACKAGES OF MARBLES		
Marbles per Package	Complete Package? Yes or No	Reason
3	Yes	$1{,}200 \div 3 = 400$ packages
4	Yes	$1{,}200 \div 4 = 300$ packages
5	Yes	$1{,}200 \div 5 = 240$ packages
6	Yes	$1{,}200 \div 6 = 200$ packages
7	No	$1{,}200 \div 7 = 171$ r3 packages
8	Yes	$1{,}200 \div 8 = 150$ packages
9	No	$1{,}200 \div 9 = 133$ r3 packages

Why learn math? Explain that a person who manages a candy factory would use number theory to determine how many packages of candy could be packed each hour or how many boxes of packaged candy would be ready to ship each day. Ask: How do people in other jobs use number theory? Possible answer: A restaurant owner uses number theory to determine how many people could be seated at tables each hour.

To find out more about number theory, visit The Harcourt Learning Site.

www.harcourtschool.com

Check What You Know

Use this page to help you review and remember important skills needed for Chapter 7.

 Vocabulary

Choose the best term from the box.

composite
number
multiple
prime number

1. A number whose only factors are 1 and itself is a __?__ .
   prime number

2. A number that has more than two factors is a __?__ .
   composite number

 Prime Numbers (See p. H7.)

Decide whether the number is a prime number. Write *yes* or *no*.

3. 2 yes	**4.** 5 yes	**5.** 4 no	**6.** 9 no
7. 11 yes	**8.** 21 no	**9.** 37 yes	**10.** 26 no
11. 13 yes	**12.** 7 yes	**13.** 45 no	**14.** 70 no

 Composite Numbers (See p. H7.)

Decide whether the number is a composite number. Write *yes* or *no*.

15. 6 yes	**16.** 15 yes	**17.** 19 no	**18.** 81 yes
19. 24 yes	**20.** 53 no	**21.** 3 no	**22.** 25 yes

 Multiples (See p. H8.)

Write the next three multiples.

23. 4 4, 8, 12, ▪, ▪, ▪ 16, 20, 24	**24.** 10 10, 20, 30, ▪, ▪, ▪ 40, 50, 60	**25.** 12 12, 24, 36, ▪, ▪, ▪ 48, 60, 72
26. 8 8, 16, 24, ▪, ▪, ▪ 32, 40, 48	**27.** 5 5, 10, 15, ▪, ▪, ▪ 20, 25, 30	**28.** 11 11, 22, 33, ▪, ▪, ▪ 44, 55, 66

Write the first five multiples of each number.

29. 6 6, 12, 18, 24, 30	**30.** 22 22, 44, 66, 88, 110	**31.** 30 30, 60, 90, 120, 150
32. 7 7, 14, 21, 28, 35	**33.** 9 9, 18, 27, 36, 45	**34.** 13 13, 26, 39, 52, 65

Factors (See p. H8.)

Write all of the factors of each number.

35. 8 1, 2, 4, 8	**36.** 9 1, 3, 9	**37.** 11 1, 11
38. 18 1, 2, 3, 6, 9, 18	**39.** 54 1, 2, 3, 6, 9, 18, 27, 54	**40.** 32 1, 2, 4, 8, 16, 32

> **LOOK AHEAD**
>
> **In Chapter 7 you will**
> - use divisibility rules
> - find prime factors
> - determine the LCM and GCF of whole numbers

145

Check What You Know
INTERVENTION • Diagnose and Prescribe

Prerequisite Skill	Items (Pupil Edition p. 145)	How to Help Options
✓ Prime Numbers	3–14	• **Troubleshooting, Pupil Edition p. H7** • **Intervention Strategies and Activities** Card, Copying Master, or CD-ROM • **Skill 5**
✓ Composite Numbers	15–22	• **Troubleshooting, Pupil Edition p. H7** • **Intervention Strategies and Activities** Card, Copying Master, or CD-ROM • **Skill 6**
✓ Multiples	23–34	• **Troubleshooting, Pupil Edition p. H8** • **Intervention Strategies and Activities** Card, Copying Master, or CD-ROM • **Skill 15**
✓ Factors	35–40	• **Troubleshooting, Pupil Edition p. H8** • **Intervention Strategies and Activities** Card, Copying Master, or CD-ROM • **Skill 16**

Divisibility

LESSON PLANNING

Objective To use divisibility rules

Intervention for Prerequisite Skills

Multiples, Factors (For intervention strategies, see page 145.)

Materials *For each student* hundred chart

California Mathematics Content Standards

○━ NS 2.0 Students calculate and solve problems involving addition, subtraction, multiplication, and division.

○━ MR 1.1 Analyze problems by identifying relationships, distinguishing relevant from irrelevant information, identifying missing information, sequencing and prioritizing information, and observing patterns.

(*Also* MR 2.2, MR 3.0)

Math Background

One topic of number theory is divisibility.

- Students will use the concept of divisibility as they simplify fractions and find common denominators.

- Knowing if a number is divisible by 2, 3, 4, 5, 6, 8, 9, or 10 will help students as they find factors.

- Different observations must be made for 3 and 9, where the sum of the number's digits must be considered.

- Divisibility by 6 is determined by two considerations: divisibility by 2 and divisibility by 3.

WARM-UP RESOURCES

NUMBER OF THE DAY

Transparency
7.1

The number of the day is a common number of pizza servings. It is the smallest number divisible by 2, 3, and 4. What number is it? 12

PROBLEM OF THE DAY

Transparency
7.1

Corrine is having a party. She has 45 different party favors and wants to give each guest the same number of favors. How many guests could she invite and how many favors would they get? 1, 45; 3, 15; 5, 9; 9, 5; 15, 3; 45, 1

Solution Problem of the Day tab, p. PD7

DAILY FACTS PRACTICE

Have students practice division facts by completing Set G of *Teacher's Resource Book,* p. TR97.

ALTERNATIVE TEACHING STRATEGY ELL

Materials *For each group* centimeter cubes

Have students **use centimeter cubes to model division** of a number such as 24 by 2, 3, 4, 5, 6, 8, 9, and 10.

- Divide the class into small groups and give each group several numbers, such as 50, 35, 12, 20, 32, 27, 45. Ask them to model division of their numbers by 2, 3, 4, 5, 6, 8, 9, and 10 and record the results in a table.
- Have the groups of students compare the results.
- Use their results to develop the rules for divisibility.

50 divisible by 2, 5, 10; 35 divisible by 5; 12 divisible by 2, 3, 4, 6; 20 divisible by 2, 4, 5, 10; 32 divisible by 2, 4, 8; 27 divisible by 3, 9; 45 divisible by 3, 5, 9

KINESTHETIC

MIXED REVIEW AND TEST PREP

Cumulative Review Chapters 1–7

Refer to the Pupil Edition pages referenced in the exercises for further review. Have students go to the lesson page, review the lesson, and correct any problem they missed.

Mixed Review and Test Prep, p. 147

How to Help	
Item	Page
30	129
31	60
32	76
33	22
34	44

SPECIAL NEEDS

Divide the class into small groups and have each group **write the rules for divisibility** for 2, 3, 4, 5, and 6.

- Direct each student to say the last two digits of his or her phone number. Then ask the group to work together to decide if the number is divisible by either 2, 3, 4, 5, or 6 by using the rules they have written.
- Suggest that students make a table of their results to share with the class.

Check students' work.

AUDITORY

ADVANCED LEARNERS

Challenge students to **apply what they have learned about division.** Have students answer and give two examples for each of the following questions: Possible answers are given.

- If a number is divisible by 2 and 3, is it divisible by 6? yes; 18 and 30 are divisible by 2, 3, and 6.
- If a number is divisible by 2 and 4, is it divisible by 8? not necessarily; 12 and 20 are divisible by 2 and 4, but not by 8.
- If a number is divisible by 3 and 5, is it divisible by 15? yes; 30 and 45 are divisible by 3, 5, and 15.
- If a number is divisible by 3 and 6, is it divisible by 18? not necessarily; 30 and 42 are divisible by 3 and 6, but not by 18.

AUDITORY

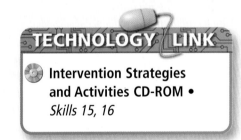

TECHNOLOGY LINK

Intervention Strategies and Activities CD-ROM •
Skills 15, 16

Objective To use divisibility rules

Vocabulary *Review* divisible

Materials *For each student* hundred chart

1 Introduce

QUICK REVIEW provides review of pre-requisite skills.

Why Learn This? You can use this skill to determine how to divide items, such as party favors, equally among your friends. *Share the lesson objective with students.*

2 Teach

Guided Instruction

• *Review the divisibility rules for 2 and 3.*

State the divisibility rule for 6 in another way. A number is divisible by 6 if it is even and the sum of the digits is divisible by 3.

• *Discuss the remaining divisibility rules.*

What is another way of stating the divisibility rule for 10? A number is divisible by 10 if it is divisible by 2 and 5.

• *As students work through the examples, ask:*

How did you decide 610 was not divisible by 3? The sum of the digits, $6 + 1 + 0$, is not divisible by 3.

REASONING **If a number is not divisible by 3, will it be divisible by 9? Explain.** No; if it does not have a factor of 3, it cannot have a factor of 9.

ADDITIONAL EXAMPLE

Example, p. 146

Determine whether 720 is divisible by 2, 3, 4, 5, 6, 8, 9, or 10.

2: the last digit is zero

3: the sum of the digits is divisible by 3

4: the last two digits form a number divisible by 4

5: the last digit is 0

6: the number is divisible by 2 and 3

8: the three digits form a number divisible by 8

9: the sum of the digits is divisible by 9

10: the last digit is 0

146 Chapter 7

Divisibility

Learn how to tell if a number is divisible by 2, 3, 4, 5, 6, 8, 9, or 10.

Remember that a number is divisible by another number if the remainder is zero.

QUICK REVIEW

Write *even* or *odd* for each.

1. 34,526 even
2. 5,437 odd
3. 6,230 even
4. 27,343 odd
5. 1,468 even

Chris knows that a number is divisible by 2 if the last digit is 0, 2, 4, 6, or 8. He also knows that a number is divisible by 3 if the sum of the digits is divisible by 3. He wonders if there is a rule for numbers that are divisible by 6.

MATH LAB

Activity

You need: hundred chart

• Shade all the numbers divisible by 2.

• Circle all the numbers that are divisible by 3.

• Look at the numbers that are both shaded and circled. Divide these numbers by 6. What do you notice? All these numbers are divisible by 6.

• What rule can Chris write about numbers divisible by 6? Possible answer: a number is divisible by 6 if the number is divisible by 2 and 3.

Math Idea ▶ You can use divisibility rules to help you decide if a number is divisible by another number.

A number is divisible by	Divisible	Not Divisible
2 if the last digit is even (0, 2, 4, 6, or 8).	11,994	2,175
3 if the sum of the digits is divisible by 3.	216	79
4 if the last two digits form a number divisible by 4.	1,024	621
5 if the last digit is 0 or 5.	15,195	10,007
6 if the number is divisible by 2 and 3.	1,332	44
8 if the last three digits form a number divisible by 8.	5,336	3,180
9 if the sum of the digits is divisible by 9.	144	33
10 if the last digit is 0.	2,790	9,325

EXAMPLES

Tell whether each number is divisible by 2, 3, 4, 5, 6, 8, 9, or 10.

A. 610 is divisible by
2; the last digit is even.
5; the last digit is 0 or 5.
10; the last digit is 0.

B. 459 is divisible by
3; the sum of the three digits is divisible by 3.
9; the sum of the digits is divisible by 9.

146

CALIFORNIA STANDARDS O–nNS 2.0 Students calculate and solve problems involving addition, subtraction, multiplication, and division. **MR 1.1** Analyze problems by identifying relationships, distinguishing relevant from irrelevant information, identifying missing information, sequencing and prioritizing information, and observing patterns. *also* MR 2.2, MR 3.0

RETEACH 7.1

Divisibility

The rules for divisibility are:

A number is divisible by:	If:
2	the last digit is 0, 2, 4, 6, or 8.
3	the sum of its digits is divisible by 3.
4	the number formed by the last two digits is divisible by 4.
5	the last digit is 0 or 5.
6	it is divisible by 2 and by 3.
8	the number formed by the last three digits is divisible by 8.
9	the sum of its digits is divisible by 9.
10	the last digit is 0.

To determine whether 3,882 is divisible by 3, follow these steps:

Step 1 Find the sum of the digits of 3,882:

$3 + 8 + 8 + 2 = 21$

Step 2 Decide whether the sum, 21, is divisible by 3. Since 3 divides 21 evenly (with no remainder), 21 is divisible by 3. So, 3,882 is *divisible* by 3.

To determine whether 3,882 is divisible by 9, decide whether 21, the sum of the digits, can be divided evenly by 9. Since $21 ÷ 9 = 2 \ r3$, 3,882 is *not divisible* by 9.

To determine whether 7,032 is divisible by 4, follow these steps:

Step 1 Identify the number formed by the last two digits: 32.

Step 2 Decide whether 32 is divisible by 4. Since 4 divides 32 evenly (with no remainder), 32 is divisible by 4. So, 7,032 is divisible by 4.

To determine whether 7,032 is divisible by 8, decide whether 032 (the last three digits) is a number divisible by 8. Since $032 ÷ 8 = 4$, the number 7,032 is divisible by 8.

Determine whether each number is divisible by 2, 3, 4, 5, 6, 8, 9, or 10.

1. 146   2
2. 369   3, 9
3. 195   3, 5
4. 284   2, 4
5. 444   2, 3, 4, 6
6. 512   2, 4, 8
7. 788   2, 4
8. 612   2, 3, 4, 6, 9
9. 2,865   3, 5
10. 4,470   2, 3, 5, 6, 10
11. 6,048   2, 3, 4, 6, 8, 9
12. 3,240   2, 3, 4, 5, 6, 8, 9, 10

PRACTICE 7.1

Divisibility

Tell whether each number is divisible by 2, 3, 4, 5, 6, 8, 9, or 10.

1. 30   2, 3, 5, 6, 10
2. 24   2, 3, 4, 6, 8
3. 115   5
4. 240   2, 3, 4, 5, 6, 8, 10
5. 486   2, 3, 6, 9
6. 235   5
7. 279   3, 9
8. 801   3, 9
9. 145   5
10. 650   2, 5, 10
11. 736   2, 4, 8
12. 1,200   2, 3, 4, 5, 6, 8, 10
13. 207   3, 9
14. 723   3
15. 2,344   2, 4, 8
16. 868   2, 4
17. 694   2
18. 4,464   2, 3, 4, 6, 8, 9
19. 3,894   2, 3, 6
20. 306   2, 3, 6, 9
21. 836   2, 4
22. 5,962   2
23. 2,388   2, 3, 4, 6
24. 792   2, 3, 4, 6, 8, 9
25. 14,730   2, 3, 5, 6, 10
26. 24,456   2, 3, 4, 6, 8
27. 7,677   3, 9
28. 34,248   2, 3, 4, 6, 8

For 29–31 write *T* or *F* to tell whether each statement is true or false. If it is false, give an example that shows it is false.

29. No odd number is divisible by 2.   T
30. All numbers that are divisible by 4 are also divisible by 2.   T
31. All numbers that are divisible by 3 are also divisible by 6.   F; 9
32. A number is between 40 and 50 and is divisible by both 3 and 4.

What is the number?   48

Mixed Review

Add or subtract mentally.

33. $451 - 71$ 380
34. $898 - 196$ 702
35. $109 + 46 + 54$ 209

CHECK FOR UNDERSTANDING

Think and ▶ Discuss

sum must be divisible by 3, and for 9 the sum must be divisible by 9.

Look back at the lesson to answer each question.

1. **Compare** the divisibility rules for 3 and 9.
   1. They both involve finding the sum of the digits. For 3 the (see left)
2. **Tell** the advantages of knowing the divisibility rules. See below left.

Guided ▶ Practice

Tell whether each number is divisible by 2, 3, 4, 5, 6, 8, 9, or 10.

3. 56
2, 4, 8
4. 200
2, 4, 5, 8, 10
5. 784
2, 4, 8
6. 2,345
5
7. 3,009
3

PRACTICE AND PROBLEM SOLVING

Independent ▶ Practice

Tell whether each number is divisible by 2, 3, 4, 5, 6, 8, 9, or 10.

2. Possible answer: It saves time because you don't have to do the division to find out if a number is divisible by another number; it helps you find factors of a number.

8. 75
3, 5
9. 324
2, 3, 4, 6, 9
10. 45
3, 5, 9
11. 812
2, 4
12. 501
3

13. 615
3, 5
14. 936
2, 3, 4, 6, 8, 9
15. 744
2, 3, 4, 6, 8
16. 5,188
2, 4
17. 4,335
3, 5

18. 1,407
3
19. 48,006
2, 3, 6, 9
20. 7,064
2, 4, 8
21. 12,111
3
22. 1,044
2, 3, 4, 6, 9

For 23–25 write *T* or *F* to tell whether each statement is true or false. If it is false, give an example that shows it is false.

23. All even numbers are divisible by 2. **T**

24. All odd numbers are divisible by 3. **F; Possible example: 617**

25. Some even numbers are divisible by 5. **T**

Problem Solving ▶ Applications

26. A number is between 80 and 100 and is divisible by both 5 and 6. What is the number? **90**

27. *REASONING* Use the divisibility rules you know to write a divisibility rule for 15. if it ends in 0 or 5 and the sum of the digits is divisible by 3

28. Kirk has 20 trading cards. He has 10 more hockey cards than baseball cards. How many does Kirk have of each type of card? **15 hockey cards, 5 baseball cards**

29. Amber charges $8.25 per hour to baby-sit. One Saturday she baby-sat for 3.5 hr. How much did she earn baby-sitting on Saturday? Round your answer to the nearest cent. **$28.88**

MIXED REVIEW AND TEST PREP

30. What is the lower quartile of the data 24, 26, 28, 29, 30, 32, 34, 36, 37? (p. 129) **27**

31. Write the percent for 0.05. (p. 60) **5%**

32. 36.4 ÷ 0.28 (p. 76) **130**

33. 858 × 19 (p. 22) **16,302**

34. TEST PREP Which is the value of $3^2 + 2 \times 5 - 6$? (p. 44) **A**

A 13 **B** 24 **C** 34 **D** 49

Extra Practice page H38, Set A

147

PROBLEM SOLVING 7.1

Divisibility

Write the correct answer.

1. A bolt manufacturing company has 12,885 bolts to be put into bags. The packing machine can be set to seal either 3, 5, or 6 bolts into each bag. Can the machine be set for any of the three numbers without any bolts being left over? If so, which setting or settings can be used?

yes; 3 and 5

2. Scott earned $35, $40, $40, $25, and $45 for 5 weeks of part-time work. During a school break, he worked full-time for one week and earned $187. How much greater were his mean weekly earnings with the full-time week included than without it?

$25 greater

3. What is the least number that is divisible by 2, 3, 4, 5, 6, 8, 9 and 10? What is the least number if 7 is included?

720; 5,040

4. A supermarket manager wants to make a pyramid of 110 cereal boxes for display. If cereal boxes are packed in cartons of 12, what is the least number of cartons she needs to open?

10 cartons

Choose the letter for the best answer.

5. A warehouse received 1,448 copies of a book. The manager wants to place them on shelves. Which number of shelves can he use if he wants the same number of books on each shelf?
A 3 shelves   C 5 shelves
(B) 4 shelves   D 6 shelves

6. Amy had a total of $81.60 to spend on 4 gifts. She bought 3 copies of the same book and then had $27 left to spend on a sweater. How much did she pay for each copy of the book?
F $9.00   H $27.00
(G) $18.20   J $54.60

7. Max sells popcorn and potato chips at the ballpark. During one game, he sold a total of 136 bags. He sold 12 fewer bags of chips than popcorn. How many bags of chips did he sell?
A 124 bags   C 74 bags
B 84 bags   (D) 62 bags

8. A commercial jet made 3 trips during one 24-hour period, each time carrying the same number of passengers. How many passengers might the plane have carried that day?
(F) 516 passengers H 620 passengers
G 586 passengers J 634 passengers

9. Write About It Explain how you solved Problem 8.

Possible answer: I determined which of the possible numbers

is divisible by 3, the number of flights.

CHALLENGE 7.1

Divisible or Not

Each statement below about divisibility is given as a rule. If you think the rule is correct, write Correct and give an explanation of why it is true. If you think the rule is incorrect, write Incorrect and give a counterexample. A counterexample is an example that shows the rule is not true for every possibility. Possible explanations and counterexamples are given.

1. Every number that is divisible by 4 is also divisible by 2.

Correct; if a number is divisible by 4, it must be an even number, and

all even numbers are divisible by 2.

2. If a number is divisible by 6, then it is also divisible by 3.

Correct; part of the rule for divisibility by 6 is that a number be

divisible by 3.

3. All numbers that are divisible by 2 are also divisible by 4.

Incorrect; counterexamples include 6, 10, 14, 18, ...

4. All numbers divisible by 5 are also divisible by 2.

Incorrect; counterexamples include 5, 15, 25, 35, ...

5. If a number is divisible by 9, then it is also divisible by 3.

Correct; the sum of the digits of any number divisible by 9 will be a

number that is also divisible by 3.

6. All numbers divisible by 2 and 4 are also divisible by 8.

Incorrect; counterexamples include 4, 12, 20, 28, ...

7. If the last digit of a number is 0, the number is not divisible by 9.

Incorrect; counterexamples include 90, 180, 270, 360, ...

---

3 Practice

Guided Practice

Do Check for Understanding Exercises 1–7 with your students. Identify those having difficulty and use lesson resources to help.

////// **COMMON ERROR ALERT** \\\\\\

Students may incorrectly decide that a number is divisible by 3 if the last digit is 3. Have students test several numbers with a last digit of 3, such as 43 and 203, for divisibility by 3. Review the divisibility rule. Point out that $4 + 3 = 7$ and $2 + 0 + 3 = 5$, and neither sum is divisible by 3.

Independent Practice

Assign Exercises 8–29.

As students work Exercises 8–22, have them test the numbers for divisibility using one test at a time. Have students write each exercise on a separate line, by recording the number after the exercise number. Then test each one for divisibility by 2, then repeat for 3, and so on.

MIXED REVIEW AND TEST PREP

Exercises 30–34 provide **cumulative review** (Chapters 1–7).

4 Assess

Summarize the lesson by having students:

DISCUSS How could you use a calculator to determine if one number is divisible by another? Divide, and if the answer is a whole number, the first number is divisible by the second.

WRITE How did you solve Exercise 26? Possible answer: The only number between 80 and 100 that is divisible by 30 is 90.

Lesson Quiz

Transparency
7.1

Determine whether each number is divisible by 2, 3, 4, 5, 6, 8, 9, or 10.

1. 322 **2**
2. 900 **2, 3, 4, 5, 6, 9, 10**
3. 426 **2, 3, 6**
4. 511 **none**
5. 1,888 **2, 4, 8**

147

Prime Factorization

LESSON PLANNING

Objective
To write a composite number as the product of prime factors

Intervention for Prerequisite Skills
Prime Numbers, Composite Numbers, Factors (For intervention strategies, see page 145.)

California Mathematics Content Standards

NS 2.0 Students calculate and solve problems involving addition, subtraction, multiplication, and division.

(*Also* MR 1.0, MR 2.2, MR 2.5)

Vocabulary

prime factorization a number written as the product of all its prime factors

Math Background

Understanding how to write the prime factorization of a number will help students simplify fractions and find common denominators.

These ideas will help students understand prime factorization.

- When using a factor tree, students may start with any two factors. The final results will be the same.
- When finding factors by dividing, students should use the test of divisibility to decide whether 2 is a factor, then 3, and so on.

Each composite number has only one prime factorization. Changing the order of the factors does not change the factorization. However, it is easier to write a factorization in exponent form when the factors are in order from least to greatest.

WARM-UP RESOURCES

 NUMBER OF THE DAY Transparency 7.2

Write the day of the month as a product of at least two factors. Possible answer: 12th of the month, 6×2

 PROBLEM OF THE DAY Transparency 7.2

The sum of the ages of Mr. and Mrs. Olsen and their two children is 108. Their ages are sets of twin prime numbers. What are their ages? NOTE: Twin primes are two prime numbers whose difference is 2.

$11 + 13 + 41 + 43 = 108$

Solution Problem of the Day tab, p. PD7

 DAILY FACTS PRACTICE

Have students practice multiplication facts by completing Set A of *Teacher's Resource Book*, p. TR98.

INTERVENTION AND EXTENSION RESOURCES

ALTERNATIVE TEACHING STRATEGY

Materials *For each group* 8 index cards

Have students **make factor trees.** At the top of each card, write a number such as 148, 53, 290, 107, 120, 275, 550, or 333.

1. Give each team of 3 or 4 students a set of cards. One student draws a card and begins a factor tree. Another team member continues the tree, and so on until it is finished.

2. The student who receives a card with a complete prime factorization writes the factorization in exponent form at the bottom of the card.

3. The next team member draws a new card and starts the process over. The team to finish the most correct factorizations in the shortest time wins.

$148 = 2^2 \times 37$; $53 = 1 \times 53$; $290 = 2 \times 5 \times 29$; $107 = 1 \times 107$; $120 = 2^3 \times 3 \times 5$; $275 = 5^2 \times 11$; $550 = 2 \times 5^2 \times 11$; $333 = 3^2 \times 37$

VISUAL

ENGLISH LANGUAGE LEARNERS (ELL•SDAIE)

To **reinforce the meaning of the word** *prime*, display the numbers 1 to 30. Have students circle the prime numbers and discuss with them why each number is or is not prime. Prime numbers between 1 and 30: 2, 3, 5, 7, 11, 13, 17, 19, 23, 29

- After students have identified the primes less than 30, have students write multiplication expressions using the primes as factors. Possible answer: $2 \times 3 \times 5 \times 11$

- Point out that because the expressions use only prime numbers and multiplication, they are also prime factorizations. Ask students to calculate the numbers that are represented by the factorizations.

Possible answer: $2 \times 3 \times 5 \times 11 = 330$

VISUAL

**ENG-LANG
Standards
R 1.0**

MIXED REVIEW AND TEST PREP

Cumulative Review Chapters 1–7

Refer to the Pupil Edition pages referenced in the exercises for further review. Have students go to the lesson page, review the lesson, and correct any problem they missed.

Mixed Review and Test Prep, p. 149

How to Help	
Item	Page
30	146
31	60
32	66
33	106
34	94

WRITING IN MATHEMATICS

 Provide students with additional **practice using prime factorization.** Give students a number, such as 315. Ask them to write a paragraph describing how they would find the prime factors of the number.

Encourage students to use divisibility tests in their process. Point out that making a factor tree or showing the division steps will help make their process clear and logical. Possible answer: Because 315 is divisible by 5, I begin by writing 5×63. Then I can see that 63 is divisible by 3, so I write $5 \times 3 \times 21$. I can factor 21 as 3×7, so $315 = 3 \times 3 \times 5 \times 7 = 3^2 \times 5 \times 7$.

TECHNOLOGY LINK

 Intervention Strategies and Activities CD-ROM •
Skills 5, 6, 16

Objective To write a composite number as the product of prime factors

Vocabulary prime factorization

1 Introduce

QUICK REVIEW provides review of pre-requisite skills.

Why Learn This? Prime factorization can help you find the GCF and LCM of numbers. *Share the lesson objective with students.*

2 Teach

Guided Instruction

• *Have students read the first two paragraphs.*

How is a composite number different from a prime number? A composite number has more than two factors; a prime number has exactly two factors.

• *Point out that the lesson shows two different methods of finding prime factorization.*

In Example 1, why do you divide first by 2? 2 is the smallest prime factor.

How can you find factors to use in a factor tree? Possible answer: Use divisibility rules to find a number that divides evenly into a number; that divisor and the resulting quotient are factors of the dividend.

How does a factor tree help you find a prime factorization? It provides an organized vertical list of the prime factors.

ADDITIONAL EXAMPLES

Example 1, p. 148

Divide to find the prime factorization of 56.

$2 \times 2 \times 2 \times 7$, or $2^3 \times 7$

Example 2, p. 148

Use a factor tree for the prime factorization of 70.

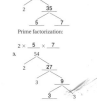

The prime factorization of 70 is $2 \times 5 \times 7$.

Prime Factorization

Learn how to write a composite number as the product of prime numbers.

Vocabulary

prime factorization

QUICK REVIEW

Write the equal factors for each.

1. 3^2 **2.** 2^4 **3.** 4^3 **4.** 9^2 **5.** 5^4
3×3 $2 \times 2 \times 2 \times 2$ $4 \times 4 \times 4$ 9×9 $5 \times 5 \times 5 \times 5$

A prime number is a whole number greater than 1 whose only factors are itself and 1. Here are the prime numbers less than 50.

2, 3, 5, 7, 11, 13, 17, 19, 23, 29, 31, 37, 41, 43, 47

A composite number, like 104, has more than two factors. You can write a composite number as the product of prime factors. This is called the **prime factorization** of the number.

You can divide to find the prime factors of a composite number.

EXAMPLE 1

Find the prime factorization of 104.

$2\overline{)104}$
$2\overline{)52}$
$2\overline{)26}$
$13\overline{)13}$
1

Repeatedly divide by the smallest possible prime factor until the quotient is 1.

$2 \times 2 \times 2 \times 13$

List the prime numbers you divided by. These are the prime factors.

So, the prime factorization of 104 is $2 \times 2 \times 2 \times 13$, or $2^3 \times 13$.

Use a factor tree to find the prime factors of a composite number.

EXAMPLE 2

Find the prime factorization of 156.

Choose any two factors of 156. Continue until only prime factors are left.

156
2 × 78   ← 2 is prime. 78 is not prime.
2 × 39   ← 39 is not prime.
3 × 13   ← prime factors

156
3 × 52   ← 3 is prime. 52 is not prime.
2 × 26   ← 26 is not prime.
2 × 13   ← prime factors

So, the prime factorization of 156 is $2 \times 2 \times 3 \times 13$, or $2^2 \times 3 \times 13$.

Math Idea ▶ Every composite number can be written as a product of two or more prime factors. No matter how you find the prime factors, you will get the same factors, but maybe in a different order.

148 CALIFORNIA STANDARDS ○━┓NS 2.0 Students calculate and solve problems involving addition, subtraction, multiplication, and division. *also* MR 1.0, MR 2.2, MR 2.5

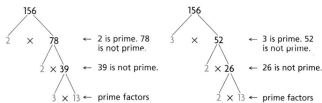

RETEACH 7.2

Prime Factorization

When you write a composite number as the product of prime factors, you have found the **prime factorization** of the number. A factor tree can help you find the prime factors of a composite number.

What is the prime factorization of 36?

Step 1 Choose any two factors of 36. Draw two lines from 36. Write one factor at the end of each line.

36
4   9

Step 2 Look at the factors. Are they prime? composite? Since they are composite, you must continue to find more factors.

36
4   9   ← factors not prime
2 2 3 3   ← all factors prime

Step 3 Look at the new bottom row of factors. Are they prime? composite? Since they are prime, you have found the prime factors of 36.

You can write the prime factorization of 36 as $2 \times 2 \times 3 \times 3$, or $2^2 \times 3^2$.

Complete each factor tree to find the prime factors of the number.

1.   70
2   35
5   7
Prime factorization:
$2 \times \underline{5} \times \underline{7}$

2.   63
3   21
3   7
Prime factorization:
$3 \times \underline{3} \times \underline{7}$ or $\underline{3^2} \times \underline{7}$

3.   54
2   27
3   9
3   3
Prime factorization:
$2 \times 3 \times \underline{3} \times 3$ or $2 \times \underline{3^3}$

4.   200
2   100
2   50
2   25
5   5
Prime factorization:
$2 \times 2 \times 2 \times \underline{5} \times \underline{5}$
or $\underline{2^3} \times \underline{5^2}$

PRACTICE 7.2

Prime Factorization

Vocabulary

1. Write *true* or *false*. Prime factorization renames a composite number as the product of prime factors. _**true**_

Use division or a factor tree to find the prime factorization.

2. 28   **3.** 50   **4.** 76   **5.** 108
$2 \times 2 \times 7$ _$2 \times 5 \times 5$_ _$2 \times 2 \times 19$_ _$2 \times 2 \times 3 \times 3 \times 3$_

6. 55   **7.** 120   **8.** 92
5×11 _$2 \times 2 \times 2 \times 3 \times 5$_ _$2 \times 2 \times 23$_

Write the prime factorization in exponent form.

9. 27   **10.** 100   **11.** 780
$3 \times 3 \times 3; 3^3$ _$2 \times 2 \times 5 \times 5; 2^2 \times 5^2$_ _$2 \times 2 \times 3 \times 5 \times 13;$_
$2^2 \times 3 \times 5 \times 13$

Solve for *n* to complete the prime factorization.

12. $n \times 17 = 51$ _$n = 3$_   **13.** $3^n \times 2 = 18$ _$n = 2$_   **14.** $2 \times 2 \times 2 \times n = 40$ _$n = 5$_

Mixed Review

For 15–18, find the mean, median, and mode.

15. 28, 35, 40, 28, 33, 36, 39, 31   **16.** 7, 7, 8, 9, 6, 6, 7, 10, 10, 9
_33.75; 34; 28_ _7.9; 7.5; 7_

17. 428, 472, 510, 386, 440   **18.** 78, 80, 95, 83, 100, 89, 88, 95
447.2; 440; no mode _88.5; 88.5; 95_

19. There are 24 students in Mrs. Garcia's class. She wants to divide the class evenly into groups of at least 4 students. Write the ways in which she can divide the class.

2 groups of 12, 3 groups of 8,
4 groups of 6, or 6 groups of 4

CHECK FOR UNDERSTANDING

Think and ▶ Discuss

Look back at the lesson to answer each question.

1. **Tell** what the prime factorization would be in Example 2 if you started with 4 and 39. $2^2 \times 3 \times 13$

2. **Tell** how you know when you have finished the prime factorization of a number. **All factors are prime numbers.**

Guided ▶ Practice

Use division or a factor tree to find the prime factorization.

3. 12	4. 65	5. 16	6. 42
$2 \times 2 \times 3$	5×13	$2 \times 2 \times 2 \times 2$	$2 \times 3 \times 7$

Write the prime factorization in exponent form.

7. 21	8. 28	9. 254	10. 908
3×7	$2 \times 2 \times 7; 2^2 \times 7$	2×127	$2 \times 2 \times 227;$ $2^2 \times 227$

PRACTICE AND PROBLEM SOLVING

Independent ▶ Practice

11. $2 \times 2 \times 2 \times 2 \times 2 \times 2$
15. $2 \times 3 \times 3; 2 \times 3^2$
19. $2 \times 2 \times 7 \times 19;$ $2^2 \times 7 \times 19$

Use division or a factor tree to find the prime factorization.

11. 128	12. 50	13. 76	14. 108
	$2 \times 5 \times 5$	$2 \times 2 \times 19$	$2 \times 2 \times 3 \times 3 \times 3$

Write the prime factorization in exponent form.

15. 18	16. 302	17. 49	18. 217
	2×151	$7 \times 7; 7^2$	7×31
19. 532	20. 45	21. 746	22. 99
	$3 \times 3 \times 5; 3^2 \times 5$	2×373	$3 \times 3 \times 11;$ $3^2 \times 11$

Solve for *n* to complete the prime factorization.

23. $2 \times n \times 5 = 20$	24. $44 = 2^2 \times n$	25. $75 = 3 \times 5 \times n$
$n = 2$	$n = 11$	$n = 5$

Problem Solving ▶ Applications

26. *REASONING* The prime factorization of 50 is 2×5^2. Without dividing or using a factor tree, tell the prime factorization of 100. **Possible answer: $2^2 \times 5^2$**

$c = 2$ or 3   27. *REASONING* A number, *c*, is a prime factor of both 12 and 60. What is *c*?

16 and 24   28. Chris bathed his pet every eighth day in June, beginning on June 8. On what other dates did he bathe his pet in June?

No, the order of factors does not affect the value of their product.   29. ✏️ **Write About It** Do the prime factors of a number differ depending on which factors you choose first? Explain.

MIXED REVIEW AND TEST PREP

30. Is 3,543 divisible by 2, 3, or 9? (p. 146) **3**

31. Write the percent for 0.6. (p. 60) **60%**

32. $18.3 + 22.6 + 17.03 + 21.99$ (p. 66) **79.92**

33. Find the median for the data 13, 8, 9, 16, 18. (p. 106) **13**

34. **TEST PREP** A sign is placed in a toy store, asking shoppers to complete a survey about their favorite video game. Which type of sampling is this? (p. 94) **A**
   A convenience   C systematic
   B random   D compatible

Extra Practice page H38, Set B

149

---

3 Practice

Guided Practice

Do Check for Understanding Exercises 1–10 with your students. Identify those having difficulty and use lesson resources to help.

//// COMMON ERROR ALERT \\\\

Simple mistakes can be avoided if students check their work. Remind students that if they multiply the prime factors, the product will be the original number.

Independent Practice

Assign Exercises 11–29.

Algebraic Thinking Writing the factorization in exponent form will help students gain facility working with exponents.

MIXED REVIEW AND TEST PREP

Exercises 30–34 provide **cumulative review** (Chapters 1–7).

4 Assess

Summarize the lesson by having students:

DISCUSS Is $3^2 \times 5 \times 7$ the prime factorization for 305? **Explain.** No; all the factors are prime, but their product is 315, not 305.

✏️ **WRITE** To find the prime factorization of a number, do you prefer the method shown in Example 1 or the method shown in Example 2? Why? Possible answer: Example 2; drawing a diagram helps me understand the problem.

Lesson Quiz

Transparency
7.2

Write the prime factorization in exponent form.

1. 36 $2^2 \times 3^2$ 2. 54 2×3^3
3. 120 $2^3 \times 3 \times 5$ 4. 63 $3^2 \times 7$

Solve for *y*.

5. $90 = 2 \times 3^2 \times y$ $y = 5$
6. $84 = 2^2 \times y \times 7$ $y = 3$

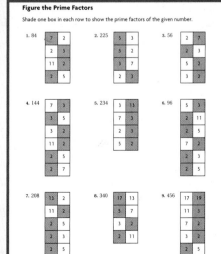

PROBLEM SOLVING 7.2

Prime Factorization
Write the correct answer.

1. Write the prime factorization of 42.

   $2 \times 3 \times 7$

3. The prime factors of a number are greater than 6 and less than 12. The smallest prime factor is used twice; the other(s), only once. What are the factors? What is the number?

   $7^2 \times 11; 539$

2. List the factors of 30.

   1, 2, 3, 5, 6, 10, 15, 30

4. Roger agreed to watch his younger siblings on August 7th and every seventh day after that. How many days will Roger watch his younger siblings in August?

   4 days

Choose the letter for the best answer.

5. What is the prime factorization of 18 in exponent form?
   A $2^2 \times 3^2$
   B 2×9
   C 3×6
   D 2×3^2

7. Lucille is having a party. She invited 8 friends and wants to have between 4 and 8 balloons for herself and each friend. What is a reasonable number of balloons to buy for the party?
   A 27 balloons
   B 32 balloons
   C 45 balloons
   D 81 balloons

9. **Write About It** Explain how you can tell which prime factorization is for the greater number.
   $2^3 \times 3^2$ $2^2 \times 3^3$

6. Which number is composite?
   F 13
   G 21
   H 23
   J 29

8. In her last 4 basketball games, Tara scored 26, 18, 34, and 27 points. Which is the best estimate of Tara's total points scored for the 4 games?
   F Less than 100
   G Between 100 and 120
   H Between 120 and 140
   J Between 140 and 160

$2^2 \times 3^3 > 2^3 \times 3^2$. Both numbers have five factors. Four of the factors
(2, 2, 3, 3) are the same. In the greater number the fifth factor is 3.
In the lesser number the fifth factor is 2.

CHALLENGE 7.2

Figure the Prime Factors
Shade one box in each row to show the prime factors of the given number.

149

Least Common Multiple and Greatest Common Factor

LESSON PLANNING

Objective To find the least common multiple and greatest common factor of numbers and use them to solve problems

Intervention for Prerequisite Skills

Multiples, Factors (For intervention strategies, see page 145.)

 California Mathematics Content Standards

➤ NS 2.4 Determine the least common multiple and the greatest common divisor of whole numbers; use them to solve problems with fractions.

(*Also* MR 3.2, MR 3.3)

Vocabulary

least common multiple (LCM) the smallest of common multiples

greatest common factor (GCF) the largest of common factors

Math Background

Prime factorization can be used to find both the least common multiple and the greatest common factor of two or more numbers.

- One way to find a common multiple of two or more numbers is to find their product. The multiple will not necessarily be the LCM. The LCM will contain enough factors so that all the factors of each number are present.

- Some numbers have only one common factor, 1. Others have several. The GCF is the largest of these common factors. One way to find the GCF is to list all the factors of each of the numbers.

In each case, prime factorization provides the most straightforward way to solve LCM and GCF problems.

WARM-UP RESOURCES

NUMBER OF THE DAY

Transparency **7.3**

The day of the month is today's number. Find the sum of the first five multiples of the day of the month. Possible answers: 6th: 6 + 12 + 18 + 24 + 30 = 90; 30th: 30 + 60 + 90 + 120 + 150 = 450

PROBLEM OF THE DAY

Transparency **7.3**

Find the least values for n and m such that the value of the first expression is twice that of the second. HINT: n and m are both less than 6.

$114 \times n$ and $95 \times m$
$n = 5$ and $m = 3$

Solution Problem of the Day tab, p. PD7

DAILY FACTS PRACTICE

Have students practice division facts by completing Set B of *Teacher's Resource Book*, p. TR98.

INTERVENTION AND EXTENSION RESOURCES

ALTERNATIVE TEACHING STRATEGY (ELL)

Ask students to **find the GCF and LCM by using prime factorization.** Have them find the prime factors of 45 and 75.

$$45 = 3 \times 3 \times 5 \qquad 75 = 3 \times 5 \times 5$$

Have them identify factors that are shared by the two numbers and underline them.

$$45 = 3 \times \underline{3 \times 5} \qquad 75 = \underline{3 \times 5} \times 5$$

Explain that 3×5, or 15, is the GCF, or greatest common factor, for 45 and 75.

Have students write the prime factorization for the LCM of 45 and 75 by writing all the factors that are common and all the factors that are not common.

$$3 \times \underline{3 \times 5} \times 5 = 225$$

So, the LCM of 45 and 75 is 225.

See also page 152.

VISUAL

MIXED REVIEW AND TEST PREP

Cumulative Review Chapters 1–7

Refer to the Pupil Edition pages referenced in the exercises for further review. Have students go to the lesson page, review the lesson, and correct any problem they missed.

Mixed Review and Test Prep, p. 153

How to Help	
Item	Page
44	148
45	28
46	40
47	40
48	60

MATH CONNECTION

Materials reference books

Introduce students to Euclid's ideas about geometry and **ways to find the greatest common factor** by sharing the following:

A famous math book titled *Elements* is more than 2,300 years old. It was written in about 300 B.C. by a Greek mathematician called Euclid. He wrote about geometry and different ways to find the greatest common factor.

Have students find out more about Euclid and his book and share with the class what they learn. Check students' work. The Euclidean algorithm is explained in the Alternative Teaching Strategy, page 152.

VISUAL

EARLY FINISHERS

Materials *For each pair* two number cubes labeled 1 to 6

Have students **practice finding the least common multiple.** Give each pair two number cubes. Have them play the following game.

- Roll the number cubes.
- Find and record the LCM of the numbers rolled.
- After five turns each, the winner is the player with the greater number of least common multiples that are 10 or less.

Check students' work.

KINESTHETIC

TECHNOLOGY LINK

Intervention Strategies
and Activities CD-ROM •
Skills 15, 16

Objective To find the least common multiple and greatest common factor of numbers and use them to solve problems

Vocabulary least common multiple (LCM), greatest common factor (GCF)

1 Introduce

QUICK REVIEW provides review of pre-requisite skills.

Why Learn This? You can use these skills to add, subtract, multiply, and divide fractions and to write them in simplest form. *Share the lesson objective with students.*

2 Teach

Guided Instruction

- As students look at Examples 1 and 2, help them think about the difference between a common multiple and the least common multiple. Ask:

In the opening problem about Kirk and Amber, the least common multiple is the same as the product of the two numbers. Would that method work for Examples 1 and 2? Explain. No; the resulting multiple would be much greater than the least common multiple.

Why can you find the least common multiple in the opening problem by multiplying the two numbers? 3 and 4 don't have any common factors.

ADDITIONAL EXAMPLE

Example 1, p. 150

Evelyn is making pumpkin pies for the school bake sale. Pie crusts are sold in packages of three. Pie filling is sold in 4-can packages. What is the least number of pie crusts and cans of pie filling Evelyn can buy to have the same number of each? 12 pie crusts and 12 cans of pie filling How many packages of each should she buy? 4 of pie crusts and 3 of filling

See also page 151.

150   Chapter 7

LESSON 7.3

Least Common Multiple and Greatest Common Factor

Learn how to find the LCM and GCF of numbers and use them to solve problems.

1. 4, 8, 12, 16, 20
2. 2, 4, 6, 8, 10
3. 3, 6, 9, 12, 15
4. 9, 18, 27, 36, 45
5. 6, 12, 18, 24, 30

List the first five multiples of each number. See left.
1. 4   2. 2   3. 3
4. 9   5. 6

Vocabulary

least common multiple (LCM)

greatest common factor (GCF)

Kirk and Amber volunteer during December. Kirk volunteers every fourth day beginning December 4. Amber volunteers every third day beginning December 3. Find the first day they will volunteer together by listing the multiples of 4 and 3.

multiples of 4:   4, 8, 12, 16, 20, 24, 28

multiples of 3:   3, 6, 9, 12, 15, 18, 21, 24, 27, 30

The multiples that appear in blue are called common multiples. The smallest of the common multiples is called the **least common multiple**, or **LCM**. The LCM of 4 and 3 is 12, the product of the two numbers. So, the first day they volunteer together is December 12.

Examples 1 and 2 show two ways to find the LCM.

EXAMPLE 1

Find the LCM of 12 and 8.

12: 12, 24, 36, 48, 60, 72, 84, 96   *List the first eight multiples.*
 8: 8, 16, 24, 32, 40, 48, 56, 64   *Find the common multiples.*

So, the LCM of 12 and 8 is 24.   *Find the LCM.*

EXAMPLE 2

Find the LCM of 6, 9, and 18.

Write the prime factorizations.
$6 = 2 \times 3$ $9 = 3 \times 3 = 3^2$ $18 = 2 \times 3 \times 3 = 2 \times 3^2$

Write a product using each prime factor only once.
2×3

For each factor, write the greatest exponent used with that factor in any of the prime factorizations. Multiply.
$2 \times 3^2 = 18$

So, the LCM of 6, 9, and 18 is 18.

150

CALIFORNIA STANDARDS O—n NS 2.4 Determine the least common multiple and the greatest common divisor of whole numbers; use them to solve problems with fractions. *also* MR 3.2, MR 3.3

RETEACH 7.3

Least Common Multiple and Greatest Common Factor

The greatest common factor, or GCF, of two numbers is the largest common factor of both numbers. You can use prime factors to find the GCF of two numbers.

What is the GCF of 28 and 36?

Step 1 Use factor trees to find the prime factors of the numbers.
$28 = 2 \times 2 \times 7$
$36 = 2 \times 2 \times 3 \times 3$

Step 2 Find the prime factors that are in both trees.   2 and 2

Step 3 Multiply the common factors. $2 \times 2 = 4$

Using this method, you discover that the GCF of 28 and 36 is 4.

To find the least common multiple, or LCM, of two numbers, you can list the multiples of each number. The smallest number in both lists is the LCM.

To find the LCM for 8 and 12:
8 → 8, 16, 24, 32, . . .
12 → 12, 24, 36, 48, . . .
The LCM for 8 and 12 is 24.

Complete to find the GCF of 12 and 72. Factor trees may vary.
1. Use factor trees to find the prime factors of the numbers.
2. Find the common prime factors. **2, 2, and 3**
3. Multiply the common factors. **2 × 2 × 3 = 12**
4. The GCF of 12 and 72 is **12**

Find the GCF of each pair of numbers.
5. 6 and 15 **3**   6. 18 and 81 **9**   7. 24 and 84 **12**

Find the LCM of each pair of numbers.
8. 9 and 12 **36**   9. 20 and 15 **60**   10. 18 and 24 **72**

PRACTICE 7.3

Least Common Multiple and Greatest Common Factor

Vocabulary

Complete.
1. The smallest of the common multiples is called the
   least common multiple, or LCM
2. The largest of the common factors is called the
   greatest common factor, or GCF

List the first five multiples of each number.
3. 9   4. 14   5. 22
   9, 18, 27, 36, 45   **14, 28, 42, 56, 70**   **22, 44, 66, 88, 110**

Find the LCM of each set of numbers.
6. 12, 18   7. 7, 14   8. 16, 20   9. 4, 5, 6   10. 2, 6, 7
   36   **14**   **80**   **60**   **42**

Find the GCF of each set of numbers.
11. 15, 45   12. 6, 14   13. 24, 40   14. 8, 12, 52   15. 16, 24, 32
    15   **2**   **8**   **4**   **8**

Find a pair of numbers for each set of conditions.
16. The LCM is 35.   17. The LCM is 36.   18. The LCM is 120.
    The GCF is 7.   The GCF is 1.   The GCF is 10.
    7 and 35   **4 and 9**   **30 and 40**

Mixed Review
Determine whether each number is divisible by 2, 3, 4, 5, 6, 8, 9, or 10.
19. 72 **2, 3, 4, 6, 8, 9**   20. 80 **2, 4, 5, 8, 10**
21. 324 **2, 3, 4, 6, 9**   22. 1,500 **2, 3, 4, 5, 6, 10**

Solve for n to complete the prime factorization.
23. $2 \times n \times 7 = 42$ **$n = 3$**   24. $3^2 \times n = 63$ **$n = 7$**   25. $5 \times 7 \times n = 385$ **$n = 11$**

Find the quotient.
26. $24.14 \div 7.1$ **3.4**   27. $17.29 \div 3.8$ **4.55**   28. $65.024 \div 6.35$ **10.24**

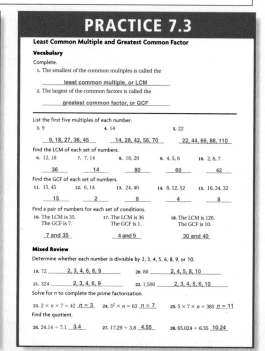

Greatest Common Factor

Factors shared by two or more numbers are called common factors. The largest of the common factors is called the **greatest common factor**, or **GCF**.

To find the GCF of two or more numbers, list all the factors of each number, find the common factors, and then find the greatest common factor.

45: 1, 3, 5, 9, 15, 45   *The common factors are 1, 3, and 9.*

27: 1, 3, 9, 27   *The GCF of 45 and 27 is 9.*

The GCF can be used to solve problems.

EXAMPLE 3

Carlyn has 12 pens and 36 pencils. She is making packages with the same number of each item. What is the greatest number of packages she can make without any items left over? How many of each item will be in each package?

You can find the greatest number of packages by finding the GCF of 12 and 36.

12: 1, 2, 3, 4, 6, 12   *List the factors.*
36: 1, 2, 3, 4, 6, 9, 12, 18, 36   *Find the common factors.*

The GCF of 12 and 36 is 12.   *Find the GCF.*

So, Carlyn can make 12 packages without any items left over.

To find the number of each item, divide the number of pens and the number of pencils by the number of packages.

Pens: $12 \div 12 = 1$ Pencils: $36 \div 12 = 3$

So, there will be 1 pen and 3 pencils in each package.

To find the GCF of two numbers, you can also use their prime factors. List the prime factors, find the common prime factors, and then find their product.

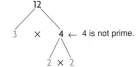
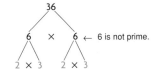

12   36

3    $\times$ 4 ← 4 is not prime.   6 $\times$ 6 ← 6 is not prime.

2 $\times$ 2   2 $\times$ 3   2 $\times$ 3

The prime factors of 12 are $2 \times 2 \times 3$.

The prime factors of 36 are $2 \times 2 \times 3 \times 3$.

The common prime factors are 2, 2, and 3.

Find the product of the common factors: $2 \times 2 \times 3$, or $2^2 \times 3 = 12$.

The GCF of 12 and 36 is 12.

151

LESSON 7.3

- *Using the prime factorization in Example 4, demonstrate the relationship between the product of two numbers and the product of their GCF and LCM.*

Compare the product of 48 and 72 to the product of their GCF and LCM.

GCF of 48 and 72 = 24

LCM of 48 and 72: $2 \times 2 \times 2 \times 2 \times 3 \times 3$

$2^4 \times 3^2 = 16 \times 9 = 144$

$48 \times 72 = 3,456 \quad 24 \times 144 = 3,456$

The product of two numbers and the product of their GCF and LCM are equal.

ADDITIONAL EXAMPLE

Example 4, p. 152

Use prime factors to find the GCF of 30 and 12.

$30 = 2 \times 3 \times 5$

$12 = 2 \times 2 \times 3$

The prime factors are 2, 3, and 5. The common prime factors are 2 and 3. $2 \times 3 = 6$.

So, the GCF of 30 and 12 is 6.

3 | Practice

Guided Practice

Do Check for Understanding Exercises 1–14 with your students. Identify those having difficulty and use lesson resources to help.

Independent Practice

Assign Exercises 15–43.

EXAMPLE 4

Use prime factors to find the GCF of 48 and 72.

48: $2 \times 2 \times 2 \times 2 \times 3$ *Find the prime factors.*
72: $2 \times 2 \times 2 \times 3 \times 3$

2, 2, 2, and 3   *Find the common prime factors.*

$2 \times 2 \times 2 \times 3 = 24$ *Multiply the common factors.*

So, the GCF of 48 and 72 is 24.

CHECK FOR UNDERSTANDING

Think and ▶ Discuss

Look back at the lesson to answer each question.

1. Possible answer: A number has a limited number of factors, but its multiples are unlimited.

  1. **Explain** why you are able to find a greatest common factor but not a greatest common multiple of 2 or more numbers.

  2. **Tell** the number of pens and pencils there would be in each package in Example 3 if Carlyn made 6 packages.
       2 pens and 6 pencils

Guided ▶ Practice

List the first five multiples of each number.

3. 3   **4.** 7   **5.** 11   **6.** 15
3, 6, 9, 12, 15   7, 14, 21, 28, 35   11, 22, 33, 44, 55   15, 30, 45, 60, 75

Find the LCM of each set of numbers.

7. 3, 7   **8.** 2, 3   **9.** 6, 9   **10.** 5, 8, 20
21   6   18   40

Find the GCF of each set of numbers.

11. 6, 9   **12.** 4, 20   **13.** 9, 24   **14.** 12, 16, 20
3   4   3   4

PRACTICE AND PROBLEM SOLVING

Independent ▶ Practice

List the first five multiples of each number.

15. 4   4, 8, 12, 16, 20   **16.** 8   8, 16, 24, 32, 40   **17.** 16   16, 32, 48, 64, 80   **18.** 55   55, 110, 165, 220, 275

19. 10   10, 20, 30, 40, 50   **20.** 27   27, 54, 81, 108, 135   **21.** 14   14, 28, 42, 56, 70   **22.** 39   39, 78, 117, 156, 195

Find the LCM of each set of numbers.

23. 3, 8, 24   24   **24.** 32, 128   128   **25.** 12, 20   60   **26.** 40, 105   840

27. 24, 30   120   **28.** 18, 21, 36   252   **29.** 12, 27   108   **30.** 48, 116   1,392

Find the GCF of each set of numbers.

31. 16, 18   **2**   **32.** 15, 18   **3**   **33.** 21, 306   **3**   **34.** 16, 24, 40   **8**

35. 25, 33   **1**   **36.** 200, 215   **5**   **37.** 24, 32, 40   **8**   **38.** 630, 712   **2**

Find a pair of numbers for each set of conditions.

39. The LCM is 36. The GCF is 3. **9 and 12**

40. The LCM is 24. The GCF is 2. **6 and 8**

Alternative Teaching Strategy

Purpose Students use the Euclidean algorithm as an alternate method for finding GCF for greater numbers.

Explain to students that some numbers are too large to use methods such as listing all factors or prime factors in order to find their GCF. Tell them there is another method they can use to find the GCF of greater whole numbers.

Display the following numbers and rules:

791 and 2,034

1. Divide the larger number by the smaller number.

2. If the remainder is not 0, divide the divisor by the remainder.

3. Continue dividing the divisor by the remainder until the remainder is 0.

4. The final divisor is the GCF.

Demonstrate this method of finding the GCF.

$$
\begin{array}{llll}
2 & 1 & 1 & 3 \\
791\overline{)2034} & 452\overline{)791} & 339\overline{)452} & 113\overline{)339} \\
\underline{1582} & \underline{452} & \underline{339} & \underline{339} \\
452 & 339 & 113 & 0
\end{array}
$$

The final divisor is 113, so the GCF for 791 and 2,034 is 113.

Have students work in pairs to use the Euclidean algorithm to find the GCF of 388 and 1,067.

When finished, have a volunteer show his or her solution:

$$
\begin{array}{lll}
2 & 1 & 3 \\
388\overline{)1067} & 291\overline{)388} & 97\overline{)291} \\
\underline{776} & \underline{291} & \underline{291} \\
291 & 97 & 0
\end{array}
$$

The final divisor is 97, so the GCF for 388 and 1,067 is 97.

41. Peter will distribute cereal samples with pamphlets about good nutrition. The samples come in packages of 15. The pamphlets come in packages of 20.

  a. What is the least number of cereal samples and pamphlets needed to have equal amounts? **60**

  b. How many packages of each does he need? **4 packages of cereal samples, 3 packages of pamphlets**

42. Ruth has 36 markers and 48 erasers. She will put them in bags with the same number of each item. What is the greatest number of bags she can make? **12 bags**

43. (?) **What's the Error?** Jan says the LCM of 10 and 15 is 5. Find her error and the correct answer.
She found the GCF instead of LCM. The LCM is 30.

MIXED REVIEW AND TEST PREP

44. Write the prime factorization for 45 in exponent form. (p. 148) 5×3^2

45. Evaluate $a \div c$, for $a = 4,602$ and $c = 37$. (p. 28) **124 r14**

46. Find the value of 5^4. (p. 40) **625**

47. TEST PREP Which is the exponential notation for
$3 \times 3 \times 3 \times 4 \times 4 \times 5 \times 5$? (p. 40) **C**

  A $3 \times 4 \times 5^7$ **B** $3^3 \times 2^4 \times 2^5$ **C** $3^3 \times 4^2 \times 5^2$ **D** $3^3 \times 4^4 \times 5^5$

48. TEST PREP Which shows the decimal for 46%? (p. 60) **G**

  F 0.046   **G** 0.46   **H** 4.6   **J** 46

LiNKUP to Careers

NASA Scientist When astronauts service and repair the Hubble Space Telescope, NASA scientists must set the orbit of the space shuttle so it will meet the Hubble Space Telescope in its orbit. The Hubble Space Telescope takes about 95 minutes to make one orbit around Earth. The space shuttle takes about 90 minutes to go around Earth.

One way to find when the two objects will meet is to find the LCM of the orbit times.

90: 90, 180, 270, 360, 450, 540, … 1,350; 1,440; 1,530; 1,620; 1,710

95: 95, 190, 285, 380, 475, 570, … 1,330; 1,425; 1,520; 1,615; 1,710

So, the space shuttle will meet the Hubble Space Telescope about every 1,710 minutes, or $28\frac{1}{2}$ hours.

• The Russian Mir space station orbits Earth about every 93 minutes. How often would Mir and the space shuttle meet? **about every 2,790 min, or $46\frac{1}{2}$ hrs**

Extra Practice page H38, Set C

153

READING STRATEGY

K-W-L Chart Before having students read the Link Up, have them look at the title and scan the text for proper nouns. Ask them to predict what the Link Up will be about. Then have students make a three-column chart headed What I Know, What I Want to Know, and What I Learned. Ask them to fill in the first two columns. Have them fill in the third column as they read the paragraph.

K-W-L Chart

What I Know	What I Want to Know	What I Learned

ENG-LANG ARTS Standards R 2.4

MIXED REVIEW AND TEST PREP
Exercises 44–48 provide **cumulative review** (Chapters 1–7).

LiNKUP to CAREERS

• *Have students read the Link Up. Encourage students to share what they know about NASA history.*

REASONING The Hubble Telescope passes overhead at noon. After 8:00 P.M., when will it pass overhead again? **9:30 P.M.**

4 Assess

Summarize the lesson by having students:

DISCUSS David is serving treats at his sister's birthday party. He has 14 cookies and 35 sticks of gum. Does he have enough to give the same number of each type of treat to each of 7 guests? Explain. Yes; the GCF of 14 and 35 is 7. Each guest will get 2 cookies and 5 sticks of gum.

WRITE Explain the difference between the LCM and the GCF. The LCM is the least number that is a multiple of two or more numbers. The GCF is the greatest number that is a factor of two or more numbers.

Lesson Quiz

Transparency **7.3**

Find the LCM of each set of numbers.

1. 12, 16 48   **2.** 12, 20 60

3. 4, 12 12   **4.** 10, 12 60

Find the GCF of each set of numbers.

5. 18, 30 6   **6.** 8, 24 8

7. 4, 26 2   **8.** 20, 50 10

Problem Solving Strategy: Make an Organized List

LESSON PLANNING

Objective To solve problems by using the strategy *make an organized list*

Intervention for Prerequisite Skills

Multiples (For intervention strategies, see page 145.)

Lesson Resources Problem Solving Think Along, p. TR1

California Mathematics Content Standards

⊶ NS 2.4 Determine the least common multiple and the greatest common divisor of whole numbers; use them to solve problems with fractions.

MR 3.2 Note the method of deriving the solution and demonstrate a conceptual understanding of the derivation by solving similar problems.

(*Also* MR 2.0)

Math Background

The strategy *make an organized list* is useful when there are several possibilities that can occur in a problem. These ideas may help students to use this strategy:

- Combine this strategy with that of *make a table* to keep track of all possibilities.
- Organize information in a list to avoid omitting possibilities.

WARM-UP RESOURCES

NUMBER OF THE DAY

Transparency 7.4

Today's number is the current time. Write the digits of the time in order. Then find the prime factorization of the number. Possible answer for 11:12 A.M.: 1,112 = 2 × 2 × 2 × 139

PROBLEM OF THE DAY

Transparency 7.4

Jon is making birdhouses. He is cutting 1-in. by 6-in. boards into pieces that are 11 in. long to make the sides of the birdhouses. Which board length would produce the least waste—4 ft, 6 ft, 8 ft, or 10 ft? Explain. 4 ft; possible multiples of 11 are 44, 55, 66, 77, 88, 99, and 110; board lengths are 48 in., 72 in., 96 in., and 120 in.; subtract multiples of 11 from next largest board length to find waste; 48 − 44 = 4; 72 − 66 = 6; 96 − 88 = 8; 120 − 110 = 10.

Solution Problem of the Day tab, p. PD7

DAILY FACTS PRACTICE

Have students practice multiplication facts by completing Set C of *Teacher's Resource Book*, p. TR98.

ALTERNATIVE TEACHING STRATEGY (ELL)

Materials 2 different colors of chalk

Students can **use a number line model to solve the problem** on page 154. Put a large number line on the classroom floor numbered from 0 to 70.

- Ask two volunteers to play the role of wheels with 4-ft and 18-ft circumferences. Give each volunteer a piece of colored chalk.

- Have students call out multiples of four as the person representing the 4-ft wheel marks them on one side of the number line. Repeat the process as the 18-ft wheel volunteer marks multiples of 18 on the opposite side of the number line. Ask:

How many turns each did it take for the wheels to line up again? 9 for the 4-ft wheel; 2 for the 18-ft wheel

How is this way of solving the problem like making an organized list? The number line is like a table or list. The multiples of 4 and 18 are recorded, in order, on the two sides of the number line.

KINESTHETIC

READING STRATEGY

Synthesize Information Have the students use the reading strategy *synthesize information* to bring together the parts of the problem on page 154. They should recognize that they need to know that if the circumference of the smaller wheel is 4 ft, it will travel 4 ft with each revolution. Ask:

What do the multiples of 4 and 18 represent in this problem? the distance each wheel has rolled after 1 turn, 2 turns, and so on

SPECIAL NEEDS

Materials *For each pair* 1 cardboard circle with diameter $3\frac{3}{16}$ in., 1 cardboard circle with diameter $3\frac{13}{16}$ in., 10 ft of butcher paper

Direct students to **build models of wheels to solve a problem.** Ask students to label the smaller cardboard circle with a circumference of 10 and the larger circle with a circumference of 12. Then, ask them to mark a small line at the edge of each circle and a starting line on the butcher paper.

- Have volunteers roll the circles along the sides of the paper starting with the mark on each circle touching the starting line. As one volunteer rolls a circle, another marks each spot where the mark on the circle touches the paper.

- After students have rolled each circle several times and marked the paper, ask:

What does each mark represent for the smaller circle? for the larger circle? 10, 20, 30, and so on; 12, 24, 36, and so on

- Direct students to use their drawings to find the LCM of 10 and 12. 60

KINESTHETIC

CAREER CONNECTION

Students can **apply problem solving skills to a career.** Share the following:

- A track and field coach trains athletes for various track and field events. Track events involve running—for example, sprints and relays. Field events involve jumping and throwing—for example, high jump and shot put.

- Marie trains runners for a competition. She wants both runners to run the same distance each day. One runner trains on a 400 yd track, and the other trains on a 300 yd one. What is the least number of laps each should run so that they run the same distance? first runner: 3 laps; second runner: 4 laps

VISUAL

TECHNOLOGY LINK

- **Intervention Strategies and Activities CD-ROM** • *Skill 15*

- **The Harcourt Learning Site**

Objective To solve problems by using the strategy *make an organized list*

Lesson Resources Problem Solving Think Along, p. TR1

1 Introduce

QUICK REVIEW provides review of pre-requisite skills.

Why Learn This? Making organized lists is helpful when you need to sort, rename, and rearrange files or folders on a computer. *Share the lesson objective with students.*

2 Teach

Guided Instruction

• *As you discuss the Boneshaker problem with the class, ask:*

REASONING Do you think your feet would go around more often if the larger wheel were in the front or if the smaller wheel were in front? Possible answer: more times with the smaller wheel in the front because it has to go around more times to cover the same distance as the larger wheel.

• *Discuss the remaining steps in the solution.*

What two things do 4, 8, . . . represent? multiples of 4 and the number of feet the small wheel has rolled as it completes a revolution

• *After students read the What If question, ask:*

What multiples will you use to solve the What if question? 8, 16, 24, 32, 40, . . . ; 18, 36, 54, . . .

Modifying Instruction Once students realize this type of problem calls for the LCM, they may choose to solve by using prime factorization instead of the organized list strategy.

PROBLEM SOLVING STRATEGY
Make an Organized List

Analyze
Choose
Solve
Check

*L**earn** how to solve problems by making an organized list.*

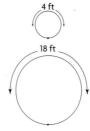
4 ft

18 ft

QUICK REVIEW

List the first four multiples of each number.

1. 3   **2.** 5   **3.** 9
3, 6, 9, 12   5, 10, 15, 20   9, 18, 27, 36
4. 11   **5.** 20
11, 22, 33, 44 20, 40, 60, 80

Like many early bicycles, the Boneshaker had different sized wheels. Suppose the circumferences of the wheels were 4 ft and 18 ft. How many revolutions would each wheel make before marks on their rims would both be in the same positions again?

The Boneshaker was invented in 1865. The wooden wheels made for an uncomfortable ride.

Analyze What are you asked to find? The number of revolutions each wheel will make before the marks would both be in the same positions again.

What facts are given? The distance around each wheel.

Choose What strategy will you use?

You can use the strategy *make an organized list*. List the total distance traveled by each wheel for every complete turn.

Solve How will you solve the problem?

Make a list of multiples of 4 and 18.
 multiples of 4: 4, 8, 12, 16, 20, 24, 28, 32, 36, 40
 multiples of 18: 18, 36, 54

The least common multiple is 36. When the wheels have traveled 36 ft, the marks will both be in the same positions again.

36 is the ninth multiple of 4, so the small wheel makes 9 revolutions.

36 is the second multiple of 18, so the large wheel makes 2 revolutions.

Check How can you check your answer? Possible answer: draw a diagram

What if the smaller wheel had a circumference of 8 ft? How many revolutions would each wheel make before the marks were both in the same positions again? smaller, 9 revolutions; larger, 4 revolutions

  CALIFORNIA STANDARDS O¬NS 2.4 Determine the least common multiple and the greatest common divisor of whole numbers; use them to solve problems with fractions. **MR 3.2** Note the method of deriving the solution and demonstrate a conceptual understanding of the derivation by solving similar problems. *also* **MR 2.0**

RETEACH 7.4

Problem Solving Strategy: Make an Organized List

Organizing data into a list is one way of making sure that you have considered every possibility for a given situation.

Two trains that ran in Great Britain in the 1930s were the Night Scotsman and the Bournemouth Belle. They both ran between London and other cities. The Night Scotsman left London every 4 days and the Bournemouth Belle left every 6 days. If they both left London on Thursday, March 1, on which other dates in March did they leave London on the same day?

Step 1 Think about what you know and what you are asked to find.
 • You know how often each train left from London:
  The Night Scotsman left London every 4 days.
  The Bournemouth Belle left every 6 days.
  You know that they both left London on Thursday, March 1.
 • You are asked to find the other dates in March on which both trains left London on the same day.

Step 2 Plan a strategy to solve.
 • Use the strategy *make an organized list.*
 • Make a list of the multiples of 4 and the multiples of 6.
 • Use the common multiples to determine the other dates in March on which both trains left London on the same day.

Step 3 Solve.
 • Carry out the strategy. Make lists of the multiples.
  multiples of 4: 4, 8, **12**, 16, 20, **24**, 28, 32, ...
  multiples of 6: 6, **12**, 18, **24**, 30, 36, 42, ...
 The common multiples of 4 and 6 that are less than 31 (the number of days in March) are 12 and 24.

So, the trains both left London together 12 days after March 1 and again 24 days after March 1. So, the dates they left on the same day were:
  1 + 12, or March 13   and   1 + 24, or March 25.

Solve the problem by making an *organized list.*

1. A bus company has routes between Chicago and several other cities. Every 5 hours a bus leaves from Chicago for Detroit and every 3 hours another bus leaves for Cleveland. If buses leave for both cities at 6:00 A.M., when is the next time two buses will leave together for these two cities?

   9:00 P.M. that same day

2. Some buses have seats for 40 people. Other buses can seat only 36. One of each type of bus is filled with families. There are no empty seats and all the families are the same size. What is the greatest number of members that each family can possibly have?

   4 members

PRACTICE 7.4

Problem Solving Strategy: Make an Organized List

Solve the problem by making an organized list.

1. Jack and Ashley begin jogging around a quarter-mile track at the same time. Ashley takes 2 minutes to complete each lap and Jack takes 3 minutes. How many laps will each have run the first time they are side-by-side again at the point where they began?

   Ashley: 3 laps; Jack: 2 laps

2. Terrence is taking two medications for his flu. He begins taking them both at 10:00 P.M. on Tuesday. If he takes one every 8 hours and the other every 10 hours, on what day and at what time will he take the two medications together again?

   2:00 P.M. on Thursday

3. A large high school has a marching band with 64 woodwind players and 72 brass players. All members of the band line up in rows of equal size. Only musicians playing the same instruments are in each row. What is the greatest number of musicians who can be in one row?

   8 musicians

4. Brice plays in a basketball league. In his last game, he scored more than 20 but fewer than 30 points by making a combination of 2- and 3-point shots. If he made 5 more 2-point shots than 3-point shots, how many of each type did he make?

   8 2-point shots, 3 3-point shots

5. Aki is buying franks and buns for a field trip. She sees franks in packages of 6 and buns in packages of 8. There are 70 people going on the trip. What is the least number of each she can buy so there are franks and buns for everyone, with no extra packages?

   9 packages of buns,
   12 packages of franks

6. Kiona has 235 CDs. She is buying CD holders for her collection. The two types that she likes hold 20 CDs and 12 CDs each. She wants to buy the same number of each type. What is the least number of each type of CD holder that Kiona will have to buy to hold her entire CD collection?

   8 of each type

Mixed Review

Estimate the sum or difference. Possible estimates are given.

7. 80 + 31 + 87   8. 710 − 189   9. 1,208 + 877 + 439
      200   500   2,500

10. 7,151 − 2,993   11. 67 + 123 + 804   12. 920 − 592
      4,000   1,000   300

PROBLEM SOLVING PRACTICE

Solve the problem by making an organized list.

1. Justin and Amy help with the shopping for their individual families. Justin goes to the store every 3 days and Amy goes every 5 days. They see each other at the store on September 30. On what date will Justin and Amy see each other at the store again? **October 15**

For 2–3, use the information below.

Susanna buys one bag with 40 snacks and another with 32. She wants to make up small snack packs for a party. All snack packs must have the same number of each snack.

2. If you make lists to find the greatest number of snack packs Susanna can make, what will you include in the lists? **B**

   A addends   **B** factors   **C** multiples   **D** fractions

3. What is the greatest number of snack packs Susanna can make? **H**

   F 2 packs   **G** 4 packs   **H** 8 packs   **J** 15 packs

PROBLEM SOLVING STRATEGIES

Draw a Diagram or Picture
Make a Model
Predict and Test
Work Backward
▶ Make an Organized List
Find a Pattern
Make a Table or Graph
Solve a Simpler Problem
Write an Equation
Use Logical Reasoning

MIXED STRATEGY PRACTICE

4. Ray begins an eight-week exercise program. He exercises 30 min during the first week, 45 min the second week, and 60 min the third week. If this pattern continues, how many hours and minutes will Ray exercise the sixth week? **1 hr 45 min**

5. DeAnn has a total of 74 in. of yarn to make gifts. She uses 13 in. of yarn for each of the 5 gifts she is making. Find how many inches of yarn DeAnn will have left after making the 5 gifts. **9 in.**

6. A total of 316 middle school teachers are going to a meeting. There are 30 more male teachers than female. How many teachers are male? **173 are male**

7. Christi rides her bicycle 7 blocks south, 3 blocks east, 5 blocks north, and 8 blocks west. How many blocks has she ridden when she crosses her own path? **18 blocks**

8. Use the graph at the right. Look at the area in square miles for each lake. How much larger is Lake Michigan than Lake Erie and Lake Ontario together? **4,920 sq mi**

9. **What's the Question?** Laura wants to buy the same number of plums and kiwis. Plums are sold in bags of 4 and kiwis are sold in bags of 7. The answer is 28 plums. **Possible question: What is the least number of plums Laura can buy?**

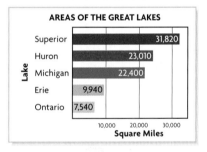

AREAS OF THE GREAT LAKES

Lake	Square Miles
Superior	31,820
Huron	23,010
Michigan	22,400
Erie	9,940
Ontario	7,540

Guided Practice

Do Problem Solving Practice Exercises 1–3 with your students. Identify those having difficulty and use lesson resources to help.

Independent Practice

Assign Exercises 4–9.

Before students begin the exercises, refer them to the list of strategies on the PE page that they might use to solve the problems.

4 Assess

Summarize the lesson by having students:

DISCUSS Describe how to find the first ten multiples of a number such as 18. Possible answer: Multiply 18 by 1, by 2, by 3, and so on.

WRITE Describe how to find the LCM of two numbers such as 8 and 14. Possible answer: First, list some multiples of 8. Then list some multiples of 14. Find the smallest number that appears on both lists.

Lesson Quiz

Transparency **7.4**

1. Karena shops for groceries every 6 days and for gas every 5 days. How many times a month does she shop for both on the same day? for 28- to 30-day months—0 times; for 31-day months—1 time

2. Tim is supposed to give an equal number of red cubes and blue cubes to students in his class. He has 28 red cubes and 35 blue cubes. What is the greatest number of students to whom he can give cubes? 7 students

---

READING STRATEGY 7.4

Synthesize Information

Analyze | Choose | Solve | Check

To **synthesize** means to form a whole by combining parts. You can combine new information to make something from the separate parts. One way to do this is to make an organized list. Read the following problem.

VOCABULARY
synthesize

Al, Jo-Jo, and Tom are standing on the first step of a staircase. There are 16 steps in all. Al goes up the staircase one step at a time. Jo-Jo skips one step each time. Tom skips two steps each time. On which steps will they all place a foot?

1. Make a list to show on which step each person steps.

   Al: 2, 3, 4, 5, 6, 7, 8, 9, 10, 11, 12, 13, 14, 15, 16

   Jo-Jo: 3, 5, 7, 9, 11, 13, 15

   Tom: 4, 7, 10, 13, 16

2. Synthesize the information by finding the number that appears in all three lists. Solve the problem.

   seventh and thirteenth steps

Synthesize the information by making an organized list. Solve

3. Al, Jo-Jo, and Tom are climbing the staircase, as described above. All boys start on their left foot. Which is the next step on which they will all place their left foot?

   thirteenth step

4. Al walks 1 mi in 14 min. Jo-Jo bikes 1 mi in 6 min. Tom runs 1 mi in 7 min. If they all start from the same place on a 1-mi track, how many miles will each boy have traveled when they are all on that spot again?

   Al: 3 mi; Jo-Jo: 7 mi; Tom: 6 mi

5. Al, Jo-Jo, and Tom are climbing the staircase. They all start on their left foot. Will all three boys ever step on the same stair with their right foot? Explain.

   No. They all step on the seventh stair, but only Jo-Jo steps with his right foot. They all step on the thirteenth stair, but with their left feet.

6. Jo-Jo jogs every fourth day of each month. Al jogs every sixth day of each month. On which days of each month can they jog together?

   the twelfth and the twenty-fourth

CHALLENGE 7.4

Organization is the Key!

Solve each problem by making an organized list of the data.

1. Ana and Juan are going shopping for gifts. They need to go to a toy store (T), a stationery store (S), and a jewelry store (J). Make a list of all the possible orders in which they can visit the stores. How many choices do they have for the order in which they visit the stores?

   S-T-J; S-J-T; J-S-T; J-T-S; T-J-S; T-S-J; 6 choices

2. Suppose Ana needs to stop at her bank before going to any stores. In how many different orders can they make their four stops?

   6 different orders

3. Assume it does not matter whether Ana goes to the bank before shopping or after shopping. In how many different orders can they then make their four stops?

   12 different orders

4. Juan and his three friends, Amy, Vijay, and Yoko, will each talk to one another on the phone today before agreeing where to meet after he finishes shopping. If each friend speaks to the others once, how many phone calls will there be in all? (Keep in mind that once Juan calls Amy, for example, there is no need for Amy to call Juan.)

   6 phone calls

5. When wrapping the three gifts that she has bought, Ana has a choice of three different wrapping papers to use: one with stripes, one with balloons, and one with elephants. She cannot decide whether to wrap all the gifts in the same paper or to use a different paper for each gift. In how many different ways can she wrap the three gifts? (Count each combination of wrapping papers only once.)

   10 ways

   SSS, SSB, SSE, BBB, BBS, BBE, EEE, EES, EEB, SEB

6. If Ana decides to use a different wrapping paper for each gift, in how many different ways can she wrap her three gifts?

   6 ways

CHAPTER 7

REVIEW/TEST

Purpose To check understanding of concepts, skills, and problem solving presented in Chapter 7

USING THE PAGE

The Chapter 7 Review/Test can be used as a **review** or a **test**.

- Items 1–3 check understanding of concepts and new vocabulary.
- Items 4–36 check skill proficiency.
- Items 37–40 check students' abilities to choose and apply problem solving strategies to real-life problems involving number theory.

 Suggest that students place the completed Chapter 7 Review/Test in their portfolios.

USING THE ASSESSMENT GUIDE

- Multiple-choice format of Chapter 7 Posttest—See *Assessment Guide*, pp. AG49–50.
- Free-response format of Chapter 7 Posttest—See *Assessment Guide*, pp. AG51–52.

USING STUDENT SELF-ASSESSMENT

The How Did I Do? survey helps students assess what they have learned and how they learned it. This survey is available as a copying master in *Assessment Guide*, p. AGxvii.

CHAPTER 7 REVIEW/TEST

1. **VOCABULARY** Writing a composite number as the product of prime factors is called __?__. (p. 148) **prime factorization**

2. **VOCABULARY** The largest of the common factors of two or more numbers is the __?__. (p. 150) **GCF**

3. **VOCABULARY** The smallest of the multiples of two or more numbers is the __?__. (p. 150) **LCM**

Tell whether each number is divisible by 2, 3, 4, 5, 6, 8, 9, or 10. (pp. 146–147)

4. 42 2, 3, 6   5. 64 2, 4, 8   6. 96 2, 3, 4, 6, 8   7. 225 3, 5, 9

8. 330 2, 3, 5, 6, 10   9. 963 3, 9   10. 450 2, 3, 5, 6, 9, 10   11. 2,385 3, 5, 9

Use division or a factor tree to find the prime factorization. Write the prime factorization in exponent form. (pp. 148–149)

12. 9 3^2 13. 8 2^3 14. 14 2×7 15. 18 2×3^2

16. 80 $2^4 \times 5$ 17. 12 $2^2 \times 3$ 18. 33 3×11 19. 50 2×5^2

20. 49 7^2 21. 98 2×7^2 22. 504 $2^3 \times 3^2 \times 7$ 23. 891 $3^4 \times 11$

24. List the first twenty multiples of 4 and the first twenty multiples of 10. What is the least common multiple? What multiples greater than 80 do they have in common? (pp. 150–153)
LCM: 20; all numbers that are multiples of 20

Find the LCM and the GCF of each set of numbers. (pp.150–153)

25. 3, 9 9; 3   26. 2, 6 6; 2   27. 6, 4 12; 2   28. 10, 15 30; 5

29. 8, 12 24; 4   30. 9, 27 27; 9   31. 15, 25 75; 5   32. 25, 115 575; 5

33. 27, 189 189, 27   34. 6, 8, 12 24; 2   35. 6, 9, 12 36; 3   36. 8, 16, 20 80; 4

Solve. (pp. 146–155)

37. A number is between 60 and 70. It is divisible by 3 and 9. What is the number? **63**

38. Meat patties are sold in packages of 12. Buns are sold in packages of 8. What is the least number of meat patties and buns needed to have an equal number of each? **24 patties and 24 buns**

39. Cashews are sold in 8-oz jars, almonds in 12-oz jars, and peanuts in 16-oz jars. What is the least number of ounces of each type of nuts you can buy to make mixed nuts with equal amounts of each? How many jars of each would you need? **48 oz; 6 jars of cashews, 4 jars of almonds, 3 jars of peanuts**

40. Alissa jogs in the park every 3 days. Erin jogs in the park once a week on Saturday. If they met in the park on Saturday, April 30, when will they meet in the park again? **Saturday, May 21**

CHAPTER 7 TEST, page 1

Choose the best answer.

For 1–2, choose the list that contains all the numbers from 2 to 10 by which the given number is divisible.

1. 24
- A 2
- B 2, 3, 4
- C 2, 3, 4, 6, 8
- D 2, 3, 4, 6, 8, 9

2. 245
- F 2
- G 5, 7
- H 3, 5
- J 3, 5, 9

3. Which number is divisible by both 5 and 9?
- A 550
- B 801
- C 2,345
- D 4,005

4. Which pair of numbers is divisible by both 6 and 9?
- F 136 and 594
- G 234 and 458
- H 270 and 369
- J 414 and 630

5. What are the first five multiples of 21?
- A 1, 3, 7, 21, 63
- B 3, 7, 21, 63, 147
- C 21, 42, 63, 84, 105
- D 21, 42, 84, 168, 336

6. What is the prime factorization of 594 in exponent form?
- F $2^3 \times 3^2 \times 11$
- G $3^3 \times 4 \times 11$
- H $2 \times 3^3 \times 11$
- J $2^2 \times 3^2 \times 11$

7. What is the prime factorization of 936 in exponent form?
- A $2^3 \times 3^2$
- B $2^3 \times 3^2 \times 13$
- C $2^3 \times 3 \times 13$
- D $8 \times 9 \times 13$

8. What is the prime factorization of 52?
- F $2^2 \times 13$
- G 4×13
- H 2×26
- J $2 \times 3 \times 7$

9. Which number is prime?
- A 37
- B 54
- C 75
- D 91

10. Find the GCF of 52 and 195.
- F 780
- G 26
- H 15
- J 13

11. Find the LCM of 70 and 105.
- A 35
- B 42
- C 210
- D 7,350

12. Emily is making treats that need 1 chocolate bar and 1 marshmallow each. Chocolate bars come in packages of 12. Marshmallows come in packages of 30. What is the least number of packages of each she will have to buy in order to have equal numbers of chocolate bars and marshmallows?
- F 2 chocolate, 5 marshmallow
- G 5 chocolate, 2 marshmallow
- H 30 chocolate, 10 marshmallow
- J 60 chocolate, 60 marshmallow

13. Find a pair of numbers whose LCM is 360 and whose GCF is 3.
- A 15 and 18
- B 18 and 24
- C 24 and 45
- D 45 and 1,280

14. What is the 25th number in the pattern?
137, 134, 131, 128, 125, …
- F 26
- G 62
- H 65
- J 74

Go On

CHAPTER 7 TEST, page 2

15. There are 12 cheerleaders and 45 band members. All of the cheerleaders and band members will work in groups at the car wash. Each group will have the same number of cheerleaders and the same number of band members. What is the greatest number of groups that can be formed?
- A 3
- B 5
- C 6
- D 12

16. Five weeks ago, Jules typed 8 words per min. During the next 4 weeks his speed increased to 12 words, 16 words, 20 words, and then 24 words per min. To get a job, Jules must type 60 words per min. If his improvement continues to follow this pattern, in how many more weeks will he reach 60 words per min?
- F 12 weeks
- G 9 weeks
- H 6 weeks
- J 3 weeks

17. If you fold a piece of paper in half once, there are 2 parts. Folding twice gives you 4 parts. Three folds gives you 8 parts, and so on. How many folds would be necessary to get 128 parts?
- A 4
- B 7
- C 24
- D 64

18. Find the LCM of 8, 12, and 18.
- F 1,728
- G 216
- H 96
- J 72

19. By which pair of numbers below is 16,728 divisible?
- A 2 and 9
- B 3 and 9
- C 3 and 8
- D 4 and 7

20. Joshua swims every 4 days and Katarina swims every 7 days. They both swam on July 4. How many more times will they swim on the same day by September 4?
- F 1
- G 2
- H 5
- J 10

21. Hot dogs are sold 12 in a package. Buns are sold 8 in a package. Ketchup packets come 100 in a box. What is the least number of each item you can buy and have the same number of hot dogs, buns, and ketchup packets?
- A 4
- B 600
- C 1,200
- D 9,600

22. Carbon-14 (C-14) has a half-life of about 6,000 yr. If you start with 6,400 g of C-14, there would be 3,200 g left after 6,000 yr, 1,600 g after 12,000 yr, and 800 g after 18,000 yr. How long would it be until only 100 g were left?
- F 17,984 yr
- G 24,000 yr
- H 30,000 yr
- J 36,000 yr

23. Find the GCF of 15, 18, and 54.
- A 2
- B 3
- C 5
- D 270

24. The prime factorization of 378 is $2 \times 3^n \times 7$. What is the value of n?
- F 3
- G 4
- H 7
- J 27

25. Which pair of numbers has 36 as the LCM?
- A 3, 6
- B 3, 12
- C 6, 9
- D 9, 12

Stop

TIP! **Get the information you need. See item 2.**

You know that juice boxes are sold in packages of 8 and rice snacks are sold in packages of 10. Use the least common multiple to find an equal number of treats before you determine how many packages to buy.

Also see problem 3, p. H63.

1. What is the prime factorization of 90? **A**

   A $2 \times 3^2 \times 5$ **C** $2^2 \times 3 \times 5^2$

   B $2 \times 3 \times 5$ **D** $2^2 \times 3^2 \times 5^2$

2. Hu is buying treats for a party. Juice boxes are sold in packages of 8. Rice snacks are sold in packages of 10. What is the least number of packages of juice and rice snacks he should buy to have an equal number of juice boxes and rice snacks? **G**

   F 4 juice packs, 5 boxes of rice snacks

   G 5 juice packs, 4 boxes of rice snacks

   H 9 juice packs, 9 boxes of rice snacks

   J 10 juice packs, 8 boxes of rice snacks

3. What is the least common multiple of 18 and 27? **C**

   A 3   **C** 54

   B 9   **D** 486

4. What is the prime factorization of 24? **G**

   F 2×2^3 **H** $2^4 \times 3$

   G $2^3 \times 3$ **J** 6×2^2

5. Which number is divisible by both 6 and 9? **B**

   A 45   **C** 243

   B 216   **D** 768

6. Carni earned the following amounts baby-sitting: $17, $15, $12, $17, $14. What was the mean amount that Carni earned? **G**

   F $14   **H** $16

   G $15   **J** Not here

7. What is the greatest common factor of 16 and 24? **B**

   A 4   **C** 48

   B 8   **D** 384

8. Marcus has a baseball game every fifth day in April. His first game is on April 5. How many games will there be in April? **J**

   F 3   **H** 5

   G 4   **J** 6

9. A theater holds 381 people. All the available tickets for 18 shows were sold. Which is a good estimate for the number of people who attended the shows? **C**

   A Less than 4,000 people

   B Between 4,000 and 6,000 people

   C Between 6,000 and 8,000 people

   D More than 8,000 people

10. Eleni bakes brownies for a bake sale at school. She wants to make 4 batches of brownies and package the brownies in boxes of 8. How many boxes will she need if there are 32 brownies in each batch? **G**

    F 12   **H** 20

    G 16   **J** 32

157

CUMULATIVE REVIEW •
Chapters 1–7

USING THE PAGE

This page may be used to help students get ready for standardized tests. The test items are written in the same style and arranged in the same format as those on many state assessments. The page is cumulative. It covers math objectives and essential skills that have been taught up to this point in the text. Most of the items represent skills from the current chapter, and the remainder represent skills from earlier chapters.

This page can be assigned at the end of the chapter as classwork or as a homework assignment. You may want to have students use individual recording sheets presented in a multiple-choice (standardized) format. A Test Answer Sheet is available as a blackline master in *Assessment Guide* (p. AGxlii).

You may wish to have students describe how they solved each problem and share their solutions.

Fraction Concepts

CHAPTER PLANNER

Getting Ready for Chapter 8 • Assessing Prior Knowledge and INTERVENTION (See PE and TE page 159.)

LESSON	CALIFORNIA STANDARDS	PACING	VOCABULARY*	MATERIALS	RESOURCES AND TECHNOLOGY
8.1 Equivalent Fractions and Simplest Form pp. 160–163 **Objective** To identify and write equivalent fractions and to write fractions in simplest form	O—¬ NS 2.4 (*Also* O—¬ NS 2.0 MR 2.2, MR 2.5)	2 Days	**equivalent fractions** **simplest form**	*For each group* fraction bars or fraction strips	Reteach, Practice, Problem Solving, Challenge 8.1 Worksheets Extra Practice p. H39, Set A ▭ Transparency 8.1 🌐 **E-Lab** • *Equivalent Fractions*; E-Lab Recording Sheet 💿 **Number Heroes** • *Fraction Fireworks*
8.2 Mixed Numbers and Fractions pp. 164–165 **Objective** To write fractions as mixed numbers and mixed numbers as fractions	O—¬ NS 1.0 (*Also* O—¬ NS 2.0 MR 2.2, MR 2.5)	1 Day	**mixed number**		Reteach, Practice, Problem Solving, Challenge 8.2 Worksheets Extra Practice p. H39, Set B ▭ Transparency 8.2 💿 **Calculating Crew** • *Nautical Number Line*
8.3 Compare and Order Fractions pp. 166–167 **Objective** To compare and order fractions	O—¬ NS 2.4 (*Also* O—¬ NS 1.0 MR 1.0, MR 2.4, MR 2.5)	1 Day			Reteach, Practice, Problem Solving, Challenge 8.3 Worksheets Extra Practice p. H39, Set C ▭ Transparency 8.3
8.4 Math Lab: Explore Fractions and Decimals p. 168 **Objective** To convert fractions to decimals	MR 2.0, MR 2.4 (*Also* MR 2.5)			*For each student* graph paper, scissors, colored pencils	🌐 **E-Lab** • *Equivalent Fractions, Decimals, and Mixed Numbers*; E-Lab Recording Sheet 💿 **Astro Algebra** • *Red* 💿 **Number Heroes** • *Fraction Fireworks*
8.5 Fractions, Decimals, and Percents pp. 169–171 **Objective** To convert fractions to decimals, decimals to fractions, and fractions to percents	O—¬ NS 1.0 (*Also* O—¬ NS 2.0 MR 2.2, MR 2.4, MR 2.5)	1 Day (For Lessons 8.4 and 8.5)	**terminating** **decimal** **repeating** **decimal** percent		Reteach, Practice, Problem Solving, Challenge 8.5 Worksheets Extra Practice p. H39, Set D ▭ Transparency 8.5 💿 **Astro Algebra** • *Red* 💿 **Calculating Crew** • *Nautical Number Line*

Ending Chapter 8 • Chapter 8 Review/Test, p. 172 • **Cumulative Review,** p. 173

*****Boldfaced** terms are new vocabulary. Other terms are review vocabulary.

CHAPTER AT A GLANCE

Vocabulary Development

The boldfaced words are the new vocabulary terms in the chapter. Have students record the definitions in their Math Journals.

equivalent fractions, p. 160

simplest form, p. 161

mixed number, p. 164

terminating decimal, p. 169

repeating decimal, p.169

> equivalent
> fractions

Vocabulary Cards
Have students use the Vocabulary Cards on *Teacher's Resource Book* **pp. TR125–128** to make graphic organizers or word puzzles. The cards can also be added to a file of mathematics terms.

Writing Opportunities

PUPIL EDITION
- **What's the Question?**, p. 163
- **What's the Error?**, pp. 165, 167
- **Write About It**, pp. 165, 171

- **Write a Problem**, p. 163

TEACHER'S EDITION
- **Write**—See the *Assess* section of each TE lesson.
- **Writing in Mathematics**, p. 164B

ASSESSMENT GUIDE
- **How Did I Do?**, p. xvii

California Mathematics Content Standards for Grade 6

Strands

Number Sense

Lesson 8.1: NS 2.0, 2.4

Lesson 8.2: NS 1.0, 2.0

Lesson 8.3: NS 1.0, 1.1, 2.4

Lesson 8.5: NS 1.0, 2.0

Algebra and Functions

Measurement and Geometry

Statistics, Data Analysis, and Probability

Mathematical Reasoning

Lesson 8.1: MR 2.2, 2.5

Lesson 8.2: MR 2.2, 2.5

Lesson 8.3: MR 1.0, 2.4, 2.5

Lesson 8.4: MR 2.0, 2.4, 2.5

Lesson 8.5: MR 2.2, 2.4, 2.5

Family Involvement Activities

These activities provide:
- Letter to the Family
- Information about California Standards
- Model of Essential Skills
- Math Vocabulary
- Family Game

Family Involvement Activities, p. FA29

Fraction Concepts

MATHEMATICS ACROSS THE GRADES

SKILLS TRACE ACROSS THE GRADES

GRADE 5	GRADE 6	GRADE 7
Write equivalent fractions; write fractions in simplest form; compare and order fractions	**Write fractions in equivalent and simplest form; convert between, compare, and order fractions and mixed numbers; represent and use equivalent representations for fractions, decimals, and percents**	Write fractions and mixed numbers in equivalent and simplest form; represent fractions as terminating or repeating decimals

SKILLS TRACE FOR GRADE 6

LESSON	FIRST INTRODUCED	TAUGHT AND PRACTICED	TESTED	REVIEWED
8.1	Grade 4	PE pp. 160–163, H39, p. RW36, p. PW36, p. PS36	PE p. 172, pp. AG53–56	PE pp. 172, 173, 222–223
8.2	Grade 4	PE pp. 164–165, H39, p. RW37, p. PW37, p. PS37	PE p. 172, pp. AG53–56	PE pp. 172, 173, 222–223
8.3	Grade 4	PE pp. 166–167, H39, p. RW38, p. PW38, p. PS38	PE p. 172, pp. AG53–56	PE pp. 172, 173, 222–223
8.4	Grade 4	PE p. 168	PE p. 172, pp. AG53–56	PE pp. 172, 173, 222–223
8.5	Grade 6	PE pp. 169–171, H39, p. RW39, p. PW39, p. PS39	PE p. 172, pp. AG53–56	PE pp. 172, 173, 222–223

KEY **PE** Pupil Edition **PS** Problem Solving Workbook **RW** Reteach Workbook
PW Practice Workbook **AG** Assessment Guide

Looking Back Prerequisite Skills

To be ready for Chapter 8, students should have the following understandings and skills:

- **Vocabulary**—*denominator, numerator*

- **Compare and Order Whole Numbers and Decimals**—use <,>, and = symbols to compare whole numbers and decimals; order whole numbers and decimals from greatest to least

- **Model Fractions**—write the fraction that names the shaded part of a model

- **Model Percents**—write the percent that names the shaded part of a model

Check What You Know

Use page 159 to determine students' knowledge of prerequisite concepts and skills.

Intervention

Help students prepare for the chapter by using the intervention resources described on TE page 159.

Looking at Chapter 8 Essential Skills

Students will

- develop skill in writing equivalent fractions and fractions in simplest form.

- write fractions as mixed numbers and mixed numbers as fractions.

- compare and order fractions.

- **make the connection between graphic representations for fractions, decimals, and percents and converting among fractions, decimals, and percents.**

EXAMPLE

Write the fraction as a decimal.

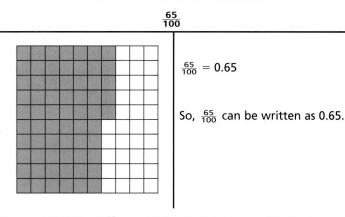

$$\frac{65}{100} = 0.65$$

So, $\frac{65}{100}$ can be written as 0.65.

Looking Ahead Applications

Students will apply what they learn in Chapter 8 to the following new concepts:

- Add and Subtract Fractions and Mixed Numbers (Chapter 9)
- Multiply and Divide Fractions and Mixed Numbers (Chapter 10)
- Number Relationships (Chapter 11)
- Rate, Ratio, Percent, and Proportion (Chapter 20)

Fraction Concepts

INTRODUCING THE CHAPTER

Tell students that fractions are used to name equal parts of a whole or of a group. Have students focus on the photo and write a fraction to describe the number of animals. Possible answer: $\frac{2}{3}$ (2 babies to 3 animals)

USING DATA

To begin the study of this chapter, have students

- Find which cat is about half the length of the jaguar. bobcat
- Write a fraction to compare the length of the bobcat to that of the tiger. about $\frac{1}{3}$
- Write three more fractions that could be used to express data relationships on the graph. Answers will vary.

PROBLEM SOLVING PROJECT

Purpose To use fractions to solve a problem

Grouping pairs or small groups

Background The largest member of the cat family is the Siberian tiger. The average length, tip of nose to tail, is 10 ft 4 in.

Analyze, Choose, Solve, and Check

Have students

- Research the average lengths of cats that live in each of five different areas of the world, such as Canada, India, and Brazil.
- Make a table or graph of their results.
- Write fractions that describe the data they have collected.

Check students' work.

 Suggest that students place the tables and graphs in their portfolios.

CHAPTER **8** **Fraction Concepts**

Around the world, there are more than 30 different species of cats living in forests, grasslands, deserts, and mountains. The body lengths of cats range from 2 feet to 10 feet. The average tiger is $9\frac{1}{4}$ feet long, and the average lion is $6\frac{1}{2}$ feet long. The average bobcat is about $3\frac{1}{4}$ feet long. Compare the average length of a tiger to that of a lion.

$9\frac{1}{4} > 6\frac{1}{2}$; the length of a tiger is greater.

158 Chapter 8

Why learn math? Explain that wildlife biologists collect data about wild animals, including their height, length, and weight. They use these data to study the health and viability of these animals. Ask: What other professions might involve data that contain mixed numbers? Possible answer: architects, chefs, web-page designers

Check What You Know

Use this page to help you review and remember important skills needed for Chapter 8.

✓ Vocabulary

Choose the best term or symbol from the box.

denominator
<
numerator
>

1. The symbol for "is greater than" is ___?___ . >
2. The top number of a fraction is called the ___?___ . numerator
3. The bottom number of a fraction is called the ___?___ . denominator

✓ Compare and Order Whole Numbers
(See p. H3.)

Write <, >, or = for each ●.

4. 408 ● 480   <
5. 4,279 ● 4,277   >
6. 30 tens ● 3 hundreds   =
7. 9,315 ● 9,351   <
8. 18,808 ● 18,880   <
9. 356,782 ● 356,482   >

Order the numbers from greatest to least.

10. 3,400; 3,439; 3,399
    3,439; 3,400; 3,399
11. 61,060; 62,000; 61,600
    62,000; 61,600; 61,060
12. 98,450; 98,405; 98,540
    98,540; 98,450; 98,405

✓ Model Fractions (See p. H8.)

Write the fraction for the shaded part. 13. $\frac{5}{6}$ 14. $\frac{2}{5}$ 15. $\frac{1}{3}$ 16. $\frac{4}{8}$

13.   14.   15.   16.

✓ Model Percents (See p. H9.)

Write the percent for the shaded part.

17.
20%

18.
13%

19.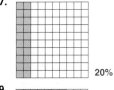
75%

20.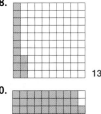
98%

> **LOOK AHEAD**

In Chapter 8 you will
- find equivalent fractions
- write fractions in simplest form
- write fractions as mixed numbers and mixed numbers as fractions
- compare and order fractions
- find relationships among fractions, decimals, and percents

159

ASSESSING PRIOR KNOWLEDGE

Use the **Check What You Know** page to determine whether your students have mastered the prerequisite skills critical for this chapter.

INTERVENTION

- **Diagnose and Prescribe**

  Evaluate your students' performance on this page to determine whether intervention is necessary. **How to Help Options** that provide instruction, practice, and a check are listed in the chart below.

- **Review Prerequisite Skills**

  The following resources provide a review for the prerequisite vocabulary and skills.

  Option 1—Check What You Know, Pupil Edition p. 159

  Option 2—Troubleshooting, Pupil Edition pp. H3, H8–9

TEACHER'S NOTES

Check What You Know
INTERVENTION • Diagnose and Prescribe

Prerequisite Skill	Items (Pupil Edition p. 159)	How to Help Options
✓ Compare and Order Whole Numbers and Decimals	4–12	• **Troubleshooting, Pupil Edition p. H3** • **Intervention Strategies and Activities** Card, Copying Master, or CD-ROM • **Skills 3, 34**
✓ Model Fractions	13–16	• **Troubleshooting, Pupil Edition p. H8** • **Intervention Strategies and Activities** Card, Copying Master, or CD-ROM • **Skill 20**
✓ Model Percents	17–20	• **Troubleshooting, Pupil Edition p. H9** • **Intervention Strategies and Activities** Card, Copying Master, or CD-ROM • **Skill 21**

Equivalent Fractions and Simplest Form

LESSON PLANNING

Objective **To identify and write equivalent fractions and to write fractions in simplest form**

Intervention for Prerequisite Skills

Model Fractions (For intervention strategies, see page 159.)

Materials *For each group* fraction bars or fraction strips, p. TR18

Lesson Resources E-Lab Recording Sheet • *Equivalent Fractions*

 California Mathematics Content Standards

○━ NS 2.4 Determine the least common multiple and the greatest common divisor of whole numbers; use them to solve problems with fractions.

(*Also* ○━ NS 2.0, MR 2.2, MR 2.5)

 **Vocabulary**

equivalent fractions fractions that name the same amount or the same part of a whole

simplest form a fraction in which the numerator and denominator have no common factors other than 1

Math Background

The following experiences will help students understand the concepts of equivalent fractions and fractions in simplest form:

- Using fraction bars to show equivalent fractions.
- Finding equivalent fractions by multiplying or dividing the numerator and denominator of a fraction by the same number.
- Finding the simplest form of a fraction by dividing the numerator and denominator by the greatest common factor.

WARM-UP RESOURCES

 NUMBER OF THE DAY
Transparency **8.1**

4 and 24 are multiples of this number; 2 and 3 are not. What number is it? 4

 PROBLEM OF THE DAY
Transparency **8.1**

John has 3 coins, 2 of which are the same. Ellen has 1 fewer coin than John, and Anna has 2 more coins than John. Each girl has only 1 kind of coin. Who has coins that could equal the value of a half-dollar? Ellen and Anna

Solution Problem of the Day tab, p. PD8

 DAILY FACTS PRACTICE

Have students practice addition facts by completing Set D of *Teacher's Resource Book,* p. TR98.

INTERVENTION AND EXTENSION RESOURCES

ALTERNATIVE TEACHING STRATEGY

Materials *For each pair* 2 square sheets of paper

Help students **visualize equivalent fractions.** Ask each student to fold one square lengthwise, not diagonally, to model halves, and to label each part $\frac{1}{2}$. Next, have pairs fold and label their squares to solve $\frac{1}{2} = \frac{\blacksquare}{4}$, $\frac{1}{2} = \frac{\blacksquare}{8}$, and $\frac{3}{4} = \frac{\blacksquare}{8}$. 2, 4, 6

See also page 162.

KINESTHETIC

ENGLISH LANGUAGE LEARNERS ELL•SDAIE

To help students **understand the concept of fractions,** discuss these part-to-whole relationships. Have them write each relationship in fraction form.

- A room is part of a house. $\frac{room}{house}$
- A flower is part of a garden. $\frac{flower}{garden}$
- A tree is part of a forest. $\frac{tree}{forest}$

Ask volunteers to give other examples of part-to-whole relationships. Possible answer: An egg is part of a dozen eggs.

AUDITORY

MIXED REVIEW AND TEST PREP

Cumulative Review Chapters 1–8

Refer to the Pupil Edition pages referenced in the exercises for further review. Have students go to the lesson page, review the lesson, and correct any problem they missed.

Mixed Review and Test Prep, p. 163

How to Help	
Item	**Page**
67	44
68	44
69	70
70	70
71	70

EARLY FINISHERS

Have students **demonstrate their understanding of equivalent fractions and simplest form.**

Ask students to write two additional equivalent fractions for the fractions in Exercises 23–26 on page 162. Circle the simplest form fraction. Possible answers: 23: $\frac{4}{8}$, $\frac{10}{20}$, 24: $\frac{20}{30}$, $\frac{6}{9}$, 25: $\frac{32}{40}$, $\frac{8}{10}$, 26: $\frac{18}{54}$, $\frac{3}{9}$

Simplest form: 23: $\frac{1}{2}$; 24: $\frac{2}{3}$; 25: $\frac{4}{5}$; 26: $\frac{1}{3}$

VISUAL

E-LAB RECORDING SHEET

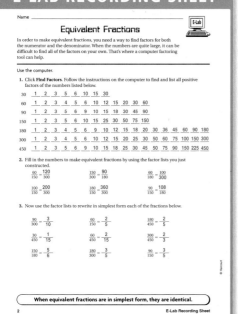

The E-Lab Recording Sheets and activities are available on the E-Lab website.

www.harcourtschool.com/elab2002

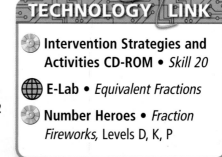

TECHNOLOGY LINK

- **Intervention Strategies and Activities CD-ROM** • *Skill 20*
- **E-Lab** • *Equivalent Fractions*
- **Number Heroes** • *Fraction Fireworks,* Levels D, K, P

Objective To identify and write equivalent fractions and to write fractions in simplest form

Vocabulary equivalent fractions, simplest form

Materials *For each group* fraction bars or fraction strips, p. TR18

Lesson Resources E-Lab Recording Sheet • *Equivalent Fractions*

1 Introduce

QUICK REVIEW provides review of prerequisite skills.

Why Learn This? You will use equivalent fractions to set up and solve proportions and use simplest form to express solutions to problems. *Share the lesson objective with students.*

2 Teach

Guided Instruction

• *Check students' understanding of the opening model.*

  How could you use fraction bars to find how many eighths are equivalent to $\frac{1}{4}$? Place $\frac{1}{8}$ fraction bars along the $\frac{1}{4}$ bar until the lengths are equal.

  How many eighths are equivalent to $\frac{1}{4}$? 2

• *Explain that in Example 1, students are being asked to identify a fraction that is equivalent to $\frac{2}{4}$ and has a denominator of 12.*

  How do you know which number to multiply the numerator and denominator by? by finding the factor you multiply 4 by to get a product of 12

  What is that factor? 3

ADDITIONAL EXAMPLE

Example 1, p. 160

Complete: $\frac{3}{5} = \frac{\blacksquare}{15}$

$\frac{3 \times \boxed{3}}{5 \times \boxed{3}} = \frac{9}{15}$

So, $\frac{3}{5} = \frac{9}{15}$

LESSON **8.1**

Equivalent Fractions and Simplest Form

Learn how to identify and write equivalent fractions, and how to write fractions in simplest form.

Vocabulary

equivalent fractions

simplest form

Write all the factors.

1. 12	**2.** 10	**3.** 16	**4.** 25	**5.** 20
1, 2, 3, 4, 6, 12	1, 2, 5, 10	1, 2, 4, 8, 16	1, 5, 25	1, 2, 4, 5, 10, 20

Fractions that name the same amount or the same part of a whole are called **equivalent fractions**. The figures show that the fractions $\frac{1}{4}$ and $\frac{2}{8}$ are equivalent, because they name the same part of a whole circle.

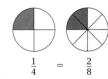

$\frac{1}{4} = \frac{2}{8}$

There are several ways to find equivalent fractions.

Activity

You need: fraction bars

Find how many eighths are equivalent to $\frac{1}{2}$.

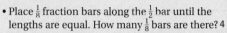

• Place $\frac{1}{8}$ fraction bars along the $\frac{1}{2}$ bar until the lengths are equal. How many $\frac{1}{8}$ bars are there? **4**

• Complete: $\frac{1}{2} = \frac{\blacksquare}{8}$ **4**

• Use fraction bars. How many fourths are equivalent to $\frac{1}{2}$? **2**

• Complete: $\frac{1}{2} = \frac{\blacksquare}{4}$ **2**

Another way to find an equivalent fraction is to multiply or divide the numerator and denominator of a fraction by the same number, except 0. Doing this does not change the fraction's value, because this is the same as multiplying or dividing by 1.

EXAMPLE 1

Complete: $\frac{2}{4} = \frac{\blacksquare}{12}$

$\frac{2}{4} = \frac{6}{12}$

THINK: To get the denominator 12, I need to multiply the denominator 4 by 3. So, to get the missing numerator, I should multiply the numerator 2 by 3.

$\frac{2 \times \boxed{3}}{4 \times \boxed{3}} = \frac{6}{12}$

$\frac{3}{3} = 1$, so the product is still equal to $\frac{2}{4}$.

160

CALIFORNIA STANDARDS O—nNS 2.4 Determine the least common multiple and the greatest common divisor of whole numbers; use them to solve problems with fractions (e.g., to find a common denominator to add two fractions or to find the reduced form for a fraction). also O—nNS 2.0, MR 2.2, MR 2.5

RETEACH 8.1

Equivalent Fractions and Simplest Form

When the numerator and denominator of a fraction have no common factors other than 1, the fraction is in **simplest form**. You can use a GCF to write a fraction in simplest form.

What is the simplest form of $\frac{32}{56}$?

Step 1 Find the GCF of 32 and 56 by listing the factors of each. The GCF is 8.

32: 1, 2, 4, <u>8</u>, 16, 32
56: 1, 2, 4, 7, <u>8</u>, 14, 28, 56

Step 2 Divide the numerator and denominator by the GCF.

$\frac{32}{56} = \frac{32 \div 8}{56 \div 8} = \frac{4}{7}$

So, $\frac{4}{7}$ is the simplest form of $\frac{32}{56}$.

Complete to find the simplest form of $\frac{88}{104}$.

1. Find the GCF of 88 and 104. 88: <u>1, 2, 4, 8, 11, 22, 44, 88</u>

   The GCF is <u>8</u>. 104: <u>1, 2, 4, 8, 13, 26, 52, 104</u>

2. Divide the numerator and denominator by the GCF. $\frac{88 \div 8}{104 \div 8} = \frac{11}{13}$

3. So, <u>$\frac{11}{13}$</u> is the simplest form of $\frac{88}{104}$.

Complete to find the simplest form of $\frac{78}{120}$.

4. Find the GCF of 78 and 120. 78: <u>1, 2, 3, 6, 13, 26, 39, 78</u>

   The GCF is <u>6</u>. 120: <u>1, 2, 3, 4, 5, 6, 8, 10, 12, 15, 20, 24, 30, 40, 60, 120</u>

5. Divide the numerator and denominator by the GCF. $\frac{78 \div 6}{120 \div 6} = \frac{13}{20}$

6. So, <u>$\frac{13}{20}$</u> is the simplest form of $\frac{78}{120}$.

Find the GCF of the pair of numbers. Then write the fraction in simplest form.

7. 4, 10; $\frac{4}{10}$ 8. 8, 12; $\frac{8}{12}$ 9. 18, 36; $\frac{18}{36}$ 10. 21, 60; $\frac{21}{60}$

   2; $\frac{2}{5}$ 4; $\frac{2}{3}$ 18; $\frac{1}{2}$ 3; $\frac{7}{20}$

PRACTICE 8.1

Equivalent Fractions and Simplest Form

Vocabulary

Complete.

1. When the numerator and denominator of a fraction have no common factor other than 1, the fraction is in <u>simplest form</u>.

2. Fractions that name the same amount or the same part of a whole are called <u>equivalent fractions</u>.

Write the factors common to the numerator and denominator.

3. $\frac{8}{32}$ 4. $\frac{10}{50}$ 5. $\frac{2}{13}$ 6. $\frac{14}{49}$ 7. $\frac{1}{19}$

   1, 2, 4, 8   1, 2, 5, 10   1   1, 7   1

8. $\frac{12}{18}$ 9. $\frac{25}{75}$ 10. $\frac{15}{40}$ 11. $\frac{9}{54}$ 12. $\frac{6}{33}$

   1, 2, 3, 6   1, 5, 25   1, 5   1, 3, 9   1, 3

Write the fraction in simplest form.

13. $\frac{9}{36}$ 14. $\frac{15}{50}$ 15. $\frac{11}{121}$ 16. $\frac{15}{36}$ 17. $\frac{14}{28}$

    $\frac{1}{4}$ $\frac{3}{10}$ $\frac{1}{11}$ $\frac{5}{12}$ $\frac{1}{2}$

18. $\frac{30}{66}$ 19. $\frac{63}{72}$ 20. $\frac{27}{81}$ 21. $\frac{25}{65}$ 22. $\frac{12}{42}$

    $\frac{5}{11}$ $\frac{7}{8}$ $\frac{1}{3}$ $\frac{5}{13}$ $\frac{2}{7}$

Complete.

23. $\frac{36}{72} = \frac{1}{2}$ 24. $\frac{50}{75} = \frac{2}{3}$ 25. $\frac{17}{85} = \frac{1}{5}$ 26. $\frac{63}{84} = \frac{3}{4}$ 27. $\frac{2}{3} = \frac{64}{96}$

Mixed Review

Tell whether you would use a bar, line, or circle graph to display the data.

28. The number of students in each grade at your school <u>bar</u>

29. A hospital patient's temperature taken each hour for 8 hours <u>line</u>

30. The part of each day you spend at various activities <u>circle</u>

EXAMPLE 2

Complete: $\frac{6}{10} = \frac{\blacksquare}{5}$

THINK: I can get the denominator 5 by dividing the denominator 10 by 2. So, to get the missing numerator, I should divide the numerator 6 by 2.

$\frac{6}{10} = \frac{3}{5}$

$\frac{6 \div 2}{10 \div 2} = \frac{3}{5}$ $\frac{2}{2} = 1$, so the quotient is still equal to $\frac{6}{10}$.

Math Idea ▶ When the numerator and denominator of a fraction have no common factors other than 1, the fraction is in **simplest form**.

$\frac{9}{16}$ **is** in simplest form because 9 and 16 have no common factors other than 1.

$\frac{9}{15}$ **is not** in simplest form because 9 and 15 have the common factor 3.

EXAMPLE 3

The sun is much farther from the Earth than the moon is. So, even though the sun is much larger than the moon, the sun's tide-raising force is only $\frac{12}{30}$ of the moon's force. Write $\frac{12}{30}$ in simplest form.

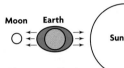

Tides are caused by the gravitational pull of the sun and the moon on Earth's oceans.

12: 1, 2, 3, 4, 6, 12   *Find the common factors of 12 and 30.*
30: 1, 2, 3, 5, 6, 10, 15, 30

$\frac{12}{30} = \frac{12 \div 3}{30 \div 3} = \frac{4}{10}$ *Divide the numerator and denominator by a common factor.*

$\frac{4}{10} = \frac{4 \div 2}{10 \div 2} = \frac{2}{5}$ *Repeat until the fraction is in simplest form.*

So, $\frac{2}{5}$ is the simplest form of $\frac{12}{30}$.

Bay of Fundy during low tide

In Example 3, the numerator and denominator were divided by common factors twice to find the simplest form. You can find it in just one step if you divide by the greatest common factor.

EXAMPLE 4

The world's highest tides occur in Canada's Bay of Fundy. Tides in Seattle, Washington, average only about $\frac{12}{42}$ of tidal heights in the Bay of Fundy. Write $\frac{12}{42}$ in simplest form.

12: 1, 2, 3, 4, 6, 12
42: 1, 2, 3, 6, 7, 14, 21, 42   *Find the GCF of 12 and 42.*
GCF = 6

$\frac{12}{42} = \frac{12 \div 6}{42 \div 6} = \frac{2}{7}$ *Divide the numerator and denominator by the GCF.*

So, $\frac{2}{7}$ is the simplest form of $\frac{12}{42}$.

Bay of Fundy during high tide

161

• *Focus on how Examples 1 and 2 are related.*

REASONING How are the solutions to **Example 1** and **Example 2** different? In Example 1, you multiply to change to a greater denominator. In Example 2, you divide to change to a lesser denominator.

• *Point out that students can apply what they learned in Example 4 to Example 3.*

How could you have used the GCF to write Example 3 in simplest form? I could have divided 12 and 30 by the GCF 6.

ADDITIONAL EXAMPLES

Example 2, p. 161

Complete: $\frac{2}{16} = \frac{\blacksquare}{8}$

$\frac{2 \div 2}{16 \div 2} = \frac{1}{8}$

So, $\frac{2}{16} = \frac{1}{8}$.

Example 3, p. 161

In the sixth-grade class, $\frac{12}{18}$ of the students ride the bus to school. Write $\frac{12}{18}$ in simplest form.

12: 1, 2, 3, 4, 6, 12

18: 1, 2, 3, 6, 9, 18

$\frac{12}{18} = \frac{12 \div 3}{18 \div 3} = \frac{4}{6}$

$\frac{4 \div 2}{6 \div 2} = \frac{2}{3}$

So, $\frac{2}{3}$ is the simplest form of $\frac{12}{18}$.

Example 4, p. 161

The weather in central Florida is very warm for more than $\frac{8}{12}$ of the year. Write $\frac{8}{12}$ in simplest form.

8: 1, 2, 4, 8

12: 1, 2, 3, 4, 6, 12

GCF = 4

$\frac{8 \div 4}{12 \div 4} = \frac{2}{3}$

So, $\frac{2}{3}$ is the simplest form of $\frac{8}{12}$.

PROBLEM SOLVING 8.1

Equivalent Fractions and Simplest Form   Analyze Choose Solve Check

Write the correct answer.

1. Write $\frac{12}{20}$ in simplest form.

$\frac{3}{5}$

2. What is the LCM of 4 and 6?

12

3. Pauline has 8 adventure books, 4 books of poems, and 6 animals books. What fraction of the books are books of poems? Write the fraction in simplest form.

$\frac{4}{18} = \frac{2}{9}$

4. Vickie made 20 cookies to share equally with friends. She will give the same number of cookies to each friend and keep that same number for herself. With how many friends can she share the cookies? List all the possible numbers of friends.

19, 9, 4, 3, 1

Choose the letter for the best answer.

5. What number is missing from the factor tree?

36
2 × 18
2 × ■
3 × 3

A 2   C 9
B 3   D 16

6. What are the factors common to the numerator and denominator of $\frac{24}{54}$?

F 1, 2, 3, 6
G 1, 2, 3, 6, 8
H 1, 2, 3, 4, 6
J 1, 2, 3, 6, 18

7. Which is the simplest form of the fraction $\frac{36}{72}$?

A $\frac{2}{5}$ C $\frac{8}{18}$
B $\frac{4}{9}$ D $\frac{1}{2}$

8. Abigail saved $3.58, $12.64, $9.45, and $23.60 in the last four weeks. What is a good estimate of how much Abigail saved in the last four weeks?

F Less than $20
G Between $20 and $40
H Between $40 and $60
J Between $60 and $80

9. **Write About It** Explain why dividing the numerator and the denominator of a fraction by the GCF is the most efficient way of simplifying the fraction.

If you use the GCF, you only have to divide the numerator and denominator once.

CHALLENGE 8.1

Fraction Flowers

Shade each petal that contains a fraction in simplest form. Then write the other fractions in simplest form.

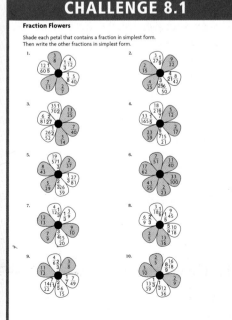

3 | Practice

Guided Practice

Do Check for Understanding Exercises 1–22 with your students. Identify those having difficulty and use lesson resources to help.

Independent Practice

Assign Exercises 23–66.

To help students with Exercises 23–34, have them decide if they need to multiply or divide because of the given numerators or denominators. Then display the following pattern of boxes and have students copy and complete the appropriate pattern for each exercise:

$$\blacksquare \frac{\times \blacksquare}{\times \blacksquare} = \frac{\blacksquare}{\blacksquare} \quad \text{or} \quad \blacksquare \frac{\div \blacksquare}{\div \blacksquare} = \frac{\blacksquare}{\blacksquare}$$

CHECK FOR UNDERSTANDING

Think and ▸ Discuss

Look back at the lesson to answer each question.

1. Also multiply the denominator by 5; $\frac{10}{15}$

1. **Describe** what you must do to find a fraction equivalent to $\frac{2}{3}$ if you first multiply the numerator by 5. What is the equivalent fraction?

2. **Explain** how you know that $\frac{5}{12}$ is in simplest form.
5 and 12 have no common factors other than 1.

Guided ▸ Practice Complete.

3. $\frac{3}{5} = \frac{\blacksquare}{20}$ 12 4. $\frac{3}{24} = \frac{\blacksquare}{8}$ 1 5. $\frac{8}{12} = \frac{\blacksquare}{6}$ 4 6. $\frac{3}{4} = \frac{\blacksquare}{24}$ 18

7. $\frac{4}{8} = \frac{\blacksquare}{2}$ 1 8. $\frac{9}{24} = \frac{\blacksquare}{8}$ 3 9. $\frac{8}{18} = \frac{\blacksquare}{36}$ 16 10. $\frac{12}{54} = \frac{\blacksquare}{9}$ 2

Write the factors common to the numerator and denominator.

11. $\frac{4}{8}$ 1, 2, 4 12. $\frac{9}{24}$ 1, 3 13. $\frac{8}{18}$ 1, 2 14. $\frac{12}{54}$ 1, 2, 3, 6

Write the fraction in simplest form.

15. $\frac{4}{32}$ $\frac{1}{8}$ 16. $\frac{14}{21}$ $\frac{2}{3}$ 17. $\frac{9}{54}$ $\frac{1}{6}$ 18. $\frac{48}{54}$ $\frac{8}{9}$

19. $\frac{22}{8}$ $\frac{11}{4}$ 20. $\frac{18}{5}$ $\frac{18}{5}$ 21. $\frac{9}{30}$ $\frac{3}{10}$ 22. $\frac{48}{32}$ $\frac{3}{2}$

PRACTICE AND PROBLEM SOLVING

Independent ▸ Practice Complete.

23. $\frac{1}{2} = \frac{\blacksquare}{10}$ 5 24. $\frac{10}{15} = \frac{\blacksquare}{3}$ 2 25. $\frac{16}{20} = \frac{\blacksquare}{5}$ 4 26. $\frac{9}{27} = \frac{\blacksquare}{3}$ 1

27. $\frac{2}{12} = \frac{1}{\blacksquare}$ 6 28. $\frac{\blacksquare}{36} = \frac{2}{9}$ 8 29. $\frac{21}{24} = \frac{7}{\blacksquare}$ 8 30. $\frac{40}{\blacksquare} = \frac{5}{8}$ 64

31. $\frac{9}{\blacksquare} = \frac{3}{4}$ 12 32. $\frac{3}{\blacksquare} = \frac{12}{16}$ 4 33. $\frac{16}{28} = \frac{4}{\blacksquare}$ 7 34. $\frac{25}{40} = \frac{\blacksquare}{8}$ 5

TECHNOLOGY LINK
More Practice: Use E-Lab, *Equivalent Fractions*. www.harcourtschool.com/elab2002

Write the factors common to the numerator and denominator.

35. $\frac{1}{7}$ 1 36. $\frac{9}{30}$ 1, 3 37. $\frac{6}{27}$ 1, 3 38. $\frac{9}{63}$ 1, 3, 9

39. $\frac{10}{35}$ 1, 5 40. $\frac{16}{40}$ 1, 2, 4, 8 41. $\frac{3}{5}$ 1 42. $\frac{8}{10}$ 1, 2

Write the fraction in simplest form.

43. $\frac{4}{24}$ $\frac{1}{6}$ 44. $\frac{9}{12}$ $\frac{3}{4}$ 45. $\frac{6}{48}$ $\frac{1}{8}$ 46. $\frac{10}{15}$ $\frac{2}{3}$

47. $\frac{10}{18}$ $\frac{5}{9}$ 48. $\frac{20}{15}$ $\frac{4}{3}$ 49. $\frac{18}{90}$ $\frac{1}{5}$ 50. $\frac{28}{42}$ $\frac{2}{3}$

51. $\frac{22}{33}$ $\frac{2}{3}$ 52. $\frac{24}{30}$ $\frac{4}{5}$ 53. $\frac{60}{42}$ $\frac{10}{7}$ 54. $\frac{24}{28}$ $\frac{6}{7}$

55. $\frac{16}{64}$ $\frac{1}{4}$ 56. $\frac{8}{12}$ $\frac{2}{3}$ 57. $\frac{18}{90}$ $\frac{1}{5}$ 58. $\frac{48}{18}$ $\frac{8}{3}$

59. $\frac{4^2}{32}$ $\frac{1}{2}$ 60. $\frac{3^2}{12}$ $\frac{3}{4}$ 61. $\frac{2^3}{12}$ $\frac{2}{3}$ 62. $\frac{3^2}{6^2}$ $\frac{1}{4}$

Alternative Teaching Strategy

Purpose Students use divisibility rules to write greater fractions in simplest form.

Explain that divisibility rules can be used to find factors. Remind students that a fraction is in simplest form when the numerator and denominator have no common factors other than 1. Model this process for $\frac{84}{93}$.

1. Write 1, 2, 3, 4, 5, 6, 7, 8, and 9. Underline the numerator's factors.

84: <u>1</u> <u>2</u> <u>3</u> 4 5 <u>6</u> <u>7</u> 8 9

2. Write 1, 2, 3, 4, 5, 6, 7, 8, and 9. Underline the denominator's factors.

93: <u>1</u> 2 <u>3</u> 4 5 6 7 8 9

3. Circle the greatest common factor (GCF) and use it to divide the fraction.

84: <u>1</u> <u>2</u> ③ <u>4</u> 5 <u>6</u> <u>7</u> 8 9
93: <u>1</u> 2 ③ 4 5 6 7 8 9
$\frac{84 \div 3}{93 \div 3} = \frac{28}{31}$

4. Check the new fraction for common factors.

28: <u>1</u> <u>2</u> 3 <u>4</u> 5 6 <u>7</u> 8 9
31: <u>1</u> 2 3 4 5 6 7 8 9

The simplest form for $\frac{84}{93}$ is $\frac{28}{31}$.

5. If there are common factors greater than 1, repeat steps 3 and 4 until 1 is the only common factor.

Have pairs of students write these fractions in simplest form: $\frac{36}{84}$ and $\frac{125}{200}$. $\frac{3}{7}$, $\frac{5}{8}$

Then have each pair write two fractions and challenge other students to write them in simplest form.

Note: This method will work for numerators and denominators less than 221. It may miss common factors for greater numbers.

Check students' work.

Problem Solving ▶ Applications

AMERICAN METEOR SOCIETY FIREBALL REPORT, 1998	
Month	Number
January	13
February	8
March	20
April	18
May	8
June	13

65. What fraction of the muffins are bran?

63. Use Data Look at the table at the left. A "fireball" is an extremely bright meteor occasionally seen streaking across the night sky. What fraction of the fireballs reported to the American Meteor Society during the first 6 months of 1998 occurred in March? $\frac{1}{4}$

64. Technology Some calculators have a SIMP key that can be used to simplify fractions. What fraction would this key sequence give? 10 / 15 SIMP = $\frac{2}{3}$

65. ? **What's the Question?** Esteban has 6 apple muffins, 2 corn muffins, and 4 bran muffins. The answer is $\frac{1}{3}$ of the muffins.

66. ✎ **Write a problem** about everyday life that involves finding the simplest form of a fraction. **Answers will vary.**

MIXED REVIEW AND TEST PREP

Evaluate each expression.

67. $(6 \div 3)^3 + 2^4$ (p. 44) **24**   **68.** $(6^2 \div 3^2) + 1$ (p. 44) **5**   **69.** 3.5×0.01 (p. 70) **0.035**

70. TEST PREP 0.5×1.2 (p. 70) **B**

  A 0.06   **B** 0.6   **C** 6   **D** 6.2

71. TEST PREP An adult's movie ticket costs $7.50, and a child's ticket costs $5.50. Find the total cost for 2 adults and 3 children. (p. 70) **J**

  F $13.00   **G** $20.50   **H** $24.00   **J** $31.50

Thinker's CORNER

Algebra You can use what you know about equivalent fractions to solve some types of algebraic equations.

A. $\frac{2}{3} = \frac{x-5}{27}$

THINK: I need to find a fraction equivalent to $\frac{2}{3}$ that has 27 as its denominator. I'll multiply by 9.

$$\frac{2}{3} = \frac{\blacksquare}{27} \qquad \frac{2 \times 9}{3 \times 9} = \frac{18}{27}$$

So, $x - 5 = 18$. If 5 less than some number is 18, that number must be 23. So, $x = 23$.

B. $\frac{3}{s+2} = \frac{18}{24}$

THINK: I need to find a fraction equivalent to $\frac{18}{24}$ that has 3 as its numerator. I'll divide by 6.

$$\frac{3}{\blacksquare} = \frac{18}{24} \qquad \frac{3}{4} = \frac{18 \div 6}{24 \div 6}$$

So, $s + 2 = 4$. If some number plus 2 equals 4, that number must be 2. So, $s = 2$.

Solve the equation.

1. $\frac{x+3}{10} = \frac{1}{2}$ $x = 2$ **2.** $\frac{5}{8} = \frac{c-5}{40}$ $c = 30$ **3.** $\frac{3}{b-4} = \frac{9}{15}$ $b = 9$

4. $\frac{1}{(2+y)} = \frac{6}{24}$ $y = 2$ **5.** $\frac{4}{9} = \frac{(w+4)}{18}$ $w = 4$ **6.** $\frac{(k-5)}{8} = \frac{12}{32}$ $k = 8$

Extra Practice page H39, Set A

163

Thinker's Corner

• *Focus on the order of the steps students must follow to solve the equations.*

In Example A, after you know the factor for 3 and 27, what must you do before you can solve the equation? Explain. Find the numerator; you need to know what $x - 5$ equals before you can solve for x.

In Example B, after you know the factor for 3 and 18, what do you need to do before you can solve the equation? Explain. Find the denominator; you need to know what $s + 2$ equals before you can solve for s.

REASONING Find an equivalent fraction for $\frac{5}{6}$, then use the equivalent fraction to write and solve an addition equation for the numerator. Possible answer: $\frac{15}{18}$; $\frac{5}{6} = \frac{x+4}{18}$; $x = 11$

4 | Assess

Summarize the lesson by having students:

DISCUSS Can you multiply the numerator and denominator of a fraction by a factor other than 1 and write the fraction in simplest form? Explain. No; the simplest form means the numerator and denominator have only 1 as a common factor.

 WRITE Which of the methods shown in Examples 3 and 4 on page 161 is the more efficient way to write a fraction in simplest form? Explain. Example 4; Example 4's method is more efficient because you divide only once.

Lesson Quiz

Transparency
8.1

Write the fraction in simplest form.

1. $\frac{21}{24}$ $\frac{7}{8}$ **2.** $\frac{12}{16}$ $\frac{3}{4}$ **3.** $\frac{24}{60}$ $\frac{2}{5}$

4. $\frac{12}{18}$ $\frac{2}{3}$ **5.** $\frac{55}{60}$ $\frac{11}{12}$ **6.** $\frac{40}{50}$ $\frac{4}{5}$

7. There are 30 students in the sixth grade. 15 are girls. What fraction of the students are girls? $\frac{1}{2}$

8. The school band has 24 members. $\frac{1}{4}$ of them play the flute. How can you use equivalent fractions to find the number of flute players in the band? $\frac{1}{4} = \frac{6}{24}$; 6 flute players

Mixed Numbers and Fractions

LESSON PLANNING

Objective To write fractions as mixed numbers and mixed numbers as fractions

Intervention for Prerequisite Skills

Model Fractions (For intervention strategies, see page 159.)

 California Mathematics Content Standards

⊶ **NS 1.0** Students compare and order positive and negative fractions, decimals, and mixed numbers. Students solve problems involving fractions, ratios, proportions, and percentages.

(*Also* ⊶ NS 2.0, MR 2.2, MR 2.5)

Vocabulary

mixed number a number that includes a whole-number part that is not 0 and a fraction part

Math Background

Consider the following ideas to help students understand how mixed numbers are related to whole numbers and fractions:

- A mixed number can be written as an equivalent fraction whose numerator is greater than its denominator.

- Division can be used to change a fraction greater than 1 to a mixed number.

- Both mathematically and in real-life, fractions greater than 1 are extremely common and useful. So, there is nothing "wrong" with "improper" fractions.

WARM-UP RESOURCES

 NUMBER OF THE DAY

What fraction of a dollar is a quarter? What fraction of a dollar are 5 dimes? $\frac{1}{4}$; $\frac{1}{2}$

 PROBLEM OF THE DAY

At the car show there are 20 vehicles on display. Some are motorcycles and some are cars. All 56 wheels on the vehicles need to be polished. What fraction of the vehicles are motorcycles? $\frac{3}{5}$

Solution Problem of the Day tab, p. PD8

 DAILY FACTS PRACTICE

Have students practice subtraction facts by completing Set E of *Teacher's Resource Book*, p. TR98.

ALTERNATIVE TEACHING STRATEGY ELL

Materials *For each group* play money—3 one-dollar bills, 20 quarters

Model mixed numbers and fractions greater than 1 with play money. Present 2 one-dollar bills and 1 quarter. Have a volunteer display an equivalent amount using quarters only.

Display the mixed number and the fraction: $2\frac{1}{4}$ and $\frac{9}{4}$.

Have students repeat the activity by using other amounts. Check students' work.

KINESTHETIC

MIXED REVIEW AND TEST PREP

Cumulative Review Chapters 1–8

Refer to the Pupil Edition pages referenced in the exercises for further review. Have students go to the lesson page, review the lesson, and correct any problem they missed.

Mixed Review and Test Prep, PE p. 165

How to Help	
Item	Page
37	148
38	148
39	148
40	98
41	66

WRITING IN MATHEMATICS

 Have students demonstrate their understanding of how to **write mixed numbers as fractions and fractions as mixed numbers.** Ask them to describe the procedure they would use to write $3\frac{1}{2}$ as a fraction. Then have them write the procedure they would use to express $\frac{15}{6}$ as a mixed number. Possible answers: multiply 3×2 and add 1 to get 7 for the numerator: $\frac{7}{2}$; divide 15 by 6 to get 2 and a remainder of 3 to make the mixed number $2\frac{3}{6}$

VISUAL

ADVANCED LEARNERS

Materials *For each student* index card

Challenge students to **write mixed numbers as fractions.** Working in small groups, each student should write his or her name and age in years and months on an index card.

Within their groups, have students discuss how to write their ages as mixed numbers and as fractions and then write them on the cards. Have each group order the numbers on the cards from least to greatest. Check students' work.

VISUAL

TECHNOLOGY LINK

 Intervention Strategies and Activities CD-ROM • *Skill 20*

 Calculating Crew • *Nautical Number Line*, Level K

Objective To write fractions as mixed numbers and mixed numbers as fractions

Vocabulary mixed number

1 Introduce

QUICK REVIEW provides review of pre-requisite skills.

Why Learn This? You can use this skill to help you express units of measurement, such as feet and yards, as a fraction or a mixed number. *Share the lesson objective with students.*

2 Teach

Guided Instruction

- *Discuss the symbols in the graph.*

  How many quarter sections represent 1 minute? 2 minutes? 4; 8

- *In Example 1, emphasize the usefulness of changing a fraction to a mixed number.*

  How can changing $\frac{11}{4}$ and $\frac{15}{2}$ to mixed numbers help you compare the lengths of the eclipses in 2017 and 2186? Possible answer: It is easier to compare the whole numbers 2 and 7 than fractions with different denominators.

- *Have students compare Examples 1 and 2.*

  What operations are used to change a fraction to a mixed number? a mixed number to a fraction? division, multiplication, and subtraction; multiplication and addition

Modifying Instruction Demonstrate for students another way to solve Example 2:
$$3\frac{2}{5} = 3 + \frac{2}{5} = \frac{3 \times 5}{1 \times 5} + \frac{2}{5}$$
$$= \frac{15}{5} + \frac{2}{5}$$
$$= \frac{17}{5}$$

ADDITIONAL EXAMPLES

Example 1, p. 164

Harrison studied $\frac{43}{2}$ minutes for his math test. Write $\frac{43}{2}$ as a mixed number. $21\frac{1}{2}$ minutes

Example 2, p. 164

Write $4\frac{5}{6}$ as a fraction. $\frac{29}{6}$

Mixed Numbers and Fractions

A total solar eclipse occurs when the moon passes between the sun and the Earth, "eclipsing" the sun's light.

Learn how to write fractions as mixed numbers and mixed numbers as fractions.

Vocabulary

mixed number

QUICK REVIEW

1. $4 \times 7 + 2$ 30
2. $19 + 11$ 30
3. $2 \times 7 + 5$ 19
4. $35 + 9$ 44
5. $8 \times 4 + 6$ 38

Total solar eclipses are rare, with only three visible in most of the U.S. since 1963. Eclipses last different times. In the graph, each quarter-section of a circle represents $\frac{1}{4}$ minute. How long will the 2017 eclipse last? It is represented by 11 sections, or $\frac{11}{4}$ minutes.

The graph shows that 11 sections equal 2 whole minutes plus $\frac{3}{4}$ of another minute. So, $\frac{11}{4} = 2\frac{3}{4}$. The 2017 eclipse will last $2\frac{3}{4}$ minutes.

The fraction $\frac{11}{4}$ has a value greater than 1 because the numerator is greater than the denominator. Sometimes a fraction such as $\frac{11}{4}$ is called an "improper fraction." Any such fraction can be written as a **mixed number**, like $2\frac{3}{4}$.

APPROXIMATE LENGTH OF U.S. TOTAL SOLAR ECLIPSES

1963	
1970	
1979	
2017	

$\square = \frac{1}{4}$ minute

Math Idea ▶ A mixed number has a whole-number part that is not 0 and a fraction part.

EXAMPLE 1

The longest total solar eclipse in the next 200 years will take place in 2186. It will last about $\frac{15}{2}$ minutes. Write $\frac{15}{2}$ as a mixed number.

$$\frac{15}{2} \rightarrow 2\overline{)15} \quad \begin{array}{r} 7\frac{1}{2} \\ \underline{-14} \\ 1 \end{array}$$

Divide the numerator by the denominator. For the fraction part of the quotient, use the remainder as the numerator and the divisor as the denominator. Write the fraction in simplest form.

So, $\frac{15}{2} = 7\frac{1}{2}$. The 2186 eclipse will last $7\frac{1}{2}$ minutes.

You can also write a mixed number as a fraction.

EXAMPLE 2

Write the mixed number $3\frac{2}{5}$ as a fraction.

$$3\frac{2}{5} = \frac{3 \times 5}{5} + \frac{2}{5} = \frac{(3 \times 5) + 2}{5} = \frac{17}{5}$$

Multiply the whole number by the denominator. Add the numerator. Use the same denominator.

So, $3\frac{2}{5} = \frac{17}{5}$.

164

CALIFORNIA STANDARDS NS 1.0 Students compare and order positive and negative fractions, decimals, and mixed numbers. Students solve problems involving fractions, ratios, proportions, and percentages. *also* ⚷NS 2.0, MR 2.2, MR 2.5

RETEACH 8.2

Mixed Numbers and Fractions

A mixed number is made up of two parts: a whole number and a fraction.
- You can rewrite a mixed number as an equivalent fraction. This type of fraction will have a numerator that is greater than the denominator.
- You can also rewrite a fraction with a numerator greater than the denominator as a mixed number.

Write $4\frac{2}{3}$ as an equivalent fraction.	Write $\frac{19}{4}$ as a mixed number.
Step 1 Multiply the whole number by the denominator of the fraction. $4 \times 3 = 12$	**Step 1** Divide the numerator by the denominator. $19 \div 5 = 3$ r4
Step 2 Add the numerator. This sum is the numerator of the equivalent fraction. $12 + 2 = 14$	**Step 2** Use the remainder as the numerator in the fraction part of the mixed number. The denominator is the divisor.
Step 3 Use the same denominator to write the equivalent fraction. $\frac{14}{3}$	$3\frac{4}{5}$ ←remainder ←divisor

Complete.

1. Write $7\frac{3}{5}$ as a fraction.

Step 1 Multiply the whole number by the denominator of the fraction $7 \times \boxed{5} = \boxed{35}$

Step 2 Add the numerator. This sum is the numerator of the equivalent fraction. $\boxed{35} + \boxed{3} = \boxed{38}$

Step 3 Use the same denominator to write the equivalent fraction. $\frac{\boxed{38}}{\boxed{5}}$

Write the mixed number as a fraction.

2. $5\frac{1}{3}$ $\frac{16}{3}$
3. $4\frac{1}{5}$ $\frac{21}{5}$
4. $5\frac{2}{7}$ $\frac{37}{7}$
5. $6\frac{1}{3}$ $\frac{19}{3}$
6. $7\frac{4}{5}$ $\frac{39}{5}$

Write the fraction as a mixed number.

7. $\frac{17}{3}$ $5\frac{2}{3}$
8. $\frac{19}{6}$ $3\frac{1}{6}$
9. $\frac{37}{8}$ $4\frac{5}{8}$
10. $\frac{52}{9}$ $5\frac{7}{9}$
11. $\frac{69}{11}$ $6\frac{3}{11}$

PRACTICE 8.2

Mixed Numbers and Fractions

Vocabulary

Complete.

1. A _____mixed number_____ has a whole-number part and a fraction part.

Write the fraction as a mixed number or a whole number.

2. $\frac{20}{5}$ 4
3. $\frac{19}{4}$ $4\frac{3}{4}$
4. $\frac{22}{7}$ $3\frac{1}{7}$
5. $\frac{39}{10}$ $3\frac{9}{10}$
6. $\frac{19}{10}$ $1\frac{9}{10}$
7. $\frac{75}{15}$ 5
8. $\frac{44}{13}$ $3\frac{5}{13}$
9. $\frac{50}{7}$ $7\frac{1}{7}$
10. $\frac{63}{21}$ 3
11. $\frac{45}{8}$ $5\frac{5}{8}$
12. $\frac{25}{6}$ $4\frac{1}{6}$
13. $\frac{72}{12}$ 6
14. $\frac{55}{9}$ $6\frac{1}{9}$
15. $\frac{46}{5}$ $9\frac{1}{5}$
16. $\frac{77}{11}$ 7

Write the mixed number as a fraction.

17. $6\frac{2}{7}$ $\frac{44}{7}$
18. $4\frac{6}{11}$ $\frac{50}{11}$
19. $9\frac{2}{3}$ $\frac{29}{3}$
20. $11\frac{1}{5}$ $\frac{56}{5}$
21. $2\frac{2}{3}$ $\frac{8}{3}$
22. $7\frac{2}{9}$ $\frac{65}{9}$
23. $12\frac{4}{5}$ $\frac{64}{5}$
24. $4\frac{5}{8}$ $\frac{37}{8}$
25. $8\frac{2}{3}$ $\frac{26}{3}$
26. $13\frac{1}{2}$ $\frac{27}{2}$

Mixed Review

Write the prime factorization of each number using exponents.

27. 84 $2^2 \times 3 \times 7$
28. 72 $2^3 \times 3^2$
29. 300 $2^2 \times 3 \times 5^2$

Write the fraction in simplest form.

30. $\frac{35}{45}$ $\frac{7}{9}$
31. $\frac{16}{42}$ $\frac{8}{21}$
32. $\frac{56}{72}$ $\frac{7}{9}$
33. $\frac{22}{55}$ $\frac{2}{5}$
34. $\frac{18}{81}$ $\frac{2}{9}$
35. $\frac{24}{30}$ $\frac{4}{5}$
36. $\frac{16}{40}$ $\frac{2}{5}$
37. $\frac{24}{36}$ $\frac{2}{3}$
38. $\frac{27}{63}$ $\frac{3}{7}$
39. $\frac{72}{88}$ $\frac{9}{11}$

CHECK FOR UNDERSTANDING

Think and ▶ Look back at the lesson to answer the question.
Discuss

1. **Tell** how you know that a given number is a mixed number.
   It has a whole-number part and a fraction part.
   Write the fraction as a mixed number or a whole number.

2. $\frac{5}{3}$ $1\frac{2}{3}$ 3. $\frac{7}{2}$ $3\frac{1}{2}$ 4. $\frac{15}{5}$ 3   5. $\frac{11}{3}$ $3\frac{2}{3}$ 6. $\frac{13}{4}$ $3\frac{1}{4}$

Guided ▶ Write the mixed number as a fraction.
Practice

7. $1\frac{1}{4}$ $\frac{5}{4}$ 8. $1\frac{3}{5}$ $\frac{8}{5}$ 9. $2\frac{2}{3}$ $\frac{8}{3}$ 10. $3\frac{4}{5}$ $\frac{19}{5}$ 11. $5\frac{2}{7}$ $\frac{37}{7}$

PRACTICE AND PROBLEM SOLVING

Independent ▶ Write the fraction as a mixed number or a whole number.
Practice

12. $\frac{7}{4}$ $1\frac{3}{4}$ 13. $\frac{9}{2}$ $4\frac{1}{2}$ 14. $\frac{11}{2}$ $5\frac{1}{2}$ 15. $\frac{23}{4}$ $5\frac{3}{4}$ 16. $\frac{27}{3}$ 9

34. She forgot the
denominator when
she wrote the
number of fourths
in 3;

17. $\frac{31}{6}$ $5\frac{1}{6}$ 18. $\frac{18}{11}$ $1\frac{7}{11}$ 19. $\frac{90}{7}$ $12\frac{6}{7}$ 20. $\frac{104}{13}$ 8   21. $\frac{150}{9}$ $16\frac{2}{3}$

$3\frac{1}{4} = \frac{(3 \times 4) + 1}{4} = \frac{13}{4}$

22. $\frac{x}{y}$ for $x = 18$ and $y = 12$ $1\frac{1}{2}$ 23. $\frac{a}{b}$ for $a = 55$ and $b = 15$ $3\frac{2}{3}$

Write the mixed number as a fraction.

24. $3\frac{2}{3}$ $\frac{11}{3}$ 25. $6\frac{1}{2}$ $\frac{13}{2}$ 26. $5\frac{1}{3}$ $\frac{16}{3}$ 27. $1\frac{9}{10}$ $\frac{19}{10}$ 28. $4\frac{1}{9}$ $\frac{37}{9}$

29. $9\frac{1}{4}$ $\frac{37}{4}$ 30. $2\frac{3}{8}$ $\frac{19}{8}$ 31. $4\frac{9}{11}$ $\frac{53}{11}$ 32. $11\frac{4}{9}$ $\frac{103}{9}$ 33. $18\frac{3}{5}$ $\frac{93}{5}$

Problem Solving ▶ 34. **What's the Error?**   Marti changed $3\frac{1}{4}$ to $12\frac{1}{4}$.
   What mistake did she make? What is the correct answer?
   See above left.

35. **Write About It**   Can any fraction be written as a mixed
   number? Explain. **No, only a fraction whose numerator is greater
   than its denominator**

36. **Astronomy**   On June 20, 1955, a total solar eclipse lasted 7 min
   7 sec. On June 20, 1974, a total solar eclipse lasted 5 min 8 sec.
   Which lasted longer? How much longer? **June 20, 1955; 1 min
   59 sec**

MIXED REVIEW AND TEST PREP

Write the prime factorization of each number. (p.148)

37. 36 $2^2 \times 3^2$ 38. 42 $2 \times 3 \times 7$ 39. 23 23×1

40. Is the following question biased? If so, rewrite it so that it is   **yes; possible answer: Did**
   unbiased: The film *Time Warp* is great, isn't it? (p. 98)   **you enjoy the film *Time***
                                                                Warp*?

41. **TEST PREP**   Noella is hiking a 25-km trail. She has hiked 3.8 km
   to the first overlook and another 6.5 km to the second overlook.
   How many kilometers does she have left to hike? (p. 66) **C**

   A 9.3 km   **B** 10.3 km   **C** 14.7 km   **D** 15.7 km

Extra Practice   page H39, Set B   165

---

3 Practice

Guided Practice

Do Check For Understanding Exercises 1–11
with your students. Identify those having difficulty and use lesson resources to help.

//// COMMON ERROR ALERT \\\\

When changing mixed numbers to fractions,
students often make careless errors in multiplying and/or adding. To check for errors,
have students change the fractions back to
mixed numbers and compare.

Independent Practice

Assign Exercises 12–36.

MIXED REVIEW AND TEST PREP

Exercises 37–41 provide **cumulative review**
(Chapters 1–8).

4 Assess

Summarize the lesson by having students:

DISCUSS Jo has $\frac{11}{4}$ cups of milk. She needs
$3\frac{1}{4}$ cups of milk for a recipe. How can Jo tell
if she has enough? Change $\frac{11}{4}$ to a mixed
number. Compare it to $3\frac{1}{4}$.

WRITE Compare the numerator
with the denominator in a fraction
less than one and in a fraction greater than
1. The numerator is less than the denominator
in a fraction less than one and the numerator is
greater than the denominator in a fraction
greater than one.

Lesson Quiz   Transparency

Write the fraction as a mixed number
or a whole number.

1. $\frac{12}{5}$ $2\frac{2}{5}$ 2. $\frac{10}{7}$ $1\frac{3}{7}$ 3. $\frac{49}{7}$ 7

Write the mixed number as a fraction.

4. $2\frac{3}{5}$ $\frac{13}{5}$ 5. $1\frac{7}{8}$ $\frac{15}{8}$ 6. $9\frac{1}{3}$ $\frac{28}{3}$

PROBLEM SOLVING 8.2

Mixed Numbers and Fractions   [Analyze] [Choose] [Solve] [Check]
Write the correct answer.

1. Write $4\frac{3}{5}$ as a fraction.
   $\frac{23}{5}$

2. Write $\frac{24}{40}$ in simplest form.
   $\frac{3}{5}$

3. Alex found a piece of lumber in the
   wood pile that is $\frac{7}{4}$ feet long. He needs
   3 feet to do a project. Does he have
   enough lumber for the project?
   Explain.
   No; $\frac{7}{4} = 1\frac{3}{4}$.

4. Jane has envelopes in packets of 4 and
   note cards in packets of 6. What is the
   least number of packets of each she
   needs in order to have an equal
   number of envelopes and note cards?
   3 packets of envelopes, and 2
   packets of note cards

Choose the letter for the best answer.

5. Which fraction is equivalent to $5\frac{7}{8}$?
   A $\frac{61}{8}$ C $\frac{40}{8}$
   Ⓑ $\frac{47}{8}$ D $\frac{35}{8}$

6. Which mixed number is equivalent
   to $\frac{85}{9}$?
   F $8\frac{7}{9}$ H $9\frac{5}{9}$
   G $9\frac{4}{9}$ Ⓙ $9\frac{2}{9}$

7. Betty's father earned $38,967.43 last
   year. Each month $245.32 was taken out
   of his pay for deductions. Which number
   sentence could be used to find m, the
   amount of money he took home each
   month?
   A $m = (\$38,967.43 \div 12) + \$245.32$
   Ⓑ $m = (\$38,967.43 \div 12) - \$245.32$
   C $m = (\$38,967.43 - \$245.32) \div 12$
   D $m = (\$38,967.43 + \$245.32) \div 12$

8. Devin has between $12 and $20
   deducted from his check every month
   for charity. What is a reasonable
   estimate for the amount of money he
   will have deducted for donations to
   charity in a year?
   F $50
   Ⓖ $200
   H $300
   J $400

9. Write About It   Can any whole number be written as a fraction?
   Explain.
   Yes. You can simply write the whole number as the numerator and
   a 1 as the denominator.

CHALLENGE 8.2

Fraction Squares
Shade the squares that show fractions equivalent to the mixed
number in the center.

165

Compare and Order Fractions

LESSON PLANNING

Objective To compare and order fractions

Intervention for Prerequisite Skills

Compare and Order Whole Numbers (For intervention strategies, see page 159.)

California Mathematics Content Standards

NS 1.1 Compare and order positive and negative fractions, decimals, and mixed numbers and place them on a number line.

NS 2.4 Determine the least common multiple and the greatest common divisor of whole numbers; use them to solve problems with fractions.

(*Also* NS 1.0, MR 1.0, MR 2.4, MR 2.5)

Math Background

Share these ideas with students as they learn how to compare and order fractions:

- Use mental math to compare fractions with the same denominators.
- When comparing fractions with unlike denominators, a number line can be used to find the greater fraction.
- Another way to compare fractions with unlike denominators is to find equivalent fractions with the same denominators.

WARM-UP RESOURCES

NUMBER OF THE DAY

Transparency 8.3

Marcus is in the sixth grade. He says he is 105,120 _____ old. Which word belongs in the blank: *months, days,* or *hours*? Explain. hours; Possible answer: Marcus is about 12 years old. 10 years × 12 months = 120; 10 years × 365 days = 3,650; 4,000 days × 25 = 100,000 hours.

PROBLEM OF THE DAY

Transparency 8.3

From 4:00 to 5:30, Jacob, Lisa, and Chelsea took turns playing the same computer game. Jacob played for $\frac{1}{2}$ hour and Lisa played for $\frac{3}{4}$ hour. For how many minutes did Chelsea play the game? 15 minutes

Solution Problem of the Day tab, p. PD8

DAILY FACTS PRACTICE

Have students practice addition and subtraction facts by completing Set F of *Teacher's Resource Book,* page TR98.

ALTERNATIVE TEACHING STRATEGY (ELL)

Materials *For each student* fraction strips, p. TR18

Have students demonstrate how to **use fraction strips to compare fractions with unlike denominators.**

Ask: Which is greater: $\frac{2}{3}$ or $\frac{5}{6}$? $\frac{5}{6}$

| $\frac{1}{3}$ | | $\frac{1}{3}$ | | |
| $\frac{1}{6}$ | $\frac{1}{6}$ | $\frac{1}{6}$ | $\frac{1}{6}$ | $\frac{1}{6}$ |

Have volunteers model comparisons of other fraction pairs. Display the comparisons. Check students' work.

VISUAL

MIXED REVIEW AND TEST PREP

Cumulative Review Chapters 1–8

Refer to the Pupil Edition pages referenced in the exercises for further review. Have students go to the lesson page, review the lesson, and correct any problem they missed.

Mixed Review and Test Prep, p. 167

How to Help	
Item	**Page**
29	82
30	82
31	150
32	150
33	22

CAREER CONNECTION

Materials *For each group* reference books

Ask students to **determine how fractions are used** in various careers. Have them work in small groups to prepare an oral report about one of the following careers: stockbroker, engineer, architect, chef. Direct students to describe how fractions relate to each career.

Encourage them to use reference materials and, if possible, to interview a person working in that career. Check students' work.

AUDITORY

PHYSICAL FITNESS/HEALTH CONNECTION

Have students **order fractions with unlike denominators** from the survey results below. The data show the fraction of those surveyed who ranked each factor as most important for a good night's sleep.

Good mattress: $\frac{8}{25}$; Healthy diet: $\frac{1}{10}$; Daily exercise: $\frac{1}{5}$; Good pillows: $\frac{2}{25}$; Other factors: $\frac{3}{10}$

Ask students to list the factors in order of importance from greatest to least. good mattress, other factors, daily exercise, healthy diet, good pillows

VISUAL

TECHNOLOGY LINK

Intervention Strategies and Activities CD-ROM • *Skill 3*

LESSON 8.3 ORGANIZER

Objective To compare and order fractions

1 Introduce

QUICK REVIEW provides review of pre-requisite skills.

Why Learn This? You can use this skill to help compare customary units of measurement that are expressed as fractions. *Share the lesson objective with students.*

2 Teach

Guided Instruction

- *Work through the Example, and discuss how finding the LCM helps you compare fractions.*

How did you use the LCM to compare fractions? I wrote an equivalent fraction with the LCM 20 as the denominator for each fraction. The fraction with the greater numerator was the greater number.

REASONING Another way to solve the Example is to compare each fraction to $\frac{1}{2}$: $\frac{7}{10} > \frac{1}{2}$ and $\frac{1}{4} < \frac{1}{2}$, so $\frac{1}{4} < \frac{7}{10}$.

Modifying Instruction Some students may need to review comparing fractions with like denominators before comparing those with unlike denominators.

ADDITIONAL EXAMPLE

Example, p. 166

About $\frac{3}{5}$ of the class are bus riders and about $\frac{1}{6}$ are walkers. Are there more bus riders or walkers?

To compare $\frac{3}{5}$ and $\frac{1}{6}$, find the LCM of the denominators, 5 and 6.

5: 5, 10, 15, 20, 25, 30

6: 6, 12, 18, 24, 30

LCM = 30 $\frac{3}{5} = \frac{3 \times 6}{5 \times 6} = \frac{18}{30}$ $\frac{1}{6} = \frac{1 \times 5}{6 \times 5} = \frac{5}{30}$

$\frac{18}{30} > \frac{5}{30}$ so $\frac{3}{5} > \frac{1}{6}$

So, there are more bus riders.

166 Chapter 8

Compare and Order Fractions

Learn how to compare and order fractions.

Remember that values increase as you move to the right on a number line. Values decrease as you move left.

increase ⟶

⟵ decrease

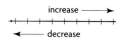

QUICK REVIEW

1. $\frac{1}{2} = \frac{\blacksquare}{10}$ 5   2. $\frac{2}{3} = \frac{\blacksquare}{9}$ 6   3. $\frac{4}{5} = \frac{\blacksquare}{20}$ 16   4. $\frac{3}{8} = \frac{\blacksquare}{24}$ 9

5. Write the first four multiples of 12. 12, 24, 36, 48

If two fractions have the same denominator, the fraction with the greater numerator is greater. So, $\frac{7}{12} > \frac{5}{12}$ because 7 > 5.

If fractions do not have common denominators, you can use a number line to compare and order the fractions. The number line shows that $\frac{1}{4} < \frac{3}{8} < \frac{1}{2}$. From least to greatest the order is $\frac{1}{4}, \frac{3}{8}, \frac{1}{2}$.

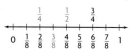

You can also use the least common multiple (LCM) to compare and order fractions.

EXAMPLE

George Washington Carver, one of America's most honored scientists, was born a slave in 1864.

George Washington Carver made over 500 useful agricultural products using peanuts, sweet potatoes, and pecans. About $\frac{7}{10}$ of the products used peanuts and about $\frac{1}{4}$ used sweet potatoes. Did Carver make more products with sweet potatoes or with peanuts?

To compare $\frac{7}{10}$ and $\frac{1}{4}$, find the LCM of the denominators, 10 and 4.

10: 10, 20, 30, 40   *Write multiples of 10.*

4: 4, 8, 12, 16, 20, 24, 28   *Write multiples of 4.*

LCM = 20

$\frac{7}{10} = \frac{7 \times 2}{10 \times 2} = \frac{14}{20}$ *Rewrite the fractions, using the LCM*

$\frac{1}{4} = \frac{1 \times 5}{4 \times 5} = \frac{5}{20}$ *as a common denominator.*

$\frac{14}{20} > \frac{5}{20}$, so $\frac{7}{10} > \frac{1}{4}$.   *Compare $\frac{14}{20}$ and $\frac{5}{20}$.*

So, Carver made more products with peanuts.

CHECK FOR UNDERSTANDING

Look back at the lesson to answer each question.

1. **Explain** how to compare $\frac{4}{9}$ and $\frac{5}{9}$.

1. The fractions have the same denominator. So, compare the numerators. 4 < 5, so $\frac{4}{9} < \frac{5}{9}$.

Think and ▸ Discuss

166

CALIFORNIA STANDARDS O—ɴ NS 1.1 Compare and order positive and negative fractions, decimals, and mixed numbers and place them on a number line. O—ɴ NS 2.4 Determine the least common multiple and the greatest common divisor of whole numbers; use them to solve problems with fractions. *also* O—ɴ NS 1.0, MR 1.0, MR 2.4, MR 2.5

RETEACH 8.3

Compare and Order Fractions

To compare fractions without using a number line, you can use a flowchart approach. Here are the steps for comparing $\frac{1}{3}$ and $\frac{2}{5}$.

	$\frac{1}{3}$ $\frac{2}{5}$
Step 1 Are the denominators the same? If YES, then the fraction with the greater numerator is the greater fraction. If NO, go on.	Since the denominators are not the same, go on to the next step.
Step 2 Are the numerators the same? If YES, then the fraction with the smaller denominator is the greater fraction. If NO, go on.	$\frac{1}{3}$ $\frac{2}{5}$ Since the numerators are not the same, go on to the next step.
Step 3 Find the least common denominator of the two fractions.	multiples of 3: 3, 6, 9, 12, 15, 18, ... multiples of 5: 5, 10, 15, 20, 25, ... 15 is the least common multiple of 3 and 5. So, it is the least common denominator of the fractions.
Step 4 Write fractions equivalent to the original fractions using the common denominator.	$\frac{1}{3} \times \frac{5}{5} = \frac{5}{15}$ $\frac{2}{5} \times \frac{3}{3} = \frac{6}{15}$
Step 5 Compare the fractions using the common denominator.	$\frac{5}{15} < \frac{6}{15}$
Step 6 Write the comparison of the original fractions in the same order.	$\frac{1}{3} < \frac{2}{5}$

Compare the fractions. Write <, >, or = in each ◯.

1. $\frac{4}{9} \; \text{>} \; \frac{4}{11}$ 2. $\frac{3}{4} \; \text{>} \; \frac{2}{5}$ 3. $\frac{3}{8} \; \text{<} \; \frac{3}{7}$ 4. $\frac{8}{9} \; \text{>} \; \frac{4}{9}$

5. $\frac{2}{3} \; \text{<} \; \frac{5}{6}$ 6. $\frac{1}{6} \; \text{<} \; \frac{3}{11}$ 7. $\frac{6}{15} \; \text{=} \; \frac{2}{5}$ 8. $\frac{6}{11} \; \text{<} \; \frac{5}{9}$

9. $\frac{2}{7} \; \text{<} \; \frac{1}{3}$ 10. $\frac{3}{5} \; \text{<} \; \frac{6}{9}$ 11. $\frac{7}{9} \; \text{>} \; \frac{5}{12}$ 12. $\frac{9}{10} \; \text{>} \; \frac{7}{8}$

13. $\frac{2}{9} \; \text{<} \; \frac{1}{3}$ 14. $\frac{4}{8} \; \text{<} \; \frac{2}{11}$ 15. $\frac{4}{7} \; \text{>} \; \frac{8}{14}$ 16. $\frac{9}{14} \; \text{<} \; \frac{9}{10}$

PRACTICE 8.3

Compare and Order Fractions

Compare the fractions. Write <, >, or = for each ●.

1. $\frac{5}{6} \; \text{>} \; \frac{3}{4}$ 2. $\frac{1}{4} \; \text{>} \; \frac{1}{5}$ 3. $\frac{2}{3} \; \text{>} \; \frac{3}{8}$ 4. $\frac{5}{8} \; \text{<} \; \frac{3}{4}$

5. $\frac{9}{10} \; \text{>} \; \frac{7}{8}$ 6. $\frac{7}{12} \; \text{<} \; \frac{3}{4}$ 7. $\frac{13}{16} \; \text{<} \; \frac{5}{6}$ 8. $\frac{1}{4} \; \text{<} \; \frac{1}{2}$

9. $\frac{2}{5} \; \text{<} \; \frac{3}{4}$ 10. $\frac{9}{15} \; \text{<} \; \frac{3}{4}$ 11. $\frac{4}{7} \; \text{<} \; \frac{3}{5}$ 12. $\frac{9}{10} \; \text{<} \; \frac{17}{20}$

13. $\frac{4}{5} \; \text{<} \; \frac{16}{20}$ 14. $\frac{7}{9} \; \text{>} \; \frac{2}{3}$ 15. $\frac{5}{9} \; \text{<} \; \frac{2}{3}$ 16. $\frac{5}{6} \; \text{>} \; \frac{6}{11}$

Use the number line to order the fractions from least to greatest.

17. $\frac{1}{6}, \frac{5}{12}, \frac{1}{3}$ 18. $\frac{5}{6}, \frac{7}{12}, \frac{1}{2}$ 19. $\frac{3}{4}, \frac{11}{12}, \frac{2}{3}$

20. $\frac{2}{3}, \frac{7}{12}, \frac{5}{12}$ 21. $\frac{1}{2}, \frac{5}{6}, \frac{1}{6}$ 22. $\frac{7}{12}, \frac{1}{6}, \frac{3}{3}$

Order the fractions from least to greatest.

23. $\frac{1}{4}, \frac{1}{6}, \frac{2}{5}$ 24. $\frac{4}{5}, \frac{2}{3}, \frac{3}{10}$ 25. $\frac{1}{5}, \frac{3}{8}, \frac{4}{5}$

26. $\frac{7}{8}, \frac{4}{5}, \frac{9}{10}$ 27. $\frac{3}{4}, \frac{7}{10}, \frac{3}{7}$ 28. $\frac{3}{5}, \frac{1}{8}, \frac{3}{10}$

Mixed Review

Find the mean, median, and mode.

29. 6, 6, 2, 4, 8, 6, 5, 3   30. 23, 26, 24, 19, 31, 33   31. 12, 9, 21, 11, 15, 15, 8

5, 5.5, 6   26, 25, no mode   13, 12, 15

Compare the fractions. Write <, >, or = for each ●.

2. $\frac{13}{20}$ ● $\frac{9}{20}$ >   3. $\frac{1}{4}$ ● $\frac{9}{20}$ <   4. $\frac{5}{6}$ ● $\frac{2}{3}$ >   5. $\frac{3}{8}$ ● $\frac{6}{16}$ =

Use the number line to order the fractions from least to greatest.

0   $\frac{1}{12}$ $\frac{1}{6}$ $\frac{1}{4}$ $\frac{1}{3}$ $\frac{5}{12}$ $\frac{1}{2}$ $\frac{7}{12}$ $\frac{2}{3}$ $\frac{3}{4}$ $\frac{5}{6}$ $\frac{11}{12}$ 1

6. $\frac{3}{4}, \frac{1}{3}, \frac{11}{12}$ $\frac{1}{3}, \frac{3}{4}, \frac{11}{12}$ 7. $\frac{2}{3}, \frac{1}{4}, \frac{6}{12}$ $\frac{1}{4}, \frac{6}{12}, \frac{2}{3}$ 8. $\frac{1}{3}, \frac{5}{12}, \frac{2}{4}$ $\frac{1}{3}, \frac{5}{12}, \frac{2}{4}$

PRACTICE AND PROBLEM SOLVING

Compare the fractions. Write <, >, or = for each ●.

9. $\frac{6}{7}$ ● $\frac{4}{7}$ >   10. $\frac{3}{11}$ ● $\frac{4}{11}$ <   11. $\frac{4}{12}$ ● $\frac{1}{3}$ =   12. $\frac{17}{20}$ ● $\frac{3}{5}$ >

13. $\frac{5}{6}$ ● $\frac{15}{18}$ =   14. $\frac{7}{9}$ ● $\frac{11}{12}$ <   15. $\frac{3}{4}$ ● $\frac{5}{8}$ >   16. $\frac{11}{15}$ ● $\frac{2}{3}$ >

Use the number line to order the fractions from least to greatest.

0   $\frac{1}{12}$ $\frac{1}{6}$ $\frac{1}{4}$ $\frac{1}{3}$ $\frac{5}{12}$ $\frac{1}{2}$ $\frac{7}{12}$ $\frac{2}{3}$ $\frac{3}{4}$ $\frac{5}{6}$ $\frac{11}{12}$ 1

17. $\frac{9}{12}, \frac{1}{2}, \frac{2}{6}, \frac{2}{2}, \frac{1}{2}, \frac{9}{12}$ 18. $\frac{4}{12}, \frac{4}{6}, \frac{7}{12}, \frac{4}{12}, \frac{7}{12}, \frac{4}{6}$ 19. $\frac{7}{12}, \frac{5}{6}, \frac{1}{2}, \frac{1}{2}, \frac{7}{12}, \frac{5}{6}$

Order the fractions from least to greatest.

20. $\frac{5}{8}, \frac{1}{2}, \frac{3}{4}, \frac{1}{2}, \frac{5}{8}, \frac{3}{4}$ 21. $\frac{2}{5}, \frac{3}{10}, \frac{1}{2}, \frac{3}{10}, \frac{2}{5}, \frac{1}{2}$ 22. $\frac{11}{16}, \frac{3}{4}, \frac{5}{8}, \frac{5}{8}, \frac{11}{16}, \frac{3}{4}$

23. $\frac{1}{3}, \frac{1}{6}, \frac{1}{2}, \frac{1}{6}, \frac{1}{3}, \frac{1}{2}$ 24. $\frac{2}{3}, \frac{2}{9}, \frac{2}{6}, \frac{2}{9}, \frac{2}{6}, \frac{2}{3}$ 25. $\frac{3}{4}, \frac{1}{12}, \frac{5}{8}, \frac{1}{12}, \frac{5}{8}, \frac{3}{4}$

27. Three pieces of each pizza remain. That is $\frac{3}{8}$ of the mushroom and $\frac{3}{12}$ of the cheese pizza. $\frac{3}{12} = \frac{1}{4} = \frac{2}{8} < \frac{3}{8}$, so more of the mushroom pizza is left.

26. During a physical education class, $\frac{1}{3}$ of the students chose to play basketball, $\frac{4}{15}$ chose flag football, and $\frac{2}{5}$ chose tetherball. Which activity was chosen by the most students? tetherball

27. ❓ **What's the Error?** For dinner, a mushroom pizza is cut into eighths and a cheese pizza into twelfths. After the meal there are 3 pieces of each left. Pablo tells his mother that the same amount of each pizza is left. What mistake did he make? **See above left.**

28. *REASONING* Find a fraction that has a denominator of 15 and is between $\frac{2}{3}$ and $\frac{4}{5}$. $\frac{11}{15}$

MIXED REVIEW AND TEST PREP

Evaluate each expression for $a = 2.3$, $b = 0.7$, and $c = 5.4$. (p. 82)

29. $a - b + c$ **7**   30. $(b \times 5) + a$ **5.8**

31. Find the LCM of 8 and 12. (p. 150) **24**   32. Find the GCF of 16 and 40. (p. 150) **8**

33. **TEST PREP** There are 12 cans of soup in 1 case. How many cases should you order if you need 132 cans of soup? (p. 22) **B**

A 10   B 11   C 1,200   D 1,584

Extra Practice page H39, Set C

---

3 Practice

When fractions have like numerators, students often choose the fraction with the greater denominator as the greater fraction.

Error	Correction
$\frac{1}{4} > \frac{1}{2}$	$\frac{1}{2} > \frac{1}{4}$

Have students work with fraction circles or fraction bars to reinforce the concept that the fraction with the greater denominator is the lesser fraction. Compare the parts to see that $\frac{1}{4} < \frac{1}{2}$.

Guided Practice

Do Check For Understanding Exercises 1–8 with your students. Identify those having difficulty and use lesson resources to help.

Independent Practice

Assign Exercises 9–28.

MIXED REVIEW AND TEST PREP

Exercises 29–33 provide **cumulative review** (Chapters 1–8).

4 Assess

Summarize the lesson by having students:

DISCUSS Describe a situation where you would want to compare fractions. Possible answer: I ate $\frac{1}{3}$ of my pizza and Jan ate $\frac{2}{5}$ of hers. I want to know who ate more.

WRITE Explain how to compare fractions with unlike denominators. Possible answer: Change the fractions to equivalent fractions with like denominators and then compare the numerators.

Lesson Quiz

Transparency **8.3**

Compare the fractions. Write <, >, or = for each ●.

1. $\frac{1}{3}$ ● $\frac{1}{4}$ >   2. $\frac{3}{12}$ ● $\frac{7}{12}$ <

3. $\frac{2}{7}$ ● $\frac{6}{21}$ =

4. Kit used $\frac{5}{8}$ yd of orange string and $\frac{3}{4}$ yd of blue string for her project. Which color did she use more of? blue

---

PROBLEM SOLVING 8.3

Compare and Order Fractions

Write the correct answer.

Analyze Choose Solve Check

1. Beth has a box of 20 red pencils and a box of 16 blue pencils. If she makes equal-size groups of all red or all blue pencils, what is the greatest number that can be in each group so that no pencils will be left over?

4 pencils

2. Kim called her brother from her hotel after stopping for the night while on a trip. She told him she had completed $\frac{5}{8}$ of her trip. Had she completed at least half the trip? Explain.

Yes; $\frac{5}{8} > \frac{1}{2}$.

3. A doughnut shop uses the following formula when selling its doughnuts: $P = \$0.75 \times d$, where d is the number of doughnuts purchased and P is the price the customer pays. What is the greatest number of doughnuts a customer can buy with $5?

6 doughnuts

4. José read a cake recipe that called for $\frac{3}{4}$ cup flour, $\frac{1}{3}$ cup sugar, and $\frac{2}{5}$ cup milk. He lined up the ingredients in order by the amount, from least to greatest. Which ingredient did José put at the end of the line?

flour

Choose the letter for the best answer.

5. Evelyn said that she had finished less than half of her homework problems. What fraction of the problems might Evelyn have completed?
A $\frac{3}{5}$ C $\frac{5}{8}$
B $\frac{3}{8}$ D $\frac{4}{5}$

6. Four friends are all reading the same book. Gordon has read $\frac{1}{2}$ the book, Nick has read $\frac{3}{4}$, Yvonne has read $\frac{2}{5}$, and Curtis has read $\frac{2}{3}$. Which of them has read the greatest part of the book?
F Gordon   H Nick
G Yvonne   J Curtis

7. This year's sixth grade in Glenn Middle School has 6 classes. Which is the number of sixth-grade students if there are the same number of students in each class?
A 184 students   C 170 students
B 172 students   D 168 students

8. Di has 1 red marker, 1 blue marker, and 1 green marker. She plans to make a design having 3 vertical stripes, one of each color. How many different designs can Di make?
F 3 designs   H 9 designs
G 6 designs   J 12 designs

9. **Write About It** What are some different ways to compare a fraction to $\frac{1}{2}$? Possible answer: Use a number line, find and use the least common denominator, or determine if the denominator of the fraction is greater or less than twice the numerator.

CHALLENGE 8.3

Let's Compare

For each exercise, choose a fraction from the box at the right.

$\frac{19}{24}$ $\frac{7}{24}$ $\frac{7}{10}$ $\frac{1}{2}$

1. Carl, Philip, and Monica were discussing how they had spent last summer. Carl said that he stayed at his grandmother's house for half the summer. Philip said he stayed at his aunt's house for $\frac{5}{6}$ of the summer. Monica said she was away for a greater fraction of the summer than either of the two boys. If she was away for less than $\frac{3}{4}$ of the summer, what fraction of the summer was she away?

$\frac{7}{10}$ of the summer

2. When her cat had kittens, Mrs. Banks gave three of them to neighbors while they were still very small. The one she gave to Elise weighed $\frac{2}{5}$ pound. The one that Carmela received weighed $\frac{3}{5}$ pound. The kitten that Denise took home weighed more than Carmela's kitten, but less than Elise's. What fraction of a pound did Denise's kitten weigh?

$\frac{1}{2}$ lb

3. Each morning, Maria rides her bike $\frac{1}{3}$ mile to school. Angela walks the $\frac{1}{4}$ mile between her home and school. James skateboards to school, a distance less than Maria rides, but more than Angela walks. What fraction of a mile does James skateboard to school? **$\frac{7}{24}$ mi**

4. Sandra, Jackson, and Shari all have the same size box of markers. Sandra still has $\frac{5}{8}$ of all the markers that were originally in her box. Jackson has $\frac{3}{4}$ of the original number. Shari has more markers than one of her friends, but less than the other. What fraction of the original number of markers does Shari still have? **$\frac{19}{24}$ of the markers**

ORGANIZER

Objective To convert fractions to decimals

Materials *For each student* 1-cm graph paper, p. TR64, or two 10 × 10 grids (decimal squares), p. TR7; scissors; colored pencils

Lesson Resources E-Lab Recording Sheet • *Equivalent Fractions, Decimals, and Mixed Numbers*

Intervention for Prerequisite Skills Model Fractions (For intervention strategies, see page 159.)

Using the Page

Activity

Some students may confuse tenths with hundredths. Remind students that a 10 × 10 grid column represents one tenth and a square represents one hundredth.

Think and Discuss

What is the same about showing $\frac{6}{10}$ and $\frac{62}{100}$ on a 10 × 10 grid? What is different? For both you need to shade 6 columns; for $\frac{62}{100}$, you need to shade 2 more squares.

Practice

Ask students to explain the difference in their models for Exercises 3 and 4. The model for $\frac{7}{10}$ shows 70 shaded squares because $\frac{7}{10} = \frac{70}{100}$. The model for $\frac{7}{100}$ shows 7 shaded squares.

Oral Assessment

Write $\frac{1}{4}$ as a decimal. Describe your work. $\frac{1}{4} = \frac{25}{100} = 0.25$; First I write an equivalent fraction with 100 as the denominator. Then I use the numerator to write the decimal as hundredths.

Explore Fractions and Decimals

MATH LAB

Explore how to convert fractions to decimals.

You need graph paper, scissors, colored pencils.

You can use decimal squares to help you convert fractions to decimals.

Activity

• Cut out a 10 × 10 grid from graph paper. Fold it into 2 equal parts. Then use a colored pencil to shade one of the equal parts. What fraction of the grid is shaded? $\frac{1}{2}$

100 squares; 50 squares; $\frac{50}{100}$; 0.50

• How many small squares are in the whole grid? How many of these squares are shaded? What fraction compares these shaded squares to those in the whole grid? What decimal can you write for this fraction?

10 columns; 5 columns; $\frac{5}{10}$; 0.5

• How many columns are in the whole grid? How many columns are shaded? What fraction compares the shaded columns to the whole grid? What decimal can you write for this fraction?

• Are the fractions $\frac{1}{2}$, $\frac{5}{10}$, and $\frac{50}{100}$ equivalent? How do you know? What are two ways to write the fraction $\frac{1}{2}$ as a decimal? Yes; they all describe the same part of the grid; 0.50, 0.5.

• Cut out another 10 × 10 grid. Fold the grid into 5 equal parts and shade one part. How many rows or columns are shaded? How can you write $\frac{1}{5}$ as a decimal? 2 rows or columns; 0.2 or 0.20

Think and Discuss

• How can you show tenths in a 10 × 10 grid? full rows or columns

• How can you show hundredths in a 10 × 10 grid? small squares

• What fractions are easiest to write as decimals? fractions with denominators of 10 or 100

• How is the 10 × 10 grid helpful for writing fractions as decimals? The 10 × 10 grid has 100 squares, so each square is one hundredth of the whole.

TECHNOLOGY LINK

More Practice: Use E-Lab, *Equivalent Fractions, Decimals, and Mixed Numbers.* www.harcourtschool.com/elab2002

Practice

Write the fraction as a decimal. Use decimal squares.

1. $\frac{3}{10}$ 0.3   2. $\frac{60}{100}$ 0.60   3. $\frac{7}{10}$ 0.7   4. $\frac{7}{100}$ 0.07   5. $\frac{90}{100}$ 0.90

6. $\frac{2}{10}$ 0.2   7. $\frac{40}{100}$ 0.40   8. $\frac{6}{10}$ 0.6   9. $\frac{85}{100}$ 0.85   10. $\frac{8}{10}$ 0.8

CALIFORNIA STANDARDS **MR 2.0** Students use strategies, skills, and concepts in finding solutions. **MR 2.4** Use a variety of methods, such as words, numbers, symbols, charts, graphs, tables, diagrams, and models, to explain mathematical reasoning. *also* **MR 2.5**

E-LAB RECORDING SHEET

Name

Equivalent Fractions, Decimals, and Mixed Numbers

Fractions, mixed numbers, and decimals are different ways of writing the positive rational numbers you have been studying.

1. Write the number $\frac{3}{4}$ as a fraction in eighths. ____ $\frac{6}{8}$
   Write the number 3 as a fraction in tenths. ____ $\frac{30}{10}$

2. If you can write the number $2\frac{3}{8}$ by using a fraction in fourths, write it in the blank. Otherwise, write *no*. no
   If you can write the number $3\frac{3}{8}$ as a decimal, write it in the blank. Otherwise, write *no*. 3.375

3. Express the point on the number line halfway between $\frac{3}{4}$ and $1\frac{1}{2}$ as both a mixed number and a decimal. $1\frac{1}{8}$; 1.125

4. What is another way to write the decimal 3.333333...? $3\frac{1}{3}$

Use the computer. Answers will vary for Problems 5–19.

Click **Decimal**. Follow the directions on the screen, and click on a decimal that names the same number as the fraction. When the round is over, record both. Do this six times.

5. ____   6. ____   7. ____

8. ____   9. ____   10. ____

Click **Fraction**. Enter a fraction or mixed number that names the same number as the decimal given. When the round is over, record both. Do this six times.

11. ____   12. ____   13. ____

14. ____   15. ____   16. ____

Click **All**. Choose the fraction, mixed number, or decimal that does not name the same number as the other two. Move fast before they reach the target. Select your own speed and keep practicing. In each case, record the two that match. Do this six times.

17. ____   18. ____   19. ____

Every rational number greater than 0 can be expressed both as a decimal and as a fraction.

E-Lab Recording Sheet   3

USING E-LAB

Students use visual thinking as they play a game that relates fractions and decimals.

The E-Lab Recording Sheets and activities are available on the E-Lab website.

www.harcourtschool.com/elab2002

TECHNOLOGY LINK

 Intervention Strategies and Activities CD-ROM • *Skill 20*

 E-Lab • *Equivalent Fractions, Decimals, and Mixed Numbers*

 Astro Algebra • *Red*, Level C; **Number Heroes** • *Fraction Fireworks*, Levels Q, Y

Fractions, Decimals, and Percents

LESSON PLANNING

Objective To convert fractions to decimals, decimals to fractions, and fractions to percents

Intervention for Prerequisite Skills

Compare and Order Whole Numbers, Model Percents (For intervention strategies, see page 159.)

 California Mathematics Content Standards

NS 1.0 Students compare and order positive and negative fractions, decimals, and mixed numbers. Students solve problems involving fractions, ratios, proportions, and percentages.

(*Also* NS 2.0, MR 2.2, MR 2.4, MR 2.5)

Vocabulary

terminating decimal a decimal, such as $\frac{1}{2} = 0.5$, for which the division operation results in a remainder of zero

repeating decimal a decimal, such as $\frac{1}{3} = 0.333\ldots$ or $0.\overline{3}$, which shows a pattern of repeating digits

Math Background

Consider the following as you help students understand the relationship between fractions, decimals, and percents.

- Use a decimal's place value to write a decimal as a fraction.
- To write a fraction as a decimal, divide the numerator by the denominator.
- To compare fractions and decimals, rewrite the fractions as decimals so that all the numbers are in the same form.
- To write fractions as percents, first rewrite the fractions as decimals, and then convert the decimals to percents.

WARM-UP RESOURCES

 NUMBER OF THE DAY Transparency **8.5**

Write the part of the month that has elapsed as 2 equivalent fractions. Possible answer: $\frac{12}{30} = \frac{6}{15}$

 PROBLEM OF THE DAY Transparency **8.5**

A pizza has 8 slices. Milton ate $\frac{1}{4}$ of the pizza. Earl ate $\frac{1}{2}$ of what was left over. Did Earl eat more or fewer than 4 pieces? Explain. fewer; $\frac{1}{4}$ of 8 = 2; 8 − 2 = 6; Earl ate $\frac{1}{2}$ of 6 pieces, or 3 pieces

Solution Problem of the Day tab, p. PD8

 DAILY FACTS PRACTICE

Have students practice multiplication and division facts by completing Set A of *Teacher's Resource Book*, p. TR99.

INTERVENTION AND EXTENSION RESOURCES

ALTERNATIVE TEACHING STRATEGY

Have students **use equivalent fractions with denominators of 100 to change fractions to percents.** Display: $\frac{1}{4} = \frac{\blacksquare}{100}$

Ask a volunteer to suggest a number to multiply 4 by to equal 100. Then complete the process.

$$\frac{1}{4} = \frac{1 \times 25}{4 \times 25} = \frac{25}{100} = 0.25 = 25\%$$

Direct students to change these fractions to percents.

$\frac{7}{20} = \frac{\blacksquare}{100}\ 35\%$ $\frac{13}{25} = \frac{\blacksquare}{100}\ 52\%$

VISUAL

MIXED REVIEW AND TEST PREP

Cumulative Review Chapters 1–8

Refer to the Pupil Edition pages referenced in the exercises for further review. Have students go back to the lesson page, review the lesson, and correct any problem they missed.

Mixed Review and Test Prep, p. 171

How to Help	
Item	Page
57	164
58	164
59	66
60	66
61	109

ENGLISH LANGUAGE LEARNERS ELL·SDAIE

Reinforce vocabulary by having students **identify numbers as fractions, decimals, or percents.**

- Display the words *decimal, fraction,* and *percent.* Have students copy the words into their math journals leaving a few lines between each word.

- Ask students to list ten examples of a decimal after the word *decimal.*

- Then have them rewrite the decimals as fractions and percents, recording their answers after the appropriate words.

Ask volunteers to share examples with the class.

Check students' work.

VISUAL

ENG-LANG ARTS
Standards
R 1.0

SPECIAL NEEDS

Materials *For each student* two 10 x 10 grids (decimal squares), p. TR7; 2 different colored markers

Have students **model a decimal and a fraction** that they have compared in one of the Exercises 38–43 on page 171. Tell students to model the decimal in one color on one of the grids and to model the fraction in another color on the other grid to show that their answer is correct. Check students' work.

KINESTHETIC

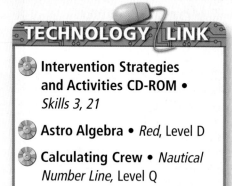

TECHNOLOGY LINK

- **Intervention Strategies and Activities CD-ROM** • *Skills 3, 21*

- **Astro Algebra** • *Red,* Level D

- **Calculating Crew** • *Nautical Number Line,* Level Q

LESSON 8.5

Fractions, Decimals, and Percents

Learn how to convert fractions to decimals, decimals to fractions, and fractions to percents.

QUICK REVIEW

1. 24 ÷ 4 **6** **2.** 144 ÷ 6 **24** **3.** 155 ÷ 5 **31**
4. Write 0.73 in words.
seventy-three hundredths
5. Write 0.026 in words.
twenty-six thousandths

There are many ways to write numbers. Some ways are as fractions, decimals, and percents.

Sometimes you may have to rewrite a given number in a different form. The easiest conversion is from a decimal to a fraction.

Vocabulary

terminating decimal

repeating decimal

EXAMPLE 1

Remember that *percent* means "out of one hundred." For example, 25% means "25 out of 100."

Write each decimal as a fraction.
A. 0.7 **B.** 0.29

Use the decimal's place value to write each fraction.

$0.7 = \frac{7}{10}$ **THINK:** *"seven tenths"* $0.29 = \frac{29}{100}$ **THINK:** *"twenty-nine hundredths"*

To rewrite a fraction as a decimal, use long division or a calculator.

EXAMPLE 2

A newborn koala is about 19 mm long. This is about $\frac{3}{4}$ in. Change $\frac{3}{4}$ to a decimal.

Use long division.

$$\begin{array}{r} 0.75 \\ 4\overline{)3.00} \end{array}$$ *Divide the numerator by the denominator.*

So, $\frac{3}{4} = 0.75$.

Use a calculator.

3 ÷ 4 =

0.75

The decimal 0.75 is an example of a **terminating decimal**. The decimal comes to an end at 5. You know that a decimal terminates if you reach a remainder of zero when you are using long division.

The decimal for the fraction $\frac{4}{11}$ does not terminate. When you divide 4 by 11, you never reach a remainder of zero. This decimal is a **repeating decimal** because it shows a pattern of repeating digits.

To write a repeating decimal, show three dots or draw a bar over the repeating part.

$\frac{4}{11} = 0.363636\dots$ $\frac{4}{11} = 0.\overline{36}$

$$\begin{array}{r} 0.3636 \\ 11\overline{)4.0000} \\ -3\,3 \\ \hline 70 \\ -66 \\ \hline 40 \\ -33 \\ \hline 70 \\ -66 \\ \hline 4 \end{array}$$

 CALIFORNIA STANDARDS ⊶ **NS 1.0** Students compare and order positive and negative fractions, decimals, and mixed numbers. Students solve problems involving fractions, ratios, proportions, and percentages. *also* ⊶ **NS 2.0, MR 2.2, MR 2.4, MR 2.5**

169

RETEACH 8.5

Fractions, Decimals, and Percents

When you need to change a fraction to a decimal, you can use division.
Write the fraction $\frac{3}{5}$ as a decimal.

Step 1 Set up a division problem, dividing the numerator by the denominator. $5\overline{)3}$

Step 2 Place a decimal point after the numerator. Write a zero. $5\overline{)3.0}$

Step 3 Divide as you would with whole numbers. $\begin{array}{r}0.6\\5\overline{)3.0}\\3\,0\\\hline 0\end{array}$

So, written as a decimal, $\frac{3}{5} = 0.6$. Recall that 0.6 is a terminating decimal because it ends after the tenths place.

When you need to change a decimal to a fraction, use place value.

Change 0.364 to a fraction.

Step 1 Identify the place value of the last digit in the decimal number. $\begin{array}{c}0.364\\\uparrow\\\text{thousandths}\end{array}$

Step 2 Use the place value of the last digit as the denominator. $\frac{364}{1,000}$

So, $0.364 = \frac{364}{1,000}$.

Answer the questions to change the fraction to a decimal.

1. $\frac{1}{4}$ **2.** $\frac{3}{8}$

a. What division problem will you use?   **a.** What division problem will you use?
  1 ÷ 4   3 ÷ 8

b. What is the quotient?   **b.** What is the quotient?
  0.25   0.375

Use place value to write the decimal as a fraction.

3. 0.6 $\frac{6}{10}$ **4.** 0.92 $\frac{92}{100}$ **5.** 0.48 $\frac{48}{100}$ **6.** 0.137 $\frac{137}{1,000}$

PRACTICE 8.5

Fractions, Decimals, and Percents

Write the decimal as a fraction.

1. 0.5 $\frac{5}{10}$ **2.** 0.14 $\frac{14}{100}$ **3.** 0.06 $\frac{6}{100}$ **4.** 0.83 $\frac{83}{100}$

5. 0.62 $\frac{62}{100}$ **6.** 0.317 $\frac{317}{1,000}$ **7.** 0.805 $\frac{805}{1,000}$ **8.** 0.955 $\frac{955}{1,000}$

Write as a decimal. Tell whether the decimal terminates or repeats.

9. $\frac{3}{10}$ 0.3, T **10.** $\frac{6}{9}$ $0.\overline{6}$, R **11.** $\frac{7}{12}$ $0.58\overline{3}$, R **12.** $\frac{11}{20}$ 0.55, T

13. $\frac{7}{30}$ $0.2\overline{3}$, R **14.** $\frac{9}{10}$ 0.9, T **15.** $\frac{7}{15}$ $0.4\overline{6}$, R **16.** $\frac{4}{11}$ $0.\overline{36}$, R

Compare. Write <, >, or = for each ●.

17. 0.24 ● $\frac{1}{4}$ < **18.** 0.18 ● $\frac{7}{50}$ > **19.** $\frac{4}{10}$ ● 0.44 <

20. $\frac{1}{5}$ ● 0.19 > **21.** $\frac{7}{20}$ ● 0.45 < **22.** $\frac{9}{20}$ ● 0.45 =

Write the fraction as a percent.

23. $\frac{3}{5}$ 60% **24.** $\frac{17}{100}$ 17% **25.** $\frac{4}{2}$ 200% **26.** $\frac{1}{500}$ 0.2%

27. $\frac{9}{25}$ 36% **28.** $\frac{7}{5}$ 140% **29.** $\frac{6}{40}$ 15% **30.** $\frac{17}{20}$ 85%

Mixed Review
Estimate. Possible estimates are given.

31. 56.09 ÷ 7.1 **8** **32.** 64.1 − 13.9 **50** **33.** 97.6 ÷ 9.8 **10** **34.** $1.79 − $0.82 **$1.00**

35. 188.2 × 21.3 **4,000** **36.** 602.5 ÷ 102.4 **700** **37.** $49.34 × 5 **$250** **38.** 711.2 + 798.5 **1,500**

Evaluate the expression.

39. 6 + 4 × 3 **18** **40.** 18 − 6 ÷ 2 **14** **41.** (10 × 3) ÷ 6 **5**

LESSON 8.5 ORGANIZER

Objective To convert fractions to decimals, decimals to fractions, and fractions to percents

Vocabulary terminating decimal, repeating decimal *Review* percent

1 Introduce

QUICK REVIEW provides review of prerequisite skills.

Why Learn This? You can use this skill to convert survey results to percents for graphic displays. *Share the lesson objective with students.*

2 Teach

Guided Instruction

• *Discuss the methods of conversion in Examples 1 and 2.*

Why is it simple to convert a decimal to a fraction? The denominator is the same as the decimal place, and the numerator is the number part of the decimal.

How would you write 0.09 as a fraction? $\frac{9}{100}$

REASONING **What kind of fraction results in a decimal containing a whole number? Explain.** A fraction greater than 1; the denominator/divisor is less than the numerator/dividend.

• *Focus on the concept of terminating and repeating decimals.*

How do you know when to stop dividing when you have a repeating decimal? when you see the pattern of numbers repeat in the quotient

REASONING If $\frac{1}{3} = 0.\overline{3}$, express $\frac{2}{3}$ as a decimal. $0.\overline{6}$

ADDITIONAL EXAMPLES

Example 1, p. 169

Write each decimal as a fraction.
A. 0.3 $\frac{3}{10}$ **B.** 0.41 $\frac{41}{100}$

Example 2, p. 169

Tracy's grade on a quiz was $\frac{7}{9}$. Change $\frac{7}{9}$ to a decimal. $0.7777\dots$ or $0.\overline{7}$

169

LESSON 8.5

- *Before discussing Example 3, review how to compare decimals.*

  How do you compare decimals? Start at the left and compare the digits in each place, one at a time.

- *Help students generalize the method for changing decimals to percents.*

  What do you do to the decimal point to change any decimal to a percent? move it 2 places to the right

REASONING **Challenge students to reverse the process and explain how to write 15% as a fraction.** Write 15% as 0.15. Then rewrite the decimal as a fraction, $\frac{15}{100}$. Finally, write the fraction in simplest form, $\frac{3}{20}$.

ADDITIONAL EXAMPLES

Example 3, p. 170

The jar of Spencer's Spices contains $\frac{1}{8}$ lb of cinnamon. The jar of Nature's Best has 0.25 lb of cinnamon. Which container holds more cinnamon? $\frac{1}{8} = 0.125$; $0.25 > 0.125$; Nature's Best

Example 4, p. 170

Stuffed animals are on sale at the zoo's souvenir shop for $\frac{1}{5}$ off. What percent off the original price is the sale price? $\frac{1}{5} = 0.20 = 20\%$

3 Practice

Guided Practice

Do Check for Understanding Exercises 1–17 with your students. Identify those having difficulty and use lesson resources to help.

Additional Answers, Check for Understanding

1. The last digit is in the thousandths place. The numerator is 26 and the denominator is 1,000, so $0.026 = \frac{26}{1000}$.

2. Possible answer: When you use long division to write a fraction as a decimal, you will reach a remainder of zero if the decimal terminates. You will reach a repeating remainder or pattern of remainders if the decimal repeats.

To compare a fraction and a decimal, you can first rewrite the fraction as a decimal. Then compare the decimals.

EXAMPLE 3

A newborn panda weighs about $\frac{1}{4}$ lb. A newborn cocker spaniel weighs about 0.4 lb. Which animal weighs less at birth?

Solve by using long division.

$$\begin{array}{r} 0.25 \\ 4\overline{)1.00} \\ -8 \\ \hline 20 \\ -20 \\ \hline 0 \end{array}$$

Divide the numerator by the denominator.

Solve by using a calculator.

1 ÷ 4 = 0.25

$0.25 < 0.4$, so $\frac{1}{4} < 0.4$.

So, a newborn panda weighs less than a newborn cocker spaniel.

To write a fraction as a percent, first convert the fraction to a decimal. Then write the decimal as a percent.

EXAMPLE 4

The barrow ground squirrel of Point Barrow, Alaska, is the world's longest-hibernating animal. The squirrel hibernates $\frac{9}{12}$ of the year. What percent of the year does it hibernate?

$\frac{9}{12} = 0.75$ *Use long division or a calculator to rewrite the fraction as a decimal.*

$0.75 = \frac{75}{100}$ THINK: *75 hundredths. Write the decimal as a fraction.*

$= 75\%$ THINK: *Percent means "out of one hundred." So, 75 hundredths is 75 percent.*

So, the barrow ground squirrel hibernates 75% of the year.

CHECK FOR UNDERSTANDING

Think and Discuss ▶ Look back at the lesson to answer each question.

1. **Explain** how to use place value to change 0.026 to a fraction. See below.
2. **Compare** a repeating decimal with a terminating decimal. See below.

Guided Practice ▶ Write the decimal as a fraction.

3. 0.7 $\frac{7}{10}$ 4. 0.39 $\frac{39}{100}$ 5. 0.105 $\frac{105}{1,000}$ 6. 0.007 $\frac{7}{1,000}$

Write as a decimal. Tell whether the decimal terminates or repeats.

7. $\frac{1}{4}$ 0.25, T 8. $\frac{7}{20}$ 0.35, T 9. $\frac{2}{3}$ 0.$\overline{6}$, R 10. $\frac{8}{11}$ 0.$\overline{72}$, R

Compare. Write <, >, or = for each ●.

11. 0.62 ● $\frac{1}{2}$ > 12. $\frac{12}{20}$ ● 0.9 < 13. $\frac{1}{8}$ ● 0.125 =

Write the fraction as a percent.

14. $\frac{7}{10}$ 70% 15. $\frac{1}{5}$ 20% 16. $\frac{1}{4}$ 25% 17. $\frac{40}{100}$ 40%

170 Chapter 8

PROBLEM SOLVING 8.5

Fractions, Decimals, and Percents

Analyze Choose Solve Check

Write the correct answer.

1. Amir had $\frac{3}{4}$ of a dollar and Dale had $0.83. Who had more money?

   Dale

2. Kate read the number 0.345 as "345 hundredths." Was she correct? Explain.

   No; the number is 345 thousandths.

3. The winning times for the men's 100-meter run in three recent Olympics are given below. Put the winning times in order from fastest to slowest.

   | 1988 | 1992 | 1996 |
   | 9.92 sec | 9.96 sec | 9.84 sec |

   9.84 sec, 9.92 sec, 9.96 sec

4. The winning times for the women's 400-meter relay in the 1988, 1992, and 1996 Olympics are given below. In which Olympic year was the fastest time run?

   | 1988 | 1992 | 1996 |
   | 41.98 sec | 41.11 sec | 41.95 sec |

   1996

Choose the letter for the best answer.

5. Polly listens to 5 hours of classical music each week. Which is the best estimate of how many minutes of classical music she listens to in 19 weeks?

   A 4,000 min
   B 6,000 min
   C 8,000 min
   D 10,000 min

6. Nancy wants to buy 24 sodas for her party. A 6-pack of soda costs $2, including tax. Which expression can be used to find the total cost of the sodas that Nancy wants to buy?

   F 24 × $2
   G 6 × $2
   H (24 ÷ 6) × $2
   J (24 − 6) × $2

7. The distance from Shania's house to school is $\frac{3}{5}$ of the distance from Faith's house to school. What percent of the distance that Faith travels each morning does Shania travel?

   A 3.5%   C 50%
   B 35%   D 60%

8. Park ran 0.8 mile. Nicholas said that he ran the same fraction of a mile. How far did Nicholas run?

   F $\frac{4}{5}$ mi   H $\frac{1}{5}$ mi
   G $\frac{3}{5}$ mi   J $\frac{1}{8}$ mi

9. **Write About It** Explain how to compare the fraction $\frac{2}{3}$ and the decimal 0.7 to see which is greater.

   Possible answer: Use Division to rewrite $\frac{2}{3}$ as a decimal. Then compare the two decimals to see that 0.7 is greater than $\frac{2}{3}$.

CHALLENGE 8.5

Decimal Patterns

Find the next three terms in the pattern. Then write the rule for the pattern.

1. $\frac{1}{5}$, $\frac{2}{5}$, $\frac{3}{5}$, $\frac{4}{5}$, $\frac{5}{5}$, $\frac{6}{5}$, $\frac{7}{5}$, $\frac{8}{5}$, $\frac{9}{5}$

   0.20 0.40 0.60 0.80 1.00 1.20 1.40 1.60 1.80
   Rule: _____ Add $\frac{1}{5}$ (0.20) to previous number.

2. $\frac{11}{2}$, $\frac{10}{2}$, $\frac{9}{2}$, $\frac{8}{2}$, $\frac{7}{2}$, $\frac{6}{2}$, $\frac{5}{2}$, $\frac{4}{2}$, $\frac{3}{2}$

   5.5 5.0 4.5 4.0 3.5 3.0 2.5 2.0 1.5
   Rule: _____ Subtract $\frac{1}{2}$ (0.5) from previous number.

3. $\frac{3}{10}$, $\frac{6}{10}$, $\frac{9}{10}$, $\frac{12}{10}$, $\frac{15}{10}$, $\frac{18}{10}$, $\frac{21}{10}$, $\frac{24}{10}$, $\frac{27}{10}$

   0.3 0.6 0.9 1.2 1.5 1.8 2.1 2.4 2.7
   Rule: _____ Add $\frac{3}{10}$ (0.3) to previous number.

4. $\frac{25}{4}$, $\frac{24}{4}$, $\frac{23}{4}$, $\frac{22}{4}$, $\frac{21}{4}$, $\frac{20}{4}$, $\frac{19}{4}$, $\frac{18}{4}$, $\frac{17}{4}$

   6.25 6.00 5.75 5.50 5.25 5.00 4.75 4.50 4.25
   Rule: _____ Subtract $\frac{1}{4}$ (0.25) from previous number.

5. $\frac{44}{10}$, $\frac{40}{10}$, $\frac{36}{10}$, $\frac{32}{10}$, $\frac{28}{10}$, $\frac{24}{10}$, $\frac{20}{10}$, $\frac{16}{10}$, $\frac{12}{10}$, $\frac{8}{10}$

   4.4 4.0 3.6 3.2 2.8 2.4 2.0 1.6 1.2 0.8
   Rule: _____ Subtract $\frac{4}{10}$ (0.4) from previous number.

6. $\frac{99}{100}$, $\frac{88}{100}$, $\frac{77}{100}$, $\frac{66}{100}$, $\frac{55}{100}$, $\frac{44}{100}$, $\frac{33}{100}$, $\frac{22}{100}$

   0.99 0.88 0.77 0.66 0.55 0.44 0.33 0.22
   Rule: _____ Subtract $\frac{11}{100}$ (0.11) from previous number.

Independent ▶ Practice

Write the decimal as a fraction.

18. 0.4 $\frac{4}{10}$ **19.** 0.06 $\frac{6}{100}$ **20.** 0.35 $\frac{35}{100}$ **21.** 0.61 $\frac{61}{100}$

22. 0.115 $\frac{115}{1,000}$ **23.** 0.205 $\frac{205}{1,000}$ **24.** 0.079 $\frac{79}{1,000}$ **25.** 0.009 $\frac{9}{1,000}$

Write as a decimal. Tell whether the decimal terminates or repeats.

26. $\frac{1}{5}$ 0.2, T **27.** $\frac{1}{6}$ $0.1\overline{6}$, R **28.** $\frac{1}{15}$ $0.0\overline{6}$, R **29.** $\frac{5}{8}$ 0.625, T

30. $\frac{11}{20}$ 0.55, T **31.** $\frac{3}{10}$ 0.3, T **32.** $\frac{5}{12}$ $0.41\overline{6}$, R **33.** $\frac{1}{9}$ $0.\overline{1}$, R

34. $\frac{11}{12}$ $0.91\overline{6}$, R **35.** $\frac{9}{25}$ 0.36, T **36.** $\frac{17}{33}$ $0.\overline{51}$, R **37.** $\frac{15}{99}$ $0.\overline{15}$, R

Compare. Write <, >, or = for each ●.

38. $\frac{1}{10}$ ● 0.04 > **39.** 0.15 ● $\frac{3}{20}$ = **40.** $\frac{1}{2}$ ● 0.52 <

41. 0.65 ● $\frac{3}{4}$ < **42.** $\frac{1}{20}$ ● 0.1 < **43.** 0.58 ● $\frac{7}{12}$ <

Write the fraction as a percent.

44. $\frac{9}{10}$ 90% **45.** $\frac{3}{4}$ 75% **46.** $\frac{1}{2}$ 50% **47.** $\frac{6}{100}$ 6%

48. $\frac{3}{5}$ 60% **49.** $\frac{25}{50}$ 50% **50.** $\frac{3}{2}$ 150% **51.** $\frac{1}{200}$ 0.5%

Problem Solving ▶ Applications

52. The goal of the East Side Animal Shelter is to have 0.8 of its animals adopted. One week, the shelter found homes for 20 of its 24 animals. Did the shelter reach its goal? Explain.
Yes; $\frac{20}{24} = \frac{5}{6} = 0.8\overline{3} > 0.8.$

Use Data For 53–55, use the table.

53. Write Brian's math test score as a decimal. 0.72

54. Did Juan get a higher score on the math or science test? science

55. Which student got a higher score on the math test than on the science test?

55. Megan

STUDENT	MATH SCORE	SCIENCE SCORE
Brian	$\frac{18}{25}$	0.95
Juan	$\frac{21}{25}$	0.85
Sabina	$\frac{17}{25}$	0.75
Megan	$\frac{23}{25}$	0.90

56. **Write About It** The decimal for $\frac{1}{9}$ is $0.\overline{1}$; for $\frac{2}{9}$, $0.\overline{2}$; and for $\frac{3}{9}$, $0.\overline{3}$. Explain how you could use this information to predict the decimal for $\frac{8}{9}$. Use division to check your method. The numerator repeats after the decimal point, so $\frac{8}{9}$ would be $0.\overline{8}$.

57. Write $4\frac{1}{2}$ as a fraction. (p. 164) $\frac{9}{2}$ **58.** Write $\frac{36}{5}$ as a mixed number. (p. 164) $7\frac{1}{5}$

59. $79.02 - 2.13$ (p. 66) **76.89** **60.** $48.541 + 11$ (p. 66) **59.541**

61. TEST PREP On his last seven math quizzes, Rashard scored 86, 88, 92, 88, 33, 96, and 84. Find the mean of his scores with and without the outlier. (p. 109) **A**
A 81, 89 **B** 84, 89 **C** 88, 88 **D** 89, 81

Independent Practice

Assign Exercises 18–56.

Algebraic Thinking In Exercises 11–13 and 38–43, students compare numbers. This skill provides a basis for understanding how to solve inequalities.

For Exercise 52, students must first write the fraction of animals that found homes. Then they should rewrite that fraction in simplest form. Finally, they should change the fraction to a decimal and compare it with 0.8.

MIXED REVIEW AND TEST PREP
Exercises 57–61 provide **cumulative review** (Chapters 1–8).

4 Assess

Summarize the lesson by having students:

DISCUSS Describe one situation in which you might have to change a percent to a fraction or a fraction to a percent. Answers may vary.

WRITE Explain how to change a decimal to a fraction and a fraction to a decimal. Possible answer: Use the decimal number as the numerator and the place value of the decimal as the denominator; divide the numerator by the denominator.

Lesson Quiz

Transparency **8.5**

Write the decimal as a fraction.

1. 0.1 $\frac{1}{10}$ **2.** 0.09 $\frac{9}{100}$

3. 0.411 $\frac{411}{1000}$

Write the fraction as a decimal. Tell whether the decimal terminates or repeats.

4. $\frac{2}{9}$ 0.222 . . ., R **5.** $\frac{4}{15}$ 0.2666 . . ., R

6. $\frac{4}{16}$ 0.25, T

CHAPTER 8

REVIEW/TEST

Purpose To check understanding of concepts, skills, and problem solving presented in Chapter 8

USING THE PAGE

The Chapter 8 Review/Test can be used as a **review** or a **test**.

- Items 1–2 check understanding of concepts and new vocabulary.
- Items 3–29 check skill proficiency.
- Items 30–33 check students' abilities to choose and apply problem solving strategies to real-life problems that involve fractions.

Suggest that students place the completed Chapter 8 Review/Test in their portfolios.

USING THE ASSESSMENT GUIDE

- Multiple-choice format of Chapter 8 Posttest—See *Assessment Guide*, pp. AG53–54.
- Free-response format of Chapter 8 Posttest—See *Assessment Guide*, pp. AG55–56.

USING STUDENT SELF-ASSESSMENT

The How Did I Do? survey helps students assess what they have learned and how they learned it. This survey is available as a copying master in *Assessment Guide*, p. AGxvii.

172   Chapter 8

CHAPTER 8 REVIEW/TEST

1. **VOCABULARY** When the numerator and denominator of a fraction have no common factors other than 1, the fraction is in __?__. (p. 161) **simplest form**

2. **VOCABULARY** A number that is made up of a whole number and a fraction is called a __?__. (p. 164) **mixed number**

Write the fraction in simplest form. (pp. 160–163)

3. $\frac{6}{12}$ $\frac{1}{2}$

4. $\frac{12}{16}$ $\frac{3}{4}$

5. $\frac{25}{30}$ $\frac{5}{6}$

Complete. (pp. 160–163)

6. $\frac{3}{5} = \frac{\blacksquare}{20}$ 12

7. $\frac{2}{\blacksquare} = \frac{10}{35}$ 7

8. $\frac{24}{32} = \frac{\blacksquare}{8}$ 6

Write the fraction as a mixed number or a whole number. (pp. 164–165)

9. $\frac{7}{3}$ $2\frac{1}{3}$

10. $\frac{30}{6}$ 5

11. $\frac{19}{4}$ $4\frac{3}{4}$

Write the mixed number as a fraction. (pp. 164–165)

12. $1\frac{5}{6}$ $\frac{11}{6}$

13. $3\frac{1}{3}$ $\frac{10}{3}$

14. $5\frac{7}{8}$ $\frac{47}{8}$

Compare the fractions. Write <, >, or = for each ●. (pp. 166–167)

15. $\frac{7}{8}$ ● $\frac{5}{8}$ >

16. $\frac{2}{3}$ ● $\frac{8}{12}$ =

17. $\frac{1}{3}$ ● $\frac{1}{2}$ <

18. $\frac{1}{2}$ ● $\frac{11}{20}$ <

19. $\frac{3}{4}$ ● $\frac{3}{8}$ >

20. $\frac{7}{25}$ ● $\frac{1}{5}$ >

Write the decimal as a fraction. (pp. 169–171)

21. 0.27 $\frac{27}{100}$

22. 0.1 $\frac{1}{10}$

23. 0.089 $\frac{89}{1,000}$

Write as a decimal. Tell whether the decimal terminates or repeats. (pp. 169–171)

24. $\frac{1}{4}$ 0.25, T

25. $\frac{5}{6}$ $0.8\overline{3}$, R

26. $\frac{7}{20}$ 0.35, T

Write the fraction as a percent. (pp. 169–171)

27. $\frac{3}{4}$ 75%

28. $\frac{9}{100}$ 9%

29. $\frac{11}{25}$ 44%

30. In the election for class president, Marcus received $\frac{5}{12}$ of the votes, Denise received $\frac{1}{4}$ of the votes, and Alonzo received $\frac{1}{3}$ of the votes. Who won the election? (pp. 166–167) **Marcus**

31. **Use Data** Use the table to find the fraction of the new November films that are rated PG-13. Write your answer in simplest form. What percent is this? (pp. 160–163) $\frac{2}{5}$; 40%

32. Of all U.S. car tunnels longer than 1 mile, $\frac{3}{8}$ are in Pennsylvania. Change $\frac{3}{8}$ to a decimal. (pp. 169–171) **0.375**

33. On Library Day, $\frac{13}{20}$ of the students at Pine Street School checked books out of the library. What percent of the students checked out books? (pp. 169–171) **65%**

NOVEMBER FILMS	
Rating	Number
G	3
PG-13	8
PG	5
R	4

172   Chapter 8

CHAPTER 8 TEST, page 1

Choose the best answer.

For 1–3, find the number that completes the equation.

1. $\frac{2}{3} = \frac{\blacksquare}{15}$
   A 5   C 12
   (B) 10   D 18

2. $\frac{12}{24} = \frac{4}{\blacksquare}$
   F 72   H 6
   (G) 8   J 2

3. $\frac{3}{\blacksquare} = \frac{6}{8}$
   A 16   (C) 4
   B 5   D 2

4. Which fraction is in simplest form?
   (F) $\frac{5}{12}$ H $\frac{9}{12}$
   G $\frac{6}{12}$ J $\frac{10}{12}$

5. Which is $\frac{6}{30}$ in simplest form?
   A $\frac{6}{5}$ (C) $\frac{1}{5}$
   B $\frac{5}{6}$ D $\frac{1}{30}$

6. Which is $\frac{10}{16}$ in simplest form?
   F $\frac{20}{32}$ H $\frac{4}{6}$
   (G) $\frac{5}{8}$ J $\frac{5}{4}$

7. Which is $\frac{8}{3}$ as a mixed number?
   A $\frac{2}{3}$ C $2\frac{1}{3}$
   B 2   (D) $2\frac{2}{3}$

8. Which fraction is equal to 4?
   (F) $\frac{20}{5}$ H $\frac{25}{5}$
   G $\frac{22}{4}$ J $\frac{24}{4}$

9. Which is $2\frac{3}{4}$ as a fraction?
   (A) $\frac{11}{4}$ C $\frac{9}{4}$
   B $\frac{10}{4}$ D $\frac{8}{4}$

10. Which is $3\frac{5}{8}$ as a fraction?
    F $\frac{5}{8}$ (H) $\frac{29}{8}$
    G $\frac{16}{8}$ J $\frac{40}{8}$

For 11–14, find the number that makes the number sentence true.

11. $\frac{5}{6} = \frac{\blacksquare}{12}$
    A 2   (C) 10
    B 6   D 11

12. $\blacksquare < \frac{11}{16}$
    F $\frac{14}{16}$ H $\frac{6}{8}$
    G $\frac{8}{10}$ (J) $\frac{5}{8}$

13. $\blacksquare > \frac{4}{7}$
    A 0.3   C 0.5
    B 0.4   (D) 0.6

14. 0.6 = $\blacksquare$
    F $\frac{60}{10}$ (H) $\frac{3}{5}$
    G $\frac{10}{6}$ J $\frac{3}{50}$

Go On →

CHAPTER 8 TEST, page 2

15. Which is 0.3 as a fraction?
    A $\frac{30}{10}$ C $\frac{3}{100}$
    (B) $\frac{3}{10}$ D $\frac{3}{1,000}$

16. Which completes the equation?
    $6\frac{7}{10} = \frac{670}{\blacksquare}$
    F 1,000   H 10
    (G) 100   J 1

17. What is $\frac{3}{4}$ in decimal form? Tell whether the decimal terminates or repeats.
    A 0.25; repeats
    B 0.25; terminates
    C 0.75; repeats
    (D) 0.75; terminates

18. What is $\frac{8}{10}$ in decimal form?
    F 0.9   H 0.8
    (G) 0.8   J 0.3

19. What is $\frac{2}{5}$ written as a percent?
    A 2%   (C) 40%
    B 20%   D 45%

20. What is $\frac{19}{100}$ written as a percent?
    F 190%   H 1.9%
    (G) 19%   J 0.19%

21. In gym class, $\frac{1}{4}$ of the students voted to play soccer, $\frac{1}{12}$ voted to play baseball, $\frac{3}{8}$ voted to play volleyball, and $\frac{7}{24}$ voted to play basketball. Which activity got the greatest part of the votes?
    (A) volleyball   C basketball
    B soccer   D baseball

22. In a sixth-grade class, $\frac{7}{20}$ of the students got 100 on a test. What percent of the students got 100 on the test?
    F 3.5%   H 21%
    G 5%   (J) 35%

23. At a film festival, $\frac{9}{15}$ of the judges gave the movie *The Last Bicycle* the highest rating. Which decimal tells what part of the group of judges gave the movie the highest rating?
    A 0.9   C 0.45
    (B) 0.6   D 0.3

24. For the class picnic, $\frac{1}{3}$ of the class voted for vanilla ice cream, $\frac{2}{5}$ voted for chocolate, $\frac{1}{6}$ voted for peach, and $\frac{1}{15}$ voted for strawberry. Which flavor received the least part of the votes?
    (F) strawberry   H chocolate
    G vanilla   J peach

For 25, use the table below.

ARTURO'S BOOKS	
Type	Number
Mystery	7
Science Fiction	6
Romance	3
Nonfiction	4

25. Which fraction tells what part of Arturo's books are science fiction?
    A $\frac{6}{7}$ (C) $\frac{3}{10}$
    B $\frac{3}{5}$ D $\frac{3}{20}$

Stop

Understand the problem.

See item **8.**

To compare fractions and decimals, change them to the same form. Use the form that will be easier to work with. Then find the numbers that are in the proper order.

Also see problem **1**, p. H62.

Choose the best answer.

1. Which group contains fractions that are all equivalent to $\frac{1}{4}$? **C**

   A $\frac{2}{8}, \frac{4}{20}, \frac{11}{44}$ C $\frac{6}{24}, \frac{15}{60}, \frac{50}{200}$

   B $\frac{3}{6}, \frac{20}{80}, \frac{3}{12}$ D $\frac{3}{12}, \frac{25}{100}, \frac{5}{9}$

2. Which is equivalent to 0.36? **G**

   F $\frac{18}{100}$

   G $\frac{9}{25}$

   H $\frac{3}{6}$

   J $\frac{36}{10}$

3. Which pair contains numbers that are equivalent? **A**

   A $3\frac{2}{3}, \frac{11}{3}$ C $4\frac{2}{5}, \frac{21}{5}$

   B $\frac{13}{4}, 2\frac{3}{4}$ D $\frac{16}{7}, 3\frac{1}{2}$

4. What is $\frac{135}{144}$ in simplest form? **H**

   F $\frac{7}{8}$ H $\frac{15}{16}$

   G $\frac{11}{12}$ J Not here

5. Eldora measured the length of a remote control sailboat course as $\frac{5}{8}$ of a mile. What is the decimal equivalent of $\frac{5}{8}$? **C**

   A 0.5

   B 0.58

   C 0.625

   D 0.8

6. In which pair are both numbers equivalent to $\frac{3}{4}$? **J**

   F 0.25; 25%   H 80%; $\frac{12}{15}$

   G 30%; $\frac{3}{10}$ J 75%; $\frac{12}{16}$

7. Evan has a bag of fruit. He has 9 apples, 4 oranges, and 3 bananas. What fraction represents the pieces of fruit that are oranges? **B**

   A $\frac{4}{18}$

   B $\frac{1}{4}$

   C $\frac{5}{16}$

   D $\frac{3}{4}$

8. Which numbers are in order from least to greatest? **F**

   F 0.3, $\frac{3}{8}, \frac{2}{5}$

   G $\frac{2}{5}$, 0.3, $\frac{3}{8}$

   H $\frac{3}{8}, \frac{2}{5}$, 0.3

   J $\frac{2}{5}, \frac{3}{8}$, 0.3

9. If 5 packages of hot dogs cost $9.25, what is the cost of 1 package? **C**

   A $0.92

   B $1.15

   C $1.85

   D $2.10

10. $\frac{5}{6} < \blacksquare$ **J**

   F $\frac{7}{12}$ H $\frac{7}{9}$

   G $\frac{7}{10}$ J $\frac{7}{8}$

173

CUMULATIVE REVIEW •
Chapters 1–8

USING THE PAGE

This page may be used to help students get ready for standardized tests. The test items are written in the same style and arranged in the same format as those on many state assessments. The page is cumulative. It covers math objectives and essential skills that have been taught up to this point in the text. Most of the items represent skills from the current chapter, and the remainder represent skills from earlier chapters.

This page can be assigned at the end of the chapter as classwork or as a homework assignment. You may want to have students use individual recording sheets presented in a multiple-choice (standardized) format. A Test Answer Sheet is available as a blackline master in *Assessment Guide* (p. AGxlii).

You may wish to have students describe how they solved each problem and share their solutions.

Add and Subtract Fractions and Mixed Numbers

CHAPTER PLANNER

PACING OPTIONS	
Compacted	6 Days
Expanded	11 Days

Getting Ready for Chapter 9 • Assessing Prior Knowledge and INTERVENTION (See PE and TE page 175.)

LESSON	CALIFORNIA STANDARDS	PACING	VOCABULARY*	MATERIALS	RESOURCES AND TECHNOLOGY
9.1 Estimate Sums and Differences pp. 176–179 **Objective** To estimate sums and differences of fractions and mixed numbers	NS 2.1 (*Also* O➡ NS 2.0, MR 2.4)	2 Days	mixed number		Reteach, Practice, Problem Solving, Challenge 9.1 Worksheets Extra Practice p. H40, Set A ▢ Transparency 9.1 ◉ **Harcourt Math Newsroom Video** • *Portable Planetarium*
9.2 Math Lab: Model Addition and Subtraction pp. 180–181 **Objective** To use fraction bars to add and subtract fractions with unlike denominators	NS 2.1 (*Also* O➡ NS 2.0, O➡NS 2.4, MR 2.4, MR 2.5)		**unlike fractions** least common multiple (LCM)	*For each group* fraction bars or fraction strips	🌐 **E-Lab** • *Addition and Subtraction of Unlike Fractions*; E-Lab Recording Sheet
9.3 Add and Subtract Fractions pp. 182–185 **Objective** To add and subtract fractions	O➡ NS 2.0 O➡ NS 2.4 MR 2.1 (*Also* O➡ NS 1.0, NS 2.1, MR 1.0, MR 1.1)	2 Days (For Lessons 9.2 and 9.3)	**least common denominator (LCD)**		Reteach, Practice, Problem Solving, Challenge 9.3 Worksheets Extra Practice p. H40, Set B ▢ Transparency 9.3 ◉ **Number Heroes** • *Fraction Fireworks*; **Calculating Crew** • *Nautical Number Line* **Math Jingles™•CD 5–6•** *Track 14*
9.4 Add and Subtract Mixed Numbers pp. 186–189 **Objective** To add and subtract mixed numbers	O➡ NS 2.0 O➡ NS 2.4 MR 2.1 (*Also* O➡NS 1.0, NS 2.1, MR 1.0, MR 1.1O➡MR 2.4, MR 2.7)	1 Day	mixed number		Reteach, Practice, Problem Solving, Challenge 9.4 Worksheets Extra Practice p. H40, Set C ▢ Transparency 9.4 ◉ **Calculating Crew** • *Nautical Number Line*
9.5 Math Lab: Rename to Subtract pp. 190–191 **Objective** To use fraction bars to rename and subtract mixed numbers	O➡ NS 2.0 O➡ NS 2.4 (*Also* NS 2.1, MR 2.4, MR 2.5)			*For each group* fraction bars or fraction strips	🌐 **E-Lab** • *Subtracting Mixed Numbers*; E-Lab Recording Sheet
9.6 Subtract Mixed Numbers pp. 192–193 **Objective** To subtract mixed numbers involving renaming	O➡ NS 2.0 O➡ NS 2.4 MR 2.1 (*Also* O➡NS 1.0, NS 2.1, MR 2.7)	2 Days (For Lessons 9.5 and 9.6)			Reteach, Practice, Problem Solving, Challenge 9.6 Worksheets Extra Practice p. H40, Set D ▢ Transparency 9.6 ◉ **Calculating Crew** • *Nautical Number Line*
9.7 Problem Solving Strategy: Draw a Diagram pp. 194–195 **Objective** To use the strategy *draw a diagram* to solve problems	O➡ NS 2.0 (*Also* O➡NS 1.0, O➡NS 2.4, MR 2.0, MR 2.4, MR 2.7, MR 3.2)	1 Day			Reteach, Practice, Reading Strategy, Challenge 9.7 Worksheets ▢ Transparency 9.7 Problem Solving Think Along, p. TR1

Ending Chapter 9 • Chapter 9 Review/Test, p. 196 • **Cumulative Review,** p. 197

*Boldfaced terms are new vocabulary. Other terms are review vocabulary.

Vocabulary Development

The boldfaced words are the new vocabulary terms in the chapter. Have students record the definitions in their Math Journals.

unlike fractions, p. 180

least common denominator (LCD), p. 182

Vocabulary Cards

Have students use the Vocabulary Cards on *Teacher's Resource Book* **pp. TR127–128** to make graphic organizers or word puzzles. The cards can also be added to a file of mathematics terms.

California Mathematics Content Standards for Grade 6

Strands

Number Sense

Lesson 9.1: NS 2.0, 2.1

Lesson 9.2: NS 2.0, 2.1, 2.4

Lesson 9.3: NS 1.0, NS 2.0, 2.1, 2.4

Lesson 9.4: NS 2.0, 2.1, 2.4

Lesson 9.5: NS 2.0, 2.1, 2.4

Lesson 9.6: NS 1.0, 2.0, 2.1, 2.4

Lesson 9.7: NS 1.0, NS 2.0, 2.4

Algebra and Functions

Measurement and Geometry

Statistics, Data Analysis, and Probability

Mathematical Reasoning

Lesson 9.1: MR 1.0, 1.1, 2.4

Lesson 9.2: MR 2.4, 2.5

Lesson 9.3: MR 2.1

Lesson 9.4: MR 1.0, 1.1, 2.1, 2.4, 2.7

Lesson 9.5: MR 2.4, 2.5

Lesson 9.6: MR 2.1, 2.7

Lesson 9.7: MR 2.0, 2.4, 2.7, 3.2

Writing Opportunities

PUPIL EDITION

- **What's the Question?,** p. 185
- **What's the Error?,** p. 189
- **Write About It,** p. 193
- **Write a Problem,** pp. 179, 195

TEACHER'S EDITION

- **Write**—See the *Assess* section of each TE lesson.
- **Writing in Mathematics,** pp. 176B, 180, 186B

ASSESSMENT GUIDE

- **How Did I Do?,** p. AGxvii

Family Involvement Activities

These activities provide:

- Letters to the Family
- Information about California Standards
- Math Vocabulary
- Family Game
- Practice (Homework)

Family Involvement Activities, p. FA33

Add and Subtract Fractions and Mixed Numbers

MATHEMATICS ACROSS THE GRADES

SKILLS TRACE ACROSS THE GRADES

GRADE 5	GRADE 6	GRADE 7
Add and subtract fractions; add and subtract mixed numbers	**Estimate sums and differences of fractions and mixed numbers; add and subtract fractions and mixed numbers**	Estimate with fractions; add and subtract fractions and mixed numbers

SKILLS TRACE FOR GRADE 6

LESSON	FIRST INTRODUCED	TAUGHT AND PRACTICED	TESTED	REVIEWED
9.1	Grade 5	PE pp. 176–179, H40, p. RW40, p. PW40, p. PS40	PE p. 196, pp. AG57–60	PE pp. 196, 197, 222–223
9.2	Grade 4	PE pp. 180–181	PE p. 196, pp. AG57–60	PE pp. 196, 197, 222–223
9.3	Grade 4	PE pp. 182–185, H40, p. RW41, p. PW41, p. PS41	PE p. 196, pp. AG57–60	PE pp. 196, 197, 222–223
9.4	Grade 5	PE pp. 186–189, H40, p. RW42, p. PW42, p. PS42	PE p. 196, pp. AG57–60	PE pp. 196, 197, 222–223
9.5	Grade 5	PE pp. 190–191	PE p. 196, pp. AG57–60	PE pp. 196, 197, 222–223
9.6	Grade 5	PE pp. 192–193, H40, p. RW43, p. PW43, p. PS43	PE p. 196, pp. AG57–60	PE pp. 196, 197, 222–223
9.7	Grade 5	PE pp. 194–195, p. RW44, p. PW44, p. PS44	PE p. 196, pp. AG57–60	PE pp. 196, 197, 222–223

KEY   **PE**   Pupil Edition   **PS**   Problem Solving Workbook   **RW**   Reteach Workbook
        PW   Practice Workbook   **AG**   Assessment Guide

Looking Back Prerequisite Skills

To be ready for Chapter 9, students should have the following understandings and skills:

• **Vocabulary**—*divide, mixed number, estimate, simplest form, equivalent*

• **Simplify Fractions**—write fractions in simplest form

• **Add and Subtract Like Fractions**—add and subtract fractions with common denominators

Check What You Know

Use page 175 to determine students' knowledge of prerequisite concepts and skills.

Intervention

Help students prepare for the chapter by using the intervention resources described on TE page 175.

Looking at Chapter 9 Essential Skills

Students will

• understand the concepts for estimating sums and differences of fractions and mixed numbers.

• **develop skill and accuracy adding and subtracting fractions and mixed numbers.**

• use the strategy *draw a diagram* to solve problems.

EXAMPLE

Find the sum $1\frac{1}{2} + 1\frac{1}{3}$.

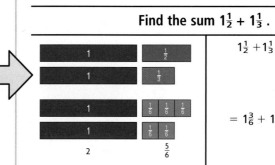

$1\frac{1}{2} + 1\frac{1}{3}$ Write each fraction with the common denominator.

$= 1\frac{3}{6} + 1\frac{2}{6}$ Add fractions. Add whole number parts.

So, the sum is $2\frac{5}{6}$.

Looking Ahead Applications

Students will apply what they learn in Chapter 9 to the following new concepts:

• Rational Numbers (Chapter 11)

• Solve Equations (Chapters 15 and 16)

• Numerical and Algebraic Expressions (Chapter 14)

• Probability (Chapters 22 and 23)

Add and Subtract Fractions and Mixed Numbers

INTRODUCING THE CHAPTER

Tell students that adding and subtracting fractions and mixed numbers involve combining or finding the difference between these values. Have students focus on each food group in Bob's diagram. Explain that 1 of the 5 dairy and protein servings is shaded, so $\frac{1}{5}$ of the daily requirement has been met. Ask students what fraction of the daily requirement has been met for grains, rice, and pasta. $\frac{2}{9}$ of the daily requirement

USING DATA

To begin the study of this chapter, have students

- Determine how many more cups of grains, rice, and pasta than of dairy and protein are recommended. 2 more cups

- Determine what fraction of the fruits and vegetables daily requirement has not yet been met. $\frac{6}{7}$

PROBLEM SOLVING PROJECT

Purpose To add or subtract fractions and mixed numbers

Grouping pairs or small groups

Background The Food Guide Pyramid appears below.

Analyze, Choose, Solve, and Check

Have students

- Make a diagram showing recommended servings for each food group.

- Shade the food servings they eat at each meal for one day.

- Record the fraction of recommended servings they eat at each meal and the total fraction of recommended servings for the day.

Check students' work.

Portfolio Suggest that students display their Food Guide Pyramids and later include them in their portfolios.

In 1992, the United States Department of Agriculture and the Department of Health and Human Services introduced the Food Guide Pyramid. Bob used the information in the pyramid to make the diagram shown. He shades the number of servings he has each day to make sure he has a balanced diet. The shaded squares show what he ate for breakfast. How many cups of food were in his breakfast?

about 2 cups

174 Chapter 9

Why learn math? Explain that a dietician's job is to help people make healthy choices about the types and amount of food they eat. Dieticians will often use fractions and mixed numbers to describe portions. Ask: In what other jobs do people use fractions and mixed numbers? Possible answer: construction, tailoring

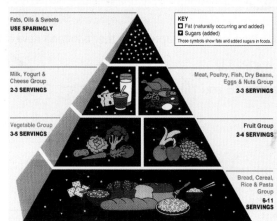

Check What You Know

Use this page to help you review and remember important skills needed for Chapter 9.

✔ Vocabulary

Choose the best term from the box.

divide
equivalent
estimate
mixed number
simplest form

1. A number with a whole-number part and a fraction part is called a(n) ? . **mixed number**

2. A fraction in which the numerator and denominator have no common factors other than 1 is in ? . **simplest form**

3. To write a fraction greater than 1 as a mixed number, ? the numerator by the denominator. **divide**

4. Fractions that name the same number or part are called ? fractions. **equivalent**

✔ Simplify Fractions (See p. H9.)

Write each fraction in simplest form.

5. $\frac{6}{8}$ **$\frac{3}{4}$**   6. $\frac{5}{10}$ **$\frac{1}{2}$**   7. $\frac{4}{12}$ **$\frac{1}{3}$**   8. $\frac{18}{27}$ **$\frac{2}{3}$**   9. $\frac{12}{9}$ **$\frac{4}{3}$, or $1\frac{1}{3}$**

10. $\frac{16}{20}$ **$\frac{4}{5}$**   11. $\frac{12}{8}$ **$\frac{3}{2}$, or $1\frac{1}{2}$**   12. $\frac{9}{15}$ **$\frac{3}{5}$**   13. $\frac{10}{20}$ **$\frac{1}{2}$**   14. $\frac{15}{18}$ **$\frac{5}{6}$**

15. $\frac{26}{39}$ **$\frac{2}{3}$**   16. $\frac{12}{16}$ **$\frac{3}{4}$**   17. $\frac{15}{9}$ **$\frac{5}{3}$, or $1\frac{2}{3}$**   18. $\frac{6}{32}$ **$\frac{3}{16}$**   19. $\frac{17}{51}$ **$\frac{1}{3}$**

20. $\frac{48}{54}$ **$\frac{8}{9}$**   21. $\frac{100}{200}$ **$\frac{1}{2}$**   22. $\frac{25}{10}$ **$\frac{5}{2}$, or $2\frac{1}{2}$**   23. $\frac{80}{64}$ **$\frac{5}{4}$, or $1\frac{1}{4}$**   24. $\frac{84}{96}$ **$\frac{7}{8}$**

✔ Add and Subtract Like Fractions (See p. H10.)

Find the sum or difference. Write each answer in simplest form.

25. $\frac{1}{3}+\frac{1}{3}$ **$\frac{2}{3}$**   26. $\frac{3}{5}+\frac{1}{5}$ **$\frac{4}{5}$**   27. $\frac{3}{8}+\frac{1}{8}$ **$\frac{1}{2}$**   28. $\frac{5}{6}+\frac{1}{6}$ **1**

29. $\frac{3}{4}-\frac{1}{4}$ **$\frac{1}{2}$**   30. $\frac{5}{8}-\frac{3}{8}$ **$\frac{1}{4}$**   31. $\frac{2}{3}-\frac{1}{3}$ **$\frac{1}{3}$**   32. $\frac{4}{5}-\frac{2}{5}$ **$\frac{2}{5}$**

33. $\frac{3}{6}+\frac{2}{6}$ **$\frac{5}{6}$**   34. $\frac{7}{8}-\frac{1}{8}$ **$\frac{3}{4}$**   35. $\frac{3}{4}+\frac{1}{4}$ **1**   36. $\frac{7}{8}-\frac{3}{8}$ **$\frac{1}{2}$**

37. $\frac{4}{9}-\frac{2}{9}$ **$\frac{2}{9}$**   38. $\frac{1}{12}+\frac{7}{12}$ **$\frac{2}{3}$**   39. $\frac{13}{14}-\frac{3}{14}$ **$\frac{5}{7}$**   40. $\frac{1}{15}+\frac{8}{15}$ **$\frac{3}{5}$**

> **LOOK AHEAD**
>
> In Chapter 9 you will
> - estimate sums and differences of fractions and mixed numbers
> - add and subtract fractions and mixed numbers

175

Assessing Prior Knowledge

Use the **Check What You Know** page to determine whether your students have mastered the prerequisite skills critical for this chapter.

Intervention

- **Diagnose and Prescribe**

  Evaluate your students' performance on this page to determine whether intervention is necessary. **How to Help Options** that provide instruction, practice, and a check are listed in the chart below.

- **Review Prerequisite Skills**

  The following resources provide a review for the prerequisite vocabulary and skills.

  Option 1—Check What You Know, Pupil Edition p. 175

  Option 2—Troubleshooting, Pupil Edition pp. H9–10

TEACHER'S NOTES

Check What You Know
INTERVENTION • Diagnose and Prescribe

Prerequisite Skill	Items (Pupil Edition p. 175)	How to Help Options
✔ Simplify Fractions	5–24	• **Troubleshooting, Pupil Edition p. H9** • **Intervention Strategies and Activities** Card, Copying Master, or CD-ROM • **Skill 22**
✔ Add and Subtract Like Fractions	25–40	• **Troubleshooting, Pupil Edition p. H10** • **Intervention Strategies and Activities** Card, Copying Master, or CD-ROM • **Skill 23**

Estimate Sums and Differences

LESSON PLANNING

Objective To estimate sums and differences of fractions and mixed numbers

Intervention for Prerequisite Skills

Simplify Fractions, Add and Subtract Like Fractions (For intervention strategies, see page 175.)

 California Mathematics Content Standards

NS 2.1 Solve problems involving addition, subtraction, multiplication, and division of positive fractions and explain why a particular operation was used for a given situation.

(*Also* o—n NS 2.0, MR 2.4)

Math Background

Students may estimate a sum or difference of fractions, as they may with whole numbers and decimals, to check an answer for reasonableness or to solve a problem in which an estimate is all that is needed.

Experiences with models will help students develop estimating skills for fractions and mixed numbers.

- By comparing fraction bar models, students can picture whether a fraction is closer to 0, $\frac{1}{2}$, or 1.

- Graphing a fraction on a number line can help students determine whether a fraction is closer to 0, $\frac{1}{2}$, or 1.

WARM-UP RESOURCES

 NUMBER OF THE DAY Transparency 9.1

The number of the day is the number that describes today as a day of the month. Write a fraction to describe what part of the current month has passed. Answer for April 10: $\frac{10}{30} = \frac{1}{3}$

 PROBLEM OF THE DAY Transparency 9.1

Mike's and Kay's numbers are both less than 1. The digit in Mike's numerator is the same as the digit in Kay's denominator. Kay's number is $\frac{1}{10}$ greater than Mike's. What are Mike's and Kay's numbers? Mike's number is $\frac{2}{5}$ and Kay's number is $\frac{1}{2}$.

Solution Problem of the Day tab, p. PD9

 DAILY FACTS PRACTICE

Have students practice addition and subtraction facts by completing Set B of *Teacher's Resource Book*, p. TR99.

INTERVENTION AND EXTENSION RESOURCES

ALTERNATIVE TEACHING STRATEGY (ELL)

Materials *For each student* index card

Have students **match exact numbers with estimates.** For half of the class, write sentences with exact numbers, one per card:

- The show lasts 55 min.
- Ginny is 62 in. tall.
- Only 5 eggs are in this carton.

Then write corresponding estimates—*around an hour, approximately 5 ft, about $\frac{1}{2}$ doz*—on cards for the remaining students. Pass out the cards to the class. Have students take turns reading aloud cards with an exact number and then cards with the matching estimates. Check students' work.

See also page 178.

AUDITORY

MIXED REVIEW AND TEST PREP

Cumulative Review Chapters 1–9

Refer to the Pupil Edition pages referenced in the exercises for further review. Have students go to the lesson page, review the lesson, and correct any problem they missed.

Mixed Review and Test Prep, p. 179

How to Help	
Item	**Page**
50–51	169
52	98
53	22
54	150

WRITING IN MATHEMATICS

Have students **complete each statement to include an exact number and an estimate.** Display the following. Possible answers are given.

- Bob watched TV for _____. 35 min, about $\frac{1}{2}$ hour
- Last year Liza grew _____. $2\frac{3}{8}$ in., about $2\frac{1}{2}$ in.
- The recipe calls for _____ of ginger. $2\frac{1}{8}$ tsp., about 2 tsp.
- _____ of the class attended the party. $\frac{2}{3}$, More than $\frac{1}{2}$

VISUAL

LANGUAGE ARTS CONNECTION

Ask students to **research the origins of math terms,** such as *fraction, addition,* and *subtraction,* and to report to the class what they discover. Explain that many English words have Latin origins. The word *fraction,* for example, comes from the Latin word *frangere,* which means "to break." Encourage students to relate this meaning to their understanding of a fraction. Check students' work.

AUDITORY

ENG-LANG ARTS Standards
R 1.0

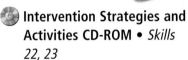

TECHNOLOGY LINK

Intervention Strategies and Activities CD-ROM • *Skills 22, 23*

Harcourt Math Newsroom Video • *Portable Planetarium*

LESSON 9.1 ORGANIZER

Objective To estimate sums and differences of fractions and mixed numbers

Vocabulary *Review* mixed number

---

1 Introduce

QUICK REVIEW provides review of pre-requisite skills.

Why Learn This? You can estimate the amount of flour needed to make muffins when you double the recipe. *Share the lesson objective with students.*

2 Teach

Guided Instruction

• *Direct students' attention to the number line.*

How do you decide whether $\frac{3}{8}$ is closer to 0, $\frac{1}{2}$, or 1? On the scale marked in eighths, $\frac{3}{8}$ is 3 spaces away from zero and 5 spaces away from 1, but only 1 space away from $\frac{1}{2}$.

REASONING **How could you use division to decide whether the numerator of a fraction is about half the denominator?** By dividing the denominator by 2 and comparing it to the numerator.

• *As students look at Example 1, ask:*

Why would you estimate the sum in Example 1? Possible answer: the problem asks for an approximate answer, not an exact answer.

How do you know the sum is less than 1? Both fractions are less than $\frac{1}{2}$.

ADDITIONAL EXAMPLE

Example 1, p. 176

Roger bought $\frac{3}{4}$ lb of broccoli and $\frac{1}{8}$ lb of cauliflower. About how many pounds of vegetables did he buy? about 1 lb

176 Chapter 9

LESSON **9.1**

Estimate Sums and Differences

Learn how to estimate sums and differences of fractions and mixed numbers.

QUICK REVIEW

Estimate the sum or difference. Possible estimates are given.

1.	2.	3.	4.	5.
823	364	736	589	6,755
+116	−232	−381	+ 42	− 482
900	**130**	**300**	**640**	**6,300**

You can decide whether a fraction is closest to 0, $\frac{1}{2}$, or 1.

One Way Use a number line.

Look at the number line below. Is $\frac{3}{8}$ closest to 0, $\frac{1}{2}$, or 1?

$$0 \quad \frac{1}{8} \quad \frac{2}{8} \quad \frac{3}{8} \quad \frac{1}{2} \quad \frac{5}{8} \quad \frac{6}{8} \quad \frac{7}{8} \quad 1$$

$\frac{3}{8}$ is closest to $\frac{1}{2}$.

Another Way Compare the numerator to the denominator.

| $\frac{1}{8}$ | $\frac{1}{6}$ | $\frac{2}{9}$ | | $\frac{4}{9}$ | $\frac{5}{8}$ | $\frac{2}{3}$ | | $\frac{7}{9}$ | $\frac{5}{6}$ | $\frac{7}{8}$ |

The numerators are much less than half the denominators. So, the fractions are close to 0.

The numerators are about one half of the denominators. So, the fractions are close to $\frac{1}{2}$.

The numerators are about the same as the denominators. So, the fractions are close to 1.

Sometimes when you add and subtract fractions, you do not need an exact answer.

EXAMPLE 1

The California section of the Pacific Crest Trail, which runs from Mexico to Canada, is 1,680 miles long. The average time it takes to hike the California section of the trail is 3–5 months. The Tanner family hiked $\frac{3}{10}$ of this section in June and July. Then they hiked $\frac{3}{8}$ of it in August and September. About how much of the trail did the Tanners hike from June through September?

Estimate $\frac{3}{10} + \frac{3}{8}$.

$$\frac{3}{10} \rightarrow \frac{1}{2} \qquad \text{\small$\frac{3}{10}$ is between 0 and $\frac{1}{2}$, but closer to $\frac{1}{2}$.}$$
$$+\frac{3}{8} \rightarrow +\frac{1}{2} \qquad \text{\small$\frac{3}{8}$ is between 0 and $\frac{1}{2}$, but closer to $\frac{1}{2}$.}$$
$$\overline{\hspace{1.2cm}1} \qquad \text{\small The sum is greater than $\frac{1}{2}$, but less than 1.}$$

So, the Tanners hiked more than $\frac{1}{2}$ of the trail, but not all of it.

176

CALIFORNIA STANDARDS NS 2.1 Solve problems involving addition, subtraction, multiplication, and division of positive fractions and explain why a particular operation was used for a given situation. *also,* NS 2.0, MR 2.4

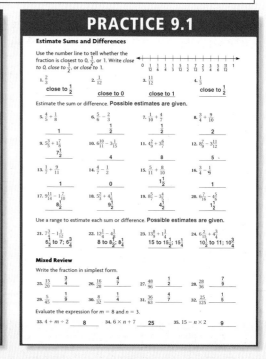

RETEACH 9.1

Estimate Sums and Differences

Some problems need only an estimated answer, not an exact answer. You can estimate with fractions by rounding them to 0, $\frac{1}{2}$, or 1.

Estimate. $\frac{4}{5} + \frac{5}{12}$

Step 1: Look at the first fraction.
• Is 4 much less than 5? No.
• Is 4 about half of 5? No.
• Is 4 almost the same as 5? Yes.
• Since the numerator is almost the same as the denominator, round the fraction to 1.

Step 2: Look at the second fraction.
• Is 5 almost the same as 12? No.
• Is 5 about half of 12? Yes.
• Since the numerator is about half of the denominator, round the fraction to $\frac{1}{2}$.

Step 3: Add the rounded fractions to get an estimated answer. $1 + \frac{1}{2} = 1\frac{1}{2}$

Follow the same steps to estimate a difference.

Estimate. $\frac{8}{9} - \frac{1}{10}$

Step 1: Look at the first fraction.
• Is 8 much less than 9? No.
• Is 8 about half of 9? No.
• Is 8 almost the same as 9? Yes.
• So, round the fraction to 1.

Step 2: Look at the second fraction.
• Is 1 much less than 10? Yes.
• So, round the fraction to 0.

Step 3: Find the difference between the rounded fractions to get an estimated answer. $1 - 0 = 1$

Estimate the sum or difference. Possible estimates are given.

1. $\frac{6}{7} - \frac{1}{3}$	2. $\frac{11}{12} + \frac{4}{7}$	3. $\frac{5}{9} + \frac{4}{8}$	4. $\frac{11}{12} - \frac{1}{15}$	5. $\frac{13}{14} - \frac{11}{12}$
about $\frac{1}{2}$	about $1\frac{1}{2}$	about $\frac{1}{2}$	about $\frac{1}{2}$	about 0

6. $\frac{5}{6} + \frac{1}{7}$	7. $\frac{7}{8} - \frac{3}{9}$	8. $\frac{3}{5} + \frac{1}{2}$	9. $\frac{11}{12} - \frac{15}{16}$	10. $\frac{3}{7} - \frac{1}{8}$
about 1	about $\frac{1}{2}$	about 1	about 0	about $\frac{1}{2}$

PRACTICE 9.1

Estimate Sums and Differences

Use the number line to tell whether the fraction is closest to 0, $\frac{1}{2}$, or 1. Write *close to 0*, *close to $\frac{1}{2}$*, or *close to 1*.

$$0 \ \frac{1}{12} \ \frac{1}{4} \ \frac{1}{3} \ \frac{5}{12} \ \frac{1}{2} \ \frac{7}{12} \ \frac{2}{3} \ \frac{3}{4} \ \frac{5}{6} \ \frac{11}{12} \ 1$$

1. $\frac{2}{3}$	2. $\frac{1}{12}$	3. $\frac{11}{12}$	4. $\frac{1}{3}$
close to $\frac{1}{2}$	close to 0	close to 1	close to $\frac{1}{2}$

Estimate the sum or difference. Possible estimates are given.

5. $\frac{4}{5} + \frac{1}{7}$	6. $\frac{5}{6} - \frac{2}{3}$	7. $\frac{1}{10} + \frac{4}{7}$	8. $\frac{3}{4} + \frac{9}{10}$
1	$\frac{1}{2}$	$\frac{1}{2}$	2

9. $5\frac{3}{5} + 1\frac{7}{8}$	10. $6\frac{10}{11} - 3\frac{1}{15}$	11. $4\frac{5}{9} + 3\frac{6}{7}$	12. $8\frac{7}{9} - 3\frac{1}{11}$
$7\frac{1}{2}$	4	8	5

13. $\frac{1}{7} + \frac{9}{11}$	14. $\frac{4}{7} - \frac{1}{2}$	15. $\frac{5}{11} + \frac{8}{9}$	16. $\frac{3}{4} - \frac{1}{9}$
1	0	$1\frac{1}{2}$	1

17. $9\frac{11}{14} - 1\frac{7}{10}$	18. $5\frac{3}{4} + 4\frac{1}{7}$	19. $8\frac{5}{7} - 3\frac{4}{9}$	20. $6\frac{7}{16} - 1\frac{4}{5}$
8	10	5	$4\frac{1}{2}$

Use a range to estimate each sum or difference. Possible estimates are given.

21. $7\frac{3}{4} - 1\frac{1}{12}$	22. $12\frac{1}{4} - 4\frac{1}{9}$	23. $13\frac{9}{10} + 1\frac{1}{4}$	24. $6\frac{5}{12} + 4\frac{3}{4}$
$6\frac{1}{2}$ to 7; $6\frac{3}{4}$	8 to $8\frac{1}{4}$; $8\frac{1}{4}$	15 to $15\frac{1}{4}$; $15\frac{1}{4}$	$10\frac{1}{2}$ to 11; $10\frac{3}{4}$

Mixed Review

Write the fraction in simplest form.

25. $\frac{15}{20}$	$\frac{3}{4}$	26. $\frac{16}{28}$	$\frac{4}{7}$	27. $\frac{48}{96}$	$\frac{1}{2}$	28. $\frac{28}{36}$	$\frac{7}{9}$
29. $\frac{5}{45}$	$\frac{1}{9}$	30. $\frac{8}{32}$	$\frac{1}{4}$	31. $\frac{36}{63}$	$\frac{4}{7}$	32. $\frac{25}{125}$	$\frac{1}{5}$

Evaluate the expression for $m = 8$ and $n = 3$.

33. $4 + m \div 2$ **8**   34. $6 \times n + 7$ **25**   35. $15 - n \times 2$ **9**

EXAMPLE 2

Estimate $\frac{7}{8} - \frac{5}{6}$.

$$\frac{7}{8} \rightarrow 1 \qquad \text{\textit{$\frac{7}{8}$ is between $\frac{1}{2}$ and 1, but closer to 1.}}$$
$$-\frac{5}{6} \rightarrow -1 \qquad \text{\textit{$\frac{5}{6}$ is between $\frac{1}{2}$ and 1, but closer to 1.}}$$
$$\overline{\phantom{-\frac{5}{6} \rightarrow}} \; 0 \qquad \text{\textit{Subtract.}}$$

The fractions are close to each other and their difference is close to 0.

Remember that a mixed number is a whole number and a fraction combined. $4\frac{2}{5}$ is a mixed number.

Look at the number line below. Is $3\frac{5}{8}$ in. closest to 3 in., $3\frac{1}{2}$ in., or 4 in.?

$3\frac{5}{8}$ in. is closest to $3\frac{1}{2}$ in.

To estimate sums and differences of mixed numbers, compare each mixed number to the nearest whole number or the nearest $\frac{1}{2}$.

EXAMPLE 3

Bianca's goal is to jog 15 miles a week. So far this week she has jogged $2\frac{5}{6}$ mi and $3\frac{1}{10}$ mi. About how many more miles must she jog to meet her goal?

Estimate $15 - \left(2\frac{5}{6} + 3\frac{1}{10}\right)$.

$$15 - \left(2\frac{5}{6} + 3\frac{1}{10}\right) \qquad \text{\textit{$2\frac{5}{6}$ is close to 3, and $3\frac{1}{10}$ is close to 3.}}$$
$$15 - (3 \; + \; 3) \qquad \text{\textit{Add.}}$$
$$15 - 6 = 9 \qquad \text{\textit{Subtract.}}$$

So, Bianca needs to jog about 9 more miles to meet her goal.

You can find a range to estimate a sum or difference.

EXAMPLE 4

Estimate $5\frac{3}{4} - 4\frac{7}{8}$.

Since $5\frac{3}{4}$ is halfway between $5\frac{1}{2}$ and 6, find two estimates.

$5\frac{3}{4} - 4\frac{7}{8}$ *$5\frac{3}{4}$ is close to 6, and $4\frac{7}{8}$ is close to 5.* $5\frac{3}{4} - 4\frac{7}{8}$ *$5\frac{3}{4}$ is close to $5\frac{1}{2}$, and $4\frac{7}{8}$ is close to 5.*

$6 - 5 = 1$ *Subtract.*   AND $5\frac{1}{2} - 5 = \frac{1}{2}$ *Subtract.*

The range is $\frac{1}{2}$ to 1. A good estimate of $5\frac{3}{4} - 4\frac{7}{8}$ would be $\frac{3}{4}$, halfway between $\frac{1}{2}$ and 1.

177

- *Direct students' attention to Example 2.*

  How is estimating the difference of fractions like estimating the sum? Possible answer: The fractions are approximated the same way—by using 0, $\frac{1}{2}$, and 1 as markers.

- *Discuss using a number line to estimate solutions with a mixed number. Then ask:*

  How would you find a number close to $3\frac{5}{8}$ without using a number line? Possible answer: $\frac{5}{8}$ is closer to $\frac{1}{2}$ than to 1, so $3\frac{5}{8}$ must be closer to $3\frac{1}{2}$ than to 4.

- *Discuss Example 3 with students.*

  What does $\left(2\frac{5}{6} + 3\frac{1}{10}\right)$ represent? the number of miles Bianca has jogged this week

  Why do you add before subtracting? Order of operations rules tell you to do operations inside parentheses before subtracting.

Modifying Instruction In Example 4, students may see $4\frac{7}{8}$ as close to 5 and subtract 5 from $5\frac{3}{4}$. Encourage students to explore this and other methods of estimating.

ADDITIONAL EXAMPLES

Example 2, p. 177

Estimate $\frac{7}{8} - \frac{5}{12}$. $\frac{1}{2}$

Example 3, p. 177

Rod wants to pick 10 pounds of apples to make cider. He fills one bag with $2\frac{5}{8}$ lb of apples, and another bag with $4\frac{3}{16}$ lb. About how many more pounds of apples does Rod need to pick? about $3\frac{1}{2}$ lb more

Example 4, p. 177

Estimate $8\frac{3}{4} - 4\frac{8}{9}$ by finding 2 estimates. $8\frac{1}{2} - 5 = 3\frac{1}{2}$; $9 - 5 = 4$; range is $3\frac{1}{2}$ to 4; $3\frac{3}{4}$

PROBLEM SOLVING 9.1

Estimate Sums and Differences

Write the correct answer.

1. Jon won $\frac{1}{3}$ of his tennis matches. Tori won 0.45 of her matches and Tim won $\frac{2}{5}$ of his. If they all played the same number of matches, who won the most?

   Tori

2. Working on the computer, Julie used 15% of the available time. At that point 60% of the time was left. How much of the computer time was available before Julie worked?

   75%

3. Mary has $\frac{3}{4}$ gal of milk. She needs to use $\frac{1}{3}$ gal in one recipe and $\frac{1}{4}$ gal in another recipe. Does she have enough milk?

   yes

4. Thad practiced playing the flute for $1\frac{3}{4}$ hr before dinner and $2\frac{1}{4}$ hr after dinner. About how long did Thad practice playing his flute?

   about 4 hr

Choose the letter for the best answer.

5. Sid has two pieces of fabric. One piece is $\frac{5}{12}$ yd and the other piece is $\frac{1}{6}$ yd. Estimate the total amount of fabric he has.

   A $\frac{1}{4}$ yd   C $\frac{3}{4}$ yd
   B $\frac{1}{2}$ yd   D 1 yd

6. Kyle has $1\frac{5}{8}$ ft of twine. He gave $\frac{1}{2}$ ft to his friend. About how much twine does he have left?

   F 2 ft   H 1 ft
   G $1\frac{1}{2}$ ft   I $\frac{1}{2}$ ft

7. On Monday 45,789 people attended a game in the stadium. On Tuesday 36,984 people attended a game in the stadium. Which is the best estimate of how many more people attended the game on Monday than on Tuesday?

   A 7,000
   B 8,000
   C 9,000
   D 10,000

8. Nancy measured her stride to be 45.7 cm. She then went for a walk and counted 352 steps. Which expression can be used to find the distance she walked in centimeters?

   F 352 − 45.7
   G 352 + 45.7
   H 352 ÷ 45.7
   I 352 × 45.7

9. **Write About It** Explain how you know whether to round a fraction to 0, $\frac{1}{2}$, or 1.

   You round to the number closest to the fraction. If the fraction is

   halfway between two numbers, you round to the greater number.

CHALLENGE 9.1

You Write the Problem

An error was made when this book was created. Somehow, the answers to the problems on this page were printed, but the problems were omitted. Help the printer out by creating an estimation problem for each answer below. Make sure your problems involve fractions. **Problems will vary.**

1. _____
2. _____

   Answer — about $3\frac{1}{2}$ mi   Answer — about 4 yd of fabric

3. _____
4. _____

   Answer — about 15 ft of wire   Answer — about 3 c of flour

5. _____
6. _____

   Answer — about $7\frac{1}{2}$ yd of ribbon   Answer — about 4 hr

7. _____
8. _____

   Answer — about 12 gal   Answer — about $5\frac{1}{2}$ in.

177

LESSON 9.1

3 | Practice

Guided Practice

Do Check for Understanding Exercises 1–14 with your students. Identify those having difficulty and use lesson resources to help.

Independent Practice

Assign Exercises 15–49.

Remind students that they need only an estimate for Exercise 45 and Exercise 47.

REASONING Ask a volunteer to explain his or her logic in answering Exercise 47. Lead students to conclude that their answer could be any number that is close to 2.

CHECK FOR UNDERSTANDING

Think and ▶
Discuss

1. Possible answer: Compare the numerator to the denominator to decide whether the fraction is closest to 0, $\frac{1}{2}$, or 1.

Guided ▶
Practice

Look back at the lesson to answer each question.

1. **Explain** how to round fractions less than 1. See left.

2. **Compare** the numerator and denominator of several fractions greater than $\frac{1}{2}$. What do you notice?
Possible answer: The numerator is greater than half the denominator.

Use the number line to tell whether the fraction is closest to 0, $\frac{1}{2}$, or 1. Write *close to 0*, *close to $\frac{1}{2}$*, or *close to 1*.

$$0 \quad \frac{1}{12} \quad \frac{1}{6} \quad \frac{1}{4} \quad \frac{1}{3} \quad \frac{5}{12} \quad \frac{1}{2} \quad \frac{7}{12} \quad \frac{2}{3} \quad \frac{3}{4} \quad \frac{5}{6} \quad \frac{11}{12} \quad 1$$

3. $\frac{11}{12}$ close to 1 4. $\frac{1}{12}$ close to 0 5. $\frac{1}{4}$ between 0 and $\frac{1}{2}$ 6. $\frac{2}{3}$ close to $\frac{1}{2}$

Estimate the sum or difference. Possible estimates are given.

7. $\frac{3}{5} + \frac{6}{7}$ $1\frac{1}{2}$ 8. $\frac{10}{12} - \frac{4}{5}$ 0 9. $\frac{7}{8} - \frac{4}{9}$ $\frac{1}{2}$ 10. $\frac{5}{16} + \frac{4}{9}$ 1

11. $4\frac{3}{8} + 2\frac{3}{4}$ $7\frac{1}{2}$ 12. $3\frac{2}{16} - \frac{8}{15}$ $2\frac{1}{2}$ 13. $4\frac{11}{12} - 3\frac{1}{5}$ 2 14. $6\frac{7}{8} + 5\frac{5}{9}$ $12\frac{1}{2}$

PRACTICE AND PROBLEM SOLVING

Independent ▶
Practice

Use the number line to tell whether the fraction is closest to 0, $\frac{1}{2}$, or 1. Write *close to 0*, *close to $\frac{1}{2}$*, or *close to 1*.

$$0 \quad \frac{1}{12} \quad \frac{1}{6} \quad \frac{1}{4} \quad \frac{1}{3} \quad \frac{5}{12} \quad \frac{1}{2} \quad \frac{7}{12} \quad \frac{2}{3} \quad \frac{3}{4} \quad \frac{5}{6} \quad \frac{11}{12} \quad 1$$

15. $\frac{5}{6}$ close to 1 16. $\frac{5}{12}$ close to $\frac{1}{2}$ 17. $\frac{1}{6}$ close to 0 18. $\frac{3}{4}$ between $\frac{1}{2}$ and 1

Estimate the sum or difference. Possible estimates are given.

19. $\frac{12}{13} + \frac{15}{17}$ 2 20. $2\frac{1}{4} + 1\frac{1}{8}$ $3\frac{1}{2}$ 21. $\frac{15}{16} - \frac{6}{10}$ $\frac{1}{2}$ 22. $7\frac{9}{16} - 4\frac{2}{9}$ $3\frac{1}{2}$

23. $12\frac{1}{12} + 4\frac{4}{5}$ 17 24. $\frac{18}{20} - \frac{3}{50}$ 1 25. $4\frac{3}{8} - 1\frac{1}{3}$ 3 26. $\frac{3}{5} + \frac{6}{7}$ $1\frac{1}{2}$

27. $\frac{5}{9} - \frac{1}{2}$ 0 28. $\frac{1}{12} + 1\frac{3}{19}$ 1 29. $9\frac{7}{12} - 5\frac{1}{5}$ $4\frac{1}{2}$ 30. $\frac{13}{15} + \frac{8}{9} + \frac{1}{7}$ 2

Use a range to estimate each sum or difference. Possible estimates are given.

31. $6\frac{1}{4} + 2\frac{5}{6}$ 9 to $9\frac{1}{2}$; $9\frac{1}{4}$ 32. $5\frac{7}{10} - 2\frac{1}{4}$ $3\frac{1}{2}$ to 4; $3\frac{3}{4}$ 33. $8\frac{3}{4} - 4\frac{1}{8}$ $4\frac{1}{2}$ to 5; $4\frac{3}{4}$

34. $3\frac{1}{4} - 1\frac{1}{8}$ 2 to $2\frac{1}{2}$; $2\frac{1}{4}$ 35. $1\frac{3}{4} + 3\frac{4}{5}$ $5\frac{1}{2}$ to 6; $5\frac{3}{4}$ 36. $4\frac{1}{9} + 5\frac{3}{4}$ $9\frac{1}{2}$ to 10; $9\frac{3}{4}$

37. Estimate the sum. $3\frac{1}{5} + 2\frac{1}{3} + 1\frac{11}{12}$ about 7

TECHNOLOGY LINK

To learn more about estimation, watch the **Harcourt Math Newsroom Video** *Portable Planetarium*.

178 Chapter 9

Alternative Teaching Strategy

Purpose Students will use fraction circles to estimate fraction sums.

Materials *For each pair* fraction circles, pp. TR19–TR20

Have each pair shade five fraction circles as follows:

- 1 circle to show a fraction close to 0
- 2 circles to show fractions close to $\frac{1}{2}$
- 2 circles to show fractions close to 1

Tell pairs to label their circles with the fractions and the estimates they represent.

Students' circles might look like those shown below.

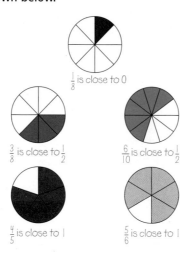

$\frac{1}{8}$ is close to 0

$\frac{3}{8}$ is close to $\frac{1}{2}$

$\frac{6}{10}$ is close to $\frac{1}{2}$

$\frac{4}{5}$ is close to 1

$\frac{5}{6}$ is close to 1

Ask volunteers to share their labeled circles. Next, ask each pair to use two circles to write an addition sentence. Have pairs trade circles and addition sentences and estimate the sum. Check students' work.

38. Estimate the difference between 8 and $2\frac{7}{18}$. **about $5\frac{1}{2}$**

39. About how much more is $8\frac{7}{10}$ feet than $2\frac{3}{8}$ feet? **about 6 feet**

40. Estimate the sum of $2\frac{1}{8}$, $7\frac{7}{9}$, $1\frac{7}{8}$, and $8\frac{1}{4}$. **about 20**

41. Estimate the sum of 8.5, $5\frac{1}{4}$, $4\frac{2}{3}$, and 6.75. **Possible answer: about 26**

42. Estimate the difference between $15\frac{3}{5}$ and $4\frac{2}{9}$. **about $11\frac{1}{2}$**

43. Estimate the sum of $18\frac{3}{10}$, $5\frac{7}{8}$, $2\frac{1}{4}$, and $3\frac{4}{5}$. **about 30**

44. About how much more is $24\frac{1}{3}$ yd than $11\frac{5}{6}$ yd? **about 12 yd**

Problem Solving ▶ Applications

Use Data The table shows data on the longest ski trails at five different mountains in the United States. For 45–46, use the table.

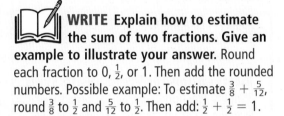

Ski Trails	
Mountain	Longest Ski Trail (mi)
Beaver Creek, CO	$2\frac{3}{4}$
Killington, VT	$10\frac{1}{5}$
Mammoth, CA	$2\frac{1}{2}$
Taos, NM	$5\frac{1}{4}$
Whiteface, NY	3

45. About how much longer is the trail at Killington than the trail at Mammoth? **about $7\frac{1}{2}$ mi longer**

46. Find the median of the trail lengths. **3 mi**

47. Leo needs $\frac{3}{4}$ yd of blue fabric, $\frac{7}{10}$ yd of purple fabric, and $\frac{1}{5}$ yd of white fabric for a sewing project. About how much fabric does he need for the sewing project? **Possible estimate: about $1\frac{1}{2}$ yd**

48. 📖 **Write a problem** about everyday life at home that can be solved by estimating fractions. Exchange with a classmate and solve. **Check students' problems.**

49. Merika mowed her yard every ninth day, beginning on March 6 and continuing through April. On what other days did she mow her yard in March? in April? **March 15, 24; April 2, 11, 20, 29**

MIXED REVIEW AND TEST PREP

Write the fraction or decimal as a percent. (p. 169)

50. $\frac{3}{4}$ **75%**   51. 0.45 **45%**

52. A survey question reads "Is blue your favorite color?" Is the question biased or unbiased? (p. 98) **biased**

53. **TEST PREP** The band members are setting up chairs for a concert in the school auditorium. They can put 25 chairs in each row. How many rows will they need to seat 350 people? (p. 22) **B**

  A 10 **B** 14 **C** 18 **D** 25

54. **TEST PREP** Find the GCF for 80, 96, and 112. (p.150) **J**

  F 6 **G** 8 **H** 14 **J** 16

(Extra Practice) page H40, Set A)   **179**

4 Assess

Summarize the lesson by having students:

DISCUSS Explain how to solve Exercise 40. Round both $2\frac{1}{8}$ and $1\frac{7}{8}$ to 2. Round both $7\frac{7}{9}$ and $8\frac{1}{4}$ to 8. Add $2 + 8 + 2 + 8 = 20$.

WRITE Explain how to estimate the sum of two fractions. Give an example to illustrate your answer. Round each fraction to 0, $\frac{1}{2}$, or 1. Then add the rounded numbers. Possible example: To estimate $\frac{3}{8} + \frac{5}{12}$, round $\frac{3}{8}$ to $\frac{1}{2}$ and $\frac{5}{12}$ to $\frac{1}{2}$. Then add: $\frac{1}{2} + \frac{1}{2} = 1$.

Lesson Quiz

Transparency **9.1**

Estimate the sum or difference. Possible estimates are given.

1. $\frac{9}{16} + \frac{5}{8}$ 1   2. $\frac{9}{10} - \frac{3}{8}$ $\frac{1}{2}$

3. $\frac{7}{8} + \frac{5}{12}$ $1\frac{1}{2}$ 4. $3\frac{2}{3} + 7\frac{5}{9}$ $11\frac{1}{2}$

5. $9\frac{1}{4} - 2\frac{8}{9}$ 6   6. $8\frac{5}{8} - 4\frac{3}{8}$ 4

ORGANIZER

Objective To use fraction bars to add and subtract fractions with unlike denominators

Vocabulary unlike fractions *Review* least common multiple (LCM)

Materials *For each group* fraction bars or fraction strips, p. TR18

Lesson Resources E-Lab Recording Sheet • *Addition and Subtraction of Unlike Fractions*

Intervention for Prerequisite Skills Simplify Fractions, Add and Subtract Like Fractions (For intervention strategies, see page 175.)

Using the Pages

Remind students of how to add two like fractions. Point out that the numerator of the answer is the sum of the numerators. Emphasize that they keep the same denominator.

Activity 1

Show students that 12 is the smallest number that is a multiple of both 6 and 4:

multiples of 6: 6, **12**, 18, 24, . . .

multiples of 4: 4, 8, **12**, 16, . . .

Because 12 is a multiple of both 6 and 4, the fractions $\frac{1}{6}$ and $\frac{1}{4}$ can be rewritten with denominators of 12. The fraction bars show that $\frac{1}{6} = \frac{2}{12}$ and $\frac{1}{4} = \frac{3}{12}$.

Think and Discuss

• *Discuss adding $\frac{2}{3}$ and $\frac{3}{8}$.*

  What must be true of a denominator that could be used to rewrite thirds and eighths? It must be a multiple of both 3 and 8.

Practice

• *After students work Exercise 1, ask:*

  How did you use the model to find the sum of $\frac{1}{4}$ and $\frac{1}{2}$? I used 2 fourths to fit across 1 half. The sum of 2 fourths plus 1 fourth is 3 fourths.

Model Addition and Subtraction

Explore how to use fraction bars to add and subtract fractions with unlike denominators.

You need fraction bars.

Vocabulary
unlike fractions

Remember that the LCM is the least of the common multiples of two or more numbers.
2: 2, 4, **6**, 8, 10, 12, . . .
3: 3, **6**, 9, 12, 15, . . .
The LCM of 2 and 3 is 6. The LCM can be used to write common denominators of two or more fractions.

QUICK REVIEW
Find the LCM for each set of numbers.
1. 2, 8 **8**   2. 6, 9 **18**
3. 4, 15 **60**   4. 4, 10 **20**
5. 2, 3, 10 **30**

Fractions with the same denominator, such as $\frac{5}{9}$ and $\frac{4}{9}$, are called like fractions. Fractions with different denominators are called **unlike fractions**. You can use fraction bars to rename the denominators before adding.

Activity 1

Find $\frac{1}{6} + \frac{1}{4}$.

• Use fraction bars to show both fractions.

• Which fraction bars fit exactly across $\frac{1}{6}$ and $\frac{1}{4}$? Think about the LCM of 6 and 4. **twelfths**

• What is $\frac{1}{6} + \frac{1}{4}$? **$\frac{5}{12}$**

$\frac{1}{6} = \frac{2}{12}$ $\frac{1}{4} = \frac{3}{12}$

Think and Discuss

• Look at the model for $\frac{1}{6} + \frac{1}{4}$. What do you know about $\frac{1}{6}$ and $\frac{2}{12}$? about $\frac{1}{4}$ and $\frac{3}{12}$? **They are equivalent; they are equivalent.**

• How are the denominators of $\frac{1}{6}$, $\frac{1}{4}$, and $\frac{1}{12}$ related? (HINT: Think about common multiples.) **12 is the LCM of 6 and 4.**

Practice

Use fraction bars to find the sum. Draw a diagram of your model. Check students' diagrams.

1. $\frac{1}{4} + \frac{1}{2}$ $\frac{3}{4}$ 2. $\frac{1}{2} + \frac{1}{3}$ $\frac{5}{6}$ 3. $\frac{1}{2} + \frac{2}{5}$ $\frac{9}{10}$ 4. $\frac{2}{3} + \frac{1}{6}$ $\frac{5}{6}$

5. $\frac{1}{3} + \frac{1}{4}$ $\frac{7}{12}$ 6. $\frac{3}{8} + \frac{1}{4}$ $\frac{5}{8}$ 7. $\frac{1}{6} + \frac{1}{2}$ $\frac{2}{3}$ 8. $\frac{3}{8} + \frac{1}{2}$ $\frac{7}{8}$

9. $\frac{1}{5} + \frac{1}{2}$ $\frac{7}{10}$ 10. $\frac{3}{4} + \frac{1}{6}$ $\frac{11}{12}$ 11. $\frac{1}{3} + \frac{1}{6}$ $\frac{1}{2}$ 12. $\frac{5}{8} + \frac{1}{4}$ $\frac{7}{8}$

180

WRITING IN MATHEMATICS

Have students **write a word problem that can be solved with these fraction bars.**

Possible answer: Jon is swimming across Blue Lake, which is $\frac{5}{6}$ mi long. He has swum $\frac{3}{4}$ mi. How far does he have to go? $\frac{1}{12}$ mi

Intervention and Extension Resources

EARLY FINISHERS

Materials *For each group* fraction bars or fraction strips, p. TR18

Students **use fraction bars or fraction strips to find the sum of fractions with compatible denominators.** Explain that when the denominator of one fraction is a multiple of the denominator of another fraction, the denominators are *compatible*. Have students solve these exercises.

• $\frac{2}{3} - \frac{1}{6}$ $\frac{1}{2}$ • $\frac{4}{5} + \frac{1}{10}$ $\frac{9}{10}$ • $\frac{3}{8} + \frac{1}{4}$ $\frac{5}{8}$

KINESTHETIC

Fraction bars also can be used to subtract unlike fractions.

TECHNOLOGY LINK
More Practice: Use E-Lab, *Addition and Subtraction of Unlike Fractions.*
www.harcourtschool.com/elab2002

Activity 2

Find $\frac{1}{2} - \frac{1}{5}$.

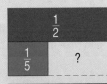

- Use fraction bars to show $\frac{1}{2}$ and $\frac{1}{5}$.
- Which fraction bars fit exactly across $\frac{1}{2}$ and $\frac{1}{5}$? Think about the LCM. **tenths**

- Compare $\frac{5}{10}$ and $\frac{2}{10}$. How much more is $\frac{5}{10}$ than $\frac{2}{10}$? $\frac{3}{10}$ **more**
- What is $\frac{5}{10} - \frac{2}{10}$? What is $\frac{1}{2} - \frac{1}{5}$? $\frac{3}{10}$; $\frac{3}{10}$

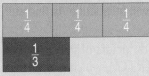

Think and Discuss
- How are the denominators of $\frac{1}{2}$, $\frac{1}{5}$, and $\frac{1}{10}$ related? **The LCM of 2 and 5 is 10.**
- Look at the model of $\frac{3}{4} - \frac{1}{3}$. Which fraction bars will fit exactly across $\frac{3}{4}$ and $\frac{1}{3}$? Explain. **Twelfths; 12 is the LCM of 4 and 3.**
- Which fraction bars will fit exactly across $\frac{1}{2} - \frac{1}{4}$? **fourths, eighths, or twelfths**

Practice
Check students' diagrams.
Use fraction bars to subtract. Draw a diagram of your model.

1. $\frac{3}{4} - \frac{1}{3}$ $\frac{5}{12}$ 2. $\frac{2}{5} - \frac{1}{10}$ $\frac{3}{10}$ 3. $\frac{1}{3} - \frac{1}{4}$ $\frac{1}{12}$ 4. $\frac{1}{2} - \frac{1}{3}$ $\frac{1}{6}$

5. $\frac{1}{2} - \frac{2}{5}$ $\frac{1}{10}$ 6. $\frac{1}{2} - \frac{5}{12}$ $\frac{1}{12}$ 7. $\frac{1}{4} - \frac{1}{6}$ $\frac{1}{12}$ 8. $\frac{1}{3} - \frac{1}{6}$ $\frac{1}{6}$

9. $\frac{1}{4} - \frac{1}{8}$ $\frac{1}{8}$ 10. $\frac{1}{2} - \frac{1}{4}$ $\frac{1}{4}$ 11. $\frac{5}{6} - \frac{1}{3}$ $\frac{1}{2}$ 12. $\frac{7}{8} - \frac{3}{4}$ $\frac{1}{8}$

MIXED REVIEW AND TEST PREP

Compare. Write <, >, or = for each ●. (p. 169)

13. $\frac{3}{8}$ ● 0.375 **=**   14. 0.15 ● $\frac{1}{4}$ **<**   15. 0.6 ● $\frac{11}{20}$ **>**

16. Multiply. 9.25×3.2 (p. 70) **29.6**

17. **TEST PREP** Which is $9 \times 9 \times 9 \times 9 \times 9$ written with exponents? (p.40) **B**

   A 9^9 **B** 9^5 **C** 9×5 **D** 9×9

Activity 2

- *Help students relate the fractions used in Activity 2.*

What do you notice about these pairs of fractions: $\frac{1}{2}$ and $\frac{5}{10}$; $\frac{1}{5}$ and $\frac{2}{10}$? The fractions in each pair are equivalent.

Think and Discuss

- *Discuss the relationship between $\frac{3}{4}$ and $\frac{1}{3}$.*

How many twelfths will fit across $\frac{3}{4}$? across $\frac{1}{3}$? What is $\frac{3}{4} - \frac{1}{3}$? 9; 4; $\frac{5}{12}$

Why might you use fourths instead of other common denominators to find $\frac{1}{2} - \frac{1}{4}$? Possible answer: 4 is the LCM, so the lesser number is easier to work with than other common denominators.

Practice

- *Before students begin, ask:*

How do Exercises 2, 6, and 8 differ from Exercises 1, 3, 4, 5, and 7? In Exercises 2, 6, and 8, the LCM is the denominator of one of the fractions.

MIXED REVIEW AND TEST PREP
Exercises 13–17 provide **cumulative review** (Chapters 1–9).

Oral Assessment

In which of these exercises do you need to rename before you add or subtract?
Exercises 1 and 3

1. $\frac{3}{4} + \frac{2}{3}$ 2. $\frac{4}{9} - \frac{2}{9}$
3. $\frac{5}{8} - \frac{1}{4}$ 4. $\frac{4}{5} + \frac{2}{5}$

What fraction bars would you use to model $\frac{3}{4} + \frac{2}{3}$? thirds, fourths, twelfths

---

E-LAB RECORDING SHEET

Name _____

Addition and Subtraction of Unlike Fractions

Use the computer.

1. Follow the directions on the computer to complete the table of multiples.

| 4 | 8 | 12 | 16 | 20 | 24 | 28 | 32 | 36 | 40 | 44 | 48 | 52 | 56 | 60 |
| 5 | 10 | 15 | 20 | 25 | 30 | 35 | 40 | 45 | 50 | 55 | 60 | 65 | 70 | 75 |

2. Circle all numbers in the table that appear in both rows. 20 40 60
3. The smallest number circled in your table is the least common multiple of 4 and 5.
   What number is the least common multiple of 4 and 5? ___20___
4. Click Reset. Complete the table of multiples.

3	6	9	12	15	18	21	24	27	30	33	36	39	42	45
4	8	12	16	20	24	28	32	36	40	44	48	52	56	60
6	12	18	24	30	36	42	48	54	60	66	72	78	84	90

5. Circle all numbers in the table that appear in all three rows. 12, 24, 36
6. What number is the least common multiple of 3, 4, and 6? ___12___
7. Use the least common multiple of 4 and 5, computed in Problem 3, as the least common denominator for adding the fractions $\frac{1}{4}$ and $\frac{1}{5}$. $\frac{1}{4} + \frac{1}{5} = \frac{5}{20} + \frac{4}{20} = \frac{9}{20}$
8. Use the least common multiple of 3, 4, and 6, computed in Problem 6, as the least common denominator for adding the fractions $\frac{1}{3}$, $\frac{1}{4}$, and $\frac{1}{6}$. $\frac{1}{3} + \frac{1}{4} + \frac{1}{6} = \frac{4}{12} + \frac{3}{12} + \frac{2}{12} = \frac{9}{12}$ or $\frac{3}{4}$

Use E-Lab to find the least common denominator for each of the following addition problems.

	Least Common Denominator
9. $\frac{1}{4} + \frac{1}{10} + \frac{1}{12}$	60
10. $\frac{1}{6} + \frac{1}{9} + \frac{1}{12}$	36
11. $\frac{1}{6} + \frac{1}{10} + \frac{1}{15}$	30
12. $\frac{1}{2} + \frac{1}{3} + \frac{1}{4}$	12
13. $\frac{1}{3} + \frac{1}{5} + \frac{1}{9}$	45
14. $\frac{1}{2} + \frac{1}{3} + \frac{1}{7}$	42

The least common multiple of the denominators of two or more fractions can be used as the common denominator for addition.

E-Lab Recording Sheet

USING E-LAB

Students use a computer tool for finding multiples to add fractions with unlike denominators.

The E-Lab Recording Sheets and activities are available on the E-Lab website.

www.harcourtschool.com/elab2002

TECHNOLOGY LINK

Intervention Strategies and Activities CD-ROM • *Skills 22, 23*

E-Lab • *Addition and Subtraction of Unlike Fractions*

Add and Subtract Fractions

LESSON PLANNING

Objective To add and subtract fractions

Intervention for Prerequisite Skills

Simplify Fractions, Add and Subtract Like Fractions (For intervention strategies, see page 175.)

 California Mathematics Content Standards

○━ NS 2.0 Students calculate and solve problems involving addition, subtraction, multiplication, and division.

○━ NS 2.4 Determine the least common multiple and greatest common divisor of whole numbers; use them to solve problems with fractions.

MR 2.1 Use estimation to verify the reasonableness of calculated results.

(*Also* ○━ NS 1.0, NS 2.1, MR 1.0, MR 1.1)

Vocabulary

least common denominator (LCD)
the least number, other than zero, that is a multiple of two or more denominators

Math Background

These ideas will help students find sums and differences of fractions.

- Multiples or factors of the given denominators can be used to find their LCM, which is the LCD of the given fractions.
- To find the numerator of the sum or difference of two fractions with a common denominator, add or subtract their numerators.
- Use an estimate to decide if an answer is reasonable.

WARM-UP RESOURCES

 NUMBER OF THE DAY

 Transparency 9.3

We are two common fractions. Our numerators are 1 and the LCM of our denominators is 20. What fractions are we? Possible answer: $\frac{1}{5}$ and $\frac{1}{4}$

 PROBLEM OF THE DAY

 Transparency 9.3

Kim used $\frac{6}{8}$ of a tank of gas. She bought $\frac{5}{8}$ of a tank and then used $\frac{4}{8}$ of a tank. Kim was almost out of money, so she filled the tank to half full by adding $\frac{2}{8}$ of a tank of gas. What part of a tank of gas did she start with? Kim started with $\frac{7}{8}$ tank of gas.

Solution Problem of the Day tab, p. PD9

 DAILY FACTS PRACTICE

Have students practice addition and subtraction facts by completing Set D of *Teacher's Resource Book*, p. TR99.

ALTERNATIVE TEACHING STRATEGY

To **reinforce students' understanding of the least common denominator (LCD),** begin by displaying two fractions, such as $\frac{2}{3}$ and $\frac{5}{6}$.

- Ask four or five volunteers to name possible common denominators. Possible answers: 6, 12, 18, 24, 30

- Ask a volunteer to explain how to choose the LCD. The LCD must be a multiple of 6 because 6 is the greater number; because 6 can also be divided by 3, the LCD is 6.

Repeat with other pairs of fractions.

See also page 184.

AUDITORY

MIXED REVIEW AND TEST PREP

Cumulative Review Chapters 1–9

Refer to the Pupil Edition pages referenced in the exercises for further review. Have students go to the lesson page, review the lesson, and correct any problem they missed.

Mixed Review and Test Prep, p. 185

How to Help	
Item	**Page**
51	160
52	160
53	20
54	94
55	52

SPECIAL NEEDS ELL

Materials *For each group* fraction bars or fraction strips, p. TR18

Ask groups to **use fraction bars or strips to find sums and differences.** Have each group write two fractions using denominators from the fraction bars and then find a sum and a difference: for example, $\frac{5}{8} + \frac{1}{4}$ and $\frac{5}{8} - \frac{1}{4}$. Then have students model the sum and the difference using fractions bars. Finally, have each group write the sum and difference by finding the LCD of the fractions. $\frac{5}{8} + \frac{1}{4} = \frac{7}{8}, \frac{5}{8} - \frac{1}{4} = \frac{3}{8}$

KINESTHETIC

ADVANCED LEARNERS

Challenge students to **complete the magic square.** Explain to students that the sums of the rows, columns, and diagonals are all the same. The sum in this square is 1.

$\frac{2}{15}$	$\frac{7}{15}$	$\frac{2}{5}$
$\frac{3}{5}$	$\frac{1}{3}$	$\frac{1}{15}$
$\frac{4}{15}$	$\frac{1}{5}$	$\frac{8}{15}$

VISUAL

TECHNOLOGY LINK

- **Intervention Strategies and Activities CD-ROM** • *Skills 22, 23*

- **Number Heroes** • *Fraction Fireworks,* Levels T, U, W

- **Calculating Crew** • *Nautical Number Line,* Level M

Objective To add and subtract fractions

Vocabulary least common denominator (LCD)

1 Introduce

QUICK REVIEW provides review of pre-requisite skills.

Why Learn This? You can use adding and subtracting fractions to solve problems involving time and food preparation. *Share the lesson objective with students.*

2 Teach

Guided Instruction

• *Direct students to read Example 1.*

Why is 12 the LCM of 4 and 3? 12 is the least multiple of 4 which is also a multiple of 3.

• *As you discuss Example 2, ask:*

Why can we multiply $\frac{1}{2}$ by $\frac{5}{5}$ and $\frac{3}{5}$ by $\frac{2}{2}$? Both $\frac{5}{5}$ and $\frac{2}{2}$ are equal to 1, and you can multiply any number by 1 without changing its value.

Modifying Instruction For Example 2, have students who are having difficulty use fraction bars or strips to make models. Discuss how the models relate to the process shown in the example.

ADDITIONAL EXAMPLES

Example 1, p. 182

Aaron is making chocolate pudding. He combines $\frac{1}{2}$ c of sugar with $\frac{1}{3}$ c of cocoa. What is the total amount of the two ingredients? $\frac{5}{6}$ c

Example 2, p. 182

Find the sum. $\frac{3}{4} + \frac{3}{5}$ $1\frac{7}{20}$

182 Chapter 9

Add and Subtract Fractions

Learn how to add and subtract fractions.

Vocabulary

least common denominator (LCD)

$\mathbf{Y}$ou can use a diagram to add and subtract fractions. To help you, think about the LCM of the denominators and about equivalent fractions.

EXAMPLE 1

Kayla is making two recipes. One recipe calls for $\frac{1}{4}$ c raisins, and the other recipe calls for $\frac{1}{3}$ c raisins. How many total cups of raisins does Kayla need?

Complete the diagram to find the sum of $\frac{1}{4}$ and $\frac{1}{3}$.

The LCM of 4 and 3 is 12. Draw twelfths under $\frac{1}{4}$ and $\frac{1}{3}$.

THINK: $\frac{1}{4} = \frac{3}{12}$ and $\frac{1}{3} = \frac{4}{12}$.

So, Kayla needs $\frac{7}{12}$ c of raisins.

Math Idea ▶ To add fractions without using diagrams, you can write equivalent fractions by using the **least common denominator**, or **LCD**. The LCD is the LCM of the denominators.

EXAMPLE 2

Find $\frac{1}{2} + \frac{3}{5}$.

Estimate. Each fraction is close to $\frac{1}{2}$, so the sum is about 1.

$$\frac{1}{2} = \frac{1 \times 5}{2 \times 5} = \frac{5}{10}$$
$$+\frac{3}{5} = +\frac{3 \times 2}{5 \times 2} = +\frac{6}{10}$$

The LCM of 2 and 5 is 10, so the LCD of $\frac{1}{2}$ and $\frac{3}{5}$ is 10. Multiply to write equivalent fractions using the LCD.

$$\frac{1}{2} = \frac{5}{10}$$
$$+\frac{3}{5} = +\frac{6}{10}$$

Add the numerators. Write the sum over the denominator.

$$\frac{11}{10}, \text{ or } 1\frac{1}{10}$$

Write the answer as a fraction or as a mixed number.

Compare the answer to your estimate. Since $1\frac{1}{10}$ is close to the estimate of 1, the answer is reasonable. So, $\frac{1}{2} + \frac{3}{5} = 1\frac{1}{10}$.

182   **CALIFORNIA STANDARDS** O━┓NS 2.0 Students calculate and solve problems involving addition, subtraction, multiplication, and division. O━┓NS 2.4 Determine the least common multiple and the greatest common divisor of whole numbers; use them to solve problems with fractions. **MR 2.1** Use estimation to verify the reasonableness of calculated results. *also,* O━┓NS 1.0, NS 2.1, MR 1.0, MR 1.1

RETEACH 9.3

Add and Subtract Fractions

To add or subtract unlike fractions, first change them to equivalent fractions with the same denominator.

Find the sum. $\frac{1}{4} + \frac{2}{3}$

Step 1: Find the LCM of the denominators. The LCM of 4 and 3 is 12. So, the LCD of $\frac{1}{4}$ and $\frac{2}{3}$ is 12.

Step 2: Multiply to write equivalent fractions, using the LCD.

$$\frac{1}{4} = \frac{1 \times 3}{4 \times 3} = \frac{3}{12}$$
$$\frac{2}{3} = \frac{2 \times 4}{3 \times 4} = \frac{8}{12}$$

Step 3: Add the numerators. Write the sum over the denominator.

$$\frac{3}{12} + \frac{8}{12} = \frac{11}{12}$$

Remember, keep the denominator the same.

Step 4: Write the answer as a fraction or as a mixed number in simplest form.

$$\frac{1}{4} + \frac{2}{3} = \frac{11}{12}$$

$\frac{11}{12}$ is already in simplest form.

Follow the same steps to subtract unlike fractions.

Complete to find each sum. Write the answer in simplest form.

1. Find $\frac{2}{5} + \frac{3}{10}$.
The LCM of 5 and 10 is 10.
So, $\frac{2}{5} + \frac{3}{10} = \frac{4}{10} + \frac{3}{10} = \frac{7}{10}$.

2. Find $\frac{7}{8} + \frac{2}{3}$.
The LCM of 8 and 3 is 24.
So, $\frac{7}{8} + \frac{2}{3} = \frac{21}{24} + \frac{16}{24} = \frac{37}{24} = 1\frac{13}{24}$.

3. Find $\frac{1}{4} + \frac{5}{6}$.
The LCM of 4 and 6 is 12.
So, $\frac{1}{4} + \frac{5}{6} = \frac{3}{12} + \frac{10}{12} = \frac{13}{12} = 1\frac{1}{12}$.

4. Find $\frac{1}{6} + \frac{3}{8}$.
The LCM of 6 and 8 is 24.
So, $\frac{1}{6} + \frac{3}{8} = \frac{4}{24} + \frac{9}{24} = \frac{13}{24}$.

Find the sum or difference. Write the answer in simplest form.

5. $\frac{5}{7} + \frac{1}{2}$ $\frac{11}{14}$ 6. $\frac{11}{12} - \frac{7}{8}$ $\frac{1}{24}$ 7. $\frac{4}{5} + \frac{1}{3}$ $\frac{17}{15}$, or $1\frac{2}{15}$ 8. $\frac{3}{4} - \frac{1}{5}$ $\frac{11}{20}$

PRACTICE 9.3

Add and Subtract Fractions

Use the LCD to rewrite the problem by using equivalent fractions.

1. $\frac{3}{8} + \frac{1}{2}$ $\frac{3}{8} + \frac{4}{8}$
2. $\frac{3}{4} - \frac{1}{6}$ $\frac{9}{12} - \frac{2}{12}$
3. $\frac{2}{3} + \frac{4}{15}$ $\frac{10}{15} + \frac{12}{15}$
4. $\frac{8}{9} - \frac{1}{3}$ $\frac{8}{9} - \frac{3}{9}$
5. $\frac{1}{4} + \frac{3}{7}$ $\frac{7}{28} + \frac{12}{28}$

Write the sum or difference in simplest form. Estimate to check.

6. $\frac{1}{2} + \frac{1}{5}$ $\frac{7}{10}$
7. $\frac{6}{7} - \frac{1}{4}$ $\frac{17}{28}$
8. $\frac{9}{10} - \frac{3}{5}$ $\frac{3}{10}$
9. $\frac{7}{8} - \frac{1}{2}$ $\frac{3}{8}$
10. $\frac{3}{4} + \frac{5}{8}$ $1\frac{3}{8}$

11. $\frac{4}{5} - \frac{1}{3}$ $\frac{7}{15}$
12. $\frac{5}{8} + \frac{1}{10}$ $\frac{29}{40}$
13. $\frac{1}{2} - \frac{1}{6}$ $\frac{1}{3}$
14. $\frac{7}{10} + \frac{1}{4}$ $\frac{19}{20}$
15. $\frac{5}{6} + \frac{1}{3}$ $1\frac{1}{6}$

16. $\frac{11}{12} - \frac{1}{4}$ $\frac{2}{3}$
17. $\frac{7}{10} + \frac{1}{2}$ $1\frac{1}{5}$
18. $\frac{1}{4} + \frac{7}{12}$ $\frac{5}{6}$
19. $\frac{5}{6} - \frac{1}{7}$ $\frac{11}{21}$
20. $\frac{4}{5} - \frac{1}{6}$ $\frac{19}{30}$

21. $\frac{3}{4} + \frac{1}{2}$ $1\frac{1}{4}$
22. $\frac{2}{3} - \frac{3}{8}$ $\frac{7}{24}$
23. $\frac{3}{5} + \frac{1}{15}$ $\frac{2}{3}$
24. $\frac{13}{14} - \frac{2}{7}$ $\frac{9}{14}$
25. $\frac{1}{3} - \frac{1}{5}$ $\frac{2}{15}$

26. $\frac{7}{10} - \frac{2}{5}$ $\frac{3}{10}$
27. $\frac{1}{7} + \frac{1}{2}$ $\frac{9}{14}$
28. $\frac{7}{12} - \frac{1}{4}$ $\frac{1}{3}$
29. $\frac{7}{15} - \frac{2}{5}$ $\frac{1}{15}$
30. $\frac{2}{5} + \frac{1}{3}$ $\frac{11}{15}$

31. $\frac{4}{9} + \frac{1}{2}$ $\frac{17}{18}$
32. $\frac{5}{8} - \frac{2}{3}$ $\frac{1}{21}$
33. $\frac{5}{8} + \frac{1}{3}$ $\frac{23}{24}$
34. $\frac{2}{9} + \frac{1}{3}$ $\frac{7}{9}$
35. $\frac{5}{6} - \frac{1}{2}$ $\frac{1}{3}$

Mixed Review

Find the mean, median, and mode.

36. 57, 71, 50, 57, 53, 60   58, 57, 57
37. 21, 25, 29, 18, 31, 27, 24   25, 25, no mode

Find the quotient.

38. $26.98 \div 3.8$ 7.1   39. $1.365 \div 0.07$ 19.5   40. $174.08 \div 27.2$ 6.4

You can use a similar method to subtract unlike fractions.

EXAMPLE 3

Kayla is preparing a pasta dish for a small dinner party. Kayla has $\frac{1}{2}$ c of grated mozzarella cheese. The recipe calls for $\frac{2}{3}$ c of grated mozzarella cheese. How much more mozzarella cheese does Kayla need to grate?

Find $\frac{2}{3} - \frac{1}{2}$.

Estimate. $\frac{2}{3}$ is a little more than $\frac{1}{2}$, so the difference is close to 0.

$$\frac{2}{3} = \frac{2 \times \boxed{2}}{3 \times \boxed{2}} = \frac{4}{6}$$ *The LCD of $\frac{2}{3}$ and $\frac{1}{2}$ is 6.*

$$-\frac{1}{2} = -\frac{1 \times \boxed{3}}{2 \times \boxed{3}} = -\frac{3}{6}$$ *Multiply to find the equivalent fractions using the LCD.*

$$\frac{2}{3} = \frac{4}{6}$$
$$-\frac{1}{2} = -\frac{3}{6}$$
$$\frac{1}{6}$$

Subtract the numerators. Write the difference over the denominator.

Compare the answer to your estimate. Since $\frac{1}{6}$ is close to the estimate of 0, the answer is reasonable.

So, Kayla needs to grate $\frac{1}{6}$ c more cheese.

EXAMPLE 4

A. $\frac{5}{6} = \frac{5 \times \boxed{3}}{6 \times \boxed{3}} = \frac{15}{18}$

   $-\frac{7}{9} = -\frac{7 \times \boxed{2}}{9 \times \boxed{2}} = -\frac{14}{18}$

                $\frac{1}{18}$

B. $\frac{5}{12} \quad\quad = \frac{5}{12}$

   $-\frac{1}{4} = -\frac{1 \times \boxed{3}}{4 \times \boxed{3}} = -\frac{3}{12}$

                $\frac{2}{12} = \frac{1}{6}$

CHECK FOR UNDERSTANDING

Think and Discuss ▶ Look back at the lesson to answer each question.

1. **Tell** how much more cheese Kayla would need to grate if she had $\frac{1}{4}$ c of grated cheese. $\frac{5}{12}$ c more

2. **REASONING Tell** when the LCD of two fractions is equal to the product of the denominators. when the denominators have 1 as their GCF

Guided Practice ▶ Use the LCD to rewrite the problem by using equivalent fractions.

3. $\frac{7}{10} + \frac{1}{5}$ $\frac{7}{10} + \frac{2}{10}$ 4. $\frac{1}{3} + \frac{1}{8}$ $\frac{8}{24} + \frac{3}{24}$ 5. $\frac{4}{5} - \frac{1}{3}$ $\frac{12}{15} - \frac{5}{15}$

183

• *Before discussing Examples 3 and 4, ask:*

REASONING **How do you think the method for subtracting fractions will be like the method for adding fractions?** For both, it is necessary to find the LCD.

• *Direct student's attention to Example 3.*

Why is the LCD of 2 and 3 equal to their product? They have no lesser multiple in common.

REASONING **How do you know what to multiply the numerator and denominator by when writing the equivalent fractions?** Divide the LCD by the denominator of each fraction.

ADDITIONAL EXAMPLES

Example 3, p. 183

Kayla's dessert calls for $\frac{3}{4}$ c of syrup. She has only $\frac{2}{3}$ c left in the bottle. How much syrup must she use from the new bottle? $\frac{1}{12}$ c

Example 4, p. 183

A. $\frac{9}{10} - \frac{7}{8}$ $\frac{1}{40}$ B. $\frac{11}{12} - \frac{1}{4}$ $\frac{8}{12}$, or $\frac{2}{3}$

3 Practice

Guided Practice

Do Check for Understanding Exercises 1–13 with your students. Identify those having difficulty and use lesson resources to help.

To help students understand Exercise 2, show that they can find the LCM of two numbers by dividing the product of the numbers by the GCF. For example, the GCF of 6 and 9 is 3, so the LCM of 6 and 9 is $6 \times 9 \div 3 = 18$.

So, if the GCF of two numbers is 1:

LCD (= LCM) = product of numbers ÷ GCF
               = product of numbers ÷ 1
               = product of numbers

PROBLEM SOLVING 9.3

Add and Subtract Fractions

Write the correct answer.

1. List all the factors of 24.

   1, 2, 3, 4, 6, 8, 12, 24

2. What is the prime factorization $3 \times 3 \times 5 \times 7 \times 11 \times 11$ written in exponent form?

   $3^2 \times 5 \times 7 \times 11^2$

3. Olga has $\frac{3}{4}$ yd of blue ribbon. She also has $\frac{3}{8}$ yd of red ribbon. How much ribbon does she have altogether?

   $1\frac{1}{8}$ yd

4. Bruce walks $\frac{7}{8}$ mi to school and his friend walks $\frac{1}{3}$ mi to school. How much farther does Bruce have to walk than his friend?

   $\frac{13}{24}$ mi

Choose the letter for the best answer.

5. What is the prime factorization of 48?

   A $2 \times 2 \times 3$
   B $2 \times 2 \times 2 \times 2 \times 2$
   Ⓒ $2 \times 2 \times 2 \times 2 \times 3$
   D $2 \times 2 \times 2 \times 3 \times 3$

6. Todd had $\frac{7}{8}$ gal of paint. He used $\frac{1}{4}$ gal on one project and $\frac{1}{2}$ gal on another project. How much paint does he have left?

   Ⓕ $\frac{1}{8}$ gal   H $\frac{5}{8}$ gal
   G $\frac{3}{8}$ gal   J $1\frac{5}{8}$ gal

7. The third-grade class painted $\frac{1}{4}$ of the school fence, the fourth-grade class painted $\frac{1}{6}$ of it, and the fifth-grade class painted $\frac{2}{5}$ of it. How much of the fence has been painted?

   A $\frac{4}{5}$
   B $\frac{13}{15}$
   Ⓒ $\frac{7}{20}$
   D $\frac{9}{10}$

8. In the last four days, the local swimming pool has been used by 348 people, 276 people, 573 people, and 621 people. Which is the best estimate of the total number of people who have used the pool in the last four days?

   Ⓕ 1,850
   G 2,000
   H 2,200
   J 2,350

9. **Write About It** Explain how you found the least common denominator for Exercise 6.

   The least common denominator is the least common multiple of the denominators. The LCM of 2, 4, and 8 is 8.

CHALLENGE 9.3

Sum It Up

The shaded portion of each figure below models a fraction. Use the figures to find each sum. Write your answer in simplest form.

1. $A + C =$ $\frac{5}{8}$
2. $F - B =$ $\frac{1}{32}$
3. $E - D =$ $\frac{1}{16}$
4. $C + F =$ $\frac{19}{32}$
5. $A + B =$ $\frac{11}{16}$
6. $E - C =$ $\frac{1}{4}$
7. $B + D =$ $\frac{3}{4}$
8. $A + F =$ $\frac{23}{32}$
9. $D - A =$ $\frac{1}{16}$
10. $C + B =$ $\frac{9}{16}$
11. $E + A =$ $\frac{7}{8}$
12. $D - F =$ $\frac{3}{32}$
13. $C + D =$ $\frac{11}{16}$
14. $E - B + C =$ $\frac{7}{16}$
15. $F + A - D =$ $\frac{9}{32}$
16. $A - B + C =$ $\frac{5}{16}$
17. $E - F + D =$ $\frac{19}{32}$
18. $A + F - B =$ $\frac{13}{32}$

Write the sum or difference in simplest form. Estimate to check.

9. $\frac{17}{12}$, or $1\frac{5}{12}$

6. $\frac{1}{5} + \frac{3}{5}$ $\frac{4}{5}$

7. $\frac{7}{9} - \frac{4}{9}$ $\frac{1}{3}$

8. $\frac{7}{9} - \frac{1}{6}$ $\frac{11}{18}$

9. $\frac{2}{3} + \frac{3}{4}$

10. $\frac{3}{4} - \frac{3}{8}$ $\frac{3}{8}$

11. $\frac{2}{5} - \frac{1}{3}$ $\frac{1}{15}$

12. $\frac{2}{5} + \frac{2}{4}$ $\frac{9}{10}$

13. $\frac{4}{9} + \frac{1}{3}$ $\frac{7}{9}$

COMMON ERROR ALERT

Some students may add both the numerators and the denominators when adding fractions. Have these students use fraction bars to show that the sum of $\frac{1}{2}$ and $\frac{1}{4}$ is $\frac{3}{4}$, not $\frac{3}{8}$.

Error

$\frac{1}{2} + \frac{1}{4} = \frac{2}{4} + \frac{1}{4} = \frac{3}{8}$

Correction

$\frac{1}{2} + \frac{1}{4} = \frac{2}{4} + \frac{1}{4} = \frac{3}{4}$

PRACTICE AND PROBLEM SOLVING

Independent Practice ▶ Use the LCD to rewrite the problem by using equivalent fractions.

14. $\frac{9}{10} - \frac{1}{5}$ $\frac{9}{10} - \frac{2}{10}$

15. $\frac{6}{7} - \frac{3}{4}$ $\frac{24}{28} - \frac{21}{28}$

16. $\frac{1}{4} + \frac{5}{8}$ $\frac{2}{8} + \frac{5}{8}$

Write the sum or difference in simplest form. Estimate to check.

17. $\frac{1}{6} + \frac{2}{3}$ $\frac{5}{6}$

18. $\frac{4}{7} - \frac{1}{7}$ $\frac{3}{7}$

19. $\frac{1}{2} + \frac{3}{10}$ $\frac{4}{5}$

20. $\frac{1}{3} - \frac{1}{4}$ $\frac{1}{12}$

21. $\frac{5}{7} - \frac{1}{2}$ $\frac{3}{14}$

22. $\frac{1}{3} + \frac{2}{3}$ 1

23. $\frac{6}{10} - \frac{4}{10}$ $\frac{1}{5}$

24. $\frac{3}{8} + \frac{1}{3}$ $\frac{17}{24}$

25. $\frac{11}{8}$, or $1\frac{3}{8}$

25. $\frac{3}{4} + \frac{5}{8}$

26. $\frac{7}{12} + \frac{2}{3}$

27. $1 - \frac{3}{8}$ $\frac{5}{8}$

28. $\frac{1}{2} - \frac{2}{5}$ $\frac{1}{10}$

26. $\frac{15}{12}$, or $1\frac{1}{4}$

29. $\frac{4}{5} - \frac{1}{3}$ $\frac{7}{15}$

30. $\frac{1}{4} + \frac{2}{3}$ $\frac{11}{12}$

31. $\frac{5}{9} - \frac{1}{3}$ $\frac{2}{9}$

32. $\frac{3}{8} + \frac{3}{20}$ $\frac{21}{40}$

33. $\frac{6}{8}$, or $\frac{3}{4}$

33. Find the sum of $\frac{1}{8}$, $\frac{3}{8}$, and $\frac{2}{8}$.

34. Find $\frac{1}{2} + \frac{2}{3} + \frac{1}{6}$. $\frac{4}{3}$, or $1\frac{1}{3}$

35. Find $\frac{3}{4} + 0.5 + 0.75$. 2

36. Find $0.6 - \frac{3}{8}$. 0.225, or $\frac{9}{40}$

37. How much longer than $\frac{1}{4}$ mile is $\frac{2}{3}$ mile? $\frac{5}{12}$ mile

Solve each equation mentally. Write the answer in simplest form.

38. $p + \frac{1}{4} = \frac{3}{4}$ $p = \frac{1}{2}$

39. $r = \frac{5}{12} + \frac{7}{12}$ $r = 1$

40. $\frac{4}{5} - q = \frac{2}{5}$ $q = \frac{2}{5}$

41. $c = \frac{7}{10} - \frac{1}{10}$ $c = \frac{3}{5}$

42. $\frac{3}{7} + s = \frac{5}{7}$ $s = \frac{2}{7}$

43. $m - \frac{1}{6} = \frac{5}{6}$ $m = 1$

Problem Solving ▶
Applications

Use Data For 44–46, use the recipe at the right.

44. Yuji has $\frac{7}{8}$ c of orange juice. How much orange juice does he have left to drink after he makes the fruit cups? $\frac{5}{8}$ c

45. How many total teaspoons of $\frac{5}{8}$ tsp vanilla and orange extract does Yuji need to make the fruit cups?

46. Yuji used $\frac{1}{4}$ tsp of orange extract. By how much did he exceed the amount of orange extract in the recipe? $\frac{1}{8}$ tsp

Fruit Cups

2 cups of orange sections

1 cup blueberries

$\frac{1}{4}$ cup orange juice

1 tbsp sugar

1 tsp lemon juice

$\frac{1}{2}$ tsp vanilla extract

$\frac{1}{8}$ tsp orange extract

184 Chapter 9

Independent Practice

Assign Exercises 14–50.

In Exercise 47, students will need to subtract the sum of the given fractions from 1 to answer the question.

In Exercise 49, students should begin by finding the numbers between 21 and 30 that are multiples of 4. Those numbers are 24 and 28. Students can then verify that the GCF of 24 and 28 is 4.

Alternative Teaching Strategy

Purpose Students add and subtract fractions to complete number squares.

Materials *For each group* an addition and a subtraction square; fraction bars or fraction strips, p. TR18

Display the following addition number square.

$\frac{1}{4}$	$\frac{1}{12}$	? $\frac{1}{3}$
$\frac{1}{3}$	$\frac{1}{6}$	? $\frac{1}{2}$
? $\frac{7}{12}$	? $\frac{1}{4}$	? $\frac{5}{6}$

Have students work in groups to copy the addition square and then complete it. Let them use fraction bars if they wish. Discuss any difficulties that students encounter.

Next, display the following subtraction number square. Have students follow the same process as with the addition square.

$\frac{8}{9}$	$\frac{1}{3}$	? $\frac{5}{9}$
$\frac{1}{2}$	$\frac{1}{6}$	? $\frac{1}{3}$
? $\frac{7}{18}$	? $\frac{1}{6}$	? $\frac{2}{9}$

Finally, have groups make number squares for addition and/or subtraction. Tell students that they may write any four fractions to start an addition square. In subtraction squares, the fractions in the top row must be greater than those in the second row. The fractions in the left column must be greater than those in the second column. Have groups find the missing fractions in their squares.

Then ask groups to exchange number squares, solve, and compare solutions. Check students' work.

47. Each week, Reina spends $\frac{2}{3}$ of her allowance on school lunches and saves $\frac{1}{5}$ of it. What fraction of her allowance is left? Which operation(s) did you use? Why? **$\frac{2}{15}$ is left; add to find the total spent and saved; subtract to find how much is left.**

48. ❓ **What's the Question?** In Mrs. Lucero's class, $\frac{1}{10}$ of the students are wearing blue shirts and $\frac{3}{5}$ of the students are wearing white shirts. The answer is $\frac{3}{10}$ of the class. **What part of Mrs. Lucero's class is wearing *neither* blue nor white shirts?**

49. *REASONING* Joaquin is thinking of two numbers. Each number is between 21 and 30. The GCF of the numbers is 4. What are the numbers? **24 and 28**

50. One cup of whole milk contains 166 calories and one cup of skim milk contains 88 calories. How many more calories are there in 4 cups of whole milk than in 4 cups of skim milk? **312 more calories**

MIXED REVIEW AND TEST PREP

For 51-52, write in simplest form. (p.160)

51. $\frac{36}{81}$ **$\frac{4}{9}$**   52. $\frac{95}{200}$ **$\frac{19}{40}$**   53. Subtract. $9,285 - 3,153$ (p. 20) **6,132**

54. **TEST PREP** A teacher selects 50 students by picking names out of a box without looking. What type of sample is this? (p. 94) **C**

   A biased   **B** convenience   **C** random   **D** systematic

55. **TEST PREP** Eric skated 500 meters in 37.14 seconds. Andre skated the same distance in 37.139 seconds, and Al in 37.12 seconds. What is the correct order of their times in seconds, from fastest to slowest times? (p. 52) **H**

   F 37.14, 37.139, 37.12   **H** 37.12, 37.139, 37.14

   G 37.12, 37.14, 37.139   **J** 37.139, 37.12, 37.14

Thinker's CORNER

MATH FUN • FRACTION GAME
Materials: 9 index cards per group
Have students write these numbers on the cards, one to a card:

A student shuffles the cards. Each student in the group picks two cards and subtracts the lesser number from the greater number. Students compare answers. The one whose answer is the greatest number scores a point. Reshuffle the cards after each round. Three points are needed to win the game.

⟨ Extra Practice ⟩ page H40, Set B **185**

MIXED REVIEW AND TEST PREP
Exercises 51–55 provide **cumulative review** (Chapters 1–9).

Thinker's Corner

• *Have students prepare the cards and read the directions for the game.*

Which two cards will give the greatest difference? $\frac{11}{12} - \frac{1}{5}$

Which pairs of cards would not require finding the LCD? $\frac{2}{3} - \frac{1}{3}$ and $\frac{5}{8} - \frac{3}{8}$

What is the greatest LCD that a pair of cards could have? Pair $\frac{11}{12}$ and $\frac{1}{5}$ and pair $\frac{11}{12}$ and $\frac{7}{10}$; both have an LCD of 60.

REASONING **Is there a strategy you can use to win? Explain.** No; the numbers are picked at random.

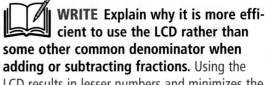

Summarize the lesson by having students:

DISCUSS Kari wants to subtract $\frac{1}{4}$ from $\frac{7}{8}$. What does she need to do? Rewrite the fractions with an LCD of 8. Then subtract the numerators and write the difference over 8.

✏️ **WRITE Explain why it is more efficient to use the LCD rather than some other common denominator when adding or subtracting fractions.** Using the LCD results in lesser numbers and minimizes the need to simplify answers.

Lesson Quiz

Transparency **9.3**

Write the sum or difference in simplest form. Estimate to check.

1. $\frac{1}{3} + \frac{5}{8}$ **$\frac{23}{24}$**   **2.** $\frac{3}{4} - \frac{1}{3}$ **$\frac{5}{12}$**

3. $\frac{9}{10} - \frac{2}{5}$ **$\frac{1}{2}$**   **4.** $\frac{5}{8} + \frac{5}{12}$ **$1\frac{1}{24}$**

5. $\frac{1}{3} + \frac{5}{6}$ **$1\frac{1}{6}$**   **6.** $\frac{5}{6} - \frac{5}{8}$ **$\frac{5}{24}$**

Add and Subtract Mixed Numbers

LESSON PLANNING

Objective To add and subtract mixed numbers

Intervention for Prerequisite Skills

Simplify Fractions, Add and Subtract Like Fractions (For intervention strategies, see page 175.)

California Mathematics Content Standards

○┐NS 2.0 Students calculate and solve problems involving addition, subtraction, multiplication, and division.

○┐NS 2.4 Determine the least common multiple and greatest common divisor of whole numbers; use them to solve problems with fractions.

MR 2.1 Use estimation to verify the reasonableness of calculated results.

(*Also* NS 2.1, MR 2.4, MR 2.7)

Math Background

Because a mixed number is the sum of a whole number and a fraction, two mixed numbers can be added by first adding the fraction parts and then adding the whole numbers. The Associative and Commutative properties justify this procedure. In the lesson, models help students grasp the steps in the algorithm.

To help students master addition and subtraction of mixed numbers, they should follow these steps:

- Write equivalent fractions for the fraction parts, using the LCD of the given fractions.
- Add or subtract the fraction parts.
- Add or subtract the whole numbers next.
- Write the answer in simplest form.

WARM-UP RESOURCES

NUMBER OF THE DAY

Transparency 9.4

Use the number 3, the number of the month, and your age. Write the greatest possible mixed number in simplest form with these three numbers. Possible answer for 3, 10, and 12: $12\frac{3}{10}$

PROBLEM OF THE DAY

Transparency 9.4

Complete the Magic Square. The sum is $1\frac{1}{4}$.

$\frac{1}{2}$	$\frac{7}{12}$	$\frac{1}{6}$
$\frac{1}{12}$	$\frac{5}{12}$	$\frac{3}{4}$
$\frac{2}{3}$	$\frac{1}{4}$	$\frac{1}{3}$

Solution Problem of the Day tab, p. PD9

DAILY FACTS PRACTICE

Have students practice addition and subtraction facts by completing Set E of *Teacher's Resource Book,* p. TR99.

INTERVENTION AND EXTENSION RESOURCES

ALTERNATIVE TEACHING STRATEGY (ELL)

To **reinforce the method for adding fractions and mixed numbers,** present a mixed number, such as $4\frac{1}{4}$. Have pairs of students write and model two different number sentences that have $4\frac{1}{4}$ as the sum.

Possible answer: $2\frac{1}{2} + 1\frac{3}{4} = 4\frac{1}{4}$; $3\frac{3}{4} + \frac{1}{2} = 4\frac{1}{4}$

See also page 188.

AUDITORY

MIXED REVIEW AND TEST PREP

Cumulative Review Chapters 1–9

Refer to the Pupil Edition pages referenced in the exercises for further review. Have students go to the lesson page, review the lesson, and correct any problem they missed.

Mixed Review and Test Prep, p. 189

How to Help	
Item	Page
37	182
38	66
39	166
40	44
41	30

WRITING IN MATHEMATICS

Materials reference books, cookbooks

Have students **apply fractions and mixed numbers** by writing a paragraph about the ingredients in a recipe for a popular rice dish. Tell students that the January harvest festival in South India is called Pongal. A popular rice dish served in India goes by the same name. Challenge students to find this recipe or some other recipe that features rice, copy it into their journals, and then write a paragraph about the recipe that includes the use of fractions and mixed numbers.

Check students' work.

SCIENCE CONNECTION

Have students **apply operations with mixed numbers by using the data below to write two word problems.**

City	Annual Rainfall
Houston, TX	$44\frac{3}{4}$ in.
Phoenix, AZ	$7\frac{1}{10}$ in.
Atlanta, GA	$48\frac{3}{5}$ in.
Chicago, IL	$33\frac{1}{3}$ in.

Check students' work.

VISUAL

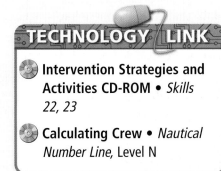

TECHNOLOGY LINK

- **Intervention Strategies and Activities CD-ROM** • *Skills 22, 23*

- **Calculating Crew** • *Nautical Number Line,* Level N

Objective To add and subtract mixed numbers

Vocabulary *Review* mixed number

1 Introduce

QUICK REVIEW provides review of prerequisite skills.

Why Learn This? You can use this skill to find the sum of two weights given as mixed numbers. *Share the lesson objective with students.*

2 Teach

Guided Instruction

• *Discuss Example 1.*

Describe how you would draw a diagram to show $2\frac{3}{4}$. Draw two unit bars the same size and then draw one bar $\frac{3}{4}$ of that size, divided into three equal sections.

REASONING **What do the models show you about how to add mixed numbers?** Possible answer: Add the fractions and then, separately, add the whole numbers.

In Example 1, what would you estimate the sum to be? Does the estimate help you confirm the answer? 4; yes, 4 is close to $3\frac{11}{12}$.

Modifying Instruction Before doing Example 2, review changing fractions greater than 1 to mixed numbers. Have students write these fractions as mixed numbers:

$\frac{7}{2}, \frac{13}{6}, \frac{15}{4}, \frac{14}{3}$ $3\frac{1}{2}, 2\frac{1}{6}, 3\frac{3}{4}, 4\frac{2}{3}$

ADDITIONAL EXAMPLES

Example 1, p. 186

Draw a diagram to find the sum. $1\frac{1}{4} + 1\frac{1}{6}$ Check students' work; $2\frac{5}{12}$.

Example 2, p. 186

Find the sum. $3\frac{3}{4} + 5\frac{2}{5}$ $9\frac{3}{20}$

Add and Subtract Mixed Numbers

Learn how to add and subtract mixed numbers.

QUICK REVIEW

Write in simplest form.

1. $\frac{4}{16}$ $\frac{1}{4}$ 2. $\frac{14}{21}$ $\frac{2}{3}$ 3. $\frac{10}{16}$ $\frac{5}{8}$

4. $\frac{10}{30}$ $\frac{1}{3}$ 5. $\frac{25}{30}$ $\frac{5}{6}$

A flock of birds is migrating from Canada to Florida for the winter. One day they fly $2\frac{3}{4}$ hours before stopping to rest. Then they fly $1\frac{1}{6}$ more hours. For how long do the birds fly?

One Way You can draw a diagram.

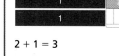 EXAMPLE 1

Remember that to write a fraction as a mixed number, you divide the numerator by the denominator. The quotient is the mixed number.

$$\frac{13}{3} \rightarrow 3)\overline{13} \quad \begin{array}{r} 4\frac{1}{3} \\ \underline{-12} \\ 1 \end{array}$$

Show $2\frac{3}{4} + 1\frac{1}{6}$.

Combine whole numbers. Combine fractions. Draw equivalent fractions with the LCD, 12.

$2 + 1 = 3$ $\frac{9}{12} + \frac{2}{12} = \frac{11}{12}$

Add fractions. Add whole numbers.

So, the birds fly for $3\frac{11}{12}$ hours.

Another Way You can use the LCD to write equivalent fractions.

EXAMPLE 2

Find $4\frac{2}{3} + 5\frac{4}{5}$.

$$\begin{array}{r} 4\frac{2}{3} = \ 4\frac{10}{15} \\ +5\frac{4}{5} = +5\frac{12}{15} \\ \hline 9\frac{22}{15} = 9 + 1\frac{7}{15} = 10\frac{7}{15} \end{array}$$

Write equivalent fractions, using the LCD, 15. Add fractions. Add whole numbers.

Rename the fraction as a mixed number. Rewrite the sum.

So, $4\frac{2}{3} + 5\frac{4}{5} = 10\frac{7}{15}$.

186

 CALIFORNIA STANDARDS ⌐NS 2.0 Students calculate and solve problems involving addition, subtraction, multiplication, and division. ⌐NS 2.4 Determine the least common multiple and the greatest common divisor of whole numbers; use them to solve problems with fractions. MR 2.1 Use estimation to verify the reasonableness of calculated results. *also,* ⌐NS 1.0, NS 2.1, MR 1.0, MR 1.1, MR 2.4, MR 2.7

RETEACH 9.4

Add and Subtract Mixed Numbers

Zack is working on a science project. He needs a $1\frac{1}{8}$-ft piece of wire and a $2\frac{1}{4}$-ft piece of wire. Zack wants to know the total amount of wire he needs for the project. He decides to make a diagram to find the total.

Step 1 Zack draws a diagram that represents each piece of wire.

$\boxed{1} \ \boxed{\frac{1}{8}} \leftarrow 1\frac{1}{8}$
$\boxed{1} \ \boxed{\frac{1}{4}} \leftarrow 2\frac{1}{4}$
$\boxed{1}$

Step 2 Zack combines the whole numbers. He draws equivalent fractions with the LCD of 8 to combine the fractions.

$1 + 2 = 3 \quad \frac{1}{8} + \frac{2}{8} = \frac{3}{8}$

Step 3 Then Zack adds the whole numbers and the fractions.

$3 + \frac{3}{8} = 3\frac{3}{8}$

So, Zack needs $3\frac{3}{8}$ ft of wire.

Draw a diagram to find each sum or difference. Check students' drawings.

1. $3\frac{1}{4} + 2\frac{1}{2} = \frac{5\frac{3}{4}}{}$ 2. $2\frac{5}{6} - 1\frac{1}{3} = \frac{1\frac{1}{2}}{}$

3. $1\frac{3}{4} + 2\frac{1}{8} = \frac{3\frac{7}{8}}{}$ 4. $3\frac{4}{5} - 1\frac{1}{2} = \frac{2\frac{3}{10}}{}$

PRACTICE 9.4

Add and Subtract Mixed Numbers

Draw a diagram to find each sum or difference. Write the answer in simplest form. Check students' diagrams.

1. $1\frac{2}{5} + 1\frac{2}{5}$ $2\frac{4}{5}$ 2. $2\frac{3}{8} - 1\frac{1}{4}$ $1\frac{1}{8}$ 3. $2\frac{1}{6} + 1\frac{1}{3}$ $3\frac{3}{6}$, or $3\frac{1}{2}$

4. $3\frac{1}{2} - 1\frac{1}{4}$ $2\frac{1}{4}$ 5. $2\frac{3}{8} + 1\frac{1}{2}$ $3\frac{7}{8}$ 6. $2\frac{2}{3} - 1\frac{1}{6}$ $1\frac{3}{6}$, or $1\frac{1}{2}$

Write the sum or difference in simplest form. Estimate to check.

7. $1\frac{1}{5} + 1\frac{1}{4}$ $2\frac{9}{20}$ 8. $2\frac{1}{4} - 1\frac{1}{8}$ $1\frac{1}{8}$ 9. $8\frac{5}{6} - 1\frac{3}{4}$ $7\frac{1}{12}$

10. $1\frac{1}{6} + 2\frac{2}{3}$ $3\frac{5}{6}$ 11. $4\frac{3}{8} - 2\frac{3}{4}$ $2\frac{3}{8}$ 12. $2\frac{1}{5} + 4\frac{1}{2}$ $7\frac{3}{10}$

13. $5\frac{7}{9} - 3\frac{2}{3}$ $2\frac{1}{9}$ 14. $4\frac{3}{5} - 3\frac{1}{10}$ $1\frac{1}{2}$ 15. $1\frac{1}{6} + 4\frac{3}{4}$ $5\frac{11}{12}$

16. $7\frac{1}{3} - 2\frac{1}{4}$ $5\frac{1}{12}$ 17. $5\frac{2}{3} - 1\frac{1}{4}$ $4\frac{1}{12}$ 18. $3\frac{2}{5} + 4\frac{1}{6}$ $7\frac{17}{30}$

19. $3\frac{1}{2} + 1\frac{5}{8}$ $5\frac{1}{8}$ 20. $3\frac{7}{8} + 4\frac{1}{3}$ $8\frac{5}{24}$ 21. $6\frac{5}{8} - 2\frac{1}{5}$ $4\frac{9}{40}$

Mixed Review

Write the fraction as a percent.

22. $\frac{1}{4}$ _25%_   23. $\frac{3}{10}$ _30%_   24. $\frac{2}{5}$ _40%_

25. $\frac{5}{100}$ _5%_   26. $\frac{10}{5}$ _200%_   27. $\frac{9}{50}$ _18%_

Write the numbers in order from least to greatest.

28. 0.303, 0.03, 0.33, 0.033   29. 11.10, 10.01, 11.01, 10.10

0.03, 0.033, 0.303, 0.33   10.01, 10.10, 11.01, 11.10

30. 2.292, 2.922, 2.929, 2.229   31. 0.545, 0.55, 0.445, 0.45

2.229, 2.292, 2.922, 2.929   0.445, 0.45, 0.545, 0.55

32. 6.626, 6.266, 6.226, 6.662   33. 7.070, 70.07, 7.007, 7.707

6.226, 6.266, 6.626, 6.662   7.007, 7.070, 7.707, 70.07

Subtract Mixed Numbers

One Way You can use diagrams to subtract mixed numbers.

EXAMPLE 3

Find $1\frac{1}{2} - 1\frac{1}{10}$.

| 1 | $\frac{1}{2}$ |
| 1 | $\frac{1}{10}\frac{1}{10}\frac{1}{10}\frac{1}{10}\frac{1}{10}$ |

| 1 | $\frac{1}{10}\frac{1}{10}\frac{1}{10}\frac{1}{10}\frac{1}{10}$ |

*Draw $1\frac{1}{2}$.
Find the LCD for $\frac{1}{2}$ and $\frac{1}{10}$.
Change the half to tenths.*

Subtract $1\frac{1}{10}$ from $1\frac{5}{10}$.

So, $1\frac{1}{2} - 1\frac{1}{10} = \frac{4}{10}$, or $\frac{2}{5}$.

• Draw a diagram to find $2\frac{1}{2} - 1\frac{1}{3}$. $1\frac{1}{6}$; **Check students' diagrams.**

Another Way When you subtract mixed numbers with unlike fractions, you can use the LCD to write equivalent fractions.

EXAMPLE 4

The rusty-spotted cat, the smallest meat-eating feline, lives in southern India and Sri Lanka. An adult has a head-and-body length of $13\frac{2}{5}$ in. to $18\frac{9}{10}$ in. Find the difference between the greatest and least lengths.

Find $18\frac{9}{10} - 13\frac{2}{5}$.

Estimate. $18\frac{9}{10}$ is close to 19 and $13\frac{2}{5}$ is close to 13. So, the difference is about $19 - 13$, or 6.

$$18\frac{9}{10} = 18\frac{9}{10}$$ *Write equivalent fractions, using the LCD, 10.*

$$-13\frac{2}{5} = -13\frac{4}{10}$$ *Subtract the fractions.*

$$\overline{\phantom{-13\frac{2}{5}=}5\frac{5}{10}} = 5\frac{1}{2}$$ *Subtract the whole numbers.*

The exact answer is reasonable because it is close to the estimate of 6. So, the difference between the greatest and least lengths is $5\frac{1}{2}$ in.

CHECK FOR UNDERSTANDING

Think and Discuss ▸ Look back at the lesson to answer each question.
Possible answer: The fractions must have the same denominators before they can be added.
1. **Explain** why you must find equivalent fractions to add $1\frac{1}{5} + 1\frac{1}{2}$.

2. **Tell** how you know that $6\frac{1}{2} - 4\frac{1}{4}$ is more than 2. $\frac{1}{2}$ is more than $\frac{1}{4}$ and $6 - 4 = 2$.

Guided Practice ▸ Draw a diagram to find each sum or difference. Write the answer in simplest form. **Check students' diagrams.**

3. $2\frac{3}{5} + 1\frac{1}{5}$ $3\frac{4}{5}$ **4.** $1\frac{1}{4} + 2\frac{2}{3}$ $3\frac{11}{12}$ **5.** $2\frac{4}{5} - 1\frac{1}{2}$ $1\frac{3}{10}$

• *Have students study the models shown in Example 3.*

How is adding mixed numbers similar to subtracting them? Possible answer: You work first with the fractions and then with the whole numbers.

ADDITIONAL EXAMPLES

Example 3, p. 187

Draw a diagram to find the difference. $2\frac{2}{5} - 1\frac{3}{10}$ Check students' work; $1\frac{1}{10}$.

Example 4, p. 187

The river by Camp Somerset is $1\frac{3}{8}$ mile shorter than the $3\frac{1}{2}$-mile-long river by Camp Hope. How long is the river by Camp Somerset? $2\frac{1}{8}$ mi

3 Practice

Guided Practice

Do Check for Understanding Exercises 1–11 with your students. Identify those having difficulty and use lesson resources to help.

Confirm that students know that their equivalent fraction diagrams should be twelfths for Exercise 4 and tenths for Exercise 5.

PROBLEM SOLVING 9.4

Add and Subtract Mixed Numbers

Write the correct answer.

1. Write $\frac{12}{15}$ in simplest form.

$\frac{3}{5}$

2. List all of the factors of 42.

1, 2, 3, 6, 7, 14, 21, 42

3. Devon worked on her homework for $2\frac{3}{4}$ hr on Friday and $1\frac{1}{2}$ hr on Saturday. How much longer did she work on Friday than on Saturday?

$1\frac{1}{4}$ hr

4. Victoria taped a piece of ribbon that was $3\frac{1}{4}$ yd long to a piece that was $1\frac{1}{3}$ yd long. How long are the two pieces of ribbon together?

$4\frac{7}{12}$ yd

Choose the letter for the best answer.

5. What is the GCF of 30 and 40?

A 2
Ⓑ 10
C 30
D 40

6. What is $\frac{45}{7}$ written as a mixed number?

F $7\frac{3}{5}$
Ⓖ $6\frac{3}{7}$
H $6\frac{5}{9}$
J $5\frac{5}{7}$

7. Hank walks $4\frac{1}{4}$ blocks to school and his friend Jonas walks $6\frac{1}{8}$ blocks to school. How much farther does Jonas have to walk?

A $1\frac{7}{8}$ blocks
Ⓑ $2\frac{1}{8}$ blocks
C $2\frac{1}{4}$ blocks
D $2\frac{3}{8}$ blocks

8. At a flea market, Theresa bought $5\frac{1}{4}$ yd of lace trim and $8\frac{3}{4}$ yd of ribbon trim. How much trim did she buy altogether?

F $13\frac{3}{8}$ yd
G $13\frac{5}{12}$ yd
H $13\frac{1}{2}$ yd
Ⓘ $14\frac{5}{12}$ yd

9. Write About It When adding mixed numbers, what do you do when the fraction part of the sum has a numerator that is greater than the denominator?

You rewrite the fraction part as a mixed number and add the mixed number to the whole number part of the sum.

CHALLENGE 9.4

Addition Patterns

Write the next three terms. Then identify the rule.

1. 10; $14\frac{1}{5}$; $18\frac{2}{5}$; $22\frac{3}{5}$; $26\frac{4}{5}$; 31 ; $35\frac{1}{5}$

Rule: _____ Add $4\frac{1}{5}$ to previous term.

2. 1; $2\frac{1}{4}$; $3\frac{1}{2}$; $4\frac{3}{4}$; 6 ; $7\frac{1}{4}$; $8\frac{1}{2}$

Rule: _____ Add $1\frac{1}{4}$ to previous term.

3. 5; $7\frac{1}{5}$; $9\frac{2}{5}$; $11\frac{3}{5}$; $13\frac{4}{5}$; 16 ; $18\frac{1}{5}$

Rule: _____ Add $2\frac{1}{5}$ to previous term.

4. 1; $2\frac{3}{8}$; $3\frac{3}{4}$; $5\frac{1}{8}$; $6\frac{1}{2}$; $7\frac{7}{8}$; $9\frac{1}{4}$

Rule: _____ Add $1\frac{3}{8}$ to previous term.

5. 4; $7\frac{2}{9}$; $10\frac{4}{9}$; $13\frac{6}{9}$; $16\frac{8}{9}$; $20\frac{1}{9}$; $23\frac{3}{3}$

Rule: _____ Add $3\frac{2}{9}$ to previous term.

6. 2; $4\frac{3}{10}$; $6\frac{3}{5}$; $8\frac{9}{10}$; $11\frac{1}{5}$; $13\frac{1}{2}$; $15\frac{4}{5}$

Rule: _____ Add $2\frac{3}{10}$ to previous term.

7. 3; $4\frac{1}{3}$; $5\frac{2}{3}$; 7; $8\frac{1}{3}$; $9\frac{2}{3}$; 11

Rule: _____ Add $1\frac{1}{3}$ to previous term.

8. 1; $3\frac{1}{2}$; $5\frac{1}{3}$; $7\frac{1}{2}$; $9\frac{2}{3}$; $11\frac{5}{6}$; 14

Rule: _____ Add $2\frac{1}{6}$ to previous term.

9. 8; $9\frac{1}{8}$; $10\frac{1}{4}$; $11\frac{3}{8}$; $12\frac{1}{2}$; $13\frac{5}{8}$; $14\frac{3}{4}$

Rule: _____ Add $1\frac{1}{8}$ to previous term.

10. 12; $14\frac{3}{4}$; $17\frac{1}{2}$; $20\frac{1}{4}$; 23 ; $25\frac{3}{4}$; $28\frac{2}{2}$

Rule: _____ Add $2\frac{3}{4}$ to previous term.

Independent Practice

Assign Exercises 12–36.

Review the properties of addition and order of operations rules before assigning Exercises 27–29.

Students can solve Exercise 35 by using the strategy *make a table*.

Write the sum or difference in simplest form. Estimate to check.

6. $1\frac{1}{8} + 1\frac{5}{8}$ $2\frac{6}{8}$, or $2\frac{3}{4}$ 7. $2\frac{1}{4} + 4\frac{1}{3}$ $6\frac{7}{12}$ 8. $5\frac{3}{8} - 1\frac{1}{4}$ $4\frac{1}{8}$

9. $4\frac{1}{3} - 3\frac{1}{6}$ $1\frac{1}{6}$ 10. $3\frac{3}{4} + 4\frac{5}{12}$ $8\frac{1}{6}$ 11. $6\frac{5}{6} - 5\frac{7}{9}$ $1\frac{1}{18}$

PRACTICE AND PROBLEM SOLVING

Independent ▶ Practice

12. $2\frac{8}{12}$, or $2\frac{2}{3}$

Draw a diagram to find each sum or difference. Write the answer in simplest form. Check students' diagrams.

12. $1\frac{5}{12} + 1\frac{1}{4}$ 13. $1\frac{1}{3} + 1\frac{1}{6}$ $2\frac{1}{2}$ 14. $4\frac{1}{2} - 2\frac{2}{5}$ $2\frac{1}{10}$

Write the sum or difference in simplest form. Estimate to check.

15. $4\frac{1}{2} + 3\frac{4}{5}$ $8\frac{3}{10}$ 16. $4\frac{1}{3} - 2\frac{1}{4}$ $2\frac{1}{12}$ 17. $5\frac{5}{6} + 4\frac{2}{9}$ $10\frac{1}{18}$

18. $3\frac{1}{4} - 1\frac{1}{6}$ $2\frac{1}{12}$ 19. $7\frac{1}{2} - 3\frac{2}{5}$ $4\frac{1}{10}$ 20. $3\frac{2}{7} + 8\frac{1}{3}$ $11\frac{13}{21}$

TECHNOLOGY LINK
More Practice: Use **Mighty Math Calculating Crew**, *Nautical Number Line*, Level N.

21. $7\frac{3}{4} + 3\frac{2}{5}$ $11\frac{3}{20}$ 22. $5\frac{5}{6} - 2\frac{7}{9}$ $3\frac{1}{18}$ 23. $4\frac{5}{7} + 3\frac{1}{2}$ $8\frac{3}{14}$

24. How much greater is $5\frac{3}{4}$ than 3? $2\frac{3}{4}$

25. What is the sum of $25\frac{3}{8}$ and $2\frac{3}{4}$? $28\frac{1}{8}$

26. What is the sum of $4\frac{5}{8}$ and 7.8? **12.425**, or $12\frac{17}{40}$

Find the missing number and identify which property of addition you used.

27. $3\frac{7}{8} + \blacksquare = 2\frac{1}{4} + 3\frac{7}{8}$ 28. $3\frac{3}{4} + 0 = \blacksquare$ 29. $\left(\frac{2}{3} + 1\frac{5}{6}\right) + \frac{1}{6} = \frac{2}{3} + \left(\blacksquare + \frac{1}{6}\right)$
Commutative, $2\frac{1}{4}$ Identity, $3\frac{3}{4}$ Associative, $1\frac{5}{6}$

Problem Solving ▶ Applications

Use Data The graph shows the head-and-body lengths of five small mammals. For 30–31, use the graph.

30. How much longer is the harvest mouse than the Kitti's hognosed bat? $1\frac{1}{6}$ in.

31. The masked shrew is $1\frac{2}{3}$ in. long. Is it longer or shorter than the little brown bat? How much? Which operation did you use? Why?

longer; $\frac{1}{6}$ in.; subtraction; to find the difference between the lengths

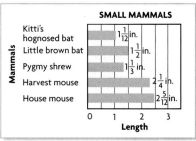

SMALL MAMMALS

Kitti's hognosed bat $1\frac{1}{12}$ in.
Little brown bat $1\frac{1}{2}$ in.
Pygmy shrew $1\frac{1}{3}$ in.
Harvest mouse $2\frac{1}{4}$ in.
House mouse $2\frac{5}{12}$ in.

Mammals

Length 0 1 2 3

Alternative Teaching Strategy

Purpose Students will add and subtract mixed numbers by using fractions greater than one.

Give students a mixed-number addition or subtraction problem, such as $3\frac{1}{2} + 1\frac{2}{5}$. Tell them that they can solve a problem like this by changing the mixed numbers to fractions greater than 1. Have students solve the following problem by using both the process shown in the lesson and this method.

Lesson method: $3\frac{1}{2}$ = $3\frac{5}{10}$
                 $+1\frac{2}{5}$ = $+1\frac{4}{10}$
                         $4\frac{9}{10}$

Changing mixed numbers to fractions method:

$3\frac{1}{2}$ = $\frac{7}{2}$ = $\frac{35}{10}$
$+1\frac{2}{5}$ = $+\frac{7}{5}$ = $+\frac{14}{10}$
                    $\frac{49}{10} = 4\frac{9}{10}$

Then ask students to find the difference by using both methods.

$3\frac{1}{2}$ = $3\frac{5}{10}$ $3\frac{1}{2}$ = $\frac{7}{2}$ = $\frac{35}{10}$
$-1\frac{2}{5}$ = $-1\frac{4}{10}$ $-1\frac{2}{5}$ = $-\frac{7}{5}$ = $-\frac{14}{10}$
       $2\frac{1}{10}$ $\frac{21}{10} = 2\frac{1}{10}$

Have students compare and contrast the two methods and discuss which one they prefer.

Check students' work.

32. On its way to the shore, a sea turtle traveled $4\frac{1}{4}$ hr the first day. The second day, the turtle traveled $3\frac{1}{2}$ hr. How many hours did the sea turtle travel in the two days? **$7\frac{3}{4}$ hr**

33. Mrs. Myers used $1\frac{1}{2}$ c of flour to make muffins, $4\frac{1}{4}$ c to make bread, and $\frac{3}{4}$ c to make gravy. If she has $3\frac{1}{4}$ c left, how much flour did Mrs. Myers have before she started the meal? **$9\frac{3}{4}$ c**

34. (?) **What's the Error?** Izumi added $3\frac{1}{4}$ and $2\frac{2}{3}$ and got $5\frac{3}{12}$. Explain the error. What is the correct sum? **see left**

35. Betty, Jim, Manuel, and Rosa won the first four prizes in a design contest. Jim won second prize. Manuel did not win third prize. Rosa won fourth prize. What prize did Betty win? **3rd prize**

34. Izumi used the LCD, 12, but he forgot to change the numerators before adding; $5\frac{11}{12}$

36. Alexis needs a new blender. She found the same blender on sale at five different stores. The prices are $22.95, $21.85, $22.05, $20.95, and $21.99. Order the prices from least to greatest. **$20.95, $21.85, $21.99, $22.05, $22.95**

MIXED REVIEW AND TEST PREP

37. Find the sum of $\frac{2}{3}$ and $\frac{2}{5}$. (p. 182) **$\frac{16}{15}$, or $1\frac{1}{15}$**

38. Subtract. $425.2 - 51.05$ (p. 66) **374.15**

39. Order $\frac{1}{2}$, $\frac{4}{5}$, and $\frac{2}{3}$ from greatest to least. (p. 166) **$\frac{4}{5}, \frac{2}{3}, \frac{1}{2}$**

40. TEST PREP Find the value of $(6 + 4)^2 \div 5$. (p. 44) **D**

   A 4   **B** 4.4   **C** 9.2   **D** 20

41. TEST PREP Which is the solution of $x + 3 = 10$? (p. 30) **B**

   A $x = 3$ **B** $x = 7$ **C** $x = 10$ **D** $x = 13$

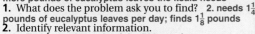

LiNKUP to Reading

Strategy • Choose Relevant Information

Sometimes a word problem contains more information than you need. You must decide which information is relevant, or needed to solve the problem.

The koala of eastern Australia feeds mostly on eucalyptus leaves. It nibbles on about 6 of the 500 species of eucalyptus per day and selects certain trees and leaves over others to find the $1\frac{1}{4}$ pounds of food that it needs. Suppose the koala finds only $1\frac{1}{8}$ pounds of food by the end of the day. How many more pounds of eucalyptus leaves does the koala need? **1. how many more pounds of eucalyptus leaves the koala needs**

1. What does the problem ask you to find? **2. needs $1\frac{1}{4}$ pounds of eucalyptus leaves per day; finds $1\frac{1}{8}$ pounds**

2. Identify relevant information.

3. What information is not relevant? **3. it nibbles on about six of the 500 species**

4. Solve the problem. **4. $1\frac{1}{4} - 1\frac{1}{8} = 1\frac{2}{8} - 1\frac{1}{8} = \frac{1}{8}$; $\frac{1}{8}$ lb of eucalyptus leaves**

Extra Practice page H40, Set C

189

LiNKUP to READING

• *After students read the paragraph about the koala, ask:*

How can you decide whether you have too much information? Possible answer: Choose the information you need to solve the problem and see if any is not relevant.

What LCD did you use? 8

REASONING Is it reasonable to assume that a koala eats exactly $1\frac{1}{2}$ lb of food each day? Explain. No; that is probably the average amount a koala eats.

4 Assess

Summarize the lesson by having students:

DISCUSS How could you use diagrams to add $1\frac{1}{2} + 1\frac{1}{3}$? Possible answer: Model $1\frac{1}{2}$ using 1 bar and $\frac{1}{2}$ bar. Model $1\frac{1}{3}$ using 1 bar and $\frac{1}{3}$ bar. Add $\frac{1}{2} + \frac{1}{3}$ by modeling and adding equivalent fractions $\frac{3}{6} + \frac{2}{6} = \frac{5}{6}$. Add the two whole bars for a sum of 2. So, $1\frac{1}{2} + 1\frac{1}{3} = 2\frac{5}{6}$

 WRITE Explain how to add two mixed numbers with unlike fractions. Write each fraction part using a common denominator, add the fractions and then the whole numbers, simplify.

Lesson Quiz

Transparency
9.4

Draw a diagram to find each sum or difference. Write the answer in simplest form.

1. $1\frac{1}{8} + 4\frac{3}{4}$ $5\frac{7}{8}$ **2.** $2\frac{2}{3} - 1\frac{1}{12}$ $1\frac{7}{12}$

3. $5\frac{1}{2} - 2\frac{2}{5}$ $3\frac{1}{10}$ **4.** $5\frac{2}{3} + 3\frac{5}{6}$ $9\frac{1}{2}$

5. $2\frac{2}{3} - 1\frac{1}{9}$ $1\frac{5}{9}$ **6.** $1\frac{1}{6} + 2\frac{5}{6}$ 4

READING STRATEGY

K-W-L Chart Before having students read Linkup to Reading, have them read the strategy—*Choose Relevant Information.* Ask them to predict how they will apply this strategy to math. Then have students make a three-column chart headed What I Know, What I Want to Know, and What I Learned. Ask them to fill in the first two columns. Have them fill in the third column as they read through the paragraph and questions.

K-W-L Chart

What I Know	What I Want to Know	What I Learned

ORGANIZER

Objective To use fraction bars to rename and subtract mixed numbers

Materials *For each group* fraction bars or fraction strips, p. TR18

Lesson Resources E-Lab Recording Sheet • *Subtracting Mixed Numbers*

Intervention for Prerequisite Skills Simplify Fractions, Add and Subtract Like Fractions (For intervention strategies, see page 175.)

Using The Pages

Point out to students that in some subtraction problems, the first mixed number must be renamed so that the fraction part is greater than the fraction part of the mixed number being subtracted.

Activity

As students look at the subtraction $2\frac{1}{5} - 1\frac{4}{5}$*, ask:*

Why can't you do the subtraction as it is given? $\frac{4}{5}$ is greater than $\frac{1}{5}$.

How are the two models in A alike and how are they different? They name the same amount; the first model displays 2 wholes, while the second displays 1 whole plus a second whole divided into fifths.

Modifying Instruction Reinforce the idea that it is possible to model a whole number as a whole or as a fraction. This process is similar to renaming tens and greater place values as necessary when subtracting whole numbers.

Show the similarity between Activity A and regrouping when you subtract $45 - 37$.

$$
\begin{array}{r}
\overset{3\ \ 15}{\cancel{4}\cancel{5}} = 30 + 10 + 5 = 30 + 15 \\
-3\,7 = 30 + 7 = 30 + 7 \\
\hline
8
\end{array}
$$

Rename to Subtract

MATH LAB

Explore how to use fraction bars to subtract mixed numbers.

You need fraction bars.

QUICK REVIEW

Write the difference in simplest form.

1. $\frac{4}{7} - 1\frac{3}{7}$ 2. $\frac{3}{4} - 1\frac{1}{4}\frac{1}{2}$ 3. $\frac{7}{10} - \frac{5}{10}\frac{1}{5}$

4. $\frac{8}{12} - \frac{4}{12}\frac{1}{3}$ 5. $\frac{5}{9} - \frac{2}{9}\frac{1}{3}$

Sometimes you need to rename mixed numbers before you can subtract.

Activity

A. Find $2\frac{1}{5} - 1\frac{4}{5}$.

• Use fraction bars to model $2\frac{1}{5}$.

| 1 | 1 | $\frac{1}{5}$ | ← $2\frac{1}{5}$ |

• Here is another way to model $2\frac{1}{5}$.

| 1 | $\frac{1}{5}$ $\frac{1}{5}$ $\frac{1}{5}$ $\frac{1}{5}$ $\frac{1}{5}$ $\frac{1}{5}$ | ← $1\frac{6}{5}$ |

• From which model can you subtract $1\frac{4}{5}$? **the second one**

• Subtract $1\frac{4}{5}$ from $1\frac{6}{5}$. What is $2\frac{1}{5} - 1\frac{4}{5}$? **$\frac{2}{5}$**

B. Find $2\frac{1}{6} - 1\frac{5}{12}$.

• Use fraction bars to model $2\frac{1}{6}$.

| 1 | 1 | $\frac{1}{6}$ | ← $2\frac{1}{6}$ |

• Since you are subtracting twelfths, think of the LCD for $\frac{1}{6}$ and $\frac{5}{12}$. Change the sixths to twelfths.

| 1 | 1 | $\frac{1}{12}$ $\frac{1}{12}$ | ← $2\frac{2}{12}$ |

• Can you subtract $1\frac{5}{12}$ from either of these models? **no**

• Here is another way to model $2\frac{2}{12}$.

| 1 | $\frac{1}{12}$ $\frac{1}{12}$ $\frac{1}{12}$ $\frac{1}{12}$ $\frac{1}{12}$ $\frac{1}{12}$ $\frac{1}{12}$ $\frac{1}{12}$ $\frac{1}{12}$ $\frac{1}{12}$ $\frac{1}{12}$ $\frac{1}{12}$ $\frac{1}{12}$ $\frac{1}{12}$ | ← $1\frac{14}{12}$ |

• Subtract $1\frac{5}{12}$ from $1\frac{14}{12}$. What is $2\frac{1}{6} - 1\frac{5}{12}$? **$\frac{9}{12}$, or $\frac{3}{4}$**

190

CALIFORNIA STANDARDS O—n**NS 2.0** Students calculate and solve problems involving addition, subtraction, multiplication, and division. O—n**NS 2.4** Determine the least common multiple and the greatest common divisor of whole numbers; use them to solve problems with fractions. *also,* **MR 2.4, MR 2.5, NS 2.1**

SPECIAL NEEDS (ELL)

Materials *For each group* three whole bars or strips and four $\frac{1}{4}$ bars or strips, p. TR18

Ask each group to **use fraction bars or strips to model and record two different mixed-number subtraction sentences.** When the groups have finished, have students compare their exercises and solutions. Check students' work.

KINESTHETIC

Intervention and Extension Resources

MATH CONNECTION: MEASUREMENT

Materials *For each group* inch rulers, p. TR22; fraction bars or fraction strips, p. TR18

Have groups **measure the lengths of various items and determine the difference** between the longest and shortest measurements. Tell students to measure several books, pencils, and erasers. Then ask groups to model the difference in length between the longest and shortest of each type of item. Check students' work.

KINESTHETIC

C. Find $2\frac{1}{4} - 1\frac{3}{8}$.

- Use fraction bars to model $2\frac{1}{4}$.

| 1 | 1 | $\frac{1}{4}$ | $\leftarrow 2\frac{1}{4}$

- Since you are subtracting eighths, think of the LCD for $\frac{1}{4}$ and $\frac{3}{8}$. Change the fourth to eighths.

| 1 | 1 | $\frac{1}{8}$ $\frac{1}{8}$ | $\leftarrow 2\frac{2}{8}$

TECHNOLOGY LINK
More Practice: Use E-Lab, *Subtraction of Mixed Numbers.*
www.harcourtschool.com/elab2002

- Can you subtract $1\frac{3}{8}$ from either of these models? **no**

- Here is another way to model $2\frac{2}{8}$.

| 1 | $\frac{1}{8}$ $\frac{1}{8}$ $\frac{1}{8}$ $\frac{1}{8}$ $\frac{1}{8}$ $\frac{1}{8}$ $\frac{1}{8}$ $\frac{1}{8}$ $\frac{1}{8}$ $\frac{1}{8}$ | $\leftarrow 1\frac{10}{8}$

- Subtract $1\frac{3}{8}$ from $1\frac{10}{8}$. What is $2\frac{1}{4} - 1\frac{3}{8}$? $\frac{7}{8}$

Think and Discuss

- Think about $2\frac{5}{6} - 1\frac{1}{6}$. Do you need to rename before you subtract? Explain. No; $\frac{5}{6}$ is greater than $\frac{1}{6}$, and the denominators are the same.

- Think about $5\frac{2}{5} - 3\frac{4}{5}$. Do you need to rename before you subtract? Explain. Yes; $\frac{2}{5}$ is less than $\frac{4}{5}$.

Practice

Check students' diagrams.

Use fraction bars to subtract. Draw a diagram of your model.

1. $3\frac{1}{3} - 1\frac{2}{3}$ $1\frac{2}{3}$ 2. $3\frac{3}{8} - \frac{3}{4}$ $2\frac{5}{8}$ 3. $3\frac{1}{9} - 1\frac{1}{3}$ $1\frac{4}{9}$ 4. $2\frac{3}{8} - 1\frac{1}{2}$ $\frac{7}{8}$

5. $1\frac{1}{2} - \frac{4}{5}$ $\frac{7}{10}$ 6. $3\frac{1}{5} - 1\frac{3}{10}$ $1\frac{9}{10}$ 7. $2\frac{2}{3} - 1\frac{3}{4}$ $\frac{11}{12}$ 8. $3\frac{1}{12} - 2\frac{5}{6}$ $\frac{1}{4}$

MIXED REVIEW AND TEST PREP

9. Draw a diagram to find the sum of $2\frac{1}{2}$ and $1\frac{1}{4}$. Write the answer in simplest form. (p. 186) $3\frac{3}{4}$

10. Write $\frac{2}{5}$ as a decimal and as a percent. (p. 169) **0.4, 40%**

11. Evaluate $a \times b$ for $a = 4.2$ and $b = 5.1$. (p. 82) **21.42**

12. Write the prime factorization of 245 in exponent form. (p. 148) $7^2 \times 5$

13. **TEST PREP** Which is the quotient $2.79 \div 0.045$? (p. 76) **D**

   A 0.12555   **B** 2.705   **C** 2.835   **D** 62

191

Remind students that before they model the whole numbers to subtract, they need to be sure that the fractions have been modeled with a common denominator.

Think and Discuss

When discussing these two questions, help students conclude that renaming is necessary whenever the second fraction is greater than the first fraction.

Practice

Before students begin work, ask:

Which exercises require renaming a whole as a fraction? all

Which exercises require renaming the fractions with a common denominator? all but Exercise 1

MIXED REVIEW AND TEST PREP

Exercises 9–13 provide **cumulative review** (Chapters 1–9).

Oral Assessment

Use fraction bars to subtract. Draw a diagram of your model. Check students' work.

1. $2\frac{3}{4} - 1\frac{1}{3}$ $1\frac{5}{12}$

2. $3\frac{2}{5} - 2\frac{4}{5}$ $\frac{3}{5}$

3. Did you need to find the LCD to subtract in Exercise 1 or Exercise 3? Why? Yes, in Exercise 3; the denominators are not the same.

4. Did you need to rename a mixed number to subtract in Exercise 5 or Exercise 6? Why? Yes, in both; In Exercise 5, $\frac{1}{2}$ is less than $\frac{4}{5}$; in Exercise 6, $\frac{1}{5}$ is less than $\frac{3}{10}$.

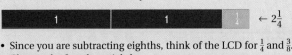

E-LAB RECORDING SHEET

Name _____

Subtracting Mixed Numbers

To subtract mixed numbers, find the least common denominator. Rename when needed.

Subtract $1\frac{1}{8}$ from $2\frac{3}{4}$.

Start with a model of the fraction $2\frac{3}{4}$. Change to eighths, the LCD. Subtract $1\frac{1}{8}$ from $2\frac{6}{8}$.

1. What is $2\frac{3}{4} - 1\frac{1}{8}$? $1\frac{5}{8}$

Subtract $1\frac{7}{8}$ from $2\frac{1}{4}$.

Now renaming is needed. Change 1 one to 8 eighths. Subtract $1\frac{7}{8}$ from $1\frac{10}{8}$.

2. What is $2\frac{1}{4} - 1\frac{7}{8}$? $\frac{3}{8}$

Use the computer.

Click **New Problem**. Enter $2\frac{1}{2}$ for the first number. Subtract the following numbers, one at a time. You may need to use the **Rename Fraction** and **Rename Mixed Number** buttons before you can click **Subtract**. Record each result.

3. $2\frac{1}{2} - \frac{3}{4} =$ $1\frac{3}{4}$
4. $2\frac{1}{2} - \frac{7}{8} =$ $1\frac{5}{8}$
5. $2\frac{1}{2} - 1\frac{5}{6} =$ $\frac{5}{6}$
6. $2\frac{1}{2} - 1\frac{5}{8} =$ $\frac{7}{8}$
7. $2\frac{1}{2} - 1\frac{7}{10} =$ $\frac{8}{10}$ or $\frac{4}{5}$
8. $2\frac{1}{2} - 1\frac{11}{12} =$ $\frac{7}{12}$

Select your own number pairs for subtraction. Both numbers of each pair must be less than 3, and the second number must be less than the first. Complete the subtractions yourself. Then use the computer to check your answers. **Answers will vary for Problems 9–14.**

9. ___ – ___ = ___
10. ___ – ___ = ___
11. ___ – ___ = ___
12. ___ – ___ = ___
13. ___ – ___ = ___
14. ___ – ___ = ___

When subtracting mixed numbers, think of the LCD and rename as needed.

E-Lab Recording Sheet   5

USING E-LAB

Students use visual thinking, reasoning, and a fraction model to subtract mixed numbers.

The E-Lab Recording Sheets and activities are available on the E-Lab website.

www.harcourtschool.com/elab2002

TECHNOLOGY LINK

Intervention Strategies and Activities CD-ROM • *Skills 22, 23*

E-Lab • *Subtracting Mixed Numbers*

191

Subtract Mixed Numbers

LESSON PLANNING

Objective To subtract mixed numbers involving renaming

Intervention for Prerequisite Skills

Simplify Fractions, Add and Subtract Like Fractions (For intervention strategies, see page 175.)

California Mathematics Content Standards

NS 2.0 Students calculate and solve problems involving addition, subtraction, multiplication, and division.

NS 2.4 Determine the least common multiple and greatest common divisor of whole numbers; use them to solve problems with fractions (e.g., to find a common denominator to add two fractions or to find the reduced form for a fraction).

MR 2.1 Use estimation to verify the reasonableness of calculated results.

(*Also* NS 1.0, 2.1, MR 2.7)

Math Background

As with whole numbers and decimals, mixed numbers sometimes must be renamed in order to subtract one from the other.

The following ideas may help students master this algorithm:

- It is easier to compare fractions if they have the same denominator, so the first step is to find the LCD.
- The fraction part of a mixed number must be renamed if it is less than the fraction part of the mixed number to be subtracted from it.
- When renaming a whole, it is helpful to write the whole number as a sum; for example, rewrite 5 as $4 + 1$. The 1 can be renamed as a fraction, for example, $\frac{3}{3}$, $\frac{5}{5}$, or $\frac{8}{8}$.

WARM-UP RESOURCES

 NUMBER OF THE DAY Transparency 9.6

Write your age in years and months as a mixed number.
Possible answer: for 11 years 4 months: $11\frac{1}{3}$

 PROBLEM OF THE DAY Transparency 9.6

Melissa rides the bus $1\frac{2}{3}$ mi north and $3\frac{1}{8}$ mi east to get to school. Brandon rides his bike $2\frac{3}{4}$ mi south and $2\frac{1}{6}$ mi west to get to the same school. Who rides farther? Estimate the distances. What can you conclude about the estimates? Brandon rides farther. From the estimates, the distance appears to be the same. To answer the question, you need to find the exact answer.

Solution Problem of the Day tab, p. PD9

 DAILY FACTS PRACTICE

Have students practice subtraction facts by completing Set G of *Teacher's Resource Book*, p. TR99.

INTERVENTION AND EXTENSION RESOURCES

ALTERNATIVE TEACHING STRATEGY

To help students **gain proficiency in renaming mixed numbers for subtraction,** have them work with simpler exercises first.

- Tell students to rename $1\frac{2}{3}$, $1\frac{1}{6}$, and $1\frac{3}{4}$ as fractions greater than 1. $\frac{5}{3}$, $\frac{7}{6}$, $\frac{7}{4}$

- Have students use their answers to help them rename $5\frac{2}{3}$, $6\frac{1}{6}$, and $3\frac{3}{4}$ as mixed numbers with fractions greater than 1. $4\frac{5}{3}$, $5\frac{7}{6}$, $2\frac{7}{4}$

VISUAL

MIXED REVIEW AND TEST PREP

Cumulative Review Chapters 1–9

Refer to the Pupil Edition pages referenced in the exercises for further review. Have students go to the lesson page, review the lesson, and correct any problem they missed.

Mixed Review and Test Prep, p. 193

How to Help	
Item	Page
24	186
25	160
26	106
27	28
28	70

SPECIAL NEEDS ELL

Materials *For each group* play money (one-dollar bills, quarters, dimes)

- Discuss the fractional parts of a dollar that a quarter and a dime represent. $\frac{1}{4}$, $\frac{1}{10}$

- Have students use play money to model these differences: $3\frac{1}{4} - 1\frac{3}{4}$; $5\frac{3}{10} - 2\frac{7}{10}$ 3 dollars, 1 quarter − 1 dollar, 3 quarters; 5 dollars, 3 dimes − 2 dollars, 7 dimes

- Ask what needs to be renamed to find the differences and then solve. 3 dollars, 1 quarter = 2 dollars, 5 quarters; 5 dollars, 3 dimes = 4 dollars, 13 dimes; $1\frac{2}{4} = 1\frac{1}{2}$; $2\frac{6}{10} = 2\frac{3}{5}$

- Repeat for similar subtraction problems.

Check students' work.

KINESTHETIC

ADVANCED LEARNERS

Challenge students to **find the next four mixed numbers in the patterns and describe the pattern.** Give students the following:

$1\frac{1}{2}$, $3\frac{1}{6}$, $4\frac{5}{6}$, $6\frac{1}{2}$ $8\frac{1}{6}$, $9\frac{5}{6}$, $11\frac{1}{2}$, $13\frac{1}{6}$; $+ 1\frac{2}{3}$

$2\frac{3}{4}$, $4\frac{1}{4}$, $3\frac{5}{12}$, $4\frac{11}{12}$, $4\frac{1}{12}$ $5\frac{7}{12}$, $4\frac{3}{4}$, $6\frac{1}{4}$, $5\frac{5}{12}$; $+ 1\frac{1}{2}$, $- \frac{5}{6}$

After checking the answers, have each student write a sequence. Then ask pairs of students to exchange and continue each other's sequence. Finally, have pairs compare solutions.

VISUAL

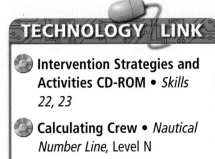

TECHNOLOGY LINK

- **Intervention Strategies and Activities CD-ROM** • *Skills 22, 23*

- **Calculating Crew** • *Nautical Number Line,* Level N

Objective To subtract mixed numbers involving renaming

1 Introduce

QUICK REVIEW provides review of prerequisite skills.

Why Learn This? You can use this skill to find out how much farther you have to travel on a hike to reach a known destination. *Share the lesson objective with students.*

2 Teach

Guided Instruction

• *Direct students' attention to the problem about the blizzard.*

How do you determine the greatest and least amounts? The greatest amount is $4\frac{1}{3}$ ft because 4 is the greatest whole number. The least amount is $1\frac{5}{12}$ because $\frac{5}{12}$ is less than $\frac{7}{12}$.

Modifying Instruction Have students model the exercises with fraction bars or strips.

• *Discuss the Example with students.*

Why is it necessary to rename the 5 as a mixed number? so that there is a fraction from which $\frac{4}{5}$ can be subtracted

How do you decide what denominator to use for the whole number you are renaming? Use the denominator of the fraction in the mixed number.

REASONING **How can you check that the answer in the Example is correct?** Possible answer: Add $3\frac{1}{5}$ and $1\frac{4}{5}$. The sum should equal 5.

ADDITIONAL EXAMPLE

Additional example, p. 192

Find the difference. $8 - 3\frac{3}{10}$ $4\frac{7}{10}$

Subtract Mixed Numbers

Learn how to subtract mixed numbers involving renaming.

QUICK REVIEW

Write the number that makes the fraction equivalent to $\frac{1}{2}$.

1. $\frac{\blacksquare}{8}$ 4 2. $\frac{\blacksquare}{6}$ 3 3. $\frac{\blacksquare}{20}$ 10 4. $\frac{\blacksquare}{14}$ 7 5. $\frac{\blacksquare}{100}$ 50

A 1993 blizzard called The Storm of the Century brought record cold, wind, and snow to many cities in the southern and eastern United States.

How much more snow did Mount LeConte receive than Birmingham received?

Find $4\frac{1}{3} - 1\frac{5}{12}$.

STORM OF THE CENTURY	
City	Snow (ft)
Birmingham, AL	$1\frac{5}{12}$
Asheville, NC	$1\frac{7}{12}$
Pittsburgh, PA	$2\frac{1}{2}$
Syracuse, NY	$3\frac{7}{12}$
Mount LeConte, TN	$4\frac{1}{3}$

Estimate. $4\frac{1}{3}$ is close to $4\frac{1}{2}$ and $1\frac{5}{12}$ is close to $1\frac{1}{2}$. So, the difference is about $4\frac{1}{2} - 1\frac{1}{2}$, or 3.

Subtract.

$$4\frac{1}{3} = 4\frac{4}{12}$$
$$-1\frac{5}{12} = -1\frac{5}{12}$$

The LCD of $\frac{1}{3}$ and $\frac{5}{12}$ is 12.
Write equivalent fractions, using the LCD, 12.

$$4\frac{1}{3} = 4\frac{4}{12} = 3\frac{16}{12}$$
$$-1\frac{5}{12} = -1\frac{5}{12} = -1\frac{5}{12}$$
$$\overline{\qquad\qquad\quad 2\frac{11}{12}}$$

Since $\frac{5}{12}$ is greater than $\frac{4}{12}$, rename $4\frac{4}{12}$.
$4\frac{4}{12} = 3 + \frac{12}{12} + \frac{4}{12} = 3\frac{16}{12}$.
Subtract the fractions.
Subtract the whole numbers.

The answer is reasonable because it is close to the estimate of 3 ft. So, Mount LeConte received $2\frac{11}{12}$ ft more snow than Birmingham.

EXAMPLE

Jake is running in a 5-km race. So far he has run $1\frac{4}{5}$ km. How far does he have to go?

Find the difference. $5 - 1\frac{4}{5}$

$$5 = 4\frac{5}{5}$$
$$-1\frac{4}{5} = -1\frac{4}{5}$$
$$\overline{\qquad\quad 3\frac{1}{5}}$$

Since you are subtracting fifths, rename 5 as $4\frac{5}{5}$.

Subtract the fractions.
Subtract the whole numbers.

So, Jake has $3\frac{1}{5}$ km to go.

192

CALIFORNIA STANDARDS O—¬NS 2.0 Students calculate and solve problems involving addition, subtraction, multiplication, and division. O—¬NS 2.4 Determine the least common multiple and the greatest common divisor of whole numbers; use them to solve problems with fractions. MR 2.1 Use estimation to verify the reasonableness of calculated results. *also,* NS 1.0, NS 2.1, MR 2.7

RETEACH 9.6

Subtract Mixed Numbers

Mrs. Ruiz buys $4\frac{1}{2}$ lb of apples. She uses $1\frac{2}{3}$ lb to bake apple tarts. How many pounds of apples are left?

Step 1 The LCD of $\frac{1}{2}$ and $\frac{2}{3}$ is 6.
Rename the fractions using the LCD.

$$4\frac{1}{2} = 4\frac{3}{6}$$
$$-1\frac{2}{3} = 1\frac{4}{6}$$

Step 2 Since you can't subtract $\frac{4}{6}$ from $\frac{3}{6}$, rename $4\frac{3}{6}$.
Think: $4\frac{3}{6} = 3 + \frac{6}{6} + \frac{3}{6} = 3\frac{9}{6}$

$$4\frac{1}{2} = 4\frac{3}{6} = 3\frac{9}{6}$$
$$-1\frac{2}{3} = 1\frac{4}{6} = 1\frac{4}{6}$$
$$\overline{\qquad\qquad\quad 2\frac{5}{6}}$$

Now, subtract the fractions. Then subtract the whole numbers.

So, $4\frac{1}{2} - 1\frac{2}{3} = 2\frac{5}{6}$

Mrs. Ruiz has $2\frac{5}{6}$ lbs of apples left.

Find the difference. Write the answer in simplest form.

1. $6\frac{2}{5}$ 2. $4\frac{1}{6}$ 3. $9\frac{3}{7}$
   $-3\frac{7}{10}$ $-2\frac{3}{4}$ $-5\frac{5}{7}$
   $\overline{2\frac{7}{10}}$ $\overline{1\frac{5}{12}}$ $\overline{3\frac{13}{14}}$

4. $11\frac{1}{3}$ 5. $10\frac{3}{8}$ 6. $6\frac{1}{10}$
   $-7\frac{8}{9}$ $-3\frac{1}{2}$ $-4\frac{4}{5}$
   $\overline{3\frac{4}{9}}$ $\overline{6\frac{7}{8}}$ $\overline{1\frac{3}{10}}$

7. $9\frac{1}{8}$ 8. $12\frac{2}{5}$ 9. $8\frac{2}{3}$
   $-4\frac{3}{4}$ $-6\frac{1}{2}$ $-5\frac{5}{6}$
   $\overline{4\frac{3}{8}}$ $\overline{5\frac{9}{10}}$ $\overline{2\frac{5}{6}}$

PRACTICE 9.6

Subtract Mixed Numbers

Write the difference in simplest form. Estimate to check.

1. $8\frac{3}{4} - 6\frac{1}{2}$ 2. $4\frac{3}{5} - 2\frac{7}{10}$ 3. $7\frac{1}{4} - 2\frac{2}{3}$ 4. $6\frac{5}{9} - 3\frac{2}{3}$
   $2\frac{1}{4}$ $1\frac{9}{10}$ $4\frac{7}{12}$ $1\frac{8}{9}$

5. $3\frac{1}{2} - 2\frac{3}{5}$ 6. $5\frac{3}{8} - 4\frac{1}{2}$ 7. $6\frac{1}{3} - 2\frac{3}{4}$ 8. $1\frac{7}{9} - 1\frac{2}{3}$
   $\frac{9}{10}$ $\frac{7}{8}$ $3\frac{7}{12}$ $\frac{1}{9}$

9. $4\frac{2}{5} - 1\frac{1}{4}$ 10. $5\frac{4}{5} - 3\frac{1}{4}$ 11. $3\frac{1}{5} - 1\frac{4}{9}$ 12. $4\frac{5}{8} - 2\frac{1}{2}$
    $3\frac{3}{20}$ $2\frac{11}{20}$ $1\frac{34}{45}$ $2\frac{1}{8}$

13. $5\frac{1}{6} - 3\frac{2}{3}$ 14. $4\frac{3}{8} - 2\frac{7}{10}$ 15. $4\frac{1}{8} - 2\frac{3}{4}$ 16. $3\frac{1}{2} - 1\frac{7}{10}$
    $1\frac{1}{2}$ $1\frac{27}{40}$ $1\frac{3}{8}$ $1\frac{8}{10}$

17. $5\frac{1}{4} - 2\frac{3}{8}$ 18. $6\frac{1}{4} - 4\frac{2}{5}$ 19. $9\frac{3}{8} - 4\frac{1}{3}$ 20. $5\frac{1}{6} - 1\frac{5}{8}$
    $2\frac{7}{8}$ $1\frac{17}{20}$ $5\frac{1}{24}$ $3\frac{13}{24}$

Evaluate each expression for $a = 3\frac{1}{3}$, $b = 2\frac{1}{4}$, $c = 5\frac{1}{6}$.

21. $c - a$ 22. $c - b$ 23. $a - b$
    $1\frac{5}{6}$ $2\frac{11}{12}$ $1\frac{1}{12}$

Mixed Review

Write in exponential form.

24. $5 \times 5 \times 5 \times 5$ 5^4 25. $10 \times 10 \times 10$ 10^3

26. $k \times k \times k \times k \times k$ k^5 27. $w \times w$ w^2

Evaluate each expression.

28. $17.61 - s$ for $s = 12.18$ 29. $75.6 \div v$ for $v = 6.3$ 30. $5f$ for $f = 8.7$
    5.43   12   43.5

CHECK FOR UNDERSTANDING

Think and ▶
Discuss

Look back at the lesson to answer each question.

1. **Explain** how to rename $3\frac{1}{3}$ so you could subtract $1\frac{2}{3}$. $3\frac{1}{3} = 2 + \frac{3}{3} + \frac{1}{3} = 2\frac{4}{3}$.

2. **What if** you wanted to find $4\frac{5}{12} - 2\frac{3}{8}$? What equivalent fractions would you write using the LCD? $4\frac{10}{24}$ and $2\frac{9}{24}$

Guided Practice ▶

Write the difference in simplest form. Estimate to check.

3. $4\frac{1}{3} - 2\frac{1}{4}$ $2\frac{1}{12}$

4. $6 - 2\frac{2}{3}$ $3\frac{1}{3}$

5. $7\frac{3}{10} - 3\frac{2}{5}$ $3\frac{9}{10}$

6. $6\frac{1}{5} - 3\frac{7}{10}$ $2\frac{1}{2}$

7. $8\frac{5}{6} - 4\frac{8}{9}$ $3\frac{17}{18}$

8. $16\frac{3}{8} - 7\frac{1}{2}$ $8\frac{7}{8}$

PRACTICE AND PROBLEM SOLVING

Independent ▶
Practice

Write the difference in simplest form. Estimate to check.

9. $3\frac{1}{6} - 1\frac{1}{4}$ $1\frac{11}{12}$

10. $5\frac{1}{2} - 3\frac{7}{10}$ $1\frac{4}{5}$

11. $12\frac{1}{9} - 7\frac{1}{3}$ $4\frac{7}{9}$

12. $4\frac{1}{4} - 2\frac{2}{5}$ $1\frac{17}{20}$

13. $8\frac{1}{4} - 5\frac{2}{3}$ $2\frac{7}{12}$

14. $7\frac{5}{9} - 2\frac{5}{6}$ $4\frac{13}{18}$

15. $11\frac{1}{4} - 9\frac{7}{8}$ $1\frac{3}{8}$

16. $5.25 - 2\frac{3}{8}$ $2\frac{7}{8}$, or 2.875

17. $6.2 - 3\frac{1}{2}$ $2\frac{7}{10}$, or 2.7

Evaluate each expression for $j = 5\frac{1}{2}$, $k = 4\frac{3}{5}$, and $m = 2\frac{7}{10}$.

18. $j - k$ $\frac{9}{10}$

19. $j - m$ $2\frac{4}{5}$

20. $k - m$ $1\frac{9}{10}$

Problem Solving ▶
Applications

21. $\frac{7}{8}$ mi shorter

21. Whit usually drives $4\frac{7}{8}$ mi on the expressway to work. Sometimes traffic is bad due to weather conditions and he takes another route which is $5\frac{3}{4}$ mi long. How much shorter is his usual route?

22. ✏ **Write About It** Why do you write equivalent fractions before you rename? Can you rename before you write equivalent fractions? because it is easier to tell whether renaming is necessary when fractions are equivalent; yes

23. **Number Sense** Prime numbers that differ by 2, such as 3 and 5, or 59 and 61, are called twin primes. Write two other pairs of twin primes between 1 and 50. possible answer: 5, 7; 29, 31

MIXED REVIEW AND TEST PREP

24. Find the sum of $1\frac{1}{3}$ and $2\frac{1}{6}$. (p. 186) $3\frac{1}{2}$

25. Tell which are equivalent numbers. $\frac{11}{3}$, $7\frac{1}{3}$, $6\frac{1}{3}$, $\frac{22}{3}$ (p. 160) $7\frac{1}{3}$, $\frac{22}{3}$

26. Find the median for the data. 30, 36, 39, 38, 36, 33 (p. 106) 36

27. Evaluate $b \div d$, for $b = 2,260$ and $d = 41$. (p. 28) 55 r5

28. **TEST PREP** Alexander buys 3 boxes of computer paper for $10.79 per box, including tax. How much change will he get from $50? (p. 70) **C**

 A $39.21   C $17.63
 B $32.37   D $11.00

(Extra Practice) page H40, Set D) **193**

PROBLEM SOLVING 9.6

Subtract Mixed Numbers

Write the correct answer.

1. Write $7\frac{2}{9}$ as a fraction.

$\frac{65}{9}$

2. Write $\frac{52}{11}$ as a mixed number or whole number.

$4\frac{8}{11}$

3. The nature club hiked $5\frac{1}{8}$ km on Saturday and $4\frac{3}{4}$ km on Sunday. How much farther did they hike on Saturday than on Sunday?

$\frac{3}{8}$ km

4. Rachel bought $8\frac{1}{2}$ yd of fabric. She used $4\frac{2}{3}$ yd to make a blouse and skirt. How much fabric did she have left?

$3\frac{5}{6}$ yd

Choose the letter for the best answer.

5. What is the LCM of 4, 7, and 8?

 A 14
 B 28
 Ⓒ 56
 D 224

6. What is the GCF of 20 and 28?

 F 2
 Ⓖ 4
 H 5
 J 7

7. The electrician had $45\frac{1}{2}$ ft of wire. He used $3\frac{3}{8}$ ft of it to wire a CD player. How much wire did he have left?

 Ⓐ $41\frac{7}{8}$ ft
 B $41\frac{5}{8}$ ft
 C $42\frac{3}{8}$ ft
 D $42\frac{5}{8}$ ft

8. In 1998, a northern city had $24\frac{2}{3}$ ft of snow. In 1999 that same city had only $8\frac{3}{4}$ ft of snow. What was the difference in the snowfall amounts?

 F $16\frac{7}{12}$ ft
 G $16\frac{5}{8}$ ft
 Ⓗ $15\frac{11}{12}$ ft
 J $15\frac{7}{12}$ ft

9. **Write About It** Explain how to write a mixed number as a fraction.

Multiply the denominator by the whole number and add the numerator.

This result becomes the numerator of the fraction. The denominator

stays the same.

CHALLENGE 9.6

Puzzling Fractions

Match each exercise in Column 1 with its sum or difference in Column 2. Then, to discover the Math Tip in the box, write each corresponding letter above the line marked with the exercise number.

Column 1	Letter	Column 2
1. $2\frac{1}{3} - 1\frac{3}{4}$	H	A. $1\frac{8}{9}$
2. $5\frac{1}{2} - 3\frac{1}{4}$	O	B. $3\frac{7}{12}$
3. $4\frac{2}{9} - 2\frac{8}{9}$	A	D. $2\frac{5}{6}$
4. $6\frac{2}{3} - 5\frac{1}{3}$	S	E. $2\frac{1}{8}$
5. $4\frac{2}{3} - 1\frac{5}{6}$	D	F. $2\frac{1}{2}$
6. $5\frac{3}{10} - 1\frac{4}{5}$	L	H. $\frac{7}{12}$
7. $5\frac{1}{6} - 2\frac{2}{3}$	U	I. $6\frac{7}{12}$
8. $6\frac{3}{4} - 3\frac{1}{6}$	B	L. $3\frac{1}{2}$
9. $2\frac{5}{9} - 1\frac{1}{7}$	N	M. $6\frac{8}{15}$
10. $7\frac{11}{12} - 5\frac{1}{6}$	W	N. $1\frac{2}{35}$
11. $3\frac{5}{8} - 1\frac{1}{4}$	E	O. $2\frac{1}{4}$
12. $6\frac{5}{12} - 1\frac{7}{20}$	P	P. $1\frac{1}{20}$
13. $8\frac{5}{12} - 1\frac{5}{6}$	I	R. $\frac{8}{9}$
14. $5\frac{3}{7} - 1\frac{1}{3}$	T	S. $1\frac{1}{3}$
15. $9\frac{5}{6} - 3\frac{1}{21}$	M	T. $3\frac{20}{21}$
16. $4\frac{7}{10} - 2\frac{13}{20}$	F	U. $2\frac{1}{2}$
17. $6\frac{1}{2} - 3\frac{1}{4}$	R	W. $3\frac{3}{4}$

Math Tip

```
A  N  S  W  E  R  S        S  H  O  U  L  D
3  9  4  10 11 17 4        4  1  2  7  8  6  5
               B  E     I  N
               8  11    13 9
S  I  M  P  L  E  S  T        F  O  R  M
4  13 15 12 6  11 4  14       16 2  17 15
```

---

3 Practice

Guided Practice

Do Check for Understanding Exercises 1–8 with your students. Identify those having difficulty and use lesson resources to help.

**/// COMMON ERROR ALERT **

Some students may have difficulty writing mixed numbers when renaming one whole. Have them work through the renaming step by first modeling it with fraction bars or strips and recording equivalent values.

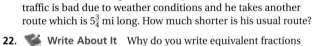

Independent Practice

Assign Exercises 9–23.

Algebraic Thinking Review with students how to find prime numbers to answer Exercise 23. They should use factoring and divisibility rules to eliminate composite numbers; for example, all even numbers can be divided by 2, so none, other than 2 itself, can be prime numbers.

MIXED REVIEW AND TEST PREP

Exercises 24–28 provide **cumulative review** (Chapters 1–9).

4 Assess

Summarize the lesson by having students:

DISCUSS Describe the steps in solving **Exercise 9.** Possible answer: Rename both fractions with the common denominator, 12; rename $3\frac{1}{6}$ as $2\frac{14}{12}$; subtract.

 WRITE Describe a way to solve **Exercise 4 mentally.** Possible answer: Think that $6 - 3 = 3$ and $1 - \frac{2}{3} = \frac{1}{3}$, so the difference is $3\frac{1}{3}$.

Lesson Quiz

Find the difference. Write the answer in simplest form.

Transparency 9.6

1. $2\frac{1}{8} - 1\frac{3}{8}$ $\frac{3}{4}$

2. $2\frac{1}{4} - 1\frac{1}{3}$ $\frac{11}{12}$

3. $3\frac{1}{12} - 1\frac{5}{6}$ $1\frac{1}{4}$

4. $5\frac{1}{2} - 1\frac{7}{10}$ $3\frac{4}{5}$

5. $3\frac{1}{2} - 1\frac{6}{7}$ $1\frac{9}{14}$

6. $12\frac{1}{8} - 9\frac{1}{6}$ $2\frac{23}{24}$

193

Problem Solving Strategy: *Draw a Diagram*

LESSON PLANNING

Objective To use the strategy *draw a diagram* to solve problems

Intervention for Prerequisite Skills

Simplify Fractions, Add and Subtract Like Fractions (For intervention strategies, see page 175.)

Lesson Resources Problem Solving Think Along, p. TR1

 California Mathematics Content Standards

○━ NS 2.0 Students calculate and solve problems involving addition, subtraction, multiplication, and division.

(*Also* NS 1.0, NS 2.4, MR 2.0, MR 2.4, MR 3.2)

Math Background

By drawing a diagram showing how the data in a problem are related, students often see more clearly how to solve the problem. This is particularly true for problems that involve a physical situation, such as the following:

• distance and direction.

• geometric shapes and perimeter or area.

• patterns, as when students find the number of diagonals in a polygon.

WARM-UP RESOURCES

 NUMBER OF THE DAY

 Transparency **9.7**

Write the present time (hours and minutes) as a mixed number. Estimate what time it will be in $4\frac{5}{6}$ hours.
Possible answer for 10:20 A.M.: $10\frac{1}{3}$; 3:10 P.M.

 PROBLEM OF THE DAY

 Transparency **9.7**

Write the next 4 numbers. How does each number relate to the one before it?

A. 10, $8\frac{3}{4}$, $7\frac{1}{2}$, $6\frac{1}{4}$ 5, $3\frac{3}{4}$, $2\frac{1}{2}$, $1\frac{1}{4}$; it is $1\frac{1}{4}$ less.

B. 9, $7\frac{7}{8}$, $6\frac{3}{4}$, $5\frac{5}{8}$ $4\frac{1}{2}$, $3\frac{3}{8}$, $2\frac{1}{4}$, $1\frac{1}{8}$; it is $1\frac{1}{8}$ less.

C. $11\frac{7}{10}$, $10\frac{2}{5}$, $9\frac{1}{10}$, $7\frac{4}{5}$ $6\frac{1}{2}$, $5\frac{1}{5}$, $3\frac{9}{10}$, $2\frac{3}{5}$; it is $1\frac{3}{10}$ less.

Solution Problem of the Day tab, p. PD9

 DAILY FACTS PRACTICE

Have students practice addition facts by completing Set A of *Teacher's Resource Book*, p. TR100.

INTERVENTION AND EXTENSION RESOURCES

ALTERNATIVE TEACHING STRATEGY

Materials *For each student* ruler (inches), p. TR23

To **review and apply relationships in a rectangle,** have students:

- find and measure the sides of rectangles on this page and other pages in the text.

- state the relationship between opposite sides of a rectangle. They are equal in length.

- write the distances represented by the sides of the rectangle showing the taxi's route. $8\frac{1}{4}$ mi, $1\frac{1}{3}$ mi, $8\frac{1}{4}$ mi, $1\frac{1}{3}$ mi

- find the distance from location B to where the taxi crosses its own path. $2\frac{2}{3}$ mi

- Add to find the rectangle's perimeter. $19\frac{1}{6}$ mi

KINESTHETIC

ENGLISH LANGUAGE LEARNERS ELL•SDAIE

Ask students to **model distances** and **use the strategy** *draw a diagram*.

- Select a unit, such as a volunteer's shoe length. Have the volunteer pace out several distances in the room. For each, state the length and draw a labeled line on the board to represent the distance.

- Use the sentence frame *How far is it from [Tim's desk] to [the door]?* to ask students about the labeled distances.

- Make up problems like the one on page 194, based on distances in your room. Tell groups to use *draw a diagram* to solve them.

Check students' work.

VISUAL

READING STRATEGY

Summarize To use this strategy, students must include the main ideas and all the information they need to solve a problem. As they look at the opening problem on page 194, have them describe:

- what the diagram shows as the given information in the problem. the distances AB, BC, CD, DE, and EF

- how the diagram shows how to find the distances from the point of intersection to C and to E. by showing a rectangle with congruent opposite sides

- how the diagram helps solve the problem. Possible answer: It quickly shows the given data and how they relate to one another.

EARLY FINISHERS

Materials *For each group* a map of a foreign country with distances between major cities labeled

Each group **uses a map to calculate the distance** to a mystery destination. Have each group:

- choose a destination and use the map scale to find the distance from a city to their destination.

- write a description of their destination's location, using the distance and needed directions, such as *north of Athens.*

Tell groups to exchange descriptions and discover each other's destinations. Ask them to draw a diagram that shows directional lines and distances. Check students' work.

VISUAL

TECHNOLOGY LINK

Intervention Strategies and Activities CD-ROM • *Skills 22, 23*

Objective To use the strategy *draw a diagram* to solve problems

Lesson Resources Problem Solving Think Along, p. TR1

1 Introduce

QUICK REVIEW provides review of prerequisite skills.

Why Learn This? You can use this skill to display data and find solutions to complex word problems. *Share the lesson objective with students.*

2 Teach

Guided Instruction

• *Read the problem with students.*

Why are there right angles in the diagram at locations B, C, D, and E? The problem states that the taxi changes directions at each point to a new direction at right angles to the previous one.

From the point where the taxi crosses its own path, how far is it to location C? to location E? Explain. $1\frac{1}{3}$ mi; $8\frac{1}{4}$ mi; the diagram shows a rectangle, which has opposite sides that are the same length.

• *Have volunteers explain steps in the problem solving process.*

What is the advantage of drawing a diagram in this problem? Possible answer: It shows the key points in the taxi's travels, and how they relate to each other geometrically.

How else could you find a solution in the Solve step? Possible answer: Add the distances from A to B and from B to the point of intersection, plus the lengths of the sides of the rectangle.

PROBLEM SOLVING STRATEGY
Draw a Diagram

Analyze
Choose
Solve
Check

Learn how to use the strategy *draw a diagram* to solve problems.

QUICK REVIEW

1. $\frac{3}{4} - 1\frac{1}{4}$ $\frac{1}{2}$ 2. $\frac{4}{5} - 1\frac{3}{5}$ $\frac{3}{5}$ 3. $\frac{2}{3} - \frac{2}{3}$ 0   4. $\frac{1}{5} + \frac{4}{5}$ 1   5. $\frac{9}{10} - \frac{6}{10}$ $\frac{3}{10}$

A taxicab travels $1\frac{1}{3}$ mi west, 4 mi north, $8\frac{1}{4}$ mi east, $1\frac{1}{3}$ mi south, and then 10 mi west. How far has the taxicab traveled when it crosses its own path?

Analyze   What are you asked to find?
how far the taxicab has traveled when it crosses its own path
What information is given?
distances and directions in which the taxicab travels
Is there numerical information you will not use? If so, what? No

Choose   What strategy will you use?

You can draw a diagram that shows the taxicab's route.

Solve   How will you solve the problem?

Draw a diagram and label the distances and locations.

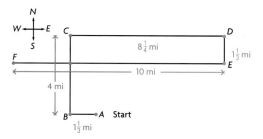

Add all the distances from A to E. Then add the distance from E to the point where the taxicab crosses its own path. This will be the same as the distance from C to D.

$$1\frac{1}{3} + 4 + 8\frac{1}{4} + 1\frac{1}{3} + 8\frac{1}{4}$$

Write equivalent fractions by using the LCD, 12.

$$1\frac{4}{12} + 4 + 8\frac{3}{12} + 1\frac{4}{12} + 8\frac{3}{12} = 22 + \frac{14}{12} = 22 + 1\frac{2}{12} = 23\frac{1}{6}$$

So, the taxicab has traveled $23\frac{1}{6}$ mi when it crosses its own path.

Check   How can you check to see if your answer is reasonable?

estimate the sum

194

CALIFORNIA STANDARDS O➜NS 2.0 Students calculate and solve problems involving addition, subtraction, multiplication, and division. *also,* NS 1.0, NS 2.4, MR 2.0, MR 2.4, MR 2.7, MR 3.2

RETEACH 9.7

Problem Solving Strategy: Draw a Diagram

Some problems become clearer when you draw a diagram to represent the information you are given.

Ms. Kaminsky is teaching her class a game in which students stand in a circle. Two girls stand together, then 1 boy, then 2 girls, then 1 boy, and so on. Altogether, 7 boys are standing in the circle along with all the girls in the class. If there are 27 students in the class, how many boys are not participating?

Step 1: Think about what you know and what you are asked to find.
• You know that all the girls in the class are in the circle.
• You know that there are 7 boys in the circle.
• You know that for every 2 girls in the circle, there is 1 boy.
• You are asked to find how many boys in the class are not in the circle.

Step 2: Plan a strategy to solve.
• Use the strategy *draw a diagram.*
• Draw what you know from the problem.

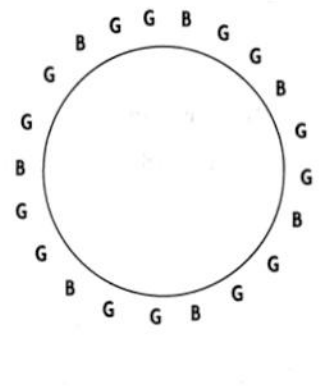

Step 3: Solve.
• Carry out the strategy.
The diagram shows that if 7 boys are in the circle, then there must be 14 girls.
$7 + 14 = 21$ and $27 - 21 = 6$.
So, 6 boys in the class are not participating.

Use the strategy *draw a diagram* to help you solve.
1. In another game, the arrangement around the circle is reversed. Two boys stand together, then 1 girl, then 2 boys, then 1 girl, and so on. In this version of the game, what is the greatest number of students in Ms. Kaminsky's class that can participate at one time?

   18 students: 12 boys and 6 girls

2. The desks are arranged in rows of 6 from the front of the room to the back. In all, there are 5 rows. Arthur sits in the fourth seat of the first row. Andrea sits 3 rows over and 1 seat back. Charles sits 3 seats in front of Andrea. Juan sits 2 rows over and 2 seats farther back than Charles. Where is Juan compared to Arthur?

   next to Arthur

PRACTICE 9.7

Problem Solving Strategy: Draw a Diagram

Solve by drawing a diagram.

1. In the school art room the students use square tables. Each side of a table is $4\frac{1}{2}$ ft. If some of the tables are placed end-to-end, they form a rectangle with a perimeter of 36 ft. How many tables are used to make the rectangle?

   3 tables

2. The art room is on one side of the hallway with an office, a classroom, and the music room. The art room is between the classroom and the office. The classroom is between the music room and the art room. Which two rooms are on the ends of the hallway?

   office, music room

3. During art class, 2 students can sit at each side of a square table. The students decide to make a large rectangular table by placing 5 square tables end-to-end. How many students will be able to sit at this large table?

   24 students

4. Richard is cutting a hole in a wall to hold an air conditioner. The front of the air conditioner is a rectangle 26 in. wide and 16 in. high. The wall is 72 in. wide. If the air conditioner is centered in the wall, how wide will the wall be on either side of it?

   23 in.

5. Cassandra is training for a charity walk between two towns. The towns are 12 mi apart. On her first day of training, she walks $4\frac{1}{2}$ mi. If she increases her distance by $1\frac{1}{2}$ mi every 3 days, how many days will it take until Cassandra has walked at least 10 mi?

   13 days

6. Marla wants to wrap a present that is in the shape of a cube. She wants to put one piece of ribbon around the top and two sides. She wants to put a second piece around the top, bottom, and other two sides. The box is $8\frac{1}{2}$ in. on each edge. What is the shortest length of ribbon she needs?

   68 in.

Mixed Review

Write the number in standard form.

7. six hundred and three tenths   **600.3**
8. ninety-one hundredths   **0.91**
9. ninety and seven hundredths   **90.07**
10. eighty and nine tenths   **80.9**

Find the GCF for each set of numbers.

11. 10, 15   **5**   12. 16, 40   **8**   13. 18, 45   **9**   14. 20, 28   **4**   15. 24, 56   **8**

PROBLEM SOLVING PRACTICE

Solve by drawing a diagram.

1. A tour bus travels $7\frac{1}{2}$ mi south, $3\frac{1}{3}$ mi east, $4\frac{1}{3}$ mi north, and $11\frac{1}{2}$ mi west. How far has the tour bus traveled when it crosses its own path? **$18\frac{1}{2}$ mi**

2. Tanisha needs a fence that is 33 ft long to separate her two gardens. If she puts one post in the ground every $5\frac{1}{2}$ ft, how many posts will Tanisha need for the fence? **7 posts**

For 3–4, use the information below.

Carla drives south $2\frac{1}{2}$ mi from her home. Next, she drives east $\frac{1}{3}$ mi. Then, she drives south 3 mi.

3. How many total miles does Carla drive from her home? **C**

   A 5 mi   C $5\frac{5}{6}$ mi

   B $5\frac{1}{5}$ mi   D 6 mi

4. In which directions must Carla drive to return home? **H**

   F east and north   H west and north

   G east and south   J west and south

PROBLEM SOLVING STRATEGIES

▶ Draw a Diagram or Picture
   Make a Model
   Predict and Test
   Work Backward
   Make an Organized List
   Find a Pattern
   Make a Table or Graph
   Solve a Simpler Problem
   Write an Equation
   Use Logical Reasoning

MIXED STRATEGY PRACTICE

5. A display in a store has 24 cans in the bottom row, 21 in the second row, and 18 in the third row. If the pattern continues, how many cans are in the fifth row? **12 cans**

6. Tickets to see an Irish dance group cost $52 and $28. Mario bought 7 tickets for his family and paid a total of $316. How many tickets at each price did he buy? **five $52 tickets and two $28 tickets**

7. Ms. Lopez travels north from home to pick up Maria at school. Then she travels $3\frac{1}{2}$ mi east to pick up Marcos and $4\frac{1}{4}$ mi south to pick up Carter. If Ms. Lopez has driven a total of $12\frac{1}{2}$ mi, what is the distance from home to Maria's school? **$4\frac{3}{4}$ mi**

8. Tim has a job in the city. He has to commute $6\frac{1}{2}$ km to work. The bus he takes to work travels about $3\frac{1}{4}$ km in 10 minutes. About how much time does Tim spend on the bus going to and from work? **40 minutes**

9. In a recent contest, Gary scored more points than Catherine, who scored more points than Clara. Christopher scored more points than Clara but fewer than Gary. Who had the most points? **Gary**

10. Use the table below. What is Joshua's total bill if he rented 3 videos and kept them for 6 days? **$20.34**

Video Rental Prices	
1 movie for 1 day	$2.99
Each additional day	$0.99
5 additional days	$3.79

11. ✎ **Write a problem** that can be solved by using the strategy *draw a diagram*. Explain the steps you would use to solve the problem, and draw the diagram. **Check students' problems and explanations.**

195

---

3 Practice

Guided Practice

Do Problem Solving Practice Exercises 1–4 with your students. Identify those having difficulty and use lesson resources to help.

As students draw diagrams for Exercise 1, review the compass directions.

Independent Practice

Assign Exercises 5–11.

Students may use either the strategy *make a table* or *predict and test* in Exercise 6.

Encourage students to use the *make a diagram* strategy to solve Exercise 7.

4 Assess

Summarize the lesson by having students:

DISCUSS What kinds of problems do you think the strategy *draw a diagram* works well with? Possible answer: those involving distance or geometric figures

WRITE Describe the steps you used to solve Exercise 7. Possible answer: I drew a line segment north from Ms. Lopez's home, then another one east that I marked $3\frac{1}{2}$ mi, then another one south that I marked $4\frac{1}{4}$ mi. Then I subtracted the sum of $3\frac{1}{2}$ mi and $4\frac{1}{4}$ mi from $12\frac{1}{2}$ mi.

Lesson Quiz

Transparency **9.7**

Draw a diagram to solve. Check students' work.

1. Kendra rides her bike $4\frac{7}{10}$ mi west from her home to the park. She then rides west to the library. From there, she rides $3\frac{1}{2}$ mi west to Sean's house. If she rides her bike 12 mi in all, how far is it from the park to the library? $3\frac{4}{5}$ mi

2. Aaron plans to put braid around the edge of a square tablecloth that measures $6\frac{3}{4}$ ft on each side. How many feet of braid will he need? 27 ft

---

READING STRATEGY 9.7

Summarize

Analyze Choose Solve Check

To **summarize** is to state something in a brief way. Knowing how to summarize information is a useful skill. Sometimes drawing a diagram to display information is a good way to summarize information.

VOCABULARY summarize

Read the following problem.

Rosie walks dogs to earn money. She leaves home with her own dog, Loki, and picks up a poodle, Dante, $\frac{1}{2}$ mi east of her home. Next she gets Noni, another poodle, who lives $\frac{3}{4}$ mi east of Dante. Another $\frac{1}{4}$ mi east, she picks up a spaniel, Higgins. Rosie then drops off the dogs at their houses in this order: first Loki, then Dante, then Noni, then Higgins. Then Rosie walks home. How far have Rosie and each dog walked?

1. Draw a diagram to summarize the information.

   Check students' diagrams.

2. Solve the problem.
   Rosie walked $\frac{6}{}$ mi.   Loki walked $\frac{3}{}$ mi.   Dante walked $\frac{3}{}$ mi.
   Noni walked $\frac{3}{}$ mi.   Higgins walked $\frac{3}{}$ mi.

Draw a diagram to summarize the information. Solve the problem.

3. Bill, Samantha, and Tim are doing a science project together. Samantha lives $\frac{7}{10}$ mi west of the school. Tim lives $\frac{2}{5}$ mi west of Samantha. Bill lives $\frac{1}{2}$ mi east of the school. After school, they walk to Bill's house to pick up some equipment. Then they go to Tim's house to work. When they are finished, Bill and Samantha walk home. How far did each student walk after school?

   Check students' diagrams.

   Bill walked $\frac{3\frac{1}{5}}{}$ mi.   Samantha walked $\frac{2\frac{1}{6}}{}$ mi.   Tim walked $\frac{1\frac{23}{30}}{}$ mi.

CHALLENGE 9.7

Pyramid Patterns in a Diagram

Pascal's Triangle is a diagram that has been used for many years to solve problems. It was named for a French mathematician who may have discovered it.

					1						Row 0
				1		1					Row 1
			1		2		1				Row 2
		1		3		3		1			Row 3
	1		4		6		4		1		Row 4
1		5		10		10		5		1	Row 5

Use Pascal's Triangle to answer the following questions.

1. Find each group of numbers in the diagram.

   1   2 3 1   3 3   4 6
        3   3 1   4   10

   From these groups, can you describe the pattern that is used to create the triangle?
   The bottom number is the sum of the two numbers above it.

2. The next row of the triangle contains these numbers.
   1   $\underline{6}$ 15   20 $\underline{15}$ 6   1
   Use the pattern to fill in the row.

3. A section further down the triangle contains the following numbers.
   1   7   21   35   35   21   7   1
   1   $\underline{8}$ 28 $\underline{56}$ 70 $\underline{56}$ $\underline{28}$ 8   1
   Use the pattern to fill in the row.

4. When you add the numbers in the rows, an interesting pattern develops. Add the numbers in rows 0 through 5. Describe what you find.
   The sums of the rows are the powers of 2.

5. What will the sum be for row 6? row 7? **64, 128**

6. Find the diagonals that represent the first 5 counting numbers (1, 2, 3, 4, and 5). If the pattern is extended, in which row will the eighth counting number be found? **row 8**

195

REVIEW/TEST

Purpose To check understanding of concepts, skills, and problem solving presented in Chapter 9

USING THE PAGE

The Chapter 9 Review/Test can be used as a **review** or a **test**.

- Items 1–37 check skill proficiency.
- Items 38–40 check students' abilities to choose and apply problem solving strategies to real-life addition and subtraction problems.

 Suggest that students place the completed Chapter 9 Review/Test in their portfolios.

USING THE ASSESSMENT GUIDE

- Multiple-choice format of Chapter 9 Posttest—See *Assessment Guide*, pp. AG57–58.
- Free-response format of Chapter 9 Posttest—See *Assessment Guide*, pp. AG59–60.

USING STUDENT SELF-ASSESSMENT

The How Did I Do? survey helps students assess what they have learned and how they learned it. This survey is available as a copying master in *Assessment Guide*, p. AGxvii.

Estimate the sum or difference. (pp. 176–179) Possible estimates are given.

1. $\frac{7}{12} + \frac{1}{4}$ 1
2. $\frac{4}{5} - \frac{2}{7}$ $\frac{1}{2}$
3. $\frac{4}{5} + \frac{3}{8}$ 1
4. $\frac{3}{4} - \frac{1}{3}$ 1

5. $4\frac{2}{9} - \frac{1}{7}$ 4
6. $\frac{9}{20} + 1\frac{4}{5}$ $2\frac{1}{2}$
7. $6\frac{1}{4} + 3\frac{2}{9}$ $9\frac{1}{2}$
8. $9\frac{4}{5} - 2\frac{7}{9}$ 7

Write the sum or difference in simplest form. Estimate to check. (pp. 182–185)

9. $\frac{1}{2} + \frac{1}{3}$ $\frac{5}{6}$
10. $\frac{3}{4} + \frac{1}{6}$ $\frac{11}{12}$
11. $\frac{2}{5} + \frac{2}{4}$ $\frac{9}{10}$
12. $\frac{2}{3} + \frac{3}{4}$ $\frac{17}{12}$, or $1\frac{5}{12}$

13. $\frac{5}{6} + \frac{2}{3}$ $\frac{3}{2}$, or $1\frac{1}{2}$
14. $\frac{1}{3} + \frac{5}{6}$ $\frac{7}{6}$, or $1\frac{1}{6}$
15. $\frac{3}{8} + \frac{3}{4}$ $\frac{9}{8}$, or $1\frac{1}{8}$
16. $\frac{5}{8} + \frac{1}{6}$ $\frac{19}{24}$

17. $\frac{3}{4} - \frac{1}{3}$ $\frac{5}{12}$
18. $\frac{7}{8} - \frac{1}{4}$ $\frac{5}{8}$
19. $\frac{5}{6} - \frac{2}{9}$ $\frac{11}{18}$
20. $\frac{8}{9} - \frac{1}{6}$ $\frac{13}{18}$

21. $\frac{7}{8} - \frac{5}{6}$ $\frac{1}{24}$
22. $\frac{7}{12} - \frac{5}{12}$ $\frac{1}{6}$
23. $\frac{3}{5} - \frac{1}{4}$ $\frac{7}{20}$
24. $\frac{4}{5} - \frac{1}{10}$ $\frac{7}{10}$

Draw a diagram to find the sum or difference. Write the answer in simplest form. (pp. 186–189) Check students' diagrams.

25. $2\frac{3}{8} + 1\frac{1}{4}$ $3\frac{5}{8}$
26. $6\frac{2}{3} - 3\frac{1}{4}$ $3\frac{5}{12}$
27. $5\frac{2}{5} - 3\frac{3}{10}$ $2\frac{1}{10}$
28. $2\frac{1}{6} + 1\frac{1}{3}$ $3\frac{1}{2}$

Write the sum or difference in simplest form. Estimate to check. (pp. 186–189, 192–193)

29. $1\frac{1}{6} + 3\frac{2}{3}$ $4\frac{5}{6}$
30. $2\frac{3}{4} + 3\frac{1}{8}$ $5\frac{7}{8}$
31. $1\frac{1}{2} + 2\frac{1}{4}$ $3\frac{3}{4}$

32. $1\frac{1}{5} + 1\frac{3}{10}$ $2\frac{1}{2}$
33. $7\frac{3}{4} - 5\frac{1}{3}$ $2\frac{5}{12}$
34. $8\frac{1}{3} - 3\frac{1}{8}$ $5\frac{5}{24}$

35. $3\frac{1}{4} - 2\frac{1}{2}$ $\frac{3}{4}$
36. $4\frac{1}{2} - 1\frac{2}{3}$ $2\frac{5}{6}$
37. $7\frac{1}{5} - 5\frac{4}{9}$ $1\frac{34}{45}$

Solve each problem by drawing a diagram. (pp. 194–195)

38. A minibus leaves the garage and travels $9\frac{5}{6}$ mi north to pick up Tanya. Then it travels $3\frac{1}{6}$ mi west to pick up Luis, $4\frac{1}{4}$ mi south to pick up Alissa, and $4\frac{5}{12}$ mi east to the school. How far does the minibus travel before crossing its own path? **$20\frac{5}{12}$ mi**

39. Satoko has a board that is 9 ft long. She needs to cut the board into $2\frac{1}{4}$-ft sections. How many cuts will she have to make? **3 cuts**

40. Del drives $3\frac{1}{4}$ mi north from his home. Next, he drives west $\frac{3}{4}$ mi. Then, he drives north $\frac{1}{2}$ mi. In which directions must Del drive to return home? **east and south**

Decide on a plan.
See item **2**.

Show the hours practiced as an addition sentence. Find the *least common denominator* before you add.

Also see problem **4**, p. H64.

Choose the best answer.

1. Bryce had $\frac{13}{15}$ gallon of paint. He used $\frac{1}{3}$ gallon for a project. How much paint did he have left? **A**

   A $\frac{8}{15}$ gal   C $\frac{1}{3}$ gal

   B $\frac{1}{2}$ gal   D $\frac{1}{5}$ gal

2. Tirzah practiced the piano for $1\frac{2}{3}$ hours on Monday, $\frac{3}{4}$ hour on Wednesday, and $1\frac{1}{2}$ hours on Friday. Which is the total amount of time she spent practicing the piano? **H**

   F $3\frac{2}{5}$ hr   H $3\frac{11}{12}$ hr

   G $3\frac{3}{4}$ hr   J 4 hr

3. Last week Jessie's swimming practice lasted for $\frac{3}{5}$ hour on Monday, $\frac{5}{6}$ hour on Wednesday, and $\frac{9}{10}$ hour on Friday. How many hours did she have swimming practice during the week? **D**

   A $1\frac{1}{3}$ hr   C 2 hr

   B $1\frac{2}{3}$ hr   D $2\frac{1}{3}$ hr

4. What is the value of $n + \frac{1}{2}$ for $n = \frac{5}{6}$? **J**

   F $\frac{1}{3}$ H $1\frac{1}{6}$

   G $\frac{11}{12}$ J $1\frac{1}{3}$

5. In which pair are both numbers equivalent to $\frac{2}{5}$? **C**

   A 0.2; 20%

   B 25%; $\frac{4}{10}$

   C 40%; 0.4

   D 0.6; $\frac{6}{15}$

6. $14\frac{2}{3} - 9\frac{5}{12}$ **H**

   F $4\frac{1}{3}$ H $5\frac{1}{4}$

   G $4\frac{1}{2}$ J Not here

7. The mean of 5 numbers is 25.6. What is the sum of the numbers? **A**

   A 128   C 26.1

   B 30.6   D Not here

8. Bart passed a sign that read, "City Limit $5\frac{1}{2}$ miles." If he drives $2\frac{1}{4}$ miles farther, how far will he be from the city limit? **J**

   F $2\frac{1}{4}$ mi   H 3 mi

   G $2\frac{1}{2}$ mi   J $3\frac{1}{4}$ mi

9. Which is a reasonable estimate of the sum of the fractions $\frac{1}{12}$, $\frac{4}{9}$, $\frac{5}{8}$, and $\frac{11}{12}$? **B**

   A 1   C 4

   B 2   D $4\frac{1}{2}$

10. Mel hiked $\frac{9}{16}$ mile on Saturday and $\frac{7}{8}$ mile on Sunday. Which is a good estimate for how far Mel hiked in all? **G**

    F about 2 mi

    G about $1\frac{1}{2}$ mi

    H about 1 mi

    J about $\frac{1}{2}$ mi

11. $1\frac{7}{8} - \frac{9}{10}$ **D**

    A $1\frac{1}{2}$ C $1\frac{1}{40}$

    B $1\frac{1}{10}$ D $\frac{39}{40}$

12. $115,371.9 + 22,671.25$ **G**

    F 138,043.015   H 138,043.259

    G 138,043.15   J Not here

CUMULATIVE REVIEW •
Chapters 1–9

USING THE PAGE

This page may be used to help students get ready for standardized tests. The test items are written in the same style and arranged in the same format as those on many state assessments. The page is cumulative. It covers math objectives and essential skills that have been taught up to this point in the text. Most of the items represent skills from the current chapter, and the remainder represent skills from earlier chapters.

This page can be assigned at the end of the chapter as classwork or as a homework assignment. You may want to have students use individual recording sheets presented in a multiple-choice (standardized) format. A Test Answer Sheet is available as a blackline master in *Assessment Guide* (p. AGxlii).

You may wish to have students describe how they solved each problem and share their solutions.

Multiply and Divide Fractions and Mixed Numbers

CHAPTER PLANNER

PACING OPTIONS	
Compacted	5 Days
Expanded	9 Days

Getting Ready for Chapter 10 • Assessing Prior Knowledge and INTERVENTION (See PE and TE page 199.)

LESSON	CALIFORNIA STANDARDS	PACING	VOCABULARY*	MATERIALS	RESOURCES AND TECHNOLOGY
10.1 Estimate Products and Quotients pp. 200–201 **Objective** To estimate products and quotients of fractions and mixed numbers	○━ NS 2.0 NS 2.2 (*Also* ○━ NS 1.0, MR 2.5)	1 Day			Reteach, Practice, Problem Solving, Challenge 10.1 Worksheets Extra Practice p. H41, Set A ▭ Transparency 10.1
10.2 Multiply Fractions pp. 202–205 **Objective** To multiply fractions	○━ NS 2.0 NS 2.2 MR 2.1 (*Also* ○━ NS 1.0, NS 2.1, ○━ NS 2.4, MR 1.3, MR 2.5)	1 Day			Reteach, Practice, Problem Solving, Challenge 10.2 Worksheets Extra Practice p. H41, Set B ▭ Transparency 10.2 ◉ **Calculating Crew** • *Nautical Number Line* ◉ **Number Heroes** • *Fraction Fireworks*
10.3 Multiply Mixed Numbers pp. 206–207 **Objective** To multiply mixed numbers	○━ NS 2.0 MR 2.1 NS 2.2 (*Also* ○━ NS 1.0, NS 2.1, ○━ NS 2.4, MR 1.3, MR 2.5)	1 Day			Reteach, Practice, Problem Solving, Challenge 10.3 Worksheets Extra Practice p. H41, Set C ▭ Transparency 10.3
10.4 Math Lab: Division of Fractions pp. 208–209 **Objective** To model division with fractions	○━ NS 2.0 NS 2.2 (*Also* NS 2.1, ○━ NS 2.4)		reciprocal	For each student fraction circles	🌐 **E-Lab** • *Exploring Division of Fractions;* E-Lab Recording Sheet **Math Jingles™ CD 5-6** • *Track 15*
10.5 Divide Fractions and Mixed Numbers pp. 210–213 **Objective** To divide fractions and mixed numbers	○━ NS 2.0 NS 2.2 (*Also* ○━ NS 1.0, NS 2.1, ○━ NS 2.4, MR 2.1)	2 Days (For Lessons 10.4 and 10.5)			Reteach, Practice, Problem Solving, Challenge 10.5 Worksheets Extra Practice p. H41, Set D ▭ Transparency 10.5
10.6 Problem Solving Skill: *Choose the Operation* pp. 214–215 **Objective** To *choose the operation* to solve a problem	○━ NS 2.0 MR 3.2 (*Also* NS 2.1, NS 2.2)	1 Day			Reteach, Practice, Reading Strategy, Challenge 10.6 Worksheets ▭ Transparency 10.6 Problem Solving Think Along, p. TR1
10.7 Algebra: Fraction Expressions and Equations pp. 216–217 **Objective** To evaluate expressions with fractions and to solve equations with fractions by using mental math and substitution	AF 1.0 ○━ AF 1.1 (*Also* NS 2.1, NS 2.2)	1 Day			Reteach, Practice, Problem Solving, Challenge 10.7 Worksheets Extra Practice p. H41, Set E ▭ Transparency 10.7 **Math Jingles™ CD 5-6** • *Tracks 8-9*

Ending Chapter 10 • Chapter 10 Review/Test, p. 218 • **Cumulative Review,** p. 219

Ending Unit 3 • Math Detective, p. 220; **Challenge,** p. 221; **Study Guide and Review,** pp. 222–223; **California Connections,** pp. 224–225

* **Boldfaced** terms are new vocabulary. Other terms are review vocabulary.

Vocabulary Development

The boldfaced word is the new vocabulary term in the chapter. Have students record the definition in their Math Journals.

reciprocal, p. 209

> reciprocal

Vocabulary Cards
Have students use the Vocabulary Cards on *Teacher's Resource Book* **pp. TR127–128** to make graphic organizers or word puzzles. The cards can also be added to a file of mathematics terms.

California Mathematics Content Standards for Grade 6

Strands

Number Sense

Lesson 10.1: NS 1.0, 2.0, 2.2

Lesson 10.2: NS 1.0, 2.0, 2.1, 2.2, 2.4

Lesson 10.3: NS 1.0, 2.0, 2.1, 2.2, 2.4

Lesson 10.4: NS 2.0, 2.1, 2.2, 2.4

Lesson 10.5: NS 1.0, 2.0, 2.1, 2.2, 2.4

Lesson 10.6: NS 2.0, 2.1, 2.2

Lesson 10.7: NS 2.1, 2.2

Algebra and Functions

Lesson 10.7: AF 1.0, 1.1

Measurement and Geometry

Statistics, Data Analysis, and Probability

Mathematical Reasoning

Lesson 10.1: MR 2.5

Lesson 10.2: MR 1.3, 2.1, 2.5

Lesson 10.3: MR 1.3, 2.1, 2.5

Lesson 10.4: MR 2.1

Lesson 10.6: MR 3.2

Writing Opportunities

PUPIL EDITION
- **Write About It,** pp. 201, 207, 215
- **What's the Error?,** pp. 213, 217
- **What's the Question?,** p. 205

TEACHER'S EDITION
- **Write** — See the *Assess* section of each TE lesson.
- **Writing in Mathematics,** pp. 202B, 208, 216B

ASSESSMENT GUIDE
- **How Did I Do?,** p. AGxvii

Family Involvement Activities

These activities provide:
- Letter to the Family
- Information about California Standards
- Math Vocabulary
- Family Game
- Practice (Homework)

GRADE 6
Chapter 10

WHAT WE ARE LEARNING
Multiplying and Dividing Fractions and Mixed Numbers

VOCABULARY
Here is a vocabulary term we use in class:

Reciprocal One of two numbers whose product is 1
$\frac{3}{4} \times \frac{4}{3} = 1$
$\frac{3}{4}$ and $\frac{4}{3}$ are reciprocals.

The California Math Standards
Your child's **Harcourt Math** book lists the California Math Standards that are taught in every lesson. If you have questions about the standards, be sure to consult *California Standards for Grade 6* that was sent home at the beginning of the school year.

Date

Dear Family,

Your child is continuing the study of fractions. *This is how your child is learning to estimate products and quotients.*

Step 1
Round mixed numbers to the nearest whole number and fractions to 1, $\frac{1}{2}$, or 0, whichever is nearest.

$48\frac{7}{10} \times 5\frac{2}{3}$ 49×5
$48\frac{7}{10} \div 5\frac{2}{3}$ $49 \div 5$

Step 2
Perform the operation.
$49 \times 5 = 245$ $49 \div 5 = 9\frac{4}{5}$

How would you estimate the product $9\frac{1}{8} \times \frac{7}{8}$? Your child might suggest: The first thing to do is round the numbers. $9\frac{1}{8}$ is close to 9 and $\frac{7}{8}$ is close to 1.

What do you do next? Your child might respond: I perform the operation in my head.

$9 \times 1 = 9$

How would you estimate the quotient $9\frac{1}{8} \div \frac{1}{3}$?

$9\frac{1}{8}$ is close to 9 and $\frac{1}{3}$ is close to $\frac{1}{2}$.

$9 \div \frac{1}{2} = 18$

Why is your estimate for the quotient of $9\frac{1}{8} \div \frac{1}{3}$ so much greater than the dividend? One way to think about $9\frac{1}{8} \div \frac{1}{3}$ is "how many $\frac{1}{3}$ pieces are in $9\frac{1}{8}$ pieces?" The answer is greater than $9\frac{1}{8}$.

Family Involvement Activities, p. FA37

Multiply and Divide Fractions and Mixed Numbers

MATHEMATICS ACROSS THE GRADES

SKILLS TRACE ACROSS THE GRADES

GRADE 5	GRADE 6	GRADE 7
Write products of fractions and mixed numbers; write quotients of fractions divided by fractions and quotients of fractions divided by whole numbers	**Estimate and write products and quotients of fractions and mixed numbers; evaluate expressions and use mental math to solve equations involving fractions**	Multiply and divide rational numbers; solve multistep equations involving rational numbers

SKILLS TRACE FOR GRADE 6

LESSON	FIRST INTRODUCED	TAUGHT AND PRACTICED	TESTED	REVIEWED
10.1	Grade 6	PE pp. 200–201, H41, p. RW45, p. PW45, p. PS45	PE p. 218, pp. AG61–64	PE pp. 218, 219, 222–223
10.2	Grade 5	PE pp. 202–205, H41, p. RW46, p. PW46, p. PS46	PE p. 218, pp. AG61–64	PE pp. 218, 219, 222–223
10.3	Grade 5	PE pp. 206–207, H41, p. RW47, p. PW47, p. PS47	PE p. 218, pp. AG61–64	PE pp. 218, 219, 222–223
10.4	Grade 5	PE pp. 208–209	PE p. 218, pp. AG61–64	PE pp. 218, 219, 222–223
10.5	Grade 5	PE pp. 210–213, H41, p. RW48, p. PW48, p. PS48	PE p. 218, pp. AG61–64	PE pp. 218, 219, 222–223
10.6	Grade 4	PE pp. 214–215, p. RW49, p. PW49, p. PS49	PE p. 218, pp. AG61–64	PE pp. 218, 219, 222–223
10.7	Grade 6	PE pp. 216–217, H41, p. RW50, p. PW50, p. PS50	PE p. 218, pp. AG61–64	PE pp. 218, 219, 222–223

KEY **PE** Pupil Edition   **PS** Problem Solving Workbook   **RW** Reteach Workbook
PW Practice Workbook   **AG** Assessment Guide

Looking Back Prerequisite Skills

To be ready for Chapter 10, students should have the following understandings and skills:

- **Vocabulary**—*fraction, mixed number, equation*
- **Round Fractions**—round fractions to 0, $\frac{1}{2}$, or 1
- **Mental Math and Equations**—use mental math to solve equations involving addition, subtraction, multiplication, and division
- **Fractions and Mixed Numbers**—write mixed numbers as fractions and fractions as mixed numbers

Check What You Know

Use page 199 to determine students' knowledge of prerequisite concepts and skills.

Intervention

Help students prepare for the chapter by using the intervention resources described on TE page 199.

Looking at Chapter 10 Essential Skills

Students will

- estimate products and quotients of fractions and mixed numbers.
- **make connections between the algorithm and graphic representations of operations with fractions.**
- develop skill and accuracy writing products and quotients of fractions and mixed numbers.
- use the skill *choose the operation* to solve problems.
- evaluate expressions with fractions and solve equations with fractions by using mental math and substitution.

EXAMPLE

Find $\frac{1}{2} \times \frac{2}{3}$.

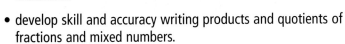

Model	Algorithm
	Multiply the numerators. Multiply the denominators.
	$\frac{1}{2} \times \frac{2}{3} = \frac{1 \times 2}{2 \times 3} = \frac{2}{6}$
	For simplest form, divide the numerator and the denominator by the GCF, 2.
	$\frac{2 \div 2}{6 \div 2} = \frac{1}{3}$
	So, the product $\frac{1}{2} \times \frac{2}{3}$ is $\frac{1}{3}$.

Looking Ahead Applications

Students will apply what they learn in Chapter 10 to the following new concepts:

- Expressions (Chapter 14)
- Operations with Rational Numbers (Grade 7)
- Multiplication and Division Equations (Chapter 16)

Multiply and Divide Fractions and Mixed Numbers

INTRODUCING THE CHAPTER

Tell students that as with whole numbers, division of fractions and mixed numbers is the inverse operation of multiplication. Have students estimate the number of cyclists pictured in the photograph. Ask them how many $\frac{1}{2}$ that number is. about 25 cyclists

USING DATA

To begin the study of this chapter, have students

- Find the approximate number of kilometers covered during $\frac{1}{2}$ of Stages 9–12. about 417 km

- Determine to the nearest hour how long it would take to complete Stages 5–8 at a rate of $17\frac{1}{2}$ km per hour. about 39 hours

PROBLEM SOLVING PROJECT

Purpose To use fractions to solve a problem

Grouping pairs or small groups

Background 1 km is equivalent to about $\frac{5}{8}$ mi.

Analyze, Choose, Solve, and Check

Have students

- Convert the distance for each group of stages of the Tour de France to the nearest mile. Pro.–4: 487 mi, 5–8: 430 mi; 9–12: 521 mi; 13–16: 500 mi; 17–20: 367 mi

- Use an atlas to map out a bike tour in the United States that is equivalent in distance to the Tour de France.

- Draw a map of the bike tour. Label the distances in miles.

Check students' work.

Portfolio Suggest that students display the maps in the classroom and then place them in their portfolios.

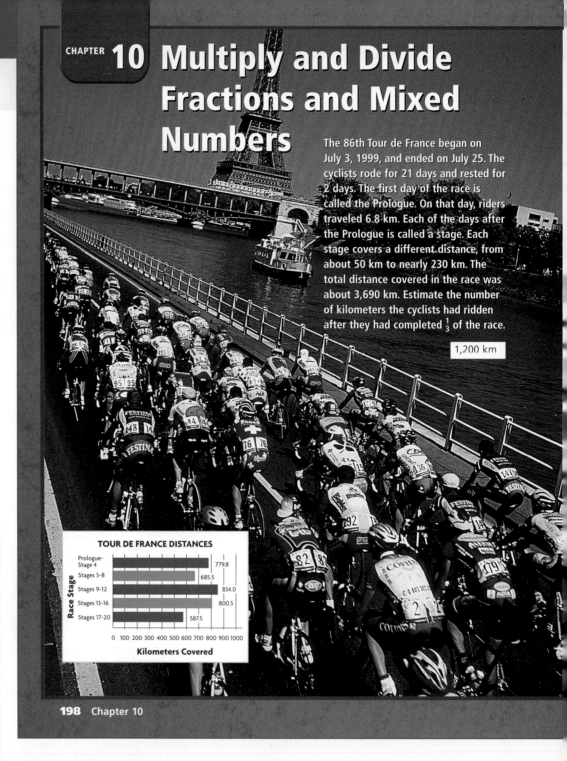

CHAPTER 10 Multiply and Divide Fractions and Mixed Numbers

The 86th Tour de France began on July 3, 1999, and ended on July 25. The cyclists rode for 21 days and rested for 2 days. The first day of the race is called the Prologue. On that day, riders traveled 6.8 km. Each of the days after the Prologue is called a stage. Each stage covers a different distance, from about 50 km to nearly 230 km. The total distance covered in the race was about 3,690 km. Estimate the number of kilometers the cyclists had ridden after they had completed $\frac{1}{3}$ of the race.

1,200 km

TOUR DE FRANCE DISTANCES

Race Stage	Kilometers Covered
Prologue–Stage 4	779.8
Stages 5-8	685.5
Stages 9-12	834.0
Stages 13-16	800.5
Stages 17-20	587.5

0 100 200 300 400 500 600 700 800 900 1000
Kilometers Covered

198 Chapter 10

Why learn math? Explain that cyclists can use fractions to help them calculate their speed as they race. For example, if they decide they want to complete each quarter of a race in a certain amount of time, they can multiply the total distance by $\frac{1}{4}$ to check their time as they complete each quarter. Graphic artists use fractions as they design a page. Architects multiply and divide fractions when they design blueprints. Ask: In what other jobs do people multiply and divide fractions and mixed numbers?
Possible answers: construction work; buying fabric

Check What You Know

Use this page to help you review and remember important skills needed for Chapter 10.

✓ Vocabulary

Choose the best term from the box.

> fraction
> mixed number
> equation

1. An algebraic or numerical sentence that shows two quantities are equal is a(n) __?__ . **equation**

2. A number that is made up of a whole number and a fraction is a(n) __?__ . **mixed number**

✓ Round Fractions (See p. H10.)

Round each fraction to 0, $\frac{1}{2}$, or 1.

3. $\frac{2}{9}$ 0   4. $\frac{7}{8}$ 1   5. $\frac{7}{15}$ $\frac{1}{2}$ 6. $\frac{5}{8}$ $\frac{1}{2}$ 7. $\frac{1}{4}$ $\frac{1}{2}$

8. $\frac{2}{15}$ 0   9. $\frac{3}{8}$ $\frac{1}{2}$ 10. $\frac{5}{6}$ 1   11. $\frac{1}{3}$ $\frac{1}{2}$ 12. $\frac{10}{11}$ 1

13. $\frac{11}{20}$ $\frac{1}{2}$ 14. $\frac{7}{12}$ $\frac{1}{2}$ 15. $\frac{1}{6}$ 0   16. $\frac{4}{7}$ $\frac{1}{2}$ 17. $\frac{2}{6}$ $\frac{1}{2}$

✓ Mental Math and Equations (See p. H11.)

Use mental math to solve.

18. $9.3 + x = 12.5$
$x = 3.2$

19. $4c = 128$
$c = 32$

20. $x - 160 = 520$
$x = 680$

21. $5.11 = 5.28 - x$
$x = 0.17$

22. $0.12 = \frac{x}{0.6}$
$x = 0.072$

23. $35 - t = 21$
$t = 14$

24. $6y = 0.24$
$y = 0.04$

25. $r + 3.7 = 6.3$
$r = 2.6$

✓ Fractions and Mixed Numbers (See p. H11.)

Write each fraction as a mixed number.

26. $\frac{18}{5}$ $3\frac{3}{5}$ 27. $\frac{7}{6}$ $1\frac{1}{6}$

28. $\frac{16}{15}$ $1\frac{1}{15}$ 29. $\frac{4}{3}$ $1\frac{1}{3}$

Write each mixed number as a fraction.

30. $1\frac{5}{8}$ $\frac{13}{8}$ 31. $7\frac{1}{2}$ $\frac{15}{2}$

32. $3\frac{2}{3}$ $\frac{11}{3}$ 33. $2\frac{4}{5}$ $\frac{14}{5}$

> **LOOK AHEAD**
>
> In Chapter 10 you will
> - estimate products and quotients
> - multiply and divide fractions and mixed numbers
> - use fractions in expressions and equations

Check What You Know
INTERVENTION • Diagnose and Prescribe

Prerequisite Skill	Items (Pupil Edition p. 199)	How to Help Options
✓ Round Fractions	3–17	• **Troubleshooting, Pupil Edition p. H10** • **Intervention Strategies and Activities** Card, Copying Master, or CD-ROM • **Skill 24**
✓ Mental Math and Equations	18–25	• **Troubleshooting, Pupil Edition p. H11** • **Intervention Strategies and Activities** Card, Copying Master, or CD-ROM • **Skill 41**
✓ Fractions and Mixed Numbers	26–33	• **Troubleshooting, Pupil Edition p. H11** • **Intervention Strategies and Activities** Card, Copying Master, or CD-ROM • **Skills 25–26**

Estimate Products and Quotients

LESSON PLANNING

Objective To estimate products and quotients of fractions and mixed numbers

Intervention for Prerequisite Skills

Round Fractions (For intervention strategies, see page 199.)

California Mathematics Content Standards

○→ NS 2.0 Students calculate and solve problems involving addition, subtraction, multiplication, and division.

NS 2.2 Explain the meaning of multiplication and division of positive fractions and perform the calculations.

(*Also* ○→ NS 1.0, MR 2.5)

Math Background

Students may use an estimate of fraction or mixed number products and quotients to check an answer's reasonableness. Or, they may estimate a product or quotient because that is all the problem requires.

- Products of mixed numbers can be estimated by rounding. You can round to the nearest whole number or $\frac{1}{2}$ and multiply.

- When working with fractions, products, and quotients, you can get a closer estimate by finding the average of a high estimate and a low estimate.

- Sometimes it is easiest to estimate quotients by using compatible numbers.

WARM-UP RESOURCES

 NUMBER OF THE DAY

Write fractions with a denominator of 7 that are close to 0, $\frac{1}{2}$, and 1. Possible answer: $\frac{1}{7}$, $\frac{4}{7}$, $\frac{6}{7}$

 PROBLEM OF THE DAY

A is a whole number between 55 and 60. The product of *A* and *B* is between 1,045 and 1,500. Between what two numbers is *B*? between 19 and 26

Solution Problem of the Day tab, p. PD10

 DAILY FACTS PRACTICE

Have students practice multiplication and division facts by completing Set B of *Teacher's Resource Book*, p. TR100.

ALTERNATIVE TEACHING STRATEGY

Have students **use number lines to estimate fraction quotients**, such as $8 \div \frac{3}{4}$. Ask them to draw number lines divided into fourths showing 0 through 8. Have them use the number lines to find the number of 1's in 8 and the number of $\frac{1}{2}$'s in 8, since $\frac{3}{4}$ is halfway between 1 and $\frac{1}{2}$.

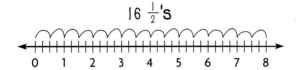

$16 \frac{1}{2}$'s

Then, to demonstrate that the average of these first two estimates, 8 and 16, is a reasonable estimate for the quotient, have students use the number line to estimate the number of $\frac{3}{4}$'s in 8. about 11

VISUAL

MIXED REVIEW AND TEST PREP

Cumulative Review Chapters 1–10

Refer to the Pupil Edition pages referenced in the exercises for further review. Have students go to the lesson page, review the lesson, and correct any problem they missed.

Mixed Review and Test Prep, p. 201

How to Help	
Item	Page
28	177
29	198
30	110
31	28
32	158

ENGLISH LANGUAGE LEARNERS (ELL•SDAIE)

Review vocabulary with students by discussing and displaying the words *product, quotient, estimate, mixed number,* and *fraction.* Call on volunteers to write an example of each of the terms.

Then combine the words into phrases and ask for volunteers to write examples. For example, *estimate the product of two fractions.* Possible answer: $\frac{7}{8} \times \frac{2}{3}$ is about $\frac{1}{2}$

VISUAL

EARLY FINISHERS

Materials *For each pair* 2 number cubes, labeled 1–6 and 7–12, p. TR75

Have students **practice estimating fraction products.** Working in pairs, each student rolls the cubes and writes a fraction less than 1 from the two numbers. Then students work together to estimate the product of the two fractions they have formed. Possible answer: For $\frac{4}{7} \times \frac{3}{10}$, students might estimate $\frac{1}{4}$.

KINESTHETIC

TECHNOLOGY LINK

Intervention Strategies and
Activities CD-ROM • *Skill 24*

1 Introduce

QUICK REVIEW provides review of prerequisite skills.

Why Learn This? You can estimate the number of $\frac{3}{4}$-hr activities you can schedule between 1:00 P.M. and 5:30 P.M. *Share the lesson objective with students.*

2 Teach

Guided Instruction

- *Direct students' attention to the opening problem.*
- *Direct students to understand that 1,000 million is the same as 1 billion.*

REASONING **Why is an estimate an appropriate answer?** Possible answer: The number $4\frac{2}{5}$ is already an estimate, so it is reasonable to find an estimate rather than an exact answer.

Modifying Instruction Don't discourage students from reasonable rounding, which may not always be to the nearest whole number. Had the population been $247\frac{7}{10}$ million, rounding to the nearest 10 would make the operation easier.

- *Demonstrate the quotient estimate in the Example and ask:*

Why would you not estimate with average estimates if the division were $\frac{5}{6}$? $\frac{5}{6}$ is halfway between $\frac{2}{3}$ and 1, and $\frac{2}{3}$ is not an easy divisor with which to estimate.

ADDITIONAL EXAMPLE

Example, p. 200

Mrs. Keenan's students are decorating their classroom with a paper chain for a party. Using construction paper, they are cutting strips $\frac{3}{4}$ in. wide by 9 in. long. Lee has only one sheet of paper, which is 9 in. × 12 in. About how many loops can she make? Estimate. $12 \div \frac{3}{4}$

$12 \div 1 = 12 \qquad 12 \div \frac{1}{2} = 24$

$12 + 24 = 36; 36 \div 2 = 18$
So, Lee can make about 18 loops.

LESSON **10.1**

Estimate Products and Quotients

Learn how to estimate products and quotients of fractions and mixed numbers.

Remember that when rounding fractions, round to 0, $\frac{1}{2}$, or 1. When rounding mixed numbers, round to the nearest whole number.

In a landfill, bulldozers spread and compact the garbage into 10-foot layers. Every layer is covered with clean soil.

The landfills in more than half of the states in the United States will soon be full. It is estimated that each person in the United States produces $4\frac{2}{5}$ pounds of garbage a day. If the population of the United States was $249\frac{7}{10}$ million, about how many pounds of garbage would be produced every day?

One way to estimate the answer is to round the mixed numbers to the nearest whole number.

Estimate. $4\frac{2}{5} \times 249\frac{7}{10}$

$$4\frac{2}{5} \times 249\frac{7}{10} \quad \textit{Round to the nearest whole number.}$$
$$\downarrow \qquad \downarrow \quad \textsf{THINK: } \tfrac{2}{5} \textit{ rounds to 0, and } \tfrac{7}{10} \textit{ rounds to 1.}$$
$$4 \ \times 250 = 1{,}000 \quad \textit{Multiply.}$$

So, about 1,000 million pounds would be produced each day.

You can also estimate by averaging two estimates.

EXAMPLE

Estimate. $8 \div \frac{3}{4}$
Since $\frac{3}{4}$ is halfway between $\frac{1}{2}$ and 1, find the two estimates and then find their average.

Round up.   *Round down.*

$8 \div \frac{3}{4} \rightarrow 8 \div 1 = 8$ $8 \div \frac{3}{4} \rightarrow 8 \div \frac{1}{2} = 16$

$8 + 16 = 24; 24 \div 2 = 12$ So, $8 \div \frac{3}{4}$ is about 12.

You can use compatible numbers to estimate a product or quotient.

$23\frac{3}{4} \div 4\frac{1}{2} \ \rightarrow \ 25 \div 5 = 5$

So, $23\frac{3}{4} \div 4\frac{1}{2}$ is about 5.

200 **CALIFORNIA STANDARDS** O—n NS 20 Students calculate and solve problems involving addition, subtraction, multiplication, and division. NS 2.2 Explain the meaning of multiplication and division of positive fractions and perform the calculations. *also* O—n NS 1.0, MR 2.5

RETEACH 10.1

Estimate Products and Quotients

You can often estimate the product or quotient of two mixed numbers by rounding each of them to the nearest whole number. Using a number line may help you round in the appropriate direction.

$\frac{3}{5}$ $\frac{4}{5}$ $2\frac{1}{4}$ $5\frac{5}{8}$ $10\frac{1}{8}$ $12\frac{3}{4}$

0 1 2 3 4 5 6 7 8 9 10 11 12 13

Use rounding to multiply $2\frac{3}{4} \times 10\frac{1}{8}$

Step 1 Round each mixed number to the nearest whole number.

$2\frac{3}{4} \times 10\frac{1}{8}$
$\downarrow \qquad \downarrow$
$3 \ \times \ 10$

Step 2 Multiply the rounded values.

$3 \times 10 = 30$
The product is about 30.

Use rounding to divide $12\frac{1}{4} \div 5\frac{7}{8}$

Step 1 Round each mixed number to the nearest whole number.

$12\frac{1}{4} \div 5\frac{7}{8}$
$\downarrow \qquad \downarrow$
$12 \div 6$

Step 2 Divide the rounded values.

$12 \div 6 = 2$
The quotient is about 2.

When a fraction is between 0 and 1, round it to 0, $\frac{1}{2}$, or 1, whichever is closest. Remember that you cannot divide by 0.

Use rounding to multiply $\frac{4}{5} \times 10\frac{1}{8}$

$\frac{4}{5} \times 10\frac{1}{8} \rightarrow 1 \times 10$
The product is about 1 × 10, or 10.

Use rounding to divide $12\frac{1}{4} \div \frac{3}{5}$

$12\frac{1}{4} \div \frac{3}{5} \rightarrow 12 \div \frac{1}{2}$
The quotient is about $12 \div \frac{1}{2} = 12 \times 2$, or 24.

Complete the estimation of each product or quotient. Possible answers are given.

1. Estimate $15\frac{5}{6} \times 1\frac{7}{8}$

$15\frac{5}{6} \times 1\frac{7}{8} \rightarrow \underline{15} \times \underline{2}$

$= \underline{30}$

2. Estimate $24\frac{5}{6} \div 4\frac{4}{5}$

$24\frac{5}{6} \div 4\frac{4}{5} \rightarrow \underline{25} \div \underline{5}$

$= \underline{5}$

3. Estimate $\frac{3}{5} \times 48$

$\frac{3}{5} \times 48 \rightarrow \underline{\tfrac{1}{2}} \times \underline{48}$

$= \underline{24}$

4. Estimate $59\frac{7}{8} \div 15\frac{1}{8}$

$59\frac{7}{8} \div 15\frac{1}{8} \rightarrow \underline{60} \div \underline{15}$

$= \underline{4}$

PRACTICE 10.1

Estimate Products and Quotients

Estimate each product or quotient. Possible answers are given.

1. $4\frac{1}{4} \times 3\frac{3}{4}$ __16__
2. $20\frac{5}{6} \div 6\frac{3}{4}$ __3__
3. $\frac{3}{4} \times \frac{5}{6}$ __1__
4. $\frac{3}{4} \div \frac{2}{3}$ __1__
5. $45\frac{1}{3} \div 8\frac{2}{3}$ __5__
6. $17\frac{2}{7} \times 1\frac{2}{7}$ __17__
7. $2\frac{3}{5} \div \frac{2}{5}$ __5__
8. $19 \times 6\frac{1}{3}$ __114__
9. $2\frac{3}{4} \times 2\frac{4}{5}$ __9__
10. $36\frac{3}{7} \div 11\frac{3}{4}$ __3__
11. $\frac{7}{9} \times 13\frac{1}{9}$ __13__
12. $\frac{1}{5} \div 20$ __0__
13. $3\frac{3}{4} \div 4\frac{1}{2}$ __1__
14. $42\frac{1}{6} \times 14\frac{4}{9}$ __630__
15. $\frac{1}{10} \times \frac{1}{10}$ __0__
16. $8\frac{1}{3} \times 6\frac{4}{5}$ __56__
17. $12\frac{1}{6} \div 3\frac{2}{3}$ __3__
18. $40\frac{2}{9} \div 7\frac{4}{5}$ __5__
19. $10\frac{5}{6} \times 3\frac{7}{8}$ __44__
20. $18\frac{3}{10} \div 1\frac{6}{7}$ __9__
21. $9\frac{3}{4} \times 17\frac{1}{5}$ __170__

Estimate to compare. Write < or > for each ●.

22. $3\frac{1}{5} \times 5$ ● $12 \div \frac{9}{10}$ __>__
23. $6\frac{1}{2} \div 12$ ● $\frac{5}{8} \div \frac{1}{3}$ __>__
24. $5\frac{2}{7} \div 1\frac{3}{8}$ ● $2\frac{1}{8} \div 3\frac{4}{7}$ __>__
25. $3\frac{3}{4} \times 1\frac{1}{4}$ ● $31\frac{3}{4} \div 8\frac{1}{4}$ __>__
26. $15\frac{1}{5} \div 4\frac{2}{9}$ ● $1\frac{3}{4} \div 3\frac{4}{5}$ __>__
27. $7\frac{2}{9} \times 1\frac{5}{7}$ ● $36\frac{1}{2} \div 2\frac{7}{8}$ __<__

Mixed Review

Write the fraction as a percent.

28. $\frac{3}{4}$ __75%__
29. $\frac{7}{10}$ __70%__
30. $\frac{1}{20}$ __5%__
31. $\frac{3}{25}$ __12%__
32. $\frac{29}{50}$ __58%__
33. $\frac{13}{10}$ __130%__
34. $\frac{1}{8}$ __12.5%__
35. $\frac{5}{8}$ __62.5%__

Think and ▸
Discuss

1. $2 \times 250 = 500$; about 500 million pounds

2. Possible answer: $84 \div 12$

Guided ▸
Practice

Look back at the lesson to answer each question.

1. **What if** each person in the United States produced $2\frac{1}{5}$ pounds of garbage? About how many pounds of garbage would be produced?

2. **Tell** what compatible numbers you could use to find $81\frac{3}{5} \div 12\frac{7}{8}$.

Estimate each product or quotient. Possible answers are given.

3. $\frac{7}{8} \times \frac{7}{16}$ **$\frac{1}{2}$**   4. $10\frac{8}{11} \div 2\frac{1}{5}$ **5**   5. $78\frac{3}{7} \div 4\frac{1}{6}$ **20**   6. $\frac{3}{5} \times 38$ **19**

7. $1\frac{3}{4} \times 35$ **70**   8. $21\frac{3}{8} \div 17\frac{1}{3}$ **1**   9. $58\frac{3}{4} \times 1\frac{5}{6}$ **118**   10. $98\frac{7}{8} \div 23\frac{1}{5}$ **4**

Independent ▸
Practice

Estimate each product or quotient. Possible answers are given.

11. $\frac{7}{9} \times \frac{1}{3}$ **$\frac{1}{2}$**   12. $10\frac{8}{9} \times \frac{5}{6}$ **11**   13. $\frac{5}{6} \div \frac{11}{12}$ **1**   14. $67\frac{9}{12} \div 2\frac{7}{10}$ **23**

15. $24\frac{9}{10} \div 6\frac{2}{3}$ **4**   16. $36\frac{5}{8} \div 13\frac{3}{5}$ **4**   17. $67\frac{2}{3} \div 23\frac{1}{8}$ **3**   18. $97\frac{2}{9} \div 52\frac{5}{8}$ **2**

19. $3\frac{11}{12} \times 4\frac{6}{7}$ **20**   20. $12\frac{5}{24} \div \frac{8}{12}$ **24**   21. $\frac{5}{9} \times \frac{7}{12}$ **$\frac{1}{4}$**   22. $\frac{2}{5} \div \frac{10}{21}$ **1**

Problem Solving ▸
Applications

Estimate to compare. Write < or > for each ●.

23. $4\frac{1}{6} \times 3\frac{2}{3}$ ● $7\frac{5}{8} \div 2\frac{1}{3}$ **>**   24. $7\frac{2}{3} \div 5$ ● $2\frac{4}{8} \times 3\frac{1}{8}$ **<**

25. Cal runs $5\frac{3}{10}$ miles in $33\frac{4}{5}$ minutes. About how many minutes does it take for Cal to run one mile? **about 7 min**

26. **Write About It** Explain how you would estimate a quotient of mixed numbers. **Possible answer: Choose two compatible numbers about equal to the given numbers and find their quotient.**

27. Doris picked up used newspapers around her neighborhood for six days. She picked up 0.5 kg the first day, 2 kg the second day, and 3.5 kg the third day. If this pattern continued, how much newspaper did she pick up on the sixth day? **8 kg**

28. Write $\frac{7}{20}$ as a percent. (p. 169) **35%**

29. $5\frac{7}{9} - 2\frac{1}{3}$ (p. 186) **$3\frac{4}{9}$**

30. Find the mean, median, and mode for the data.
27, 48, 83, 76, 48, 27 (p. 110) **51.5; 48; 27 and 48**

31. Evaluate the expression $m - 4^2$ for $m = 3^3$. (p. 28) **11**

32. **TEST PREP** Which is the LCM of 18 and 24? (p.150) **C**
A 2   B 8   C 72   D 128

Extra Practice page H41, Set A

201

Guided Practice

Do Check for Understanding Exercises 1–10 with your students. Identify those having difficulty and use lesson resources to help.

Independent Practice

Assign Exercises 11–27.

For Exercise 27, students may find a number line helpful to see the pattern.

MIXED REVIEW AND TEST PREP
Exercises 28–32 provide **cumulative review** (Chapters 1–10).

Summarize the lesson by having students:

DISCUSS Ask students to explain how they find an estimate of the product of two fractions that are less than 1. Possible answer: Round each fraction to 0, $\frac{1}{2}$, or 1 and then multiply.

 WRITE Why is it important to estimate products and quotients of mixed numbers and fractions? Possible answer: An estimate allows you to check the reasonableness of a computation. Also, many times an estimate is all you need to solve a problem.

Lesson Quiz

Transparency **10.1**

Estimate each product or quotient. Possible answers are given.

1. $\frac{5}{6} \times \frac{3}{8}$ **$\frac{1}{2}$**   2. $34\frac{1}{3} \times \frac{3}{5}$ **17**

3. $10 \div \frac{2}{5}$ **20**   4. $14\frac{2}{3} \div 3\frac{1}{3}$ **5**

PROBLEM SOLVING 10.1

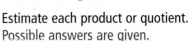

Estimate Products and Quotients

Analyze   Choose   Solve   Check

Write the correct answer.

1. The water behind a dam begins rising at a rate of $1\frac{3}{4}$ in. per hr during a spring thaw. The water will spill over the dam if it rises 72 in. Estimate the number of hours before the dam will overflow.
about 36 hours

2. Dillon wants to survey 1 out of every 10 adults in his neighborhood between the ages of 25 and 40. He has generated a list of 220 people in this age group. How many people should he survey?
22 people

3. Mikel used $3\frac{1}{8}$ qt of potting soil per plant to pot 15 small shrubs. About how much potting soil did Mikel use for all of the shrubs?
about 45 qt

4. Ann is 136.8 centimeters tall and Theresa is 128.9 centimeters tall. How much taller is Ann than Theresa?
7.9 centimeters taller

Write the letter of the best answer.

5. Al is filling $\frac{3}{4}$ lb packages of chocolate chip cookies. About how many packages can be filled from a 44 lb container of chocolate chip cookies?
A about 33 packages
B about 44 packages
C about 60 packages
D about 66 packages

6. Nikki's 8 dogs each get $4\frac{1}{8}$ c of dry dog food every day. Estimate the total amount of dry dog food that she provides for the dogs each day.
F about 4 c
G about 12 c
H about 33 c
J about 100 c

7. Karl found that a garden measured $4\frac{7}{8}$ yd by $12\frac{2}{3}$ yd. Which is the best estimate of the area of the garden?
A (4×12) yd²
B (4×13) yd²
C (5×12) yd²
D (5×13) yd²

8. About how many $\frac{2}{3}$ lb boxes of raisins can be filled from a $15\frac{1}{2}$ lb bag of raisins?
F about 10 boxes
G about 15 boxes
H about 20 boxes
I about 25 boxes

9. **Write About It** When is it appropriate to use an estimate?
Possible answer: An estimate is appropriate for checking a calculation or whenever an approximate answer will be close enough.

CHALLENGE 10.1

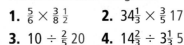

Estimation Sense

If you estimate without thinking about the situation, you can get results that simply do not make any sense. Such errors can lead to other more serious errors. **Possible answers are given.**

Solve.

1. Mr. Axel won $7,328,493 in the state lottery. He promised to give $\frac{1}{10}$ of the money to several charities and keep the rest for himself. He rounded $\frac{1}{10}$ to 0, and then multiplied to see that each charity would get $0! What is wrong with Mr. Axel's approach to this problem? What might he do to get a more accurate estimate?
$\frac{1}{10}$ of such a large amount of money is a lot more than $0.
Mr. Axel might remember that multiplying by $\frac{1}{10}$ is the
same as dividing by 10 or multiplying by 0.1.

2. The Martin family started a savings account with $1,000 that grew at the same rate every year. There was always $1\frac{1}{8}$ times as much money at the end of each year than at the beginning of the year. The Martin's rounded the growth rate of $1\frac{1}{8}$ times to 1, and estimated how much they would have in 10 years. What was their estimated total? What is wrong with their approach to this problem?
The Martin's estimation showed that they would end up with
$1,000, because they were always multiplying by 1. They
should have realized that rounding to 1 can be a problem
when dealing with a repeating situation like bank account
interest.

3. Think about the situations in Problems 1 and 2 above. What would you say to someone who estimates by rounding small fractions to 0 and any fraction near 1 to 1?
You might warn them to use common sense when
applying rounding rules so that they don't make a
mistake. They should ask, "Does my estimate make
sense in this situation?"

Multiply Fractions

LESSON PLANNING

Objective To multiply fractions

Intervention for Prerequisite Skills

Round Fractions, Write a Fraction as a Mixed Number, Write a Mixed Number as a Fraction (For intervention strategies, see page 199.)

 California Mathematics Content Standards

⊶ NS 2.0 Students calculate and solve problems involving addition, subtraction, multiplication, and division.

NS 2.2 Explain the meaning of multiplication and division of positive fractions and perform the calculations.

MR 2.1 Use estimation to verify the reasonableness of calculated results.

(*Also* ⊶NS 1.0, NS 2.1, ⊶NS 2.4, MR 1.3, MR 2.5)

Math Background

If you multiply a whole number by a fraction, such as $4 \times \frac{1}{2}$, you can think of it as $\frac{1}{2} + \frac{1}{2} + \frac{1}{2} + \frac{1}{2} = 2$. However, to multiply $\frac{1}{2} \times 4$ or $\frac{1}{2} \times \frac{1}{2}$, you need to think of taking the fractional part of a set or of a fraction.

- Because multiplication is commutative, $\frac{1}{2} \times 4$ is the same as $4 \times \frac{1}{2}$, or 2. So, you can think of half of 4, or one of two equal parts of 4.

- In the same way, you can think of $\frac{1}{2} \times \frac{1}{2}$ as one of two equal parts of $\frac{1}{2}$, or $\frac{1}{4}$.

Both of these problems can be illustrated on a number line or with models, leading to the common algorithm for multiplication of fractions.

WARM-UP RESOURCES

 NUMBER OF THE DAY Transparency 10.2

The number of the day is the total number of days in the current month. If each day this month you save a half-dollar, how much money will you have at the end of the month? Possible answer: for month with 30 days, $15

 PROBLEM OF THE DAY Transparency 10.2

In a jump-rope marathon, Cara earns $5 for charity for each half hour or fraction of a half hour that she jumps rope. How much money will Cara earn if she jumps rope for 175 min? $30

Solution Problem of the Day tab, p. PD10

 DAILY FACTS PRACTICE

Have students practice multiplication facts by completing Set C of *Teacher's Resource Book*, p. TR100.

INTERVENTION AND EXTENSION RESOURCES

ALTERNATIVE TEACHING STRATEGY ⓔⓛⓛ

Materials *For each pair* 2 number cubes, labeled 1–6 and 4–9, p. TR75

Ask student pairs to **practice multiplying fractions.**

- The pairs roll 2 number cubes twice. The players form 2 fractions.
- The first player estimates whether the product will be equal to, greater than, or less than 1.
- Students check the estimation by finding the product. If the estimation was correct, the first player earns a point.
- Have students take turns estimating the product. The first student to reach 5 points wins. Check students' work.

See also page 204.

VISUAL

MIXED REVIEW AND TEST PREP

Cumulative Review Chapters 1–10

Refer to the Pupil Edition pages referenced in the exercises for further review. Have students go to the lesson page, review the lesson, and correct any problem they missed.

Mixed Review and Test Prep, p. 205

How to Help	
Item	Page
38	208
39	82
40	66
41	98
42	158

SPECIAL NEEDS

Materials *For each group* spinner with 8 sections, p. TR72

Have students **practice the multiplication algorithm for fractions.**

- Have the groups of 2 or 3 write a simple fraction in each section of the spinner, such as $\frac{1}{2}$ and $\frac{2}{3}$.
- Each group should use the spinner to form multiplication problems by spinning twice and recording each fraction.
- Then, have the groups find the products.

Check students' work.

VISUAL

WRITING IN MATHEMATICS

 Have students **apply their knowledge of the multiplication of fractions** by writing problems.

- Have them work in pairs to choose a topic, such as practicing the piano or making a pizza.
- Then ask each student to write a problem and provide a solution.
- Each pair can share their problems with another pair and talk about the solutions.

Call on volunteers to share their problems with the class. Check students' work.

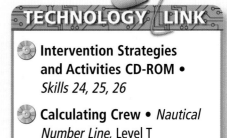

TECHNOLOGY LINK

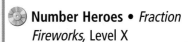

- **Intervention Strategies and Activities CD-ROM** • *Skills 24, 25, 26*

- **Calculating Crew** • *Nautical Number Line,* Level T

- **Number Heroes** • *Fraction Fireworks,* Level X

Objective To multiply fractions

1 Introduce

QUICK REVIEW provides review of pre-requisite skills.

Why Learn This? You can find out how much of each of the ingredients of a recipe you will need if you cut the recipe in half. *Share the lesson objective with students.*

2 Teach

Guided Instruction

• *Refer students to the model.*

Why is the paper folded into 4 equal parts? to show fourths

Does it make sense that the product is in eighths? Explain. Yes; An eighth is half of a fourth.

• *Have students explain the relationship between the factors and the product.*

How do you find the denominator of the product? multiply the denominators of the factors

REASONING **Why is multiplying fractions usually easier than adding or subtracting fractions?** You don't have to find a common denominator in order to multiply.

• *After students make the model for $\frac{1}{3} \times \frac{3}{4}$, ask:*

What did you do differently to find $\frac{1}{3} \times \frac{3}{4}$ than to find $\frac{1}{2} \times \frac{3}{4}$? The second fold is in thirds rather than in halves.

LESSON **10.2**

Multiply Fractions

Learn how to multiply fractions.

QUICK REVIEW

Write each fraction in simplest form.

1. $\frac{8}{10}$ $\frac{4}{5}$ 2. $\frac{21}{28}$ $\frac{3}{4}$ 3. $\frac{36}{54}$ $\frac{2}{3}$

4. $\frac{18}{30}$ $\frac{3}{5}$ 5. $\frac{12}{8}$ $1\frac{1}{2}$

Carolyn asked $\frac{3}{4}$ of her classmates what time they leave for school in the morning. Of those she asked, $\frac{1}{2}$ leave at 7:00 A.M. What fractional part of the class told her that they leave for school at 7:00 A.M.?

One way to find the fractional part of a fraction is to make a model.

Find $\frac{1}{2}$ of $\frac{3}{4}$, or $\frac{1}{2} \times \frac{3}{4}$.

Fold a piece of paper into 4 equal parts.

Shade 3 parts to show $\frac{3}{4}$.

Fold the paper in half. Shade $\frac{1}{2}$ of the paper.

Of the $2 \times 4 = 8$ parts, $1 \times 3 = 3$ are shaded, so $\frac{3}{8}$ of the paper is shaded twice. These parts represent $\frac{1}{2} \times \frac{3}{4}$.

$$\frac{1}{2} \times \frac{3}{4} = \frac{3}{8}$$

So, $\frac{3}{8}$ of the students Carolyn asked leave at 7:00 A.M.

The product of numerators is the numerator of the product, and the product of the denominators is the denominator of the product.

• Compare the numerator and denominator of the product with the numerators and denominators of the factors. What relationship do you see?

You can see this relationship in the solution to the problem.

$$\frac{\text{numerator} \times \text{numerator}}{\text{denominator} \times \text{denominator}} = \frac{\text{numerator}}{\text{denominator}}$$

↑   ↑   ↑

factor   factor   product

• Make a model to find $\frac{1}{3} \times \frac{3}{4}$. **Check students' models;** $\frac{3}{12}$

202 **CALIFORNIA STANDARDS** O⌐NS 2.0 Students calculate and solve problems involving addition, subtraction, multiplication, and division. **NS 2.2** Explain the meaning of multiplication and division of positive fractions and perform the calculations. **MR 2.1** Use estimation to verify the reasonableness of calculated results. *also* O⌐NS 1.0, NS 2.1, O⌐NS 2.4, MR 1.3, MR 2.5

RETEACH 10.2

Multiply Fractions

Bo knows that $\frac{2}{3}$ of the students in his class play soccer. Of those students, $\frac{1}{6}$ are in the school band. Bo wants to know what fraction of his class play soccer and are in the school band.

Step 1 Write a multiplication sentence. $\frac{2}{3} \times \frac{1}{6} = \blacksquare$

Step 2 Multiply the numerators. $\frac{2 \times 1}{3 \times 6} = \frac{2}{18}$
Multiply the denominators.

Step 3 Divide the numerator and denominator by the GCF, 2. $= \frac{2 \div 2}{18 \div 2}$

Step 4 Write the product in simplest form. $= \frac{1}{9}$

So, $\frac{1}{9}$ of Bo's class play soccer and are in the school band.

Complete to find each product.

1. $\frac{3}{4} \times \frac{2}{9} = \frac{3 \times \boxed{2}}{\boxed{4} \times 9}$

$= \frac{6}{\boxed{36}}$

$= \frac{6 \div \boxed{6}}{36 \div \boxed{6}}$

$= \frac{1}{\boxed{6}}$

2. $\frac{1}{8} \times \frac{2}{3} = \frac{1 \times 2}{8 \times \boxed{3}}$

$= \frac{2}{\boxed{24}}$

$= \frac{2 \div \boxed{2}}{24 \div \boxed{2}}$

$= \frac{1}{\boxed{12}}$

Use GCFs to simplify the fractions. Write the product in simplest form.

3. $\frac{5}{6} \times \frac{2}{5}$ 4. $\frac{3}{4} \times \frac{5}{9}$ 5. $\frac{5}{6} \times \frac{3}{10}$ 6. $\frac{3}{4} \times \frac{6}{9}$
$\frac{1}{3}$ $\frac{5}{12}$ $\frac{1}{4}$ $\frac{1}{2}$
$\frac{2}{9}$ $\frac{5}{16}$ $\frac{1}{6}$ $\frac{6}{14}$

7. $\frac{4}{5} \times \frac{5}{8}$ 8. $\frac{5}{6} \times \frac{12}{25}$ 9. $\frac{2}{3} \times \frac{9}{20}$ 10. $\frac{3}{5} \times \frac{4}{15}$
$\frac{1}{2}$ $\frac{2}{5}$ $\frac{3}{10}$ $\frac{1}{10}$

PRACTICE 10.2

Multiply Fractions

Make a model to find the product. Check students' models.

1. $\frac{1}{2} \times 6$ 2. $\frac{2}{5} \times \frac{1}{2}$ 3. $\frac{1}{8} \times \frac{1}{2}$ 4. $10 \times \frac{1}{2}$ 5. $\frac{1}{2} \times \frac{1}{3}$
$\frac{1}{5}$ $\frac{1}{16}$
3    $\frac{1}{5}$ $\frac{1}{16}$ 5 $\frac{1}{6}$

Multiply. Write the answer in simplest form.

6. $\frac{1}{4} \times \frac{1}{6}$ 7. $\frac{1}{5} \times \frac{1}{2}$ 8. $\frac{3}{8} \times \frac{1}{4}$ 9. $\frac{3}{5} \times \frac{1}{4}$ 10. $\frac{4}{5} \times \frac{1}{2}$
$\frac{1}{24}$ $\frac{1}{10}$ $\frac{3}{32}$ $\frac{3}{20}$ $\frac{2}{5}$

11. $\frac{1}{4} \times \frac{8}{9}$ 12. $\frac{3}{4} \times \frac{2}{7}$ 13. $\frac{5}{9} \times \frac{9}{10}$ 14. $\frac{6}{7} \times \frac{1}{5}$ 15. $\frac{6}{7} \times \frac{2}{3}$
$\frac{2}{9}$ $\frac{3}{14}$ $\frac{1}{2}$ $\frac{6}{35}$ $\frac{4}{7}$

16. $\frac{3}{4} \times \frac{8}{9}$ 17. $\frac{3}{4} \times \frac{8}{15}$ 18. $\frac{6}{8} \times \frac{8}{9}$ 19. $\frac{7}{8} \times 24$ 20. $\frac{3}{4} \times \frac{1}{3}$
$\frac{2}{3}$ $\frac{2}{5}$ $\frac{4}{27}$ 21 $\frac{1}{8}$

21. $\frac{5}{6} \times \frac{3}{10}$ 22. $\frac{9}{10} \times \frac{2}{3}$ 23. $30 \times \frac{4}{5}$ 24. $\frac{1}{2} \times \frac{12}{13}$ 25. $\frac{9}{11} \times \frac{22}{27}$
$\frac{1}{4}$ $\frac{3}{5}$ 24 $\frac{6}{13}$ $\frac{2}{3}$

Compare. Write <, >, or = for ●.

26. $\frac{1}{2} \times \frac{2}{3} ● \frac{2}{3}$ <   27. $\frac{3}{4} \times 8 ● 6$ =   28. $\frac{1}{4} \times 4 ● 1\frac{1}{4}$ >

Mixed Review

Write each mixed number as a fraction.

29. $4\frac{2}{22}$ 30. $6\frac{3}{45}$ 31. $2\frac{8}{30}$ 32. $5\frac{3}{28}$
$\frac{22}{5}$ $\frac{45}{7}$ $\frac{30}{11}$ $\frac{28}{5}$

Write each fraction as a mixed number.

33. $\frac{12}{5}$ 34. $\frac{41}{12}$ 35. $\frac{25}{6}$ 36. $\frac{50}{9}$
$2\frac{2}{5}$ $3\frac{5}{12}$ $4\frac{1}{6}$ $5\frac{5}{9}$

You can use this relationship to multiply fractions without making a model.

EXAMPLE 1

Find $\frac{1}{3} \times \frac{3}{7}$. Write the product in simplest form.

Remember that to write a fraction in simplest form, divide the numerator and the denominator by the greatest common factor (GCF).

$$\frac{1}{3} \times \frac{3}{7} = \frac{1 \times 3}{3 \times 7} = \frac{3}{21}$$

Multiply the numerators.
Multiply the denominators.

$$= \frac{3 \div 3}{21 \div 3}$$

Divide the numerator and the denominator by the GCF, 3.

$$= \frac{1}{7}$$

Write the product in simplest form.

So, $\frac{1}{3} \times \frac{3}{7} = \frac{1}{7}$.

- Explain why the product, $\frac{1}{7}$, is less than the factor $\frac{3}{7}$. **Possible answer: both factors are less than 1.**

You can also multiply a whole number and a fraction without making a model.

EXAMPLE 2

Ms. Jones's car is being repaired after being in an accident. Her daughter Cindy will have to walk a total of $\frac{9}{10}$ mi to and from school every day for 11 days. How far will Cindy walk in all?

Find $11 \times \frac{9}{10}$.

Estimate. $11 \times 1 = 11$

$$11 \times \frac{9}{10} = \frac{11}{1} \times \frac{9}{10}$$

Write the whole number as a fraction.

$$= \frac{11 \times 9}{1 \times 10}$$

Multiply the numerators.
Multiply the denominators.

$$= \frac{99}{10}, \text{ or } 9\frac{9}{10}$$

Write the answer as a fraction or as a mixed number in simplest form.

Compare the product to your estimate. $9\frac{9}{10}$ is close to the estimate of 11. The product is reasonable.

So, Cindy will walk $9\frac{9}{10}$ mi.

- **What if** Cindy walked to school for 21 days? How far would Cindy walk in all? **$18\frac{9}{10}$ mi**

- *Draw students' attention to the Remember. Ask:*

  How do you find the greatest common factor of two numbers? Possible answer: Find all the factors of both numbers and determine the greatest one that is a factor of both.

- *As students look at Example 1, ask:*

  How could you estimate the product? Round $\frac{1}{3}$ to $\frac{1}{2}$ and $\frac{3}{7}$ to $\frac{1}{2}$ and then multiply $\frac{1}{2} \times \frac{1}{2}$, which is $\frac{1}{4}$.

  Why isn't the answer $\frac{3}{21}$? $\frac{3}{21}$ isn't in simplest form.

- *As students look at Example 2, ask:*

  Why would you want to report the answer as a mixed number? Possible answer: The answer to a word problem is more clearly expressed as a mixed number than as a fraction greater than 1.

ADDITIONAL EXAMPLES

Example 1, p. 203

Find $\frac{4}{5} \times \frac{3}{4}$. Write the product in simplest form. $\frac{3}{5}$

Example 2, p. 203

Nathan is training for a swim meet, which will take place in 2 weeks. He swims $\frac{5}{8}$ mi 6 days a week. How far will Nathan swim before the meet? $\frac{60}{8}$, or $7\frac{1}{2}$ mi

203

PROBLEM SOLVING 10.2

Multiply Fractions

Write the correct answer.

Analyze Choose Solve Check

1. Write $\frac{10}{15}$ in simplest form.

   $\frac{2}{3}$

2. List the first four multiples of 9.

   9, 18, 27, 36

3. Write the multiplication shown by the model. Then write the product.

   $\frac{3}{8} \times \frac{1}{2} = \frac{3}{16}$

4. Write the multiplication shown by the model. Then write the product.

   $\frac{1}{4} \times \frac{1}{3} = \frac{1}{12}$

Write the letter of the best answer.

5. Which is the missing number?

   $\frac{7}{8} \times \frac{\blacksquare}{5} = \frac{7}{10}$

   A 1
   B 2
   C 3
   D 4

6. Which is a list of all the factors of 50?

   F 5, 10
   G 2, 5, 10, 25
   H 1, 2, 5, 10, 25, 50
   J 1, 2, 5, 10, 15, 20, 25, 50

7. Luke exercises $\frac{3}{4}$ hr each morning. He spends $\frac{1}{3}$ of this time riding an exercise bike. What part of an hour does Luke spend riding the bike?

   A $\frac{1}{4}$ hr
   B $\frac{1}{3}$ hr
   C $\frac{1}{2}$ hr
   D $\frac{3}{4}$ hr

8. Sally is reading a book for school. She has read 27 pages every day for the last 15 days. How many pages has Sally read so far?

   F 42 pages
   G 300 pages
   H 405 pages
   J 450 pages

9. **Write About It** Look at the model in Problem 3. Explain how you can tell which two fractions are factors and which fraction is the product.

   Possible answer: The fraction for the first factor is shown by the shaded columns. 3 of the 8 columns are shaded. The fraction for the second factor is shown by the shaded rows. 1 of the 2 rows is shaded. The product is shown by the parts that are shaded twice. 3 of the 16 parts are shaded twice.

CHALLENGE 10.2

Fraction Flowers

Color the petals containing factors of the product in the circle. Remember to use GCFs to simplify the factors before multiplying!

203

- *Direct students' attention to the follow-up question to Example 3.*

What is the GCF for the numerators and the denominators? 2

Modifying Instruction Show with Example 3 why you can simplify before you multiply when a numerator and a denominator have a common factor. The Identity Property of 1 allows you to divide the numerator and denominator by the GCF 2:

$$\frac{2 \times 3}{5 \times 4} = \frac{2 \times 3}{5 \times 4} \div 1 = \frac{2 \times 3}{5 \times 4} \div \frac{2}{2}$$

$$= \frac{(2 \div 2) \times 3}{5 \times (4 \div 2)} = \frac{1 \times 3}{5 \times 2} = \frac{3}{10}$$

ADDITIONAL EXAMPLES

Example 3, p. 204

Jeff has $\frac{3}{8}$ of his candy bar supply left over from the candy sale. Kristin helped by selling $\frac{5}{6}$ of his left-over bars. What part of Jeff's candy bar supply was Kristin able to sell? *Kristin sold $\frac{5}{16}$ of Jeff's candy bars.*

Example 4, p. 204

Find $\frac{2}{3} \times \frac{9}{14}$. Use the GCF to simplify the fractions before you multiply.

$$\overset{1}{\underset{1}{\cancel{2}}} \times \frac{\overset{3}{\cancel{9}}}{\underset{7}{\cancel{14}}} = \frac{1 \times 3}{1 \times 7} = \frac{3}{7}$$

So, $\frac{2}{3} \times \frac{9}{14} = \frac{3}{7}$.

When a numerator and a denominator have a common factor, you can simplify before you multiply.

EXAMPLE 3

Cheryl has $\frac{3}{4}$ of a box of snacks left from a school party. She gives $\frac{2}{5}$ of the snacks to the people in the school office. What part of the box of snacks does she give the people in the office?

Find $\frac{2}{5} \times \frac{3}{4}$.

Estimate. $\frac{1}{2} \times 1 = \frac{1}{2}$

$\frac{2}{5} \times \frac{3}{4}$ ← The GCF of 2 and 4 is 2.   *Look for a numerator and denominator with common factors. Find the GCF.*

$\frac{\overset{1}{\cancel{2}}}{5} \times \frac{3}{\underset{2}{\cancel{4}}}$ ← $2 \div 2 = 1$
← $4 \div 2 = 2$ *Divide the numerator and denominator by the GCF, 2.*

$\frac{\overset{1}{\cancel{2}}}{5} \times \frac{3}{\underset{2}{\cancel{4}}} = \frac{1 \times 3}{5 \times 2} = \frac{3}{10}$ *Multiply.*

So, Cheryl gives away $\frac{3}{10}$ of the box of snacks.

- What is $\frac{1}{8} \times \frac{6}{7}$? Simplify the fractions before you multiply. $\frac{3}{28}$

EXAMPLE 4

Find $\frac{8}{9} \times \frac{3}{4}$. Use the GCF to simplify the fractions before you multiply.

$\frac{8}{9} \times \frac{3}{4}$ ← The GCF of 8 and 4 is 4.
← The GCF of 3 and 9 is 3.

$\frac{\overset{2}{\cancel{8}}}{\underset{3}{\cancel{9}}} \times \frac{\overset{1}{\cancel{3}}}{\underset{1}{\cancel{4}}} = \frac{2 \times 1}{3 \times 1} = \frac{2}{3}$ *Divide the numerators and denominators by the GCFs, 3 and 4. Multiply.*

So, $\frac{8}{9} \times \frac{3}{4} = \frac{2}{3}$.

CHECK FOR UNDERSTANDING

Think and ▶ Discuss Look back at the lesson to answer each question.

rectangle into 3 equal parts and shade 1. The 3 parts shaded twice show $\frac{3}{24}$, or $\frac{1}{8}$.

1. **Explain** how to make a model to show $\frac{1}{3} \times \frac{3}{8}$. *Divide a rectangle into 8 equal parts and shade 3. Divide the (see left)*
2. **Tell** how you can rewrite a whole number before you multiply it by a fraction. *write the whole number as a fraction*

Guided ▶ Practice Make a model to find the product. *Check students' models.*

3. $\frac{3}{4} \times \frac{1}{2}$ $\frac{3}{8}$
4. $\frac{1}{3} \times \frac{5}{8}$ $\frac{5}{24}$
5. $\frac{2}{5} \times \frac{1}{2}$ $\frac{2}{10}$, or $\frac{1}{5}$
6. $\frac{1}{3} \times \frac{1}{2}$ $\frac{1}{6}$

Alternative Teaching Strategy

Purpose Students use fraction strips to investigate multiplication of fractions.

Materials *For each group* 3 pages of fraction strips, p. TR18

Provide each group of 4 with simple multiplication problems such as $\frac{1}{2} \times \frac{3}{4}$.

One student should trace 3 of the 4 fourths on the $\frac{1}{4}$-fraction strip.

Then have another student cut out the traced $\frac{3}{4}$ fraction strip and vertically fold it in half.

Finally, have another student match the folded section to an equivalent portion of another fraction strip, in this case showing 8 eighths.

| $\frac{1}{8}$ | $\frac{1}{8}$ | $\frac{1}{8}$ | $\frac{1}{8}$ | $\frac{1}{8}$ | $\frac{1}{8}$ | $\frac{1}{8}$ | $\frac{1}{8}$ |

| $\frac{1}{4}$ | |

The last student should write the problem with the solution: $\frac{1}{2} \times \frac{3}{4} = \frac{3}{8}$.

Students should take turns playing different roles modeling other similar problems.

Check students' work.

Multiply. Write the answer in simplest form.

7. $\frac{3}{4} \times \frac{2}{5}$ $\frac{3}{10}$ 8. $\frac{2}{5} \times \frac{7}{8}$ $\frac{7}{20}$ 9. $2 \times \frac{6}{7}$ $\frac{12}{7}$, or $1\frac{5}{7}$ 10. $\frac{2}{3} \times 16$ $\frac{32}{3}$, or $10\frac{2}{3}$

11. $\frac{2}{3} \times 4$ $\frac{8}{3}$, or $2\frac{2}{3}$ 12. $9 \times \frac{2}{3}$ 6   13. $\frac{5}{6} \times \frac{2}{3}$ $\frac{5}{9}$ 14. $\frac{3}{5} \times \frac{5}{6}$ $\frac{1}{2}$

PRACTICE AND PROBLEM SOLVING

Independent Practice

Make a model to find the product. Check students' models.

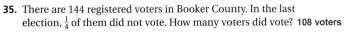
15. $\frac{3}{4} \times \frac{1}{4}$ $\frac{3}{16}$ 16. $\frac{3}{4} \times \frac{2}{3}$ $\frac{6}{12}$ or $\frac{1}{2}$ 17. $\frac{1}{8} \times \frac{1}{2}$ $\frac{1}{16}$ 18. $3 \times \frac{1}{4}$ $\frac{3}{4}$

Multiply. Write the answer in simplest form.

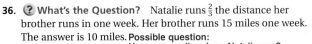
19. $\frac{1}{3} \times \frac{2}{3}$ $\frac{2}{9}$ 20. $\frac{3}{4} \times \frac{1}{3}$ $\frac{1}{4}$ 21. $\frac{1}{5} \times \frac{2}{3}$ $\frac{2}{15}$ 22. $\frac{1}{4} \times \frac{2}{7}$ $\frac{1}{14}$

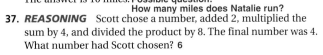
23. $\frac{4}{5} \times \frac{7}{8}$ $\frac{7}{10}$ 24. $\frac{2}{9} \times \frac{3}{4}$ $\frac{1}{6}$ 25. $\frac{1}{8} \times \frac{4}{5}$ $\frac{1}{10}$ 26. $\frac{5}{9} \times \frac{3}{10}$ $\frac{1}{6}$

27. $\frac{4}{9} \times \frac{3}{5}$ $\frac{4}{15}$ 28. $\frac{2}{3} \times 21$ 14   29. $24 \times \frac{1}{12}$ 2   30. $\frac{1}{8} \times 16$ $\frac{2}{1}$, or 2

Compare. Write <, >, or = for ●.

31. $\frac{2}{9} \times \frac{3}{10}$ ● $\frac{2}{9}$ <   32. $\frac{5}{6} \times 5$ ● $\frac{5}{6}$ >   33. $8 \times \frac{1}{9}$ ● 8 <

Problem Solving Applications

34. Sandra takes $\frac{1}{2}$ hr to walk to school. She spends $\frac{1}{2}$ of that time walking down her street. What part of an hour does Sandra spend walking down her street? How many minutes is this? $\frac{1}{4}$ hr; 15 min

35. There are 144 registered voters in Booker County. In the last election, $\frac{1}{4}$ of them did not vote. How many voters did vote? 108 voters

36. (?) What's the Question? Natalie runs $\frac{2}{3}$ the distance her brother runs in one week. Her brother runs 15 miles one week. The answer is 10 miles. **Possible question: How many miles does Natalie run?**

37. *REASONING* Scott chose a number, added 2, multiplied the sum by 4, and divided the product by 8. The final number was 4. What number had Scott chosen? 6

MIXED REVIEW AND TEST PREP

38. $3\frac{2}{3} \times 2\frac{1}{7}$ (p. 206) $7\frac{6}{7}$ 39. Solve. $5b = 60.45$ (p. 82) $b = 12.09$ 40. 267.45×2.8 (p. 70) 748.86

41. **TEST PREP** The manager of a grocery store asks customers in the store on a given day to fill out a card naming their favorite cookie. Which type of sample is this? (p. 98) **A**

   A convenience   B biased   C random   D systematic

42. **TEST PREP** Which shows the GCF for 130 and 75? (p. 150) **H**

   F 3   G 4   H 5   J 6

(Extra Practice) page H41, Set B   205

//// COMMON ERROR ALERT \\\\

When multiplying a whole number by a fraction, some students may multiply the whole number by the denominator as well as by the numerator. Encourage students always to rewrite the whole number as a fraction before multiplying.

Error	Correction
$1 \times \frac{4}{5} = \frac{7 \times 4}{7 \times 5} = \frac{28}{35}$	$\frac{7}{1} \times \frac{4}{5} = \frac{28}{5} = 5\frac{3}{5}$

Guided Practice

Do Check for Understanding Exercises 1–14 with your students. Identify those having difficulty and use lesson resources to help.

Independent Practice

Assign Exercises 15–37.

MIXED REVIEW AND TEST PREP
Exercises 38–42 provide **cumulative review** (Chapters 1–10).

4 | Assess

Summarize the lesson by having students:

DISCUSS Why is the product the same whether you multiply and then simplify or simplify and then multiply? Possible answer: In either case you divide by the same common factors.

WRITE Why does $\frac{3}{4} \times \frac{8}{5} = \frac{3}{1} \times \frac{2}{5}$? The denominator/numerator pair of 4 and 8 are divided by the common factor of 4, resulting in the simplified form.

Lesson Quiz

Transparency
10.2

Multiply. Write the answer in simplest form.

1. $14 \times \frac{5}{7}$ 10   2. $\frac{7}{12} \times \frac{3}{14}$ $\frac{1}{8}$
3. $\frac{6}{7} \times \frac{7}{8}$ $\frac{3}{4}$ 4. $\frac{3}{4} \times \frac{1}{6}$ $\frac{1}{8}$

205

Multiply Mixed Numbers

LESSON PLANNING

Objective To multiply mixed numbers

Intervention for Prerequisite Skills

Write a Fraction as a Mixed Number, Write a Mixed Number as a Fraction (For intervention strategies, see page 199.)

 California Mathematics Content Standards

⊶NS 2.0 Students calculate and solve problems involving addition, subtraction, multiplication, and division.

NS 2.2 Explain the meaning of multiplication and division of positive fractions and perform the calculations.

MR 2.1 Use estimation to verify the reasonableness of calculated results.

(*Also* ⊶NS 1.0, ⊶NS 2.4, NS 2.1, MR 1.3, MR 2.5)

Math Background

The rule for multiplying mixed numbers is the same as that for multiplying fractions, so students must first write each mixed number as a fraction and then apply the rule for multiplying fractions.

Consider the following as you help students understand how to multiply mixed numbers:

- The estimate is important because it provides a check of how reasonable your answer is. If you make a mistake writing a mixed number as a fraction or simplifying the answer, the check may alert you to the error.
- Before you multiply numerators and denominators, apply the GCF process so that the answer will be in simplest form.
- The solution is not complete until the answer is written in simplest form or as a whole or mixed number.

WARM-UP RESOURCES

 NUMBER OF THE DAY

Write your age in years and months as a mixed number. Then express it as a fraction greater than one. Possible answer for 11 yr, 9 mo: $11\frac{3}{4}$, $\frac{47}{4}$

 PROBLEM OF THE DAY

It took André 1 min to fill his aquarium $\frac{1}{3}$ full. How long will it take him to fill the aquarium $\frac{3}{4}$ full? $2\frac{1}{4}$ min

Solution Problem of the Day tab, p. PD10

 DAILY FACTS PRACTICE

Have students practice multiplication facts by completing Set D of *Teacher's Resource Book,* p. TR100.

INTERVENTION AND EXTENSION RESOURCES

ALTERNATIVE TEACHING STRATEGY (ELL)

Materials *For each pair* eight $\frac{1}{2}$-fraction strips, p. TR18

Have students **model multiplication of mixed numbers.** To illustrate $2\frac{1}{2} \times 1\frac{3}{5}$, or $\frac{5}{2} \times \frac{8}{5}$, have students use fraction strips to model $\frac{5}{2}$. Then, ask them to model $\frac{1}{5}$ of $\frac{5}{2}$, which is $\frac{1}{2}$. Finally, have them model 8 of the $\frac{1}{2}$ portions, which is $8 \times \frac{1}{2}$, or 4.

Students can also use fraction strips to model the Example on page 206. Have them compare their modeling to the use of the Distributive Property and the renaming of the mixed number in the example. Check students' work.

VISUAL

CAREER CONNECTION

Present this information and have students **solve the problem below by multiplying by a mixed number.**

A political campaign manager arranges for the press conferences, coffees, dinners, and other campaign appearances the candidate makes. He or she may also help plan the advertising that will be done and be responsible for being sure the necessary local, state, and federal reports are filed.

A campaign manager is paid $28 per hour. She works for $50\frac{3}{4}$ hr one week. How much does she make that week? $1,421

AUDITORY

MIXED REVIEW AND TEST PREP

Cumulative Review Chapters 1–10

Refer to the Pupil Edition pages referenced in the exercises for further review. Have students go to the lesson page, review the lesson, and correct any problem they missed.

Mixed Review and Test Prep, p. 207

How to Help	
Item	**Page**
28	202
29	186
30	160
31	20
32	110

ADVANCED LEARNERS

Challenge students to discover the error in the **use of the Distributive Property.** Tell students that Mai Ling used the Distributive Property to multiply $6\frac{1}{2} \times 5\frac{1}{2}$ and got $30\frac{1}{4}$ as an answer. Challenge them to show whether she is correct. No; $(6 + \frac{1}{2}) \times (5 + \frac{1}{2}) = 6 \times (5 + \frac{1}{2}) + \frac{1}{2} \times (5 + \frac{1}{2}) = (6 \times 5) + (6 \times \frac{1}{2}) + (\frac{1}{2} \times 5) + (\frac{1}{2} \times \frac{1}{2}) = 30 + 3 + 2\frac{1}{2} + \frac{1}{4} = 35\frac{3}{4}$

AUDITORY

TECHNOLOGY LINK

● **Intervention Strategies and Activities CD-ROM** • *Skills 25, 26*

Objective To multiply mixed numbers

1 Introduce

QUICK REVIEW provides review of pre-requisite skills.

Why Learn This? You will be able to find the perimeter of squares and the area of rectangles whose sides are given as mixed numbers. *Share the lesson objective with students.*

2 Teach

Guided Instruction

• *Have students consider the opening problem.*

How is multiplying two mixed numbers like multiplying two fractions? Once the mixed numbers are written as fractions, the process is the same. Divide by the GCFs as needed, multiply the numerators, and multiply the denominators.

• *Guide students to compare the relative values of products and their factors when multiplying fractions and mixed numbers.*

Describe the size of the factors in relation to the product in each of the following: $\frac{1}{2} \times \frac{3}{4} = \frac{3}{8}$, $3 \times \frac{1}{2} = 1\frac{1}{2}$, $1\frac{1}{3} \times 2\frac{1}{4} = 3$. The product of two fractions is less than either factor. The product of a whole number and a fraction is less than the whole number and greater than the fraction. The product of two mixed numbers is greater than either factor.

Algebraic Thinking Point out to students that it is possible to use the Distributive Property to multiply the two mixed numbers from the opening problem.

$$2\frac{1}{2} \times 3\frac{1}{5} = (2 \times 3) + (2 \times \frac{1}{5}) + (\frac{1}{2} \times 3) + (\frac{1}{2} \times \frac{1}{5})$$
$$= 6 + \frac{2}{5} + \frac{3}{2} + \frac{1}{10}$$
$$= 8$$

ADDITIONAL EXAMPLE

Example, p. 206

Multiply. $4 \times 2\frac{7}{9}$

$4 \times 2\frac{7}{9} = (4 \times 2) + (4 \times \frac{7}{9})$
$\qquad = 8 + \frac{28}{9} = 8 + 3\frac{1}{9} = 11\frac{1}{9}$
So, $4 \times 2\frac{7}{9} = 11\frac{1}{9}$

Multiply Mixed Numbers

Learn how to multiply mixed numbers.

QUICK REVIEW

Write the missing numerator.

1. $1\frac{2}{3} = \frac{\blacksquare}{3}$ 5
2. $6\frac{3}{5} = \frac{\blacksquare}{5}$ 33
3. $7\frac{3}{7} = \frac{\blacksquare}{7}$ 52
4. $9\frac{3}{8} = \frac{\blacksquare}{8}$ 75
5. $3\frac{2}{5} = \frac{\blacksquare}{5}$ 17

Remember that you can write a mixed number as a fraction.

$2\frac{3}{4} = \frac{(2 \times 4) + 3}{4}$

$\qquad = \frac{11}{4}$

Ann and Sheri are training for a bicycle race. On one day, Ann rides $3\frac{1}{5}$ mi. Sheri rides $2\frac{1}{2}$ times as far as Ann. How many miles does Sheri ride?

Find $2\frac{1}{2} \times 3\frac{1}{5}$. Estimate. $3 \times 3 = 9$

$2\frac{1}{2} \times 3\frac{1}{5} = \frac{5}{2} \times \frac{16}{5}$ *Write the mixed numbers as fractions.*

$\qquad = \frac{\overset{1}{\cancel{5}}}{\underset{1}{\cancel{2}}} \times \frac{\overset{8}{\cancel{16}}}{\underset{1}{\cancel{5}}}$ *Simplify the fractions. Multiply.*

$\qquad = \frac{8}{1}$, or 8 *Write the answer in simplest form or as a whole or mixed number.*

So, Sheri rides 8 mi. The answer is reasonable since it is close to the estimate of 9 mi.

You can use the Distributive Property to multiply a whole number by a mixed number.

EXAMPLE

Multiply. $5 \times 2\frac{3}{8}$

$5 \times 2\frac{3}{8} = 5 \times (2 + \frac{3}{8})$

$\qquad = (5 \times 2) + (5 \times \frac{3}{8})$ *Use the Distributive Property.*

$\qquad = (5 \times 2) + (\frac{5}{1} \times \frac{3}{8})$ *Write the whole number as a fraction. Find 5×2 and $\frac{5}{1} \times \frac{3}{8}$.*

$\qquad = 10 + \frac{15}{8}$

$\qquad = 10 + 1\frac{7}{8} = 11\frac{7}{8}$ *Write the fraction as a mixed number. Find the sum.*

So, $5 \times 2\frac{3}{8} = 11\frac{7}{8}$.

206

RETEACH 10.3

Multiply Mixed Numbers

Barbara bought $2\frac{1}{4}$ dozen donuts. Her family ate $\frac{2}{3}$ of them. How many dozen did her family eat?

Step 1 What is $\frac{2}{3}$ of $2\frac{1}{4}$? $\frac{2}{3} \times 2\frac{1}{4} = \blacksquare$

Find $\frac{2}{3} \times 2\frac{1}{4}$.

Step 2 Write the mixed number as a fraction. $\frac{2}{3} \times 2\frac{1}{4} = \frac{2}{3} \times \frac{9}{4}$

Step 3 Use the GCF to simplify. $= \frac{\overset{1}{\cancel{2}}}{3} \times \frac{9}{\underset{2}{\cancel{4}}}$
The GCF of 2 and 4 is 2.
The GCF of 3 and 9 is 3. $\frac{\cancel{1}}{\cancel{1}} \qquad \cancel{2}$

Step 4 Multiply. $= \frac{1}{1} \times \frac{3}{2} = \frac{3}{2} = 1\frac{1}{2}$

So, Barbara's family ate $1\frac{1}{2}$ dozen.

Find the product. Write it in simplest form.

1. $\frac{2}{5} \times 1\frac{2}{3}$ $\frac{2}{3}$
2. $4\frac{1}{2} \times 6\frac{2}{3}$ 30
3. $2\frac{1}{2} \times 3\frac{1}{8}$ $6\frac{7}{8}$
4. $\frac{8}{9} \times 3\frac{3}{4}$ $3\frac{1}{3}$
5. $1\frac{3}{5} \times 1\frac{5}{9}$ $2\frac{2}{9}$
6. $2\frac{1}{2} \times 1\frac{3}{7}$ 4
7. $\frac{5}{8} \times 4\frac{4}{5}$ 3
8. $2\frac{3}{4} \times 1\frac{3}{5}$ $4\frac{2}{5}$
9. $1\frac{1}{3} \times 5\frac{3}{4}$ $7\frac{2}{3}$
10. $2\frac{4}{9} \times 1\frac{1}{2}$ $3\frac{2}{3}$
11. $1\frac{5}{8} \times \frac{5}{7}$ $\frac{5}{8}$
12. $3\frac{5}{6} \times 2\frac{1}{4}$ $8\frac{5}{8}$
13. $1\frac{1}{2} \times \frac{9}{10}$ $1\frac{1}{35}$
14. $\frac{4}{7} \times 2\frac{3}{8}$ $1\frac{5}{14}$
15. $\frac{5}{6} \times 4\frac{1}{5}$ 3

PRACTICE 10.3

Multiply Mixed Numbers

Multiply. Write your answer in simplest form.

1. $2\frac{1}{2} \times 1\frac{1}{3}$ $3\frac{1}{3}$
2. $3\frac{1}{5} \times 2\frac{1}{2}$ 8
3. $8\frac{3}{4} \times \frac{2}{5}$ $3\frac{1}{2}$
4. $3\frac{1}{3} \times 1\frac{1}{5}$ 4
5. $3\frac{1}{3} \times 2\frac{2}{5}$ 8
6. $1\frac{3}{4} \times \frac{3}{14}$ $\frac{3}{8}$
7. $4\frac{2}{5} \times \frac{10}{11}$ 4
8. $\frac{6}{7} \times 2\frac{1}{10}$ $1\frac{4}{5}$
9. $3\frac{1}{2} \times 1\frac{1}{4}$ $4\frac{3}{8}$
10. $2\frac{3}{5} \times 1\frac{2}{3}$ $4\frac{1}{3}$
11. $4\frac{3}{8} \times \frac{1}{2}$ $2\frac{3}{16}$
12. $6\frac{1}{5} \times \frac{5}{9}$ $4\frac{4}{9}$
13. $2\frac{1}{4} \times 3\frac{1}{2}$ $7\frac{7}{8}$
14. $9\frac{1}{3} \times 1\frac{2}{7}$ 12
15. $\frac{3}{5} \times 1\frac{2}{3}$ 1
16. $12\frac{1}{3} \times 1\frac{1}{2}$ $18\frac{1}{2}$
17. $1\frac{1}{8} \times \frac{1}{3}$ $\frac{3}{8}$
18. $3\frac{3}{4} \times 1\frac{5}{6}$ $6\frac{7}{8}$
19. $2\frac{2}{3} \times 1\frac{5}{9}$ $3\frac{9}{10}$
20. $5\frac{3}{5} \times 1\frac{2}{7}$ $7\frac{1}{5}$

Use the Distributive Property to multiply.

21. $7 \times 4\frac{1}{6}$ $29\frac{1}{6}$
22. $1\frac{1}{4} \times 8$ 10
23. $5\frac{3}{8} \times 3$ $16\frac{1}{8}$
24. $6 \times 2\frac{4}{5}$ $16\frac{4}{5}$

Compare. Write <, >, or = for ●.

25. $2\frac{1}{2} \times 2\frac{3}{4}$ ● $3\frac{1}{2} \times 4$ <
26. $6\frac{3}{5} \times 3\frac{3}{4}$ ● $3\frac{3}{4} \times 6\frac{3}{5}$ =

Mixed Review

Use the data in the chart for 27–28.

Quiz Scores								
30	27	21	27	25	30	29	19	15
26	27	28	22	25	23	26	18	17

27. Make a stem-and-leaf plot of the data.

28. Use the stem-and-leaf plot to find the median and mode. 25.5; 27

Stem	Leaves
1	5 7 8 9
2	1 2 3 5 5 6 6 7 7 7 8 9
3	0 0

Think and Discuss ▶

Look back at the lesson to answer each question.

1. $3 \times 4\frac{2}{3} = (3 \times 4) +$ $\left(3 \times \frac{2}{3}\right)$; $12 + 2 = 14$.

1. **Show** how to use the Distributive Property to find $3 \times 4\frac{2}{3}$.

2. **Discuss** whether the product of two mixed numbers is greater than or less than the factors. Give two examples.
greater than; Possible example: $4\frac{1}{2} \times 6\frac{1}{3} = 28\frac{1}{2}$, $3\frac{2}{5} \times 5\frac{3}{5} = 20\frac{8}{15}$

Guided ▶ Practice

Multiply. Write your answer in simplest form.

3. $\frac{3}{4} \times 1\frac{1}{2}$ $1\frac{1}{8}$
4. $\frac{1}{2} \times 2\frac{1}{3}$ $1\frac{1}{6}$
5. $1\frac{1}{2} \times 1\frac{1}{2}$ $2\frac{1}{4}$
6. $1\frac{2}{5} \times 2\frac{1}{4}$ $3\frac{3}{20}$

Use the Distributive Property to multiply.

7. $6\frac{1}{8} \times 3$ $18\frac{3}{8}$
8. $3 \times 9\frac{4}{5}$ $29\frac{2}{5}$
9. $1\frac{1}{8} \times 2$ $2\frac{1}{4}$
10. $6 \times 4\frac{1}{4}$ $25\frac{1}{2}$

Independent ▶ Practice

Multiply. Write your answer in simplest form.

11. $4\frac{2}{3} \times 1\frac{3}{4}$ $8\frac{1}{6}$
12. $1\frac{3}{8} \times 4\frac{2}{3}$ $6\frac{5}{12}$
13. $5\frac{1}{2} \times 6$ 33
14. $2 \times 3\frac{1}{7}$ $6\frac{2}{7}$

15. $4\frac{1}{6} \times 3\frac{3}{5}$ 15
16. $1\frac{3}{4} \times 3$ $5\frac{1}{4}$
17. $10\frac{1}{5} \times 8\frac{1}{3}$ 85
18. $5 \times 1\frac{5}{6}$ $9\frac{1}{6}$

Use the Distributive Property to multiply.

19. $3 \times 2\frac{2}{5}$ $7\frac{1}{5}$
20. $4 \times 8\frac{5}{6}$ $35\frac{1}{3}$
21. $3\frac{3}{4} \times 6$ $22\frac{1}{2}$
22. $1\frac{1}{2} \times 12$ 18

Compare. Write $<$, $>$, or $=$ for each ●.

23. $3\frac{1}{3} \times 2\frac{1}{7}$ ● $3\frac{1}{4} \times 5$ $<$
24. $7 \times 7\frac{3}{7}$ ● $6\frac{3}{4} \times 4\frac{4}{5}$ $>$

Problem Solving ▶ Applications

25. Mr. Jackson rides his bicycle $1\frac{2}{3}$ mi every day. His wife rides $1\frac{1}{4}$ times as far as he does. How many miles does Mrs. Jackson ride her bicycle? $2\frac{1}{12}$ mi

26. John works part time for \$6.50 an hour. He works $3\frac{1}{2}$ hr each on Monday, Tuesday, and Thursday afternoons. How much does he earn those three days? **\$68.25**

27. ✎ **Write About It** Without multiplying, tell whether the product of $\frac{2}{3} \times \frac{3}{4}$ is a fraction, a whole number, or a mixed number. **Since both factors are fractions less than 1, the product is a fraction.**

MIXED REVIEW AND TEST PREP

28. $\frac{4}{9} \times \frac{2}{3}$ (p. 202) $\frac{8}{27}$
29. $8\frac{3}{4} - 2\frac{2}{5}$ (p. 186) $6\frac{7}{20}$
30. Simplify. $\frac{27}{45}$ (p. 160) $\frac{3}{5}$
31. $414{,}089 - 62{,}036$ (p. 20) **352,053**

32. **TEST PREP** Which is the mean of the data?
90, 94, 65, 90, 84, 94, 85 (p. 110) **B**
A 29   **B** 86   **C** 90   **D** 94

Extra Practice page H41, Set C

207

PROBLEM SOLVING 10.3

Multiply Mixed Numbers

Write the correct answer.

Analyze Choose Solve Check

1. Rewrite the problem by changing each mixed number to a fraction. Then multiply; write the answer in simplest form.

$$4\frac{2}{3} \times 3\frac{2}{5}$$
$$\frac{14}{3} \times \frac{17}{5}; \ 15\frac{13}{15}$$

2. Rewrite the problem by changing each mixed number to a fraction. Then multiply; write the answer in simplest form.

$$7\frac{1}{4} \times 5\frac{2}{9}$$
$$\frac{29}{4} \times \frac{47}{9}; \ 37\frac{31}{36}$$

3. Peter needs $\frac{1}{2}$ of a cup of butter to make cookies and $\frac{1}{8}$ of a cup of butter to make bread. How much butter in all does Peter need to make cookies and bread?

$\frac{1}{4}$ c

4. Darla needs to exercise $\frac{1}{2}$ hour each day. So far today she has exercised for $\frac{1}{4}$ hour. How much longer does Darla need to exercise today?

$\frac{1}{4}$ hr

Write the letter of the best answer.

5. In the long jump, Bryn's longest jump is $14\frac{1}{8}$ ft. April's best jump is $1\frac{1}{8}$ times as far as Bryn's. What is April's longest jump?

A $13\frac{11}{24}$ ft   **C** $16\frac{1}{8}$ ft
B $15\frac{11}{24}$ ft   **D** $16\frac{1}{2}$ ft

6. Andrew has a collection of 36 baseball cards. Jared has $1\frac{1}{3}$ times as many baseball cards as Andrew. How many baseball cards does Jared have in his collection?

F 38 cards   **H** 66 cards
G 60 cards   **J** 396 cards

7. Derick spent $1\frac{1}{2}$ hours cleaning up after an event. Charles spent $2\frac{1}{4}$ times as many hours as Derick did cleaning up. Which number sentence can be used to find c, the amount of time Charles spent cleaning up?

A $c = 2\frac{1}{4} + 1\frac{1}{2}$ **C** $c = 2\frac{1}{4} + 1\frac{1}{2}$
B $c = 2\frac{1}{4} - 1\frac{1}{2}$ **D** $c = 2\frac{1}{4} \times 1\frac{1}{2}$

8. Sam worked four different jobs last week. On the first job he earned \$28.75, on the second job he earned \$18.03, on the third job he earned \$50, and on the fourth job he earned \$68.93. Which is the best estimate of how much Sam earned last week?

F \$200   **H** \$120
G \$170   **J** \$100

9. **Write About It** When rewriting a mixed number as a fraction, why do you multiply the whole number by the denominator of the fraction?

Possible answer: You need to write the whole number part of the mixed number as a fraction with the same denominator as the fraction part.

CHALLENGE 10.3

Fraction Analogies

Read each analogy. Explain how each pair of numbers are related. The first one is done for you.

1. $2\frac{1}{3}$ is to $3\frac{1}{2}$ as $4\frac{3}{8}$ is to $6\frac{9}{16}$.

Think: What number times $2\frac{1}{3}$ equals $3\frac{1}{2}$?
$3\frac{1}{2}$ is the product of $2\frac{1}{3}$ and $1\frac{1}{2}$, just as $6\frac{9}{16}$ is the product of $4\frac{3}{8}$ and $1\frac{1}{2}$.

2. $1\frac{2}{5}$ is to $2\frac{9}{20}$ as $3\frac{1}{2}$ is to $6\frac{1}{8}$.
$2\frac{9}{20}$ is the product of $1\frac{2}{5}$ and $1\frac{3}{4}$, as $6\frac{1}{8}$ is the product of
$3\frac{1}{2}$ and $1\frac{3}{4}$.

3. $4\frac{3}{8}$ is to $1\frac{3}{32}$ as $5\frac{3}{4}$ is to $1\frac{7}{16}$.
$1\frac{3}{32}$ is the product of $4\frac{3}{8}$ and $\frac{1}{4}$, as $1\frac{7}{16}$ is the product of
$5\frac{3}{4}$ and $\frac{1}{4}$.

4. $3\frac{4}{5}$ is to $9\frac{1}{2}$ as $4\frac{7}{8}$ is to $12\frac{3}{16}$.
$9\frac{1}{2}$ is the product of $3\frac{4}{5}$ and $2\frac{1}{2}$, as $12\frac{3}{16}$ is the product of
$4\frac{7}{8}$ and $2\frac{1}{2}$.

5. $5\frac{1}{3}$ is to $1\frac{1}{15}$ as $6\frac{3}{4}$ is to $1\frac{7}{20}$.
$1\frac{1}{15}$ is the product of $5\frac{1}{3}$ and $\frac{1}{5}$, as $1\frac{7}{20}$ is the product of
$6\frac{3}{4}$ and $\frac{1}{5}$.

6. $9\frac{5}{8}$ is to $11\frac{7}{16}$ as $3\frac{1}{4}$ is to $3\frac{21}{32}$.
$11\frac{7}{16}$ is the product of $9\frac{5}{8}$ and $1\frac{3}{16}$, as $3\frac{21}{32}$ is the product of
$3\frac{1}{4}$ and $1\frac{3}{16}$.

7. $2\frac{1}{12}$ is to $3\frac{5}{9}$ as $4\frac{5}{18}$ is to $6\frac{4}{9}$.
$3\frac{5}{9}$ is the product of $2\frac{5}{12}$ and $1\frac{7}{15}$, as $6\frac{4}{9}$ is the product of
$4\frac{5}{6}$ and $1\frac{1}{3}$.

---

3 | Practice

Guided Practice

Do Check for Understanding Exercises 1–10 with your students. Identify those having difficulty and use lesson resources to help.

Independent Practice

Assign Exercises 11–27.

Encourage students to estimate each product to check for reasonableness after they multiply.

MIXED REVIEW AND TEST PREP
Exercises 28–32 provide **cumulative review** (Chapters 1–10).

4 | Assess

Summarize the lesson by having students:

DISCUSS What steps did you follow to find the answer for Exercise 12? Write the mixed numbers as fractions, $\frac{11}{8}$ and $\frac{14}{3}$. Divide by the GCF, multiply the numerators, and multiply the denominators: $\frac{11}{4} \times \frac{7}{3} = \frac{77}{12}$. Write as a mixed number: $6\frac{5}{12}$.

WRITE Explain how to use the Distributive Property to multiply a whole number and a mixed number.
Possible answer: First multiply the whole number times the whole number part of the mixed number. Then write the whole number as a fraction and multiply that times the fraction part of the mixed number. Find the sum of the two products.

Lesson Quiz

Transparency 10.3

Multiply. Write your answer in simplest form.

1. $3 \times \frac{3}{8}$ $1\frac{1}{8}$
2. $4\frac{1}{3} \times 2\frac{2}{5}$ $10\frac{2}{5}$
3. $5\frac{5}{6} \times 2\frac{1}{4}$ $13\frac{1}{8}$
4. $6 \times 3\frac{1}{3}$ 20

ORGANIZER

Objective To model division of fractions

Vocabulary reciprocal

Materials *For each student* fraction circles, pp. TR19–20

Lesson Resources E-Lab Recording Sheet • *Exploring Division of Fractions*

Intervention for Prerequisite Skills Write a Fraction as a Mixed Number, Write a Mixed Number as a Fraction (For intervention strategies, see page 199.)

Using the Pages

Encourage students to discuss times they have used fractions or division of fractions, such as with crafts and cooking.

Activity 1

Students expect the quotient to be less than the dividend. This thinking must be revised with the division of fractions. The modeling process shows that the quotient is greater than the dividend when dividing a whole number by a fraction.

REASONING **How many $\frac{1}{3}$'s of a circle do you need to make $\frac{1}{6}$?** only $\frac{1}{2}$ of a $\frac{1}{3}$ section

Think and Discuss

As they discuss the meaning of $2 \div \frac{1}{6} = 12$, you may want to have students model the division. Then ask: **How can you use the inverse to write the division sentence as a multiplication sentence?** $12 \times \frac{1}{6} = 2$

Practice

Even though students may know the answers to the first two exercises without modeling, encourage them to model the divisions. This ability will help them solve more complex problems.

Division of Fractions

Explore how to model division of fractions.

You need fraction circles.

QUICK REVIEW

1. $3 \times \frac{1}{3}$ 1   2. $\frac{1}{4} \times 4$ 1   3. $7 \times \frac{3}{2}$ $\frac{21}{2}$

4. $2 \times \frac{8}{12}$ $1\frac{1}{3}$ 5. $\frac{2}{5} \times \frac{5}{2}$ 1

Vocabulary

reciprocal

TECHNOLOGY LINK

More Practice: Use E-Lab, *Exploring Division of Fractions.* www.harcourtschool.com/elab2002

Using models will help you understand division of fractions.

Activity 1

A. Use fraction circles to find $4 \div \frac{1}{3}$, or the number of thirds in 4 wholes.

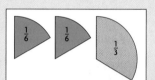

- Trace 4 whole circles on your paper.

- Model $4 \div \frac{1}{3}$ by tracing $\frac{1}{3}$-circle pieces on the 4 circles.

One whole equals three thirds.

- How many thirds are in 4 wholes? What is $4 \div \frac{1}{3}$? **12; 12**

B. Use fraction circles to find $\frac{1}{3} \div \frac{1}{6}$, or the number of sixths in $\frac{1}{3}$.

- Place as many $\frac{1}{6}$ pieces as you can on the $\frac{1}{3}$ piece.

- How many sixths are in $\frac{1}{3}$? What is $\frac{1}{3} \div \frac{1}{6}$? **2; 2**

Think and Discuss

- If $4 \div \frac{1}{3} = 12$, explain what $8 \div \frac{1}{3}$ must be. **24**

- If $2 \div \frac{1}{6} = 12$, explain what $8 \div \frac{1}{6}$ must be. **48**

Practice

Use fraction circles to model each problem. Draw a diagram of your model. Check students' models.

1. $3 \div \frac{1}{3}$ **9**   2. $4 \div \frac{1}{4}$ **16**   3. $\frac{1}{2} \div \frac{1}{8}$ **4**   4. $\frac{3}{4} \div \frac{1}{8}$ **6**

CALIFORNIA STANDARDS ○┐NS 2.0 Students calculate and solve problems involving addition, subtraction, multiplication, and division. NS 2.2 Explain the meaning of multiplication and division of positive fractions and perform the calculations (e.g., $\frac{5}{8} \div \frac{15}{16} = \frac{5}{8} \times \frac{16}{15} = \frac{2}{3}$). *also* ○┐NS 2.1, NS 2.4

ALTERNATIVE TEACHING STRATEGY

Materials *For each group* play money— 5 one-dollar bills, 10 half-dollars, and 20 quarters

Have students **use play money to model division with fractions.** Have students identify what part of a dollar each coin is. Then present problems such as $3 \div \frac{1}{2}$ and $4 \div \frac{1}{4}$. Have volunteers model the divisions with the play money, first showing the amounts with dollars and then using the coins to represent the fractions.

KINESTHETIC

Intervention and Extension Resources

WRITING IN MATHEMATICS

Have students **describe applications of fractions** by writing a description of how a person in one of various occupations would use fractions in his or her work.

Occupations: stockbroker, chef, tailor, dietitian, fitness trainer, musician

Check students' work.

VISUAL

Two numbers are **reciprocals** if their product is 1.

$$\frac{1}{2} \times 2 = 1 \qquad \frac{3}{4} \times \frac{4}{3} = 1 \qquad 6 \times \frac{1}{6} = 1$$

$$\uparrow \quad \uparrow \qquad\qquad \uparrow \quad \uparrow \qquad\qquad \uparrow \quad \uparrow$$

reciprocals $\qquad$ reciprocals $\qquad$ reciprocals

By using inverse operations, you can write related number sentences.

$$1 \div \frac{1}{2} = 2 \qquad 1 \div \frac{3}{4} = \frac{4}{3} \qquad 1 \div 6 = \frac{1}{6}$$

$$1 \div 2 = \frac{1}{2} \qquad 1 \div \frac{4}{3} = \frac{3}{4} \qquad 1 \div \frac{1}{6} = 6$$

You can use reciprocals and inverse operations when you divide.

Activity 2

• Study these problems.

Find $6 \div \frac{1}{2}$.

$1 \div \frac{1}{2} = 2$ *Think of the reciprocal of $\frac{1}{2}$.*

Since $1 \div \frac{1}{2} = 1 \times 2$, $6 \div \frac{1}{2} = 6 \times 2$.

So, $6 \div \frac{1}{2} = 6 \times 2 = 12$.

Find $\frac{3}{4} \div \frac{1}{3}$.

$1 \div \frac{1}{3} = 3$ *Think of the reciprocal of $\frac{1}{3}$.*

Since $1 \div \frac{1}{3} = 1 \times 3$, $\frac{3}{4} \div \frac{1}{3} = \frac{3}{4} \times 3$.

So, $\frac{3}{4} \div \frac{1}{3} = \frac{3}{4} \times 3 = \frac{9}{4}$, or $2\frac{1}{4}$.

Think and Discuss

• When you divide 1 by a number, what is the quotient? **the reciprocal of the number**

• If $1 \div \frac{1}{3} = 3$, then what is $2 \div \frac{1}{3}$? What is $5 \div \frac{1}{3}$? **$2 \times 3 = 6$; $5 \times 3 = 15$**

• If $1 \div \frac{2}{5} = \frac{5}{2}$, then what is $2 \div \frac{2}{5}$? What is $\frac{1}{2} \div \frac{2}{5}$? **$2 \times \frac{5}{2} = 5$; $\frac{1}{2} \times \frac{5}{2} = \frac{5}{4}$, or $1\frac{1}{4}$**

Practice

Find the value of n.

1. If $1 \div \frac{1}{2} = 2$, then $2 \div \frac{1}{2} = n$. **$n = 4$**

2. If $1 \div \frac{4}{5} = \frac{5}{4}$, then $4 \div \frac{4}{5} = n$. **$n = 5$**

3. If $1 \div \frac{2}{3} = \frac{3}{2}$, then $\frac{1}{2} \div \frac{2}{3} = n$. **$n = \frac{3}{4}$**

4. If $1 \div \frac{3}{5} = \frac{5}{3}$, then $\frac{3}{4} \div \frac{3}{5} = n$. **$n = \frac{5}{4}$, or $1\frac{1}{4}$**

Find the quotient.

5. $6 \div \frac{3}{4}$ **8**

6. $4 \div \frac{1}{2}$ **8**

7. $\frac{1}{2} \div \frac{1}{3}$ **$\frac{3}{2}$, or $1\frac{1}{2}$**

8. $\frac{2}{3} \div \frac{1}{8}$ **$\frac{16}{3}$, or $5\frac{1}{3}$**

MIXED REVIEW AND TEST PREP

9. $2\frac{4}{5} \times 3\frac{3}{8}$ (p. 206) **$9\frac{9}{20}$**

10. Complete. $\frac{3}{8} = \frac{\blacksquare}{24}$ (p. 160) **9**

11. Compare 606.64 and 606.074.

Use $<$, $>$, or $=$. (p. 52)   **606.64 > 606.074**

12. $46.08 - 19.204$ (p. 66) **26.876**

13. TEST PREP Which shows $\frac{24}{60}$ in simplest form? (p. 160) **B**

  A $\frac{1}{3}$ **B** $\frac{2}{5}$ **C** $\frac{8}{20}$ **D** $\frac{6}{15}$

209

Activity 2

As students look at the examples of reciprocals before they begin the activity, encourage them to give examples of other reciprocal pairs. They should see that exchanging the numerator and denominator of a fraction forms the fraction's reciprocal.

Direct students' attention to the problems. Discuss with students that the phrases "divided by $\frac{1}{2}$" and "divided into halves" or "divided by 2" sound very much alike and can easily be confused.

Think and Discuss

When discussing the first question, refer students back to the definition of *reciprocal* and to the related number sentences.

Practice

After students complete Exercises 1–4, have them describe the relationship between each n and the quotient given in the *if* part of each statement. Students should conclude that the n is the product of that quotient and the dividend of the *then* part of the problem.

Remind students to rewrite each division as multiplication when completing Exercises 5–8.

MIXED REVIEW AND TEST PREP

Exercises 9–13 provide **cumulative review** (Chapters 1–10).

Oral Assessment

How would you use a model to show $3 \div \frac{1}{6}$? Trace 3 wholes. Then see how many $\frac{1}{6}$ pieces will fit on the 3 wholes.

Dividing by the fraction $\frac{2}{3}$ is the same as multiplying by what fraction? $\frac{3}{2}$

E-LAB RECORDING SHEET

Name _____

Exploring Division of Fractions

1. Two fractions are **equivalent** if they both simplify to the same fraction. Simplify the fractions and see whether they are equivalent. **Both fractions reduce to $\frac{2}{3}$; they are equivalent.**

$\frac{4}{6} = \frac{2}{3}$ $\frac{8}{12} = \frac{2}{3}$

2. Convert $\frac{3}{4}$ to an equivalent fraction with a denominator of 12. $\frac{3}{4} = \frac{9}{12}$

The following example shows one way to divide fractions by using equivalent fractions.

A. First, write both fractions as equivalent fractions that have the same denominator.

$\frac{4}{6} \div \frac{3}{4} = \frac{8}{12} \div \frac{9}{12}$

B. Think of equal parts divided by equal parts.

$\frac{8}{12} \div \frac{9}{12} \rightarrow \frac{8\text{ equal parts}}{9\text{ equal parts}}$

C. Write the quotient.

$\frac{4}{6} \div \frac{3}{4} = \frac{8}{12} \div \frac{9}{12} = \frac{8}{9}$

Use the computer.

Divide by finding equivalent fractions with common denominators. Record each problem and result in the tables below. **Answers will vary.**

3. Original Fractions	Equivalent Fractions	Quotient

4. Original Fractions	Equivalent Fractions	Quotient

5. Original Fractions	Equivalent Fractions	Quotient

6. Original Fractions	Equivalent Fractions	Quotient

You can divide two fractions by writing both as equivalent fractions with common denominators. The quotient is the quotient of the two numerators.

6   E-Lab Recording Sheet

USING E-LAB

Students use a computer model as they develop a new algorithm for division of fractions.

E-Lab Recording Sheets and activities are available on the E-Lab website.

www.harcourtschool.com/elab2002

TECHNOLOGY LINK

Intervention Strategies and Activities CD-ROM • *Skills 25, 26*

E-Lab • *Exploring Division of Fractions*

209

Divide Fractions and Mixed Numbers

LESSON PLANNING

Objective To divide with fractions and mixed numbers

Intervention for Prerequisite Skills

Write a Fraction as a Mixed Number, Write a Mixed Number as a Fraction (For intervention strategies, see page 199.)

 California Mathematics Content Standards

○━ NS 2.0 Students calculate and solve problems involving addition, subtraction, multiplication, and division.

NS 2.2 Explain the meaning of multiplication and division of positive fractions and perform the calculations.

(*Also* ○━ NS 1.0, NS 2.1, ○━ NS 2.4, MR 2.1)

Math Background

The first step in dividing one fraction by another is to rewrite the problem as a multiplication problem in which the divisor is replaced by its reciprocal. As with the rule for multiplication of fractions and of mixed numbers, the rule for division of fractions applies to dividing with mixed numbers.

Consider the following as you help students master the division algorithm for fractions.

- Before applying the division algorithm, both the dividend and the divisor must be written in fraction form.
- The reciprocal of the divisor is formed by exchanging the numerator with the denominator.
- An estimate is especially helpful because it can alert you to a possible error in rewriting the divisor.

WARM-UP RESOURCES

 NUMBER OF THE DAY
Transparency

Take your age and multiply it by $2\frac{1}{2}$. Possible answer: $12 \times 2\frac{1}{2} = 30$

 PROBLEM OF THE DAY
Transparency

A hawk flies $\frac{1}{3}$ mi in 30 sec. How far can the hawk fly in 1 min? How fast does it fly in miles per hour? $\frac{2}{3}$ mi; 40 mph

Solution Problem of the Day tab, p. TR10

 DAILY FACTS PRACTICE

Have students practice division facts by completing Set F of *Teacher's Resource Book,* p. TR100.

ALTERNATIVE TEACHING STRATEGY

Materials *For each pair* 6 index cards

Have students work in pairs to **practice the division algorithm for fractions.** Have each pair choose 3 exercises from Exercises 26–37, page 212, and copy the exercises one to a card. On the remaining 3 cards, have them write the multiplication step showing the divisor's reciprocal.

Have pairs trade their sets of cards. Ask students to work together to match the divisions with the multiplications and then solve the problems. Check students' work.

See also page 212.

VISUAL

MIXED REVIEW AND TEST PREP

Cumulative Review Chapters 1–10

Refer to the Pupil Edition pages referenced in the exercises for further review. Have students go to the lesson page, review the lesson, and correct any problem they missed.

Mixed Review and Test Prep, p. 213

How to Help	
Item	Page
54	206
55	186
56	82
57	20
58	172

ENGLISH LANGUAGE LEARNERS (ELL•SDAIE)

Review with students the steps for **dividing one mixed number by another.** Display the steps below and have students illustrate each step with an example.

- Write the mixed numbers as fractions.
- Use the reciprocal of the divisor to write the problem as a multiplication problem.
- Simplify.
- Multiply.
- Write the answer in simplest form.

Ask volunteers to present their examples to the class.

Check students' work.

AUDITORY

ALGEBRA CONNECTION

Challenge students to **solve mixed number and fraction riddles** using mental math. Call on volunteers to explain their answers.

- What number times $3\frac{1}{2}$ is $10\frac{1}{2}$? 3
- $\frac{3}{4}$ divided by what number is $\frac{15}{16}$? $\frac{4}{5}$
- What number times $\frac{7}{10}$ is 1? $\frac{10}{7}$, or $1\frac{3}{7}$
- $3\frac{1}{3}$ divided by what number is 3? $1\frac{1}{9}$

AUDITORY

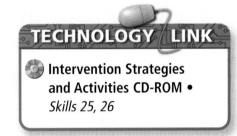

TECHNOLOGY LINK

Intervention Strategies and Activities CD-ROM •
Skills 25, 26

Objective To divide with fractions and mixed numbers

1 Introduce

QUICK REVIEW provides review of pre-requisite skills.

Why Learn This? You can use division of fractions to find out how many half-cup servings are in a container of juice. *Share the lesson objective with students.*

2 Teach

Guided Instruction

• *Direct students' attention to the Math Idea. Ask:*

How does the reciprocal relate to this method? You multiply the reciprocal of the divisor by the dividend.

Review with students the meaning of reciprocal.

What is the product of a number and its reciprocal? 1

• *Work through Example 1. Then display for students a follow-up problem,* $\frac{1}{8} \div \frac{4}{5}$.

For which fraction do you need to write the reciprocal? $\frac{4}{5}$

Algebraic Thinking Using the reciprocal of the divisor to write a multiplication problem provides the opportunity to teach students about inverse operations as they apply to dividing with fractions. Understanding the relationship between inverse operations provides a foundation for understanding the process of solving equations.

ADDITIONAL EXAMPLE

Example 1, p. 210

Find $\frac{7}{8} \div \frac{1}{3}$.

$\frac{7}{8} \div \frac{1}{3} = \frac{7}{8} \times \frac{3}{1}$

$\quad\quad = \frac{21}{8}$, or $2\frac{5}{8}$

So, $\frac{7}{8} \div \frac{1}{3} = 2\frac{5}{8}$.

Divide Fractions and Mixed Numbers

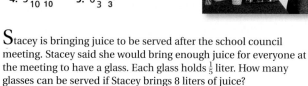

Learn how to divide with fractions and mixed numbers.

QUICK REVIEW

Write each mixed number as a fraction.

1. $2\frac{1}{3}$ $\frac{7}{3}$ 2. $1\frac{3}{8}$ $\frac{11}{8}$ 3. $4\frac{1}{2}$ $\frac{9}{2}$

4. $3\frac{9}{10}$ $\frac{39}{10}$ 5. $6\frac{2}{3}$ $\frac{20}{3}$

Stacey is bringing juice to be served after the school council meeting. Stacey said she would bring enough juice for everyone at the meeting to have a glass. Each glass holds $\frac{1}{5}$ liter. How many glasses can be served if Stacey brings 8 liters of juice?

Find $8 \div \frac{1}{5}$.

Math Idea ▶ When you divide by a fraction, you can use multiplication to find the quotient.

Rewrite the division problem as a multiplication problem by using the reciprocal.

$8 \div \frac{1}{5} = \frac{8}{1} \div \frac{1}{5}$ *Write the whole number as a fraction.*

$\quad\quad = \frac{8}{1} \times \frac{5}{1}$ *Use the reciprocal of the divisor to write a multiplication problem.*

$\quad\quad = \frac{8}{1} \times \frac{5}{1} = \frac{40}{1}$, or 40   *Multiply.*

So, 8 liters can fill 40 glasses.

You can also use the reciprocal of the divisor to divide fractions and mixed numbers.

EXAMPLE 1

Find $\frac{2}{3} \div \frac{4}{7}$.

$\frac{2}{3} \div \frac{4}{7} = \frac{2}{3} \times \frac{7}{4}$ *Use the reciprocal of the divisor to write a multiplication problem.*

$\quad\quad = \frac{\overset{1}{2}}{3} \times \frac{7}{\underset{2}{4}}$ *Divide the numerator and denominator by the GCF, 2.*

$\quad\quad = \frac{7}{6}$, or $1\frac{1}{6}$ *Multiply.*

So, $\frac{2}{3} \div \frac{4}{7} = 1\frac{1}{6}$.

210

RETEACH 10.5

Divide Fractions and Mixed Numbers

Beth is working on a science project. She needs $\frac{2}{3}$-yd pieces of wire for the project. She bought a 6-yd piece of wire at the hardware store. How many $\frac{2}{3}$-yd pieces can she cut from this piece?

Step 1 Write a division sentence to find this amount. $\frac{6}{1} \div \frac{2}{3} = \blacksquare$

Step 2 Use the reciprocal of the divisor to write a multiplication problem. $\frac{6}{1} \div \frac{2}{3} = \frac{6}{1} \times \frac{3}{2}$ **Think:** the reciprocal of $\frac{2}{3}$ is $\frac{3}{2}$.

Step 3 Simplify. $= \frac{\overset{3}{6}}{1} \times \frac{3}{2}$

Step 4 Multiply. $= \frac{3}{1} \times \frac{3}{1} = \frac{9}{1} = 9$

So, Beth can cut 9 pieces of wire.

Find the quotient. Write it in simplest form.

1. $8 \div \frac{3}{4}$ 2. $\frac{5}{9} \div \frac{2}{3}$ 3. $2\frac{4}{5} \div \frac{2}{3}$
   $10\frac{2}{3}$ $\frac{5}{6}$ $4\frac{1}{5}$

4. $2\frac{1}{10} \div \frac{3}{5}$ 5. $12 \div \frac{4}{5}$ 6. $2\frac{5}{8} \div \frac{3}{4}$
   $3\frac{1}{2}$ 15 $3\frac{1}{2}$

7. $4\frac{2}{5} \div 1\frac{2}{3}$ 8. $2\frac{1}{5} \div 1\frac{3}{10}$ 9. $3\frac{2}{7} \div 1\frac{6}{7}$
   $2\frac{16}{25}$ $1\frac{9}{13}$ $1\frac{10}{13}$

10. $5\frac{5}{6} \div 3\frac{1}{3}$ 11. $6\frac{1}{2} \div 2\frac{3}{4}$ 12. $\frac{5}{12} \div \frac{5}{8}$
    $1\frac{3}{4}$ $2\frac{4}{11}$ $\frac{2}{3}$

13. $27 \div \frac{3}{8}$ 14. $\frac{4}{7} \div \frac{1}{2}$ 15. $\frac{5}{8} \div \frac{1}{4}$
    72 $1\frac{1}{7}$ $3\frac{1}{2}$

PRACTICE 10.5

Divide Fractions and Mixed Numbers

Write the reciprocal of the number.

1. $\frac{6}{7}$ 2. $\frac{1}{9}$ 3. 5   4. $\frac{8}{5}$ 5. $3\frac{1}{3}$
   $\frac{7}{6}$ 9 $\frac{1}{5}$ $\frac{5}{8}$ $\frac{3}{10}$

Find the quotient. Write the answer in simplest form.

6. $\frac{4}{5} \div \frac{8}{15}$ 7. $\frac{7}{10} \div \frac{1}{2}$ 8. $\frac{8}{6} \div \frac{2}{3}$ 9. $24 \div \frac{1}{2}$
   $1\frac{1}{2}$ $1\frac{2}{5}$ $1\frac{2}{3}$ 48

10. $9 \div \frac{1}{6}$ 11. $\frac{9}{9} \div \frac{2}{3}$ 12. $\frac{9}{10} \div \frac{2}{5}$ 13. $\frac{9}{20} \div \frac{3}{4}$
    54 $1\frac{5}{6}$ $2\frac{1}{4}$ $\frac{3}{5}$

14. $\frac{5}{8} \div \frac{5}{16}$ 15. $\frac{5}{6} \div \frac{2}{3}$ 16. $\frac{12}{21} \div \frac{4}{7}$ 17. $\frac{5}{8} \div \frac{1}{4}$
    2 $1\frac{1}{4}$ 1 $2\frac{1}{2}$

18. $\frac{3}{4} \div \frac{2}{3}$ 19. $\frac{5}{6} \div \frac{5}{9}$ 20. $\frac{7}{8} \div 12$ 21. $15 \div \frac{5}{9}$
    $1\frac{1}{8}$ $1\frac{1}{2}$ $\frac{7}{96}$ 27

22. $\frac{5}{12} \div \frac{3}{4}$ 23. $\frac{3}{8} \div 18$ 24. $\frac{7}{10} \div 14$ 25. $24 \div \frac{4}{5}$
    $\frac{5}{9}$ $\frac{1}{48}$ $\frac{1}{20}$ 30

Use mental math to find each quotient.

26. $10 \div \frac{1}{4}$ 27. $12 \div \frac{1}{6}$ 28. $3 \div \frac{1}{10}$ 29. $15 \div \frac{1}{2}$
    40 72 30 30

Mixed Review

Find the mean, median, and mode.

30. 8, 10, 12, 11, 8, 9, 10, 10   31. 228, 209, 195, 187, 251
    9.75; 10; 10   214; 209; no mode

Compare. Write <, >, or = for ●.

32. $\frac{4}{5}$ ● $\frac{8}{5}$ 33. $\frac{5}{9}$ ● $\frac{4}{13}$ 34. $\frac{6}{15}$ ● $\frac{2}{5}$ 35. $\frac{6}{7}$ ● $\frac{14}{15}$
    $<$ $>$ $=$ $<$

EXAMPLE 2

Each member of the school council will write his or her name on a strip of paper at the meeting. Jeremy has pieces of paper $5\frac{1}{4}$ in. long. Each strip of paper should be $1\frac{3}{4}$ in. How many strips can Jeremy cut from the length of one piece of paper?

Find $5\frac{1}{4} \div 1\frac{3}{4}$.

Estimate. $5 \div 2 = 2\frac{1}{2}$

$5\frac{1}{4} \div 1\frac{3}{4} = \frac{21}{4} \div \frac{7}{4}$ *Write the mixed numbers as fractions.*

$= \frac{21}{4} \times \frac{4}{7}$ *Use the reciprocal of the divisor to write a multiplication problem.*

$= \frac{\overset{3}{\cancel{21}}}{\underset{1}{\cancel{4}}} \times \frac{\overset{1}{\cancel{4}}}{\underset{1}{\cancel{7}}}$ *Simplify and multiply.*

$= \frac{3}{1}$, or 3

Compare the product to your estimate. 3 is close to the estimate of $2\frac{1}{2}$. The product is reasonable.

So, Jeremy can cut 3 strips from each piece of paper.

- What is $2\frac{3}{4} \div 1\frac{2}{5}$? $1\frac{27}{28}$

Sometimes you can use mental math to divide whole numbers and fractions.

EXAMPLE 3

Use mental math to solve.

A $9 \div \frac{1}{2}$ **THINK:** $9 \times 2 = 18$.   *Dividing by $\frac{1}{2}$ is the same as multiplying by 2.*
So, $9 \div \frac{1}{2} = 18$.   *There are 18 halves in 9.*

B $13 \div \frac{1}{3}$ **THINK:** $13 \times 3 = 39$.   *Dividing by $\frac{1}{3}$ is the same as multiplying by 3.*
So, $13 \div \frac{1}{3} = 39$.   *There are 39 thirds in 13.*

C $20 \div \frac{2}{5}$ **THINK:** $20 \times 5 = 100$.   *Dividing by $\frac{2}{5}$ is the same as multiplying by $\frac{5}{2}$.*
$100 \div 2 = 50$.
So, $20 \div \frac{2}{5} = 50$.

- Use mental math to find $15 \div \frac{1}{6}$. 90

211

- *Have students consider the word problem for Example 2.*

Which mixed number is the dividend and which is the divisor? $5\frac{1}{4}$ is the dividend and $1\frac{3}{4}$ is the divisor.

In the follow-up problem, how would you rewrite the mixed numbers? $2\frac{3}{4}$ as $\frac{11}{4}$, and $1\frac{2}{5}$ as $\frac{7}{5}$

- *Encourage students to explain in their own words the mental math in Example 3.*

How could you describe dividing by a unit fraction in terms of multiplying? Possible answer: Multiply by the denominator of the unit fraction.

REASONING **How could you use mental math to divide 9 by $\frac{3}{2}$?** Think $9 \times 2 = 18$. Then $18 \div 3 = 6$.

Example 2, p. 211

The recipe for Thirst Ender drink requires $1\frac{1}{2}$ cups of sugar for each gallon of water. If you have only 9 cups of sugar, how many gallons of Thirst Ender can you make? 6 gallons

Example 3, p. 211

Use mental math to solve.

A. $12 \div \frac{1}{5}$ Think: $12 \times 5 = 60$.
So, $12 \div \frac{1}{5} = 60$.

B. $7 \div \frac{1}{8}$ Think: $7 \times 8 = 56$.
So, $7 \div \frac{1}{8} = 56$.

C. $12 \div \frac{2}{3}$ Think: $12 \times 3 = 36$.
$36 \div 2 = 18$.
So, $12 \div \frac{2}{3} = 18$.

PROBLEM SOLVING 10.5

Divide Fractions and Mixed Numbers   Analyze Choose Solve Check

Write the correct answer.

1. Write the reciprocal of $\frac{5}{9}$.
$\frac{9}{5}$

2. Write the reciprocal of 15.
$\frac{1}{15}$

3. Bill used $7\frac{1}{8}$ cups of flour to bake a batch of bread. He started with $12\frac{1}{2}$ cups of flour. Does Bill have enough flour to bake another batch of bread? Explain.
No, he has only $5\frac{3}{8}$ c left.

4. Nancy has $19\frac{3}{4}$ feet of wallpaper border. She bought an additional $23\frac{5}{8}$ feet. How much wallpaper border does Nancy have in all?
$43\frac{3}{8}$ ft.

Write the letter of the best answer.

5. Which is a list of all the factors of 26?
   A 1, 2, 3, 9, 13, 26
   B 1, 13, 26
   C 1, 2, 13, 26
   D 26, 52, 78, 104

6. Which is a list of the first four multiples of 5?
   F 1, 5, 10, 15
   G 5, 10, 15, 20
   H 5, 15, 25, 35
   J 10, 20, 30, 40

7. Julie is hanging wallpaper in her house. The job requires $5\frac{1}{4}$ rolls of wallpaper. If she can hang $1\frac{1}{2}$ rolls of wallpaper each hour, how long will it take her to complete the job?
   A $2\frac{1}{4}$ hr   C $3\frac{1}{2}$ hr
   B $3\frac{1}{2}$ hr   D $7\frac{1}{4}$ hr

8. Evan has a board that is 8 feet long. He wants to cut it into pieces that are $\frac{3}{4}$ foot each. Which number sentence can be used to determine p, the number of pieces he will get from the board?
   F $p = 8 + \frac{3}{4}$ H $p = 8 \div \frac{3}{4}$
   G $p = 8 - \frac{3}{4}$ J $p = 8 \times \frac{3}{4}$

9. **Write About It** Explain what a reciprocal is and how to find the reciprocal of a fraction and of a whole number.
Possible answer: A reciprocal is one of two numbers whose product is 1. To find the reciprocal of a fraction, you "flip" the numerator and the denominator. To find the the reciprocal of a whole number, you write the whole number over 1 and then "flip." The reciprocal of $\frac{2}{3}$ is $\frac{3}{2}$. The reciprocal of 3 is $\frac{1}{3}$.

CHALLENGE 10.5

Divide to Find a Message

Match each exercise in Column 1 with its quotient in Column 2. Then write each corresponding letter on the line below marked with the exercise number to discover the Math Tip.

Column 1

1. $\frac{3}{4} \div \frac{1}{2}$ L
2. $6 \div \frac{1}{9}$ Q
3. $\frac{8}{11} \div \frac{1}{3}$ G
4. $10 \div \frac{2}{5}$ A
5. $\frac{11}{12} \div \frac{1}{3}$ N
6. $\frac{1}{10} \div 5$ C
7. $\frac{3}{4} \div \frac{1}{8}$ T
8. $\frac{5}{7} \div 10$ X
9. $\frac{4}{5} \div \frac{2}{10}$ Z
10. $3 \div \frac{2}{9}$ E
11. $8 \div \frac{3}{8}$ V
12. $\frac{7}{8} \div \frac{1}{2}$ B
13. $\frac{1}{2} \div 12$ S

14. $12 \div \frac{1}{6}$ U
15. $\frac{2}{7} \div \frac{1}{8}$ P
16. $18 \div \frac{2}{3}$ J
17. $\frac{3}{20} \div \frac{3}{10}$ I
18. $15 \div \frac{1}{3}$ W
19. $\frac{3}{5} \div \frac{1}{3}$ R
20. $11 \div \frac{1}{2}$ D
21. $\frac{5}{7} \div \frac{10}{14}$ F
22. $\frac{2}{3} \div \frac{8}{9}$ Y
23. $5 \div \frac{1}{15}$ H
24. $\frac{7}{8} \div \frac{1}{4}$ O
25. $10 \div \frac{1}{5}$ K
26. $\frac{5}{8} \div \frac{1}{3}$ M

Column 2

A. 25   N. $2\frac{3}{4}$
B. $1\frac{3}{4}$ O. $3\frac{1}{2}$
C. $\frac{1}{50}$ P. $2\frac{2}{7}$
D. 22   Q. 54
E. $13\frac{1}{2}$ R. $1\frac{4}{5}$
E I   S. $\frac{1}{4}$
G. $2\frac{2}{11}$ T. 6
H. 75   U. 72
L. $\frac{1}{2}$ V. $21\frac{1}{3}$
J. 27   W. 45
K. 50   X. $\frac{1}{14}$
L. $1\frac{1}{2}$ Y. $\frac{3}{4}$
M. $1\frac{7}{8}$ Z. 4

M T   H   E   P   R   O   D   U   C   T
   7   23 10   15 19 24 20 14 6   7

T O   F   A   N   U   M   B   E   R
   24 21   4   5   14 26 12 10 19

H A   N   D   I   T   S
   4   5   20   17 7   13

T R   E   C   I   P   R   O   C   A   L
I 19 10 6   17 15 19 24 6   4   1

P I   S   O   N   E
   17 13   24 5   10

211

LESSON 10.5

3 Practice

/// **COMMON ERROR ALERT** \\\

When dividing two fractions, students may find the reciprocal for the dividend instead of the divisor.

Have students copy the division and then circle the divisor to help them remember for which fraction they need to write the reciprocal.

Error	Correction
$\frac{3}{4} \div \frac{1}{5} = \frac{4}{3} \times \frac{1}{5}$	$\frac{3}{4} \div \boxed{\frac{1}{5}} = \frac{3}{4} \times \frac{5}{1}$

Guided Practice

Do Check for Understanding Exercises 1–15 with your students. Identify those having difficulty and use lesson resources to help.

Independent Practice

Assign Exercises 16–53.

For Exercises 42–47, encourage students to recopy the division, making the substitution before writing the expression as a multiplication expression and evaluating the expression.

CHECK FOR UNDERSTANDING

Think and Discuss ▶ Look back at the lesson to answer each question.

1. **Tell** what the reciprocal of a number is. Give an example. **See left.**

2. **Give** an example of a fraction or mixed-number division problem where the quotient is greater than the dividend. **See left.**

Guided ▶ **Practice**

1. Possible answer: a number that when multiplied by the given number gives a product of 1; $\frac{4}{3}$ is the reciprocal of $\frac{3}{4}$

2. Possible answer: $3\frac{1}{4} \div \frac{3}{4} = 4\frac{1}{3}$ or $\frac{3}{4} \div \frac{1}{3} = 2\frac{1}{4}$

Write the reciprocal of the number.

3. $\frac{2}{3}$ $\frac{3}{2}$ 4. $\frac{3}{4}$ $\frac{4}{3}$ 5. 7 $\frac{1}{7}$ 6. $2\frac{3}{8}$ $\frac{8}{19}$ 7. $4\frac{1}{3}$ $\frac{3}{13}$

Find the quotient. Write the answer in simplest form.

8. $\frac{1}{3} \div \frac{1}{2}$ $\frac{2}{3}$ 9. $\frac{1}{5} \div \frac{1}{4}$ $\frac{4}{5}$ 10. $\frac{1}{4} \div \frac{1}{2}$ $\frac{1}{2}$ 11. $\frac{1}{8} \div 3$ $\frac{1}{24}$

12. $4 \div \frac{2}{3}$ 6 13. $3\frac{3}{5} \div 1\frac{1}{5}$ 3 14. $2\frac{3}{5} \div 4$ $\frac{13}{20}$ 15. $3\frac{1}{4} \div 2\frac{2}{3}$ $1\frac{7}{32}$

PRACTICE AND PROBLEM SOLVING

Independent ▶ **Practice**

Write the reciprocal of the number.

16. $\frac{5}{8}$ $\frac{8}{5}$ 17. $10\frac{1}{10}$ 18. $\frac{1}{6}$ 6 19. $\frac{2}{9}$ $\frac{9}{2}$ 20. $3\frac{1}{2}$ $\frac{2}{7}$

21. $\frac{15}{7}$ $\frac{7}{15}$ 22. $\frac{1}{5}$ 5 23. 9 $\frac{1}{9}$ 24. $1\frac{5}{6}$ $\frac{6}{11}$ 25. $2\frac{3}{5}$ $\frac{5}{13}$

Find the quotient. Write the answer in simplest form.

26. $\frac{3}{8} \div \frac{1}{2}$ $\frac{3}{4}$ 27. $\frac{2}{3} \div \frac{4}{7}$ $1\frac{1}{6}$ 28. $\frac{7}{8} \div \frac{1}{3}$ $2\frac{5}{8}$ 29. $8 \div \frac{6}{7}$ $9\frac{1}{3}$

30. $12 \div \frac{3}{5}$ 20 31. $\frac{3}{4} \div \frac{1}{3}$ $2\frac{1}{4}$ 32. $\frac{4}{9} \div \frac{3}{5}$ $\frac{20}{27}$ 33. $4 \div \frac{4}{5}$ 5

34. $3\frac{2}{5} \div 1\frac{1}{5}$ $2\frac{5}{6}$ 35. $3\frac{4}{5} \div \frac{3}{4}$ $5\frac{1}{15}$ 36. $4\frac{1}{2} \div \frac{1}{4}$ 18 37. $4\frac{1}{5} \div 2\frac{2}{5}$ $1\frac{8}{13}$

Use mental math to find each quotient.

38. $10 \div \frac{1}{2}$ 20 39. $12 \div \frac{2}{3}$ 18 40. $6 \div \frac{1}{4}$ 24 41. $8 \div \frac{1}{4}$ 32

Algebra Evaluate the expression.

42. $4 \div a$ for $a = \frac{2}{3}$ 6 43. $b \div 2\frac{1}{3}$ for $b = 5\frac{1}{2}$ $2\frac{5}{14}$

44. $1\frac{4}{5} \div a$ for $a = 2\frac{3}{5}$ $\frac{9}{13}$ 45. $c \div 7\frac{4}{5}$ for $c = 2\frac{1}{6}$ $\frac{5}{18}$

46. $b \div 7$ for $b = \frac{1}{5}$ $\frac{1}{35}$ 47. $3\frac{1}{5} \div b$ for $b = 4\frac{4}{5}$

212 Chapter 10

Alternative Teaching Strategy

Purpose Students use an activity to reinforce the concept of division of fractions.

Materials large cards or sheets of paper

Write a number of division problems, such as $\frac{1}{2} \div \frac{2}{3}$, $\frac{2}{5} \div 3\frac{1}{2}$, and so on, on large cards, one to a card.

$$\frac{1}{2} \div \frac{2}{3} \qquad \frac{2}{5} \div 3\frac{1}{2}$$

On a second set of cards, write the corresponding multiplication problems, one to a card.

$$\frac{1}{2} \times \frac{3}{2} \qquad \frac{2}{5} \times \frac{2}{7}$$

Hold up the first division problem and ask students what they would do to solve. Encourage them to give answers describing the process rather than solving the division.

Then mix up the division and multiplication cards and distribute them one to a student. Ask students with the division problems to stand around the room and hold up their cards. Then have students with multiplication cards find the corresponding division cards. Have each pair show their cards to the class, and ask for volunteers to simplify and solve. Check students' work.

---

212 Chapter 10

48. The members of the school council were told they could divide the 15 acres of land next to the school into $1\frac{1}{2}$-acre sections to be used for new building projects for the school. How many $1\frac{1}{2}$-acre sections will there be? **10 sections**

49. How many $\frac{1}{4}$-lb turkey burgers can Katie make with 12 lb of ground turkey? **48 burgers**

50. In a $\frac{1}{4}$-mi relay, each runner on a team runs $\frac{1}{16}$ mi. How many runners are in the relay? **4 runners**

51. Gerald has $8\frac{3}{4}$ yd of fabric. This is 7 times the amount he needs to make one costume for the school play. How much fabric does he need for each costume? **$1\frac{1}{4}$ yd**

52 She wrote the reciprocal of the dividend instead of the divisor; $1\frac{1}{2}$

52. ❓ **What's the Error?** Jamie worked the problem below. What mistake did Jamie make? What is the correct answer in simplest form?

$$3\frac{1}{3} \div 2\frac{2}{9} = \frac{10}{3} \div \frac{20}{9} = \frac{3}{10} \times \frac{20}{9} = \frac{2}{3}$$

53. Jacki wants to buy a blouse for $12.95, a T-shirt for $15.95, a book for $10.50, and two pens for $3.75 each. What is the total cost? **$46.90**

MIXED REVIEW AND TEST PREP

54. $3\frac{1}{3} \times 2\frac{2}{5}$ (p. 206) **8**

55. $10\frac{1}{2} + 2\frac{7}{8}$ (p. 186) **$13\frac{3}{8}$**

56. Evaluate $5.2x$ for $x = 3.41$. (p. 82) **17.732**

57. **TEST PREP** Which is the sum for $234{,}607 + 84{,}395$? (p. 20) **D**

   A 218,002   **B** 218,992   **C** 318,902   **D** 319,002

58. **TEST PREP** Which shows $4\frac{3}{8}$ as a fraction? (p. 172) **H**

   F $\frac{11}{8}$ **G** $\frac{15}{8}$ **H** $\frac{35}{8}$ **J** $\frac{39}{8}$

LiNKUP to Careers

Carpenter A carpenter builds and repairs structures. A carpenter can frame a house, put on siding and insulation, put up the rafters and roof, hang doors and windows, and lay floors. Carpenters usually work with wood. They need to measure accurately and work with fractions and mixed numbers when they buy and cut wood for projects.

- Mark is hired to do interior trim work. The molding that he will use comes in 8-ft lengths. He needs strips of wood that are $\frac{5}{6}$ ft long. How many $\frac{5}{6}$ ft pieces can he cut from each 8-ft length? **9 pieces**

Extra Practice page H41, Set D)

213

MIXED REVIEW AND TEST PREP
Exercises 54–58 provide **cumulative review** (Chapters 1–10).

LiNKUP to CAREERS

- *Draw students' attention to the Link Up. Have them tell what they know about the work a carpenter does.*

Why is it important for a carpenter to know fractions? Dimensions are often given in fractions and mixed numbers, and boards must be cut for exact fit. (Even 2-by-4's are actually $1\frac{1}{2}$-in. $\times$ $3\frac{1}{2}$-in.)

REASONING If Mark cuts a total of 101 of the $\frac{5}{6}$ ft. pieces, describe the leftover pieces of wood. **11 pieces that are 6 in. long and 1 piece that is 76 in. long**

4 Assess

Summarize the lesson by having students:

DISCUSS What division expression would you use to solve Exercise 49 and what would be the divisor's reciprocal? $12 \div \frac{1}{4}$; $\frac{4}{1}$, or 4

 WRITE How is a reciprocal used in division of fractions? To divide by a fraction, you multiply by the reciprocal of the divisor.

Lesson Quiz

Write the reciprocal of the number.

1. $\frac{1}{5}$ **5**
2. $\frac{3}{7}$ **$\frac{7}{3}$**
3. $6\frac{1}{3}$ **$\frac{3}{19}$**

Find the quotient. Write the answer in simplest form.

4. $\frac{3}{7} \div \frac{3}{8}$ **$\frac{8}{7}$, or $1\frac{1}{7}$**
5. $3\frac{1}{7} \div \frac{2}{7}$ **11**
6. $9 \div \frac{1}{5}$ **45**

Transparency **10.5**

READING STRATEGY

K-W-L Chart Before having students read the Link Up, have them look at the picture and the title. Ask them to predict what the Link Up will be about. Then have students make a three-column chart headed What I Know, What I Want to Know, and What I Learned. Ask them to fill in the first two columns. Have them fill in the third column as they read through the paragraph.

K-W-L Chart

What I Know	What I Want to Know	What I Learned

ENG-LANG ARTS Standards R 2.4

Problem Solving Skill:
Choose the Operation

LESSON PLANNING

Objective To *choose the operation* to solve a problem

Intervention for Prerequisite Skills

Write a Fraction as a Mixed Number, Write a Mixed Number as a Fraction (For intervention strategies, see page 199.)

Lesson Resources Problem Solving Think Along, p. TR1

California Mathematics Content Standards

○━ NS 2.0 Students calculate and solve problems involving addition, subtraction, multiplication, and division.

MR 3.2 Note the method of deriving the solution and demonstrate a conceptual understanding of the derivation by solving similar problems.

(*Also* NS 2.1, NS 2.2)

Math Background

Choosing the correct operation is a very important skill for students. The following ideas will help them understand this process.

- Not all problems involving several numbers indicate addition. Some numbers may be extraneous to the solution.

- Joining groups of equal sizes implies multiplication, while joining different-sized groups requires addition.

- Modeling the problem may help students determine the operation needed.

- Using whole numbers in place of fractions or decimals may make it easier to select the needed operation.

WARM-UP RESOURCES

NUMBER OF THE DAY

Transparency 10.6

Write a number sentence dividing the number of the day of the month by $\frac{1}{4}$. Possible answer: $5 \div \frac{1}{4} = 20$

PROBLEM OF THE DAY

Transparency 10.6

Maria has $2\frac{1}{2}$ as many trading cards as Roberto, who has $\frac{1}{4}$ as many as Julia. Karen and Tim each have 25, which is 15 fewer than Julia has. Who has the most cards? Julia

Solution Problem of the Day tab, p. PD10

DAILY FACTS PRACTICE

Have students practice multiplication and division facts by completing Set G of *Teacher's Resource Book*, p. TR100.

INTERVENTION AND EXTENSION RESOURCES

ALTERNATIVE TEACHING STRATEGY

To help students **analyze word problems for choosing the operation,** call on a volunteer to read Problem A on page 214. Have students discuss the concepts that indicate addition and multiplication. joining groups of different sizes and joining equal-sized groups

Call on volunteers to change the problem so a different operation would be needed. For example, "How much farther did José drive to Jim's house than to play practice?"

Repeat the activity for Problems B, C, and D.

Check students' work.

VISUAL

READING STRATEGY

Multiple-meaning Words Some words or phrases can have more than one meaning, depending on the surrounding words or sentences. Have students analyze the use of the words *how much* in Problems C and D on page 214 and in Exercises 1 and 2 on page 215. Point out that those words themselves do not indicate an operation. In fact, they suggest different operations, based on the context. Have students make up two problems using the phrase *how much* to indicate two different operations. Check students' work.

 ENG-LANG ARTS Standards R 1.2

ENGLISH LANGUAGE LEARNERS (ELL·SDAIE)

Materials *For each group* poster board

Have students work in small groups to make a poster to **illustrate one of the four operations.** Review the descriptions given on page 214. Have each group choose an operation and make a poster that includes a description of the operation, a word problem that uses the operation, and an illustration. Encourage students to share their posters and display them for the class.

Check students' work.

VISUAL

EARLY FINISHERS

Materials *For each group* 4 index cards

Have students **practice choosing the operation** needed to solve word problems.

- Give each group of students 4 index cards.
- Have them write one operation on each card: add, subtract, multiply, and divide.
- Ask students to take turns drawing a card and then finding a word problem in their textbook whose solution requires that operation.
- Another student verifies that the operation is correct. Check students' work.

VISUAL

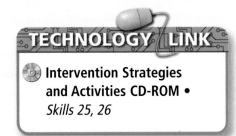

TECHNOLOGY LINK

Intervention Strategies and Activities CD-ROM • *Skills 25, 26*

LESSON **10.6** ORGANIZER

Objective To *choose the operation* to solve a problem

Lesson Resources Problem Solving Think Along, p. TR1

1 Introduce

QUICK REVIEW provides review of pre-requisite skills.

Why Learn This? This skill will be useful in solving a wide variety of real-life problems, such as finding the total number of hours the library is open during a week. *Share the lesson objective with students.*

2 Teach

Guided Instruction

• *Direct students' attention to the four operations outlined on this page.*

Describe a problem situation where you would add. Possible answer: I know how many people are in our class and how many are in another class. I would add to find how many in all.

• *Ask similar questions about the other three operations. Then discuss the examples.*

When would you combine addition and multiplication to solve a problem?
Possible answer: in a 2-step problem when you want to join a variety of equal-sized groups

---

LESSON **10.6**

PROBLEM SOLVING SKILL
Choose the Operation

Analyze
Choose
Solve
Check

Learn how to choose the operation needed to solve a problem.

Use the chart to help you decide how the numbers in a problem are related.

Then choose the operation needed to solve each problem.

ADD	• Joining groups of different sizes
SUBTRACT	• Taking away or comparing groups
MULTIPLY	• Joining equal-sized groups
DIVIDE	• Separating into equal-sized groups • Finding out how many in each group

Read each problem and decide how you would solve it.

A In one week, José drove $3\frac{1}{4}$ mi to play practice, $3\frac{1}{4}$ mi to the hardware store to buy supplies, and $7\frac{4}{5}$ mi to Jim's house to work on the costumes for the play. How many miles did he drive in all?	**B** Carla bought 6 yd of terry cloth to make collars for some of the costumes for the play. Each collar takes $\frac{2}{3}$ yd of fabric. How many collars can Carla make?
C Leanne makes props for the school play. She uses $4\frac{1}{8}$ lb of clay to make each vase and $2\frac{3}{4}$ lb to make each bowl. How much more clay does Leanne use to make one vase than one bowl?	**D** Sean bought $12\frac{2}{3}$ yd of pine lumber for $6 per yd to build some scenery for the school play. How much money did he spend?

A add, or multiply and add
B divide
C subtraction
D multiply

• What operation would you use to solve each problem?

• Which problems could you solve by using a combination of operations? **Problem A; add or multiply and add**

• How did the chart above help you decide which operation to use for each problem? **Answers will vary.**

214 **CALIFORNIA STANDARDS** O—n**NS 2.0** Students calculate and solve problems involving addition, subtraction, multiplication, and division. **MR 3.2** Note the method of deriving the solution and demonstrate a conceptual understanding of the derivation by solving similar problems. *also* **NS 2.1, NS 2.2**

RETEACH 10.6

Problem Solving Skill: Choose the Operation

It is often helpful to think about the kind of answer you need to solve a problem before you decide which operation or operations to use. Here are some different problem types and the operations used to solve them.

• **Add to combine two or more like measures, such as length or weight.**

Lolly put $3\frac{1}{2}$ lb of sugar into a can containing 6 lb of sugar. The total amount of sugar in the can is $3\frac{1}{2} + 6$, or $9\frac{1}{2}$ lb.

• **Subtract to take away an amount or to compare like measures.**

Perry spilled $2\frac{2}{3}$ lb of flour out of a 10-lb bag. The flour remaining in the bag weighs $10 - 2\frac{2}{3}$, or $7\frac{1}{3}$ lb. There is $7\frac{2}{3} - 2\frac{1}{3}$, or $5\frac{1}{3}$ lb more flour in the bag than was spilled.

• **Multiply to combine a number of equal measures or to calculate a new type of measure.**

A square $3\frac{1}{2}$ yd on each side has a perimeter of $4 \times 3\frac{1}{2}$, or 14 yd. The square also has an area of $3\frac{1}{2} \times 3\frac{1}{2}$, or $12\frac{1}{4}$ yd².

• **Divide to determine how many parts of equal size are in a measure or to determine the size of several equal parts.**

A $9\frac{1}{2}$ in. long board is cut into 4 equal lengths. Each piece has a length of $9\frac{1}{2} \div 4$, or $2\frac{3}{8}$ in. If a 6 ft board is cut in $1\frac{1}{2}$ ft lengths, there will be $6 \div 1\frac{1}{2}$, or 4 pieces.

Name the operation you would use to solve the problem. Then solve it.

1. Orange juice comes in 1-gal (128-oz) containers. William uses $12\frac{1}{2}$ oz of orange juice to make his favorite fruit smoothie. How many smoothies should he be able to make from one container of orange juice?

   divide: $128 \div 12\frac{1}{2}$;
   _____
   about 10 smoothies

2. William spills about $3\frac{1}{2}$ oz of liquid each time he makes a smoothie. He makes an average of 44 smoothies each day. How many ounces of liquid would he spill on a typical day?

   multiply: $3\frac{1}{2} \times 44$;
   _____
   about 154 oz

PRACTICE 10.6

Problem Solving Skill: Choose the Operation

Solve. Name the operations used.

1. Marie practiced piano a total of $17\frac{1}{2}$ hr last week. If she practiced the same amount of time each day, how long did she practice daily?

   $2\frac{1}{2}$ hr, division

2. Sylvan withdrew $\frac{2}{5}$ of the amount in his savings account, and spent $\frac{7}{10}$ of that money. What fraction of his total savings does he still have?

   $\frac{18}{25}$, multiplication and subtraction

3. Ike practices guitar $2\frac{1}{3}$ hr per day, but Jenn only practices $\frac{3}{4}$ hr. How much longer does Ike practice?

   $1\frac{3}{4}$ hr, subtraction

4. A painter is going to paint a wall that measures $2\frac{3}{5}$ yd by $4\frac{1}{2}$ yd. What is the area of the wall?

   12 yd², multiplication

5. José gives each of his 15 patio plants $\frac{3}{4}$ qt of water daily in warm weather. How much water does José use on his plants on a warm day?

   $11\frac{1}{4}$ qt, multiplication

6. José waters each of his 15 patio plants with $\frac{1}{2}$ qt water daily in cool weather. How much water can José expect to use on his patio plants during a cool week?

   52.5 qt, multiplication

7. Marisol rode her scooter $1\frac{1}{2}$ mi to Athena's home, then $\frac{3}{4}$ mi to Ariel's home, then $1\frac{1}{4}$ mi back to her home. How far did Marisol ride?

   $3\frac{1}{2}$ mi, addition

8. Bill can polish a car in $2\frac{1}{4}$ hr. Lara and Danny can do the same job working together in $1\frac{1}{2}$ hr. How much faster than Bill can Lara and Danny do the job when working together?

   $1\frac{1}{4}$ hr faster, subtraction

Mixed Review

Write each fraction in simplest form.

9. $\frac{5}{10}$
   $\frac{1}{2}$

10. $\frac{20}{50}$
    $\frac{2}{5}$

11. $\frac{15}{25}$
    $\frac{3}{5}$

12. $\frac{22}{32}$
    $\frac{11}{16}$

13. $\frac{21}{24}$
    $\frac{7}{8}$

Solve. Name the operations used.

1. It takes Karen $5\frac{1}{2}$ minutes to walk to the community center. It takes Jackie $7\frac{1}{3}$ minutes. How much longer does it take Jackie? **$1\frac{5}{6}$ min; subtraction**

2. Rob makes candles that weigh $1\frac{3}{16}$ lb each. How much do 24 of them weigh? **$28\frac{1}{2}$ lb; multiplication**

3. Katie decorates travel bags. Each bag requires $1\frac{1}{3}$ yd of trim around the top and 1 yd of trim on the handle.

   a. Which operations could you use to find how much trim is needed for a number of bags? **B**

   b. How much trim would it take to make 4 bags? **H**

   A subtraction and division
   B addition and multiplication
   C division and multiplication
   D addition and division

   F $8\frac{1}{3}$ yd
   G 8 yd
   H $9\frac{1}{3}$ yd
   J 9 yd

MIXED APPLICATIONS

4. Marcie has 18 oz of dough left in a container. She needs $3\frac{3}{5}$ oz of dough to make one ornament.

   a. Write the expression you would use to find the number of ornaments she can make. Solve the problem. **$18 \div 3\frac{3}{5}$, 5 ornaments**

   b. How many ounces of dough are left in the container if she makes 4 ornaments? **$3\frac{3}{5}$ oz**

Use Data For 5–8, use the map.

5. Darrin hiked the shortest route from the trailhead to Hart Mountain in $7\frac{3}{4}$ hours. What is the average number of miles he hiked in 1 hour? **$2\frac{2}{3}$ mi**

6. How much shorter was the trail that Darrin took than the trail through Warm Springs? **$3\frac{2}{3}$ mi**

7. Elk Meadow is halfway along the trail from the trailhead to Hart Mountain. How far is it from the trailhead to Elk Meadow? **$10\frac{1}{3}$ mi**

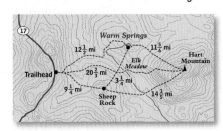

8. Sharlene left the trailhead at 8:30 A.M. for a daylong hike. She returned to the trailhead $7\frac{1}{2}$ hours after she left. What time did she return? **4 P.M.**

9. ✎ **Write About It** Explain how you decide what operation to use when solving a problem.
   Possible answer: I read the problem and see how the numbers are related.

---

3 Practice

Guided Practice

Do Problem Solving Practice Exercises 1–3 with your students. Identify those having difficulty and use lesson resources to help.

Independent Practice

Assign Exercises 4–9.

You may want to have students use fraction circles to model the solution to Exercise 4.

4 Assess

Summarize the lesson by having students:

DISCUSS **What did you do to solve Exercise 5?** Possible answer: I divided the shortest distance by $7\frac{3}{4}$.

 WRITE **Describe two ways to solve Exercise 3b. What property do these two ways illustrate?** Add $1\frac{1}{3}$ and 1 and then multiply by 4, or multiply $1\frac{1}{3}$ by 4 and 1 by 4 and then add; the Distributive Property.

Lesson Quiz

Solve.

Transparency 10.6

1. A recipe for cookies calls for $3\frac{3}{4}$ cups of flour. How much flour would you need for half a recipe? $1\frac{7}{8}$ cups

2. Kayla uses $3\frac{2}{3}$ yd of plaid material and $1\frac{1}{2}$ yd of solid-color material for each outfit she makes. How many yards does it take for 3 outfits? $15\frac{1}{2}$ yd

---

READING STRATEGY 10.6

Multiple-Meaning Words

Analyze Choose Solve Check

Some problems contain words that have more than one meaning. The words may have the same spelling and different pronunciations or the same sound but different meanings. You can use information given in the problem to determine which meaning of the word is being used. Read the following problem.

VOCABULARY
multiple-meaning

The Continental Divide, or Great Divide, is the watershed of North America. This means that it is the high point of land that separates the waters that flow east from those that flow west. The chart below shows precipitation information for the Continental Divide. How much greater is the annual precipitation at the highest elevation than at the lowest elevation?

Elevation	4,000–7,000 ft	7,000–11,000 ft	11,000–14,000 ft
Annual Precipitation	11 in.	20 in.	40 in.

1. Which word has both a mathematical meaning and an everyday meaning? **divide**

2. What operation is needed to solve the problem? **subtraction**

3. Solve the problem. **29 in.**

Read each problem carefully. Then solve.

Mr. Winston is building an addition onto his house. The area of the addition is 150 square feet. The contractor is charging him $200 per square foot. How much will the addition cost?

4. Which word has both a mathematical meaning and an everyday meaning? **addition**

5. What operation is needed to solve the problem? **multiplication**

6. Solve the problem. **$30,000**

Mr. Winston's house is in a suburban area. The original house had an area of 1,750 square feet. When construction is complete, what will be the area of the new house?

7. Which word has both a mathematical meaning and an everyday meaning? **area**

8. What operation is needed to solve the problem? **addition**

9. Solve the problem. **1,900 sq ft**

CHALLENGE 10.6

ABCD Methods

Ann, Badri, Cristina, and Devon measured a redwood deck to determine its area. They made the following sketch to record their measurement.

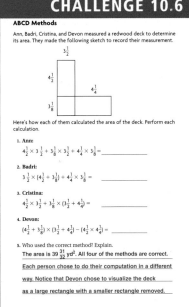

Here's how each of them calculated the area of the deck. Perform each calculation.

1. **Ann:**
   $4\frac{1}{2} \times 3\frac{1}{2} + 3\frac{1}{8} \times 3\frac{1}{2} + 4\frac{1}{4} \times 3\frac{1}{8} =$ _____

2. **Badri:**
   $3\frac{1}{2} \times (4\frac{1}{2} + 3\frac{1}{8}) + 4\frac{1}{4} \times 3\frac{1}{8} =$ _____

3. **Cristina:**
   $4\frac{1}{2} \times 3\frac{1}{2} + 3\frac{1}{8} \times (3\frac{1}{2} + 4\frac{1}{4}) =$ _____

4. **Devon:**
   $(4\frac{1}{2} + 3\frac{1}{8}) \times (3\frac{1}{2} + 4\frac{1}{4}) - (4\frac{1}{2} \times 4\frac{1}{4}) =$ _____

5. Who used the correct method? Explain.
   The area is 39 $\frac{31}{32}$ yd². All four of the methods are correct.
   Each person chose to do their computation in a different
   way. Notice that Devon chose to visualize the deck
   as a large rectangle with a smaller rectangle removed.

Algebra: Fraction Expressions and Equations

LESSON PLANNING

Objective To evaluate expressions with fractions and to solve equations with fractions by using substitution and mental math

Intervention for Prerequisite Skills

Write a Fraction as a Mixed Number, Write a Mixed Number as a Fraction, Equations (For intervention strategies, see page 199.)

California Mathematics Content Standards

AF 1.0 Students write verbal expressions and sentences as algebraic expressions and equations; they evaluate algebraic expressions, solve simple linear equations, and graph and interpret their results.

AF 1.1 Write and solve one-step linear equations in one variable.

(*Also* NS 2.1, NS 2.2)

Math Background

The skills students have learned in evaluating expressions and solving equations with whole numbers and decimals can be used in working with expressions and equations with fractions and mixed numbers.

Consider the following as you help students understand the process of working with fraction expressions and equations:

- Once the variable has been replaced with a number, use the rules for adding, subtracting, multiplying, or dividing fractions and mixed numbers.

- Rewrite a division equation as a multiplication equation before solving.

- To find solutions for addition or subtraction equations, rewrite the fractions with common denominators.

WARM-UP RESOURCES

 NUMBER OF THE DAY *Transparency* **10.7**

Take the number that represents the month of the year. Use it as the numerator in a fraction with a denominator of 8. Multiply the fraction times 4. What is the product? Possible answer: $\frac{3}{8} \times 4 = 1\frac{1}{2}$

 PROBLEM OF THE DAY *Transparency* **10.7**

Ming Li ran 90 ft from first base to second base. Each stride was about $3\frac{1}{2}$ ft long. If she takes about 2 strides per second, about how long did it take her to get to second base? Possible answer: about 13 sec

Solution Problem of the Day tab, p. PD10

 DAILY FACTS PRACTICE

Have students practice multiplication and division facts by completing Set A of *Teacher's Resource Book*, p. TR101.

ALTERNATIVE TEACHING STRATEGY (ELL)

Materials *For each group* 1 index card per student

Have smaller groups of students **work with algebraic expressions**. Have each group member choose a different fraction to write on an index card. Have the groups exchange cards. Give each group an algebraic expression such as $c \div \frac{2}{3} + \frac{3}{4}$. Have the group members work together to evaluate the expression for each of the fractions on the cards. Check students' work.

VISUAL

MIXED REVIEW AND TEST PREP

Cumulative Review Chapters 1–10

Refer to the Pupil Edition pages referenced in the exercises for further review. Have students go to the lesson page, review the lesson, and correct any problem they missed.

Mixed Review and Test Prep, p. 217

How to Help	
Item	Page
26	210
27	166
28	70
29	82
30	70

WRITING IN MATHEMATICS

Explain how you would **solve an equation** as in Exercise 24 on page 217. Possible answer: The product of $3\frac{1}{2}$ and the number of days equals the total weight of the insects, $17\frac{1}{2}$. So, for b days, $3\frac{1}{2} \times b = 17\frac{1}{2}$. To solve, make a table and substitute values for b such as 3, 4, and 5 until one works. Then check the answer by substituting it in the equation.

ADVANCED LEARNERS

Challenge students to **solve equations with mixed numbers and fractions.**

- Ask students to write number sentences involving fractions or mixed numbers. For example, $14\frac{5}{9} - 5\frac{1}{3} = 9\frac{2}{9}$ or $1\frac{1}{2} \div \frac{3}{8} = 4$.
- Have a volunteer present his or her number sentence as an algebraic equation. For example, "If I subtract $5\frac{1}{3}$ from a number, I get $9\frac{2}{9}$."
- The other students then write the equation and solve. $n - 5\frac{1}{3} = 9\frac{2}{9}$; $n = 14\frac{5}{9}$

VISUAL

TECHNOLOGY LINK

Intervention Strategies and Activities CD-ROM • *Skills 25, 26, 41*

Objective To evaluate expressions with fractions and to solve equations with fractions by using substitution and mental math

1 Introduce

QUICK REVIEW provides review of pre-requisite skills.

Why Learn This? Being able to evaluate expressions will help you check the solutions to equations that have fractions and mixed numbers. *Share the lesson objective with students.*

2 Teach

Guided Instruction

• *As you discuss the opening problem and writing an expression, guide students in determining the correct expression.*

If you wanted to find the weight of 2 brochures, how would you do it? Multiply 2 times $\frac{3}{4}$.

How can you use your answer to help find an expression? To find the weight of b brochures, multiply b by $\frac{3}{4}$.

Modifying Instruction For students having difficulty substituting values for variables in expressions or equations, display the expression and write the value on a piece of paper. Place the paper over the variable.

ADDITIONAL EXAMPLE

Example, p. 216

Solve the equation $w \times \frac{1}{3} = 4$ by using mental math.

$w \times \frac{1}{3} = 4$ *Remember that multiplying by $\frac{1}{3}$ is like dividing by 3. What number divided by 3 is 4?*

$w = 12$

$12 \times \frac{1}{3} = 4$ *Check your answer. Replace w with 12.*

$\frac{12}{1} \times \frac{1}{3} = \frac{12}{3}$, or 4

So, $w = 12$.

216   Chapter 10

ALGEBRA
Fraction Expressions and Equations

Learn how to evaluate expressions and solve equations with fractions.

Ann will be mailing some brochures about the different types of plants that eat insects. The price to mail them depends on the total weight. Each brochure weighs $\frac{3}{4}$ ounce. How much do the brochures weigh in all?

Venus's-flytrap is found in the coastal regions of North and South Carolina.

You can write and evaluate an expression. Choose a variable to represent the number of brochures.

Let $b =$ the number of brochures.

$b \times \frac{3}{4}$ or $\frac{3}{4}b$ *Write the expression.*

The number of brochures Ann mails changes every week. What was the total weight of the 23 brochures she mailed last week?

$b \times \frac{3}{4}$ or $\frac{3}{4}b$ *Write the expression.*

$23 \times \frac{3}{4}$ *Replace b with 23.*

$\frac{69}{4}$, or $17\frac{1}{4}$ *Multiply.*

So, the total weight is $17\frac{1}{4}$ oz.

You have solved equations with whole numbers and decimals by using mental math. You can use mental math to solve some equations with fractions.

 EXAMPLE

Solve the equation $n \div \frac{1}{4} = 8$ by using mental math.

$n \div \frac{1}{4} = 8$ *Remember, when dividing by $\frac{1}{4}$, you multiply by the reciprocal, 4.*

$n = 2$ *What number times 4 equals 8?*

$2 \div \frac{1}{4} = 8$ *Check your answer. Replace n with 2.*

$\frac{2}{1} \times \frac{4}{1} = \frac{8}{1}$, or 8   So, $n = 2$.

• Use mental math to solve $x + \frac{2}{3} = \frac{5}{6}$. $x = \frac{1}{6}$

216

CALIFORNIA STANDARDS ○━┑AF 1.1 Write and solve one-step linear equations in one variable. **AF 1.0** Students write verbal expressions and sentences as algebraic expressions and equations; they evaluate algebraic expressions, solve simple linear equations, and graph and interpret their results. *also* **NS 2.1, NS 2.2**

RETEACH 10.7

Algebra: Fraction Expressions and Equations

Algebraic expressions can have fractions in them. Also, fractional values can replace a variable in the expression.
Let's explore the fraction expressions $x + \frac{2}{5}$ and $\frac{3}{4}y$ for several values of the variables x and y.

x	$x + \frac{2}{5}$
$\frac{1}{5}$	$\frac{1}{5} + \frac{2}{5} = \frac{3}{5}$
1	$1 + \frac{2}{5} = 1\frac{2}{5}$
10	$10 + \frac{2}{5} = 10\frac{2}{5}$

y	$\frac{3}{4}y$
$\frac{1}{2}$	$\frac{3}{4} \times \frac{1}{2} = \frac{3}{8}$
2	$\frac{3}{4} \times 2 = 1\frac{1}{2}$
10	$\frac{3}{4} \times 10 = 7\frac{1}{2}$

Notice that the expression $x + \frac{2}{5}$ adds $\frac{2}{5}$ to any value of x, and that the expression $\frac{3}{4}y$ multiplies any value of y by $\frac{3}{4}$.

When solving an equation involving fractions and fractional expressions, often you can use your number sense to decide what value for the variable makes the equation true.
• Solve the equation $x + \frac{2}{5} = \frac{3}{5}$.
Ask yourself: *What number can I add to $\frac{2}{5}$ to get $\frac{3}{5}$?*
You can add $\frac{1}{5}$ to $\frac{2}{5}$ to get $\frac{3}{5}$. So, $x = \frac{1}{5}$.
• Solve the equation $\frac{3}{4}y = \frac{30}{4}$.
Ask yourself: *What can I multiply $\frac{3}{4}$ by to get $\frac{30}{4}$?*
You can multiply $\frac{3}{4}$ by 10 to get $\frac{30}{4}$. So, $y = 10$.

Evaluate the expression.
1. $x + \frac{1}{10}$ for $x = \frac{1}{2}$ $\frac{3}{5}$ 2. $\frac{1}{9}y$ for $y = \frac{4}{9}$ $\frac{1}{18}$ 3. $\frac{1}{3} - z$ for $z = \frac{1}{4}$ $\frac{1}{12}$

Use mental math to solve the equation.
4. $y + \frac{1}{2} = \frac{5}{2}$ $y = 2$ 5. $\frac{1}{10}m = 2$ $m = 20$ 6. $\frac{1}{3}t = 1$ $t = 3$
7. $\frac{1}{4}x = 2$ $x = 8$ 8. $n + \frac{3}{8} = \frac{1}{2}$ $n = \frac{1}{8}$ 9. $w - \frac{3}{10} = \frac{1}{5}$ $w = \frac{1}{2}$
10. $\frac{5}{6} - x = \frac{3}{4}$ $x = \frac{1}{12}$ 11. $t - \frac{1}{3} = 1$ $t = \frac{4}{3}$ 12. $a + \frac{1}{3} = 7$ $a = 6\frac{2}{3}$

PRACTICE 10.7

Algebra: Fraction Expressions and Equations

Evaluate the expression.
1. $2\frac{1}{4} + x$ for $x = 2\frac{1}{8}$ $4\frac{3}{8}$ 2. $2\frac{1}{4} + x$ for $x = \frac{1}{2}$ $2\frac{3}{4}$ 3. $2\frac{1}{4} + x$ for $x = \frac{3}{8}$ $2\frac{5}{8}$
4. $y - 2\frac{2}{5}$ for $y = 5\frac{4}{5}$ $3\frac{1}{5}$ 5. $y - 2\frac{2}{5}$ for $y = 4\frac{7}{10}$ $2\frac{1}{10}$ 6. $y - 2\frac{2}{5}$ for $y = 6$ $3\frac{2}{5}$
7. $\frac{2}{5}s$ for $s = 2$ $1\frac{1}{5}$ 8. $\frac{2}{5}s$ for $s = \frac{1}{3}$ $\frac{1}{5}$ 9. $\frac{3}{5}s$ for $s = 1\frac{3}{4}$ 1
10. $6\frac{2}{7}p$ for $p = \frac{1}{2}$ $3\frac{1}{7}$ 11. $6\frac{2}{7}p$ for $p = \frac{2}{3}$ $14\frac{2}{3}$ 12. $6\frac{2}{7}p$ for $p = 2\frac{5}{8}$ $16\frac{1}{2}$
13. $x + 1\frac{1}{4}$ for $x = 4\frac{1}{4}$ 3   14. $x + 3\frac{1}{4}$ for $x = \frac{1}{4}$ $\frac{1}{13}$ 15. $x + 2\frac{1}{4}$ for $x = 2\frac{1}{8}$ 1

Use mental math to solve the equation.
16. $x + 5\frac{3}{8} = 5\frac{7}{8}$ $x = \frac{1}{8}$ 17. $\frac{1}{6}y = \frac{1}{12}$ $y = \frac{1}{6}$ 18. $z - 8\frac{1}{6} = 12\frac{1}{3}$ $z = 20\frac{5}{6}$ 19. $w + \frac{3}{20} = \frac{5}{9}$ $w = \frac{1}{4}$
20. $\frac{1}{3}n = 3$ $n = 3\frac{3}{4}$ 21. $c + 4\frac{1}{3} = 7\frac{5}{6}$ $c = 3\frac{1}{2}$ 22. $m - 6\frac{1}{4} = 5\frac{7}{8}$ $m = 12\frac{3}{8}$ 23. $\frac{3}{4}d = 9\frac{3}{4}$ $d = 13$

Mixed Review

Add or subtract. Write the answer in simplest form.
24. $\frac{7}{8} - \frac{3}{4}$ $\frac{1}{8}$ 25. $\frac{1}{2} - \frac{1}{12}$ $\frac{5}{12}$ 26. $\frac{1}{3} + \frac{1}{2}$ $\frac{5}{6}$ 27. $\frac{2}{5} + \frac{9}{20}$ $\frac{17}{20}$
28. $\frac{4}{5} - \frac{3}{7}$ $\frac{13}{35}$ 29. $\frac{4}{9} + \frac{3}{10}$ $\frac{67}{90}$ 30. $\frac{7}{10} - \frac{1}{6}$ $\frac{8}{15}$ 31. $\frac{5}{4} + \frac{8}{15}$ $1\frac{19}{20}$
32. $4\frac{1}{2} + 2\frac{1}{4} + 1\frac{1}{8}$ $7\frac{7}{8}$ 33. $4\frac{3}{8} - 2\frac{3}{4}$ $1\frac{5}{8}$

CHECK FOR UNDERSTANDING

Think and ▶
Discuss

Look back at the lesson to answer each question.

1. **What if** Ann mails 32 brochures? Show how you would find the total weight of the brochures. $b \times \frac{3}{4}$; $32 \times \frac{3}{4}$; **24 oz**

2. **Explain** how you would solve the equation $d \div \frac{1}{3} = 9$.
Think: What number times 3 equals 9? $d = 3$

Guided ▶
Practice

Evaluate the expression.

3. $x - 1\frac{1}{5}$ for $x = 3\frac{2}{5}$ **$2\frac{1}{5}$** 4. $\frac{1}{4}y$ for $y = \frac{1}{2}$ **$\frac{1}{8}$** 5. $t + 2\frac{1}{4}$ for $t = 3\frac{3}{8}$ **$5\frac{5}{8}$**

Use mental math to solve the equation.

6. $x - 4\frac{1}{4} = 2\frac{1}{2}$ **$x = 6\frac{3}{4}$** 7. $\frac{2}{3}y = \frac{1}{4}$ **$y = \frac{3}{8}$** 8. $2\frac{5}{8} = t + 1\frac{1}{4}$ **$t = 1\frac{3}{8}$**

PRACTICE AND PROBLEM SOLVING

Independent ▶
Practice

10. $15\frac{5}{12}$ **12.** $9\frac{1}{8}$
16. $1\frac{1}{3}$

24. Possible answer: let b equal the number of days; $3\frac{1}{2}b = 17\frac{1}{2}$; $b = 5$ days

Problem Solving ▶
Applications

Evaluate the expression.

9. $c + 2\frac{2}{3}$ for $c = 5\frac{1}{6}$ **$7\frac{5}{6}$** 10. $4\frac{5}{8}m$ for $m = 3\frac{1}{3}$ 11. $b \div 2\frac{1}{2}$ for $b = 3\frac{1}{8}$ **$1\frac{1}{4}$**

12. $4\frac{5}{8} + a$ for $a = 4\frac{4}{8}$ 13. $b \times \frac{1}{5}$ for $b = \frac{1}{4}$ **$\frac{1}{20}$** 14. $\frac{5}{8} \div c$ for $c = 5$ **$\frac{1}{8}$**

15. $\frac{21}{24} - a$ for $a = \frac{1}{2}$ **$\frac{3}{8}$** 16. $c \div 1\frac{1}{4}$ for $c = 1\frac{2}{3}$ 17. $\frac{1}{3} + \frac{1}{2} + d$ for $d = \frac{1}{6}$ **1**

Use mental math to solve the equation.

18. $x - 3\frac{1}{2} = 2\frac{1}{4}$ **$x = 5\frac{3}{4}$** 19. $\frac{1}{5}x = \frac{2}{5}$ **$x = 2$** 20. $14\frac{2}{3} + x = 28$ **$x = 13\frac{1}{3}$**

21. $8x = 2$ **$x = \frac{1}{4}$** 22. $\frac{2}{3}t = 2$ **$t = 3$** 23. $3\frac{1}{3} + x = 4\frac{2}{3}$ **$x = 1\frac{1}{3}$**

24. Ann's brochures tell about the eating habits of pitcher plants, sundew plants, and Venus's-flytraps. Suppose one type of plant traps about $3\frac{1}{2}$ oz of insects each day. Write and solve an equation to find how many days the plant takes to trap a total of $17\frac{1}{2}$ oz of insects.

Sundew Plant

25. **?** **What's the Error?** Robin evaluated $\frac{3}{4}h$ for $h = \frac{3}{8}$ in this way:
$\frac{3}{4} \times \frac{3}{8} = \frac{6}{8} \times \frac{3}{8} = \frac{9}{8}$. Explain her mistake. **Robin did not multiply the numerators or multiply the denominators to get $\frac{9}{32}$.**

MIXED REVIEW AND TEST PREP

26. $4\frac{5}{8} \div 2\frac{1}{6}$ (p. 210) **$2\frac{7}{52}$**

27. Order from greatest to least. $\frac{3}{4}, \frac{3}{8}, \frac{3}{5}$ (p. 166) **$\frac{3}{4}, \frac{3}{5}, \frac{3}{8}$**

28. 25.95×13.3 (p. 70) **345.135**

29. Solve. $1.5 = \frac{a}{3}$ (p. 82) **$a = 4.5$**

30. **TEST PREP** Which decimal is 10 times as great as 34.62? (p. 70) **D**

A 0.34 **B** 3.4 **C** 3.46 **D** 346.2

Extra Practice page H41, Set E

217

---

3 Practice

Guided Practice

Do Check for Understanding Exercises 1–8 with your students. Identify those having difficulty and use lesson resources to help.

Independent Practice

Assign Exercises 9–25.

As students evaluate the expressions in Exercises 9–17, encourage them to think about how the value of the expressions will relate to the number being substituted.

MIXED REVIEW AND TEST PREP
Exercises 26–30 provide **cumulative review** (Chapters 1–10).

4 Assess

Summarize the lesson by having students:

DISCUSS **What if you decided 32 was the correct answer to the Example on page 216? What would you do to check it?**
Possible answer: Check by substituting 32 into the original equation. When you multiply by 4 and see that it is wrong, rethink your solution.

 WRITE **Explain how you solve an equation such as the one in**
Exercise 18. Possible answer: I think of number families and remember that the sum of the difference and the number subtracted equals the number you subtracted from. I also remember the check procedure for subtraction.

Lesson Quiz
Transparency **10.7**

Evaluate the expression.

1. $\frac{3}{4}x$ for $x = 5\frac{1}{3}$ **4**

2. $2\frac{3}{5} + b$ for $b = 4\frac{7}{15}$ **$7\frac{1}{15}$**

Use mental math to solve the equation.

3. $n + \frac{3}{4} = 1\frac{1}{2}$ **$n = \frac{3}{4}$**

4. $a \div 3 = \frac{1}{5}$ **$a = \frac{3}{5}$**

217

PROBLEM SOLVING 10.7

Algebra: Fraction Expressions and Equations Analyze Choose Solve Check

Write the correct answer.

1. Use GCFs to simplify the factors. Write the new problem.
$\frac{2}{5} \times \frac{5}{9}$
$\frac{2}{1} \times \frac{1}{9}$

2. Use GCFs to simplify the factors. Write the new problem.
$\frac{4}{7} \times \frac{3}{8}$
$\frac{1}{7} \times \frac{3}{2}$

3. A 45-inch-tall rain barrel is filling up with water at a rate of $\frac{3}{4}$ in. per hr. The time it takes to fill can be found by solving the equation $45 = \frac{3}{4}h$ for h. How long will it take the rain barrel to fill?
60 hr

4. Some videotapes are made so that the first $1\frac{1}{3}$ ft of the tape cannot be recorded on. Find how much of a 180-foot videotape can be recorded on by solving the equation $180 = t + 1\frac{1}{3}$ for t.
$178\frac{2}{3}$ ft

Write the letter of the best answer.

5. $x = \frac{3}{5}$ is the solution to which of the following equations?
A $3 = \frac{3}{5}x$
B $3 = 5 + x$
C $\frac{2}{5} = 1 - x$
D $\frac{5}{3} = 3x$

6. What is the value of the expression $\frac{2}{7} - \frac{3}{7}y$ for $y = \frac{3}{7}$?
F $\frac{3}{7}$
G 0
H $\frac{9}{49}$
J $\frac{12}{49}$

7. Carlos rode his skateboard for 48 min each day for the last 25 days. How many hours has Carlos ridden on his skateboard over the last 25 days?
A 20 hr
B 23 hr
C 25 hr
D 1200 hr

8. Brad bought a new basketball for $35.87, including tax. He gave the cashier a $100 bill. How much change did the cashier give back to Brad?
F $75.87
G $64.87
H $64.13
J $35.87

9. **Write About It** How is evaluating expressions involving fractions different from evaluating expressions that do not involve fractions?
Possible answer: You must remember the rules for adding, subtracting, multiplying, and dividing fractions as well as whole numbers.

CHALLENGE 10.7

Expression Maps

In the expression map at the right, it is possible to move from location A to location C in two different ways. One way is to go from location A to location B, and then from location B to location C.

Notice the algebraic expressions along the paths between each pair of locations. Suppose you start with $x = 4$ at location A. From A to B the value is $\frac{3}{4} \times 4 = 3$. Then moving from location B to location C the value is $\frac{7}{4} \times 4 = 7$. From A to B to C = 3 + 7 = 10.

If you start with $x = 4$ at location A and move along the path directly to location C, the value is $\frac{5}{2} \times 4 = 10$. Notice that you get the same result regardless of which way you chose to go from location A to location C.

Start at location A with several other values for x. Verify that both paths result in the same final value.

For 1–3, use expression map P-Q-R at the right.

1. Start at location P with $x = \frac{1}{4}$ and move to location Q. What is the value of the algebraic expression $x + 3\frac{1}{2}$?
$3\frac{3}{4}$

2. What is the value from location Q to location R? What is the value from P to Q to R?
$4\frac{3}{8}; 8\frac{1}{8}$

3. Now start at location P with $x = \frac{1}{4}$ and move directly to location R. What is the value?
$8\frac{1}{8}$

For 4–6, use expression map S-T-U at the right.

4. What value do you get if you start at location S with $x = 3$ and move to location T? $3\frac{1}{6}$

5. What is the value from location T to location U? $5\frac{1}{3}$
What is the value from S to T to U? $8\frac{1}{2}$

6. What value do you get if you start at location S with $x = 3$ and move directly to location U? $8\frac{1}{2}$

217

CHAPTER 10

REVIEW/TEST

Purpose To check understanding of concepts, skills, and problem solving presented in Chapter 10

USING THE PAGE

The Chapter 10 Review/Test can be used as a **review** or a **test**.

- Item 1 checks understanding of concepts and new vocabulary.
- Items 2–35 check skill proficiency.
- Items 36–40 check students' abilities to choose and apply problem solving strategies to real-life problems involving multiplication and division of fractions.

 Suggest that students place the completed Chapter 10 Review/Test in their portfolios.

USING THE ASSESSMENT GUIDE

- Multiple-choice format of Chapter 10 Posttest—See *Assessment Guide*, pp. AG61–62.
- Free-response format of Chapter 10 Posttest—See *Assessment Guide*, pp. AG63–64.

USING STUDENT SELF-ASSESSMENT

The How Did I Do? survey helps students assess what they have learned and how they learned it. This survey is available as a copying master in *Assessment Guide*, p. AGxvii.

CHAPTER 10 REVIEW/TEST

1. VOCABULARY Two numbers are __?__ if their product is 1. (pp. 208–209) **reciprocals**

Estimate each product or quotient. (pp. 200–201) Possible answers are given.

2. $\frac{2}{9} \times \frac{1}{6}$ **0**

3. $\frac{7}{8} \div \frac{11}{12}$ **1**

4. $\frac{7}{15} \div \frac{8}{9}$ $\frac{1}{2}$

5. $2\frac{4}{5} \times 3\frac{3}{10}$ **9**

6. $4\frac{2}{15} \times 5\frac{4}{7}$ **24**

7. $31\frac{3}{8} \div 4\frac{1}{2}$ **8**

Multiply. Write the answer in simplest form. (pp. 202–207)

8. $\frac{1}{6} \times \frac{3}{5}$ $\frac{1}{10}$

9. $\frac{2}{3} \times \frac{4}{7}$ $\frac{8}{21}$

10. $16 \times \frac{5}{12}$ $\frac{20}{3}$, or $6\frac{2}{3}$

11. $\frac{3}{8} \times 10$ $\frac{15}{4}$, or $3\frac{3}{4}$

12. $1\frac{1}{2} \times \frac{3}{4}$ $\frac{9}{8}$, or $1\frac{1}{8}$

13. $4\frac{1}{2} \times 2\frac{1}{3}$ $\frac{21}{2}$, or $10\frac{1}{2}$

14. $1\frac{1}{2} \times \frac{2}{3}$ **1**

15. $2\frac{1}{3} \times 3\frac{1}{7}$ $\frac{22}{3}$, or $7\frac{1}{3}$

Find the quotient. Write it in simplest form. (pp. 210–213)

16. $\frac{6}{7} \div \frac{3}{5}$ $\frac{10}{7}$, or $1\frac{3}{7}$

17. $\frac{3}{4} \div \frac{1}{3}$ $\frac{9}{4}$, or $2\frac{1}{4}$

18. $3\frac{1}{3} \div 2\frac{4}{5}$ $1\frac{14}{21}$

19. $9\frac{1}{2} \div 1\frac{3}{8}$ $6\frac{10}{11}$

20. $8 \div \frac{6}{7}$ $\frac{28}{3}$, or $9\frac{1}{3}$

21. $\frac{4}{5} \div 4$ $\frac{1}{5}$

22. $2\frac{3}{5} \div 4\frac{1}{5}$ $\frac{13}{21}$

23. $\frac{5}{8} \div 10$ $\frac{1}{16}$

Evaluate the expression. (pp. 216–217)

24. $x - 3\frac{1}{3}$ for $x = 6\frac{1}{5}$ $2\frac{13}{15}$

25. $\frac{3}{4} \div r$ for $r = 4$ $\frac{3}{16}$

26. $25\frac{1}{8} + m$ for $m = 6\frac{2}{3}$ $31\frac{19}{24}$

27. $x + 3\frac{1}{10}$ for $x = 1\frac{1}{2}$ $4\frac{3}{5}$

28. $\frac{7}{8} a$ for $a = \frac{2}{5}$ $\frac{7}{20}$

29. $\frac{3}{4} b$ for $b = 1\frac{1}{6}$ $\frac{7}{8}$

Use mental math to solve the equation. (pp. 216–217)

30. $x - 6\frac{1}{9} = 3\frac{2}{3}$ $x = 9\frac{7}{9}$

31. $x \div \frac{1}{3} = 12$ $x = 4$

32. $12\frac{3}{4} + x = 15\frac{7}{8}$ $x = 3\frac{1}{8}$

33. $1\frac{1}{8} b = 4\frac{1}{20}$ $b = 3\frac{3}{5}$

34. $c - \frac{1}{5} = \frac{1}{2}$ $c = \frac{7}{10}$

35. $\frac{3}{7} \div a = \frac{1}{28}$ $a = 12$

Solve.

36. Mike rides his bicycle $6\frac{1}{2}$ min to school. Cami rides her bicycle $1\frac{1}{2}$ times as long. How long does it take Cami to ride to school? (pp. 206–207) $9\frac{3}{4}$ min

37. Eric practiced $\frac{3}{4}$ hr on Monday and $\frac{2}{5}$ hr on Saturday. How much longer did Eric practice on Monday? (pp. 214–215) $\frac{7}{20}$ hr

38. A race course is $\frac{3}{4}$ mi long. Racers want to run three equal sprints. How far apart should the markers be for the sprints? (pp. 210–213) $\frac{1}{4}$ mi

39. Sara has $\frac{5}{6}$ yd of ribbon and Mark has $\frac{3}{4}$ yd of ribbon. How much ribbon do Sara and Mark have altogether? (pp. 214–215) $\frac{19}{12}$ yd, or $1\frac{7}{12}$ yd

40. The sum of Kiesha's and Brent's heights is $127\frac{1}{4}$ in. Kiesha's height is $64\frac{1}{2}$ in. Write an equation to find Brent's height. (pp. 216–217) $64\frac{1}{2} + a = 127\frac{1}{4}$; $62\frac{3}{4}$ in.

218 Chapter 10

CHAPTER 10 TEST, page 1

Choose the best answer.

For 1–4, estimate the product or quotient.

1. $1\frac{3}{4} \times 4\frac{1}{3}$
A 10   C 6
B 8   D 4

2. $11\frac{2}{3} \times 8\frac{1}{8}$
F 1,200   **H 96**
G 120   J 88

3. $10\frac{1}{7} \div 1\frac{5}{6}$
A 2   C 10
B 5   D 20

4. $\frac{7}{8} + \frac{12}{13}$
F 4   H 2
G 3   **J 1**

For 5–16, find the product or quotient in simplest form.

5. $\frac{3}{5} \times \frac{1}{2}$
A $\frac{3}{10}$ C $\frac{3}{7}$
B $\frac{4}{10}$ D $1\frac{1}{5}$

6. $\frac{3}{9} \times \frac{2}{9}$
F $\frac{6}{17}$ H $\frac{6}{63}$
G $\frac{5}{17}$ **J $\frac{1}{12}$**

7. $15 \times \frac{1}{3}$
A $\frac{16}{3}$ C $\frac{45}{3}$
B 5   D 45

8. $\frac{3}{4} \times 2\frac{1}{2}$
F $\frac{3}{10}$ **H $1\frac{7}{8}$**
G $1\frac{1}{3}$ J $3\frac{3}{4}$

9. $1\frac{4}{5} \times 2\frac{2}{3}$
A $2\frac{4}{15}$ **C $3\frac{11}{15}$**
B $2\frac{1}{2}$ D $4\frac{1}{2}$

10. $4\frac{1}{6} \times 5\frac{3}{5}$
F $20\frac{1}{10}$ H $22\frac{7}{30}$
G $20\frac{4}{11}$ **J $23\frac{1}{3}$**

11. $8 \div \frac{1}{2}$
A 4   **C 16**
B 10   D 24

12. $\frac{2}{5} \div \frac{8}{15}$
F $\frac{3}{4}$ H $\frac{1}{2}$
G $\frac{30}{40}$ J $\frac{16}{75}$

13. $\frac{4}{5} \div \frac{1}{4}$
A $\frac{1}{5}$ **C $3\frac{1}{5}$**
B $\frac{5}{16}$ D 5

Go On

CHAPTER 10 TEST, page 2

14. $2\frac{1}{4} \div 1\frac{2}{3}$
F $1\frac{7}{20}$ H $3\frac{3}{4}$
G $2\frac{3}{8}$ J $3\frac{11}{12}$

15. $5 \div 3\frac{1}{2}$
A $17\frac{1}{2}$ C $3\frac{5}{7}$
B $8\frac{1}{2}$ **D $1\frac{3}{7}$**

16. $2\frac{3}{4} \div 1\frac{1}{4}$
F $1\frac{1}{4}$ H $3\frac{7}{16}$
G $2\frac{1}{5}$ J 4

17. Over a 5-day period, it took Ed $8\frac{3}{4}$ hr to read a book. He read for the same amount of time each day. How many hours did he read each day?
A $8\frac{3}{4}$ hr   C $1\frac{3}{4}$ hr
B $1\frac{3}{4}$ hr   D $\frac{3}{4}$ hr

18. Solve.
$30m = 3$
F $m = \frac{1}{10}$ H $m = 10$
G $m = \frac{1}{3}$ J $m = 90$

19. Jane drank $\frac{1}{4}$ of a carton of milk. Cliff drank $\frac{3}{8}$ of the carton. What fraction of the carton did they drink?
A $\frac{1}{24}$ carton   C $\frac{15}{24}$ carton
B $\frac{1}{2}$ carton   **D $\frac{17}{24}$ carton**

20. Felix grew $1\frac{1}{2}$ in. last year. This year he has grown $\frac{3}{4}$ as much as last year. How much has he grown this year?
F $2\frac{1}{4}$ in.   H $\frac{3}{4}$ in.
G $1\frac{1}{8}$ in.   J $\frac{1}{4}$ in.

21. Evaluate $30 \times g$ for $g = 1\frac{2}{9}$.
A $36\frac{2}{3}$ C $30\frac{9}{9}$
B $31\frac{6}{9}$ D $24\frac{6}{11}$

22. Solve.
$r \div \frac{1}{5} = 15$
F $r = 75$ H $r = \frac{3}{5}$
G $r = 3$ J $r = \frac{1}{3}$

23. Hai completed his science project in $3\frac{1}{4}$ hr. Mai-Ling took $2\frac{1}{3}$ hr. How much longer did it take Hai?
A $\frac{7}{12}$ hr   C $6\frac{1}{12}$ hr
B $1\frac{5}{7}$ hr   D $9\frac{1}{6}$ hr

24. It takes $1\frac{3}{4}$ cups of flour to make a cake. How many cups of flour does it take to make 3 cakes?
F $\frac{7}{12}$ c   H $4\frac{3}{4}$ c
G $1\frac{1}{4}$ c   **J $5\frac{1}{4}$ c**

25. Evaluate $x \div 4\frac{1}{2}$ for $x = \frac{4}{5}$.
A 5   **C $\frac{4}{21}$**
B $3\frac{3}{5}$ D $\frac{20}{120}$

Stop

Understand the problem.
See item **3**.

You know that this week's playing time is $\frac{2}{3}$ of last week's playing time. Use a *variable* to write any relationship like this one as an equation.
Also see problem **1**, p. H62.

Choose the best answer.

1. Carla rode her bicycle $1\frac{2}{5}$ miles on Monday, $2\frac{1}{4}$ miles on Wednesday, and $\frac{4}{5}$ mile on Friday. Which is a reasonable estimate of the total distance Carla rode her bicycle? **B**

   A 3 mi   C $5\frac{1}{2}$ mi

   B $4\frac{1}{2}$ mi   D $6\frac{1}{2}$ mi

2. Dan has $6\frac{2}{3}$ yards of cloth. He uses $\frac{5}{6}$ yard in each banner he makes. How many banners can Dan make from the cloth? **G**

   F 4   H 11

   G 8   J Not here

3. Vince is trying to decrease the amount of time he spends playing video games. This week he spent $5\frac{2}{3}$ hours playing video games. That was $\frac{2}{3}$ of the amount of time he played video games last week. How long did Vince play video games last week? **D**

   A $4\frac{1}{2}$ hr   C 7 hr

   B $6\frac{1}{3}$ hr   D $8\frac{1}{2}$ hr

4. Eva ordered $2\frac{1}{2}$ pounds of potato salad, $2\frac{3}{4}$ pounds of fruit salad, and $1\frac{5}{8}$ pounds of cole slaw. Which operation would be best to use to find out how much more fruit salad she ordered than coleslaw? **H**

   F addition

   G multiplication

   H subtraction

   J division

5. Which expression can be used to find $\frac{3}{5} \div \frac{1}{3}$? **C**

   A $\frac{3}{5} + \frac{1}{3}$

   B $\frac{3}{5} - \frac{1}{3}$

   C $\frac{3}{5} \times \frac{3}{1}$

   D $\frac{5}{3} \times \frac{1}{3}$

6. There are 397 students in the sixth grade at East Side School. During the first week of school, about $\frac{1}{5}$ of the sixth-grade students tried out for the band. About how many students tried out? **G**

   F 70   H 90

   G 80   J 100

7. Which is a reasonable estimate for $21\frac{4}{5} \div 3$? **D**

   A 3   C 5

   B 4   D 7

8. Solve.
   $$b - 4\frac{1}{2} = 2\frac{2}{3} \quad \textbf{J}$$

   F $b = 1\frac{5}{6}$ H $b = 6\frac{5}{6}$

   G $b = 6\frac{3}{5}$ J $b = 7\frac{1}{6}$

9. Cal has 4 bags of apples with masses of 2.5 kilograms, 2.05 kilograms, 3.12 kilograms, and 2.18 kilograms. Which shows the masses in order from lightest to heaviest? **A**

   A 2.05, 2.18, 2.5, 3.12

   B 2.5, 2.18, 3.12, 2.05

   C 3.12, 2.5, 2.18, 2.05

   D 2.18, 2.5, 2.05, 3.12

10. The sum of the prime factors of 12 is 7. What is the sum of the prime factors of 72? **F**

    F 12   H 42

    G 27   J Not here

219

CUMULATIVE REVIEW •
Chapters 1–10

USING THE PAGE

This page may be used to help students get ready for standardized tests. The test items are written in the same style and arranged in the same format as those on many state assessments. The page is cumulative. It covers math objectives and essential skills that have been taught up to this point in the text. Most of the items represent skills from the current chapter, and the remainder represent skills from earlier chapters.

This page can be assigned at the end of the chapter as classwork or as a homework assignment. You may want to have students use individual recording sheets presented in a multiple-choice (standardized) format. A Test Answer Sheet is available as a blackline master in *Assessment Guide* (p. AGxlii).

You may wish to have students describe how they solved each problem and share their solutions.

MATH DETECTIVE
On a Roll

Purpose To use deductive reasoning to solve problems involving fractions

USING THE PAGE

- *Direct students' attention to the Reasoning section. Have students read through each of the Fraction Mystery clues before they complete the mystery fractions. Ask them to solve Fraction Mystery 1.*

- **How did you pick the numbers to write the pair of equivalent fractions for Fraction Mystery 1?** Answers will vary.

- *Have students read the clue for Fraction Mystery 2.*

  When is a fraction greater than 1? when the numerator is greater than the denominator

- *After students solve Fraction Mysteries 3 and 4, have them explain their thinking.*

  How did you find a fraction to solve Fraction Mystery 3? Answers will vary.

  Were you able to solve both Fraction Mysteries 3 and 4 using the numbers you rolled? Explain. Answers will vary.

  If you were not able to complete Fraction Mysteries 3 and/or 4, could you complete them using numbers that you used in Fraction Mysteries 1 and 2? Explain. Answers will vary.

  Think It Over! After students complete the Write About It, have them compare the numbers they rolled and their solutions to the Fraction Mystery numbers.

MATH DETECTIVE

On a Roll

REASONING Roll a number cube ten times. Record the numbers that you roll. Use your knowledge of fractions to attempt to solve the problems below. You may use each of your ten numbers exactly once. Once you use a number, cross it out so that you don't use it again. Depending on which numbers you roll, you may or may not be able to solve all four mysteries.
Check students' solutions.

Fraction Mystery 1
Write a pair of equivalent fractions.

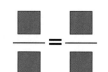

Fraction Mystery 2
Write a fraction with a value greater than 1.

Fraction Mystery 3
Write a fraction with a value greater than $\frac{1}{2}$ and less than 1.

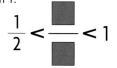

Fraction Mystery 4
Write a fraction that is not in simplest form.

Think It Over!

Using just 2's and 6's, you can't write a fraction with a value greater than $\frac{1}{2}$ and less than 1 (Mystery 3).

- **Write About It** Salvador rolled all 2's and 6's. Explain why he couldn't solve all four mysteries.

- **Stretch Your Thinking** Write a set of ten numbers with which you could solve only two of the mysteries. Possible answer: 1, 1, 1, 1, 1, 3, 3, 3, 3, 3. Neither Mystery 3 nor Mystery 4 can be solved using these numbers.

Intervention and Extension Resources

SPECIAL NEEDS

MATERIALS *For each pair* index cards

Have students **use index cards to model fractions.** Working in pairs, students should record each number they roll on a separate index card. Then have them use the index cards to make and stack fractions.

Have pairs use the index cards to model several different fractions. Then allow them to use their cards more than once to find each Fraction Mystery number. Finally ask pairs to find each Fraction Mystery number using each index card only once.
Check students' work.
KINESTHETIC

Mixed Numbers and Time

Learn how to write times as mixed numbers, and how to add and subtract times.

The ticket agent at the airport told Mario that his flight from Portland, OR, to St. Paul, MN, would take "about $4\frac{1}{2}$ hours." The agent expressed the time as a mixed number.

To write a time as a mixed number, use the fact that there are 60 minutes in 1 hour.

EXAMPLE 1

Mario's flight from Portland to St. Paul took 4 hours 24 minutes. Write the time as a mixed number.

$24 \text{ min} = 24 \times \frac{1}{60} \text{ hr} = \frac{24}{60} \text{ hr}$ *Think: 60 min = 1 hr. So, $1 \text{ min} = \frac{1}{60} \text{ hr}$.*

$= \frac{2}{5} \text{ hr}$ *Write the fraction in simplest form.*

$4 \text{ hr } 24 \text{ min} = 4\frac{2}{5} \text{ hr}$ *Write the time.*

So, Mario's flight took $4\frac{2}{5}$ hr.

To add or subtract times, use the same methods you use to add or subtract mixed numbers.

EXAMPLE 2

Solve.

A.
$$\begin{array}{r} 2 \text{ hr } 18 \text{ min} \\ + 3 \text{ hr } 52 \text{ min} \\ \hline 5 \text{ hr } 70 \text{ min} \end{array}$$

$= 5 \text{ hr} + (60 + 10) \text{ min}$
$= 5 \text{ hr} + 1 \text{ hr} + \frac{10}{60} \text{ hr}$
$= 6 \text{ hr} + \frac{1}{6} \text{ hr}$
$= 6\frac{1}{6} \text{ hr}$

B.
$$\begin{array}{rcl} 8 \text{ hr } 14 \text{ min} & \rightarrow & 7 \text{ hr } (60 + 14) \text{ min} \\ -3 \text{ hr } 20 \text{ min} & \rightarrow & -3 \text{ hr } 20 \text{ min} \end{array}$$

$$\begin{array}{r} 7 \text{ hr } 74 \text{ min} \\ -3 \text{ hr } 20 \text{ min} \\ \hline 4 \text{ hr } 54 \text{ min} \end{array}$$

$= 4 \text{ hr} + \frac{54}{60} \text{ hr}$
$= 4\frac{9}{10} \text{ hr}$

TALK ABOUT IT

- Tell how you would write the time 7 hours 35 minutes as a mixed number. Write 35 minutes as $\frac{35}{60}$, simplify the fraction, and then add it to 7 to get $7\frac{7}{12}$ hr.

TRY IT

Write as a mixed number.

1. 1 hr 30 min $1\frac{1}{2}$ hr   **2.** 4 hr 55 min $4\frac{11}{12}$ hr   **3.** 1 hr 19 min $1\frac{19}{60}$ hr

4. 28 min $\frac{7}{15}$ hr   **5.** 45 min $\frac{3}{4}$ hr   **6.** 3 hr 42 min $3\frac{7}{10}$ hr

Solve. Write as a mixed number.

7. 5 hr 12 min + 8 hr 18 min $13\frac{1}{2}$ hr   **8.** 6 hr 10 min − 4 hr 20 min $1\frac{5}{6}$ hr

221

Intervention and Extension Resources

EARLY FINISHERS

Have students **extend their understanding of mixed numbers and time**. Ask them to make a list of common fractional times with which they are familiar, including $\frac{1}{2}$, $\frac{1}{3}$, $\frac{1}{4}$, $\frac{1}{5}$, and $\frac{1}{6}$ of an hour, and multiples of the fractional times. Then have them write the number of minutes that correspond to each fractional unit of time.
Check students' work. Answers should include the following (and appropriate multiples): $\frac{1}{2}$ hr = 30 min, $\frac{1}{3}$ hr = 20 min, $\frac{1}{4}$ hr = 15 min, $\frac{1}{5}$ hr = 12 min, $\frac{1}{6}$ hr = 10 min.

CHALLENGE
Mixed Numbers and Time

Objective To extend the concepts and skills of Chapters 7–10

USING THE PAGE

- *Have a volunteer read the introduction. Then direct students' attention to Example 1.*

  What fraction that relates the number of minutes in an hour is equivalent to 1 hour? $\frac{60 \text{ min}}{60 \text{ min}} = 1$ hr

  If Mario's flight took 4 hours 12 minutes, how would you write the time as a mixed number? $4\frac{1}{5}$ hr

- *After students have read Example 2, ask:*

  Why do you rename 70 minutes in the first example? 70 minutes is greater than 1 hour, and you want to write the answer in simplest form.

  Explain how to rename to subtract in the second example. 14 is less than 20, so you cannot subtract the minutes. Since 1 hr = 60 min, you must change 8 hr 14 min to 7 hr 74 min.

- *Have students complete the Talk About It and then extend their thinking.*

  Reasoning If you wanted to add 15 minutes to $7\frac{7}{12}$ hr, explain how you would find the sum as a mixed number. Possible answer: 15 min = $\frac{1}{4}$ hr, so add $7\frac{7}{12} + \frac{1}{4} = 7\frac{7}{12} + \frac{3}{12} = 7\frac{10}{12} = 7\frac{5}{6}$ hr

Try It Before assigning Try It Exercises 1–6, remind students that when they write time as a mixed number, the minutes are expressed as a fraction of an hour. So, the units of time for each of Exercises 1–6 will be expressed as hours.

Have students write Exercises 7–8 in vertical form to solve. Remind students to write these answers as mixed numbers.

STUDY GUIDE AND REVIEW

Purpose To help students review concepts and skills presented in Chapters 7–10

USING THE PAGES

✔ Assessment Checkpoint

The Study Guide and Review includes content from Chapters 7–10.

The blue page numbers in parentheses provided with each group of exercises indicate the pages on which the concept or skill was presented. The red number given with each group of exercises identifies the Learning Goal for the concept or skill.

VOCABULARY

1. The largest of the common factors of two numbers is the __?__ . (p. 151) **greatest common factor**
2. To add unlike fractions, you can write equivalent fractions by using the __?__ . (p. 182) **least common denominator**

EXAMPLES	EXERCISES

Chapter 7

• **Write the prime factorization of a number.** (pp. 148–149) **7B**

Find the prime factorization of 150.

$$150$$
$$15 \times 10$$
$$3 \times 5 \times 2 \times 5$$

$$2 \times 3 \times 5^2$$

Write the prime factorization of each number in exponent form.

3. 52 $2^2 \times 13$
4. 125 5^3
5. 180 $2^2 \times 3^2 \times 5$
6. 27 3^3
7. 100 $2^2 \times 5^2$
8. 72 $2^3 \times 3^2$

• **Find the GCF and LCM of two or more numbers.** (pp. 150–153) **7C**

Find the LCM of 9 and 15.

9: 9, 18, 27, 36, 45   *Find multiples of 9*
15: 15, 30, 45   *and 15.*
LCM = 45   *Find the LCM.*

Find the GCF for each set of numbers.

9. 15, 30   15
10. 9, 12   3
11. 8, 16, 12   4

Find the LCM for each set of numbers.

12. 6, 10   30
13. 6, 8   24
14. 5, 9, 12   180

Chapter 8

• **Write fractions in simplest form.** (pp. 160–163) **8A**

Write $\frac{18}{30}$ in simplest form.

$$\frac{18}{30} = \frac{18 \div 6}{30 \div 6} = \frac{3}{5}$$ *Divide by the GCF.*

Write the fraction in simplest form.

15. $\frac{8}{12}$ $\frac{2}{3}$
16. $\frac{15}{20}$ $\frac{3}{4}$
17. $\frac{40}{50}$ $\frac{4}{5}$
18. $\frac{36}{48}$ $\frac{3}{4}$
19. $\frac{18}{21}$ $\frac{6}{7}$
20. $\frac{90}{40}$ $\frac{9}{4}$

• **Write mixed numbers as fractions and fractions as mixed numbers.** (pp. 164–165) **8B**

Write $3\frac{5}{6}$ as a fraction.

$$3\frac{5}{6} = \frac{(3 \times 6)}{6} + \frac{5}{6} = \frac{23}{6}$$

Write the mixed number as a fraction.

21. $4\frac{2}{3}$ $\frac{14}{3}$
22. $2\frac{8}{9}$ $\frac{26}{9}$
23. $8\frac{1}{2}$ $\frac{17}{2}$

Write the fraction as a mixed number.

24. $\frac{17}{2}$ $8\frac{1}{2}$
25. $\frac{40}{7}$ $5\frac{5}{7}$
26. $\frac{33}{4}$ $8\frac{1}{4}$

• **Convert among fractions, decimals, and percents.** (pp. 169–171) **8C**

Write $\frac{1}{8}$ as a percent.

$$\frac{1}{8} = 1 \div 8 = 0.125$$ *Change $\frac{1}{8}$ to a decimal.*
0.125 = 12.5%
So, $\frac{1}{8}$ = 12.5%.

Write the decimal as a fraction.

27. 0.75 $\frac{3}{4}$
28. 0.6 $\frac{6}{10}$, or $\frac{3}{5}$
29. 0.43 $\frac{43}{100}$

Write the fraction as a percent.

30. $\frac{5}{8}$ 62.5%
31. $\frac{2}{5}$ 40%
32. $\frac{5}{2}$ 250%

Chapter 9

- **Add and subtract fractions and mixed numbers.** (pp. 186–193) **9A**

Subtract. $4\frac{1}{4} - 2\frac{2}{3}$

$$4\frac{1}{4} = 4\frac{3}{12} = 3\frac{15}{12}$$
Write equivalent fractions.

$$-2\frac{2}{3} = -2\frac{8}{12} = -2\frac{8}{12}$$
Rename as needed.

$$\overline{\hspace{3cm}}$$

$$1\frac{7}{12}$$
Subtract fractions.
Subtract whole numbers.

Add or subtract. Write the answer in simplest form.

33. $\frac{3}{4} + \frac{1}{3}$ $\frac{13}{12}$, or $1\frac{1}{12}$

34. $\frac{3}{5} + \frac{1}{2}$ $\frac{11}{10}$, or $1\frac{1}{10}$

35. $\frac{9}{10} - \frac{3}{5}$ $\frac{3}{10}$

36. $\frac{5}{6} - \frac{1}{4}$ $\frac{7}{12}$

37. $2\frac{3}{8} + 3\frac{3}{4}$ $6\frac{1}{8}$

38. $4\frac{3}{5} + 2\frac{1}{3}$ $6\frac{14}{15}$

39. $4\frac{1}{3} - 1\frac{5}{6}$ $2\frac{1}{2}$

40. $5\frac{1}{8} - 3\frac{2}{3}$ $1\frac{11}{24}$

Chapter 10

- **Multiply and divide fractions and mixed numbers.** (pp. 202–213) **10B**

Divide. $3\frac{3}{4} \div 4\frac{1}{2}$

$$3\frac{3}{4} \div 4\frac{1}{2} = \frac{15}{4} \div \frac{9}{2}$$
Write mixed numbers as fractions.

$$= \frac{15}{4} \times \frac{2}{9}$$
Multiply by the reciprocal.

$$= \frac{5}{6}$$

Multiply or divide. Write the answer in simplest form.

41. $\frac{1}{3} \times \frac{2}{5}$ $\frac{2}{15}$

42. $\frac{5}{8} \times \frac{7}{10}$ $\frac{7}{16}$

43. $\frac{5}{9} \div \frac{1}{3}$ $\frac{5}{3}$, or $1\frac{2}{3}$

44. $9 \div \frac{4}{5}$ $\frac{45}{4}$, or $11\frac{1}{4}$

45. $3\frac{3}{4} \times 3\frac{1}{3}$ $12\frac{1}{2}$

46. $3\frac{1}{8} \times 1\frac{1}{5}$ $3\frac{3}{4}$

47. $1\frac{2}{3} \div 3\frac{5}{6}$ $\frac{10}{23}$

48. $1\frac{7}{9} \div 2\frac{2}{5}$ $\frac{20}{27}$

- **Evaluate an algebraic expression using fractions.** (pp. 216–217) **10C**

Evaluate $f + 5\frac{1}{8}$ for $f = 2\frac{1}{3}$.

$$f + 5\frac{1}{8}$$

$$2\frac{1}{3} + 5\frac{1}{8}$$
Replace f with $2\frac{1}{3}$.

$$2\frac{8}{24} + 5\frac{3}{24} = 7\frac{11}{24}$$ *Add.*

Evaluate each expression.

49. $d + 2\frac{2}{3}$ for $d = 2\frac{5}{6}$ $5\frac{1}{2}$

50. $k \times \frac{3}{4}$ for $k = 1\frac{3}{5}$ $1\frac{1}{5}$

51. $m - 3\frac{4}{9}$ for $m = 6\frac{5}{18}$ $2\frac{5}{6}$

52. $w \div 1\frac{1}{3}$ for $w = 2\frac{1}{2}$ $1\frac{7}{8}$

PROBLEM SOLVING APPLICATIONS

53. Katelynn has two sheets of paper $8\frac{1}{2}$ in. by 11 in. She cuts out a 3-in. square from the center top edge of one of the sheets. Which has the greater perimeter, the sheet with the square cut out or the uncut sheet? How much greater? (pp. 194–195) cut sheet; 6 in. greater **9C**

54. Juan goes to the fruit market every 6 days. Anita goes to the market every 4 days. They meet at the market on August 31. When will they meet at the market again? (pp. 154–155) September 12 **7D**

223

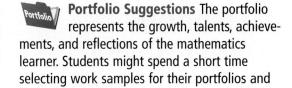

✓ Assessment Checkpoint

Portfolio Suggestions The portfolio represents the growth, talents, achievements, and reflections of the mathematics learner. Students might spend a short time selecting work samples for their portfolios and completing A Guide to My Math Portfolio from *Assessment Guide*, page AGxix.

You may want to have students respond to the following questions:

- **What new understanding of math have I developed in the past several weeks?**
- **What growth in understanding or skills can I see in my work?**
- **What can I do to improve my understanding of math ideas?**
- **What would I like to learn more about?**

For information about how to organize, share, and evaluate portfolios, see *Assessment Guide*, page AGxviii.

Use the item analysis in the **Intervention** chart to diagnose students' errors. You may wish to reinforce content or remediate misunderstandings by using the text pages or lesson resources.

STUDY GUIDE AND REVIEW INTERVENTION

How to Help Options

Learning Goal	Items	Text Pages	Reteach and Practice Resources
7B *See page 144C for Chapter 7 learning goals*	3–8	148–149	Worksheets for Lesson 7.2
7C *See page 144C for Chapter 7 learning goals*	9–14	150–153	Worksheets for Lesson 7.3
7D *See page 144C for Chapter 7 learning goals*	54	154–155	Worksheets for Lesson 7.4
8A *See page 144C for Chapter 8 learning goals*	15–20	160–163	Worksheets for Lesson 8.1
8B *See page 144C for Chapter 8 learning goals*	21–26	164–165	Worksheets for Lesson 8.2
8C *See page 144C for Chapter 8 learning goals*	27–32	169–171	Worksheets for Lesson 8.5
9A *See page 144C for Chapter 9 learning goals*	33–40	186–189, 190, 191, 192–193	Worksheets for Lessons 9.4, 9.5, 9.6
9C *See page 144C for Chapter 9 learning goals*	53	194–195	Worksheets for Lesson 9.7
10B *See page 144C for Chapter 10 learning goals*	41–48	202–205, 206–207, 208–209, 210–215	Worksheets for Lessons 10.2, 10.3, 10.4, 10.5
10C *See page 144C for Chapter 10 learning goals*	49–52	20–21, 22–25	Worksheets for Lesson 10.2

CALIFORNIA CONNECTIONS

Purpose To provide additional practice for concepts and skills in Chapters 7–10

USING THE PAGE

Trees

• *Have students refer to the table comparing tree heights.*

How can you use percents to compare the data in the table to the General Sherman tree? Tallest grand fir: $\frac{19}{20}$ = 95%; tallest ponderosa pine: $\frac{41}{50}$ = 82%; tallest sugar pine: $\frac{21}{25}$ = 84%

Are the fractions or the percents easier to relate to the height of the General Sherman tree? Explain. Answers will vary. Possible answer: Percents; The percents are in the same form and are easier to order.

How tall is the tallest sugar pine? 232 ft

Extension Discuss students' solutions to Exercise 6. Then challenge students to make up a similar problem using a diagram. They can compare the height, length, width, depth, weight, mass, or any single dimension of objects or figures. Check students' work.

Trees

California is home to some of the world's most famous trees. Here you will find the largest tree, the oldest tree, and the second-tallest tree. California also has the tallest individuals of many species of trees.

The General Sherman giant sequoia tree, in Sequoia National Park, is one of the largest trees in the world. Its weight is estimated to be equal to the combined weights of 740 elephants.

1. The world's tallest bluegum eucalyptus tree is located in Sonoma County, California. It is 165 ft tall. The General Sherman giant sequoia tree is 275 ft tall. Express the eucalyptus tree's height as a fraction of the General Sherman tree's height, in simplest form. $\frac{3}{5}$

2. The diameter of the General Sherman tree is shown in the diagram. Write the diameter as a fraction. $\frac{662}{25}$ $26\frac{12}{25}$ ft

Use Data For 3, use the table.

3. The world's tallest grand fir, ponderosa pine, and sugar pine are found in California. The table shows how the heights of the three trees compare with that of the General Sherman tree. Order the trees from tallest to least tall. **grand fir, sugar pine, ponderosa pine**

4. California's tallest tree, and the world's second tallest, is a coast redwood found in Redwoods State Park. It is 313 ft tall. Classify the number 313 as prime or composite. **prime**

5. The world's oldest tree is a 4,700-year-old bristlecone pine growing in California's White Mountains, near the town of Bishop. Write the prime factorization of 4,700. $47 \times 5^2 \times 2^2$

HEIGHTS COMPARED TO THE GENERAL SHERMAN TREE	
Tallest grand fir	$\frac{19}{20}$
Tallest ponderosa pine	$\frac{41}{50}$
Tallest sugar pine	$\frac{21}{25}$

Use Data For 6, use the drawing.

6. The world's tallest incense cedar and the world's tallest sugar pine grow in California. The height of each tree is a multiple of the height of a redwood seedling. What is the tallest the redwood seedling could be? **8 ft**

232 ft

152 ft

redwood seedling   incense cedar   sugar pine

224 Chapters 7–10

SCIENCE Standards LS6.b

Joshua Tree National Park

The Joshua tree is one of the most unusual and easily recognized trees in the world. The Joshua tree is a member of the lily family. The best examples of this rare tree are found in Joshua Tree National Park, in Southern California.

The unusual spiny-leaved Joshua tree can grow up to 40 feet tall and live up to 1,000 years.

SCIENCE Standards LS6.b

Use Data For 1–9, use the table.

1. Which trail is longer, Indian Cove or Oasis of Mara? How much longer? **Indian Cove; $\frac{1}{10}$ mi**

2. One of the trails listed is half the length of the Ryan Mountain Trail. Which trail is it? **Skull Rock**

3. What is the combined length of the two longest trails listed? **$23\frac{7}{8}$ mi**

4. How much longer than the Skull Rock Trail is the Mastodon Peak Trail? **$1\frac{2}{5}$ mi**

5. Malcolm hiked the Boy Scout Trail at an average rate of $2\frac{2}{3}$ mph. How long did the hike take? **6 hr**

Mr. Ristorcelli has hiked the Lost Palms Oasis Trail every summer for the past 16 years.

6. How far has he hiked altogether? **126 mi**

7. How many times would he have to hike the 49 Palms Oasis Trail in order to cover the same total distance? **35 times**

8. Kendra hiked four trails for a total of $11\frac{3}{4}$ mi. Three of the trails she hiked are Mastodon Peak, High View, and Ryan Mountain. What is the name of the fourth trail Kendra hiked? **Lost Horse Mine**

9. The Lost Horse Mine trail is $8\frac{1}{2}$ times as long as the trail Mesha and her brother hiked. Which trail did Mesha and her brother hike? **Oasis of Mara**

TRAILS IN JOSHUA TREE NATL. PARK	
Trail	**Approx. Length (mi)**
Boy Scout	16
49 Palms Oasis	$3\frac{3}{5}$
High View	$1\frac{3}{10}$
Indian Cove	$\frac{3}{5}$
Lost Horse Mine	$4\frac{1}{4}$
Lost Palms Oasis	$7\frac{7}{8}$
Mastodon Peak	3
Oasis of Mara	$\frac{1}{2}$
Ryan Mountain	$3\frac{1}{5}$
Skull Rock	$1\frac{3}{5}$

225

Teaching Notes

Additional Ideas:

Good Questions to Ask:

Additional Resources:

Notes for Next Time:

UNIT 4 Algebra: Integers

UNIT AT A GLANCE

Assessment Options

What types of assessment are available?

Assessing Prior Knowledge

Determine whether students have the required prerequisite concepts and skills.

Check What You Know PE pp. 227, 241, 255

Test Preparation

Provide review and practice for chapter and standardized tests.

Cumulative Review PE pp. 239, 253, 265

Mixed Review and Test Prep
See the last page of each PE skill lesson.

Study Guide and Review, PE pp. 268–269

Formal Assessment

Assess students' mastery of chapter concepts and skills.

Chapter Review/Test
PE pp. 238, 252, 264

Pretest and Posttest Options
  Chapter Test, Form A
    pp. AG73–74, 77–78, 81–82
  Chapter Test, Form B
    pp. AG75–76, 79–80, 83–84

Unit 4 Test • Chapters 11–13, pp. AG85–92

Harcourt Electronic Test System Math Practice and Assessment

Make and grade chapter tests electronically.

This software includes:
- **multiple-choice items**
- **free-response items**
- **customizable tests**
- **the means to make your own tests**

Daily Assessment

Obtain daily feedback on students' understanding of concepts.

Quick Review
See the first page of each PE lesson.

Mixed Review and Test Prep
See the last page of each PE skill lesson.

Number of the Day
See the first page of each TE skill lesson.

Problem of the Day
See the first page of each TE skill lesson.

Lesson Quiz
See the *Assess* section of each TE skill lesson.

Performance Assessment

Assess students' understanding of concepts applied to real-world situations.

Performance Assessment (Tasks A–B)
pp. PA30–31

Student Self-Assessment

Have students evaluate their own work.

How Did I Do?, p. AGxvii

A Guide to My Math Portfolio, p. AGxix

Math Journal
See *Write* in the *Assess* section of each TE skill lesson and TE pages 230B, 250B, 262B.

Portfolio

Portfolio opportunities appear throughout the Pupil and Teacher's Editions.

Suggested work samples:

Problem Solving Project TE pp. 226, 240, 254

Write About It, PE pp. 235, 263

Chapter Review/Test PE pp. 238, 252, 264

KEY   **AG** Assessment Guide   **TE** Teacher's Edition
       PA Performance Assessment   **PE** Pupil Edition

How does the Unit 4 content correlate to standardized tests and California Mathematics Content Standards?

LEARNING GOAL	TAUGHT IN LESSONS	STANDARDIZED TESTS					CALIFORNIA MATHEMATICS STANDARDS
		CAT	CTBS/ TERRA NOVA	ITBS	MAT	SAT	
11A To identify and write integers, opposites, and absolute values	11.1	●		●	●	●	MR 2.4
11B To identify and represent relationships among sets of numbers by using a variety of methods, including number lines	11.2	●	●		●	●	O━┓ NS 1.0 O━┓ NS 1.1
11C To compare and order rational numbers	11.3	●	●	●	●	●	O━┓ NS 1.0 O━┓ NS 1.1
11D To solve problems by using an appropriate strategy such as *use logical reasoning*	11.4	●	●	●	●	●	MR 2.4 MR 3.2
12A To write sums of integers by using a variety of methods, including models and number lines	12.1, 12.2	●			●	●	O━┓ NS 2.3
12B To write differences of integers by using a variety of methods, including models	12.3, 12.4	●					O━┓ NS 2.3
13A To write products of integers	13.1, 13.2	●	●		●	●	O━┓ NS 2.3
13B To write quotients of integers	13.3	●	●		●	●	O━┓ NS 2.3
13C To perform a combination of operations with integers	13.4	●	●		●	●	O━┓ NS 2.3

Technology Links

🌐 The Harcourt Learning Site

Visit The Harcourt Learning Site for related links, activities, and resources:

- Integers activity *(Use with Chapter 12.)*
- *Animated Math Glossary*
- E-Lab interactive learning experiences
- current events stories that feature mathematics
- professional development and instructional resources

www.harcourtschool.com

Harcourt Math Newsroom Videos

These videos bring exciting news events to your classroom from the leaders in news broadcasting. For each unit, there is a **Harcourt Math Newsroom Video** that helps students see the relevance of math concepts to their lives. You may wish to use the data and concepts shown in the video for real-life problem solving or class projects.

TECHNOLOGY CORRELATION

Intervention Strategies and Activities This CD-ROM helps you assess students' knowledge of prerequisite concepts and skills.

Mighty Math CD-ROM Series includes *Astro Algebra*. It provides levels of difficulty that increase from A up to Z.

E-Lab is a collection of electronic learning activities.

The chart below correlates technology activities to specific lessons.

LESSON	ACTIVITY/LEVEL	SKILL
11.2	**Astro Algebra** • *Red*, Level K	Classify rational numbers
11.3	**Astro Algebra** • *Red*, Level L **Harcourt Math Newsroom Video** • *Slow Down Light*	Compare and order rational numbers
12.1	**Astro Algebra** • *Red*, Level A	Add integers
12.2	**Astro Algebra** • *Red*, Level A	Add integers
12.3	**E-Lab** • *Modeling Subtraction of Integers* **Astro Algebra** • *Red*, Level F	Model subtraction of integers
12.4	**Astro Algebra** • *Red*, Level F	Subtract integers
13.2	**Astro Algebra** • *Red*, Level G	Multiply integers
13.3	**Astro Algebra** • *Red*, Level M	Divide integers

For the Student

Intervention Strategies and Activities

Review and practice the prerequisite skills for Chapters 11–13.

 E-LAB These interactive learning experiences reinforce and extend the skills taught in Chapters 11–13.

- Skill development
- Practice

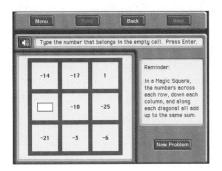

Mighty Math

The learning activities in this comprehensive math software series complement, enrich, and enhance the Pupil Edition lessons.

Astro Algebra • *Red*

For the Teacher

Teacher Support Software

- **Intervention Strategies and Activities** Provide instruction, practice, and a check of the prerequisite skills for each chapter.
- **Electronic Lesson Planner** Quickly prepare daily and weekly lessons for all subject areas.
- **Harcourt Electronic Test System Math Practice and Assessment** Edit and customize Chapter Tests or construct unique tests from large item banks.

For the Parent

The Harcourt Learning Site

- Encourage parents to visit The Harcourt Learning Site to help them reinforce mathematics vocabulary, concepts, and skills with their children.
- Have them click on *Math* for vocabulary, activities, real-life connections, and homework tips for Chapters 11–13.

www.harcourtschool.com

Internet

Teachers can find rational number activities and resources.

Students can learn more about integers and reinforce the critical concepts and skills for Chapters 11–13.

Parents can use The Harcourt Learning Site's resources to help their children with the vocabulary, concepts, and skills needed for Chapters 11–13.

Visit The Harcourt Learning Site www.harcourtschool.com

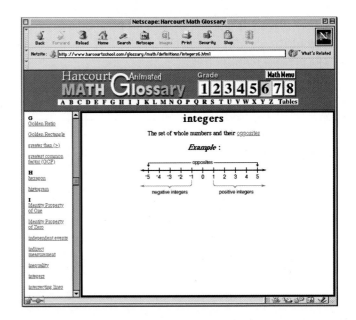

Reaching All Learners

ADVANCED LEARNERS

Challenge students to **apply their knowledge of multiplication of integers**. Have them determine if there is a rule for finding the sign of the product of more than two integers. Suggest that students make and complete a table, such as the following, to develop a pattern and then use the pattern to decide on the rule.

PRODUCT OF INTEGERS		
Integers	Number of Negative Integers	Sign of Product
$^-2 \times 4$	1	–
$^-2 \times ^-2$	2	+
$^-2 \times ^-2 \times ^-2$	3	–

Students should conclude that for an even number of negative integers the product is positive, and that for an odd number of negative integers the product is negative. *Use with Lessons 13.1–13.2.*
VISUAL

SPECIAL NEEDS

MATERIALS *For each pair* 2 pennies

Reinforce the concept of addition and multiplication of integers. Ask students working in pairs to toss two pennies at the same time and record the results in a table. Have them keep a running total of their scores by using the point system below.

$$(H,T) = {}^+5 \text{ points} \quad (H,H) = {}^-5 \text{ points}$$

$$(T,T) = {}^-5 \text{ points} \quad (T,H) = {}^+5 \text{ points}$$

Then have students calculate their final scores by multiplying the number of tosses with a positive value by 5; multiplying the number of tosses with a negative value by $^-5$; adding the two products to the running total to determine the final score. *Use with Lessons 12.1–12.2 and 13.1–13.2.*

VISUAL, KINESTHETIC

BLOCK SCHEDULING

INTERDISCIPLINARY COURSES
- Science — Connect integers to the Celsius and Fahrenheit temperature scales.
- Geography — Use positive and negative integers to compare the altitudes of various mountains and seafloor features.
- Physical Science — Explore the charged particles called electrons and protons.
- Physical Education — Use absolute value to describe how runners' times differ from the mean. If the mean is 11 sec, then 14 sec and 8 sec each differ from the mean by 3.

COMPLETE UNIT

Unit 4 may be presented in
- six 90-minute blocks.
- seven 75-minute blocks.

INTERDISCIPLINARY SUGGESTIONS

PURPOSE To connect *Algebra: Integers* to other subjects with these activities

CHAPTER 11 — Physical Education

Students research the procedure and ratings for the sit-and-reach flexibility test. For example, Good: 2 to 4 in.; Average: 0 to 2 in.; Fair: $^-2$ to 0 in.; and so on.

CHAPTER 12 — Earth Science

In the winter, people feel colder when the wind is blowing. Students write a summary explaining any patterns they see in the wind-chill table on page TE250B.

VISUAL

Students who finish their work early can
- make visual aids for lessons that teach the concept of rational numbers. Early finishers can also make a chart that shows the rules to apply when adding, subtracting, multiplying, and dividing positive and negative integers. Ask students to include sample problems that illustrate each rule.
- assemble and play the Practice Game. *See Operation Calculation.*
- solve the *Problem of the Day.*
  Use with TE Lessons 11.1–13.4.

VOCABULARY PREVIEW Have students make a math dictionary for the vocabulary in the unit. The dictionary will provide students with an easy review tool for tests and will help them build toward independence when answering word problems. Have students make a three-column chart and label the columns. As students learn about each new term, they can fill in their dictionary. *Use with Lessons 11.1–12.1.*

Term	Example	Explanation

Negative Integer Relate the terms *negative integer* and *positive integer* to right and left of zero. *Use with Lesson 11.1.*

Absolute Value The absolute value of a number is its distance from zero. Have students work with a number line and ask questions about positive and negative integers and their distance from zero. *Use with Lesson 11.1.*

VISUAL, AUDITORY

Operation Calculation

PURPOSE To perform integer operations

MATERIALS *For each group* game cards, p. TR81; paper

About the Game Players write the four operation signs down the side of a sheet of paper. Two cards are dealt to each player. Players decide which operation to use and perform the calculation using the numbers they were dealt. Players explain their choice of operation and their calculation. In four rounds, all players must perform each operation once. After four rounds, players add the answers for each round. The player with the highest total wins. *Use with Lesson 13.3.*

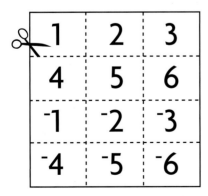

VISUAL

These books provide students with additional ways to explore integers and other rational numbers.

Snow Bound by Harry Mazer (Bantam, 1975) tells of two teen runaways who find themselves trapped in a car in a snowstorm and who must work together to survive.

- The average minimum temperature in upstate New York is ⁻8°C. Have students find the current temperature in °C and tell how many degrees warmer it is compared to that average. *Use with Lesson 12.4.*

The Facts on File Children's Atlas by David and Jill Wright (Facts on File, Inc., 1993) includes photos, maps, comparative facts, figures, puzzles, and activity boxes that enhance the study of geography.

- Use the fact box on Asia to find the locations of and the difference between the highest and lowest points in that continent. *Use with Lessons 12.3–12.4.*

CHAPTER 11 Number Relationships

CHAPTER PLANNER

PACING OPTIONS	
Compacted	4 Days
Expanded	7 Days

Getting Ready for Chapter 11 • Assessing Prior Knowledge and INTERVENTION (See PE and TE page 227.)

LESSON	📞 CALIFORNIA STANDARDS	PACING	VOCABULARY*	MATERIALS	RESOURCES AND TECHNOLOGY
11.1 Understand Integers pp. 228–229 **Objective** To identify integers and to find absolute value	MR 2.4 (*Also* MR 2.2, MR 3.0, MR 3.2, MR 3.3)	1 Day	**integers** **opposites** **positive integers** **negative integers** **absolute value**		Reteach, Practice, Problem Solving, Challenge 11.1 Worksheets Extra Practice p. H42, Set A ▢ Transparency 11.1 **Math Jingles™ CD 5-6** • *Track 17*
11.2 Rational Numbers pp. 230–233 **Objective** To classify sets of numbers and to find another rational number between two rational numbers	⊙ NS 1.0 ⊙ NS 1.1 (*Also* MR 1.0, MR 2.0, MR 3.0, MR 3.2, MR 3.3)	2 Days	**ratio** **rational number** **Venn diagram**		Reteach, Practice, Problem Solving, Challenge 11.2 Worksheets Extra Practice p. H42, Set B ▢ Transparency 11.2 💿 **Astro Algebra** • *Red*
11.3 Compare and Order Rational Numbers pp. 234–235 **Objective** To compare and order rational numbers	⊙ NS 1.0 (*Also* MR 1.0, MR 2.0, MR 2.4, MR 3.0)	1 Day			Reteach, Practice, Problem Solving, Challenge 11.3 Worksheets Extra Practice p. H42, Set C ▢ Transparency 11.3 💿 **Astro Algebra** • *Red* 📼 **Harcourt Math Newsroom Video** • *Slow Down Light*
11.4 Problem Solving Strategy: *Use Logical Reasoning* pp. 236–237 **Objective** To solve problems by using the strategy *use logical reasoning*	MR 2.0 MR 3.2 (*Also* MR 1.0, MR 3.0, MR 3.3)	1 Day			Reteach, Practice, Reading Strategy, Challenge 11.4 Worksheets ▢ Transparency 11.4 Problem Solving Think Along, p. TR1

Ending Chapter 11 • Chapter 11 Review/Test, p. 238 • **Cumulative Review,** p. 239

*****Boldfaced** terms are new vocabulary. Other terms are review vocabulary.

CHAPTER AT A GLANCE

Vocabulary Development

The boldfaced words are the new vocabulary terms in the chapter. Have students record the definitions in their Math Journals.

integers, p. 228

opposites, p. 228

positive integers, p. 228

negative integers, p. 228

absolute value, p. 228

ratio, p. 230

rational number, p. 230

Venn diagram, p. 230

integers

Vocabulary Cards
Have students use the Vocabulary Cards on *Teacher's Resource Book* **pp. TR127–130** to make graphic organizers or word puzzles. The cards can also be added to a file of mathematics terms.

Writing Opportunities

PUPIL EDITION	TEACHER'S EDITION	ASSESSMENT GUIDE
• **Write a Problem,** p. 229	• Write—See the *Assess* section of each TE lesson.	• **How Did I Do?,** p. AGxvii
• **What's the Error?,** p. 233	• **Writing in Mathematics,** p. 230B	
• **Write About It,** p. 235		
• **What's the Question?,** p. 237		

California Mathematics Content Standards for Grade 6

Strands

Number Sense

Lesson 11.2: ○━ NS 1.0, ○━ 1.1

Lesson 11.3: ○━ NS 1.0, ○━ 1.1

Algebra and Functions

Measurement and Geometry

Statistics, Data Analysis, and Probability

Mathematical Reasoning

Lesson 11.1: MR 2.2, 2.4, 3.0, 3.2, 3.3

Lesson 11.2: MR 1.0, 2.0, 3.0, 3.2, 3.3

Lesson 11.3: MR 1.0, 2.0, 2.4, 3.0

Lesson 11.4: MR 1.0, 2.0, 3.0, 3.2, 3.3

Family Involvement Activities

These activities provide:
- Letter to the Family
- Information about California Standards
- Math Vocabulary
- Family Game
- Practice (Homework)

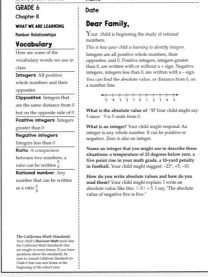

Family Involvement Activities, p. FA41

226I

Number Relationships

MATHEMATICS ACROSS THE GRADES

SKILLS TRACE ACROSS THE GRADES

GRADE 5	GRADE 6	GRADE 7
Represent and order integers on a number line; find opposites and absolute values of integers	Identify and write integers, opposites, and absolute values; represent relationships among sets of numbers using a variety of methods; compare and order rational numbers	Compare and order integers and rational numbers; represent relationships among sets of numbers

SKILLS TRACE FOR GRADE 6

LESSON	FIRST INTRODUCED	TAUGHT AND PRACTICED	TESTED	REVIEWED
11.1	Grade 4	PE pp. 228–229, H42, p. RW51, p. PW51, p. PS51	PE p. 238, pp. AG73–76	PE pp. 238, 239, 268–269
11.2	Grade 6	PE pp. 230–233, H42, p. RW52, p. PW52, p. PS52	PE p. 238, pp. AG73–76	PE pp. 238, 239, 268–269
11.3	Grade 6	PE pp. 234–235, H42, p. RW53, p. PW53, p. PS53,	PE p. 238, pp. AG73–76	PE pp. 238, 239, 268–269
11.4	Grade 4	PE pp. 236–237, p. RW54, p. PW54, p. PS54	PE p. 238, pp. AG73–76	PE pp. 238, 239, 268–269

KEY **PE** Pupil Edition   **PS** Problem Solving Workbook   **RW** Reteach Workbook
       PW Practice Workbook   **AG** Assessment Guide

Looking Back Prerequisite Skills

To be ready for Chapter 11, students should have the following understandings and skills:

- **Vocabulary**—*positive numbers, negative numbers, whole numbers*

- **Locate Points on a Number Line**—locate integers on a number line

- **Sets of Numbers**—classify numbers as counting, whole, even, odd

- **Compare Fractions**—compare fractions as $<$, $>$, or $=$

- **Temperature**—read temperature on a thermometer

Check What You Know

Use page 227 to determine students' knowledge of prerequisite concepts and skills.

Intervention

Help students prepare for the chapter by using the intervention resources described on TE page 227.

Looking at Chapter 11 Essential Skills

Students will

- develop skill identifying and writing integers, opposites, and absolute values.

- **understand the relationships among the sets of rational numbers, integers, and whole numbers.**

- develop skill comparing and ordering rational numbers.

- use the strategy *use logical reasoning* to solve problems.

EXAMPLE

Find a rational number between ⁻5.5 and ⁻5.0.

Venn Diagram	Number Line
Rational Numbers Integers Whole Numbers	Think of a number line to find a number between the two numbers. ⁻5.5 ⁻5.4 ⁻5.3 ⁻5.2 ⁻5.1 ⁻5.0 So ⁻5.4, ⁻5.3, and ⁻5.2 are some of the numbers between ⁻5.5 and ⁻5.0

Looking Ahead Applications

Students will apply what they learn in Chapter 11 to the following new concepts:

- Operations with Integers (Chapters 12 and 13)

- Addition and Subtraction Equations (Chapter 15)

- Expressions with Squares and Square Roots (Chapter 14)

- Multiplication and Division Equations (Chapter 16)

Number Relationships

INTRODUCING THE CHAPTER

Tell students that integers are used to describe real-life relationships. Have students focus on the photograph. Ask them what kind of integer they would use to describe how many feet below the summit the climbers are. a negative integer

USING DATA

To begin the study of this chapter, have students

- Name an integer that describes the altitude that is 500 ft below the base camp. ⁻500

- Name an integer that describes any altitude between Camp 2 and Camp 3. Possible answer: ⁺10,000

- Make a graph to show the camp and altitude data in the table. Check students' work.

PROBLEM SOLVING PROJECT

Purpose To use integers to solve a problem

Grouping pairs or small groups

Background Mt. Everest in Nepal is the highest mountain in the world at 29,028 ft above sea level.

Analyze, Choose, Solve, and Check

Have students

- Use an almanac or other reference to find the five highest mountains in North America and the five highest mountains in South America.

- Record the altitudes of the mountains on a graph to the nearest hundred feet.

- Order the mountains from highest to lowest.

Check students' work.

 Suggest that students place the graphs and ordered data in their portfolios.

The elevation of Mt. McKinley is 20,320 feet. It is the highest mountain in North America and has one of Earth's steepest vertical rises. With the high altitude, unpredictable weather, and steep, icy slopes, this mountain is a challenge to climb. Climbers are flown into base camp, where they start their climb at 7,200 ft. If a climb takes 20 days, what is the average altitude gained per day?

Mt. McKINLEY		
Camp	**Altitude**	**Possible Time**
Base Camp	7,200 ft	0 day
Camp 2	9,500 ft	1st day
Camp 3	11,000 ft	3rd day
Camp 4	14,200 ft	10th day
Camp 5	16,200 ft	12th day
High Camp	17,200 ft	15th day
Summit	20,320 ft	20th day

656 ft

226 Chapter 11

Why learn math? Explain that mountain climbers can use integers to describe the distance they have climbed or have left to climb. For example, 250 ft from the top of the mountain can be described as ⁻250 ft since it is 250 ft below the summit. Ask: If you were a mountain climber, how would you use an integer to describe where you are if you climbed 2,500 ft from the base of the mountain? ⁺2,500 ft

Check What You Know

Use this page to help you review and remember important skills needed for Chapter 11.

✓ Vocabulary

Choose the best term from the box.

> positive numbers
> negative numbers
> whole numbers

1. Numbers to the left of zero on the number line are ___?___ . **negative numbers**
2. Numbers greater than zero are ___?___ . **positive numbers**

✓ Locate Points on a Number Line (See p. H13.)

Copy each number line. Graph the numbers on the number line. **Check students' answers.**

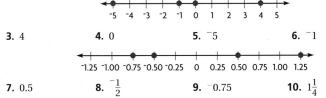

3. 4   4. 0   5. ⁻5   6. ⁻1

7. 0.5   8. ⁻$\frac{1}{2}$ 9. ⁻0.75   10. $1\frac{1}{4}$

✓ Sets of Numbers (See p. H12.)

Give four examples from each set of numbers. **Possible answers are given.**

11. whole numbers   12. counting numbers   13. odd numbers
    0, 1, 2, 3, 4   1, 2, 3, 4   1, 3, 5, 7

✓ Compare Fractions (See p. H12.)

Compare. Write <, >, or = for each ●.

14. $9\frac{1}{2}$ ● $9\frac{3}{4}$ <   15. $\frac{2}{3}$ ● $\frac{3}{2}$ <   16. $\frac{3}{4}$ ● $\frac{3}{5}$ >

17. $\frac{16}{2}$ ● $\frac{24}{3}$ =   18. $2\frac{3}{5}$ ● $2\frac{1}{4}$ >   19. $\frac{12}{2}$ ● $2\frac{1}{12}$ >

✓ Temperature (See p. H12.)

Tell the temperature shown by each letter on the thermometer.

20. A 0°F   21. B 32°F   22. C 78°F

23. D ⁻16°F   24. E ⁻20°F   25. F 60°F

> **LOOK AHEAD**
>
> In Chapter 11 you will
> • identify integers and rational numbers
> • compare and order rational numbers
> • use number lines

227

227

Understand Integers

LESSON PLANNING

Objective To identify integers and to find absolute value

Intervention for Prerequisite Skills

Locate Points on a Number Line, Temperature (For intervention strategies, see page 227.)

 California Mathematics Content Standards

MR 2.4 Use a variety of methods, such as words, numbers, symbols, charts, graphs, tables, diagrams, and models, to explain mathematical reasoning.

(*Also* MR 2.2, MR 3.0, MR 3.2, MR 3.3)

Vocabulary

integers all whole numbers and their opposites

opposites pairs of integers that are the same distance from 0

positive integers integers greater than 0

negative integers integers less than 0

absolute value the distance of an integer from 0 on the number line

Math Background

Integers include the set of whole numbers and their opposites. Integers allow us to find solutions to equations such as $x + 4 = 2$, and answers to subtraction problems such as $4 - 9$.

These ideas will help students understand integers.

- Every integer has an opposite. The opposite of a positive integer is negative, the opposite of a negative integer is positive, and the opposite of zero is itself, zero.

- The absolute value of an integer is the integer's distance from zero on the number line. Because distance is always non-negative, the absolute value of an integer is always non-negative.

WARM-UP RESOURCES

 NUMBER OF THE DAY   Transparency **11.1**

Two consecutive whole numbers have a product of 110. What is the greater number? 11

 PROBLEM OF THE DAY   Transparency **11.1**

One side of Jessica's square array is 2 tiles longer than a side of Dave's square array. Together they use a total of 100 tiles. How many tiles are on each side of Dave's array? 6 tiles on a side

Solution Problem of the Day tab, p. PD11

 DAILY FACTS PRACTICE

Have students practice addition facts by completing Set B of *Teacher's Resource Book,* p. TR101.

ALTERNATIVE TEACHING STRATEGY

Materials red and blue chalk or markers

Use a thermometer to **provide examples of applications of negative numbers.** Make a large thermometer showing temperatures from ⁻10°F to 20°F without the signs. Have students identify temperatures above zero and below zero. Ask volunteers to insert the positive signs in red and the negative signs in blue on the thermometer. Point out that positive temperatures are warmer than negative temperatures, so positive numbers are greater than negative numbers. Use the thermometer to illustrate the concept of absolute value and have students identify the absolute values of several positive and negative integers.

Check students' work.

VISUAL

MIXED REVIEW AND TEST PREP

Cumulative Review Chapters 1–11

Refer to the Pupil Edition pages referenced in the exercises for further review. Have students go to the lesson page, review the lesson, and correct any problem they missed.

Mixed Review and Test Prep, p. 229

How to Help	
Item	Page
29	202
30	76
31	44
32	70
33	154

ENGLISH LANGUAGE LEARNERS ⟨ELL•SDAIE⟩

Reinforce vocabulary associated with integers. Draw a large number line from ⁻10 to ⁺10. Display these vocabulary words above the number line: *integers, opposites, positive integers, negative integers.*

Have volunteers find the number that matches a description that you give. For example,

- negative 2 ⁻2
- positive 8 ⁺8
- the opposite of 6 ⁻6
- a positive integer Possible answer: ⁺5

Then, reverse the process by asking students to practice describing the integer you point out on the number line. Check students' work.

VISUAL

VOCABULARY STRATEGY

Have students **illustrate the integer vocabulary.** Make a bulletin board display with separate areas labeled: *integers, positive integers, negative integers, opposites,* and *absolute value.*

Group students and assign each group an area. Have them make and display examples to illustrate the concept. Discuss their completed bulletin board and refer to it as needed.

VISUAL

ENG-LANG ARTS Standards
R 1.0

TECHNOLOGY LINK

Intervention Strategies and Activities CD-ROM •
Skills 42, 56

Objective To identify integers and to find absolute value

Vocabulary integers, opposites, positive integers, negative integers, absolute value

1 Introduce

QUICK REVIEW provides review of pre-requisite skills.

Why Learn This? You can use this skill to describe positive or negative values, such as bank deposits and withdrawals. *Share the lesson objective with students.*

2 Teach

Guided Instruction

• *After introducing the lesson vocabulary, draw students' attention to the number line.*

REASONING Are there any integers between ⁺1 and ⁺2? Explain. No; integers are positive whole numbers and their opposites.

• *As students look at the number line showing absolute value, ask:*

Why do both 3 and ⁻3 have the same absolute value? They are the same distance from 0.

REASONING Relate 0 to the absolute value of integers. Absolute value is defined as the distance from zero on a number line.

Modifying Instruction Use a thermometer as you discuss examples of negative integers.

ADDITIONAL EXAMPLES

Example 1, p. 228

Name an integer to represent the situation:

A. a loss of 9 yards in a football game ⁻9

B. a temperature of 3° above zero ⁺3

C. a bank withdrawal of $40 ⁻40

Example 2, p. 228

Use the number line to find absolute value.

A. |⁻2| 2 **B.** |⁺3| 3

C. |⁺1| 1 **D.** |⁺4| 4

Understand Integers

Learn how to identify integers and find absolute value.

QUICK REVIEW
Order from greatest to least.
1. 1, 0, 3   2. 21, 17, 19   3. 46, 64, 55
4. 201, 199, 200   5. 800, 808, 880

1. 3, 1, 0   2. 21,19,17
3. 64, 55, 46 4. 201, 200, 199
5. 880, 808, 800

Death Valley is the country's hottest and driest spot.

Vocabulary
integers
opposites
positive integers
negative integers
absolute value

Mount McKinley is 20,320 ft above sea level. Death Valley is 282 ft below sea level. Sea level equals 0 ft. You can use the integers ⁺20,320 and ⁻282 to represent these elevations.

Integers include all whole numbers and their **opposites**. Each integer has an opposite that is the same distance from 0 but on the opposite side of 0. The opposite of positive 8 (⁺8) is negative 8 (⁻8). The opposite of 0 is 0.

Integers greater than 0 are **positive integers**. Integers less than 0 are **negative integers**. The integer 0 is neither positive nor negative.

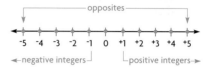

Negative integers are written with a negative sign, ⁻.

Positive integers can be written with or without a positive sign, ⁺.

EXAMPLE 1

Name an integer to represent the situation.

A. a gain of 12 yd   **B.** 30° below zero   **C.** a deposit of $100
    ⁺12   ⁻30°   ⁺100

The **absolute value** of an integer is its distance from 0. Look at ⁺3 and ⁻3. They are both 3 units from 0.

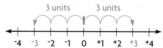

Write: |⁻3| = 3 **Read:** The absolute value of negative three is three.
Write: |⁺3| = 3 **Read:** The absolute value of positive three is three.

EXAMPLE 2

Use the number line to find each absolute value.

A. |⁻4| **B.** |⁺2| **C.** |⁻1| **D.** |⁺3|
    4   2   1   3

228

RETEACH 11.1

Understand Integers

A diver started out at the bottom of the ocean, 250 feet below sea level. He came to the surface and then climbed a hill 300 feet above sea level. How can you represent these numbers?

Integers are numbers that can show opposite directions.

250 feet below sea level is ⁻250 ft.   300 feet above sea level is ⁺300 ft.

Every integer, except zero, has an opposite.

The absolute value of a number is used to show how far a number is from 0.

Find |⁻2| This is read as the absolute value of negative 2.

So, |⁻2| = 2.

Write the opposite integer.

1. ⁻8	2. ⁺7	3. ⁺11	4. ⁻9	5. ⁻14	6. ⁺17
⁺8	⁻7	⁻11	⁺9	⁺14	⁻17
7. ⁻3	8. ⁺12	9. ⁺23	10. ⁻30	11. ⁺33	12. ⁻50
⁺3	⁻12	⁻23	⁺30	⁻33	⁺50

Find the absolute value.

13. |⁻6|	14. |⁺6|	15. |⁻8|	16. |⁻21|	17. |⁺13|	18. |⁻26|
6	6	8	21	13	26
19. |⁻45|	20. |⁺56|	21. |⁻77|	22. |⁺92|	23. |⁻345|	24. |⁺880|
45	56	77	92	345	880

PRACTICE 11.1

Understand Integers

Vocabulary

Complete.

1. ____Integers____ include all whole numbers and their opposites.

2. The ____absolute value____ of an integer is its distance from 0.

Write an integer to represent each situation.

3. earning 7 dollars   4. digging a hole 2 feet deep
   ⁺7   ⁻2
5. taking 10 steps backward   6. climbing up a mountain 20 feet
   ⁻10   ⁺20

Find the absolute value.

7. |⁻3|	8. |⁺3|	9. |⁻2|	10. |⁻6|	11. |⁺9|	12. |⁻15|
3	3	2	6	9	15
13. |⁻32|	14. |⁺32|	15. |⁻47|	16. |⁺78|	17. |⁻180|	18. |⁺574|
32	32	47	78	180	574

Write the opposite integer.

19. ⁻5	20. ⁺13	21. ⁺21	22. ⁻19	23. ⁻25	24. ⁺37
⁺5	⁻13	⁻21	⁺19	⁺25	⁻37

Mixed Review

Multiply. Write the answer in simplest form.

25. $\frac{1}{5} \times \frac{6}{7}$ 26. $\frac{4}{9} \times \frac{3}{5}$ 27. $\frac{4}{5} \times 30$
    $\frac{6}{35}$ $\frac{4}{15}$ 24

28. $2\frac{7}{10} \times \frac{2}{4}$ 29. $3\frac{3}{4} \times 2\frac{2}{5}$ 30. $1\frac{1}{2} \times 3\frac{1}{3}$
    $\frac{9}{5}$, or $1\frac{4}{5}$ 9   5

CHECK FOR UNDERSTANDING

Think and ▶ Discuss

Look back at the lesson to answer each question.

1. **Give an example** of a scale in real life in which zero is used together with other integers. **Possible answer: temperature**

2. **Tell** what the absolute value of an integer is. **It is its distance from zero on a number line.**

Guided ▶ Practice

Write an integer to represent each situation.

3. 350 ft below sea level **⁻350**

4. an increase of 78 points **⁺78**

5. 14 degrees below zero **⁻14**

Write the opposite integer.

6. ⁻289
⁺289

7. ⁻25
⁺25

8. ⁺315
⁻315

9. ⁺742
⁻742

10. ⁺993
⁻993

PRACTICE AND PROBLEM SOLVING

Independent ▶ Practice

Write an integer to represent each situation.

11. a $5.00 decline in value **⁻5**

12. an increased attendance of 477 **⁺477**

13. a gain of 12,000 ft in altitude **⁺12,000**

14. a decrease of 50 points **⁻50**

Write the opposite integer.

15. ⁻2
⁺2

16. ⁻14
⁺14

17. ⁻31
⁺31

18. ⁺88
⁻88

19. ⁺207
⁻207

Find the absolute value.

20. |⁺390|
390

21. |⁻28|
28

22. |⁻727|
727

23. |⁺660|
660

24. |⁺795|
795

Problem Solving ▶ Applications

The Dead Sea

25. The elevation of the Dead Sea is about 1,310 ft below sea level. Write the elevation using an integer. **⁻1,310 ft**

26. **REASONING** What values can *n* have if |*n*| = 5? **⁺5 or ⁻5**

27. Chris has a stack of coins containing 5 quarters, 5 dimes, and 15 nickels. What fraction of the number of coins are quarters? **$\frac{1}{5}$**

28. ✏️ **Write a problem** about two campers who camped at altitudes of 9,470 ft and 7,200 ft. Use positive and negative integers to describe the change in elevation. **Check students' problems.**

MIXED REVIEW AND TEST PREP

29. Multiply. $\frac{4}{5} \times \frac{3}{4}$ **$\frac{12}{20}$, or $\frac{3}{5}$** (p. 202)

30. Lisa works for $6.50 an hour, 3 hours a day, 4 days a week. How many weeks will it take her to earn more than $300? (p. 76) **4 weeks**

31. Find the value of the expression $9 \times (12 - 4) \div 2^3 + 4$ (p. 44) **13**

32. Write the prime factorization of 72. (p. 148) **$3 \times 3 \times 2 \times 2 \times 2$, or $3^2 \times 2^3$**

33. **TEST PREP** Six soccer teams compete for the regional play-offs. Each team plays each of the other teams only once. How many games do they play? (p. 154) **C**

A 6   B 12   C 15   D 30

Extra Practice page H42, Set A

229

PROBLEM SOLVING 11.1

Understand Integers

Write the correct answer.

Analyze · Choose · Solve · Check

1. Write an integer that represents the situation.

52 feet above sea level

⁺52 or 52

2. Write an integer that represents the situation.

losing 25 yards in football

⁻25

3. There are three bags of apples. They weigh 3.1 pounds, 3.2 pounds, and 3.05 pounds. Write the weights in order from greatest to least. Use >.

3.2 > 3.1 > 3.05

4. A hiker is 30 feet above sea level, on a cliff. His friend is 15 feet below sea level, in a valley below the hiker. What is the difference in elevation of the two hikers?

45 ft

Choose the letter for the best answer.

5. Maggie went deep-sea diving. She explored a sunken ship at 78 feet below sea level and a reef at 45 feet below sea level. Which is the position of the sunken ship written as an integer?

A ⁺78
B ⁺45
C ⁻45
D ⁻78

6. Jon was in a hot-air balloon at 23,500 feet above sea level. Phil was in a hot-air balloon at 15,200 feet above sea level. Which is the elevation of Jon's hot-air balloon written as an integer?

F ⁺23,500
G ⁺15,200
H ⁻15,200
J ⁻23,500

7. Luis scored 98, 88, 76, 78, 98, and 65 on his last 6 test. What is the range of Luis's test scores?

A 98
B 83
C 33
D 22

8. Kim works between 32 and 38 hours a week. Which is a reasonable estimate of how many hours Kim works in a year?

F Less than 2,000 hr
G Between 2,000 and 3,000 hr
H Between 3,000 and 4,000 hr
J Between 4,000 and 5,000 hr

9. **Write About It** On a number line, what value would best represent sea level? Explain.

Sea level would best be represented by zero. Elevations above

sea level would be represented by positive integers and elevations

below sea level would be represented by negative integers.

CHALLENGE 11.1

Name That Floor

The floor selection keys found in a hotel's elevator are shown. Each of the following describes a ride in the elevator.

Use integers to show how each rider's position changed. Then name the floor on which each person left the elevator. The first one is done for you.

1. Suki entered the elevator on the seventh floor. She traveled up three floors and then down five floors before leaving the elevator.

⁺3, ⁻5; fifth floor

2. Josh entered the elevator at the lobby. He went up six floors and then down two before leaving the elevator.

⁺6, ⁻2; third floor

3. Rob got on the elevator on the twelfth floor. He rode down to the mezzanine and then up four floors before leaving the elevator.

⁻12, ⁺4; fourth floor

4. Tomás entered the elevator from the garage. He rode up eight floors, down two floors, and then up another three floors before exiting.

⁺8, ⁻2, ⁺3; seventh floor

5. Jon entered the elevator on the ninth floor. He rode up five floors, down six floors, and then down another two floors before leaving the elevator.

⁺5, ⁻6, ⁻2; sixth floor

6. Tina got on the elevator at the lobby. She rode up to the fourteenth floor, down six floors, up four floors, and then she exited the elevator.

⁺15, ⁻6, ⁺4; twelfth floor

7. Evan entered the elevator on the fifth floor. He rode down to the mezzanine, down to the garage, and up four floors before leaving.

⁻5, ⁻2, ⁺4; second floor

8. Carole got on the elevator on the first floor. She rode up six floors, down to the mezzanine, and then up two floors before exiting.

⁺6, ⁻7, ⁺2; second floor

---

3 Practice

Students may read numbers such as ⁺3 and ⁻2 as "plus 3" and "minus 2." Urge them to say "positive 3" and "negative 2." Explain that the words *plus* and *minus* are used for addition or subtraction of numbers.

Guided Practice

Do Check for Understanding Exercises 1–10 with your students. Identify those having difficulty and use lesson resources to help.

Independent Practice

Assign Exercises 11–28.

Algebraic Thinking As students approach Exercise 28, remind them that some equations can have more than one solution.

MIXED REVIEW AND TEST PREP

Exercises 29–33 provide **cumulative review** (Chapters 1–11).

4 Assess

Summarize the lesson by having students:

DISCUSS When you write an integer, what does the + or − sign tell you about where the integer is? Possible answer: The + sign indicates that the integer is to the right of 0, and the − sign indicates that the integer is to the left of 0.

WRITE What are integers? Integers are all whole numbers and their opposites.

Lesson Quiz

Transparency **11.1**

Write the opposite integer.

1. ⁺60 **⁻60**   2. ⁻100 **⁺100**

3. ⁺75 **⁻75**   4. ⁻97 **⁺97**

Find the absolute value.

5. |⁻13| **13**   6. |⁺27| **27**

7. |⁻350| **350**   8. |⁺105| **105**

229

Rational Numbers
LESSON PLANNING

Objective To classify sets of numbers and to find another rational number between two rational numbers

Intervention for Prerequisite Skills

Locate Points on a Number Line, Sets of Numbers, Compare Fractions (For intervention strategies, see page 227.)

California Mathematics Content Standards

NS 1.0 Students compare and order positive and negative fractions, decimals, and mixed numbers. Students solve problems involving fractions, ratios, proportions, and percentages.

NS 1.1 Compare and order positive and negative fractions, decimals, and mixed numbers and place them on a number line.

(*Also* MR 1.0, MR 2.0, MR 3.0, MR 3.2, MR 3.3)

Vocabulary

ratio a comparison of two numbers

rational number any number that can be written as a ratio $\frac{a}{b}$ where a and b are integers and $b \neq 0$

Venn diagram a diagram that shows the relationships between sets

Math Background

The set of rational numbers includes fractions and mixed numbers as well as integers and decimals. Any number that can be written in the form $\frac{a}{b}$, where a and b are integers and $b \neq 0$, is a rational number.

To help students understand rational numbers, stress these points.

- A mixed number can be written in the form $\frac{a}{b}$ by multiplying the whole number by the denominator of the fraction, adding the numerator, and writing the result over the denominator.

- Any terminating decimal can be written in the form $\frac{a}{b}$ by using place value: $4.5 = 4\frac{5}{10} = \frac{45}{10}$.

- You can find a rational number between any two given rational numbers by finding their mean.

WARM-UP RESOURCES

 NUMBER OF THE DAY Transparency 11.2

Write the opposite of the number representing the day of the month. Possible answer for April 4: ⁻4

 PROBLEM OF THE DAY Transparency 11.2

I am a palindrome number, and the sum of my 7 digits is 25. My tens digit is 4 times as great as my ones digit and 4 more than my hundreds digit. My thousands digit and my thousandths digit are each 7 greater than my ones digit. What number am I? 8,041.408

Solution Problem of the Day tab, p. PD11

 DAILY FACTS PRACTICE

Have students practice subtraction facts by completing Set C of *Teacher's Resource Book,* p. TR101.

INTERVENTION AND EXTENSION RESOURCES

ALTERNATIVE TEACHING STRATEGY (ELL)

Materials *For each student* ruler, p. TR22; tracing paper

Reinforce the concept of rational numbers. Have students draw a number line from ⁻5 to ⁺5 on tracing paper, marking equal increments. After discussing positive rational numbers, ask students to identify 10 positive rational numbers. Have them write the numbers in the form $\frac{a}{b}$ and graph them on the number line.

Then have students fold the number line at the zero point and mark the opposites of all the rational numbers they have graphed so far.

Discuss the negative rational numbers as opposites, and have students write them in the form $\frac{a}{b}$. Finally, have them graph another negative rational number between two pairs of adjacent numbers.

Check students' work.

See also page 232.

VISUAL

MIXED REVIEW AND TEST PREP

Cumulative Review Chapters 1–11

Refer to the Pupil Edition pages referenced in the exercises for further review. Have students go to the lesson page, review the lesson, and correct any problem they missed.

Mixed Review and Test Prep, p. 233

How to Help	
Item	**Page**
36	228
37	169
38	182
39	106
40	150

WRITING IN MATHEMATICS

Have students copy the Venn diagram showing the **relationship between whole numbers, integers, and rational numbers.** Then, write a paragraph describing how to determine into which box to place a number such as 2.5.

Possible answer: First check to see if the number is a whole number or an integer. 2.5 is neither. Then, to decide if it is a rational number, see if the number can be written as a ratio of two whole numbers. Because $2.5 = 2\frac{5}{10} = \frac{25}{10}$, it is a rational number. If the number could not be written as a whole number, integer, or rational number, it would not be placed in any of the boxes.

GEOMETRY CONNECTION

Materials reference materials

Enhance students' knowledge of a commonly-used irrational number. This decimal used in geometry is the approximate value of π, a number that never terminates or repeats.

3.14159265358979...

The fact that it never terminates or repeats was proven in 1767 by Johann Lambert. Have students research pi. Possible answer: In 1989, Yasumasa Kanada and Yoshiaki Tamura proved once again when they computed π to 1,073,740,000 places that it never terminates or repeats.

AUDITORY

TECHNOLOGY LINK

- **Intervention Strategies and Activities CD-ROM** • *Skills 7, 27, 42*
- **Astro Algebra** • *Red,* Level K

LESSON 11.2 ORGANIZER

Objective To classify sets of numbers and to find another rational number between two rational numbers

Vocabulary ratio, rational number, Venn diagram

1 Introduce

QUICK REVIEW provides review of pre-requisite skills.

Why Learn This? This skill is necessary in algebra to identify and understand how different types of numbers are related. *Share the lesson objective with students.*

2 Teach

Guided Instruction

• *As you discuss the sample rational numbers and Example 1, ask:*

How can you write any whole number as a ratio of integers? Possible answer: Write it as a fraction that has the whole number in the numerator and 1 in the denominator.

How can you write a mixed number as a ratio? Write it as a fraction greater than one.

• *Before discussing A–D in Example 2, draw another Venn diagram showing how cats, mammals, and animals are related. Ask:*

Are all cats mammals? yes

Are all animals mammals? no

Modifying Instruction Have students verbalize the relationships between sets of numbers: *The set of whole numbers is contained in the set of integers. Every integer is also a rational number.*

ADDITIONAL EXAMPLE

Example 1, p. 230

Write each rational number as a ratio $\frac{a}{b}$.

A. $1\frac{5}{8}$ **B.** 0.1   **C.** 65   **D.** $^-1.5$

$1\frac{5}{8} = \frac{13}{8}$ $0.1 = \frac{1}{10}$ $65 = \frac{65}{1}$ $^-1.5 = \frac{^-3}{2}$

See also page 231.

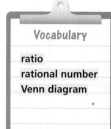

LESSON 11.2 Rational Numbers

Learn how to classify rational numbers and find another rational number between two rational numbers.

Vocabulary
ratio
rational number
Venn diagram

QUICK REVIEW

Write as a decimal and as a fraction.
1. eight tenths   2. fifty-four hundredths   3. three tenths
4. nineteen hundredths   5. forty thousandths

1. 0.8, $\frac{8}{10}$ 2. 0.54, $\frac{54}{100}$ 3. 0.3, $\frac{3}{10}$ 4. 0.19, $\frac{19}{100}$ 5. 0.040, $\frac{40}{1,000}$

A **ratio** is a comparison of two numbers, a and b, written as a fraction $\frac{a}{b}$. A **rational number** is any number that can be written as a ratio $\frac{a}{b}$, where a and b are integers and $b \neq 0$. The numbers below are all rational numbers since they can be expressed as a ratio $\frac{a}{b}$.

$$3\frac{2}{5} \qquad 0.6 \qquad 42 \qquad ^-2.5$$

Write each rational number as a ratio $\frac{a}{b}$.

EXAMPLE 1

A. $3\frac{2}{5}$ **B.** 0.6   **C.** 42   **D.** $^-2.5$

$3\frac{2}{5} = \frac{17}{5}$ $0.6 = \frac{6}{10}$ $42 = \frac{42}{1}$ $^-2.5 = \frac{^-5}{2}$

The **Venn diagram** shows how the sets of rational numbers, integers, and whole numbers are related.

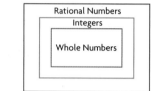

EXAMPLE 2

Use the Venn diagram to determine in which set or sets each number belongs.

A. 80   The number 80 belongs in the sets of whole numbers, integers, and rational numbers.

B. $^-2$ The number $^-2$ belongs in the sets of integers and rational numbers but not in the set of whole numbers.

C. $6\frac{1}{2}$ The number $6\frac{1}{2}$ belongs in the set of rational numbers but not in the set of integers or the set of whole numbers.

D. 7.09   The number 7.09 belongs in the set of rational numbers but not in the set of integers or the set of whole numbers.
Possible answer: $^-7, ^-4$

• Name two integers that are not also whole numbers.

CALIFORNIA STANDARDS ⚏ **NS 1.0** Students compare and order positive and negative fractions, decimals, and mixed numbers. Students solve problems involving fractions, ratios, proportions, and percentages. ⚏ **NS 1.1** Compare and order positive and negative fractions, decimals, and mixed numbers and place them on a number line. *also,* **MR 1.0, MR 2.0, MR 3.0, MR 3.2, MR 3.3**

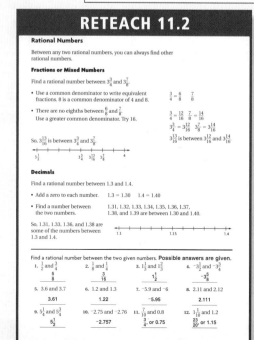

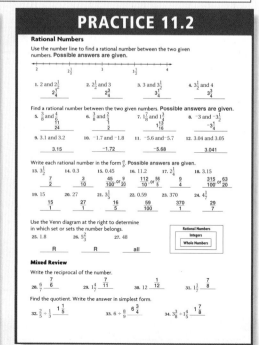

Christopher is training to run in a 5-km road race. Yesterday he ran $4\frac{1}{4}$ km, and he plans to run $4\frac{1}{2}$ km tomorrow. What distance could he run today if he wants to run between $4\frac{1}{4}$ km and $4\frac{1}{2}$ km?

Think of the distances of Christopher's training runs as rational numbers.

One Way You can use a number line to find numbers between two rational numbers.

EXAMPLE 3

Find a distance between $4\frac{1}{4}$ km and $4\frac{1}{2}$ km, using the number line.

Notice that there is a mark between $4\frac{1}{4}$ and $4\frac{1}{2}$. That could be a distance Christopher could run.

So, Christopher could run $4\frac{3}{8}$ km today.

Another Way You can use a common denominator to find a number between two rational numbers.

EXAMPLE 4

Find a number between $4\frac{1}{4}$ and $4\frac{1}{2}$.

$4\frac{1}{4} = 4\frac{2}{8}$ $4\frac{1}{2} = 4\frac{4}{8}$ *Use a common denominator to write equivalent fractions.*

$4\frac{3}{8}$ is between $4\frac{2}{8}$ and $4\frac{4}{8}$.   *Find a rational number between the two numbers.*

So, $4\frac{3}{8}$ is between $4\frac{1}{4}$ and $4\frac{1}{2}$.

• What are some common denominators you could use to find other rational numbers between $4\frac{1}{4}$ and $4\frac{1}{2}$? **Possible answers: 16, 24, 32**

You can also find a number between two rational numbers in decimal form.

EXAMPLE 5

Find a rational number between ⁻8.4 and ⁻8.5.

⁻8.4 = ⁻8.40   *Add a zero to each decimal.*

⁻8.5 = ⁻8.50

Use a number line to find a number between the two decimals.

$\mathcal{R}$emember that you can add any number of zeros to the right of a decimal without changing its value.

So, ⁻8.43, ⁻8.45, and ⁻8.48 are some of the numbers between ⁻8.4 and ⁻8.5.

231

• *When discussing Example 3, ask:*

If the distances were marked in sixteenths, what other distances would be between $4\frac{1}{4}$ km and $4\frac{1}{2}$ km? $4\frac{5}{16}$ km, $4\frac{6}{16}$ km, $4\frac{7}{16}$ km

• *After discussing Examples 4 and 5, demonstrate two other possibilities for finding a number between two rational numbers.*

Could you use the mean to find a rational number between the two fractions? Explain. Yes; The mean is the average of the two numbers, and would be located in between them, similar to the balance point on the line plot discussed in Chapter 6.

Modifying Instruction Point out that another simple way to find a fraction between two other fractions, such as $\frac{1}{2}$ and $\frac{3}{4}$, is to add the numerators and add the denominators: $\frac{1+3}{2+4} = \frac{4}{6} = \frac{2}{3}$. Therefore, $\frac{2}{3}$ lies between $\frac{1}{2}$ and $\frac{3}{4}$.

ADDITIONAL EXAMPLES

Example 2, p. 230

Use the Venn diagram on page 230 to determine in which set or sets each number belongs.

A. 0.06 rational numbers

B. ⁻7 integers, rational numbers

C. $5\frac{1}{2}$ rational numbers

D. 11 whole numbers, integers, rational numbers

Example 3, p. 231

Find a distance between $4\frac{1}{2}$ km and $4\frac{7}{8}$ km, using the number line on page 231. Possible answers: $4\frac{5}{8}$ or $4\frac{6}{8}$

Example 4, p. 231

Find a rational number between $3\frac{1}{2}$ and $3\frac{3}{4}$. Possible answer: $3\frac{5}{8}$

Example 5, p. 231

Find a rational number between ⁻4.5 and ⁻4.6. Possible answer: ⁻4.52

PROBLEM SOLVING 11.2

Rational Numbers

Write the correct answer.

Analyze Choose Solve Check

1. Write $8\frac{2}{3}$ as a rational number in the form $\frac{a}{b}$. $\frac{26}{3}$

2. Find a rational number between $\frac{1}{8}$ and $\frac{1}{3}$.   **Possible answer:** $\frac{1}{5}$

3. Write an integer that represents the situation.

climbing up a cliff 856 ft

⁺856 or 856

4. Write an integer that represents the situation.

a drop in temperature of 48 degrees

⁻48

Choose the letter for the best answer.

5. The temperature outside was 36°F. The temperature inside was 72°F. Which is the inside temperature written as an integer?
   Ⓐ ⁺72
   B ⁻36
   C ⁻36
   D ⁻72

6. Which rational number is equivalent to $2\frac{5}{9}$?
   F $\frac{22}{9}$
   Ⓖ $\frac{23}{9}$
   H $\frac{24}{9}$
   J $\frac{25}{9}$

7. The local newspaper wants to use a graph to report the number of tourists that have visited the town each month for the last year. Which type of graph should the newspaper use?
   A bar graph
   Ⓑ line graph
   C histogram
   D line plot

8. Nancy checked the gauge on her propane tank and found that the tank was between $\frac{1}{4}$ and $\frac{1}{2}$ full. Which fraction could represent how full the tank was when Nancy checked?
   Ⓕ $\frac{7}{16}$
   G $\frac{11}{16}$
   H $\frac{9}{16}$
   J $\frac{13}{16}$

9. **Write About It** Explain how 0 can be written in the form $\frac{a}{b}$.
   The number 0 can be written as $\frac{0}{9}$ or 0 over any number. 0 over

   any number is 0.

CHALLENGE 11.2

Math Pun

Find the numbers in the Math Pun that are between the pairs of numbers in the list below. Then write the letter for the pair of numbers above the number between them to discover the Math Pun.

S 2.7 and 2.9   L $\frac{3}{5}$ and 0.8   G ⁻2.5 and ⁻1.3

B $2\frac{1}{4}$ and 2.5   I ⁻$1\frac{1}{2}$ and ⁻0.5   R ⁻$\frac{2}{3}$ and ⁻$\frac{3}{4}$

U $1\frac{1}{3}$ and 1.4   H $\frac{1}{8}$ and $\frac{1}{4}$ O ⁻3.4 and ⁻3.5

A $\frac{1}{5}$ and 0.3   M $\frac{5}{6}$ and $\frac{7}{8}$ T $1\frac{1}{6}$ and 1.6

E ⁻3.8 and ⁻3.9   N 0 and ⁻$\frac{1}{8}$ K 2.53 and 2.43

MATH PUN:
R   A   T   I   O   N   A   L
⁻$\frac{17}{24}$ $\frac{1}{4}$ 1.25   ⁻1   ⁻3.46   ⁻$\frac{1}{16}$ $\frac{1}{4}$ 0.7

N   U   M   B   E   R   S
⁻$\frac{1}{16}$ 1.35 $\frac{41}{48}$ 2.4   ⁻3.82   ⁻$\frac{17}{24}$ 2.8

T   H   I   N   K
1.25 $\frac{3}{16}$ ⁻1   ⁻$\frac{1}{16}$ 2.5

S   T   R   A   I   G   H   T
2.8   1.25   ⁻$\frac{17}{24}$ $\frac{1}{4}$ ⁻1   1.8 $\frac{3}{16}$ 1.25

LESSON 11.2

3 | Practice

Guided Practice

Do Check for Understanding Exercises 1–11 with your students. Identify those having difficulty and use lesson resources to help.

COMMON ERROR ALERT

Students may think that integers are not rational numbers. Remind them that integers such as 5 and ⁻7 can be written in ratio form $\frac{a}{b}$.

$$5 = \frac{5}{1}; \quad ^-7 = \frac{^-7}{1}$$

Independent Practice

Assign Exercises 12–35.

Before beginning Exercises 20–25, remind students that more than one answer is possible. Another rational number can always be found between any two rational numbers.

For Exercises 20–25, you may want to help students rewrite one or both of the numbers so that they are in like form and, therefore, easier to compare.

Think and ▸ Discuss

Look back at the lesson to answer each question.

1. All integers can be written in the form $\frac{a}{1}$; possible example: $^-3 = \frac{^-3}{1}$

1. **Tell** why every integer is a rational number. Give an example to support your answer.

2. **Tell** what numbers would be between $4\frac{1}{4}$ and $4\frac{1}{2}$ if you divided a number line into sixteenths. $4\frac{5}{16}$, $4\frac{6}{16}$, $4\frac{7}{16}$

Guided ▸ Practice

3. $\frac{^-37}{100}$ 5. $\frac{889}{1,000}$

Write each rational number in the form $\frac{a}{b}$. Possible answers are given.

3. ⁻0.37   4. $2\frac{4}{5}$ $\frac{14}{5}$ 5. 0.889   6. 7.31 $\frac{731}{100}$ 7. $^-7\frac{1}{3}$ $\frac{^-22}{3}$

Use the number line to find a rational number between the two given numbers. Possible answers are given.

8. 1 and $1\frac{1}{2}$ $1\frac{1}{4}$ 9. $^-\frac{3}{4}$ and $^-\frac{1}{4}$ $^-\frac{1}{2}$ 10. $\frac{1}{2}$ and $1\frac{3}{4}$ 11. $^-\frac{1}{2}$ and $\frac{1}{2}$ 0

Independent ▸ Practice

13. $\frac{^-71}{100}$

Write each rational number in the form $\frac{a}{b}$. Possible answers are given.

12. $9\frac{2}{3}$ $\frac{29}{3}$ 13. ⁻0.71   14. 80.4 $\frac{804}{10}$ 15. $^-2\frac{5}{8}$ $^-\frac{21}{8}$ 16. 3.18 $\frac{318}{100}$

Use the number line to find a rational number between the two given numbers. Possible answers are given.

17. ⁻0.2 and ⁻0.4 ⁻0.3   18. 0 and 0.2 0.1   19. ⁻0.6 and ⁻0.8 ⁻0.7

Find a rational number between the two given numbers. Possible answers are given.

20. $\frac{3}{4}$ and $\frac{1}{2}$ $\frac{5}{8}$ 21. ⁻7 and $^-\frac{15}{2}$ $^-7\frac{1}{4}$ 22. 104.1 and 103$\frac{7}{8}$ 104

23. 16.1 and 16.01 16.05   24. $3\frac{5}{8}$ and $\frac{27}{8}$ $\frac{28}{8}$ 25. $^-\frac{3}{4}$ and $^-\frac{3}{8}$ $^-\frac{5}{8}$

Tell if the first rational number is between the second and third rational numbers. Write *yes* or *no*.

26. $\frac{1}{3}$; $\frac{1}{2}$ and $\frac{3}{4}$ no   27. 0.97; 0.85 and 0.99 yes   28. 3.29; 3.20 and 3.25 no

29. 3.07; 3.1 and 3.01 yes   30. ⁻8; $^-\frac{29}{4}$ and $^-\frac{33}{4}$ yes   31. $^-\frac{1}{8}$; $^-\frac{1}{16}$ and $^-\frac{1}{4}$ yes

Problem Solving ▸ Applications

32. Marie had already completed $\frac{1}{2}$ of the running race but had not yet reached the point $\frac{3}{4}$ of the way through the race. Could she have completed $\frac{5}{8}$ of the race? Explain. Yes; $\frac{5}{8}$ is between $\frac{1}{2}$ and $\frac{3}{4}$.

Alternative Teaching Strategy

Purpose Students play a game to reinforce understanding of rational numbers.

Materials 11 index cards labeled from ⁻1.5 through 1.5 in increments of tenths

Before playing the game, guide students to name rational numbers between tenths. Remind them that ⁻1.5 is the same as ⁻1.50 and ⁻1.4 is the same as ⁻1.40. Guide them to realize that they can use hundredths.

Ask: Name several rational numbers between ⁻1.50 and ⁻1.40. Possible answers: ⁻1.45, ⁻1.43, ⁻1.46

Display the following number line:

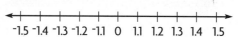

Play the following game with the class:

1. Ask two students to each pick a card and show them to the class.

2. Have players take turns picking cards. The first player to pick a card that shows a number between the first two numbers stands up and directs one of the card holders to take his or her seat.

3. Repeat Step 2 until two players have two consecutive tenths.

4. Challenge the rest of the class to name a rational number that comes between the two numbers shown.

Check students' work.

33. Susan follows the directions of a treasure map and walks 45 steps north, then $\frac{24}{3}$ steps east, $\frac{75}{5}$ steps south, and 22 steps west. How many steps does Susan walk? **90 steps**

34. Is it easier to find a rational number between $\frac{1}{2}$ and $\frac{3}{4}$ or between 0.50 and 0.75? Explain your reasoning. **See below.**

35. **What's the Error?** Jeff says that every whole number is an integer and that every integer is a whole number. Explain his error. **Not all integers are whole numbers; ⁻8 is not a whole number.**

MIXED REVIEW AND TEST PREP

36. Find the absolute value. $|{-88}|$ (p. 228) **88**

37. Write the decimal and fraction equivalents of 34%. (p. 169) **0.34; $\frac{34}{100}$**

38. $\frac{2}{5} + \frac{4}{10} + \frac{4}{5}$ (p. 182) **1$\frac{3}{5}$**

39. **TEST PREP** Which is the range of the number set 28, 8, 13, 20, and 24? (p. 106) **D**

A 4 **B** 8 **C** 15 **D** 20

40. **TEST PREP** Which is the least common multiple of 3, 5, 9, and 15? (p. 150) **H**

F 15 **G** 30 **H** 45 **J** 90

34. Possible answer: Between 0.50 and 0.75; you don't have to find a common denominator.

LiNKUP to Reading

Strategy • Use Graphic Aids Graphic aids such as Venn diagrams, charts, and tables provide specific or important information in a visual form rather than in text. Sometimes, the information needed to solve a problem may be provided only in a graphic aid.

Look at the Venn diagram to the right. It shows the relationships among whole, prime, and composite numbers.

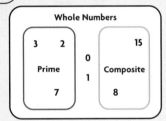

Whole Numbers
Prime: 3, 2, 7
0, 1
Composite: 15, 8

- Is a composite number always, sometimes, or never a whole number? **Always; the diagram shows that all composite numbers are also within the set of whole numbers.**
- Is a whole number always, sometimes, or never a prime number? **Sometimes; the diagram shows that some numbers within the set of whole numbers are not also prime.**

Use the Venn diagram to solve the following problems.

1. How would you describe the numbers 7 and 15? Are they whole numbers? Are they prime or composite? **yes; 7 is prime, 15 is composite**

2. Is 1 a whole number? Is it prime or composite? Explain. **yes; neither; it falls within the whole number category, but outside both prime and composite number groups**

Extra Practice page H42, Set B

233

READING STRATEGY

K-W-L Chart Before having students read the Link Up to Reading, have them look at the title and Venn diagram. Ask them to predict what the Link Up will be about. Then have students make a three-column chart headed What I Know, What I Want to Know, and What I Learned. Ask them to fill in the first two columns. Have them fill in the third column as they read the paragraph.

K-W-L Chart

What I Know	What I Want to Know	What I Learned

ENG-LANG ARTS Standards R 2.4

MIXED REVIEW AND TEST PREP
Exercises 36–40 provide **cumulative review** (Chapters 1–11).

LiNKUP to READING

- Review with students the definitions of prime numbers and composite numbers. After students have studied the Venn diagram, ask:

Why is the 0 outside the prime and composite sets? It is neither prime nor composite.

Where would the integers be in this diagram? outside the whole numbers

REASONING What is the only even prime number? 2

What is the greatest odd prime number? Since there is an infinite number of prime numbers, the greatest odd prime cannot be determined.

4 Assess

Summarize the lesson by having students:

DISCUSS If you have a positive rational number and a negative rational number, is there always a rational number between them? Explain. Yes; The number 0 is between any positive rational number and any negative rational number.

WRITE How would you find a rational number between ⁻1 and $-\frac{3}{4}$? Possible answer: Write ⁻1 as the fraction $-\frac{4}{4}$. Next use the common denominator 8 to write equivalent fractions. Then find a rational number between the two numbers.

Lesson Quiz

Transparency **11.2**

Write each rational number in the form $\frac{a}{b}$. Possible answers are given.

1. $20\frac{4}{5}$ $\frac{104}{5}$ **2.** ⁻13.5 $-\frac{135}{10}$ or $-\frac{27}{2}$

Find a rational number between the two given numbers. Possible answers are given.

3. ⁻4 and $-4\frac{1}{2}$ $-4\frac{1}{4}$ **4.** 5.7 and 5.8 5.73

233

Compare and Order Rational Numbers

LESSON PLANNING

Objective To compare and order rational numbers

Intervention for Prerequisite Skills

Locate Points on a Number Line, Compare Fractions, Temperature (For intervention strategies, see page 227.)

 ## California Mathematics Content Standards

⊶ NS 1.0 Students compare and order positive and negative fractions, decimals, and mixed numbers. Students solve problems involving fractions, ratios, proportions, and percentages.

(*Also* MR 1.0, MR 2.0, MR 2.4, MR 3.0)

Math Background

These concepts will help students understand how to compare two or more rational numbers.

- A number line can be used to compare integers. If one integer is to the left of another on the number line, it is less than the integer to the right.

- As negative integers increase in absolute value, they decrease in numeric value.

- Any negative rational number is less than every positive one.

- To compare a decimal and a fraction, write both as decimals, or write both as fractions or mixed numbers with a common denominator.

WARM-UP RESOURCES

 ### NUMBER OF THE DAY

Transparency
11.3

Graph the number associated with the month of the year on a number line. Move 10 units to the left. What number did you find? Possible answer for 2: 10 units to the left of 2 is ⁻8.

 ### PROBLEM OF THE DAY

Transparency
11.3

Leon's number is less than Bev's.

Shannon has a negative number.

Leon's and Tony's numbers were the least and the greatest.

Who has each of these numbers:

$-2\frac{1}{5}$, $\frac{19}{18}$, 2.05, -2.25?

Leon -2.25; Shannon $-2\frac{1}{5}$; Bev $\frac{19}{18}$; Tony 2.05

Solution Problem of the Day tab, p. PD11

 ### DAILY FACTS PRACTICE

Have students practice multiplication facts by completing Set D of *Teacher's Resource Book,* p. TR101.

INTERVENTION AND EXTENSION RESOURCES

ALTERNATIVE TEACHING STRATEGY

By relating the concepts of "greater than" and "less than" to numbers on a thermometer, many students will find it easier to **compare rational numbers.** Draw the number line vertically instead of horizontally.

Refer to Examples 1 and 2 on PE page 234. Call on volunteers to show the numbers you are comparing on the vertical number line. Then write the comparison statements and relate them to the numbers on the horizontal number line.

VISUAL

MIXED REVIEW AND TEST PREP

Cumulative Review Chapters 1–11

Refer to the Pupil Edition pages referenced in the exercises for further review. Have students go to the lesson page, review the lesson, and correct any problem they missed.

Mixed Review and Test Prep, p. 235

How to Help	
Item	Page
23	228
24	58
25	164
26	182
27	206

ENGLISH LANGUAGE LEARNERS ELL•SDAIE

Materials *For each student* 2 index cards

To **reinforce the concept of ordering rational numbers,** have each student write a rational number of their choosing on one index card and then write the opposite number on the other index card.

Have two volunteers each display one of their number cards. Then have a third volunteer write either $<$, $>$, or $=$ between the two numbers and explain his or her reasoning to the class. Check students' work.

VISUAL

WRITING IN MATHEMATICS

Materials *For each group* 15 index cards

Have students **practice comparing rational numbers.** Give each group of 3 students 15 index cards. Have students write a different rational number on each card, including both positive and negative rational numbers.

The groups shuffle their cards and place them face down in a pile. Each student turns over one card, and the student with the greatest number takes all the cards that are face up. They repeat the activity, but this time the student with the least number takes all the cards that are face up. Play continues, alternating greatest and least taking all, until one student has all the cards. Check students' work.

VISUAL

TECHNOLOGY LINK

- **Intervention Strategies and Activities CD-ROM** • *Skills 27, 42, 56*

- **Astro Algebra** • *Red,* Level L

- **Harcourt Math Newsroom Video** • *Slow Down Light*

Objective To compare and order rational numbers

1 Introduce

QUICK REVIEW provides review of prerequisite skills.

Why Learn This? Comparing and ordering numbers helps you decide which product has a higher rating or is more costly, and helps you organize information from a survey. *Share the lesson objective with students.*

2 Teach

Guided Instruction

- *As you discuss Example 1, display a number line to illustrate the examples. Ask:*

  How do you decide which number is less? The number farther to the left on the number line is less.

- *When students are reading Example 2, ask:*

  Why is 8.3 rewritten as 8.30? so the numbers will have the same number of decimal places and will be easier to compare

REASONING **If you compare two negative numbers and the absolute value of the first number is greater than the absolute value of the second number, which number is greater? Explain.** The second number; the number with the greater absolute value is farther to the left on the number line and, therefore, is less than the second number.

Algebraic Thinking Understanding number relationships shown by numerical inequalities will help students as they solve inequalities in algebra.

ADDITIONAL EXAMPLES

Example 1, p. 234

Compare the integers. Use $<$ and $>$. Think about their positions on a number line.

A. 1 and $^-$2 $^-$2 $<$ 1 or 1 $>$ $^-$2

B. $^-$4 and $^-$7 $^-$4 $>$ $^-$7 or $^-$7 $<$ $^-$4

Example 2, p. 234

Order $6\frac{1}{2}$, $^-6\frac{1}{3}$, and 6.4 from least to greatest. $^-6\frac{1}{3}$, 6.4, $6\frac{1}{2}$

LESSON 11.3

Learn how to compare and order rational numbers.

TECHNOLOGY LINK

To learn more about comparing rational numbers, watch the **Harcourt Math Newsroom Video** *Slow Down Light.*

Compare and Order Rational Numbers

QUICK REVIEW

Order the numbers from greatest to least.

1. 12,14,10 14; 12; 10
2. $^-$10, $^-$21, $^-$20 $^-$10, $^-$20, $^-$21
3. 3.10, 3.05, 3.15 3.15; 3.10; 3.05
4. $\frac{1}{4}$, $\frac{1}{2}$, $\frac{3}{4}$ $\frac{3}{4}$, $\frac{1}{2}$, $\frac{1}{4}$
5. $\frac{3}{5}$, $\frac{3}{6}$, $\frac{3}{4}$ $\frac{3}{4}$, $\frac{3}{5}$, $\frac{3}{6}$

Temperature commonly is measured on a scale in units of degrees. The scale contains both negative and positive numbers, like a number line. For example, the temperature in Death Valley has reached a high of 132°F, and the record low in Alaska is $^-$80°F.

You can use a number line to compare integers. On a number line, each number is greater than any number to its left and less than any number to its right. The number line below shows that $^-$80° $<$ 132° and 132° $>$ $^-$80°.

EXAMPLE 1

Compare the integers. Use $<$ and $>$. Think about their positions on a number line.

A. 2 and $^-$3
$^-$3 is to the left of 2 on the number line.
So, $^-$3 $<$ 2, or 2 $>$ $^-$3.

B. $^-$2 and $^-$4
$^-$2 is to the right of $^-$4 on the number line.
So, $^-$2 $>$ $^-$4, or $^-$4 $<$ $^-$2.

It is easier to compare and order rational numbers when they are all expressed as decimals or as fractions with a common denominator.

EXAMPLE 2

Order $8\frac{1}{4}$, $^-8\frac{1}{2}$, and 8.3 from least to greatest.

Since $^-8\frac{1}{2}$ is the only negative number, it is the least number.

Compare $8\frac{1}{4}$ and 8.3.

$8\frac{1}{4}$ = 8.25 and 8.3 = 8.30   *Write the numbers as decimals with the same number of decimal places.*

8.25 $<$ 8.30, or $8\frac{1}{4}$ $<$ 8.3   *Compare by looking at the place values.*

$^-8\frac{1}{2}$ $<$ $8\frac{1}{4}$ $<$ 8.3   *Order the three numbers.*

So, from least to greatest the numbers are $^-8\frac{1}{2}$, $8\frac{1}{4}$, and 8.3.

234

CALIFORNIA STANDARDS NS 1.0 Students compare and order positive and negative fractions, decimals, and mixed numbers. Students solve problems involving fractions, ratios, proportions, and percentages. *also,* **MR 1.0, MR 2.0, MR 2.4, MR 3.0**

RETEACH 11.3

Compare and Order Rational Numbers

You can compare rational numbers in decimal or fraction form.

Using Decimals

Compare $\frac{7}{25}$ and 0.35.

- Write the number that is not a decimal in decimal form. $\frac{7}{25} = 25\overline{)7.00}$ 0.28
- Compare decimals using place value.   0.28 $<$ 0.35

So, $\frac{7}{25} <$ 0.35.

Using Fractions

Compare $\frac{1}{4}$ and 0.3.

- Write the number that is not a fraction in fraction form.   0.3 = $\frac{3}{10}$
- Rewrite the fractions with the same denominator. Use 20 as a common denominator. $\frac{1}{4} = \frac{5}{20}$ $\frac{3}{10} = \frac{6}{20}$
- Compare the two fractions. $\frac{5}{20} < \frac{6}{20}$

So, $\frac{1}{4} <$ 0.3.

Compare. Write $<$ or $>$.

1. $\frac{2}{5}$ _>_ 0.2
2. 0.65 _<_ $\frac{2}{3}$
3. 8.9 _>_ $8\frac{4}{5}$
4. $^-4\frac{1}{8}$ _>_ $^-$4.3

Compare the rational numbers and order them from least to greatest.

5. 4.2, 2.4, $\frac{8}{2} \cdot \frac{2}{5}$
$\frac{2}{5} < 2.4 < \frac{8}{2} < 4.2$

6. $\frac{7}{5} \cdot \frac{2}{3}$, 0.2, 0.8
$0.2 < 0.8 < \frac{7}{5}$

7. 0.1, 0.6, 0.9, 0, $\frac{1}{9}$
$0 < 0.1 < \frac{1}{9} < 0.6 < 0.9$

8. $\frac{1}{3}, \frac{1}{5}, \frac{1}{8}$, 0.1
$0.1 < \frac{1}{8} < \frac{1}{5} < \frac{1}{3}$

9. $^-$1.4, $^-$1.5, 1.2, $\frac{6}{4}$
$^-1.5 < ^-1.4 < 1.2 < \frac{6}{4}$

10. 2.1, $^-$3.8, $\frac{10}{2}, \frac{^-3}{4}$
$^-3.8 < \frac{^-3}{4} < 2.1 < \frac{10}{2}$

11. 5.8, 4.9, 5.7, $2\frac{3}{5}$, 0.58
$0.58 < 2\frac{3}{5} < 4.9 < 5.7 < 5.8$

12. $^-$5.6, $^-$4.62, 2.34, $^-$4.68
$^-5.6 < ^-4.68 < ^-4.62 < 2.34$

PRACTICE 11.3

Compare and Order Rational Numbers

Compare. Write $<$ or $>$ for ◯.

1. 0.25 ◯ 0.4   _<_
2. $\frac{3}{8}$ ◯ 0.2   _>_
3. $^-2\frac{1}{2}$ ◯ $^-$2.3   _<_
4. $\frac{^-8}{8}$ ◯ $\frac{^-3}{10}$ _<_
5. 5 ◯ $^-$2   _>_
6. $\frac{^-7}{10}$ ◯ $\frac{4}{5}$ _<_
7. $^-$2.6 ◯ $^-$2.62   _>_
8. $\frac{3}{8}$ ◯ $\frac{5}{6}$ _<_
9. 3.8 + 2.2 ◯ $2\frac{1}{5} + 3\frac{4}{5}$ _>_
10. $3\frac{1}{2} \times 2$ ◯ $4\frac{1}{3} + 2.8$ _<_
11. $7\frac{1}{4} + 3\frac{1}{8}$ ◯ $1\frac{3}{8} \times 6$ _<_

Order the rational numbers from least to greatest.

12. 2.9, $^-$1.7, $\frac{9}{5}, \frac{3}{4}$
$^-1.7; \frac{3}{4}; 2.9; \frac{9}{5}$

13. $\frac{^-1}{5}, \frac{1}{10}, \frac{1}{9}$, 0.1
$\frac{^-1}{5}; 0.1; \frac{1}{10}; \frac{1}{9}$

14. 0, 0.8, $^-$1.4, $^-$0.6, $\frac{3}{5}$
$^-1.4; ^-0.6; 0; \frac{3}{5}; 0.8$

15. 8.7, $^-$9.2, $^-$7.3, 6.2, $6\frac{1}{2}$, $8\frac{7}{8}$
$^-9.2; ^-7.3; 6.2; 6\frac{1}{2}; 8.7; 8\frac{7}{8}$

16. $4\frac{1}{4}, 4\frac{3}{5}$, 4.9, 4.08, 0.49
$0.49; 4.08; 4\frac{1}{4}; 4\frac{3}{5}; 4.9$

Order the rational numbers from greatest to least.

17. 7.3, 6, $\frac{7}{8}$, 2
$7.3; 6; 2; \frac{7}{8}$

18. 2.4, $^-$1.4, $^-$3, 4.7, 3.8
$4.7; 3.8; 2.4; ^-1.4; ^-3$

19. $\frac{3}{5}, \frac{1}{10}$, 0.5, $^-$0.6, 0.42
$0.5; 0.42; \frac{3}{5}; \frac{1}{10}; ^-0.6$

Mixed Review

Find the LCM of each set of numbers.

20. 4, 10   20
21. 7, 12   84
22. 8, 18, 24   72
23. 5, 15, 20   60

Find the GCF of each set of numbers.

24. 12, 20   4
25. 16, 42   2
26. 15, 50, 75   5
27. 36, 54, 72   18

Find a pair of numbers for each set of conditions. Possible answers are given.

28. The LCM is 30. The GCF is 2.   6 and 10
29. The LCM is 36. The GCF is 6.   12 and 18

CHECK FOR UNDERSTANDING

Think and Discuss ▶ Look back at the lesson to answer each question.

1. **Describe** how you would compare 2.62 and $2\frac{3}{5}$.
   Possible answer: convert $2\frac{3}{5}$ to a decimal and compare place values.
2. **Give an example** of a rational number that is greater than $^-2.5$ and one that is less than $^-2.5$. Possible answer: $^-1.4$ and $^-3.2$

Guided Practice ▶ Compare. Write $<$, $>$, or $=$ for each ●.

```
|----|----|----|----|----|----|----|----|
-2.0 -1.5 -1.0 -0.5  0   0.5  1.0  1.5  2.0
```

3. $^-1.5$ ● $^-0.5$ 4. 0.5 ● $^-1.0$ 5. $1\frac{1}{4}$ ● 1.5 6. $^-2$ ● $^-1\frac{1}{2}$
   $<$ $>$ $<$ $<$

PRACTICE AND PROBLEM SOLVING

Independent Practice ▶ Compare. Write $<$, $>$, or $=$ for each ●.

7. $\frac{1}{2}$ ● $\frac{3}{4}$ 8. $\frac{1}{4}$ ● $^-\frac{1}{2}$ 9. 0.5 ● $\frac{3}{8}$ 10. $^-\frac{1}{4}$ ● 0.25
   $<$ $>$ $>$ $<$

11. 1.25 ● 1.75 12. $^-\frac{1}{4}$ ● $^-\frac{1}{3}$ 13. 2 ● $^-3$ 14. $\frac{4}{5}$ ● 0.9
    $<$ $>$ $>$ $<$

17. 0.4; 0.46; 0.6

15. $3.2 + 4.4$ ● $4\frac{3}{4} + 2\frac{3}{4}$ 16. $2\frac{3}{4} \times 4$ ● $3\frac{1}{4} + 8.5$
    $>$ $<$

18. $^-\frac{3}{4}$; $^-\frac{1}{2}$; $^-\frac{3}{8}$; $^-\frac{1}{8}$

Order the rational numbers from least to greatest.

19. $^-\frac{1}{4}$; $^-0.2$; 0; $\frac{1}{4}$

17. $0.6, 0.4, 0.46$ 18. $^-\frac{1}{8}, ^-\frac{1}{2}, ^-\frac{3}{8}, ^-\frac{3}{4}$ 19. $^-0.2, \frac{1}{4}, 0, ^-\frac{1}{4}$

Problem Solving Applications

22. Possible answer: The negative integer is least. Compare the positive numbers by converting the fraction to a decimal and comparing it with the decimal.

20. Lynda's times for running a mile are $5\frac{1}{2}$ min, 5.48 min, 5.51 min, and $5\frac{2}{5}$ min. What is the longest she has taken to run a mile? **5.51 min**

21. The mean temperatures for three days were $^-3°$, $^-5°$, and $1°$. Order the temperatures from highest to lowest. $1°, ^-3°, ^-5°$

22. ✎ **Write About It** Explain how you would order three numbers that include a positive fraction and decimal and a negative integer.

MIXED REVIEW AND TEST PREP

23. Write an integer to represent 450 ft below sea level. (p. 228) $^-450$

24. Round 2.0955 to the nearest thousandth. (p. 58) **2.096**

25. Write $3\frac{3}{7}$ as a fraction. (p. 164) $\frac{24}{7}$

26. $\frac{7}{8} - \frac{1}{2}$ (p. 182) $\frac{3}{8}$

27. **TEST PREP** The swim team practiced for 8 hours the first week, $1\frac{1}{4}$ times as long the second week, 12 hours the third week, and $\frac{24}{4}$ hours the fourth week. How many hours total did the swim team practice? (p. 206) **C**

   A 26   **B** 28   **C** 36   **D** 38

Extra Practice page H42, Set C   **235**

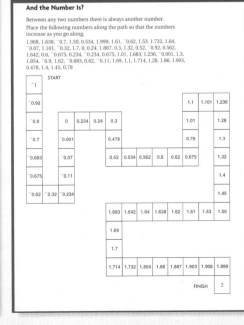

PROBLEM SOLVING 11.3

Compare and Order Rational Numbers

Analyze Choose Solve Check

Write the correct answer.

1. Compare the rational numbers and order them from least to greatest.
   $4.2, 4.083, \frac{5}{4}, \frac{9}{2}$
   $\frac{5}{4}, 4.083, 4.2, \frac{9}{2}$

2. Compare the rational numbers and order them from least to greatest.
   $5\frac{1}{4}, 5\frac{3}{8}, 5.1, 5.4$
   $5.1, 5\frac{1}{4}, 5\frac{3}{8}, 5.4$

3. Find a rational number between $\frac{1}{8}$ and $\frac{3}{4}$.
   Possible answer: $\frac{5}{8}$

4. Write $23\frac{3}{4}$ as a rational number in the form $\frac{a}{b}$.
   $\frac{95}{4}$

Choose the letter for the best answer.

5. The temperature outside was 67°F on Monday and 75°F on Tuesday. Which is the temperature on Monday written as an integer?
   A $^-75$ C $^-67$
   B $^+67$ D $^-75$

6. Jason's times for the 100-meter dash are 11.72 sec, $11\frac{3}{4}$ sec, $11\frac{1}{4}$ sec, and 11.85 sec. What is his lowest time for this race?
   F $11\frac{4}{5}$ sec   H $11\frac{3}{4}$ sec
   G 11.72 sec   J 11.85 sec

7. Larry is making punch for a large gathering of people. The recipe calls for 3 scoops of punch powder for every 10 cups. He needs to make 85 cups. Which is a reasonable estimate for how many scoops of powder Larry needs to use?
   A 18 scoops   **C** 26 scoops
   B 22 scoops   D 30 scoops

8. Which group of rational numbers is in order from least to greatest?
   F $^-\frac{2}{3}, ^-\frac{4}{5}, ^-\frac{6}{7}, ^-\frac{8}{9}$
   G $^-3.4, ^-3\frac{1}{3}, ^-3.3, ^-3.1$
   H $^-8.7, 8.07, 8.007, 8.7$
   J $^-2\frac{1}{2}, ^-2\frac{1}{3}, 0, 2\frac{1}{4}$

9. **Write About It** Explain how you would order a group of rational numbers in which some are positive and some are negative.
   Possible answer: Separate the positive and negative numbers.
   Order both groups from least to greatest. Then write the ordered list of negative numbers followed by the ordered list of positive numbers.

CHALLENGE 11.3

And the Number Is?

Between any two numbers there is always another number. Place the following numbers along the path so that the numbers increase as you go along.

1.908, 1.638, $^-0.7$, 1.50, 0.534, 1.999, 1.61, $^-0.62$, 1.53, 1.732, 1.64, $^-0.07$, 1.101, $^-0.32$, 1.7, 0, 0.24, 1.887, 0.3, 1.32, 0.52, $^-0.92$, 0.562, 1.642, 0.6, $^-0.675$, 0.234, $^-0.234$, 0.675, 1.01, 1.683, 1.236, $^-0.001$, 1.3, 1.854, $^-0.9$, 1.62, $^-0.683$, 0.62, $^-0.11$, 1.69, 1.1, 1.714, 1.28, 1.86, 1.903, 0.478, 1.4, 1.45, 0.78

	START								
$^-1$									
$^-0.92$							1.1	1.101	1.236
$^-0.9$	0	0.234	0.24	0.3			1.01		1.28
$^-0.7$	$^-0.001$			0.478			0.78		1.3
$^-0.683$	$^-0.07$		0.52	0.534	0.562	0.6	0.62	0.675	1.32
$^-0.675$	$^-0.11$								1.4
$^-0.62$	$^-0.32$	$^-0.234$							1.45
			1.683	1.642	1.64	1.638	1.62	1.61	1.53	1.50
			1.69						
			1.7						
			1.714	1.732	1.854	1.86	1.887	1.903	1.908	1.999

FINISH   2

---

3 Practice

Guided Practice

Do Check for Understanding Exercises 1–6 with your students. Identify those having difficulty and use lesson resources to help.

///// **COMMON ERROR ALERT** \\\\\

When comparing two negative numbers, students may think that the number with the greater absolute value is the greater number. Remind students that the number that is farther to the right on the number line is always greater.

Independent Practice

Assign Exercises 7–22.

Before students begin Exercises 7–16, remind them that positive numbers are always greater than negative numbers.

MIXED REVIEW AND TEST PREP
Exercises 23–27 provide **cumulative review** (Chapters 1–11).

4 Assess

Summarize the lesson by having students:

DISCUSS How does the number line show that all negative numbers are less than all positive numbers? All negative numbers are to the left of all positive numbers and zero.

 WRITE What are three ways you might compare two positive rational numbers? Possible answer: Show them on a number line. Write them as fractions with a common denominator. Compare them in decimal form.

Lesson Quiz

Transparency

Compare. Write $<$, $>$, or $=$ for each ●.

1. 3.25 ● 3.19 $>$
2. $^-1.5$ ● $^-\frac{1}{4}$ $<$
3. $\frac{1}{3}$ ● $^-\frac{2}{3}$ $>$

Order the rational numbers from least to greatest.

4. $0.1, 0.4, ^-0.2, ^-0.1$ $^-0.2, ^-0.1, 0.1, 0.4$
5. $^-2, 0.2, \frac{1}{4}, ^-\frac{1}{2}$ $^-2, ^-\frac{1}{2}, 0.2, \frac{1}{4}$

235

Problem Solving Strategy: *Use Logical Reasoning*

LESSON PLANNING

Objective To solve problems by using the strategy *use logical reasoning*

Intervention for Prerequisite Skills

Compare Fractions (For intervention strategies, see page 227.)

Lesson Resources Problem Solving Think Along, p. TR1

 California Mathematics Content Standards

MR 2.0 Students use strategies, skills, and concepts in finding solutions.

MR 3.2 Note the method of deriving the solution and demonstrate a conceptual understanding of the derivation by solving similar problems.

(*Also* MR 1.0, MR 3.0, MR 3.3)

Math Background

Students are often faced with real-life problems that can be solved with the strategy *use logical reasoning*. It is often helpful to use the strategy *make a table* when solving a problem using logical reasoning.

The following ideas will help students understand this strategy.

- When you make a table like the one on page 236, each column can contain only one "yes" because each amount of money is associated with only one person.

- Each row can contain only one "yes" because each person has only one amount of money. So, once a *yes* is entered in the table, a *no* can be written in each of the other boxes in that row and column.

- It is not necessary to take the clues in order. Sometimes later clues give pieces of information that allow the student to complete one or more boxes.

ALTERNATIVE TEACHING STRATEGY (ELL)

Materials *For each student* 8 index cards

Ask students to **use logical reasoning** to solve the problem on page 236. Have students write the four amounts and the four names given in the problem on cards, one to a card. Begin by asking students to put the numbers in order from least to greatest.

Ask students which clue can be used first. Once they have chosen the clue "Leticia has twice as much money as Shelley," have them try each pair of numbers to see which fit. Once they have chosen $5 and $10, have them match the names and the amounts. Continue working with the remaining names and amounts to solve the problem.

VISUAL

READING STRATEGY

Analyze Information Have students use the reading strategy *analyze information* to help them understand the problem on page 236.

- Direct students to focus on the phrase "but not necessarily in that order." Have students explain what the phrase tells them. that Stephen does not necessarily have $7.75 just because both are listed first

- Then ask how they will use the clue that Leticia has twice as much money as Shelley. Look for two amounts such that one is twice the other.

SPECIAL NEEDS

To help students see how to **use other strategies to solve problems involving logical reasoning,** suggest they work in groups to act out Exercise 5 on page 237.

Once students have lined up in a possible order to solve, have other students check the clues to see if the order shown fits the clues given. Encourage them to keep track of the orders they have tried so they do not repeat them.

When students have completed their activity, ask them to verbalize the correct order. Arlene, Kathy, and Helene

KINESTHETIC

VOCABULARY STRATEGY

Challenge students to work in groups of 2 or 3 to **write logical reasoning problems** similar to Exercises 1–4. Suggest that they start with data such as four people's names and information about them, such as favorite subject, number of siblings, and so on. Also suggest that two of the numbers be related in some way that is easy to describe. Then, have them write clues from the data. Remind students to check the solutions to their own problems to be sure they work before exchanging with others to solve. Check students' work.

AUDITORY

TECHNOLOGY LINK

Intervention Strategies and Activities CD-ROM • *Skill 27*

LESSON 11.4 ORGANIZER

Objective To solve problems by using the strategy *use logical reasoning*

Lesson Resources Problem Solving Think Along, p. TR1

---

1 Introduce

QUICK REVIEW provides review of pre-requisite skills.

Why Learn This? In the future, this strategy will help you solve more challenging word problems. *Share the lesson objective with students.*

2 Teach

Guided Instruction

- *After discussing the problem, and the steps "analyze" and "choose", direct students' attention to the table. Ask:*

How does the table help solve the problem? Possible answer: It helps you organize your information.

Why can you write *no* in all the other spaces in a row and in a column once you write a *yes* in that row or column?
Possible answer: A money amount can belong to only one person and each person can have only one amount.

- *Help students analyze the reasoning process.*

REASONING Which clue did you use first? Explain. Possible answer: Leticia has twice as much money as Shelley; the other clue has 2 possibilities and this clue provides 2 definite answers.

LESSON 11.4

PROBLEM SOLVING STRATEGY
Use Logical Reasoning

Analyze
Choose
Solve
Check

Learn how to solve problems by using logical reasoning.

QUICK REVIEW

Compare. Use $<$, $>$, or $=$ for each ●.

1. $\frac{3}{8}$ ● $\frac{7}{8}$ $<$ 2. 3.5 ● 3.8 $<$ 3. 2 ● $^-2$ $>$ 4. $8\frac{1}{2}$ ● $8\frac{4}{8}$ $=$

5. Order $7\frac{1}{2}$, 7.75, $\frac{21}{3}$ from least to greatest. $\frac{21}{3}$, $7\frac{1}{2}$, 7.75

Stephen, Leticia, Shelley, and Ed emptied their banks. They found $7.75, $4.35, $5.00, and $10.00, but not necessarily in that order. Leticia has twice as much money as Shelley. Stephen has an amount between Shelley's and Leticia's. Who has $4.35?

Analyze What are you asked to find? who has $4.35

What information are you given? names of people, amounts of money, plus information about how amounts are related

Choose What strategy will you use?

You can *use logical reasoning.*

Solve How will you solve the problem?

Take the clues one at a time. Use a table to help.

Only one box in each row and column can have a "yes."

	$4.35	$5.00	$7.50	$10.00
Stephen	no	no	yes	no
Leticia	no	no	no	yes
Shelley	no	yes	no	no
Ed	yes	no	no	no

Leticia has twice as much money as Shelley. So, Leticia must have $10.00 and Shelley $5.00. Fill in "yes" in those boxes, and fill in "no" in the rest of the boxes in those rows and columns.

Stephen has an amount between Shelley's and Leticia's. $7.50 is between $5.00 and $10.00, so Stephen must have $7.50. Fill in the rest of the boxes with "yes" and "no."

So, Ed has $4.35.

Check How can you check your answer? Go back to the problem and check that the numbers fit the clues.

Give the clue that Leticia has $2\frac{1}{2}$ times as much money as Shelley.

What if the amounts were $7.50, $4.35, $5.00, and $12.50? How could you change the clues in the problem? See left.

236

CALIFORNIA STANDARDS MR 2.0 Students use strategies, skills, and concepts in finding solutions. MR 3.2 Note the method of deriving the solution and demonstrate a conceptual understanding of the derivation by solving similar problems. *also,* MR 1.0, MR 3.0, MR 3.3

RETEACH 11.4

Problem Solving Strategy: Use Logical Reasoning

When a problem presents a lot of information, logical reasoning can often be used in combination with organizing the information in a table.

Chris, Keiko, Rosa, and Jamal are officers in their school's student government. One of them is president, one is vice president, one is secretary, and one is treasurer. Rosa is the president. Chris is not the treasurer. Keiko is the vice president. What office does Jamal hold?

Step 1: Think about what you know and what you are asked to find.
You know: the names of the officers and the offices;
Rosa is the president, Chris is not the treasurer, and Keiko is the vice president.
You are asked to find the office held by Jamal.

Step 2: Plan a strategy to solve.
- Use the strategy *use logical reasoning.*
- Organize the information in a table, using one at a time.

Step 3: Solve.
- Since Rosa is president, put a Y for *yes* in the box where the Rosa column and the President row cross. Put an N for *no* in the other boxes in this row and column, since Rosa cannot hold any other office and nobody else can be president.
- Since Chris is not the treasurer, put an N where the Chris column and the Treasurer row cross.
- Since Keiko is the vice president, put a Y where the Keiko column and the Vice President row cross. Put Ns in the other boxes in this row and column.
- The only office left for Chris is secretary. Put a Y where the Chris column and the Secretary row cross.
- Therefore, Jamal must be the treasurer.

	Chris	Keiko	Rosa	Jamal
President	N	N	Y	N
Vice President	N	Y	N	N
Secretary	Y	N	N	N
Treasurer	N	N	N	Y

Solve the problem using logical reasoning.

1. The Raiders, Rangers, Cougars, and Lions are in one division of a baseball league. Currently, the Raiders are ahead of the Rangers and Cougars. The Raiders and Cougars are behind the Lions. The Cougars are in last place. Who is in first place?

   Lions

2. José, Cody, and Sid are students. One of them is in sixth grade, one is in seventh, and one is in eighth. The seventh-grader and José walk to school together. Sid plays ball with the eighth-grader. Cody is in sixth grade. Who is in seventh grade?

   Sid

PRACTICE 11.4

Problem Solving Strategy: Use Logical Reasoning

Solve the problems by using logical reasoning.

1. Tamara, Alex, Elena, and Fred entered their dogs in the county dog show. The dogs were a terrier, a setter, a golden retriever, and a Great Dane. Neither girl owned the Great Dane. Neither boy entered a setter. Tamara owns a golden retriever. What breed of dog did Elena enter in the show?

   setter

2. Bobby, Ken, Sam, and Ayesha each participate in one sport at school. They play softball, football, basketball, and soccer. Ayesha plays first base. Ken does not play football. If Sam plays soccer, what sport does Bobby participate in?

   football

3. Adel, James, Erica, and An were comparing how far they live from school. An lives only $\frac{1}{3}$ as far as Adel. James lives twice as far as Erica and 4 times as far as An. If Adel lives 9 blocks from school, how far away does Erica live?

   Erica: 6 blocks

4. Ahmed looked over his math homework problems. He saw that $\frac{1}{4}$ of the problems were about fractions, $\frac{1}{3}$ were about decimals, and the rest were about geometry. If there were 4 geometry problems, how many problems did he have in all?

   24 homework problems

5. Robert, Stanley, and Keith are brothers. Robert is 4 years younger than Stanley. Keith is 3 years older than Robert. Robert is 9 years older than his cousin Richard. If Richard is 11, how old is each brother?

   Robert: 20; Keith: 23; Stanley 24

6. Adam, Carin, Dana, and Juanita are lined up for a photograph. As the photographer looks at them, Juanita is to the right of Carin. Adam is on one end. Dana is between Carin and Adam. Give their order from left to right.

   Adam, Dana, Carin, Juanita

Mixed Review

Determine whether each number is divisible by 2, 3, 4, 5, 6, 8, 9, or 10.

7. 125   8. 336   9. 1,010   10. 249   11. 9,072

   5   2, 3, 4, 6, 8   2, 5, 10   3   2, 3, 4, 6, 8, 9

Multiply. Write the answer in simplest form.

12. $\frac{1}{2} \times \frac{2}{5}$ 13. $\frac{3}{5} \times \frac{1}{3}$ 14. $\frac{5}{6} \times \frac{1}{4}$ 15. $\frac{3}{4} \times \frac{5}{6}$

   $\frac{1}{5}$ $\frac{1}{5}$ $\frac{5}{24}$ $\frac{5}{8}$

236   Chapter 11

PROBLEM SOLVING PRACTICE

Solve the problems by using logical reasoning.

1. Arthur, Victoria, and Jeffrey are in sixth, seventh, and eighth grades, although not necessarily in that order. Victoria is not in eighth grade. The sixth grader is in chorus with Arthur and in band with Victoria. Which student is in each grade? **Jeffrey, sixth grade; Victoria, seventh grade; Arthur, eighth grade**

2. Use the following information to tell which numbers in the box at the right are A, B, C, D, and E.

-3.5	$2\frac{1}{2}$
	0.43
4.3	-0.43

   • A is greater than D and less than C.
   • A and D are opposites.
   • E is the greatest number.

   A = 0.43; B = $^-$3.5; C = $2\frac{1}{2}$; D = $^-$0.43; E = 4.3

For 3–4, use this information.

Amir, Katherine, Patrick, and Lee are comparing their stamp collections. Lee has twice as many stamps as Amir. Patrick has 5 fewer stamps than Katherine, who has 5 fewer stamps than Lee. Their collections consist of 15, 20, 25, and 30 stamps.

3. If Amir has 15 stamps, how many stamps does Patrick have? **C**

   A 30   C 20
   B 25   D 15

4. The four have a total of 90 stamps. How many stamps does Katherine have? **G**

   F 30   H 20
   G 25   J 15

MIXED STRATEGY PRACTICE

5. Kathy, Arlene, and Helene are in line for concert tickets, though not necessarily in that order. Helene is behind Kathy. Kathy is not first in line. Tell the order of the three in line. **Arlene, Kathy, Helene**

6. Mel sold 25 beanbag toys at a fair. He sold some for $8 and some for $5. He made $170. How many toys did he sell for $8? **15**

7. A guidebook costs $3.75 in Canadian dollars in a Vancouver, B.C., bookstore. It also has a price of $3.50 in United States dollars. If the exchange rate is $1.12 Canadian dollars for each U.S. dollar, would you rather pay in Canadian or U.S. dollars? **$3.50 × $1.12 = $3.92, so it is cheaper in Canadian dollars.**

8. Shelters are located at regular intervals along a wilderness trail. The distance from the first shelter to the fourth shelter is 6 mi. What is the distance from the seventh shelter to the thirteenth shelter? **12 mi.**

9. Sandy has to be at the airport for a 5:20 P.M. flight. She wants to arrive 1 hr 15 min early. If it takes 50 min to drive to the airport, when should she leave for the airport? **3:15 P.M.**

10. **? What's the Question?** Anne bought 28 fish. She bought three times as many goldfish as angelfish. The answer is 7. **How many angelfish did Anne buy?**

237

3 Practice

Guided Practice

Do Problem Solving Practice Exercises 1–4 with your students. Identify those having difficulty and use lesson resources to help.

Before assigning Exercise 2, call on a volunteer to define a number's opposite.

Independent Practice

Assign Exercises 5–10.

In Exercise 8, students may find it helpful to draw a diagram.

4 Assess

Summarize the lesson by having students:

DISCUSS Which clue did you use first to solve Exercise 1? Possible answer: "The sixth grader is in chorus with Arthur and in band with Victoria."

WRITE Should you always start solving problems involving logical reasoning with the first clue? Explain. No; start with the clue that clearly eliminates one case or allows you to write a *yes* in one box.

Lesson Quiz

Transparency 11.4

1. The numbers 1.4, $^-$3.5, 5, $^-$1.2, and 1.6 are labeled A, B, C, D, and E, though not necessarily in that order. The sum of A and C is 3, and C is greater than A. D is between A and B. Tell which number goes with each letter. *A,* 1.4; *B,* $^-$3.5; *C,* 1.6; *D,* $^-$1.2; *E,* 5

2. Kelly, Maria, Rob, and Kevin participated in a school walkathon to raise money for the library. They walked 1.5 mi, 3 mi, 7 mi, and 10 mi. Kevin walked twice as far as Kelly, and Maria walked 4 more miles than Kevin. Who walked the farthest? **Rob**

READING STRATEGY 11.4

Analyze Information   Analyze Choose Solve Check

The information in a problem can offer clues about how to solve it. **Analyze,** or look carefully at, the problem. Underline or record details that help you understand the problem.

VOCABULARY analyze

Read the following problem.

Abigail, Bart, Carlotta, and Donald each play a different sport, soccer, basketball, ice hockey, or lacrosse, but not necessarily in that order. Abigail plays a sport that uses a round ball. Carlotta needs a stick to play her sport. Donald can't play his sport outside in the summer. Bart's sport isn't played on grass. Which sport does each play?

1. Analyze the problem. Underline or record details that will help you solve the problem. Which clue does each clue suggest?

   Check students' connections of each clue to the different sports.

2. Solve the problem.

   Abigail–soccer; Bart–basketball; Carlotta–lacrosse; Donald–ice hockey

Analyze the problem. Underline or record details that help you reach an understanding. Then solve.

3. Ari, Latanya, Mary, and Jed each make a different dinner course, soup, salad, main course, or dessert, but not necessarily in that order. Mary is the only one whose recipe doesn't require vegetables. Latanya is the only one who doesn't need to use a stove. Jed's course is the only one that requires a spoon. What did they each prepare?

Ari: main course	Georgia: 100%;
Latanya: salad	Fred: 92%;
Mary: dessert	Inez: 83%;
Jed: soup	Hal: 75%

4. Fred, Georgia, Hal, and Inez all participated in the Geo-Bee. Their scores were 92%, 75%, 100%, and 83%, but not necessarily in that order. Georgia's score was $\frac{3}{4}$ of Hal's score. Inez's score was 9 points less than Fred's score. What score did each receive?

CHALLENGE 11.4

Logically Speaking

1. Danielle, Effie, and Hannah are in the school orchestra. Each girl plays one instrument: the oboe, the French horn, or the clarinet. Hannah does not play the oboe, nor does she play the clarinet. Effie has never taken clarinet lessons. Which instrument does each girl play?

Danielle: clarinet; Effie: oboe;
Hannah: French horn

2. Austin and Koby each completed a reading assignment. Austin read more pages than Koby. Neither of the boys read more than 40 pages. The difference between the lengths of the reading assignments is 16 pages. The product of the lengths of the reading assignments is 720. How many pages did each boy read?

Austin: 36 pages; Koby:
20 pages

3. Sabrina, Tom, Carlos, and Fran like to go fishing. On one day they each caught a fish: a salmon, a tuna, a catfish, and a flounder. No one caught a fish that begins with the same letter as his or her name. Neither boy caught a salmon. Neither girl caught a tuna. One of the boys caught a flounder. What kind of fish did each one catch?

Sabrina: catfish; Tom: flounder
Carlos: tuna; Fran: salmon

4. Shandra is trying to guess Helen's secret number. Helen gives Shandra the following clues:
   • The number is between 1 and 10.
   • If you divide the number by 2, the result is greater than 3.
   • If you triple the number, the result is greater than 24.
   What is Helen's secret number?

   9

5. There are 12 soft drink bottles in Martha's refrigerator. The bottles are either cherry soda or root beer. If Martha takes a cherry soda and replaces it with a new bottle of root beer, there will be an equal number of each flavor. However, if she drinks a root beer and replaces it with a new bottle of cherry soda, there will be twice as many cherry sodas as root beers. How many bottles of each flavor are in the refrigerator right now?

   7 cherry, 5 root beer

6. Lori, Lisa, and Lauren are sisters. When they add their ages together, they get a sum of 19. Three years from now, Lori will be twice as old as Lisa, and Lisa will be twice as old as Lauren. How old is each girl now?

   Lori: 13, Lisa: 5, Lauren: 1

237

CHAPTER 11

REVIEW/TEST

Purpose To check understanding of concepts, skills, and problem solving presented in Chapter 11

USING THE PAGE

The Chapter 11 Review/Test can be used as a **review** or a **test**.

- Items 1–2 check understanding of concepts and new vocabulary.
- Items 3–38 check skill proficiency.
- Items 39–40 check students' abilities to choose and apply problem solving strategies to real-life problems involving integers.

 Suggest that students place the completed Chapter 11 Review/Test in their portfolios.

USING THE ASSESSMENT GUIDE

- Multiple-choice format of Chapter 11 Posttest—See *Assessment Guide*, pp. AG73–74.
- Free-response format of Chapter 11 Posttest—See *Assessment Guide*, pp. AG75–76.

USING STUDENT SELF-ASSESSMENT

The How Did I Do? survey helps students assess what they have learned and how they learned it. This survey is available as a copying master in *Assessment Guide*, p. AGxvii.

CHAPTER 11 REVIEW/TEST

1. **VOCABULARY** Positive whole numbers, their opposites, and 0 make up the set of __?__. (p. 228) **integers**

2. **VOCABULARY** A number that can be written as a ratio $\frac{a}{b}$, where a and b are integers and $b \neq 0$, is a(n) __?__. (p. 230) **rational number**

Write an integer to represent each situation. (pp. 228–229)

3. an increase of 15 points
$^+15$

4. 6 degrees below zero
$^-6°$

5. a loss of 20 pounds
$^-20$

Write the opposite integer. (pp. 228–229)

6. $^-32$ 32　　7. 12 $^-12$　　8. $^-15$ 15　　9. $^-289$ 289　　10. 0 0

Find the absolute value. (pp. 228–229)

11. $|^-12|$ 12　　12. $|^-4|$ 4　　13. $|^+17|$ 17　　14. $|^+8|$ 8　　15. $|^-347|$ 347

Write each rational number in the form $\frac{a}{b}$. (pp. 230–233) **Possible answers are given.**

16. $2\frac{2}{1}$　　17. $^-0.89$ $\frac{^-89}{100}$　　18. $3\frac{2}{3}$ $\frac{11}{3}$　　19. 5.4 $\frac{54}{10}$　　20. 14 $\frac{14}{1}$　　21. 0.334 $\frac{334}{1,000}$

Find a rational number between the two given numbers. (pp. 230–233) **Possible answers are given.**

22. $\frac{1}{4}$ and $\frac{2}{3}$ $\frac{5}{12}$　　23. 1.3 and 1.32 1.31　　24. $\frac{2}{5}$ and $\frac{3}{4}$ $\frac{9}{20}$　　25. $^-4.3$ and $^-4.4$ $^-4.36$

26. 3.4 and 3.52 3.45　　27. $2\frac{1}{5}$ and $2\frac{1}{2}$ $2\frac{1}{4}$　　28. $3\frac{5}{8}$ and $3\frac{9}{10}$ $3\frac{4}{5}$　　29. 0.9 and 0.94 0.92

Compare. Write <, >, or = for each ●. (pp. 234–235)

30. $7\frac{5}{8}$ ● $7\frac{10}{16}$ =　　31. 1.01 ● 1.10 <　　32. $^-3.4$ ● $^-4.3$ >　　33. $\frac{^-25}{3}$ ● $\frac{^-17}{2}$ <　　34. $4\frac{3}{4}$ ● 4.77 <

Order the rational numbers from greatest to least. (pp. 234–235)

35. 3.7, 3.2, $3\frac{5}{8}$　　3.7; $3\frac{5}{8}$; 3.2

36. $^-8$, $^-3$, $\frac{^-77}{11}$　　$^-3$; $\frac{^-77}{11}$; $^-8$

37. $^-1.2$, 1.2, 0.12　　1.2; 0.12; $^-1.2$

38. $\frac{5}{7}$, $\frac{9}{14}$, $\frac{11}{8}$　　$\frac{11}{8}$; $\frac{5}{7}$; $\frac{9}{14}$

39. Elizabeth, Doria, Emily, and Claudia each earned money doing odd jobs. They earned $4.50, $6.50, $8.00, and $9.00. Doria earned twice as much as Elizabeth. Emily earned $1.50 more than Claudia. Claudia earned $2.00 more than Elizabeth. How much did each person earn? (pp. 236–237) **Elizabeth: $4.50, Doria: $9.00, Emily: $8.00, Claudia: $6.50**

40. Louisa, Chris, and Vicki each have one pet: a dog, a cat, and an iguana. Louisa does not have a cat and Chris does not have a dog. Louisa's pet is a reptile. What pet does each girl have? (pp. 236–237) **Louisa: iguana, Vicki: dog, Chris: cat**

CHAPTER 11 TEST, page 1

Choose the best answer.

For 1–4, name the integer that represents each situation.

1. An increase in altitude of 2,547 ft
   A $^+2,574$　C $^-2,547$
   B $^+2,547$　D $^-2,574$

2. A drop in temperature of 16°F
   F $^-32$　H $^+16$
   G $^-16$　J $^+32$

3. The absolute value of 65
   A 65　C $^-130$
   B $^-65$　D 0

4. The opposite of 19
   F 91　H $^-19$
   G 19　J $^-91$

5. Which number is between $3\frac{1}{4}$ and $3\frac{3}{4}$?
   A $3\frac{1}{8}$　C $3\frac{7}{8}$
   B $3\frac{1}{2}$　D $3\frac{13}{16}$

6. Which number is between $^-\frac{3}{5}$ and $^-\frac{3}{4}$?
   F $^-\frac{8}{5}$　H $^-\frac{5}{8}$
   G $^-\frac{4}{5}$　J $^-\frac{2}{5}$

For 7–8, find the rational number written in the form $\frac{a}{b}$.

7. $4\frac{2}{7}$
   A $\frac{45}{7}$　C $\frac{20}{7}$
   B $\frac{33}{7}$　D $\frac{9}{7}$

8. 2.718
   F $\frac{2,718}{1,000}$　H $27\frac{18}{100}$
   G $2\frac{178}{1,000}$　J $271\frac{8}{1000}$

9. What is the value of $|^-3.14|$?
   A 3.14　C $^-3\frac{14}{1,000}$
   B $3\frac{14}{1,000}$　D $^-3.14$

10. Which rational number is between $^-\frac{5}{8}$ and $^-\frac{3}{4}$?
    F $^-\frac{13}{16}$　H $^-\frac{10}{16}$
    G $^-\frac{11}{16}$　J $^-\frac{9}{16}$

11. Order $2\frac{3}{7}$, $2\frac{5}{11}$, and 2.5 from *least to greatest*.
    A $2\frac{5}{11}$, $2\frac{3}{7}$, 2.5
    B $2\frac{3}{7}$, 2.5, $2\frac{5}{11}$
    C $2\frac{3}{7}$, $2\frac{5}{11}$, 2.5
    D 2.5, $2\frac{5}{11}$, $2\frac{3}{7}$

12. Four friends have CD collections that contain 15, 20, 30, and 35 CDs. Mike and Taylor together have 10 fewer CDs than Al and Jeff. Taylor has more CDs than Al. Who has 30 CDs?
    F Jeff　H Taylor
    G Al　J Mike

Go On

CHAPTER 11 TEST, page 2

13. Sam, Ann, and Jay play the guitar. One practices at 4:00, one at 6:00, and one at 9:00. Jay does not practice at 9:00. Ann practices 2 hours before Jay. Who practices at 4:00?
    A Sam
    B Ann
    C Jay
    D Cannot tell

14. In a race, the three fastest times were 20.3 min, $20\frac{1}{6}$ min, and 20.2 min. Order the times from *least to greatest*.
    F 20.3 min, $20\frac{1}{6}$ min, 20.2 min
    G $20\frac{1}{6}$ min, 20.2 min, 20.3 min
    H 20.2 min, $20\frac{1}{6}$ min, 20.3 min
    J 20.2 min, 20.3 min, $20\frac{1}{6}$ min

15. Which shows a correct comparison of two numbers?
    A $0 > ^-7.5$　C $^-7.5 > 0$
    B $^-7.5 > 7.5$　D $7.5 = ^-7.5$

16. Four students live in four different houses on the same block of the same street. Bob and Ceil live next door to Art. Doug lives closer to Ceil than to Art. Which two students live farthest apart?
    F Bob and Ceil　H Art and Doug
    G Ceil and Doug　J Bob and Doug

17. Gail, May, and Cara each bought a pop, rock, or jazz CD. No two girls bought the same kind of music. Gail did not buy pop music. May bought rock music. What kind of CD did each girl buy?
    A Gail, pop; May, rock, Cara, jazz
    B Gail, rock; May, rock; Cara, pop
    C Gail, rock; May, jazz; Cara, pop
    D Gail, jazz; May, rock; Cara, pop

18. What is the correct order from least to greatest for 1.1, $^-1\frac{3}{8}$, and $^-\frac{9}{8}$?
    F $^-1\frac{3}{8}$, $^-\frac{9}{8}$, 1.1
    G $^-\frac{9}{8}$, $^-1\frac{3}{8}$, 1.1
    H $^-\frac{9}{8}$, 1.1, $^-1\frac{3}{8}$
    J 1.1, $^-\frac{9}{8}$, $^-1\frac{3}{8}$

19. Temperatures on the ski slope were recorded as 17°F, $^-8$°F, $^-2$°F, and 0°F during the day. Choose the order of these temperatures from least to greatest.
    A 17°F, 0°F, $^-2$°F, $^-8$°F
    B 0°F, $^-2$°F, $^-8$°F, 17°F
    C $^-8$°F, $^-2$°F, 0°F, 17°F
    D 17°F, $^-8$°F, $^-2$°F, 0°F

20. P, Q, R, and S are integers. S is greater than Q. P is the opposite of S. R is the opposite of Q. R is to the right of 0 on the number line. Q is less than P. Which represents the greatest integer?
    F P　H R
    G Q　J S

Stop

Look for important words.
See item **8**.

Important words are *least to greatest*. Write the numbers as decimals and order them from least to greatest.

Also see problem **2**, p. H62.

Choose the best answer.

1. Which of the following can be used to represent the depth of a cave that goes 37 feet below ground level? A

   A ⁻37   **C** ⁺3.7

   B ⁻3.7   **D** ⁺37

2. Which points on the number line show opposite integers? G

   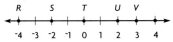

   F *R* and *S*   **H** *U* and *V*

   G *S* and *U*   **J** *T* and *R*

3. Four baseball players are standing in a line. Owen is standing between Paul and Jim. Casey is in front of Paul. Jim is last. How are they arranged in the line? D

   A Paul, Casey, Owen, Jim

   B Casey, Paul, Jim, Owen

   C Owen, Casey, Jim, Paul

   D Casey, Paul, Owen, Jim

4. With respect to sea level, the average depth of the Atlantic Ocean is ⁻11,730 feet, the Pacific Ocean is ⁻12,925 feet, and the Gulf of Mexico is ⁻5,297 feet. Which shows these values in order from least to greatest? H

   F ⁻11,730, ⁻12,925, ⁻5,297

   G ⁻11,730, ⁻5,297, ⁻12,925

   H ⁻12,925, ⁻11,730, ⁻5,297

   J ⁻12,925, ⁻5,297, ⁻11,730

5. Last week, the dance band practiced for $5\frac{1}{3}$ hours. The band usually practices for $8\frac{3}{4}$ hours per week. How many fewer hours did the band practice last week? C

   A $2\frac{3}{4}$ hr   **C** $3\frac{5}{12}$ hr

   B $3\frac{1}{3}$ hr   **D** $4\frac{1}{5}$ hr

6. Earl read that $\frac{3}{8}$ of his town's budget is spent on road repairs. Which is that amount expressed as a decimal? F

   F 0.375   **H** 0.67

   G 0.4   **J** 0.875

7. Which symbol makes this number sentence true?

   ⁻3 ● 0   A

   A <   **C** =

   B >   **D** ≥

8. Which shows the numbers in order from least to greatest?

   $$1.7, \frac{1}{2}, \ ^-0.3, \ \frac{^-3}{5} \quad \text{J}$$

   F $\frac{1}{2}$, 1.7, $\frac{^-3}{5}$, ⁻0.3

   G $\frac{^-3}{5}$, ⁻0.3, 1.7, $\frac{1}{2}$

   H ⁻0.3, $\frac{1}{2}$, $\frac{^-3}{5}$, 1.7

   J Not here

9. Which letter represents the opposite of 3 on the number line? B

   A *A*   **B** *B*   **C** *C*   **D** *D*

   ```
        A   B        C          D
   ←──┼───┼───┼───┼───┼───┼───┼──→
     -4  -3  -2  -1   0   1   2   3
   ```

10. Vicki has 8 mysteries, 6 biographies, and 10 adventure books. What part of her book collection is biographies? H

    F $\frac{1}{8}$ **H** $\frac{1}{4}$

    G $\frac{1}{6}$ **J** $\frac{1}{3}$

CUMULATIVE REVIEW •
Chapters 1–11

USING THE PAGE

This page may be used to help students get ready for standardized tests. The test items are written in the same style and arranged in the same format as those on many state assessments. The page is cumulative. It covers math objectives and essential skills that have been taught up to this point in the text. Most of the items represent skills from the current chapter, and the remainder represent skills from earlier chapters.

This page can be assigned at the end of the chapter as classwork or as a homework assignment. You may want to have students use individual recording sheets presented in a multiple-choice (standardized) format. A Test Answer Sheet is available as a blackline master in *Assessment Guide* (p. AGxlii).

You may wish to have students describe how they solved each problem and share their solutions.

Add and Subtract with Integers

CHAPTER PLANNER

Getting Ready for Chapter 12 • Assessing Prior Knowledge and INTERVENTION (See PE and TE page 241.)

LESSON	CALIFORNIA STANDARDS	PACING	VOCABULARY*	MATERIALS	RESOURCES AND TECHNOLOGY
12.1 Math Lab: Algebra—Model Addition of Integers pp. 242–243 **Objective** To use two-color counters to add integers	☛ NS 2.3 (Also ☛ NS 2.0, MR 2.4, MR 2.5)		**additive inverse**	*For each pair* 15 two-color counters	🔴 **Astro Algebra • *Red***
12.2 Algebra: Add Integers pp. 244–247 **Objective** To use a number line to add integers	☛ NS 2.3 (Also ☛ NS 2.0, MR 2.2, MR 2.4, MR 3.2)	2 Days (For Lessons 12.1 and 12.2)	absolute value		Reteach, Practice, Problem Solving, Challenge 12.2 Worksheets Extra Practice p. H43, Set A 📺 Transparency 12.2 🔴 **Astro Algebra • *Red*** **Math Jingles™•CD 5–6• *Track 17***
12.3 Math Lab: Algebra—Model Subtraction of Integers pp. 248–249 **Objective** To use two-color counters to subtract integers	☛ NS 2.3 (Also ☛ NS 2.0, MR 2.4, MR 2.5)			*For each group* 25 two-color counters	🌐 **E-Lab • *Modeling Subtraction of Integers*; E-Lab Recording Sheet** 🔴 **Astro Algebra • *Red***
12.4 Algebra: Subtract Integers pp. 250–251 **Objective** To use a number line to subtract integers	☛ NS 2.3 (Also ☛ NS 2.0, MR 2.2, MR 2.5)	1 Day (For lessons 12.3 and 12.4)			Reteach, Practice, Problem Solving, Challenge 12.4 Worksheets Extra Practice p. H43, Set B 📺 Transparency 12.4 🔴 **Astro Algebra • *Red*** **Math Jingles™•CD 5–6• *Track 17***

Ending Chapter 12 • Chapter 12 Review/Test, p. 252 • Cumulative Review, p. 253

*Boldfaced terms are new vocabulary. Other terms are review vocabulary.

Vocabulary Development

The boldfaced word is the new vocabulary term in the chapter. Have students record the definition in their Math Journals.

additive inverse, p. 243

additive inverse

Vocabulary Cards
Have students use the Vocabulary Cards on *Teacher's Resource* **pp. TR129–130** to make graphic organizers or word puzzles. The cards can also be added to a file of mathematics terms.

Writing Opportunities

PUPIL EDITION
• What's the Error?, p. 247
• What's the Question?, p. 251

TEACHER'S EDITION
• Write—See the *Assess* section of each TE lesson.
• Writing in Mathematics, p. 250B

ASSESSMENT GUIDE
• How Did I Do?, p. AGxvii

California Mathematics Content Standards for Grade 6

Strands

Number Sense
Lesson 12.1: NS 2.0, 2.3
Lesson 12.2: NS 2.0, 2.3
Lesson 12.3: NS 2.0, 2.3
Lesson 12.4: NS 2.0, 2.3

Algebra and Functions

Measurement and Geometry

Statistics, Data Analysis, and Probability

Mathematical Reasoning
Lesson 12.1: MR 2.4, 2.5
Lesson 12.2: MR 2.2. 2.4, 3.2
Lesson 12.3: MR 2.4, 2.5
Lesson 12.4: MR 2.2, 2.5

Family Involvement Activities

These activities provide:
• Letter to the Family
• Information about California Standards
• Math Vocabulary
• Family Game
• Practice (Homework)

> **HARCOURT MATH**
> **GRADE 6**
> Chapter 12
>
> **WHAT WE ARE LEARNING**
> Add and subtract with integers
>
> **Vocabulary**
> Here is a vocabulary word we use in class:
> **Additive inverse** An integer with the opposite sign of another integer
>
> **Name**
> **Date**
>
> **Dear Family,**
> Your child is studying addition and subtraction of integers. Your child learned about the rules for operations with integers by working with colored counters and also by using a number line. Your child and classmates discovered the rules listed below.
> *Rules for addition of integers*
> • To find the sum of two integers with like signs, add the absolute values of the integers and use the sign of the addends for the result.
>   4 + 3 = 7   ⁻4 + ⁻3 = ⁻7
> • To find the sum of two integers with unlike signs, subtract the lesser absolute value from the greater absolute value. Use the sign of the integer with greater absolute value for the result.
>   4 + ⁻3 = 1   ⁻4 + 3 = ⁻1
> **Let's find the value of this expression: 5 + (⁻8). How do we begin?** Your child might suggest: First, I must subtract the absolute values, so |8| − |5| = 8 − 5 = 3.
> **What is the next step?** Your child might respond: Next I apply the sign of the integer with the greater absolute value. Since ⁻8 has a greater absolute value than 5, I use the sign for ⁻8.
> **What is the value?** Your child might reply: The value of 5 + (⁻8) is ⁻3.
> *Rules for subtraction of integers*
> • To find the difference of two integers with like signs, write the expression as an addition problem and apply the rules for addition of integers.
>   ⁻12 − ⁻3 = ⁻12 + (3) = ⁻9
>   12 − 3 = 12 + (⁻3) = 9
>
> *The California Math Standards*
> Your child's **Harcourt Math** book lists the California Math Standards that are taught in every lesson. If you have questions about the standards, be sure to consult *California Standards for Grade 6* that was sent home at the beginning of the school year.

Family Involvement Activities, p. FA45

Add and Subtract with Integers

MATHEMATICS ACROSS THE GRADES

SKILLS TRACE ACROSS THE GRADES

GRADE 5	GRADE 6	GRADE 7
Add and subtract positive and negative integers	Write sums and differences of integers by using a variety of methods including models and number lines	Add, subtract, multiply, and divide integers and rational numbers

SKILLS TRACE FOR GRADE 6

LESSON	FIRST INTRODUCED	TAUGHT AND PRACTICED	TESTED	REVIEWED
12.1	Grade 5	PE pp. 242–243	PE p. 252, pp. AG77–80	PE pp. 252, 253, 268–269
12.2	Grade 5	PE pp. 244–247, H43, p. RW55, p. PW55, p. PS55	PE p. 252, pp. AG77–80	PE pp. 252, 253, 268–269
12.3	Grade 5	PE pp. 248–249	PE p. 252, pp. AG77–80	PE pp. 252, 253, 268–269
12.4	Grade 5	PE pp. 250–251, H43, p. RW56, p. PW56, p. PS56	PE p. 252, pp. AG77–80	PE pp. 252, 253, 268–269

KEY **PE** Pupil Edition   **PS** Problem Solving Workbook   **RW** Reteach Workbook
      PW Practice Workbook   **AG** Assessment Guide

Looking Back Prerequisite Skills

To be ready for Chapter 12, students should have the following understandings and skills:

- **Vocabulary**—*positive numbers, integers*
- **Understanding Integers**—use positive and negative numbers to represent situations
- **Number Lines**—write integers on a number line

Check What You Know

Use page 241 to determine students' knowledge of prerequisite concepts and skills.

Intervention

Help students prepare for the chapter by using the intervention resources described on TE page 241.

Looking at Chapter 12 Essential Skills

Students will

- **develop understanding of integer addition and subtraction by using two-color counters to add and subtract integers.**
- use number lines to add and subtract integers.
- use absolute values to add and subtract integers.

EXAMPLE

Use counters to find the sum.

$$^-2 + {}^+5$$

So, $^-2 + {}^+5 = {}^+3$.

Looking Ahead Applications

Students will apply what they learn in Chapter 12 to the following new concepts:

- Multiply and Divide with Integers (Chapter 13)
- Solve Addition and Subtraction Equations (Chapter 15)
- Evaluate Expressions (Chapter 14)

Add and Subtract with Integers

INTRODUCING THE CHAPTER

Remind students that integers show how quantities or measures compare to zero. Integers, like other numbers, can be added and subtracted. After students read the paragraph, explain that the difference between two negative numbers is the same as the difference between two positive numbers, but the sign may be different. Ask students what the estimated difference is between 193 and 129. **about 60** Have them find the opposite of 60. **⁻60**

USING DATA

To begin the study of this chapter, have students

- Draw and label a number line to show the temperature data for the Earth.
- Draw and label a number line to show the temperature data for Mars.
- Make a double bar graph of all the data in the table.

Check students' work.

PROBLEM SOLVING PROJECT

Purpose To compare data expressed as integers

Background Mars is the next planet in the solar system after the Earth. NASA's *Pathfinder* and *Sojourner* missions provided valuable scientific data, including temperature, about Mars.

Analyze, Choose, Solve, and Check

Have students

- Analyze the data given in the table and make comparisons.
- Write a paragraph that compares temperature extremes on Earth to temperature extremes on Mars.
- Support the comparison with data from the table and explain how the data was interpreted. Check students' work.

Suggest that students place their paragraphs in their portfolios.

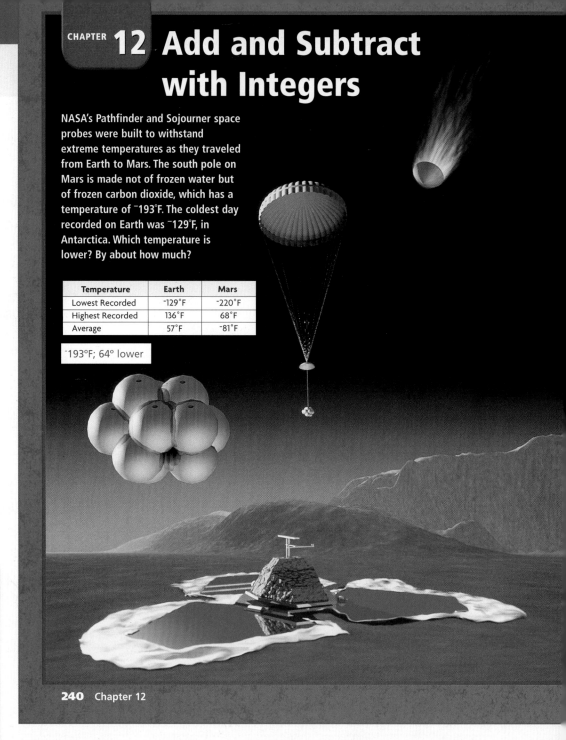

NASA's Pathfinder and Sojourner space probes were built to withstand extreme temperatures as they traveled from Earth to Mars. The south pole on Mars is made not of frozen water but of frozen carbon dioxide, which has a temperature of ⁻193°F. The coldest day recorded on Earth was ⁻129°F, in Antarctica. Which temperature is lower? By about how much?

Temperature	Earth	Mars
Lowest Recorded	⁻129°F	⁻220°F
Highest Recorded	136°F	68°F
Average	57°F	⁻81°F

⁻193°F; 64° lower

Why learn math? Explain that scientists and engineers who design equipment for space exploration must understand integers and be comfortable computing with them. Ask: How would addition and subtraction of integers be used in a career? Possible answer: A bank teller uses addition and subtraction of integers to balance accounts.

TECHNOLOGY LINK
To find out more about integers, visit The Harcourt Learning Site.
www.harcourtschool.com

Check What You Know

Use this page to help you review and remember important skills needed for Chapter 12.

 Vocabulary

Choose the best term from the box.

> positive numbers
> integers

1. The set of whole numbers and their opposites is the set of ___?___. **integers**

 Understand Integers (See p. H12.)

Write a positive or negative integer to represent each situation.

2. 14° below zero **⁻14**

3. 62 degrees above zero **⁺62**

4. 10 ft above sea level **⁺10**

5. 13 m below sea level **⁻13**

6. bottom of a well, 50 ft below the surface **⁻50**

7. a gain of 12 yards **⁺12**

8. a bank deposit of $280 **⁺280**

9. 3 ft below ground level **⁻3**

 Number Lines (See p. H13.)

Name the integer that corresponds to the point.

10. A **⁺1**

11. B **⁺11**

12. C **⁻4**

13. D **⁻8**

Use the number line to find the ending point for each move.

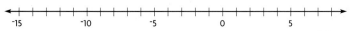

	Starting Point	Move	Ending Point
14.	⁻8	4 to the right	⁻4
15.	⁻7	6 to the left	⁻13
16.	⁺6	9 to the left	⁻3
17.	⁻1	5 to the right	⁺4
18.	⁻12	3 to the left	⁻15
19.	⁺5	5 to the left	0
20.	⁺3	7 to the left	⁻4

> **LOOK AHEAD**
>
> **In Chapter 12 you will**
> • add integers
> • subtract integers

241

Assessing Prior Knowledge

Use the **Check What You Know** page to determine whether your students have mastered the prerequisite skills critical for this chapter.

Intervention

• **Diagnose and Prescribe**

Evaluate your students' performance on this page to determine whether intervention is necessary. **How to Help Options** that provide instruction, practice, and a check are listed in the chart below.

• **Review Prerequisite Skills**

The following resources provide a review for the prerequisite vocabulary and skills.

Option 1—Check What You Know, Pupil Edition p. 241

Option 2—Troubleshooting, Pupil Edition pp. H12–13

TEACHER'S NOTES

Check What You Know
INTERVENTION • Diagnose and Prescribe

Prerequisite Skill	Items (Pupil Edition p. 241)	How to Help Options
☑ Understanding Integers	2–9	• Troubleshooting, Pupil Edition p. H12 • Intervention Strategies and Activities Card, Copying Master, or CD-ROM • **Skill 9**
☑ Number Lines	10–20	• Troubleshooting, Pupil Edition p. H13 • Intervention Strategies and Activities Card, Copying Master, or CD-ROM • **Skill 42**

ORGANIZER

Objective To use two-color counters to add integers

Vocabulary additive inverse

Materials *For each pair* 15 two-color counters

Intervention for Prerequisite Skills Understanding Integers (For intervention strategies, see page 241.)

Using the Pages

Introduce students to the counters used to model positive and negative integers. Show the yellow side of a counter and call on volunteers to describe what it represents. Repeat with the red side.

Activity 1

Ask students to explain their models and the process they used to find Lin's and Nina's scores.

Think and Discuss

Have students use their counters to show that changing the order of the addends for Lin's and Nina's scores does not change the sum. Ask:

What property of addition have you illustrated? the Commutative Property

Practice

Ask students to predict which sums in Exercises 1–4 will be positive and which will be negative. The sums in 1 and 4 are positive; the sums in 2 and 3 are negative.

LESSON **12.1**

ALGEBRA
Model Addition of Integers

MATH LAB

Explore how to use two-color counters to add integers.

You need two-color counters.

Vocabulary

additive inverse

Lin and Nina are playing a board game. To keep track of points, they are using yellow counters to represent positive points, or points gained, and red counters to represent negative points, or points lost.

Activity 1

• Lin earned 6 points during the first round. She earned 3 points during the second round. Use yellow counters to model Lin's total score.

First-round points   Second-round points
○○○○○○   ○○○

6 + 3 = 9 ← total score

• Nina lost 2 points in the first round. Then she lost 5 points in the second round. Use red counters to model Nina's total score.

First-round points   Second-round points
●●   ●●●●●

$^-2 + {}^-5 = {}^-7$ ← total score

Think and Discuss

• How is adding the scores like adding whole numbers? How is it different? You add just as you do with whole numbers. The difference is that Nina's scores are both negative numbers.
• Would changing the order when adding Lin's or Nina's points change their scores? Why or why not? No; Changing the order does not change the sum.
• How would you model 2 + 7? $^-2 + {}^-7$? by showing 2 and 7 yellow counters; by showing 2 and 7 red counters

Practice

Use counters to find the sum.

1. 4 + 9   2. $^-3 + {}^-7$ 3. $^-6 + {}^-4$ 4. 5 + 8
   $^+13$ $^-10$ $^-10$ $^+13$

242

CALIFORNIA STANDARDS O⊓NS 2.3 Solve addition, subtraction, multiplication, and division problems, including those arising in concrete situations, that use positive and negative integers and combinations of these operations. *also,* O⊓NS 2.0, MR 2.4, MR 2.5

SPECIAL NEEDS (ELL)

Materials *For each group* 30 two-color counters

Provide students with additional practice in **adding integers** by using counters to solve the word problem below. Let red counters represent the borrowed money and let yellow counters represent the money paid back.

• Peter borrowed $15 from Sarah. A week later, he paid back $5. How much does Peter still owe Sarah? $^-15 + {}^+5 = {}^-10$; Peter still owes Sarah $10.

KINESTHETIC

REACHING ALL LEARNERS
Intervention and Extension Resources

Activity 2

The **additive inverse** of an integer is its opposite. 1 and ⁻1 are the additive inverses of each other. When you add an integer and its additive inverse, the sum is always 0. You can model this using counters.

• Model the sum of 1 and its additive inverse, ⁻1.

• Model the sum of 5 and its additive inverse, ⁻5.

$$= 0$$

• During a game, Carmen gained 8 points and then lost 5 points. To find her total score, Carmen paired points gained with points lost. Use yellow and red counters to model Carmen's total score. Remember that pairs of red and yellow counters equal 0.

 $8 + ⁻5 = 3$

• Robert gained 3 points and then lost 7 points. Use yellow and red counters to model Robert's total score.

 $3 + ⁻7 = ⁻4$

Think and Discuss

• Why is Carmen's score positive? There are more yellow counters than red counters.
• Why is Robert's score negative? There are more red counters than yellow counters.

Practice

Use counters to find each sum.

1. $4 + ⁻6$ **⁻2**
2. $⁻2 + 6$ **4**
3. $7 + ⁻7$ **0**
4. $⁻3 + 8$ **5**
5. $5 + 2$ **7**
6. $3 + 1$ **4**
7. $⁻4 + ⁻5$ **⁻9**
8. $⁻3 + ⁻8$ **⁻11**

MIXED REVIEW AND TEST PREP

Order the rational numbers from least to greatest. (p. 234)

9. $⁻6.4, ⁻6.2, ⁻6.8$
   $⁻6.8, ⁻6.4, ⁻6.2$

10. $\frac{1}{3}, \frac{2}{5}, \frac{1}{4}, \frac{3}{5}$ $\frac{1}{4}, \frac{1}{3}, \frac{2}{5}, \frac{3}{5}$

11. $⁻3\frac{4}{7}, ⁻3.6, ⁻3\frac{1}{2}$
    $⁻3.6, ⁻3\frac{4}{7}, ⁻3\frac{1}{2}$

12. Evaluate the expression $c + \frac{1}{2}$ for $c = \frac{1}{3}$. (p. 216) $\frac{5}{6}$

13. **TEST PREP** Which shows the difference $6\frac{5}{6} - 5\frac{3}{4}$? (p. 186) **B**

    A $\frac{1}{9}$ **B** $1\frac{1}{12}$ **C** $1\frac{1}{2}$ **D** $1\frac{3}{4}$

243

EARLY FINISHERS

Materials *For each group* 10 two-color counters

Have students **use integers**. Explain that in golf, *par* is the standard number of strokes to hit a ball into a specific hole. Have groups use counters to find Bruce's scores.

BRUCE'S SCORES			
Hole	Par	Above or Below Par	Bruce's Score
1	4	⁻1	? ⁺3
2	3	⁻2	? ⁺1
3	5	⁺1	? ⁺6
4	5	⁺2	? ⁺7

KINESTHETIC

Activity 2

Direct students' attention to Activity 2. Ask:

How do you model a gain of 8 points? a loss of 5 points? with 8 yellow counters; with 5 red counters

How do you know from the problem that Robert's total score will be negative? Robert lost more points than he gained.

Think and Discuss

Ask:

How do the exercises in Activity 1 differ from those in Activity 2? The exercises in Activity 1 involve adding integers with the same sign; those in Activity 2 involve adding negative integers to positive integers.

Practice

Although some students may be able to solve the exercises in their heads, modeling the exercises will help them better understand the concept of adding integers. This understanding will be important in the next lesson when students add greater integers.

MIXED REVIEW AND TEST PREP

Exercises 9–13 provide **cumulative review** (Chapters 1–12).

Oral Assessment

What is the sign of the sum of two positive integers? positive

What is the sign of the sum of two negative integers? negative

What is the sign of the sum of a positive and a negative integer? the sign of the addend with the greater absolute value

What integers could you add to equal 0? Give an example. any integer and its opposite; $⁺2 + ⁻2 = 0$

Algebra: Add Integers

LESSON PLANNING

Objective To use a number line to add integers

Intervention for Prerequisite Skills

Understand Integers, Locate Points on a Number Line (For intervention strategies, see page 241.)

California Mathematics Content Standards

⊶NS 2.3 Solve addition, subtraction, multiplication, and division problems, including those arising in concrete situations, that use positive and negative integers and combinations of these operations.

(*Also* ⊶NS 2.0, MR 2.2, MR 2.4, MR 3.2)

Math Background

Adding two positive integers or two negative integers is much like adding whole numbers: the two numbers are added and then the sign of the numbers is attached. When adding a positive number and a negative number, students must first actually find the difference of the absolute values of the two numbers.

The following points may help students understand the process of adding integers:

• The sum of two positive integers is positive.

• The sum of two negative integers is negative.

• The sum of a positive and a negative number may be positive or negative. The answer is the difference of the two absolute values, and the sign is that of the number with the greater absolute value.

WARM-UP RESOURCES

 NUMBER OF THE DAY Transparency 12.2

How many minutes after the hour is it right now? Find its opposite. Possible answer for 23 minutes past the hour: ⁻23

 PROBLEM OF THE DAY Transparency 12.2

On a number line, the distance from 0 to a negative integer is four times as great as the distance to a positive integer. The sum of their absolute values is 35. What are the numbers? ⁻28, 7

Solution Problem of the Day tab, p. PD12

 DAILY FACTS PRACTICE

Have students practice addition facts by completing Set G of *Teacher's Resource Book*, p. TR101.

ALTERNATIVE TEACHING STRATEGY

Reinforce the concept of **adding integers.** Have students complete each statement with *always, sometimes,* or *never.*

- The sum of a positive integer and a negative integer is _____ positive. sometimes
- A negative integer added to a negative integer _____ equals a positive integer. never
- The sum of two positive integers is _____ positive. always
- The sum of two negative integers is _____ negative. always

See also page 246.

AUDITORY

MIXED REVIEW AND TEST PREP

Cumulative Review Chapters 1–12

Refer to the Pupil Edition pages referenced in the exercises for further review. Have students go to the lesson page, review the lesson, and correct any problem they missed.

Mixed Review and Test Prep, p. 247

How to Help	
Item	Page
42	234
43	234
44	234
45	210
46	186

ENGLISH LANGUAGE LEARNERS (ELL·SDAIE)

Materials *For each group* 20 two-color counters

Have students **model addition of integers** by solving this riddle:

- When you add <u>me</u> to 6 you get 3. What am I? $^-3$

Read the riddle aloud several times and model it with counters. Then have students work in groups to solve the riddles shown below.

- When you add <u>me</u> to $^-5$, you get 0. What am I? $^+5$
- When you add <u>me</u> to $^-9$, you get $^+2$. What am I? $^+11$

Ask students to make a riddle to share with the class. Have them read the riddle aloud, then model the answer with counters. Check students' work.

AUDITORY, KINESTHETIC

TECHNOLOGY · *CALCULATOR*

Have students use this activity to **explore integers on their calculators.**

- Have students enter 7 and press the $+/-$ key. Ask: What number is displayed? $^-7$
- Ask them to press the $+/-$ key again. Ask: Now what number is displayed? 7
- Ask students to describe the keys they would press to find the sum of $^-7$ and $^-2$. Ask: What is the sum? 7, $+/-$, $+$, 2, $+/-$, $=$; $^-9$
- Request that students repeat the above process to find the sum of $^-8$ and $^+5$. 8, $+/-$, $+$, 5, $=$; $^-3$

VISUAL

SCIENCE
Standards
IE, 7b

TECHNOLOGY LINK

 Intervention Strategies and Activities CD-ROM • *Skills 9, 42*

 Astro Algebra • *Red,* Level A

LESSON 12.2 ORGANIZER

Objective To use a number line to add integers

Vocabulary *Review* absolute value

1 Introduce

QUICK REVIEW provides review of pre-requisite skills.

Why Learn This? You can use addition of integers to determine net gain or loss of yardage in a football game and other types of games. *Share the lesson objective with students.*

2 Teach

Guided Instruction

• *Begin with a discussion of students' ideas about what kind of answer is possible when adding two integers. Direct students' attention to the first number line.*

What number does each arrow represent?
$^-3$ and $^-2$

What operation is shown by placing the tail of the arrow representing $^-2$ at the head of the one representing $^-3$? addition

• *Have students consider the second number line. Ask:*

Why do the arrows point in opposite directions? One arrow represents a positive number and the other represents a negative number.

• *Direct students' attention to Example 1.*

Can you place the tail of the arrow representing $^-6$ at 0? Explain. No; to show addition, you have to place the tail of the second arrow for $^-6$ at the same point on the number line as the head of the first arrow for 4.

REASONING **Can you draw the arrow for $^-6$ first and then the arrow for 4 and still get the same answer? Explain.** Yes; addition is commutative.

ADDITIONAL EXAMPLE

Example 1, p. 244

Use a number line to find the sum $^-3 + 5.2$

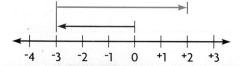

244 Chapter 12

LESSON 12.2 ALGEBRA
Add Integers

Learn how to use a number line to add integers.

QUICK REVIEW

1. 25 + 42 67 **2.** 240 − 60 180 **3.** 13 + 17 30
4. 112 + 35 147 **5.** 250 − 220 30

Jeb and Raul made up a game using a number line. Play starts at 0. A spinner is used to show positive moves and negative moves.

Jeb's first spin was $^-3$, and his second spin was $^-2$. What is Jeb's position on the number line?

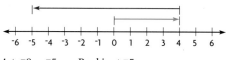

$^-3 + ^-2 = ^-5$ ← Jeb is at $^-5$.

Remember that you can write a positive number without the $^+$ sign.

$^+7 = 7$

Raul's first spin was 4, and his second spin was $^-9$. Where is Raul on the number line?

$4 + ^-9 = ^-5$ ← Raul is at $^-5$.

You can use a number line to find the sum of two integers.

EXAMPLE 1

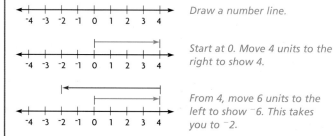

Use a number line to find the sum $4 + ^-6$.

Draw a number line.

Start at 0. Move 4 units to the right to show 4.

From 4, move 6 units to the left to show $^-6$. This takes you to $^-2$.

So, $4 + ^-6 = ^-2$.

When integers with the same sign are added, the arrows point in the same direction. When integers with different signs are added, the arrows point in different directions.

• When integers are added on a number line, when do the arrows point in the same direction and when do the arrows point in different directions? **See at left.**

RETEACH 12.2

Algebra: Add Integers

You can use a number line to help you add integers.
Find the sum $^+4 + ^-8$.
• Draw a number line.

• Start at 0. Move 4 spaces to the right to show $^+4$.

• From $^+4$, move 8 spaces to the left to show $^-8$.
So, $^+4 + ^-8 = ^-4$.

Find the sum $^-3 + ^-5$.
• Draw a number line.

• Start at 0. Move 3 spaces to the left to show $^-3$.

• From $^-3$, move 5 spaces to the left to show $^-5$.
So, $^-3 + ^-5 = ^-8$.

Use a number line to find each sum. Check students' number lines.

1. $^+7 + ^-4 =$ $^+3$
2. $^-8 + ^-2 =$ $^-10$
3. $^+5 + 3 =$ $^+2$
4. $^-6 + 3 =$ $^-9$
5. $^+5 + ^-8 =$ $^-3$
6. $^-4 + ^+9 =$ $^-13$
7. $^+7 + ^-2 =$ $^+5$
8. $^-3 + ^+5 =$ $^+2$
9. $^-1 + ^-6 =$ $^-7$
10. $^-2 + ^+6 =$ $^+4$
11. $^+8 + ^-3 =$ $^+5$
12. $^-2 + ^-5 =$ $^-7$

PRACTICE 12.2

Add Integers

Write the addition problem modeled on the number line.

1. $^+4 + ^-6 = ^-2$
2. $^-5 + ^+10 = ^+5$
3. $^-3 + ^-6 = ^-9$
4. $^-6 + ^+10 = ^+4$

Find the sum.

5. $^-8 + ^+5$ $^-13$
6. $^+14 + ^-9$ $^+5$
7. $^-20 + ^-4$ $^-24$
8. $^+31 + ^-12$ $^+19$
9. $^-14 + ^-16$ $^-30$
10. $^+35 + ^+17$ $^+52$
11. $^-23 + ^+9$ $^-32$
12. $^+39 + ^-15$ $^+24$
13. $^-59 + ^-22$ $^-81$
14. $^+47 + ^+33$ $^+14$
15. $^-37 + ^+26$ $^-63$
16. $^+49 + ^-20$ $^+29$
17. $^-19 + ^+42$ $^-61$
18. $^+17 + ^-12$ $^+5$
19. $^+44 + ^-17$ $^+27$
20. $^-64 + ^+38$ $^-102$
21. $^-23 + ^+50$ $^+27$
22. $^-31 + ^+43$ $^-74$
23. $^+85 + ^-15$ $^+70$
24. $^-59 + ^+21$ $^-80$

Mixed Review

Write the opposite of each number.

25. $^-12$ $^+12$
26. $^+81$ $^-81$
27. $^-54$ $^+54$
28. $^-17$ $^+17$

Find the absolute value.

29. $|^-45|$ 45
30. $|^+101|$ 101
31. $|^+310|$ 310
32. $|^-287|$ 287

Write each rational number in the form $\frac{a}{b}$. Possible answers are given.

33. $6\frac{7}{10}$ $\frac{67}{10}$
34. $^-9\frac{1}{8}$ $\frac{^-73}{8}$
35. $^-1.59$ $\frac{^-159}{100}$
36. 4.03 $\frac{403}{100}$

Remember that the absolute value of an integer is its distance from 0 on the number line.

When adding integers, you can use their absolute values to find the sum.

Adding with the Same Sign
When adding integers with the same sign, add the absolute values of the integers. Use the sign of the addends for the result.

EXAMPLE 2

Find the sum $^-7 + ^-2$.

$^-7 + ^-2$

$^-7 + ^-2 = 7 + 2$ *Add the absolute values of the integers.*

$= 9$

So, $^-7 + ^-2 = ^-9$.   *Use the sign of the original addends.*

Adding with Different Signs
When adding integers with different signs, subtract the lesser absolute value from the greater absolute value. Use the sign of the addend with the greater absolute value for the result.

EXAMPLE 3

A. Find the sum $^-8 + 3$.

$^-8 + 3$

Subtract the lesser absolute value from the greater absolute value.

$^-8 - 3 = 8 - 3$

$= 5$

Use the sign of the addend with the greater absolute value.

$^-8 > 3$ *The sum is negative.*

So, $^-8 + 3 = ^-5$.

B. Find the sum $^-5 + 9$.

$^-5 + 9$

Subtract the lesser absolute value from the greater absolute value.

$9 - ^-5 = 9 - 5$

$= 4$

Use the sign of the addend with the greater absolute value.

$9 > ^-5$ *The sum is positive.*

So, $^-5 + 9 = 4$.

• Find the sum $9 + ^-12$. $^-3$

EXAMPLE 4

On the first play of a football game, the Cobras gained 21 yards. On the second play, they lost 9 yards. Find the total number of yards gained or lost by the Cobras on the first two plays.

$21 + ^-9$ *Use 21 for yards gained and $^-9$ for yards lost.*

$21 - ^-9 = 21 - 9 = 12$ *Subtract the lesser absolute value from the greater absolute value.*

$21 > ^-9$ $21 + ^-9 = 12$ *Use the sign of the addend with the greater absolute value.*

So, the Cobras gained a total of 12 yards on the first two plays.

245

245

Modifying Instruction To reinforce the rules for adding integers, use a number line to model the Examples on page 245 and the Additional Examples below.

• *Review the concept of absolute value. Then ask students to think about the rule for adding two integers with the same sign and direct their attention to Example 2.*

Why is the answer negative in Example 2? The addends are both negative.

• *Ask students to consider the rule for adding two integers with opposite signs as in Example 3.*

What will be the sign of the sum in A? Why? Negative; $^-8$ has the greater absolute value.

What will be the sign of the sum in B? Why? Positive; 9 has the greater absolute value.

ADDITIONAL EXAMPLES

Example 2, p. 245

Find the sum $^-5 + ^-4$. $^-9$

Example 3, p. 245

A. Find the sum $3 + ^-7$. $^-4$

B. Find the sum $12 + ^-4$. 8

Example 4, p. 245

On the last two plays of the half, the Ramchargers gained 5 yards and lost 8 yards. Find the total number of yards gained or lost by the Ramchargers on the last two plays of the half. lost 3 yards

---

PROBLEM SOLVING 12.2

Algebra: Add Integers

Write the correct answer.

Analyze Choose Solve Check

1. Find the missing number in the pattern.

$3 + 2 = 5$
$3 + 1 = 4$
$3 + 0 = 3$
$3 + ^-1 = 2$
$3 + ^-2 = 1$
$3 + ^-3 = ▇$
0

2. Find the missing number in the pattern.

$^-3 + 1 = ^-2$
$^-3 + 0 = ^-3$
$^-3 + ^-1 = ^-4$
$^-3 + ^-2 = ^-5$
$^-3 + ^-3 = ^-6$
$^-3 + ^-4 = ▇$
$^-7$

3. Carmen wants to share her money with her cousin Jasmine. Together they have $48. If Carmen gives Jasmine $3, they will each have the same amount of money. How much money does each girl have now?

Carmen has $27,
Jasmine has $21.

4. Five students were waiting in line to return books at the library. There were 3 students ahead of John. There were 3 students behind Leila. Carla was first in line. Paul was last. What number in line was Sara?

third

Choose the letter for the best answer.

5. On three consecutive plays, a football team lost 2 yards, gained 5 yards, and gained 7 yards. Which expression could be used to find the total yards gained by the team on these three plays?

A $^-2 + ^-5 + ^-7$ C $^-2 - ^-5 + ^+7$
B $^-2 + ^-5 + ^+7$ (D) $^-2 + ^+5 + ^+7$

6. By 10:00 A.M., the temperature had risen 7°C from a morning low temperature of $^-15$°C. What was the temperature at 10:00 A.M.?

(F) $^-8$°C   H 7°C
G $^-7$°C   J 8°C

7. Kirk is 131.9 centimeters tall and Thad is 162.3 centimeters tall. Which is the best estimate of how much taller Thad is than Kirk?

A 10 cm   (C) 30 cm
B 20 cm   D 40 cm

8. Patty had 25.8 meters of wire to install lights in her backyard. She used only 19.4 meters. How much wire was left?

F 7.4 m   H 5.4 m
(G) 6.4 m   J 3.4 m

9. **Write About It** Explain why $8 + ^-3 = ^-3 + 8$.

Addition is commutative. Changing the order of the addends does not change the sum.

CHALLENGE 12.2

Sum It Up

The integer at the top of each rectangle is the sum of four addends contained in the rectangle. Shade the boxes containing the addends you use to get the sum. You will use one addend in each row.

1.

$^-2$	
$^+3$	0
$^-9$	$^+1$
$^+10$	$^-7$
$^-16$	$^-4$

2.

$^+5$	
$^+9$	$^+6$
$^-5$	$^-7$
$^-1$	$^-6$
$^+12$	0

3.

$^-4$	
$^-3$	0
$^-8$	$^-2$
$^+10$	$^-6$
$^+3$	$^+13$

4.

$^+6$	
$^+5$	$^+4$
0	$^+12$
$^+6$	$^-9$
$^+4$	$^-1$

5.

$^-3$	
$^+6$	$^-2$
$^-7$	0
$^-9$	$^+8$
$^+8$	$^+2$

6.

0	
$^+10$	$^-6$
$^-2$	$^+12$
$^-6$	$^-5$
$^-9$	$^+14$

7.

$^+2$	
$^+1$	$^-4$
$^+4$	$^-3$
$^+9$	$^+2$
$^-6$	0

8.

$^-8$	
$^-7$	$^+2$
$^-1$	$^-5$
$^-2$	$^-4$
$^+9$	$^+4$

9.

$^+4$	
$^+5$	$^-8$
$^-3$	$^-6$
$^-2$	$^+9$
$^+7$	$^-10$

LESSON 12.2

3 Practice

Guided Practice

Do Check for Understanding Exercises 1–13 with your students. Identify those having difficulty and use lesson resources to help.

///// **COMMON ERROR ALERT** \\\\\

Students may assign the wrong sign to the sum of two integers with different signs. To avoid this mistake, have students begin each exercise by circling the integer farther from zero. Remind students that this integer has the greater absolute value and the sign of this integer will be the sign used in the sum.

Independent Practice

Assign Exercises 14–41.

Algebraic Thinking For students to picture the value of x in each exercise, have them use a number line. For example, in Exercise 32 have students locate $^-5$ on a number line and then determine what number is needed to get to $^-7$.

CHECK FOR UNDERSTANDING

Think and ▶ Look back at the lesson to answer each question.
Discuss

1. **Explain** how you determine the sign of the sum of two integers with the same sign. **Use sign of the addends.**

2. **Explain** how you determine if the sum of two integers with different signs is positive or negative. **Use the sign of the addend with the greater absolute value.**

3. **Tell** how you know the Cobras had a gain of 12 yards instead of a loss of 12 yards in Example 4. **The sum was 12, which indicates a gain of 12 yards, not a loss of 12 yards.**

Guided ▶ Write the addition problem modeled on the number line.
Practice

4. 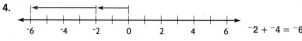 $^-2 + ^-4 = ^-6$

5. 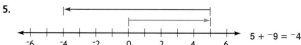 $5 + ^-9 = ^-4$

Find the sum.

6. $^-9 + 6$ $^-3$ 7. $^-3 + ^-4$ $^-7$ 8. $^-8 + 2$ $^-6$ 9. $5 + ^-7$ $^-2$

10. $^-3 + 7$ 4   11. $^-8 + ^-2$ $^-10$ 12. $11 + ^-5$ 6   13. $6 + ^-6$ 0

PRACTICE AND PROBLEM SOLVING

Independent ▶ Write the addition problem modeled on the number line.
Practice

14.  $^+2 + ^+4 = ^+6$

15.  $^-2 + ^+6 = ^+4$

Find the sum.

16. $^-5 + 8$ 3   17. $2 + ^-3$ $^-1$ 18. $7 + 2$ 9   19. $^-1 + 4$ 3

20. $8 + 7$ 15   21. $^-12 + ^-8$ $^-20$ 22. $^-15 + ^-10$ $^-25$ 23. $^-17 + 25$ 8

24. $^-2 + 5$ 3   25. $^-12 + ^-16$ $^-28$ 26. $^-17 + 5$ $^-12$ 27. $25 + ^-37$ $^-12$

28. $24 + 12$ 36   29. $30 + ^-41$ $^-11$ 30. $|16| + |^-9|$ 25   31. $|^-64| + |36|$ 100

🔢 **Algebra** Use mental math to find the value of x.

32. $^-5 + x = ^-7$ $x = ^-2$ 33. $x + ^-6 = ^-13$ $x = ^-7$

34. $x + ^-10 = ^-4$ $x = 6$ 35. $^-8 + x = ^-3$ $x = 5$

Alternative Teaching Strategy

Purpose Students use counters to add integers.

Materials *For each group* 20 two-color counters

Give each group 20 counters. Remind students that the yellow side indicates a positive number and the red side indicates a negative number. Ask each group to use their counters to show $^-3$ and $^-2$.

$^-3$ $^-2$

Then ask them to use the counters to find the sum $^-3 + ^-2$. Call on a volunteer to explain the addition process.

$^-3 + ^-2 = ^-5$

Next have students use their counters to show 4 and $^-7$. Ask them what happens when they make a pair of one counter of each color. The sum is zero. Have them use the counters to find the sum $4 + ^-7$. Ask a volunteer to explain the addition process.

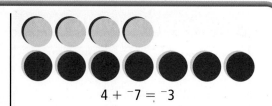

$4 + ^-7 = ^-3$

Finally, have groups use their counters to find sums for other pairs of integers. Call on volunteers to demonstrate the addition using counters, and record the number sentences. Check students' work.

Problem Solving ▶ Applications

36. In the morning the temperature was ⁻6°F. By noon it had risen 11°F. What was the temperature at noon? **5°F**

37. In the evening the temperature was ⁻9°F. By midnight it had dropped 3°F. What was the temperature at midnight? **⁻12°F**

38. Tina played a game in which she owned stock worth $33. During the game, the stock increased $11 in value and then decreased $15 in value. Write an addition sentence to find the new value of the stock. **33 + 11 + ⁻15 = 29; $29**

39. On the first three plays of a football game, the Wildcats gained 15 yards, lost 9 yards, and lost 8 yards. Find the total number of yards gained or lost by the Wildcats on the first three plays. **The Wildcats lost 2 yards.**

40. **What's the Error?** Ken says that ⁻6 + 2 = 8. What is his error? What is the correct sum? **He ignored the fact that 6 is negative; ⁻6 + 2 = ⁻4.**

41. Geometry A rectangle with an area of 180 cm² has a length of 15 cm. Find the width. **12 cm**

MIXED REVIEW AND TEST PREP

42. Is ⁻1.5 less than, greater than, or equal to ⁻1$\frac{3}{6}$? (p. 234) **equal to**

43. Is 8$\frac{3}{5}$ less than, greater than, or equal to 8.5? (p. 234) **greater than**

44. Is ⁻3.4 less than, greater than, or equal to ⁻3$\frac{1}{5}$? (p. 234) **less than**

45. TEST PREP Find the quotient 4$\frac{2}{3}$ ÷ 3$\frac{1}{2}$. (p. 210) **C**

A $\frac{3}{4}$ **B** 1$\frac{1}{4}$ **C** 1$\frac{1}{3}$ **D** 1$\frac{1}{2}$

46. TEST PREP Find the sum 5$\frac{3}{4}$ + 6$\frac{1}{3}$. (p. 186) **H**

F 11$\frac{1}{12}$ **G** 11$\frac{4}{7}$ **H** 12$\frac{1}{12}$ **J** 12$\frac{11}{12}$

Thinker's CORNER

Math Fun • Opposites Distract Remember that every number has an opposite that is the same distance from zero but is on the opposite side on the number line. Use a number line to solve these riddles.

1. I am the opposite of a number between 2$\frac{2}{3}$ and 3$\frac{5}{6}$. **Possible answer: ⁻3$\frac{3}{4}$**

2. I am the first integer that is less than the opposite of a number between 2$\frac{1}{2}$ and 2$\frac{3}{4}$. **⁻3**

3. I am the opposite of a number between ⁻4.3 and ⁻4$\frac{3}{8}$. **Possible answer: 4.37**

4. We are between ⁻2.4 and ⁻2.6. If you add our opposites, you get 5. **Possible answer: ⁻2.43 and ⁻2.57**

5. I am the opposite of the integer between the sum ⁻5 + 2 and the sum ⁻15 + 10. **4**

6. I am the second integer that is less than the sum ⁻22 + ⁻17. **⁻41**

7. I am the opposite of the even integer between the sum 35 + ⁻14 and the sum 12 + 6. **⁻20**

8. I am the integer that is 4 times the sum 42 + ⁻35. **28**

MIXED REVIEW AND TEST PREP
Exercises 42–46 provide **cumulative review** (Chapters 1–12).

Thinker's Corner

Have students work in pairs to solve these riddles. Point out that some riddles have more than one possible answer.

• As a follow-up to Exercise 4, ask:

REASONING What are two other possible answers? Possible answers: ⁻2.41 and ⁻2.59; ⁻2.44 and ⁻2.56; ⁻2.401 and ⁻2.599

4 Assess

Summarize the lesson by having students:

DISCUSS Describe what the arrows on a number line will look like to show the sum ⁻4 + ⁻6. They will both point in the negative direction. One will start at 0 and end at ⁻4 and the other will start at ⁻4 and end at ⁻10.

WRITE Describe how you would add two integers with opposite signs. Find the absolute value of each number and subtract the lesser from the greater. Then determine the sign of the sum by choosing the sign of the number with the greater absolute value.

Lesson Quiz

Transparency
12.2

Find the sum.

1. ⁻11 + 3 **⁻8**   **2.** ⁻5 + ⁻2 **⁻7**

3. 9 + ⁻16 **⁻7**   **4.** ⁻21 + 29 **8**

5. ⁻85 + 85 **0**   **6.** ⁻33 + ⁻13 **⁻46**

ORGANIZER

Objective To use two-color counters to subtract integers

Materials *For each group* 25 two-color counters

Lesson Resources E-Lab Recording Sheet • *Modeling Subtraction of Integers*

Intervention for Prerequisite Skills Understanding Integers (For intervention strategies, see page 241.)

Using the Pages

Remind students that there is more than one way to show the same value. For example, they have used two-color counters and number lines to model the addition of integers. Briefly review using counters to model integers.

How can you model 4? ⁻6? 0? with four yellow counters; with six red counters; with an equal number of red and yellow counters

Activity 1

Refer to the expression ⁻7 − 5.

Why are 5 yellow counters needed? to subtract 5

Why do we need to add both red and yellow counters to the model? Adding the same number of both colors does not change the value of the number you are subtracting from.

Refer to the expression 7 − ⁻2.

Describe the steps you will use to model 7 − ⁻2. First, model 7 with 7 yellow counters. Then, add two pairs of red and yellow counters to the model. Finally, remove the 2 red counters and write the answer 9.

Explore how to use two-color counters to subtract integers.

You need two-color counters.

ALGEBRA
Model Subtraction of Integers

QUICK REVIEW

1. 17 − 12 **5**	**2.** 42 + 20 **62**
3. 224 − 19 **205**	**4.** 132 − 18 **114**
5. 89 + 19 **108**	

You can use red and yellow counters to subtract integers. Subtracting integers is similar to subtracting whole numbers.

Activity 1

• Find ⁻9 − ⁻4. First, make a row of 9 red counters.

• Then, take away 4 of them.

   → ⁻9 − ⁻4

• How many counters are left? What is ⁻9 − ⁻4? **5; ⁻5**

Using red and yellow counters, model ⁻7 − 5.

• First, make a row of 7 red counters.

• Recall that a red counter paired with a yellow counter equals 0. Adding a red counter paired with a yellow counter does not change the value of ⁻7. Show another way to model ⁻7 that includes 5 yellow counters.

• Use your model to find ⁻7 − 5. Take away 5 yellow counters.

• What does your model show now? What is ⁻7 − 5?
12 red counters; ⁻12

Now model 7 − ⁻2.

• Model 7. Put down pairs of yellow and red counters until you can take away ⁻2. What is 7 − ⁻2? **9**

248

CALIFORNIA STANDARDS NS 2.3 Solve addition, subtraction, multiplication, and division problems, including those arising in concrete situations, that use positive and negative integers and combinations of these operations. *also,* ⟐ NS 2.0, MR 2.4, MR 2.5

SPECIAL NEEDS (ELL)

Materials *For each pair* 2 blank number cubes, p. TR75; 25 two-color counters

Ask each pair to **model subtraction of integers** by labeling the faces of one cube with positive integers 1–6 and the faces of the other with negative integers ⁻1 − ⁻6. Have each pair roll their cubes, write a subtraction problem using the numbers on the cubes, and model the subtraction with counters. Tell them to find and record the answer. Have pairs repeat the process to form 10 subtraction problems, modeling each with counters. Check students' work.

KINESTHETIC, VISUAL

Intervention and Extension Resources

Addition and subtraction of integers are related.

- Copy the model for ⁻7 below.

- Use the model to find ⁻7 − ⁻3. What is ⁻7 − ⁻3? **⁻4**

- Model ⁻7 again. Then add three yellow counters to find ⁻7 + 3. What is ⁻7 + 3? **⁻4**

TECHNOLOGY LINK

More Practice: Use E-Lab, *Modeling Subtraction of Integers.*
www.harcourtschool.com/elab2002

Think and Discuss

- The models above show that ⁻7 − ⁻3 = ⁻7 + 3. How are ⁻3 and 3 related? How are subtraction and addition related? **They are opposite, or inverse, operations.**
- How are the two models different? **One has only red counters, and the other has red and yellow counters.**
  You can write a subtraction problem as an addition problem by adding the opposite of the number you are subtracting.

$$6 - {}^-2 = 6 + 2 \leftarrow \text{Add the opposite of } {}^-2.$$

- How can you write ⁻6 − 2 as an addition problem? **by changing subtraction to addition and using ⁻2 instead of 2**

Practice

Use counters to find the difference.

1. ⁻7 − 4 **⁻11**
2. ⁻8 − ⁻5 **⁻3**
3. ⁻13 − 9 **⁻22**
4. ⁻9 − 4 **⁻13**

Complete the addition problem.

5. ⁻6 − ⁻2 = ⁻6 + ■ **2**
6. ⁻9 − ⁻3 = ⁻9 + ■ **3**
7. ⁻7 − 5 = ⁻7 + ■ **⁻5**
8. ⁻19 − 12 = ⁻19 + ■ **⁻12**

MIXED REVIEW AND TEST PREP

Find the sum. (p. 244)

9. ⁻3 + 9 **6**
10. 2 + ⁻7 **⁻5**
11. ⁻1 + ⁻7 **⁻8**

12. Write an integer to represent 217 m below sea level. (p. 228) **⁻217**

13. **TEST PREP**   Which is the value of $b + 1\frac{3}{4}$ for $b = 5\frac{2}{3}$? (p. 216) **D**

  A $6\frac{5}{7}$ B $6\frac{5}{12}$ C $7\frac{1}{12}$ D $7\frac{5}{12}$

249

E-LAB RECORDING SHEET

Name _____

Modeling Subtraction of Integers

In a magic square the numbers in each row, column, and diagonal add up to the same value. The sum associated with the magic square at the right is 15.

2	7	6
9	5	1
4	3	8

You can make a new magic square by subtracting the same value from each cell.

1. Subtract 4 from each cell to make a new magic square. Record your results in the blank grid at the right.

2. What is the new sum? All rows, columns, and diagonals should add up to this common value. ____3____

⁻2	3	2
5	1	⁻3
0	⁻1	4

3. What is the difference between the original sum and the sum for your new magic square? ____12____

Subtraction can also be used to compute a missing value in a magic square.

The sum defined in the magic square at the right is 21. In order to compute the value of the missing cell, add 6 + 5 and subtract from 21.

4	9	8
11	7	3
6	5	

4. Explain how to use the two numbers 8 and 3 in the right-hand column to compute the value of the missing cell. Add 8 and 3 and subtract the sum from 21.

Use the computer. Answers will vary for Problems 5–8.

5. Click **New Problem**. Copy the magic square from the screen onto the grid at the right.

6. Use subtraction to solve the magic square for the missing value. Write the value in the empty cell.

7. Make a new magic square from the magic square on the screen by subtracting ⁻4 from each value. Record your results in the grid at the right. (Remember that subtracting ⁻4 is the same as adding ⁻4.)

8. Copy and solve two more of the magic squares from the screen, and record the values in the grids below.

Subtracting a negative number is the same as adding the corresponding positive number.

E-Lab Recording Sheet   7

USING E-LAB

Students use addition and subtraction of integers to solve magic squares and to make new magic squares from old ones.

The E-Lab Recording Sheets and activities are available on the E-Lab website.

www.harcourtschool.com/elab2002

TECHNOLOGY LINK

- **Intervention Strategies and Activities CD-ROM** • *Skill 9*
- **E-Lab** • *Modeling Subtraction of Integers*
- **Astro Algebra** • *Red,* Level F

Algebra: Subtract Integers

LESSON PLANNING

Objective To use a number line to subtract integers

Intervention for Prerequisite Skills

Understand Integers, Locate Points on a Number Line (For intervention strategies, see page 241.)

 California Mathematics Content Standards

○━┓ NS 2.3 Solve addition, subtraction, multiplication, and division problems, including those arising in concrete situations, that use positive and negative integers and combinations of these operations.

(*Also* ○━┓ NS 2.0, MR 2.2, MR 2.5)

Math Background

Subtraction of integers is defined in terms of addition. To find the difference of two integers, add the opposite of the one being subtracted. This procedure will help students understand how to subtract integers.

- First, rewrite the subtraction problem as an addition problem. Make sure to write the opposite of the number being subtracted.
- Then use the rules of adding integers.

WARM-UP RESOURCES

 NUMBER OF THE DAY Transparency **12.4**

Write the day of the month. Add the opposite of that number to 30. What is the sum? Possible answer:
$30 + {}^-21 = 9$

 PROBLEM OF THE DAY Transparency **12.4**

Write the missing numbers. Each of the numbers in the first four rows is the sum of the two numbers below it.

$$^-4$$
$$^-3 \quad ^-1$$
$$^-1 \quad ^-2 \quad 1$$
$$^-4 \quad 3 \quad ^-5 \quad 6$$
$$^-14 \quad 10 \quad ^-7 \quad 2 \quad 4$$

Solution Problem of the Day tab, p. PD12

 **DAILY FACTS PRACTICE**

Have students practice subtraction facts by completing Set B of *Teacher's Resource Book,* p. TR102.

INTERVENTION AND EXTENSION RESOURCES

ALTERNATIVE TEACHING STRATEGY (ELL)

Reinforce the concept of using a number line to subtract integers. Draw a large number line on the floor and display the following: 14 − 6.

Place one student at 6 and another at 14. Have a third student walk from the number being subtracted, 6, to 14. Have students describe the path and record the solution. 8 steps in the positive direction

Repeat the activity for ⁻2 − 5. Place students at 5 and ⁻2. Ask a third student to start at 5, walk to ⁻2, and describe the path. 7 steps in the negative direction

KINESTHETIC

MIXED REVIEW AND TEST PREP

Cumulative Review Chapters 1–12

Refer to the Pupil Edition pages referenced in the exercises for further review. Have students go to the lesson page, review the lesson, and correct any problem they missed.

Mixed Review and Test Prep, p. 251

How to Help	
Item	Page
32	244
33	228
34	210
35	148
36	30

TECHNOLOGY LINK

 Intervention Strategies and Activities CD-ROM • *Skills 9, 42*

 Astro Algebra • *Red,* Level F

 The Harcourt Learning Site

WRITING IN MATHEMATICS

 Students can use graphic aids to practice integer subtraction. Display the graph below that shows the high and low temperatures for one week at a weather station in northern Minnesota.

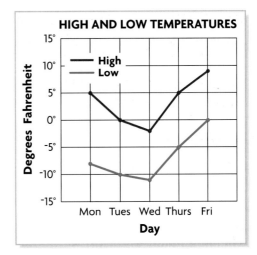

HIGH AND LOW TEMPERATURES

Have students write subtraction problems by using the graph. Check students' work.

VISUAL

ADVANCED LEARNERS

Challenge students to **apply their knowledge of subtracting integers** by using the chart below. The chart shows the windchill factor. Explain that the windchill factor is how cold it feels at a given temperature and wind speed.

WINDCHILL TEMPERATURE					
	Wind Speed (in mph)				
	0	5	10	15	20
10°	10°	6°	⁻9°	⁻18°	⁻24°
5°	5°	0°	⁻15°	⁻25°	⁻31°
0°	0°	⁻5°	⁻22°	⁻25°	⁻31°
⁻5°	⁻5°	⁻10°	⁻27°	⁻38°	⁻46°
⁻10°	⁻10°	⁻15°	⁻34°	⁻45°	⁻53°

Have students write subtraction problems based on information in the table. Check students' work.

VISUAL

Objective To use a number line to subtract integers

1 Introduce

QUICK REVIEW provides review of pre-requisite skills.

Why Learn This? You can find how much temperature changes over time by subtracting integers. *Share the lesson objective with students.*

2 Teach

Guided Instruction

• *Direct students' attention to page 250 and the description of a temperature change on Mars.*

REASONING **If the temperature had been 1°F instead of ⁻1°F, how would you write the subtraction and addition problem?**
$8 - 1 = 8 + ^-1$

Modifying Instruction Use counters to model the temperature change on Mars to help students understand the subtraction process.

• *Ask students to think about the first step in the Example while one volunteer uses counters to represent* ⁻9 − ⁻22 *and another models* ⁻9 + 22.

Are ⁻9 − ⁻22 and ⁻9 + 22 equal? Explain. Yes; they both equal 13.

Does the same kind of reasoning apply for 8 − 4? Explain. Yes; 8 − 4 = 8 + ⁻4 = 4.

Example, p. 250

When the mountain climbers started their expedition, the temperature was ⁻8°F. By late afternoon the temperature was ⁻13°F. What was the range of temperatures? 5°F

ALGEBRA
Subtract Integers

Learn how to use a number line to subtract integers.

1. 29 − 24 5
2. 14 + 8 22
3. 217 − 12 205
4. 97 + 17 114
5. 365 − 295 70

Pathfinder endured temperatures as low as ⁻89°F.

During the summer of 1997, NASA landed the Mars Pathfinder on the planet Mars. On July 9, Pathfinder reported a temperature of ⁻1°F. On July 10, Pathfinder reported a temperature of 8°F. Find the range of temperatures reported by Pathfinder from July 9 to July 10.

To find the range of temperatures, you need to find the difference of 8 and ⁻1, or 8 − ⁻1. You can find the difference of two integers by adding the opposite of the integer you are subtracting. You can then use the rules for addition of integers.

The opposite of ⁻1 is 1. So, 8 − ⁻1 becomes 8 + 1.

$8 - ^-1 = 8 + 1 = 9$

So, the range of temperatures was 9°F.

EXAMPLE

During an experiment, a scientist recorded a high temperature of ⁻9°C and a low temperature of ⁻22°C. What was the range of temperatures during the experiment?

$^-9 - ^-22 = ^-9 + 22$	*Write the subtraction problem as an addition problem. Use the rules for addition of integers.*
$^-9 + 22$	
$|22| - |^-9| = 22 - 9$	*Subtract the lesser absolute value from the greater absolute value.*
$= 13$	
$|22| > |^-9| \rightarrow ^-9 - ^-22 = 13$	*Use the sign of the addend with the greater absolute value.*

So, the range of temperatures during the experiment was 13°C.

• During the afternoon, the temperature fell from 7°F to ⁻5°F. What was the range of temperatures? **12°F**

250

CALIFORNIA STANDARDS NS 2.3 Solve addition, subtraction, multiplication, and division problems, including those arising in concrete situations, that use positive and negative integers and combinations of these operations. *also,* ⚷NS 2.0, MR 2.2, MR 2.5

RETEACH 12.4

Algebra: Subtract Integers

In New York City, the 9:00 A.M. temperature reading was ⁻5°C. By noon, the temperature had dropped 3°C. What was the temperature reading at noon?
Find ⁻5 − ⁺3.
You can find the difference of two integers by adding the opposite of the integer you are subtracting.
The opposite of ⁺3 is ⁻3.
⁻5 − ⁺3 becomes ⁻5 + ⁻3.

• Draw a number line.

• Start at 0. Move 5 spaces to the left to show ⁻5.

• From ⁻5, move 3 spaces to the left to add ⁻3.
So, at noon the temperature was ⁻8°C.

Rewrite the subtraction problem as an addition problem.

1. ⁻4 − ⁻3   2. ⁺8 − ⁻8   3. ⁺5 − ⁻9   4. ⁻6 − ⁺4
   ⁻4 + ⁺3   ⁺8 + ⁺8   ⁺5 + ⁻9   ⁻6 + ⁻4

Use a number line to find the difference. Check students' number lines.

5. ⁺6 − ⁺9 = ⁻3   6. ⁻5 − ⁻4 = ⁻1   7. ⁺7 − ⁻5 = ⁺12
8. ⁻8 − ⁺6 = ⁻14   9. ⁻6 − ⁻4 = ⁻2   10. ⁻9 − ⁺5 = ⁻14
11. ⁻3 − ⁻7 = ⁺4   12. ⁺1 − ⁻8 = ⁺7   13. ⁻3 − ⁻7 = ⁺9
14. ⁻7 − ⁺5 = ⁻12 15. ⁺9 − ⁺6 = ⁺3   16. ⁻6 − ⁺4 = ⁻10
17. ⁻4 − ⁻8 = ⁺4   18. ⁺2 − ⁺9 = ⁻7   19. ⁺4 − ⁻3 = ⁺7

PRACTICE 12.4

Subtract Integers

Use the number line to find the difference.

1. ⁻6 − ⁻9 = ⁻6 + ⁺9 = ⁺3   2. ⁻4 − ⁺5 = ⁻4 + ⁻5 = ⁻9

3. ⁻6 − ⁺5 = ⁻6 + ⁻5 = ⁻11   4. ⁻3 − ⁺7 = ⁻3 + ⁻7 = ⁻10

Find the difference.

5. ⁺8 − ⁻9   6. ⁻14 − ⁻6   7. ⁺12 − ⁻9   8. ⁺6 − ⁻2
   ⁺17   ⁻8   ⁺21   ⁺8
9. ⁺10 − ⁻3   10. ⁺11 − ⁻9   11. ⁻14 − ⁻7   12. ⁻9 − ⁺3
   ⁺13   ⁺20   ⁻7   ⁻12
13. ⁻11 − ⁻9   14. ⁻9 − ⁺4   15. ⁻13 − ⁺5   16. ⁻13 − ⁺2
   ⁻2   ⁻13   ⁻18   ⁻15
17. ⁻19 − ⁺7   18. ⁺16 − ⁺12   19. ⁺17 − ⁻11   20. ⁻18 − ⁻9
   ⁻26   ⁺4   ⁺28   ⁻9
21. ⁺15 − ⁻14 22. ⁻19 − ⁺13   23. ⁻21 − ⁺6   24. ⁻20 − ⁻8
   ⁺29   ⁻32   ⁻27   ⁻12

Mixed Review

Find a rational number between the two given numbers. Possible answers are given.

25. 8.3 and 8.26   26. ⁻4½ and ⁻4⅓   27. ⁻⅜ and ⁻0.4   28. ⁻1.9 and ⁻1¾
   8.28   ⁻4 5/12   ⁻0.38   ⁻1 7/8

Compare. Write < or > for each ●.

29. 5/8 ● 4/5   30. ⁻1.4 ● ⁻1⅜   31. ⅜ ● 0.7   32. ⁻5.5 ● ⁻5.6
   <   <   <   >

CHECK FOR UNDERSTANDING

Think and Discuss ▶ Look back at the lesson to answer the question.

1. **Tell** how you would write the subtraction problem as an addition problem if the temperature at the end of the experiment in the example was ⁻40°C. **⁻9 + 40**

Guided Practice ▶ Rewrite the subtraction problem as an addition problem.

2. $7 - 10$
$7 + {}^-10$

3. $3 - {}^-6$
$3 + 6$

4. ${}^-1 - {}^-8$
${}^-1 + 8$

5. ${}^-4 - 6$
${}^-4 + {}^-6$

Find the difference.

6. $4 - 8$
${}^-4$

7. ${}^-7 - {}^-2$
${}^-5$

8. $4 - {}^-5$
9

9. $1 - 8$
${}^-7$

PRACTICE AND PROBLEM SOLVING

Independent Practice ▶ Rewrite the subtraction problem as an addition problem.

10. $12 - 15$
$12 + {}^-15$

11. $8 - {}^-11$
$8 + 11$

12. ${}^-6 - {}^-13$
${}^-6 + 13$

13. ${}^-9 - 11$
${}^-9 + {}^-11$

Find the difference.

14. $6 - 11$
${}^-5$

15. ${}^-9 - {}^-5$
${}^-4$

16. $2 - {}^-1$
3

17. $3 - 5$
${}^-2$

18. $7 - 11$
${}^-4$

19. ${}^-5 - {}^-5$
0

20. $8 - {}^-3$
11

21. $4 - 9$
${}^-5$

22. $31 - 37$
${}^-6$

23. $35 - 39$
${}^-4$

24. $|{}^-43| - |12|$
31

25. $|{}^-27| - |{}^-32|$
${}^-5$

Evaluate.

26. ${}^-3 - {}^-5 + {}^-8$ **⁻6**

27. $6 - {}^-4 + {}^-5$ **5**

28. $8 - {}^-6 - 10$ **4**

Problem Solving Applications

29. In the morning, the temperature in Anchorage, Alaska, is ⁻12°F. Later that evening, the temperature is ⁻19°F. What is the range of temperatures? **7°F**

30. The water level of a river was 3 ft above normal. After an unusually dry season, the water level is 6 ft below normal. Find the range of the water levels of the river. **9 ft**

31. ⟨?⟩ **What's the Question?** The temperature at noon was 15°F. By midnight the temperature was ⁻3°F. The answer is 18°F. **What was the range of temperatures?**

MIXED REVIEW AND TEST PREP

32. Find the sum ⁻4 + 9. (p. 244) **5**

33. Write the opposite integer for 213. (p. 228)
⁻213

34. Find the quotient $5\frac{3}{4} \div 2\frac{1}{4}$. (p. 210) $2\frac{5}{9}$

35. Find the prime factorization of 84. (p. 148)
2 × 2 × 3 × 7

36. **TEST PREP** Solve $x + 9 = 21$ using mental math. (p. 30) **C**

   A $x = 9$ **B** $x = 11$ **C** $x = 12$ **D** $x = 30$

(**Extra Practice**) page H43, Set B   **251**

---

3 | Practice

Guided Practice

Do Check for Understanding Exercises 1–9 with your students. Identify those having difficulty and use lesson resources to help.

///// **COMMON ERROR ALERT** \\\\\

Students often remember to write the opposite of the number being subtracted but forget to change the problem to addition.

$$7 - 10 = 7 - {}^-10$$

Remind students to write the opposite of the number being subtracted *and* change the subtraction to addition.

$$7 - 10 = 7 + {}^-10$$

Independent Practice

Assign Exercises 10–31.

MIXED REVIEW AND TEST PREP
Exercises 32–36 provide **cumulative review** (Chapters 1–12).

4 | Assess

Summarize the lesson by having students:

DISCUSS **Explain how to find the opposite of an integer.** Possible answer: Write the absolute value and change the sign.

 WRITE **Explain how you solved Exercise 29.** Possible answer: Write the subtraction problem ⁻12 − ⁻19. Rewrite the problem as ⁻12 + 19. Subtract the lesser absolute value from the greater absolute value, $|19| - |12| = 7$. Then write the answer with a positive sign because the addend with the greater absolute value (19) is positive.

Lesson Quiz

Transparency [12.4]

Find the difference.

1. $6 - 14$ **⁻8**

2. ${}^-9 - {}^-11$ **2**

3. ${}^-5 - 10$ **⁻15**

4. $3 - {}^-24$ **27**

5. $31 - {}^-17$ **48**

6. ${}^-19 - 5$ **⁻24**

251

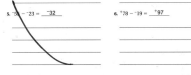

PROBLEM SOLVING 12.4

Algebra: Subtract Integers

⟨Analyze⟩⟨Choose⟩⟨Solve⟩⟨Check⟩

Write the correct answer.

1. Find the missing number in the pattern.

  $4 - 2 = 2$
  $4 - 1 = 3$
  $4 - 0 = 4$
  $4 - {}^-1 = 5$
  $4 - {}^-2 = 6$
  $4 - {}^-3 = \blacksquare$

    7

2. Find the missing number in the pattern.

  ${}^-2 - 1 = {}^-3$
  ${}^-2 - 0 = {}^-2$
  ${}^-2 - {}^-1 = {}^-1$
  ${}^-2 - {}^-2 = 0$
  ${}^-2 - {}^-3 = 1$
  ${}^-2 - {}^-4 = \blacksquare$

    2

3. Five years ago, Sean was three times as old as his brother. Today Sean is twice as old as his brother. How many years older than his brother is Sean? How old is Sean now?

  10 years older, 20 years old

4. For one week of work, Roberto earned $615. He worked 25 hours at his regular pay of $15 per hour. He also worked overtime hours, for which he was paid $20 per hour. How many overtime hours did Roberto work?

  12 hours overtime

Choose the letter for the best answer.

5. Which addition problem is equivalent to the subtraction problem ⁻8 − ⁻17?

  A $^+8 + {}^-17$
  B ${}^-8 + {}^-17$
  C $^+8 + {}^+17$
  D ${}^-8 + {}^+17$

6. Four hours ago, the temperature outside was +6°F. Since then the temperature has dropped 13°F. What is the temperature outside now?

  F $+19$°F
  G $+7$°F
  H $^-7$°F
  J $^-19$°F

7. John collected n gadgets. Frank gave him 18 more gadgets. John now has 51 gadgets. Which equation could be used to find the number of gadgets John had before Frank gave him more?

  A $n + 18 = 51$
  B $n - 51 = 18$
  C $n + 51 = 18$
  D $n - 18 = 51$

8. Maria keeps old records stored in special boxes. Each box can hold 45 old records. If she has 16 boxes full of old records, how many old records does she have?

  F 690 records
  G 700 records
  H 710 records
  J 720 records

9. **Write About It** Explain why $3 - 2 \neq 2 - 3$.

  Subtraction is not commutative. You will not get the same difference

  if you change the order of the numbers in a subtraction problem.

CHALLENGE 12.4

Create the Problem

Create a word problem that can be solved with each subtraction problem below. Then trade problems with a classmate, and solve each other's problems. Check students' problems.

1. $^-12 - {}^+7 = $ ___ **⁻19**

2. $^+15 - {}^-9 = $ ___ **⁺24**

3. $^-25 - {}^-17 = $ ___ **⁻8**

4. $^-32 - {}^+14 = $ ___ **⁻46**

5. $^-5 - {}^-23 = $ ___ **⁻32**

6. $^+78 - {}^-19 = $ ___ **⁺97**

CHAPTER 12

REVIEW/TEST

Purpose To check understanding of concepts, skills, and problem solving presented in Chapter 12

USING THE PAGE

The Chapter 12 Review/Test can be used as a **review** or a **test**.

- Item 1 checks understanding of concepts and new vocabulary.
- Items 2–35 check skill proficiency.
- Items 36–40 check students' abilities to choose and apply problem solving strategies to real-life problems involving integer addition and subtraction.

Suggest that students place the completed Chapter 12 Review/Test in their portfolios.

USING THE ASSESSMENT GUIDE

- Multiple-choice format of Chapter 12 Posttest—See *Assessment Guide*, pp. AG77–78.
- Free-response format of Chapter 12 Posttest—See *Assessment Guide*, pp. AG79–80.

USING STUDENT SELF-ASSESSMENT

The How Did I Do? survey helps students assess what they have learned and how they learned it. This survey is available as a copying master in *Assessment Guide*, p. AGxvii.

---

1. VOCABULARY The opposite of an integer is its ___?___. (p. 243) **additive inverse**

Write the addition problem modeled on each number line. (pp. 244–247)

2. 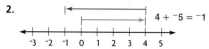 $4 + {}^-5 = {}^-1$

3.  $4 + {}^-6 = {}^-2$

Find the sum. (pp. 244–247)

4. $7 + {}^-6$ **1**	**5.** ${}^-5 + {}^-3$ **${}^-8$**	**6.** ${}^-7 + 4$ **${}^-3$**	**7.** $4 + {}^-1$ **3**
8. ${}^-3 + {}^-4$ **${}^-7$**	**9.** ${}^-2 + 6$ **4**	**10.** ${}^-8 + 3$ **${}^-5$**	**11.** ${}^-7 + {}^-9$ **${}^-16$**
12. ${}^-9 + 4$ **${}^-5$**	**13.** $9 + {}^-1$ **8**	**14.** ${}^-3 + 9$ **6**	**15.** ${}^-5 + {}^-6$ **${}^-11$**
16. ${}^-37 + 24$ **${}^-13$**	**17.** $17 + {}^-19$ **${}^-2$**	**18.** ${}^-17 + {}^-41$ **${}^-58$**	**19.** $21 + 17$ **38**

Use mental math to find the value of *x*. (pp. 244–247)

20. $x + 4 = {}^-4$ $x = {}^-8$ **21.** $x + {}^-6 = {}^-1$ **$x = 5$** **22.** $9 + x = 0$ **$x = {}^-9$** **23.** ${}^-4 + x = {}^-3$ **$x = 1$**

Find the difference. (pp. 250–251)

24. $7 - 11$ **${}^-4$**	**25.** ${}^-2 - 8$ **${}^-10$**	**26.** ${}^-3 - {}^-5$ **2**	**27.** $4 - {}^-4$ **8**
28. ${}^-1 - {}^-8$ **7**	**29.** ${}^-2 - 2$ **${}^-4$**	**30.** $3 - 8$ **${}^-5$**	**31.** $6 - 12$ **${}^-6$**
32. ${}^-1 - 4$ **${}^-5$**	**33.** ${}^-6 - {}^-8$ **2**	**34.** $51 - {}^-23$ **74**	**35.** ${}^-41 - 18$ **${}^-59$**

Solve. (pp. 242–251)

36. A submarine started one leg of its voyage at ${}^-300$ ft. At the end of that leg of the voyage, it was at ${}^-1{,}250$ ft. What was the difference between the two depths? **950 ft**

37. Neal was measuring the motion of an object. He observed that it moved 12 cm forward and 17 cm backward. What was its distance from the starting point? **5 cm**

38. Tasha needed to find the average temperature during three days in the winter. Her first step was to add the temperatures together. If the temperatures were ${}^-6°$, ${}^-8°$, and $11°$, what was the sum? **${}^-3°$**

39. At midnight the temperature was ${}^-15°F$. The temperature continued to fall until 7:00 A.M., when it was ${}^-22°F$. How many degrees had the temperature fallen during the seven hours? **7°**

40. Two explorers start a hike in a valley 12 feet below sea level. When they finish their hike they are at 22 feet above sea level. What is the difference between the two elevations? **34 ft**

CHAPTER 12 TEST, page 1

Choose the best answer.

1. Which addition problem is modeled on the number line below?

A ${}^-2 + {}^+7 = {}^+5$ C ${}^+5 + 7 = {}^-2$
B ${}^-5 + 2 = {}^-7$ D ${}^+5 - {}^+7 = {}^+12$

2. Which addition problem is modeled on the number line below?

F ${}^-4 + {}^+6 = {}^+2$ H ${}^+6 + {}^-4 = {}^+2$
G ${}^-4 + 2 = {}^-6$ J ${}^-2 + {}^-4 = {}^-6$

For 3–11, find the sum.

3. ${}^+3 + {}^+5$
A ${}^-8$ C ${}^+2$
B ${}^-2$ D ${}^+8$

4. ${}^-4 + {}^+6$
F ${}^-10$ H ${}^+2$
G ${}^-2$ J ${}^+10$

5. ${}^+2 + {}^-3$
A ${}^+5$ C ${}^-1$
B ${}^+1$ D ${}^-5$

6. ${}^-7 + {}^+3$
F ${}^-10$ H ${}^+4$
G ${}^-4$ J ${}^+10$

7. ${}^-6 + {}^-5$
A ${}^-11$ C ${}^+1$
B ${}^-1$ D ${}^+11$

8. ${}^-9 + {}^-2$
F ${}^-11$ H ${}^+7$
G ${}^-7$ J ${}^+11$

9. ${}^+13 + {}^-23$
A ${}^-36$ C ${}^+10$
B ${}^-10$ D ${}^+36$

10. ${}^+8 + {}^-15$
F ${}^+23$ H ${}^-7$
G ${}^+7$ J ${}^-23$

11. ${}^-38 + {}^+25$
A ${}^-63$ C ${}^+13$
B ${}^-13$ D ${}^+63$

For 12–13, use mental math to find the value of *x*.

12. $x + {}^-3 = {}^-5$
F $x = {}^-8$ H $x = {}^+2$
G $x = {}^-2$ J $x = {}^+8$

13. ${}^-3 + x = {}^+6$
A $x = {}^-9$ C $x = {}^+3$
B $x = {}^-3$ D $x = {}^+9$

Go On

CHAPTER 12 TEST, page 2

For 14–20, find the difference.

14. ${}^+7 - {}^-9$
F ${}^+16$ H ${}^-2$
G ${}^+2$ J ${}^-16$

15. ${}^+4 - {}^+6$
A ${}^-10$ C ${}^+2$
B ${}^-2$ D ${}^+10$

16. ${}^-3 - {}^-7$
F ${}^-10$ H ${}^+4$
G ${}^-4$ J ${}^+10$

17. ${}^+3 - {}^-3$
A ${}^+6$ C ${}^-3$
B ${}^+3$ D ${}^-6$

18. ${}^-7 - {}^+4$
F ${}^+11$ H ${}^-3$
G ${}^+3$ J ${}^-11$

19. ${}^+33 - {}^-12$
A ${}^-45$ C ${}^+21$
B ${}^-21$ D ${}^+45$

20. ${}^-17 - {}^+42$
F ${}^-59$ H ${}^-25$
G ${}^-35$ J ${}^+25$

21. At noon, the temperature was 2°F. The temperature at 8:00 P.M. was ${}^-11°F$. How many degrees did the temperature fall?

A ${}^-11°F$ C 9°F
B 2°F   D 13°F

22. Carrie walked forward 23 ft. She then walked backward 9 ft and stopped. How many feet from her starting point was she when she stopped?

F 32 ft   H 9 ft
G 14 ft   J 3 ft

23. Jiu rolled a ball toward a wall that was 12 ft away. The ball bounced back from the wall and rolled 3 ft. How many feet from Jiu was the ball when it stopped?

A 15 ft   C 9 ft
B 12 ft   D 3 ft

24. Kelly got on an elevator and went down 5 floors. The elevator then went up 9 floors, and Kelly got off. What integer describes where she got off in relation to where she got on?

F ${}^+4$ H ${}^-4$
G ${}^+2$ J ${}^-14$

25. A treasure hunter started exploring at ${}^-50$ ft from the water's surface and then went down to ${}^-85$ ft. Which of the following describes the treasure hunter's change in depth?

A ${}^-135$ ft   C ${}^-50$ ft
B ${}^-85$ ft   D ${}^-35$ ft

Stop

Get the information you need.

See item **4.**

Think about how you can write the subtraction of integers as addition. Then find the expression that has the same solution as the given subtraction problem.

Also see problem **3**, p. H63.

Choose the best answer.

1. $^-7 + 5$ **B**

   A $^-12$ **C** 2
   B $^-2$ **D** Not here

2. On Sunday, the low temperature was $^-4°F$. The low temperature on Monday was 13° higher. What was the low temperature on Monday? **J**

   F $^-13°F$

   G $^-9°F$

   H 4°F

   J 9°F

3. What is the value of $29 + k$ for $k = ^-26$? **C**

   A $^-55$ **C** 3
   B $^-3$ **D** 55

4. Which problem has the same solution as $^-3 - ^-5$? **H**

   F $^-3 - 5$ **H** $^-3 + 5$
   G $^-3 + ^-5$ **J** $3 + 5$

5. $5 + ^-8$ **A**

   A $^-3$ **C** 13
   B 3   **D** Not here

6. $^-5 - ^-3$ **G**

   F $^-8$ **H** 2
   G $^-2$ **J** Not here

7. The graph shows the number of sixth-grade students at a middle school who are in each club listed. How many more students are in the Science Club than in the Chess Club? **B**

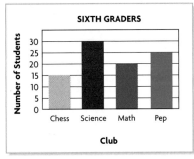

   A 2   **C** 20
   B 15   **D** 30

8. How is $2 \times 2 \times 2 \times 2$ written in exponent form with a base of 2? **F**

   F 2^4 **H** 4^2
   G 2^5 **J** 2^{10}

9. Use mental math to find the value of x. **D**

   $$x + ^-9 = 5$$

   A $x = ^-14$ **C** $x = 4$
   B $x = ^-4$ **D** $x = 14$

10. Ellen got a score of 50 on her history exam. The mean score on that exam was 45. Which claim is valid? **F**

    F Ellen's score is above the average score.
    G Ellen got the top score.
    H Ellen's score is higher than most of the other students' scores.
    J Ellen's score is below the average score.

11. $0.053 - 0.019$ **C**

    A 3.4   **C** 0.034
    B 0.34   **D** Not here

CUMULATIVE REVIEW •

Chapters 1–12

USING THE PAGE

This page may be used to help students get ready for standardized tests. The test items are written in the same style and arranged in the same format as those on many state assessments. The page is cumulative. It covers math objectives and essential skills that have been taught up to this point in the text. Most of the items represent skills from the current chapter, and the remainder represent skills from earlier chapters.

This page can be assigned at the end of the chapter as classwork or as a homework assignment. You may want to have students use individual recording sheets presented in a multiple-choice (standardized) format. A Test Answer Sheet is available as a blackline master in *Assessment Guide* (p. AGxlii).

You may wish to have students describe how they solved each problem and share their solutions.

Add and Subtract with Integers 253

Multiply and Divide with Integers

CHAPTER PLANNER

PACING OPTIONS

Compacted	2 Days
Expanded	5 Days

Getting Ready for Chapter 13 • Assessing Prior Knowledge and INTERVENTION (See PE and TE page 255.)

LESSON	CALIFORNIA STANDARDS	PACING	VOCABULARY*	MATERIALS	RESOURCES AND TECHNOLOGY
13.1 Math Lab: Algebra—Model Multiplication of Integers pp. 256–257 **Objective** To explore multiplication of integers, using two-color counters and number lines	⊶ NS 2.3 (*Also* ⊶ NS 2.0, MR 2.4)	1 Day		*For each group* two-color counters	
13.2 Algebra: Multiply Integers pp. 258–259 **Objective** To multiply integers	⊶ NS 2.3 (*Also* ⊶ NS 2.0, AF 1.3, MR 1.1, MR 2.2, MR 2.4, MR 3.3)	1 Day			Reteach, Practice, Problem Solving, Challenge 13.2 Worksheets Extra Practice p. H44, Set A ▭ Transparency 13.2 💿 **Astro Algebra • Red**
13.3 Algebra: Divide Integers pp. 260–261 **Objective** To divide integers	⊶ NS 2.3 (*Also* ⊶ NS 2.0, AF 1.3, SDAP 1.1, MR 1.1, MR 2.5, MR 3.3)	1 Day			Reteach, Practice, Problem Solving, Challenge 13.3 Worksheets Extra Practice p. H44, Set B ▭ Transparency 13.3 💿 **Astro Algebra • Red**
13.4 Combine Operations with Integers pp. 262–263 **Objective** To perform more than one operation with integers	⊶ NS 2.3 (*Also* ⊶ NS 2.0, AF 1.3, AF 1.4, MR 1.3, MR 2.2)	1 Day	order of operations		Reteach, Practice, Problem Solving, Challenge 13.4 Worksheets Extra Practice p. H44, Set C ▭ Transparency 13.4

Ending Chapter 13 • Chapter 13 Review/Test, p. 264 • Cumulative Review, p. 265

Ending Unit 4 • Math Detective, p. 266; Challenge, p. 267; Study Guide and Review, pp. 268–269; California Connections, pp. 270–271

*Boldfaced terms are new vocabulary. Other terms are review vocabulary.

CHAPTER AT A GLANCE

Vocabulary Development

There are no new words introduced in this chapter, but mathematics vocabulary is reinforced visually and verbally. Encourage students to review the mathematics vocabulary in their math journals.

Writing Opportunities

PUPIL EDITION
- **What's the Error?**, p. 259
- **What's the Question?**, p. 261
- **Write About It**, p. 263

TEACHER'S EDITION
- **Write**—See the *Assess* section of each TE lesson.
- **Writing in Mathematics**, p. 262B

ASSESSMENT GUIDE
- **How Did I Do?**, p. AGxvii

California Mathematics Content Standards for Grade 6

Strands

Number Sense

Lesson 13.1: NS 2.0, 2.3
Lesson 13.2: NS 2.0, 2.3
Lesson 13.3: NS 2.0, 2.3
Lesson 13.4: NS 2.0, 2.3

Algebra and Functions

Lesson 13.2: AF 1.3
Lesson 13.3: AF 1.3
Lesson 13.4: AF 1.3, 1.4

Measurement and Geometry

Statistics, Data Analysis, and Probability
Lesson 13.3: SDAP 1.1

Mathematical Reasoning

Lesson 13.1: MR 2.4
Lesson 13.2: MR 1.1, 2.2, 2.4, 3.3
Lesson 13.3: MR 1.1, 2.5, 3.3
Lesson 13.4: MR 1.3, 2.2

Family Involvement Activities

These activities provide:
- Letter to the Family
- Information about California Standards
- Math Vocabulary
- Family Game
- Practice (Homework)

HARCOURT MATH	Name
GRADE 6	Date
Chapter 13	

WHAT WE ARE LEARNING
Multiply and Divide with Integers

Dear Family,

Your child is studying multiplication and division of integers. Your child learned about the rules for operations with integers by working with colored counters and also by using a number line. These are the rules discovered:

Rules for multiplication of integers
- The product of two integers with unlike signs is negative.

$$4 \times {}^-3 = {}^-12 \qquad {}^-4 \times 3 = {}^-12$$

- The product of two integers with like signs is positive.

$$4 \times 3 = 12 \qquad {}^-4 \times {}^-3 = 12$$

Rules for division of integers
- The quotient of two integers with unlike signs is negative.

$$\frac{{}^-12}{3} = {}^-4 \qquad \frac{12}{{}^-3} = {}^-4$$

- The quotient of two integers with like signs is positive.

$$\frac{{}^-12}{{}^-3} = 4 \qquad \frac{12}{3} = 4$$

This is how your child is learning to perform more than one operation with integers. To guide your child's thinking while studying the operations of integers, ask the questions suggested.

Step 1
Apply the first order of operation: Operate inside the parentheses, and apply rules for operations with integers.

Can you tell me why I might say the rules for multiplying and dividing integers are the same? Your child might explain: If both signs are the same, the answer will always be positive if I multiply or if I divide. If the signs are different, the result will always be negative.

The California Math Standards
Your child's **Harcourt Math** book lists the California Math Standards that are taught in every lesson. If you have questions about the standards, be sure to consult *California Standards for Grade 6* that was sent home at the beginning of the school year.

Family Involvement Activities, p. FA51

Multiply and Divide with Integers

MATHEMATICS ACROSS THE GRADES

SKILLS TRACE ACROSS THE GRADES

GRADE 5	GRADE 6	GRADE 7
Represent and order integers on a number line; add and subtract integers	Write products and quotients of integers; evaluate expressions with a combination of operations with integers	Write products and quotients of rational numbers; evaluate expressions with rational numbers

SKILLS TRACE FOR GRADE 6

LESSON	FIRST INTRODUCED	TAUGHT AND PRACTICED	TESTED	REVIEWED
13.1	Grade 6	PE pp. 256–257	PE p. 264, pp. AG81–84	PE pp. 264, 265, 268–269
13.2	Grade 6	PE pp. 258–259, H44, p. RW57, p. PW57, p. PS57	PE p. 264, pp. AG81–84	PE pp. 264, 265, 268–269
13.3	Grade 6	PE pp. 260–261, H44, p. RW58, p. PW58, p. PS58	PE p. 264, pp. AG81–84	PE pp. 264, 265, 268–269
13.4	Grade 6	PE pp. 262–263, H44, p. RW59, p. PW59, p. PS59	PE p. 264, pp. AG81–84	PE pp. 264, 265, 268–269

KEY **PE** Pupil Edition   **PS** Problem Solving Workbook   **RW** Reteach Workbook
       PW Practice Workbook   **AG** Assessment Guide

Looking Back Prerequisite Skills

To be ready for Chapter 13, students should have the following understandings and skills:

- **Multiplication and Division Facts**—find products and quotients using mental math; solve for *n* in basic facts number sentences

- **Add and Subtract Integers**—find sums and differences of integers

- **Patterns**—find next three numbers or figures in a pattern

Check What You Know
Use page 255 to determine students' knowledge of prerequisite concepts and skills.

Intervention
Help students prepare for the chapter by using the intervention resources described on TE page 255.

Looking at Chapter 13 Essential Skills

Students will

- **understand the concepts of integer multiplication and division.**

- develop skill and accuracy applying the order of operations to integer expressions.

EXAMPLE

Use counters to find the product.

$$3 \times {}^-2$$

Each red counter represents ⁻1.

$3 \times {}^-2 = {}^-6$

So, the product is ⁻6.

Looking Ahead Applications

Students will apply what they learn in Chapter 13 to the following new concepts:

- Evaluate Expressions (Chapter 14)
- Connect Words and Equations (Chapter 15)
- Solve Multiplication and Division Equations (Chapter 16)

Multiply and Divide
with Integers

INTRODUCING THE CHAPTER

Tell students that they can think of multiplication and division of integers as repeated addition and subtraction. Ask students how many degrees of change will result if the temperature drops 3°F each hour for 8 hours. ⁻24°F

USING DATA

To begin the study of this chapter, have students

- Convert February's average low temperature to the nearest whole degree Celsius. ⁻18°C

- Make a line graph to show a steady drop in temperature from 25°F to ⁻7°F over 8 hours. Check students' work.

PROBLEM SOLVING PROJECT

Purpose To multiply and divide integers

Background The Ice Hotel is basically an igloo that is built every winter and melts each spring. About 22,000 tons of ice are carved from the Torne River to make the hotel. Artists then sculpt each room.

Analyze, Choose, Solve, and Check

Have students

- Prepare a cost analysis that shows how much of a company's $10,000 travel budget will remain if 5 people travel to and stay at the Ice Hotel for 1 night at the room rate of $250 per night.

- Research travel costs from a nearby city to Kiruna, Sweden, where the nearest airport to the Ice Hotel is located.

- Calculate the amount deducted from the budget for 5 rooms when each room costs $165, $225, and $250. $825.00; $1,125.00; $1,250.00

Check students' work.

Suggest that students place their cost analyses in their portfolios.

254

Multiply and Divide with Integers

One of the most unusual hotels in the world is located above the Arctic Circle in Sweden. The Ice Hotel is made entirely of ice, including each room, bed, fireplace, chair, and eating utensil. Each winter, adventurous travelers pay from $165 to $250 per night to stay at the hotel. On some nights, it may be 25°F in the hotel when a traveler goes to bed and the temperature will drop an average of 3°F each hour. What will be the temperature when the traveler gets up 8 hours later?

AVERAGE TEMPERATURE IN SWEDEN
(Above the Arctic Circle)

* To convert °F to °C use the formula
°C = (°F - 32) x 0.555

254 Chapter 13

Why learn math? Explain that business managers must arrange for the travel of their employees to many places around the world. Business managers are responsible for keeping track of all expenses and keeping them within a budget. In the budget, income may be recorded as positive numbers and expenses as negative numbers. Ask: When might a business manager need to multiply a negative number? Possible answer: When the same expense occurs several times within a budget.

Check What You Know

Use this page to help you review and remember important skills needed for Chapter 13.

✓ Multiplication and Division Facts (See p. H13.)

Find the product or the quotient.

1. 4×6 **24**
2. 9×7 **63**
3. $80 \div 8$ **10**
4. $24 \div 3$ **8**
5. 4×1 **4**
6. 8×7 **56**
7. 12×6 **72**
8. $108 \div 9$ **12**
9. $45 \div 9$ **5**
10. 3×11 **33**
11. $120 \div 12$ **10**
12. $81 \div 9$ **9**

Solve for n.

13. $2 \times n = 14$ **n = 7**
14. $n \times 5 = 15$ **n = 3**
15. $n \div 6 = 9$ **n = 54**
16. $88 \div n = 11$ **n = 8**
17. $42 = n \times 6$ **n = 7**
18. $11 = n \div 12$ **n = 132**

✓ Add and Subtract Integers (See p. H14.)

Find the sum or difference.

19. $8 - 15$ **⁻7**
20. $^-9 + ^-5$ **⁻14**
21. $^-15 - ^-8$ **⁻7**
22. $^-9 + 21$ **12**
23. $^-5 - 12$ **⁻17**
24. $16 - ^-13$ **29**
25. $^-31 + ^-37$ **⁻68**
26. $82 + ^-59$ **23**
27. $^-15 - 32$ **⁻47**
28. $^-50 - ^-80$ **30**
29. $12 + ^-17$ **⁻5**
30. $^-43 - ^-43$ **0**

✓ Patterns (See p. H14.)

Describe a possible pattern and find the next three numbers in your pattern.

31. $1, 2, 3, 4, 5, \ldots$ **Add 1; 6, 7, 8**
32. $16, 14, 12, 10, 8, \ldots$ **Subtract 2; 6, 4, 2**
33. $256, 128, 64, 32, 16, \ldots$ **Divide by 2; 8, 4, 2**
34. $1, 4, 7, 10, 13, \ldots$ **Add 3; 16, 19, 22**
35. $3, 6, 12, 24, 48, \ldots$ **Multiply by 2; 96, 192, 384**
36. $50,000, 10,000, 2,000, 400, \ldots$ **Divide by 5; 80, 16, 3.2**
37. $120, 112, 104, 96, 88, \ldots$ **Subtract 8; 80, 72, 64**
38. $^-6, 12, ^-24, 48, ^-96, \ldots$ **Multiply by ⁻2; 192, ⁻384, 768**

Draw a picture of the next 3 figures in the pattern. Describe the pattern.

39.
Rotate shaded triangle 90° clockwise.

40.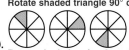
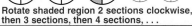
Rotate shaded region 2 sections clockwise, then 3 sections, then 4 sections, . . .

> **LOOK AHEAD**
>
> **In Chapter 13 you will**
> - multiply integers
> - divide integers
> - perform more than one operation with integers

255

Check What You Know

INTERVENTION • Diagnose and Prescribe

Prerequisite Skill	Items (Pupil Edition p. 255)	How to Help Options
✓ Multiplication and Division Facts	1–18	• **Troubleshooting, Pupil Edition p. H13** • **Intervention Strategies and Activities** Card, Copying Master, or CD-ROM • **Skills 17, 19**
✓ Add and Subtract Integers	19–30	• **Troubleshooting, Pupil Edition p. H14** • **Intervention Strategies and Activities** Card, Copying Master, or CD-ROM • **Skills 10–11**
✓ Patterns	31–40	• **Troubleshooting, Pupil Edition p. H14** • **Intervention Strategies and Activities** Card, Copying Master, or CD-ROM • **Skill 8**

ORGANIZER

Objective To explore multiplication of integers, using two-color counters and number lines

Materials *For each group* 12 two-color counters

Intervention for Prerequisite Skills Multiplication Facts, Division Facts, Patterns (For intervention strategies, see page 255.)

Using the Pages

Remind students how to use counters to model integers. Have volunteers show models of several positive and negative integers.

Activity 1

Direct students' attention to the examples in this activity. Ask:

Which number shows the number of groups? the first one

What does the second number show? the number of counters in each group

Think and Discuss

Have students relate the signs in the factors to the sign of the product.

What is the sign of the product $9 \times {}^-2$? Explain. Negative; Possible answer: You can think of it as 9 groups of $^-2$.

Practice

Ask students to describe the model they used to find the product in Exercise 4. 6 groups of $^-3$, or 6 groups of 3 red counters

---

ALGEBRA
Model Multiplication of Integers

Explore how to use two-color counters and number lines to multiply integers.

You need two-color counters.

QUICK REVIEW

1. 30×5 **150** **2.** 3×22 **66**   **3.** 8×40 **320**

4. 60×70 **4,200 5.** 250×8 **2,000**

Remember that 4×5 can be written as $4 \cdot 5$.

You can use yellow and red counters to model multiplication of integers. A yellow counter represents $^+1$ and a red counter represents $^-1$.

Activity 1

• Use yellow counters to model the product $2 \cdot 3$.

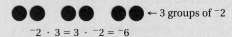 ←$^+2$ groups of 3

$2 \cdot 3 = 6$

• Use red counters to model the product $2 \cdot {}^-3$.

⬤⬤⬤ ⬤⬤⬤ ← 2 groups of $^-3$

$2 \cdot {}^-3 = {}^-6$

• Use red counters to model the product $^-2 \cdot 3$. Using the Commutative Property, you can write $^-2 \cdot 3$ as $3 \cdot {}^-2$.

⬤⬤ ⬤⬤ ⬤⬤ ← 3 groups of $^-2$

$^-2 \cdot 3 = 3 \cdot {}^-2 = {}^-6$

Write $^-3 \cdot 4$ as $4 \cdot {}^-3$ using the Commutative Property. Then use 4 groups of 3 red counters.

Think and Discuss

• How could you model the product $3 \cdot {}^-4$? **You could use 3 groups of 4 red counters.**
• How could you model the product $^-3 \cdot 4$? **See answer at left.**

• What do you notice about the product of two positive integers? of a positive integer and a negative integer? **The product is positive. The product is negative.**

Practice

Use counters to find the product.

1. $2 \cdot 4$ **8**   **2.** $3 \cdot {}^-5$ **$^-15$**   **3.** $^-5 \cdot 2$ **$^-10$**   **4.** $^-3 \cdot 6$ **$^-18$**

256

CALIFORNIA STANDARDS ⊶ **NS 2.3** Solve addition, subtraction, multiplication, and division problems, including those arising in concrete situations, that use positive and negative integers and combinations of these operations. *also* ⊶ **NS 2.0, MR 2.4**

ALTERNATIVE TEACHING STRATEGY

Materials thermometer drawn on the board or cut out of cardboard

Have students **use a thermometer to multiply integers.** First, select a temperature, such as 57°F. Have students describe how the temperature changes if it increases 3° per hour for 4 hours. Then ask students to write a multiplication sentence to show the change. $4 \times 3 = 12$ Ask: What is the temperature after 4 hours? 69°F

Repeat the activity for a drop of 2° per hour for 3 hours. $3 \times {}^-2 = {}^-6$ Ask: What is the temperature after 3 hours? 51°F

VISUAL

Intervention and Extension Resources

SPECIAL NEEDS (ELL)

Materials *For each group* 15 two-color counters

Have students **use two-color counters to model integer multiplication.** Have one student use counters to model $2 \times {}^-3 = {}^-6$. Then the other student records the number sentence: $2 \times {}^-3 = {}^-6$. Have students reverse roles and repeat the activity for different groupings of counters. Check students' work.

VISUAL

You can also use a number line to multiply integers.

- Use a number line to find the product 3 · 4. Start at 0.

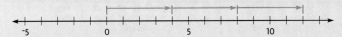

The number line shows that 3 · 4 = 4 + 4 + 4 = 12.

- Use a number line to find the product 5 · ⁻2. Start at 0.

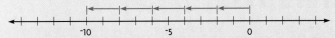

The number line shows that 5 · ⁻2 = ⁻2 + ⁻2 + ⁻2 + ⁻2 + ⁻2 = ⁻10.

- Use a number line to find the product ⁻7 · 2. Using the Commutative Property, write ⁻7 · 2 as 2 · ⁻7. Then represent 2 · ⁻7 on the number line.

The number line shows that 2 · ⁻7 = ⁻7 + ⁻7 = ⁻14. So, by the Commutative Property, ⁻7 · 2 = ⁻14.

Think and Discuss

- How could you use a number line to find the product 2 · 8?
  Start at 0 and draw 2 arrows to the right, each representing 8.
- How could you use a number line to find the product 3 · ⁻6?
  Start at 0 and draw 3 arrows to the left, each representing ⁻6.

Practice

Use a number line to find each product.

1. 4 · 5 20   2. 3 · ⁻7 ⁻21   3. 6 · ⁻3 ⁻18   4. ⁻5 · 6 ⁻30

MIXED REVIEW AND TEST PREP

Find the difference. (p. 250)

5. ⁻3 − ⁻7 4   6. 5 − 9 ⁻4   7. 12 − ⁻9 21

8. Order 0.2, $\frac{1}{8}$, and $\frac{1}{4}$ from least to greatest. (p. 234) $\frac{1}{8}$, 0.2, $\frac{1}{4}$

9. **TEST PREP** Which is the prime factorization of 28? (p. 148) B

   A 4 · 7   B $2^2 \cdot 7$ C $2 \cdot 7^2$ D $2^2 \cdot 7^2$

Remind students that they have used number lines to show addition. Since multiplication is repeated addition, a number line can be used to show multiplication. You may want to draw a single arrow above the individual arrows to show the final product.

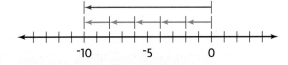

Think and Discuss

As students discuss how to show the products on a number line, ask volunteers to compare using a number line with using counters. Possible answer: The number line and the counters show the same number of equal groups. Using a number line for 2 × 8, there would be 2 groups of 8 marked. Using counters, there would be 2 groups of 8 yellow counters.

Practice

After students work through Exercise 4, ask:

How could you use counters to find the product? Possible answer: show 6 groups of 5 red counters

MIXED REVIEW AND TEST PREP

Exercises 5–9 provide **cumulative review** (Chapters 1–13).

Oral Assessment

Use a model to find the product ⁻4 × 3. Which model did you use? ⁻12; Possible answers: number line; counters

Sheandra displayed 4 groups of 2 red counters. What multiplication equation was she modeling? 4 × ⁻2 = ⁻8

SCIENCE CONNECTION

Have students **multiply negative numbers.** Students can determine the temperature at the top of three mountains if the temperature is 0°F at sea level. Explain that air temperature drops about 3°F for every 1,000 ft above sea level.

Mountain	Height (approximate)	
Le Grand	14,000 ft	⁻42°F
Combin Dom	15,000 ft	⁻45°F
Mont Blanc	16,000 ft	⁻48°F

VISUAL

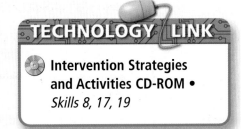

TECHNOLOGY LINK

Intervention Strategies and Activities CD-ROM •
Skills 8, 17, 19

Algebra: Multiply Integers

LESSON PLANNING

Objective To multiply integers

Intervention for Prerequisite Skills

Multiplication Facts, Division Facts, Patterns (For intervention strategies, see page 255.)

California Mathematics Content Standards

○─┐ NS 2.3 Solve addition, subtraction, multiplication, and division problems, including those arising in concrete situations, that use positive and negative integers and combinations of these operations.

(*Also* ○─┐ NS 2.0, AF 1.3, MR 1.1, MR 2.2, MR 2.4, MR 3.3)

Math Background

The following ideas will help students understand multiplication of negative integers.

• You can find multiples of a number by adding the number repeatedly.

• By establishing a pattern, it can be shown that the product of a negative number and a positive number is negative.

• By establishing a pattern, it can be shown that the product of two negative numbers is a positive number.

Although students may already know that the product of a negative and a positive integer is negative, point out that understanding patterns is necessary to understand the concept of multiplying two negative integers.

WARM-UP RESOURCES

 NUMBER OF THE DAY Transparency 13.2

The number of the day is the opposite of the day of the month. Write 2 addition number sentences using integers with the number of the day as the sum. Possible answer for January 4: opposite = ⁻4; ⁻6 + 2 = ⁻4; ⁻2 + ⁻2 = ⁻4

 PROBLEM OF THE DAY Transparency 13.2

We are two integers. Our sum is ⁻15 and our difference is 3. Who are we? ⁻6 and ⁻9

Solution Problem of the Day tab, p. PD13

 DAILY FACTS PRACTICE

Have students practice multiplication facts by completing Set D of *Teacher's Resource Book,* p. TR102.

ALTERNATIVE TEACHING STRATEGY (ELL)

Materials *For each group* two-color counters

Have students **use counters to show the product of two negative integers,** such as ⁻2 × ⁻2. Remind students that ⁻2 is the opposite of 2, and ⁻2 × ⁻2 can be thought of as removing two groups of ⁻2. Have students display 2 sets of 2 zero pairs and remove 2 sets of ⁻2.

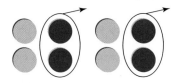

Ask: What is the product of ⁻2 × ⁻2? 4

Ask students to model other products in a similar manner. Check students' work.

VISUAL

MIXED REVIEW AND TEST PREP

Cumulative Review Chapters 1–13

Refer to the Pupil Edition pages referenced in the exercises for further review. Have students go to the lesson page, review the lesson, and correct any problem they missed.

Mixed Review and Test Prep, p. 259

How to Help	
Item	**Page**
32–34	250
35	150
36	70

SPECIAL NEEDS

Reinforce the concept of multiplying integers by discussing each of the scenarios below. Then have students write the appropriate number sentence to illustrate it. Point out that the word *not* can sometimes be translated as a negative sign.

- Finding $2 on the floor three days in a row is the same as finding $6. $3 \times 2 = 6$
- Paying $2 for lunch on 3 separate days is the same as paying out $6. $3 \times {}^-2 = {}^-6$
- Not having to pay $2 for each of 3 videos is the same as getting $6. ${}^-3 \times {}^-2 = 6$

AUDITORY

ALGEBRA CONNECTION

Have students **use another way to multiply integers.** Tell students that another way to show that the product of two negative integers is a positive integer is as follows:

$$3 + ({}^-3) = 0$$
$$(3 + ({}^-3)) \cdot {}^-5 = 0 \cdot {}^-5$$
$$(3 \cdot {}^-5) + ({}^-3 \cdot {}^-5) = 0$$
$${}^-15 + ({}^-3 \cdot {}^-5) = 0$$

Since ${}^-15 + 15 = 0$, ${}^-3 \cdot {}^-15 = 15$. Have students demonstrate this concept with the equation ${}^-2 \times {}^-6 = 12$. Check students' work.

VISUAL

TECHNOLOGY LINK

- **Intervention Strategies and Activities CD-ROM** • *Skills 8, 17, 19*

- **Astro Algebra** • *Red,* Level G

Objective To multiply integers

1 Introduce

QUICK REVIEW provides review of pre-requisite skills.

Why Learn This? You can find how much the temperature will fall over several hours if it changes the same amount each hour. *Share the lesson objective with students.*

2 Teach

Guided Instruction

- *Draw students' attention to the information about the submarine on page 258. Ask:*

  Why is a number line a better model for this situation than counters? Possible answer: It would take too many counters to model the problem.

- *Have students look at the pattern in Example 1.*

  How would you find the pattern? by looking at how the factors and the product change from number sentence to number sentence

REASONING **Describe how the pattern changes.** The second factor of each number sentence is one less than the preceding one and each product is 4 less than the previous one.

Modifying Instruction You may want to display the rules along with examples for integer multiplication after completing the lesson. Following Lesson 13.3, students can make a similar display for integer division in preparation for the lesson on combining integer operations.

ADDITIONAL EXAMPLES

Example 1, p. 258

Complete the pattern.
$3 \cdot 3 = 9$
$3 \cdot 2 = 6$
$3 \cdot 1 = 3$
$3 \cdot 0 = 0$
$3 \cdot {}^-1 = {}^-3$
$3 \cdot {}^-2 = {}^-6$
$3 \cdot {}^-3 = {}^-9$

Example 2, p. 258

Complete the pattern.
${}^-3 \cdot 3 = {}^-9$
${}^-3 \cdot 2 = {}^-6$
${}^-3 \cdot 1 = {}^-3$
${}^-3 \cdot 0 = 0$
${}^-3 \cdot {}^-1 = 3$
${}^-3 \cdot {}^-2 = 6$
${}^-3 \cdot {}^-3 = 9$

ALGEBRA
Multiply Integers

Learn how to multiply integers.

QUICK REVIEW

1. 80×6	2. 4×25	3. 50×6	4. 90×40	5. 400×10
480	100	300	3,600	4,000

A submarine is diving and its depth is changing by ${}^-30$ m every minute. If the submarine started at the surface of the ocean, how far below the surface is it after 4 minutes?

Use a number line to find the product $4 \cdot {}^-30$.

-140 -120 -100 -80 -60 -40 -20 0 20 40

The number line shows that the depth of the submarine changed ${}^-120$ m. So, the submarine is 120 m below the surface.

You can use patterns to find rules for multiplying integers.

EXAMPLE 1

Complete the pattern.

$4 \cdot 3 = 12$
$4 \cdot 2 = 8$
$4 \cdot 1 = 4$
$4 \cdot 0 = 0$
$4 \cdot {}^-1 = \blacksquare$
$4 \cdot {}^-2 = \blacksquare$
$4 \cdot {}^-3 = \blacksquare$

Study the pattern. As the second factor decreases by 1, the product decreases by 4. Assume the pattern continues.

$4 \cdot 3 = 12$
$4 \cdot 2 = 8$
$4 \cdot 1 = 4$
$4 \cdot 0 = 0$
$4 \cdot {}^-1 = {}^-4$
$4 \cdot {}^-2 = {}^-8$
$4 \cdot {}^-3 = {}^-12$

So, the missing products are ${}^-4$, ${}^-8$, and ${}^-12$. **The sign is negative.**
- What is the sign of the product of a positive and negative integer?

EXAMPLE 2

Complete the pattern.

${}^-4 \cdot 3 = {}^-12$
${}^-4 \cdot 2 = {}^-8$
${}^-4 \cdot 1 = {}^-4$
${}^-4 \cdot 0 = 0$
${}^-4 \cdot {}^-1 = \blacksquare$
${}^-4 \cdot {}^-2 = \blacksquare$
${}^-4 \cdot {}^-3 = \blacksquare$

Study the pattern. As the second factor decreases by 1, the product increases by 4. Assume the pattern continues.

${}^-4 \cdot 3 = {}^-12$
${}^-4 \cdot 2 = {}^-8$
${}^-4 \cdot 1 = {}^-4$
${}^-4 \cdot 0 = 0$
${}^-4 \cdot {}^-1 = 4$
${}^-4 \cdot {}^-2 = 8$
${}^-4 \cdot {}^-3 = 12$

TECHNOLOGY LINK

More Practice: Use **Mighty Math Astro Algebra**, Red, Level G.

So, the missing products are 4, 8, and 12.

- What is the sign of the product of two positive integers? two negative integers? **The sign is positive.**

Examples 1 and 2 lead to the rules below.

> The product of two integers with like signs is positive.
> The product of two integers with unlike signs is negative.

  CALIFORNIA STANDARDS O━┓ NS 2.3 Solve addition, subtraction, multiplication, and division problems, including those arising in concrete situations, that use positive and negative integers and combinations of these operations. *also* O━┓ NS 2.0, AF 1.3, MR 1.1, MR 2.2, MR 2.4, MR 3.3

RETEACH 13.2

Algebra: Multiply Integers

You can use patterns to think about multiplying integers.

Look at the patterns.

$4 \times 2 = 8$
$4 \times 1 = 4$
$4 \times 0 = 0$
$4 \times {}^-1 = {}^-4$
$4 \times {}^-2 = {}^-8$

${}^-2 \times 4 = {}^-8$
${}^-2 \times 2 = {}^-4$
${}^-2 \times 0 = 0$
${}^-2 \times {}^-2 = 4$
${}^-2 \times {}^-4 = 8$

When you multiply a positive integer by a negative integer, the product is a negative integer.

When you multiply two negative integers the product is a positive integer.

Find the product ${}^-8 \times 9$.
- Multiply as with whole numbers. The product of a negative integer and a positive integer is a negative integer.

${}^-8 \times 9 = {}^-72$

Find the product ${}^-6 \times {}^-4$.
- Multiply as with whole numbers. The product of two negative integers is a positive integer.

${}^-6 \times {}^-4 = 24$

Find the product.

1. $4 \times {}^-8$	2. ${}^-7 \times {}^-7$	3. ${}^-4 \times 5$	4. 9×10
${}^-32$	49	${}^-20$	90
5. $10 \times {}^-4$	6. ${}^-11 \times {}^-10$	7. ${}^-15 \times 3$	8. ${}^-12 \times {}^-6$
${}^-40$	110	${}^-45$	72
9. ${}^-11 \times 5$	10. $8 \times {}^-12$	11. ${}^-5 \times {}^-15$	12. ${}^-9 \times 8$
${}^-55$	${}^-96$	75	${}^-72$
13. $6 \times {}^-30$	14. ${}^-16 \times {}^-2$	15. ${}^-8 \times 14$	16. $20 \times {}^-20$
${}^-180$	32	${}^-112$	${}^-400$
17. 10×12	18. $8 \times {}^-11$	19. ${}^-9 \times {}^-15$	20. ${}^-13 \times 3$
120	${}^-88$	135	${}^-39$

PRACTICE 13.2

Algebra: Multiply Integers

Find the product.

1. ${}^-7 \times 3$	2. ${}^-4 \times {}^-4$	3. $9 \times {}^-2$	4. ${}^-8 \times 6$
${}^-21$	16	${}^-18$	${}^-48$
5. ${}^-4 \times 9$	6. $12 \times {}^-3$	7. ${}^-3 \times {}^-8$	8. $5 \times {}^-5$
${}^-36$	${}^-36$	24	${}^-25$
9. $8 \times {}^-2$	10. ${}^-6 \times {}^-9$	11. $3 \times {}^-11$	12. ${}^-10 \times {}^-10$
${}^-16$	54	${}^-33$	100
13. ${}^-20 \times {}^-4$	14. $14 \times {}^-7$	15. ${}^-25 \times 4$	16. $2 \times {}^-30$
80	${}^-98$	${}^-100$	${}^-60$
17. $32 \times {}^-7$	18. ${}^-45 \times {}^-2$	19. $16 \times {}^-9$	20. ${}^-18 \times {}^-5$
${}^-224$	90	${}^-144$	90
21. ${}^-3 \times {}^-15$	22. ${}^-12 \times 5$	23. $3 \times {}^-10$	24. ${}^-9 \times {}^-9$
45	${}^-60$	${}^-30$	81

ALGEBRA Use mental math to find the value of y.

25. $y \times 4 = {}^-28$	26. $y \times {}^-2 = {}^-16$	27. ${}^-5 \times y = 30$
$y = {}^-7$	$y = 8$	$y = {}^-6$
28. $9 \times y = 45$	29. $y \times 3 = {}^-45$	30. $y \times {}^-12 = 24$
$y = 5$	$y = {}^-15$	${}^-2$

Mixed Review

Find the sum.

31. $7 + {}^-3$	32. ${}^-10 + 5$	33. $4 + {}^-9$	34. ${}^-13 + {}^-7$
${}^+4$	${}^-5$	${}^-5$	${}^-20$

Write the decimal as a fraction.

35. 0.7	36. 0.15	37. 0.03	38. 0.58
$\frac{7}{10}$	$\frac{15}{100}$	$\frac{3}{100}$	$\frac{58}{100}$

CHECK FOR UNDERSTANDING

Think and ▸
Discuss

Look back at the lesson to answer each question.

1. **Tell** if the product of a negative number and zero is positive or negative. Explain. **Neither. Zero is neither positive nor negative.**

2. **Name** two possible choices for two numbers which are the same and whose product is 16. **4 · 4, or ⁻4 · ⁻4**

Guided ▸
Practice

Find the product.

3. ⁻9 · 6 **⁻54**   4. ⁻3 · ⁻4 **12**   5. ⁻8 · 2 **⁻16**   6. 8 · ⁻7 **⁻56**

7. ⁻3 · 7 **⁻21**   8. ⁻8 · ⁻2 **16**   9. 18 · ⁻5 **⁻90**   10. ⁻22 · 4 **⁻88**

PRACTICE AND PROBLEM SOLVING

Independent ▸
Practice

Find the product.

11. ⁻5 · 8 **⁻40**   12. 2 · ⁻3 **⁻6**   13. 7 · 2 **14**   14. ⁻9 · 4 **⁻36**

15. 12 · 7 **84**   16. ⁻12 · ⁻8 **96**   17. ⁻11 · ⁻10 **110**   18. ⁻8 · 3 **⁻24**

19. 24 · 12 **288**   20. 30 · ⁻12 **⁻360**   21. (⁻8 − 2) · (⁻52 + 7) **450**

 Algebra   Use mental math to find the value of *y*.

22. *y* · ⁻2 = 20   23. 4 · *y* = ⁻12   24. ⁻7 · *y* = ⁻56 ***y* = 8**
    ***y* = ⁻10**   ***y* = ⁻3**

25. *y* · ⁻6 = ⁻18   26. *y* · ⁻10 = 40   27. ⁻8 · *y* = 32 ***y* = ⁻4**
    ***y* = 3**   ***y* = ⁻4**

Problem Solving ▸
Applications

28. Drought conditions have caused the water level in a lake to change by ⁻3 in. every month for the past 4 months. Write the total change in water level over the past 4 months as a negative number. **⁻12 in.**

29. Use the Associative Property to help you find the product of ⁻3 · ⁻2 · ⁻5. **⁻30**

30. A water tank has a leak. The amount of water in the tank changes by ⁻6 gal a day. What is the total change after 7 days? **⁻42 gal**

31. **(?) What's the Error?** Beth says that ⁻5 · ⁻2 = ⁻10. What is her error? What is the correct product? **The product of integers with like signs is positive; ⁻5 · ⁻2 = 10.**

MIXED REVIEW AND TEST PREP

Find the difference. (p. 250)

32. ⁻25 − ⁻42 **17**   33. 30 − 42 **⁻12**   34. 56 − ⁻18 **74**

35. Find the LCM of 26 and 28. (p. 150) **364**

36. **TEST PREP** Evaluate 2*k* for *k* = 9.6. (p. 70) **A**

   A 19.2   **B** 11.6   **C** 7.6   **D** 4.8

Extra Practice page H44, Set A)

259

---

3 Practice

Guided Practice

Do Check for Understanding Exercises 1–10 with your students. Identify those having difficulty and use lesson resources to help.

///// **COMMON ERROR ALERT** \\\\\

Students may multiply two negative integers and show the product as negative.

$$⁻4 \times ⁻3 = ⁻12$$

Direct them to do integer multiplication in two steps. First write the sign and then write the product.

Independent Practice

Assign Exercises 11–31.

Algebraic Thinking For Exercises 25–27, have students begin by deciding whether the variable will be positive or negative.

MIXED REVIEW AND TEST PREP

Exercises 32–36 provide **cumulative review** (Chapters 1–13).

4 Assess

Summarize the lesson by having students:

DISCUSS Show the pattern you would use to solve Exercise 8. **⁻8 × 2 = ⁻16; ⁻8 × 1 = ⁻8; ⁻8 × 0 = 0; ⁻8 × ⁻1 = 8; ⁻8 × ⁻2 = 16**

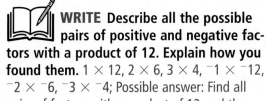 **WRITE** Describe all the possible pairs of positive and negative factors with a product of 12. Explain how you found them. **1 × 12, 2 × 6, 3 × 4, ⁻1 × ⁻12, ⁻2 × ⁻6, ⁻3 × ⁻4; Possible answer: Find all pairs of factors with a product of 12 and then write each pair again with negative signs.**

Lesson Quiz

Find the product.

1. 9 × ⁻7 **⁻63**

2. ⁻10 × ⁻10 **100**

3. ⁻150 × ⁻2 **300**

4. 30 × ⁻12 **⁻360**

Transparency
13.2

PROBLEM SOLVING 13.2

Algebra: Multiply Integers
Write the correct answer.

1. Find the missing number in the pattern.

   4 × 2 = 8
   4 × 1 = 4
   4 × 0 = 0
   4 × ⁻1 = ⁻4
   4 × ⁻2 = ⁻8
   4 × ⁻3 = ■

   ⁻12

Analyze Choose Solve Check

2. Find the missing number in the pattern.

   ⁻3 × 2 = ⁻6
   ⁻3 × 1 = ⁻3
   ⁻3 × 0 = 0
   ⁻3 × ⁻1 = 3
   ⁻3 × ⁻2 = 6
   ⁻3 × ⁻3 = ■

   9

3. Compare the rational numbers and order them from least to greatest.

   $\frac{3}{5}, \frac{4}{25}$, 0.01, 0.55

   0.01, $\frac{4}{25}$, 0.55, $\frac{3}{5}$

4. Compare the rational numbers and order them from greatest to least.

   $\frac{7}{4}, \frac{6}{3}$, 1.8, 1.74

   $\frac{6}{3}$, 1.8, $\frac{7}{4}$, 1.74

Choose the letter for the best answer.

5. The temperature dropped by 4° each hour from midnight until 5 A.M. How much did the temperature change in that time?
   A ⁻24°
   B ⁻20°
   C 20°
   D 24°

6. Stock in XYZ.com dropped 8 points each day from Monday to Friday. How much did the stock price change that week?
   F 48 points
   G 20 points
   H ⁻40 points
   J ⁻56 points

7. Which rational number is between 1.45 and 1.5?
   A 1.4
   B 1.44
   C 1.48
   D 1.52

8. Which rational number is **not** between $\frac{2}{3}$ and $\frac{7}{8}$?
   F $\frac{19}{24}$ H $\frac{3}{4}$
   G $\frac{5}{6}$ J $\frac{1}{2}$

9. **Write About It** Explain why 5 × 2 = 2 × 5.
   Multiplication is commutative. You can multiply factors
   in any order and get the same product.

CHALLENGE 13.2

Multiplication Tip
Match each product in Column 2 with its factors in Column 1. Write the corresponding letter on the line marked with the exercise number to discover the Math Tip.

	Column 1	Column 2
F	1. ⁻8 × ⁻7	A. ⁻28
R	2. 12 × ⁻4	C. 51
I	3. 13 × 3	D. 48
A	4. ⁻7 × 4	E. ⁻90
O	5. ⁻15 × ⁻3	F. 56
D	6. ⁻8 × 6	G. ⁻45
T	7. ⁻14 × ⁻2	H. 100
G	8. 9 × ⁻5	I. 39
V	9. ⁻4 × 14	N. ⁻72
C	10. ⁻17 × 3	O. 45
P	11. ⁻25 × 4	P. ⁻100
E	12. 18 × ⁻5	R. ⁻48
U	13. ⁻9 × ⁻8	S. ⁻36
S	14. ⁻6 × 6	T. 28
W	15. ⁻10 × ⁻9	U. 72
N	16. ⁻4 × 18	V. ⁻56
H	17. ⁻20 × ⁻5	W. 90

T H E __ __ P R O D U C T __ O F
7 17 12   11 2 5 6 13 10 7   5 1

T W O __ N E G A T I V E
7 15 5   16 12 8 4 7 3 9 12

I N T E G E R S __ I S __ A
3 16 7 12 8 12 2 14   3 14   4

P O S I T I V E __ I N T E G E R
11 5 14 3   7 3 9 12   3 16 7 12 8 12 2

Algebra: Divide Integers

LESSON PLANNING

Objective To divide integers

Intervention for Prerequisite Skills

Multiplication Facts, Division Facts (For intervention strategies, see page 255.)

California Mathematics Content Standards

⊶ NS 2.3 Solve addition, subtraction, multiplication, and division problems, including those arising in concrete situations, that use positive and negative integers and combinations of these operations.

(*Also* ⊶ NS 2.0, AF 1.3, SDAP 1.1, MR 1.1, MR 2.5, MR 3.3)

Math Background

Consider the following as you help students understand how to divide integers.

- Division is the inverse of multiplication.
- Every multiplication problem has a related division problem.
- The rules for determining the sign when multiplying integers are the same when dividing integers.

Students can build on their knowledge of multiplying integers and of division facts to determine the quotient of two integers.

WARM-UP RESOURCES

 NUMBER OF THE DAY Transparency 13.3

Observe the time. Determine the opposite of the number of minutes past the hour. Estimate the product of that number and 9. Possible answer for 1:22: $^-20 \times 9 = {}^-180$

 PROBLEM OF THE DAY Transparency 13.3

I am a positive integer. If I am squared, $^-5$ is added to me, $^-10$ is subtracted from me, and the result is divided by 2, the result is 7. What integer am I? 3

Solution Problem of the Day tab, p. PD13

 DAILY FACTS PRACTICE

Have students practice division facts by completing Set E of *Teacher's Resource Book,* p. TR102.

ALTERNATIVE TEACHING STRATEGY

Materials *For each group* 24 two-color counters

Have students **model integer division** by using two-color counters. Give students 24 counters and have them divide the yellow counters into 8 equal groups. Then ask them to write the number sentence they have modeled. $24 \div 8 = 3$

Next, ask students to divide 18 red counters into 3 equal groups. Again, ask students to write the number sentence they have modeled. $^-18 \div 3 = ^-6$

Finally, have students model and solve similar problems, such as $14 \div 2$ and $^-21 \div 7$. $7, ^-3$

KINESTHETIC

MIXED REVIEW AND TEST PREP

Cumulative Review Chapters 1–13

Refer to the Pupil Edition pages referenced in the exercises for further review. Have students go to the lesson page, review the lesson, and correct any problem they missed.

Mixed Review and Test Prep, p. 261

How to Help	
Item	**Page**
29	258
30	244
31	206
32	210
33	169

ENGLISH LANGUAGE LEARNERS ELL•SDAIE

Materials 2 colors of chalk or dry-erase markers

To **reinforce the terms used in the division of integers,** display the following table:

Dividend	÷ Divisor	= Quotient

Have students take turns filling in the table using Exercises 10–20 on page 261. Have them write the negative numbers in one color and the positive numbers in another color.

	Dividend	÷ Divisor	= Quotient
10.	$^-40$	8	$^-5$
16.			

VISUAL

EARLY FINISHERS

Materials *For each pair* 2 number cubes without numbers, p. TR75

Have students **practice dividing integers.** Give each pair 2 number cubes. Have them write 2, $^-9$, 6, $^-4$, 12, and $^-36$ on the faces of one cube and $^-2$, 9, $^-6$, 18, $^-4$, and 36 on the faces of the other.

Each partner rolls one of the cubes, divides 36 by the number shown, and records the number sentence. Have students repeat the activity 3 times. Then ask them to exchange cubes and repeat 3 more times. Finally have each pair list all the different number sentences they formed. Answers will vary.

TECHNOLOGY LINK

Intervention Strategies and Activities CD-ROM • *Skills 17, 19*

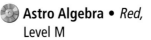
Astro Algebra • *Red, Level M*

Objective To divide integers

1 Introduce

QUICK REVIEW provides review of pre-requisite skills.

Why Learn This? You can determine the average high and low temperatures for your city. *Share the lesson objective with students.*

2 Teach

Guided Instruction

- *Remind students that addition and subtraction are inverse operations. Ask:*

  What other operations are inverse operations? multiplication and division

  What is the relationship between multiplication and division operations? For every division problem, there is a related multiplication problem that uses the same numbers.

REASONING **Describe two ways you would write 5 × 3 = 15 as a division sentence.** $15 \div 3 = 5, 15 \div 5 = 3$

- *Review the rules for dividing integers.*

  Why is the quotient ⁻5 for ⁻15 ÷ 3? The negative dividend is divided by a positive number.

  Why is the quotient 3 for ⁻15 ÷ ⁻5? The dividend and the divisor are both negative.

  Will the average in Example 2 be positive or negative? Explain. Negative; the sum is negative and it will be divided by a positive number.

ADDITIONAL EXAMPLES

Example 1, p. 260

Find the quotient.

A. $^-96 \div ^-8$ 12 B. $48 \div ^-12$ ⁻4

Example 2, p. 260

Find the average of ⁻8, 6, ⁻12, and ⁻18. ⁻8

ALGEBRA
Divide Integers

Learn how to divide integers.

QUICK REVIEW

1. $420 \div 6$ 2. $225 \div 25$ 3. $50 \div 2$ 4. $3,600 \div 4$ 5. $540 \div 60$
   70   9   25   900   9

Multiplication and division are inverse operations. To solve a division problem, think about the related multiplication problem.

$$42 \div 7 = \blacksquare \quad \textbf{THINK:}\ 7 \cdot 6 = 42, \text{ so } 42 \div 7 = 6.$$

You can use related multiplication problems to determine the sign of the quotient when dividing integers.

$8 \cdot 3 = 24$, so $24 \div 8 = 3$. $^-8 \cdot ^-3 = 24$, so $24 \div ^-8 = ^-3$.

$^-8 \cdot 3 = ^-24$, so $^-24 \div ^-8 = 3$. $8 \cdot ^-3 = ^-24$, so $^-24 \div 8 = ^-3$.

TECHNOLOGY LINK

More Practice: Use **Mighty Math Astro Algebra,** Red, Level M.

In the problems above, look at the sign of the quotients of two positive integers and the sign of the quotients of two negative integers. Then look at the sign of the quotients of a positive and negative integer. You can see that the rules below apply when dividing integers.

> The quotient of two integers with like signs is positive.
> The quotient of two integers with different signs is negative.

EXAMPLE 1

Find the quotient.

A. $^-84 \div ^-7$

Divide as with whole numbers. The quotient is positive since the integers have like signs.

$^-84 \div ^-7 = 12$

B. $^-55 \div 11$

Divide as with whole numbers. The quotient is negative since the integers have unlike signs.

$^-55 \div 11 = ^-5$

EXAMPLE 2

The low temperatures for five days in Fairbanks, Alaska, were ⁻3°F, ⁻8°F, 2°F, 3°F, and ⁻4°F. Find the average low temperature for the five days.

Find the sum. Divide the sum by 5.
$^-3 + ^-8 + 2 + 3 + ^-4 = ^-10$

$^-10 \div 5 = ^-2$

So, the average low temperature was ⁻2°F.

260

CALIFORNIA STANDARDS ⊶ NS 2.3 Solve addition, subtraction, multiplication, and division problems, including those arising in concrete situations, that use positive and negative integers and combinations of these operations. *also* ⊶ NS 2.0, AF 1.3, SDAP 1.1, MR 1.1, MR 2.5, MR 3.3

RETEACH 13.3

Algebra: Divide Integers

Multiplication and division are inverse operations. You can think of related multiplication problems to divide integers. Look at the problems below.

Division	Multiplication
$20 \div 4 = 5$	$4 \times 5 = 20$
$^-20 \div ^-4 = 5$	$^-4 \times 5 = ^-20$
$^-20 \div 4 = ^-5$	$4 \times ^-5 = ^-20$
$20 \div ^-4 = ^-5$	$^-4 \times ^-5 = 20$

When you divide two negative integers, the quotient is positive.
When you divide a positive integer by a negative integer, the quotient is negative.
When you divide a negative integer by a positive integer, the quotient is negative.

Find $^-18 \div 6$.

- Divide as with whole numbers. $^-18 \div 6 = ^-3$
  A negative integer divided by a positive integer is a negative integer.

Find $^-28 \div ^-7$.

- Divide as with whole numbers. $^-28 \div ^-7 = 4$
  A negative integer divided by a negative integer is a positive integer.

Find the quotient.

1. $^-15 \div 5$ 2. $12 \div ^-3$ 3. $^-24 \div ^-6$ 4. $30 \div 6$

   ⁻3   ⁻4   4   5

5. $^-32 \div 8$ 6. $^-40 \div ^-10$ 7. $^-45 \div ^-9$ 8. $^-72 \div ^-8$

   ⁻4   4   5   9

9. $^-400 \div 20$ 10. $^-84 \div ^-14$ 11. $72 \div ^-6$ 12. $^-120 \div 40$

   ⁻20   6   ⁻12   ⁻3

13. $75 \div ^-5$ 14. $60 \div 12$ 15. $^-125 \div 5$ 16. $^-100 \div ^-10$

   ⁻15   5   ⁻25   10

PRACTICE 13.3

Algebra: Divide Integers

Find the quotient.

1. $^-10 \div 5$ 2. $36 \div ^-9$ 3. $^-44 \div ^-11$ 4. $50 \div ^-2$

   ⁻2   ⁻4   4   ⁻25

5. $^-12 \div 4$ 6. $35 \div ^-7$ 7. $^-44 \div ^-4$ 8. $50 \div ^-5$

   ⁻3   ⁻5   11   ⁻10

9. $18 \div ^-3$ 10. $^-42 \div ^-7$ 11. $45 \div ^-5$ 12. $15 \div 3$

   ⁻6   6   ⁻9   5

13. $^-24 \div ^-8$ 14. $21 \div ^-3$ 15. $^-60 \div 6$ 16. $^-32 \div 8$

   3   ⁻7   ⁻10   ⁻4

17. $55 \div ^-5$ 18. $^-36 \div 9$ 19. $80 \div ^-4$ 20. $51 \div ^-3$

   ⁻11   ⁻4   ⁻20   ⁻17

21. $^-99 \div ^-11$ 22. $56 \div 8$ 23. $^-100 \div 5$ 24. $^-200 \div ^-4$

   9   7   ⁻20   50

25. $^-75 \div 3$ 26. $250 \div ^-25$ 27. $^-90 \div ^-18$ 28. $^-180 \div 60$

   ⁻25   ⁻10   5   ⁻3

29. $^-100 \div ^-25$ 30. $^-125 \div 5$ 31. $120 \div ^-4$ 32. $^-96 \div 16$

   4   ⁻25   ⁻30   ⁻6

33. $105 \div ^-7$ 34. $^-84 \div 12$ 35. $150 \div ^-3$ 36. $^-125 \div 25$

   ⁻15   ⁻7   ⁻50   ⁻5

37. $^-180 \div ^-90$ 38. $100 \div ^-4$ 39. $^-90 \div ^-5$ 40. $^-150 \div 50$

   2   ⁻25   18   ⁻3

ALGEBRA Use mental math to find the value of x.

41. $x \div 5 = ^-10$ 42. $27 \div x = ^-3$ 43. $x \div ^-15 = ^-4$

   $x = ^-50$ $x = ^-9$ $x = 60$

Mixed Review

Multiply. Write the answer in simplest form.

44. $\frac{2}{3} \times \frac{3}{1}$ 45. $\frac{1}{5} \times \frac{4}{1}$ 46. $\frac{3}{7} \times \frac{1}{1}$ 47. $\frac{2}{3} \times \frac{9}{1}$

   2                 $\frac{4}{20}$ $\frac{3}{28}$ $\frac{18}{15}$

Find the difference.

48. $12 - ^-9$ 49. $^-18 - 6$ 50. $4 - 10$ 51. $^-8 - ^-15$

   21   ⁻24   ⁻6   7

CHECK UNDERSTANDING

Think and ▶ Discuss

Look back at the lesson to answer the question.

1. **Tell** how the sign rules for multiplying two integers compare with the sign rules for dividing two integers. **The rules are the same.**

Guided ▶ Practice

Find the quotient.

2. ⁻9 ÷ 3 ⁻3 3. ⁻24 ÷ ⁻4 6 4. ⁻28 ÷ 7 ⁻4 5. 56 ÷ ⁻7 ⁻8

6. ⁻21 ÷ 7 ⁻3 7. ⁻16 ÷ ⁻2 8 8. 120 ÷ ⁻5 ⁻24 9. ⁻132 ÷ 6 ⁻22

PRACTICE AND PROBLEM SOLVING

Independent ▶ Practice

Find the quotient.

10. ⁻40 ÷ 8 ⁻5 11. 6 ÷ ⁻3 ⁻2 12. 14 ÷ 2 7 13. ⁻36 ÷ 4 ⁻9

14. 84 ÷ 7 12 15. ⁻72 ÷ ⁻8 9 16. ⁻63 ÷ ⁻7 9 17. ⁻70 ÷ 7 ⁻10

18. 432 ÷ 12 36 19. 255 ÷ ⁻15 ⁻17 20. (⁻40 − 4) ÷ (⁻86 + 97) ⁻4

 Algebra Use mental math to find the value of x.

21. $x ÷ ⁻6 = ⁻3$ 22. $x ÷ ⁻7 = 5$ 23. $⁻18 ÷ x = 2$
   $x = 18$ $x = ⁻35$ $x = ⁻9$

Problem Solving ▶ Applications

24. The low temperatures for a winter festival were ⁻8°F, ⁻6°F, ⁻9°F, and ⁻1°F. Find the average low temperature for the four days. ⁻6°F

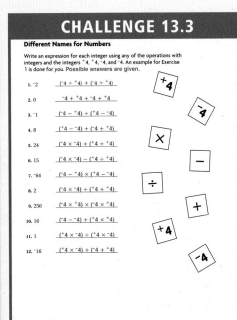

25. During the first 6 months of business, a sporting goods store showed its losses as ⁻$3,054. How would it show the average monthly loss? ⁻$509

26. The depth of a submarine changed ⁻225 ft over a period of 9 minutes. If the submarine descended at a constant rate, what was the change of depth per minute? ⁻25 ft per minute

27. The water level in a leaking swimming pool is changing ⁻4 in. per week. How many weeks will it take for the water level to change ⁻20 in.? 5 weeks

28. ❓ **What's the Question?** In a division problem, the numbers are ⁻250 and 10. The answer is ⁻25. **What's the quotient?**

MIXED REVIEW AND TEST PREP

29. Find the product 16 · ⁻6. (p. 258) ⁻96
30. Find the sum ⁻32 + ⁻42. (p. 244) ⁻74
31. Find the product $5\frac{2}{3} · 6\frac{3}{4}$. (p. 206) $38\frac{1}{4}$
32. Find the quotient $6\frac{3}{5} ÷ 2\frac{3}{4}$. (p. 210) $2\frac{2}{5}$
33. **TEST PREP** Write the fraction $\frac{5}{8}$ as a percent. (p. 169) **C**

   A 0.625%   **B** 6.25%   **C** 62.5%   **D** 625%

Extra Practice page H44, Set B **261**

---

3 Practice

Guided Practice

Do Check for Understanding Exercises 1–9 with your students. Identify those having difficulty and use lesson resources to help.

Independent Practice

Assign Exercises 10–28.

MIXED REVIEW AND TEST PREP

Exercises 29–33 provide **cumulative review** (Chapters 1–13).

4 Assess

Summarize the lesson by having students:

DISCUSS How did you solve Exercise 24? by adding the four numbers and dividing the sum by 4

WRITE Outline the steps used to find the quotient of two integers. **Give examples to show why the quotient is positive or negative.** Divide as if the integers are whole numbers and then determine the sign. If the divisor and dividend have the same sign, the quotient is positive. If they have different signs, the quotient is negative. Check students' examples.

Lesson Quiz

Transparency **13.3**

Find the quotient.

1. ⁻49 ÷ ⁻7 7 2. ⁻56 ÷ 8 ⁻7
3. ⁻99 ÷ ⁻9 11 4. 100 ÷ ⁻10 ⁻10
5. ⁻60 ÷ 12 ⁻5 6. ⁻250 ÷ ⁻50 5

PROBLEM SOLVING 13.3

Algebra: Divide Integers

Write the correct answer.

1. Find the missing number in the pattern.

   12 ÷ 3 = 4
   12 ÷ 2 = 6
   12 ÷ 1 = 12
   12 ÷ ⁻1 = ⁻12
   12 ÷ ⁻2 = ⁻6
   12 ÷ ⁻3 = ■
   ⁻4

2. Find the missing number in the pattern.

   6 ÷ ⁻2 = ⁻3
   4 ÷ ⁻2 = ⁻2
   2 ÷ ⁻2 = ⁻1
   0 ÷ ⁻2 = 0
   ⁻2 ÷ ⁻2 = 1
   ⁻4 ÷ ⁻2 = ■
   2

3. Compare the rational numbers and order them from least to greatest.

   5.62, 5.7, $5\frac{4}{5}$, $5\frac{1}{2}$

   $5\frac{1}{2}$, 5.62, 5.7, $5\frac{4}{5}$

4. Write $48\frac{5}{8}$ as a rational number in the form $\frac{a}{b}$.

   $\frac{389}{8}$

Choose the letter for the best answer.

5. The temperature changed 28° over a period of 7 hours. If the temperature dropped at a constant rate, what was the change per hour?

   A ⁻7°
   (B) ⁻4°
   C ⁻1°
   D 7°

6. A theme park recorded 1,800 fewer visitors this year than last year. What was the shortage of visitors in an average month?

   (F) ⁻150 visitors
   G ⁻140 visitors
   H ⁻130 visitors
   J ⁻120 visitors

7. Grace scored 8, 7, 8, 8, 10, 6, 7, 8, 7, 6, and 9 on her last 11 quizzes. Grace scored 8 most of the time. What term describes the most frequent score?

   A mean   **(C)** mode
   B median   **D** range

8. Mr. Frank earns $4,987.34 each month and Mrs. Frank earns $5,198.22 each month. Estimate how much the two earn together each month.

   F $8,000   **(H)** $10,000
   G $9,000   **J** $11,000

9. **Write About It** Explain why 8 ÷ 2 ≠ 2 ÷ 8.
   Division is not commutative. 8 ÷ 2 = 4 and 2 ÷ 8 = $\frac{1}{4}$.

CHALLENGE 13.3

Different Names for Numbers

Write an expression for each integer using any of the operations with integers and the integers ⁺4, ⁺4, ⁻4, and ⁻4. An example for Exercise 1 is done for you. Possible answers are given.

1. ⁻2   (⁻4 ÷ ⁺4) + (⁻4 ÷ ⁺4)
2. 0   ⁻4 + ⁺4 + ⁻4 + ⁺4
3. ⁻1   (⁻4 − ⁺4) ÷ (⁺4 − ⁻4)
4. 8   (⁺4 − ⁻4) + (⁺4 + ⁺4)
5. 24   (⁻4 × ⁻4) + (⁺4 + ⁺4)
6. 15   (⁻4 × ⁻4) − (⁺4 ÷ ⁺4)
7. ⁻64 (⁻4 − ⁺4) × (⁺4 − ⁻4)
8. 2   (⁻4 × ⁻4) ÷ (⁺4 + ⁺4)
9. 256 (⁻4 × ⁺4) × (⁻4 × ⁺4)
10. 16 (⁻4 − ⁻4) + (⁺4 × ⁺4)
11. 1   (⁺4 × ⁻4) ÷ (⁺4 × ⁻4)
12. ⁻16 (⁺4 × ⁻4) + (⁻4 + ⁺4)

261

Combine Operations with Integers

LESSON PLANNING

Objective To perform more than one operation with integers

Intervention for Prerequisite Skills

Multiplication Facts, Division Facts, Add Integers, Subtract Integers (For intervention strategies, see page 255.)

California Mathematics Content Standards

○─ NS 2.3 Solve addition, subtraction, multiplication, and division problems, including those arising in concrete situations, that use positive and negative integers and combinations of these operations.

(*Also* ○─ NS 2.0, AF 1.3, AF 1.4, MR 1.3, MR 2.2)

Math Background

Keep the following in mind as you help students perform more than one operation with integers:

* The order of operations applies, but careful attention must be given to the signs of the integers when simplifying.

* The Commutative and Associative Properties of addition and multiplication apply to integers.

* These properties often make it possible to do computation mentally rather than with pencil and paper or calculator.

WARM-UP RESOURCES

NUMBER OF THE DAY

Transparency 13.4

Begin with the number of the month of the year. Find its opposite. Then write a division sentence with that number as the quotient. Possible answer for 11: $^-22 \div 2 = ^-11$

PROBLEM OF THE DAY

Transparency 13.4

Write the missing integers.

$$^-2 \times \blacksquare 3 \times 4 = ^-24$$
$$\times \blacksquare 5 \times ^-4 \times \blacksquare 2 = \blacksquare 40$$
$$^-10 \times \blacksquare\!-12 \times ^-8 = ^-960$$

Solution Problem of the Day tab, p. PD13

DAILY FACTS PRACTICE

Have students practice multiplication and division facts by completing Set F of *Teacher's Resource Book*, p. TR102.

ALTERNATIVE TEACHING STRATEGY ELL

Materials *For each group* highlighters in four colors

To **reinforce the order of operations,** assign each step a different highlighter color. Give each student an exercise to solve from page 263 and have small groups share sets of highlighters. Each student decides which step to do first and highlights that part of the exercise in the appropriate color. He or she performs the step, highlights the relevant work, and writes the name of the step next to it. The student continues in the same way until the exercise is solved. Check students' work.

VISUAL

WRITING IN MATHEMATICS

Have students **explain the process of performing more than one operation with integers.** Ask students to determine the sign, positive or negative, of a product of more than two integers, for example, $^-2(^-4)(3)(^-6)$. Ask students to write rules with examples for how this process works. Possible answer: The sign for the product of more than two integers is positive if there are an even number of negative integers: $^-2(^-6)(^-5)(^-3) = 180$. It is negative if there are an odd number of negative integers: $^-1(^-4)(^-3) = ^-12$.

MIXED REVIEW AND TEST PREP

Cumulative Review Chapters 1–13

Refer to the Pupil Edition pages referenced in the exercises for further review. Have students go to the lesson page, review the lesson, and correct any problem they missed.

Mixed Review and Test Prep, p. 263

How to Help	
Item	Page
22–24	260
25	244
26	148

SPECIAL NEEDS

Materials *For each pair* strips of paper, each displaying a step of the order of operations; tape or glue

To **reinforce combining operations with integers,** give each pair an expression to evaluate, such as: $^-2 + 4(^-8 - ^-6) - 10$. Have partners choose the first step, in this case *work within parentheses,* and tape or glue the paper strip next to the line where they show their work. Partners continue until they have evaluated the expression. Last, have pairs share their work with the class. Check students' work.

VISUAL

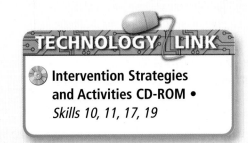

TECHNOLOGY LINK

Intervention Strategies and Activities CD-ROM •
Skills 10, 11, 17, 19

LESSON **13.4** ORGANIZER

Objective To perform more than one operation with integers

Vocabulary *Review* order of operations

1 Introduce

QUICK REVIEW provides review of prerequisite skills.

Why Learn This? You can use this skill to determine stock prices after several changes. *Share the lesson objective with students.*

2 Teach

Guided Instruction

• *Review the order of operations with students. After looking at Example 1, ask:*

REASONING How is using the order of operations with integers different from using it with whole numbers or fractions? Possible answer: The rules are the same, but you must also use the rules for integer operations.

• *Direct students' attention to Example 2.*

How would you decide by looking at a problem if it would be helpful to use the Commutative or Associative Property? by examining the problem for "friendly" number combinations, ones that are simple to multiply or that result in sums easy to add

A property other than the Commutative Property is also used to solve expression A. Explain. The Associative Property is used to add "friendly numbers": 92 + ⁻2 = 90.

ADDITIONAL EXAMPLES

Example 1, p. 262

Find the value of the expression.

⁻3 + (⁻7 − ⁻9)(3²) − 19 ⁻4

Example 2, p. 262

Find the value of the expression.

Commutative Property   Associative Property

A. ⁻7 + 24 + ⁻3 14   B. (⁻52 + ⁻3) + ⁻7
⁻62

262   Chapter 13

LESSON **13.4**

Combine Operations with Integers

Learn how to evaluate an expression with more than one operation.

QUICK REVIEW

1. (4 + 8) · 6 72   2. 100 ÷ (30 − 5) 4   3. 50 − 3² 41
4. (5 + 4) · (3 + 2) 45   5. (25 − 5) ÷ (10 − 6) 5

Sometimes you have to perform more than one operation when working with expressions involving integers. Remember the order of operations when performing more than one operation.

EXAMPLE 1

Remember that when performing more than one operation in an expression, you must use the order of operations.

1. Operate inside parentheses.
2. Clear exponents.
3. Multiply and divide from left to right.
4. Add and subtract from left to right.

Find the value of ⁻3 · (12 + 3) ÷ 3².

⁻3 · (12 + 3) ÷ 3²	*Operate inside parentheses.*
⁻3 · 15 ÷ 3²	*Clear exponents.*
⁻3 · 15 ÷ 9	*Multiply.*
⁻45 ÷ 9	*Divide.*
⁻5	

So, the value of the expression is ⁻5.

• How do you know the final answer is negative? The divisor and dividend for the last step have unlike signs.

When performing combined operations with integers, you can use properties to simplify the problem.

EXAMPLE 2

Find the value of the expression.

Commutative Property

A. 92 + 365 + ⁻2
92 + ⁻2 + 365
90 + 365
455

So, the value is 455.

Associative Property

B. (52 + 14) + ⁻14
52 + (14 + ⁻14)
52 + 0
52

So, the value is 52.

• Which property would you use to evaluate 47 + 131 + ⁻17? Explain. Commutative; 47 + ⁻17 + 131 = 30 + 131 = 161

CHECK FOR UNDERSTANDING

Think and ▶ Discuss   Look back at the lesson to answer each question.

1. **Find** the value of the expression (⁻3 + 7) · 3² ÷ ⁻18. ⁻2

2. **Explain** how the Commutative and Associative Properties simplify the problems in Example 2. They pair numbers that allow you to solve the problems by using mental math.

262

 CALIFORNIA STANDARDS O⟞ NS 2.3 Solve addition, subtraction, multiplication, and division problems, including those arising in concrete situations, that use positive and negative integers and combinations of these operations. *also* O⟞ NS 2.0, AF 1.3, AF 1.4, MR 1.3, MR 2.2

RETEACH 13.4

Combine Operations with Integers

When you use the order of operations to evaluate an expression, you may need to read through the expression several times. Each time you read the expression, think "what is the next operation I should perform?"

Find the value of the expression.

⁻5 + 6(⁻2 − 4) × 8 ÷ 2

Step 1 Read through the expression. Keep the order of operations in mind. Look to see whether there is any part of the expression inside parentheses that must be simplified.

⁻5 + 6(**⁻2 − 4**) × 8 ÷ 2   Work inside parentheses first.
⁻5 + 6(⁻6) × 8 ÷ 2

Step 2 Read through the new expression. Think about the order of operations. Look for multiplications or divisions and do them from left to right. There are three.

⁻5 + **6(⁻6)** × 8 ÷ 2   First multiply: 6(⁻6)
⁻5 + (**⁻36**) × 8 ÷ 2   Then multiply the result by 8.
⁻5 + (**⁻288**) ÷ 2   Then divide the result by 2.
⁻5 + (⁻144)

Step 3 Read through the new expression. There is only one operation left to perform: addition.

⁻5 + (⁻144)   Add the two remaining integers.
⁻149

Evaluate the expression.

1. ⁻9 + 6 ÷ ⁻2 − 5   2. (7 × 2) − ⁻8 ÷ ⁻4   3. 1 − 15 × 3 + 5

⁻17   12   ⁻39

4. ⁻10 − (⁻2 + 2) + 3   5. (⁻15 ÷ 3) + (15 ÷ ⁻3)   6. 5² − (7 + ⁻4) × 2

⁻6   ⁻10   19

7. 18 ÷ 2 + 9 ÷ ⁻3   8. (6 + ⁻4) + 4² ÷ 8   9. 12 − 10 × 2 ÷ 4

6   4   17

PRACTICE 13.4

Combine Operations with Integers

Evaluate the expression.

1. ⁻3 + 8 × 2 − 1   2. (5 − 12) × 6 + 4

12   ⁻38

3. 6 + 2 × 4 + (4 − ⁻2)   4. (⁻8 + 8) + 12 ÷ ⁻6

18   ⁻2

5. 3² − ⁻2 + (7 − 9)   6. 4 + 2³ − 7 + 1

9   6

7. 18 ÷ 6 + ⁻1 × 2   8. 7 × 6 − ⁻4 + 4²

1   62

9. (6² − 3²) × 2 − ⁻7   10. 3³ + 2 × ⁻8 − 5

61   ⁻12

11. (⁻10 − ⁻6) + (⁻1 + 8)   12. (⁻6 × ⁻4) × (⁻3 + 7)

3   ⁻96

Use a property to simplify the expression. Then evaluate the expression and identify the property you used. Possible properties are given.

13. ⁻9 + 23 + 29   14. (⁻203 + 18) + ⁻18   15. ⁻79 + ⁻187 + ⁻21

43; Commutative   ⁻203; Associative   ⁻287; Commutative

16. 13 + (47 + ⁻3)   17. ⁻9 + 16 + 9   18. 83 + (17 + ⁻18)

57; Associative   16; Commutative   82; Associative

Mixed Review

Find the sum. Write the answer in simplest form.

19. ¼ + ⅔   20. ³⁄₈ + ¼   21. ⅝ + ⅞   22. ½ + ⅜

11⁄12   5⁄8   3⁄2 or 1 ½   7⁄8

Use division to find the prime factors. Write the prime factorization.

23. 30   24. 48   25. 36   26. 35

2 × 3 × 5   2×2×2×2×3   2 × 2 × 3 × 3   5 × 7

Guided Practice

Evaluate the expression.

3. $42 \div 21 - 4 \cdot 9$ $^-34$

4. $^-15 + (^-45 \div ^-9)^2 - 29$ $^-19$

Use a property to simplify the expression. Then evaluate the expression and identify the property you used.
Possible properties are given.

5. $47 + 127 + 3$
177; commutative

6. $(223 + 24) + 6$
253; associative

7. $(576 + ^-53) + 53$
576; associative

PRACTICE AND PROBLEM SOLVING

Independent Practice

Evaluate the expression.

8. $^-4 + 7 \cdot ^-4 \div 14 - 12$ $^-18$

9. $(3 - ^-15) \div 6 \cdot (22 - 32)$ $^-30$

10. $2 - 14 + ^-8 \cdot 2^4$ $^-140$

11. $(^-15 + 7) \cdot (^-3 - 12)$ 120

12. $4^3 \div (2 - 18) \cdot (^-8 - 3)$ 44

13. $^-(3^2) \div |^-3| - ^-10$ 7

Possible properties are given. Use a property to simplify the expression. Then evaluate the expression and identify the property you used.

14. $(921 + 27) + ^-27$
921; associative

15. $85 + 321 + 15$
421; commutative

16. $^-7 + 29 + 17$
39; commutative

Problem Solving Applications

Use Data   For 17-19, use the line graph.

17. By how much did the price of Integer stock increase from January to February? **$6**

18. By how much did the price of Integer stock decrease from February to March? **$16**

19. What was the change in the price of Integer stock from January to May? Express your answer as an integer. $^-15$

Integer Stock

Price (in dollars) vs Month
Jan $26, Feb $32, Mar $16, Apr $28, May $11

20. ✎ **Write About It**   Write a problem that must be solved by performing more than one operation with integers.
Check students' problems.

21. Number Sense   How many prime numbers less than 1,000 are even? **One; 2 is prime and is an even number.**

MIXED REVIEW AND TEST PREP

Find the quotient. (p. 260)

22. $^-56 \div 8$ $^-7$

23. $^-77 \div ^-11$ 7

24. $236 \div ^-4$ $^-59$

25. Find the sum $^-79 + 42$. (p. 244) $^-37$

26. TEST PREP   Find the prime factorization of 54. (p. 148) **C**

A $2 \cdot 3$ **B** $2^3 \cdot 3$ **C** $2 \cdot 3^3$ **D** $2^3 \cdot 3^3$

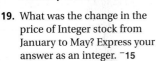
Extra Practice   page H44, Set C

263

---

3 | Practice

Guided Practice

Do Check for Understanding Exercises 1–7 with your students. Identify those having difficulty and use lesson resources to help.

Independent Practice

Assign Exercises 8–21.

To help students solve Exercises 14–16, have them identify the numbers that can be easily combined, resulting in another number that can be added mentally. Then have them decide what property they applied in determining the new combination.

MIXED REVIEW AND TEST PREP
Exercises 22–26 provide **cumulative review** (Chapters 1–13).

4 | Assess

Summarize the lesson by having students:

DISCUSS   What number would you get if you removed the parentheses from Exercise 11? $^-48$

WRITE Outline the steps you would use to solve Exercise 13.
Possible answer: First, square $^-3$. Then divide by the absolute value of $^-3$, 3. Finally subtract $^-10$.

Lesson Quiz

Transparency **13.4**

Evaluate the expression.

1. $(^-3 + 6) \times ^-9 + 15$ $^-12$

2. $^-42 + (^-2 + 12) \cdot (^-5) - ^-14$ $^-78$

3. $^-24 \div ^-6 + 8 \cdot (^-3 + 3)$ 4

Use a property to simplify the expression. Then evaluate the expression and identify the property you used.

4. $(^-25) \cdot (16) \cdot (^-2)$ 800; Commutative

5. $^-8 + (^-2 + 43)$ 33; Associative

PROBLEM SOLVING 13.4

Combine Operations with Integers
Write the correct answer.

Analyze Choose Solve Check

1. The Li family camped in a valley at an altitude of $^-25$ ft, or 25 ft below sea level. During the morning they hiked to the top of a hill where the altitude was $^+575$ ft, or 575 ft above sea level. What is the difference in altitude of the two places?

600 ft

2. Renee's checking account allows her to write checks for more than is in her account. She began with a balance of $326 and, after writing some checks, ended with a balance of $^-$108. What was the total amount of the checks she wrote?

$434

3. At 8 A.M. the outside temperature was $^-10°$ C. By noon the temperature had risen 15° C. Between noon and 5 P.M. the temperature dropped 12° C. What was the temperature at 5 P.M.?

$^-7°$ C

4. In a box of 48 candies, $\frac{1}{4}$ are green, $\frac{1}{4}$ are red, and $\frac{1}{2}$ are orange. If you give away all the candies except the green ones, how many candies will you have given away?

36 candies

Choose the letter for the best answer.

5. Chris bought a pen for $0.79. He gave the cashier a $1 bill. The cashier accidentally gave him $0.35 in change. How much extra did the cashier accidentally give Chris?
A $0.44   **C $0.14**
B $0.21   D $0.06

6. Joann dove from a 6-ft-high diving board into a 9-ft-deep pool and then touched the bottom of the pool. How far did she travel from the top of the board to the bottom of the pool?
F 3 ft   **H 15 ft**
G 6 ft   J 54 ft

7. A movie you want to see begins at 3:00 P.M. and ends at 5:15 P.M. If you leave your house 30 min before the movie begins and arrive home 15 min after it ends, how long are you away?
A 2 hr 45 min
B 3 hr
C 3 hr 15 min
D 3 hr 30 min

8. You buy several boxes of markers for an art project and spread them out on your desk. Adding 3 other markers that you already had, you now have 43 markers. How many markers could possibly come in a box?
F 6 markers
G 7 markers
H 8 markers
J 9 markers

9. Write About It How did you decide how many markers could have been in each box?

Possible answer: Subtract 3 and then find the only number that is a factor of 40.

CHALLENGE 13.4

You Need an Operation (or Maybe Several)!

Replace each □ with either +, −, ×, or ÷ to make the expression correct. Rewrite the expression on the line below. The first one is done for you.

1. $6 □ ^-4 □ 3 = ^-21$ $6 × ^-4 + 3 = ^-21$

2. $3 □ 5 = ^-2$
$3 - 5 = ^-2$

3. $10 □ ^-2 = ^-5$
$10 ÷ ^-2 = ^-5$

4. $^-12 □ ^-2 = 6 ÷$
$^-12 ÷ ^-2 = 6$

5. $17 □ ^-11 = 6 ÷$
$17 + ^-11 = 6$

6. $1 □ 8 □ ^-2 = 6 ×, +$
$1 × 8 + ^-2 = 6$

7. $5 □ 8 □ 6 = 3 -, +$
$5 - 8 + 6 = 3$

8. $20 □ 5 □ 2 = 2 ÷, ÷$
$20 ÷ 5 ÷ 2 = 2$

9. $3 □ ^-3 □ 2 = ^-18 ×, ×$
$3 × ^-3 × 2 = ^-18$

10. $6 □ ^-10 □ ^-9 = 5 +, -$
$6 + ^-10 - ^-9 = 5$

11. $2 □ 7 □ 3 = ^-8 -, -$
$2 - 7 - 3 = ^-8$

Correct each expression by adding one set of parentheses. The first one is done for you.

12. $10 - ^-3 × 2 = 16$
Without parentheses, the value of the expression is 16, since you multiply first and then subtract.
With parentheses around $^-3 × 2$, the value would still be 16, since with or without parentheses, you multiply first.
However, with parentheses around $10 - ^-3$, the value is 26, since you subtract first and then multiply.
So, the expression will be $(10 - ^-3) × 2 = 26$

13. $8 + ^-6 ÷ 2 = 1$
$(8 + ^-6) ÷ 2 = 1$

14. $5 × ^-3 + 4 = 5$
$5 × (^-3 + 4) = 5$

15. $^-20 + 6 ÷ 2 = 7$
$(^-20 + 6) ÷ ^-2 = 7$

16. $^-10 ÷ 2 + 3 = ^-2$
$^-10 ÷ (2 + 3) = ^-2$

263

CHAPTER 13

REVIEW/TEST

Purpose To check understanding of concepts, skills, and problem solving presented in Chapter 13

USING THE PAGE

The Chapter 13 Review/Test can be used as a **review** or a **test**.

- Items 1–37 check skill proficiency.
- Items 38–40 check students' abilities to choose and apply problem solving strategies to real-life problems involving integer multiplication and division.

Suggest that students place the completed Chapter 13 Review/Test in their portfolios.

USING THE ASSESSMENT GUIDE

- Multiple-choice format of Chapter 13 Posttest—See *Assessment Guide*, pp. AG81–82.
- Free-response format of Chapter 13 Posttest—See *Assessment Guide*, pp. AG83–84.

USING STUDENT SELF-ASSESSMENT

The How Did I Do? survey helps students assess what they have learned and how they learned it. This survey is available as a copying master in *Assessment Guide*, p. AGxvii.

264 Chapter 13

Find the product. (pp. 258-259)

1. $4 \times {}^-8$ ⁻32
2. $^-9 \times {}^-5$ 45
3. $7 \times {}^-2$ ⁻14
4. $^-11 \times {}^-7$ 77
5. $^-5 \times 4$ ⁻20
6. $^-8 \times {}^-10$ 80
7. $^-12 \times 5$ ⁻60
8. $^-19 \times {}^-5$ 95
9. $^-51 \times 14$ ⁻714
10. $^-18 \times {}^-7$ 126
11. $50 \times {}^-7$ ⁻350
12. $83 \times {}^-21$ ⁻1,743

Find the quotient. (pp 260-261)

13. $27 \div {}^-3$ ⁻9
14. $^-18 \div 2$ ⁻9
15. $^-36 \div {}^-6$ 6
16. $^-49 \div 7$ ⁻7
17. $144 \div {}^-12$ ⁻12
18. $^-132 \div {}^-12$ 11
19. $63 \div {}^-9$ ⁻7
20. $^-220 \div {}^-10$ 22
21. $180 \div {}^-9$ ⁻20
22. $^-216 \div 18$ ⁻12
23. $324 \div {}^-36$ ⁻9
24. $^-1,458 \div {}^-54$ 27

Evaluate the expression. (pp. 262-263)

25. $^-4 + 5 \times {}^-4 \div 2 - 12$ ⁻26
26. $(2^2 - 4^2)^2 \div {}^-24 - {}^-10$ 4
27. $(8 - {}^-4) \div 6 \times (12 - 16)$ ⁻8
28. $(6^2 - 3^2)^2 \div {}^-3 - {}^-45$ ⁻198
29. $2 - 11 + {}^-4 \times 3^3$ ⁻117
30. $2 + ({}^-11 + {}^-4) \times 5^3$ ⁻1,873
31. $(5 - 13) \times ({}^-8 \times 3)$ 192
32. $^-32 \times 11 + {}^-4 \div 2^2$ ⁻353
33. $({}^-15 \times 7) \times ({}^-12 \div {}^-3)$ ⁻420

Use a property to simplify the expression. Then evaluate the expression and identify the property you used. (pp. 262-263)

34. $(113 + 58) + {}^-28$ 143; associative
35. $^-85 + 113 + {}^-15$ 13; commutative
36. $^-117 + 49 + 17$ ⁻51; commutative
37. $(125 + {}^-13) + {}^-112$ 0; associative

Solve.

38. During the last glacial age, sea level in one body of water changed by an average of ⁻3 feet every 200 years. The glacial age lasted 10,000 years. What was the total change in sea level? (pp. 258-259) **⁻150 feet**

39. During the first nine months of the year, a worldwide club showed its total loss of members as ⁻2,718. What integer shows the average loss of members per month? (pp. 260-261) **⁻302**

40. One way to study climate is to compare the current conditions to conditions in previous years. One group studying climate found that rainfall during five months in an area showed the following changes compared with the previous year: ⁻45 in., ⁻12 in., 7 in., 23 in., ⁻3 in. What was the average change in rainfall for these five months? (pp. 260-261) **⁻6 in.**

264 Chapter 13

CHAPTER 13 TEST, page 1

Choose the best answer.

1. $^-2 \times 5$
   Ⓐ ⁻10 C 3
   B ⁻3 D 10

2. $3 \times {}^-3$
   F 6 H ⁻6
   G 0 Ⓙ ⁻9

3. $^-7 \times {}^-3$
   A ⁻21 C ⁻4
   B ⁻10 Ⓓ 21

4. $^-2 \times 7$
   Ⓕ ⁻14 H ⁻5
   G ⁻9 J 14

5. The height of a hot air balloon changed ⁻480 ft over 20 min. If the change was at a constant rate, what was the change in height per minute?
   A ⁻460 ft/min C 24 ft/min
   Ⓑ ⁻24 ft/min D 460 ft/min

6. Over the last 3 years, the changes in Mr. Chern's weight were 7 lb, ⁻7 lb, and 6 lb. What was the average yearly change in weight?
   F 20 lb Ⓗ 2 lb
   G 6 lb J ⁻2 lb

7. $^-5 \times {}^-7$
   Ⓐ 35 C ⁻12
   B 12 D ⁻35

8. $^-9 \times 0$
   F ⁻90 Ⓗ 0
   G ⁻9 J 9

9. $8 \times {}^-12$
   A 96 C ⁻4
   B 20 Ⓓ ⁻96

10. $^-6 \times 15$
    F 90 H ⁻21
    G 9 Ⓙ ⁻90

11. The change in the water level of a lake over the last 8 years has been ⁻24 in. What is the average yearly change in the water level?
    A 16 in. C ⁻16 in.
    Ⓑ ⁻3 in. D ⁻32 in.

12. The temperature rose 6°F each hour for 3 hr. What was the total temperature change over the 3-hour period?
    Ⓕ 18°F H ⁻9°F
    G 9°F J ⁻18°F

13. $35 \div {}^-7$
    A 28 Ⓒ ⁻5
    B 5 D ⁻28
    [Go On]

CHAPTER 13 TEST, page 2

14. $^-156 \div 4$
    F ⁻624 Ⓗ ⁻39
    G ⁻160 J 160

15. $360 \div {}^-12$
    A ⁻348 C 3
    Ⓑ ⁻30 D 372

16. $^-54 + {}^-9$
    F ⁻45 Ⓗ 6
    G ⁻6 J 45

17. $^-6 \times ({}^-1 + 7)$
    A 48 Ⓒ ⁻36
    B 36 D ⁻48

18. $(2 + {}^-5)^2$
    F 49 H ⁻9
    Ⓖ 9 J ⁻49

19. $^-16 \div {}^-8$
    A 24 C ⁻2
    Ⓑ 2 D ⁻24

20. $({}^-4 + 20) \div (4 - 6)^2$
    Ⓕ 4 H ⁻4
    G 2 J ⁻32

21. $({}^-8 + {}^-2)^2 + ({}^-1)^3$
    Ⓐ ⁻100 C 36
    B ⁻20 D 100

22. $(3 + 6) \times (3 - 6)$
    F 81 H 15
    G 27 Ⓙ ⁻27

For 23–24, use a property to simplify the expression. Then evaluate the expression and identify the property you used.

23. $^-5 \times 79 \div {}^-2$
    A ⁻790; Commutative
    Ⓑ 790; Commutative
    C ⁻790; Associative
    D 790; Associative

24. $(354 + 246) + {}^-246$
    F 600; Associative
    Ⓖ 354; Associative
    H 600; Commutative
    J 354; Commutative

25. Mr. and Mrs. Reyna have a bank account. Last month, Mrs. Reyna made deposits of $750 and $1,275. Mr. Reyna wrote checks that totaled $2,500. What was the change in their bank balance?
    A $575 C ⁻$375
    B $475 Ⓓ ⁻$475
    [Stop]

Eliminate choices.
See item **8.**
You can eliminate any choices that do not have the right sign.
Also see problem **5**, p. H64.

Choose the best answer.

1. $(^-5)^2 + (^-17 \cdot 20)$ **A**

   A $^-315$ **C** 315

   B 3 **D** 340

2. Which expression has a value of 10 for $m = ^-3$? **J**

   F $9 \div m + 7$

   G $m - (9 + 2)$

   H $9m + 2$

   J $9 - (m + 2)$

3. $^-54 \div ^-9$ **C**

   A $^-486$

   B $^-6$

   C 6

   D Not here

4. $8 \times ^-2 + 17$ **H**

   F $^-544$ **H** 1

   G $^-15$ **J** 33

5. $108 + (4 \times 3^2) - 76 \div 4$ **B**

   A 233

   B 125

   C 24.5

   D Not here

6. $(4^2) - (^-7 \times 2)$ **F**

   F 30 **H** $^-30$

   G 2 **J** Not here

7. Data that are divided into parts totaling 100% are best displayed in which kind of graph? **C**

   A Line graph

   B Bar graph

   C Circle graph

   D Histogram

8. Use mental math to find the value of x. **F**

   $$x \div ^-6 = 90$$

   F $x = ^-540$ **H** $x = 15$

   G $x = ^-15$ **J** $x = 96$

9. Jason's test scores are listed below. Which is the mean score? **D**

TEST SCORES					
75	85	100	91	93	87
82	76	78	100	79	98

   A 25 **C** 82

   B 75 **D** 87

10. $\frac{7}{9} - \frac{4}{6}$ **G**

    F $\frac{1}{18}$ **H** $\frac{9}{18}$

    G $\frac{1}{9}$ **J** $\frac{3}{3}$

11. $9\frac{1}{6} \div 1\frac{7}{8}$ **A**

    A $4\frac{8}{9}$ **C** $9\frac{7}{48}$

    B 5 **D** $31\frac{3}{7}$

12. $|^-2{,}187|$ **H**

    F $^-2{,}187$

    G $^-|2{,}187|$

    H $2{,}187$

    J Not here

265

CUMULATIVE REVIEW •
Chapters 1–13

USING THE PAGE

This page may be used to help students get ready for standardized tests. The test items are written in the same style and arranged in the same format as those on many state assessments. The page is cumulative. It covers math objectives and essential skills that have been taught up to this point in the text. Most of the items represent skills from the current chapter, and the remainder represent skills from earlier chapters.

This page can be assigned at the end of the chapter as classwork or as a homework assignment. You may want to have students use individual recording sheets presented in a multiple-choice (standardized) format. A Test Answer Sheet is available as a blackline master in *Assessment Guide* (p. AGxlii).

You may wish to have students describe how they solved each problem and share their solutions.

UNIT 4

MATH DETECTIVE
Play by the Rules

Purpose To use deductive reasoning to solve problems involving operations of integers

USING THE PAGE

- *Direct students' attention to the Reasoning section and Function Machines 1 and 2.*

If you know the output for Function Machine 1, how would you use the rule to find the input? Possible answer: Use the inverse operation and subtract ⁻6 from the output, or add 6 to the output.

Can you write an equivalent rule for Function Machine 1? for Function Machine 2? Subtract 6; add ⁻4.

- *Have students look at the rule and the input values for Function Machine 3.*

Do you think all of the outputs for Function Machine 3 will be positive, negative, or a combination of the two? Explain. A combination; there are both positive and negative inputs and adding 1 will not change the output as much as multiplying by ⁻3.

- *Ask students to find and discuss the rule for Function Machine 4.*

Reasoning If you know only one input and output for a function machine, can you find a unique rule for the function machine? Explain. No, Possible answer: For example, for Function Machine 4 if you know only the output for ⁻4 is 2, then the rule could be to divide by ⁻2 or it could be to add 6.

Think It Over! After students complete the Write About It, have them compare their methods for finding the rule. Guide them to understand that both forms of the rule are equivalent.

MATH DETECTIVE

Play by the Rules

REASONING Each function machine is missing something. For Machines 1, 2, and 3, an input or an output value is missing in each step. For Machine 4, the rule is missing. Use your knowledge of integer operations to find what is missing for each machine.

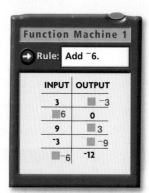

Function Machine 1
Rule: Add ⁻6.

INPUT	OUTPUT
3	⬛ ⁻3
⬛6	0
9	⬛ 3
⁻3	⬛ ⁻9
⬛ ⁻6	⁻12

Function Machine 2
Rule: Subtract 4.

INPUT	OUTPUT
5	⬛ 1
⬛ 11	7
1	⬛ ⁻3
⁻2	⬛ ⁻6
⬛ 4	0

Function Machine 3
Rule: Multiply by ⁻3. Then add 1.

INPUT	OUTPUT
3	⬛ ⁻8
1	⬛ ⁻2
0	⬛ 1
⁻2	⬛ 7
⁻10	⬛ 31

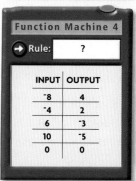

Function Machine 4
Rule: ?

INPUT	OUTPUT
⁻8	4
⁻4	2
6	⁻3
10	⁻5
0	0

Divide by ⁻2 or multiply by ⁻½.

Think It Over!

- **Write About It** Explain how you found a rule for Function Machine 4.
  Check students' answers.
- **Stretch Your Thinking** Find a rule for this function machine.
  Multiply by 2; then add 3.

INPUT	OUTPUT
0	3
1	5
2	7
3	9

Intervention and Extension Resources

ADVANCED LEARNERS

Challenge students to **find the output using each rule** below for inputs 12 and ⁻9.

Rule 1: Divide by ⁻3. Then add ⁻6. ⁻10; ⁻3

Rule 2: Multiply by ⁻⅔. Then subtract ⁻4. ⁻4; 10

Rule 3: Divide by ⁻½. Then add 8. ⁻16; 26

Rule 4: Multiply by 1⅓. Then add ⁻12. 4; ⁻24

Next ask students to make their own function table by using a rule involving two integer operations. Have them complete the table by finding the output for 5 different inputs. Then challenge them to exchange completed tables without the rule and find the rule for the table. Check students' work.

VISUAL

Challenge

Negative Exponents

Learn how to work with negative exponents and how to write small numbers by using scientific notation.

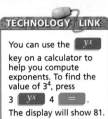

EXAMPLE

Activity

Copy and complete the pattern. Use a calculator as needed.

$10^3 = 1,000$

$10^2 = 100$

$10^1 = 10$

$10^0 = \blacksquare \ 1$

$10^{-1} = \blacksquare \ 0.1$

$10^{-2} = \blacksquare \ 0.01$

$10^{-3} = \blacksquare \ 0.001$

Notice that as the value of the exponent decreases, each number is 0.1, or $\frac{1}{10}$, as great as the previous number.

- For powers of 10, how is the negative exponent related to the number of decimal places? **The negative exponent tells the number of places to the right of the decimal.**

Negative exponents are used to write very small numbers in scientific notation.

$$0.004 = 4 \times 0.001 = 4 \times 10^{-3}$$
$$\uparrow$$
Replace 0.001 with 10^{-3}.

Look at the relationship between 0.004 and 4×10^{-3}. To write 0.004 as 4, move the decimal point 3 places to the right, multiplying by 1,000. Use $^-3$ as the exponent of 10 to show the corresponding division by 1,000.

Write 0.0000245 in scientific notation.

0.0000245
5 places

Count the number of places the decimal point must be moved to the right to form a number that is at least 1 but less than 10.

2.45×10^{-5}

Write the number. Since the decimal point moved 5 places to the right, the exponent of 10 is 10^{-5}.

TALK ABOUT IT

- When writing a very small number in scientific notation, how can you tell what should be the exponent? **Since the decimal is moved to the right, the exponent is the negative of the number of places moved.**

TRY IT

Write using scientific notation.

1. 0.002	2. 0.00034	3. 0.06	4. 0.005365
5. 0.0084	6. 0.0000794	7. 0.0000008	8. 0.000202
1. 2×10^{-3}	2. 3.4×10^{-4}	3. 6×10^{-2}	4. 5.365×10^{-3}
5. 8.4×10^{-3}	6. 7.94×10^{-5}	7. 8×10^{-7}	8. 2.02×10^{-4}

267

CHALLENGE
Negative Exponents

Objective To extend the concepts and skills of Chapters 11–13

USING THE PAGE

- *Have students complete the Activity and extend the pattern.*

  What is 0.0001 as a power of 10? 10^{-4}

  What is 10^{-6}? 0.000001

- *Work through the discussion of negative exponents and the Example.*

  Compare how to write a very small number in scientific notation to writing a very large number in scientific notation. How are they similar? different? In both cases, the number is a factor that is greater than or equal to 1 but less than 10 and multiplied by a power of 10. For large numbers, the power of 10 has a positive exponent, and for small numbers the power of 10 has a negative exponent.

- *Have students complete the Talk About It.*

  How can you check that you have written a number in scientific notation correctly? Possible answer: Convert the number back into standard form.

Try It Before assigning Try It Exercises 1–8, suggest that students copy each number and draw arrows in the standard form of the number, as shown in the Example, to help them write the needed exponent.

Intervention and Extension Resources

SCIENCE CONNECTION

Reinforce students' understanding of scientific notation. Tell students the following:

Numerical constants used in science can be very large or very small numbers. Scientific notation makes it easier to record some of these constants. For example, the mass of an electron is 9.110×10^{-31} kg, the mass of a neutron is 1.675×10^{-27} kg, and the mass of a proton is 1.673×10^{-27} kg.

Have students order the masses of the particles from greatest to least. Ask them to explain their thinking. neutron, proton, electron; Compare the exponents first. $^-31$ is less than $^-27$, so it's mass is the least. Then compare numbers that have the exponent $^-27$. 1.675 is greater than 1.673. So, a neutron's mass is the greatest.

Finally have students work in pairs to record the mass of each of the particles in standard form. Check students' work.

VISUAL

STUDY GUIDE AND REVIEW

Purpose To help students review concepts and skills presented in Chapters 11–13

USING THE PAGES

☑ Assessment Checkpoint

The Study Guide and Review includes content from Chapters 11–13.

Chapter 11
11.1 Understand Integers
11.2 Rational Numbers
11.3 Compare and Order Rational Numbers
11.4 Problem Solving Strategy: *Use Logical Reasoning*

Chapter 12
12.1 Math Lab: Algebra—Model Addition of Integers
12.2 Algebra: Add Integers
12.3 Math Lab: Algebra—Model Subtraction of Integers
12.4 Algebra: Subtract Integers

Chapter 13
13.1 Math Lab: Algebra—Model Multiplication of Integers
13.2 Algebra: Multiply Integers
13.3 Algebra: Divide Integers
13.4 Combine Operations with Integers

The blue page numbers in parentheses provided with each group of exercises indicate the pages on which the concept or skill was presented. The red number given with each group of exercises identifies the Learning Goal for the concept or skill.

VOCABULARY

1. The distance an integer is from zero is its __?__. (p. 228) **absolute value**

2. All whole numbers and their opposites are the set of __?__. (p. 228) **integers**

3. A comparison of two numbers, a and b, written as a fraction $\frac{a}{b}$, is a __?__. (p. 230) **ratio**

EXAMPLES

EXERCISES

Chapter 11

• **Write the absolute value of an integer.**
(pp. 228–229) **11A**

$|{}^{-}5| = 5$ *Write the distance $^{-}5$ is from 0 on the number line.*

Write the absolute value.

4. $|{}^{-}8|$ 8   5. $|{}^{+}6|$ 6   6. $|{}^{-}28|$ 28

7. $|{}^{-}73|$ 73   8. $|{}^{+}49|$ 49   9. $|0|$ 0

• **Classify numbers as whole numbers, integers, and rational numbers.**
(pp. 230–233) **11B**

$^{-}5$ is an integer and a rational number.

$\frac{3}{5}$ is a rational number.

Name the sets to which each number belongs.

10. $3\frac{5}{9}$ rational   11. 0.35 rational

12. $^{-}42$ rational, integer   13. $\frac{6}{3}$ whole, integer, rational

---

• **Find a rational number between two rational numbers.** (pp. 230–233) **11C**

Find a rational number between $^{-}8.5$ and $^{-}8.45$.

$^{-}8.50$ $^{-}8.45$ *Write each decimal using hundredths.*

$^{-}8.46$ is between $^{-}8.5$ and $^{-}8.45$. Some other numbers are $^{-}8.47$, $^{-}8.48$, and $^{-}8.482$.

Find a rational number between the two given numbers. Possible answers are given.

14. $\frac{1}{8}$ and $1\frac{1}{2}$ $\frac{1}{4}$ 15. $^{-}2.3$ and $^{-}2.4$ $^{-}2.35$

16. 18.01 and 18.02 18.015   17. $\frac{^{-}1}{8}$ and $\frac{1}{10}$ $\frac{^{-}1}{10}$

18. $\frac{1}{10}$ and 0.2 0.15   19. $^{-}1\frac{1}{2}$ and $^{-}1\frac{3}{4}$ $^{-}1\frac{5}{8}$

• **Compare and order rational numbers.**
(pp. 234–235) **11C**

Compare. Write $<$, $>$, or $=$ for the ●.

$^{-}5.8$ ● $^{-}5\frac{3}{4}$

$^{-}5\frac{3}{4} = {}^{-}5.75$ *Write the fraction as a decimal.*

$^{-}5.80 < {}^{-}5.75$ *Compare the decimals.*

So, $^{-}5.8 < {}^{-}5\frac{3}{4}$.

Compare. Write $<$, $>$ or $=$ for each ●.

20. $\frac{2}{5}$ ● 0.38 $>$ 21. $3\frac{3}{4}$ ● 3.89 $<$

22. $^{-}0.25$ ● $\frac{^{-}1}{4}$ $=$ 23. $4\frac{3}{10}$ ● 4.03 $>$

Order from least to greatest.

24. 1.55, $\frac{2}{3}$, $^{-}3$, 4.2, $^{-}1.8$ $^{-}3$, $^{-}1.8$, $\frac{2}{3}$, 1.55, 4.2

25. $\frac{^{-}3}{4}$, 0, 6.5, $^{-}8$, $^{-}3.6$ $^{-}8$, $^{-}3.6$, $\frac{^{-}3}{4}$, 0, 6.5

Chapter 12

- **Add and subtract integers.** (pp. 242–251) **12A, 12B**

Subtract. 6 − ⁻4
6 − ⁻4 = 6 + 4   *Write as an addition*
       = 10   *sentence.*

Add. 15 + ⁻3
15 + ⁻3 = 12   *Subtract the absolute*
                   values.

Find the sum or difference.

26. ⁻3 + 9 **6**
27. ⁻8 + ⁻9 **⁻17**
28. 12 + ⁻5 **7**
29. ⁻4 − 10 **⁻14**
30. ⁻9 − ⁻13 **4**
31. 15 − ⁻6 **21**

Chapter 13

- **Multiply and divide integers.** (pp. 258–261) **13A, 13B**

⁻4 × 7 = ⁻28   *The product or quotient of*
               a positive and a negative
               integer is negative.

⁻72 ÷ ⁻9 = 8   *The product or quotient*
               of two positive or two
               negative integers is
               positive.

Find the product or quotient.

32. ⁻16 · 3 **⁻48**
33. ⁻12 · ⁻12 **144**
34. 15 · ⁻6 **⁻90**
35. ⁻14 · ⁻9 **126**
36. ⁻54 ÷ 9 **⁻6**
37. 124 ÷ ⁻4 **⁻31**
38. ⁻75 ÷ ⁻15 **5**
39. ⁻119 ÷ 7 **⁻17**

- **Combine operations with integers.**
(pp. 262–263) **13C**

Evaluate the expression.

⁻3 + 9 × ⁻4 ÷ 3 − 8   *Do all multiplication*
                       and division from
                       left to right.

⁻3 + ⁻12 − 8   *Do all addition and*
⁻3 + ⁻12 + ⁺8   *subtraction from*
⁻23   *left to right.*

Evaluate the expression.

40. 5 − 12 ÷ ⁻2 + 4 × ⁻5 **⁻9**
41. (16 − ⁻8) ÷ (3 × ⁻2) **⁻4**
42. 2³ + (4 − ⁻6) ÷ ⁻2 **3**
43. (⁻3 + 9)² ÷ (⁻4 × 3) **⁻3**

PROBLEM SOLVING APPLICATIONS

44. Four students spent money on books. The amounts they spent were $2.50, $3.25, $5.00, and $5.75. Ari spent $3.25 more than Nina. Nina spent half as much as Jamal. Kenny spent $1.75 less than Jamal. How much did each person spend? (pp. 236–237) **Jamal: $5.00, Kenny: $3.25, Nina: $2.50, Ari: $5.75 11D**

46. Rachel is the owner of a restaurant. Her profits and losses for the past four weeks are ⁻$380, $420, ⁻$145 and $620. How much was her profit or loss for the past four weeks? (pp.244–247) **Her profit was $515. 12A**

Natalie: baseball, Aaron: swimming, Toral: soccer, Casey: hockey 11D

45. Natalie, Aaron, Toral, and Casey are each on a different sports team. Toral is not on the baseball team. Casey's team plays on the ice. Aaron's team practices in the water. They play on soccer, hockey, swimming, and baseball teams. Who plays on each team? (pp. 236–237)

47. Frances claimed that the average of the low temperatures last week was greater than ⁻4°C. Patty says that the average was less than ⁻4°C. The low temperatures last week were ⁻6°C, ⁻8°C, ⁻3°C, ⁻4°C, 0°C, ⁻9°C, and ⁻5°C. Who is correct? Explain. (pp.260–261) **Patty is correct since the average low temperature was ⁻5°C. 13B**

269

STUDY GUIDE AND REVIEW INTERVENTION

How to Help Options

Learning Goal	Items	Text Pages	Reteach and Practice Resources
11A *See page 226C for Chapter 11 learning goals*	4–9	228–229	Worksheets for Lesson 11.1
11B *See page 226C for Chapter 11 learning goals*	10–13	230–233	Worksheets for Lesson 11.2
11C *See page 226C for Chapter 11 learning goals*	14–19, 20–25	230–233, 234–235	Worksheets for Lessons 11.2, 11.3
11D *See page 226C for Chapter 11 learning goals*	44–45	236–237	Worksheets for Lesson 11.4
12A *See page 226C for Chapter 12 learning goals*	46	242–243, 244–247	Worksheets for Lessons 12.1, 12.2
12B *See page 226C for Chapter 12 learning goals*	26–31	244–247, 248–249, 250–251	Worksheets for Lessons 12.2, 12.3, 12.4
13A *See page 226C for Chapter 13 learning goals*	32–35	258–259	Worksheets for Lesson 13.2
13B *See page 226C for Chapter 13 learning goals*	36–39, 47	260–261	Worksheets for Lesson 13.3

UNIT 4

CALIFORNIA CONNECTIONS

Purpose To provide additional practice for concepts and skills in Chapters 11–13

USING THE PAGE

Temperatures

• *After Exercise 2, have students extend their thinking.*

Suppose the temperature rose 0.5°F the first hour, 1°F the second hour, and 1.5°F the third hour after the recorded low in Truckee. If this pattern continued for two more hours, what was the temperature at the end of the 5-hour period? ⁻7.5°F

• *Direct students' attention to the table showing the temperature data.*

How could you best display the data in a graph? Use a line graph or a scatterplot.

Make a line graph of the temperature data. Explain your choice of axes and scales. Check students' graphs.

Extension Have students use newspapers or the Internet to collect various temperature data about their city during different times of the year. Working in small groups ask them to display and compare the data by using graphs and tables. Encourage groups to share and explain their results. Check students' work.

Temperatures

California is a state of temperature extremes. Parts of the high and cold Sierra Nevada receive 50 *feet* or more of snow during the winter. Yet Death Valley, California, had the highest temperature ever recorded in the United States, 134°F.

SCIENCE Standards
IE 7.c

In some parts of California, you can snow ski in the morning and play tennis in the afternoon.

1. It was 64°F when Cindy's family left Santa Barbara. The temperature was 30°F when they got to Pine Mountain Summit in Los Padres National Forest. Find the temperature difference between Pine Mountain and Santa Barbara. **34°**

2. Truckee, California, sometimes has the lowest temperature outside of Alaska. One morning it was 53°F in San Francisco and ⁻15°F in Truckee. Find the temperature difference between San Francisco and Truckee. **68°**

3. Cindy's family camped near Pine Mountain. The next day, they went on to Bakersfield, where the temperature was 86°F. Find the temperature difference between Bakersfield and Pine Mountain. **56°**

4. On a February morning, these temperatures were recorded in three California mountain towns: Tahoe City, ⁻6°F; Mammoth Lakes, 0°F; Kirkwood, ⁻11°F. Order the temperatures from coldest to warmest. **⁻11°F, ⁻6°F, 0°F**

5. Here's a useful rule for estimating temperature change: temperature decreases about 5°F for every 1,000 ft that you go up in elevation. The temperature in Oakdale, California (elevation 155 ft), is 23°F. Estimate the temperature at Lake Tahoe (elevation 6,229 ft). **⁻7°F**

Because of the "wind-chill factor," air temperatures feel colder when the wind is blowing.

Use Data For 6, use the table for 10 mph winds.

CURRENT TEMPERATURES	35°F	30°F	25°F	20°F
WIND-CHILL TEMPERATURES	22°F	16°F	10°F	4°F

6. The air temperature in Quincy, California, is 5°F. A 10 mph wind is blowing. Use the patterns in the table to estimate the wind-chill temperature. **⁻14°F**

270 Chapters 11–13

Elevations

California is a state of elevation extremes, too. In California is Mount Whitney, which, at 14,494 ft, is one of the highest peaks in the country. Here, too, is Death Valley, at 282 ft below sea level ($^-$282), the country's lowest point.

Mount Whitney, California's highest point, is only about 80 miles from Death Valley, its lowest point.

Use Data   For 1–2, use the diagram at the right.

1. What is the elevation difference between the lowest point in Death Valley and the top of Mount Whitney? **14,776 ft**

2. Hikers walked from the bottom of Death Valley to the top of Mount Whitney. By about how many feet did their elevation increase, on average, every mile? **about 184.7 ft**

Use Data   For 3–4, use the diagram at the right.

3. What is the elevation difference between point P and the lowest point in Death Valley? **235 ft**

4. About how many times the elevation of point P is the elevation of the deepest point in the valley? **about 6 times**

Use Data   For 5–6, use the table.

5. Write the absolute value of Death Valley's lowest elevation and the absolute value of Long Beach's elevation. Which point is farther from sea level? Explain. **See above right.**

6. *REASONING*   Recall that air temperature decreases about 5°F for every 1,000 ft that you go up in elevation. If the temperature at Death Valley's lowest point is 90°F, which of the cities is most likely to have a temperature of about 75°F? Explain. **Victorville; it is about 3,000 ft higher and therefore likely to be 15° cooler.**

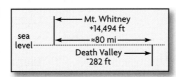

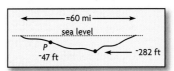

5. Death Valley: 282; Long Beach: 170; Death Valley, because 282 > 170.

ELEVATIONS OF CALIFORNIA CITIES	
Mammoth Lakes	7,860 ft
Lone Pine	3,733 ft
Victorville	2,714 ft
Ridgecrest	2,289 ft
Bakersfield	408 ft
Long Beach	170 ft

SCIENCE
Standards
IE 7.c

CALIFORNIA CONNECTIONS

Purpose To provide additional practice for concepts and skills in Chapters 11–13

USING THE PAGE

Elevations

- *Direct students' attention to the table of elevations.*

About how many times the elevation of each city in the table is the height of Mt. Whitney? Possible answers: Mammoth Lakes: about 2 times; Lone Pine: about 4 times; Victorville: about 5 times; Ridgecrest: about 6 times; Bakersfield: about 30 times; Long Beach: about 75 times

Find about how many times as great the elevation of Victorville is as the elevation of Death Valley. 2,700 − $^-$300 = 3,000
3,000 ÷ 300 = 10 The elevation of Victorville is about 10 times as great as the elevation of Death Valley.

Extension Using the diagram at the top of the page, have students plot the elevations for the cities in the table. Ask them to determine the approximate air temperatures for each if the temperature at Death Valley is 90°F. Check students' work.

271

Student Handbook

Troubleshooting H2

Prerequisite Skills Review Do you have the math skills needed to start a new chapter? Use this list of skills to review and remember your skills from last year.

Troubleshooting

Properties

The charts list the basic properties of addition and multiplication.

Addition

PROPERTY	EXAMPLE WITH NUMBERS	EXAMPLE WITH VARIABLES
Commutative	$3 + 7 = 7 + 3$	$a + b = b + a$
Associative	$(4 + 5) + 2 = 4 + (5 + 2)$	$(a + b) + c = a + (b + c)$
Identity Property of Zero	$9 + 0 = 9$ and $0 + 9 = 9$	$a + 0 = a$ and $0 + a = a$

Multiplication

PROPERTY	EXAMPLE WITH NUMBERS	EXAMPLE WITH VARIABLES
Commutative	$8 \times 6 = 6 \times 8$	$a \times b = b \times a$
Associative	$(2 \times 9) \times 5 = 2 \times (9 \times 5)$	$(a \times b) \times c = a \times (b \times c)$
Identity Property of One	$6 \times 1 = 6$ and $1 \times 6 = 6$	$a \times 1 = a$ and $1 \times a = a$
Property of Zero	$7 \times 0 = 0$ and $0 \times 7 = 0$	$a \times 0 = 0$ and $0 \times a = 0$
Distributive	$3 \times (5 + 7) = (3 \times 5) + (3 \times 7)$	$a \times (b + c) = (a \times b) + (a \times c)$

Practice

Name the property shown.

1. $0 \times 12 = 0$
Multiplication Property of Zero
2. $(8 \times 21) \times 5 = 8 \times (21 \times 5)$
Associative of Multiplication
3. $72 \times 5 = 5 \times 72$
Commutative of Multiplication
4. $4 \times (3 + 2) = (4 \times 3) + (4 \times 2)$
Distributive
5. $9 + 0 = 9$
Identity Property of Zero
6. $k + 7 = 7 + k$
Commutative of Addition
7. $(m + 4) + h = m + (4 + h)$
Associative of Addition
8. $c \times (2 + 3) = (c \times 2) + (c \times 3)$
Distributive
9. $1 \times x = x$
Identity Property of One

Represent Decimals

You can use decimal squares to represent decimals. A decimal square is divided into 100 parts. Each part represents 1 hundredth of the whole, or 0.01. Count the number of shaded parts. Write this number as hundredths.

24 out of 100 small squares are shaded.
0.24 of the whole is shaded.

Practice

Write the decimal that is represented.

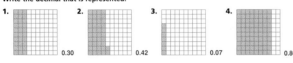

1. 0.30 **2.** 0.42 **3.** 0.07 **4.** 0.80

Write and Read Decimals

A place-value chart can help you write and read numbers. Each three-digit group, such as ones or millions, is called a **period**.

Read: "thirty million, one hundred twenty-eight thousand, five hundred ninety-seven and forty-six thousandths."

MILLIONS			THOUSANDS			ONES					
Hundreds	Tens	Ones	Hundreds	Tens	Ones	Hundreds	Tens	Ones	Tenths	Hundredths	Thousandths
	3	0	1	2	8	5	9	7	0	4	6

Example

Name the place value of the digit, 8, in the chart.

To write the value of the 8 in the chart, multiply the digit times the value of the place-value position.

Think: $8 \times 1,000$, or $8,000$.

Practice

Name the place value of the digit 4.

1. 327,489,223.78
hundred thousands
2. 198,238,042.08
tens
3. 149,678,935.91
ten millions
4. 728,035.84
hundredths

Give the value of the blue digit.

5. 538.92
8
6. 82,901,733.006
80,000,000
7. 29.35
0.05
8. 125,674.173
0.003

Compare and Order Whole Numbers

You can compare and order numbers by comparing the digits in each place-value position.

Example

Write $<$, $>$, or $=$ to compare the numbers.   14,675 ● 14,228

Step 1	Step 2	Step 3
Compare the ten thousands.	Compare the thousands.	Compare the hundreds.
14,675	14,675	14,675
↓ same number of	↓ same number of	↓ 6 > 2
14,228 ten thousands	14,228 thousands	14,228 So, 14,675 > 14,228.

Practice

Write $<$, $>$, or $=$ to compare the numbers.

1. 3,919 ● 3,991 < **2.** 188,937 ● 189,066 < **3.** 70,001 ● 70,001 =

Order the numbers from greatest to least.

4. 9,774; 9,718; 9,762
9,774; 9,762; 9,718
5. 82,056; 82,856; 81,978
82,856; 82,056; 81,978
6. 23,091; 23,910; 23,109
23,910; 23,109; 23,091

Troubleshooting

Round Whole Numbers and Decimals

Follow these steps to round a number to a given place.

Example

Round 168,279 to the nearest ten thousand.

Step 1	Step 2	Step 3
Find the digit in the place being rounded, the ten thousands place.	Look at the next digit to the right. If it is 5 or greater, round up. Otherwise, round down.	Change to zero each digit to the right of the place being rounded.
168,279	168,279 8 > 5, so round up.	168,279 → 170,000

Round to the nearest whole number.

1. 7.97 8 **2.** 15.58 16

Round to the nearest thousand.

3. 3,378 3,000 **4.** 7,607 8,000

Round to the nearest ten thousand.

5. 530,410 530,000 **6.** 12,677 10,000

Round to the nearest tenth.

7. 16.53 16.5 **8.** 2.96 3.0

Whole-Number Operations

When adding, subtracting, multiplying, and dividing whole numbers, align digits that have the same place value.

Examples

A. Find the sum. $247 + 1,496 + 89$

$$\begin{array}{r} \overset{22}{} \\ 247 \\ 1,496 \\ + 89 \\ \hline 1,832 \end{array}$$

Think: $7 + 6 + 9 = 22$
Regroup 22 ones as 2 tens 2 ones.
Add the other columns in a similar way.

B. Find the difference. $31 - 12$

$$\begin{array}{r} \overset{2\,11}{\cancel{3}\cancel{1}} \\ - 12 \\ \hline 19 \end{array}$$

Regroup when necessary.

C. Find the product. 27×86

$$\begin{array}{r} 27 \\ \times\, 86 \\ \hline 162 \\ + 2\,160 \\ \hline 2,322 \end{array}$$

Multiply by the 6 ones.
Multiply by the 8 tens.
Add the products.

D. Find the quotient. $146 \div 9$

$$\begin{array}{r} 16\ r2 \\ 9\overline{)146} \\ -\underline{9} \\ 56 \\ -\underline{54} \\ 2 \end{array}$$

Divide the 14 tens.
Multiply and subtract.
Bring down the 6 ones.
Divide the 56 ones.
Multiply and subtract.
Write the remainder.

Practice

Add, subtract, multiply, or divide.

1. $79 + 56 = 99$ 234 **2.** $345 - 26$ 319 **3.** 67×76 5,092 **4.** $376 \div 15$ 25 r1
5. $700 - 388$ 312 **6.** 19×203 3,857 **7.** $155 + 9 + 4,823$ 4,987 **8.** $524 \div 31$ 16 r28

Remainders

When dividing whole numbers, you can write a remainder as a whole number, as a decimal, or as a fraction.

Example

Divide: $15 \div 4$. Write the remainder as a decimal and as a fraction.

Step 1	Step 2	Step 3
Write the dividend as a two-place decimal.	Divide.	Write the decimal as a fraction in simplest form.
$4\overline{)15.00}$	$\begin{array}{r} 3.75 \\ 4\overline{)15.00} \end{array}$	$0.75 = \frac{75}{100} = \frac{75 \div 25}{100 \div 25} = \frac{3}{4}$
		$15 \div 4 = 3\frac{3}{4}$

Practice

Divide. Write the remainder as a decimal and as a fraction.

1. $4\overline{)30}$ 7.5; $7\frac{1}{2}$ **2.** $8\overline{)50}$ 6.25; $6\frac{1}{4}$ **3.** $10\overline{)3,315}$ 331.5; $331\frac{1}{2}$ **4.** $12\overline{)2,442}$ 203.5; $203\frac{1}{2}$
5. $6\overline{)21}$ 3.5; $3\frac{1}{2}$ **6.** $8\overline{)94}$ 11.75; $11\frac{3}{4}$ **7.** $20\overline{)74}$ 3.7; $3\frac{7}{10}$ **8.** $25\overline{)210}$ 8.4; $8\frac{2}{5}$

Read a Table

Use the title of a table to understand what the data represent. Use the labels to understand what the items represent.

Example

How far did Angie jog on Tuesday?

DAILY JOGGING RECORD (IN MILES)							
Day	Sun	Mon	Tue	Wed	Thu	Fri	Sat
Milo	4	3	5	5	0	7	6
Angie	6	3	4	0	5	8	0

The number in the row marked "Angie" and the column marked "Tue" is 4. So, Angie jogged 4 miles on Tuesday.

Practice

Use the data in the table above to answer the questions.

1. How far did Milo jog on Friday? 7 mi
2. Which person jogged 5 miles on Wednesday? Milo
3. On which day did Angie jog 6 miles? Sun
4. On which day did Milo and Angie jog the same distance? Mon
5. How far did Angie jog on the two days that she jogged the same distance? 0 mi
6. Who ran the greater total distance during the week? Milo

Troubleshooting

Mean, Median, Mode, and Range

Example

Find the mean, median, mode, and range for this set of data.
6, 19, 6, 9, 11, 15

Mean Find the sum of the data items. Divide the sum by the number of items.	$6 + 19 + 6 + 9 + 11 + 15 = 66$ mean = $66 \div 6 = 11$
Median Arrange the items from least to greatest. The median is the middle value. If there are two middle values, the median is the average of the two values.	6, 6, **9, 11**, 15, 19 9 and 11 are the middle numbers. median = $(9 + 11) \div 2 = 10$
Mode Arrange the items from least to greatest. The mode is the value or values that repeat most often. If no value repeats, there is no mode.	**6,** 6, 9, 11, 15, 19 mode = 6
Range Arrange the items from least to greatest. The range is the difference of the greatest and least values.	**6,** 6, 9, 11, 15, **19** range = $19 - 6 = 13$

Practice

Find the mean, median, mode, and range for each set of data.

1. 2, 1, 3, 5, 9
4; 3; none; 8
2. 6, 52, 41, 21, 35
31; 35; none; 46
3. 11, 15, 6, 11, 22
13; 11; 11; 16
4. 9, 5, 2, 5, 6, 1, 14
6; 5; 5; 13

Read Bar Graphs

A **bar graph** uses bars of different lengths to show and compare data.

Example

How many books did Anita read last month?

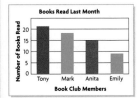
Books Read Last Month

Find the bar representing Anita. Read the scale at the left for the number the bar represents.

Anita read 15 books last month.

Practice

Use the bar graph to answer the questions.

1. How many books did Mark read? 18 books
2. Who read 22 books? Tony
3. Who read the least number of books? Emily
4. How many more books did Tony read than Anita? 7 books

H6 Prerequisite Skills Review

Read Stem-and-Leaf Plots

In a **stem-and-leaf plot**, data are organized by "stems," or the tens digits, and "leaves," or the ones digits. The stems and leaves are listed in order.

Example

Each entry in the stem-and-leaf plot gives the number of cards that were stacked in a house of cards when it collapsed. How many times were there from 40 to 49 cards when the collapse occurred?

Stem	Leaves
1	2 5 7 8 8 9
2	0 0 1 3 5 8
3	1 2 4 7
4	2 8
5	1 6

The numbers from 40 to 49 have the stem of 4, because the tens digit is 4. There are two such numbers in the table:

Stem 4, leaf 2 shows 42.
Stem 4, leaf 8 shows 48.

So, twice there were from 40 to 49 cards. Once there were 42 cards, and once there were 48.

Practice

Use the stem-and-leaf plot to answer the questions.

1. How many times were there from 10 to 19 cards when the collapse occurred? 6
2. What was the greatest number of cards stacked? the least number? 56; 12
3. How many houses of cards were built in this competition? 20
4. What are the mode, median, and range of the data in the table? mode: 18 and 20; median: 24; range: 44

Prime and Composite Numbers

A **prime number** is a whole number that has exactly two factors, itself and 1. A **composite number** has more than two factors.

Examples

Decide whether the number is *prime* or *composite*.

A. 13 13 has exactly two factors, 13 and 1. These are the only whole numbers that divide 13 evenly. So, 13 is prime.

B. 12 12 has the factors 1, 2, 3, 4, 6, and 12. Each of these whole numbers divides 12 evenly. Since 12 has more than two factors, it is composite.

Practice

Decide whether the number is *prime* or *composite*.

1. 19 prime
2. 6 composite
3. 10 composite
4. 2 prime
5. 15 composite
6. 28 composite
7. 31 prime
8. 99 composite
9. 71 prime
10. 456 composite

Student Handbook H7

Troubleshooting

Factors and Multiples

Multiples of a number are the products that result when the number is multiplied by 0, 1, 2, 3, 4, and so on.
27 is a multiple of 9 because $27 = 9 \times 3$.

Factors are numbers that divide a whole number evenly.
8 is a factor of 32 because 8 divides 32 evenly: $32 \div 8 = 4$.

Examples

A. List the next three multiples of 7: 7, 14, 21.

7,	14,	21,	**28,**	**35,**	**42**
7×1	7×2	7×3	7×4	7×5	7×6

So, the next three multiples are 28, 35, and 42.

B. Find all the factors of 20.

Think: $1 \times 20 = 20$, so 1 and 20 are factors of 20. $2 \times 10 = 20$, so 2 and 10 are factors of 20. $4 \times 5 = 20$, so 4 and 5 are factors of 20.

So, the factors of 20 are 1, 2, 4, 5, 10, and 20.

Practice

List the next three multiples of the number.

1. 5: 5, 10, 15
20, 25, 30
2. 9: 9, 18, 27
36, 45, 54
3. 6: 12, 18, 24
30, 36, 42
4. 20: 40, 60, 80
100, 120, 140

Find all of the factors of the number.

5. 13 1, 13
6. 12 1, 2, 3, 4, 6, 12
7. 30 1, 2, 3, 5, 6, 10, 15, 30
8. 24 1, 2, 3, 4, 6, 8, 12, 24
9. 15 1, 3, 5, 15
10. 22 1, 2, 11, 22
11. 28 1, 2, 4, 7, 14, 28
12. 36 1, 2, 3, 4, 6, 9, 12, 18, 36

Model Fractions

A **fraction** is a number that names a part of a whole or a part of a group.

Example

Write the fraction represented by the shaded part.

The group has 7 squares. The part that is shaded is 4 squares.

So, the fraction shaded is $\frac{4}{7}$.

Practice

Write the fraction represented by the shaded part.

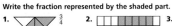

1. $\frac{3}{4}$
2. $\frac{5}{9}$
3. $\frac{3}{8}$
4. $\frac{5}{6}$

H8 Prerequisite Skills Review

Model Percents

Percent (%) means "per hundred." You can use a hundred square to model percents.

Example

Write the percent for the shaded part of the square.

There are 100 parts, and 75 of the parts are shaded. So, 75% of the parts are shaded.

Practice

Write the percent for the shaded part of the square.

1. 35%
2. 90%
3. 12%
4. 4%

Simplify Fractions

A fraction is in **simplest form** when the numerator and denominator have no common factors other than 1.

$\frac{10}{15}$ is not in simplest form, because 10 and 15 have the common factor 5.

$\frac{7}{12}$ is in simplest form, because 7 and 12 have no common factors other than 1.

You can write a fraction in simplest form by dividing the numerator and denominator by the greatest common factor (GCF).

Example

Write the fraction in simplest form. $\frac{16}{28}$

Step 1

Find the greatest common factor of 16 and 28.

factors of 16: 1, 2, 4, 8, 16
factors of 28: 1, 2, 4, 7, 14, 28

The *greatest* common factor is 4.

Step 2

Divide the numerator and the denominator by the GCF.

$\frac{16 \div 4}{28 \div 4} = \frac{4}{7}$ Since the GCF of 4 and 7 is 1, $\frac{4}{7}$ is in simplest form.

Practice

Write the fraction in simplest form.

1. $\frac{9}{15}$ $\frac{3}{5}$
2. $\frac{8}{12}$ $\frac{2}{3}$
3. $\frac{5}{20}$ $\frac{1}{4}$
4. $\frac{18}{6}$ $\frac{3}{1}$, or 3
5. $\frac{24}{32}$ $\frac{3}{4}$
6. $\frac{24}{30}$ $\frac{4}{5}$

Student Handbook H9

Add and Subtract Like Fractions

Like fractions are fractions that have the same denominator. To add or subtract like fractions, add or subtract the numerators. Keep the same denominator.

Example

Find the sum. $\frac{4}{9} + \frac{2}{9}$

Step 1

Add the numerators. Write the sum over the like denominator.

$\frac{4}{9} + \frac{2}{9} = \frac{4+2}{9} = \frac{6}{9}$

Step 2

If necessary, rewrite the fraction in simplest form.

$\frac{6}{9} = \frac{6 \div 3}{9 \div 3} = \frac{2}{3}$

Practice

Find the sum or difference. Write the answer in simplest form.

1. $\frac{1}{7} + \frac{4}{7}$
2. $\frac{4}{5} - \frac{2}{5}$
3. $\frac{3}{8} + \frac{3}{8}$
4. $\frac{3}{4} + \frac{1}{4}$
5. $\frac{7}{10} - \frac{5}{10}$
6. $\frac{8}{12} - \frac{4}{12}$
7. $\frac{15}{11} - \frac{9}{11}$
8. $\frac{5}{9} + \frac{8}{9}$, or $1\frac{4}{9}$
9. $\frac{2}{10} + \frac{6}{10}$
10. $\frac{12}{4} - \frac{8}{4}$
11. $\frac{3}{6} + \frac{1}{6}$
12. $\frac{5}{8} + \frac{1}{8}$
13. $\frac{7}{16} + \frac{5}{16}$
14. $\frac{17}{20} - \frac{9}{20}$
15. $\frac{11}{25} + \frac{4}{25}$

Round Fractions

To round a fraction to 0, $\frac{1}{2}$, or 1, compare the numerator with the denominator.

Examples

Round each fraction to 0, $\frac{1}{2}$, or 1.

A. $\frac{2}{11}$
Compared to 11, 2 is close to 0.
Round the fraction to 0.

B. $\frac{7}{15}$
7 is about half of 15.
Round the fraction to $\frac{1}{2}$.

C. $\frac{13}{16}$
13 is close to 16.
Round the fraction to 1.

Practice

Round each fraction to 0, $\frac{1}{2}$, or 1.

1. $\frac{3}{4}$
2. $\frac{1}{5}$
3. $\frac{2}{7}$
4. $\frac{6}{13}$
5. $\frac{5}{12}$
6. $\frac{14}{15}$
7. $\frac{4}{18}$
8. $\frac{3}{7}$
9. $\frac{4}{1}$
10. $\frac{12}{20}$
11. $\frac{11}{24}$
12. $\frac{17}{20}$
13. $\frac{11}{18}$
14. $\frac{3}{25}$
15. $\frac{15}{16}$

Mental Math and Equations

You can use mental math to solve equations. Try using a related equation to find the value of the variable.

Examples

Use mental math to solve the equation.

A. $k + 6 = 10$
Think: When 6 is added to k, the sum is 10. That means that $k = 10 - 6$.
So, $k = 4$. Check: $4 + 6 = 10$ ✔

B. $m - 4 = 11$
Think: When 4 is subtracted from m, the difference is 11. That means that $m = 11 + 4$.
So, $m = 15$. Check: $15 - 4 = 11$ ✔

C. $c \div 5 = 7$
Think: When c is divided by 5, the quotient is 7. That means that $c = 7 \times 5$.
So, $c = 35$. Check: $35 \div 5 = 7$ ✔

D. $h \times 4 = 36$
Think: When h is multiplied by 4, the product is 36. That means that $h = 36 \div 4$.
So, $h = 9$. Check: $9 \times 4 = 36$ ✔

Practice

Use mental math to solve the equation.

1. $g - 5 = 6$
2. $r \times 2 = 12$
3. $d \div 3 = 6$
4. $x + 9 = 17$
5. $v \div 6 = 5$
6. $y - 6 = 9$
7. $a + 3 = 15$
8. $n \times 3 = 21$

Fractions and Mixed Numbers

A **mixed number** is made up of a whole number and a fraction. You can write a mixed number as a fraction greater than 1, and a fraction greater than 1 as a mixed number.

Examples

A. Write $\frac{14}{3}$ as a mixed number.

$3\overline{)14}$ with quotient 4 r2
Divide the numerator by the denominator.

$\frac{14}{3} = 4\frac{2}{3}$
Write the remainder as the numerator of a fraction.

B. Write $3\frac{4}{5}$ as a fraction.

$3 \times 5 = 15$
Multiply the denominator by the whole number.

$15 + 4 = 19$
Add the numerator.

$3\frac{4}{5} = \frac{19}{5}$
Write the sum over the denominator.

Practice

Write the fraction as a mixed number.

1. $\frac{13}{7}$
2. $\frac{18}{5}$
3. $\frac{10}{3}$
4. $\frac{22}{9}$
5. $\frac{17}{6}$

Write the mixed number as a fraction.

6. $2\frac{4}{5}$
7. $1\frac{3}{8}$
8. $3\frac{3}{4}$
9. $2\frac{22}{25}$
10. $2\frac{11}{16}$

Compare Fractions

To compare fractions with unlike denominators, rename the fractions so that they have like denominators. Then compare the numerators.

Examples

Compare. Use <, >, or = for ●.

A. $\frac{5}{8} ● \frac{7}{8}$
The denominators are like. Compare the numerators.
$5 < 7$, so $\frac{5}{8} < \frac{7}{8}$.

B. $\frac{7}{10} ● \frac{3}{5}$
The denominators are unlike. Rename one or both fractions.
$\frac{3 \times 2}{5 \times 2} = \frac{6}{10}$
$7 > 6$, so $\frac{7}{10} > \frac{3}{5}$.

C. $2\frac{5}{12} ● 2\frac{1}{3}$
The whole numbers are equal. Rename one or both fractions.
$\frac{1 \times 4}{3 \times 4} = \frac{4}{12}$
$5 > 4$, so $2\frac{5}{12} > 2\frac{1}{3}$.

Practice

Compare. Use <, >, or = for ●.

1. $\frac{4}{5} ● \frac{3}{5}$
2. $\frac{11}{15} ● \frac{13}{15}$
3. $1\frac{4}{6} ● 1\frac{2}{3}$
4. $2\frac{5}{8} ● 2\frac{1}{2}$
5. $\frac{2}{3} ● \frac{5}{12}$
6. $\frac{7}{8} ● \frac{3}{4}$
7. $\frac{5}{15} ● \frac{2}{6}$
8. $\frac{8}{9} ● \frac{2}{3}$
9. $\frac{13}{16} ● \frac{7}{8}$
10. $\frac{5}{9} ● \frac{14}{27}$

Understand Integers

The **integers** are the whole numbers and their opposites. Integers greater than 0 are **positive integers** and are found to the right of 0 on a number line. Integers less than 0 are **negative integers** and are found to the left of 0.

Number line: $^-6\ ^-5\ ^-4\ ^-3\ ^-2\ ^-1\ 0\ 1\ 2\ 3\ 4\ 5\ 6$

Example

Name the temperatures indicated by point A and point B.

The temperature at point A is $^-35°$. The temperature at point B is $^+68°$.

Practice

Give four examples of each set of numbers. Possible answers are given.

1. whole numbers 0, 1, 2, 3
2. negative integers $^-1, ^-2, ^-3, ^-4$

Write a positive or negative integer for each situation.

3. thermometer point C 0°F
4. thermometer point D $^+105°F$
5. thermometer point E $^-7°F$
6. thermometer point F $^+32°F$
7. 35 ft above sea level $^+35$
8. a loss of $5 $^-5$

Number Lines

You can use a number line to graph numbers and to compare and order numbers. If two numbers are graphed on a number line, the number to the right is greater.

Example

Graph $^-3$, 2, and $^-1.5$ on the number line. Then order the numbers from least to greatest.

Graph each number by placing a dot on the number line.

Number line: $^-5\ ^-4\ ^-3\ ^-2\ ^-1\ 0\ 1\ 2\ 3\ 4\ 5$

Notice that $^-1.5$ appears halfway between $^-1$ and $^-2$. Since values increase as you move to the right on a number line, the order of the numbers from least to greatest is $^-3$, $^-1.5$, 2.

Practice

Name the number graphed by each point.

Number line with points A, E, C, B, D: $^-5\ ^-4\ ^-3\ ^-2\ ^-1\ 0\ 1\ 2\ 3\ 4\ 5$

1. A $^-5$
2. B 0
3. C $^-1$
4. D 3.5
5. E $^-3.5$

Graph the numbers on a number line. Then order the numbers from least to greatest. Check students' number lines.

6. 4, 2, $^-1$ / $^-1, 2, 4$
7. $^-1, ^-3, 0$ / $^-3, ^-1, 0$
8. 1.5, 2, $^-1.5$ / $^-1.5, 1.5, 2$
9. 3, $^-3, ^-4$ / $^-4, ^-3, 3$
10. $^-3.5, ^-3, ^-5$ / $^-5, ^-3.5, ^-3$

Multiplication and Division Facts

To multiply a number by a power of 10, move the decimal point one place to the right for each zero. To divide a number by a power of 10, move the decimal point one place to the left for each zero.

If you forget a multiplication fact that has 11 or 12 as a factor, think of 11 as $10 + 1$, and think of 12 as $10 + 2$.

Example

Find the product. 12×8

$12 \times 8 = (10 + 2) \times 8 = (10 \times 8) + (2 \times 8) = 80 + 16 = 96$

Practice

Find the product or quotient.

1. 56×10 560
2. $780 \div 10$ 78
3. 4.3×100 430
4. $5,280 \div 1,000$ 5.28
5. $2.61 \times 1,000$ 2,610
6. 0.48×100 48
7. $124 \div 10$ 12.4
8. $5.77 \div 100$ 0.0577
9. 11×10 110
10. 12×9 108

Add and Subtract Integers

You can add and subtract integers on a number line. To add a positive number on a number line, move right. To add a negative number, move left. To subtract a number on a number line, *add the opposite* of the number.

Examples

A. Add. $2 + {}^-6$

From 0, move to $^+2$. Move 6 units left to $^-4$.

$2 + {}^-6 = {}^-4$

B. Subtract. $^-3 - {}^-7 \rightarrow {}^-3 + {}^+7$

Add the opposite.

From 0, move to $^-3$. Move right 7 units to $^+4$.

$^-3 - {}^-7 = {}^+4$

Practice

Find the sum or difference.

1. $4 - 7$ $^-3$ **2.** $^-3 + {}^-8$ $^-11$ **3.** $5 + {}^-6$ $^-1$ **4.** $^-8 - 3$ $^-11$ **5.** $7 + {}^-3$ 4

6. $2 - {}^+5$ $^-3$ **7.** $9 - 4$ 5 **8.** $11 + {}^-7$ 4 **9.** $^-5 + {}^-6$ $^-11$ **10.** $2 - {}^-5$ 7

Patterns

Look for a rule for the pattern. Then use it to extend the pattern.

Example

Find the next three numbers in the pattern. **1, 2, 4, 8**

Step 1 Find the rule.

Each number in the series is 2 times the number before it.
$1 \times 2 = 2; 2 \times 2 = 4; 4 \times 2 = 8$

The rule is "multiply by 2."

Step 2 Use the rule.

Multiply each number by 2 to find the next number:
$8 \times 2 = 16, 16 \times 2 = 32, 32 \times 2 = 64$

So, the next three numbers are 16, 32, and 64.

Practice

Find the next three numbers in the pattern. Write the rule.

1. 10, 14, 18, 22, 26
30, 34, 38; add 4

2. 729, 243, 81, 27
9, 3, 1; divide by 3

3. 1, 4, 16 64, 256, 1,024;
multiply by 4

4. 63, 55, 47, 39
31, 23, 15; subtract 8

5. 49, 37, 25, 13
1, $^-11$, $^-23$; subtract 12

6. $2\frac{1}{2}, 1\frac{3}{4}, 1, \frac{1}{4}$
$-\frac{1}{2}, -1\frac{1}{4}, -2$; subtract $\frac{3}{4}$

Exponents

You can use exponents to express powers of numbers. An **exponent** tells how many times the **base** is used as a factor.

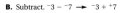

$6 \times 6 \times 6 \times 6 = 6^4$

exponent — The exponent 4 shows that the base 6 is used 4 times as a factor.

base

Examples

Find the value of 5^3.

A. $5^3 = 5 \times 5 \times 5 = 125$

Write 49 by using an exponent.

B. $49 = 7 \times 7 = 7^2$

Practice

Find the value.

1. 2^4 16   **2.** 4^3 64   **3.** 5^2 25   **4.** 10^3 1,000   **5.** 3^4 81

Write by using an exponent.

6. 9 3^2 **7.** 32 2^5 **8.** 36 6^2 **9.** 100 10^2 **10.** 27 3^3

Order of Operations

When more than one operation is used in an expression, follow these rules to evaluate the expression.

RULES FOR ORDER OF OPERATIONS	
1. First, do the operations **in parentheses**.	3. Next, **multiply and divide** from left to right.
2. Next, evaluate **exponents**.	4. Finally, **add and subtract** from left to right.

Examples

Evaluate each expression.

A. $3^2 + 5 \times 2$

1. There are no parentheses.
2. Evaluate exponents. $3^2 + 5 \times 2 = 9 + 5 \times 2$
3. Multiply. $9 + 5 \times 2 = 9 + 10$
4. Add. $9 + 10 = 19$

B. $(21 - 6) \div 3$

1. Evaluate parentheses. $(21 - 6) \div 3 = 15 \div 3$
2. There are no exponents.
3. Divide. $15 \div 3 = 5$
4. There is no addition or subtraction.

Practice

Evaluate each expression.

1. $4 + 6 \times 9$ 58   **2.** $(5 + 4) \times 3$ 27   **3.** $25 - 12 \times 3$ $^-11$ **4.** $2^2 + 3^2$ 13

5. $(2 + 3)^2$ 25   **6.** $\frac{10 - 4}{2} \times 4^2$ 48   **7.** $5^2 \div (1^5 + 4)$ 5   **8.** $2 + 3 \times 3 \times 3$ 29

Add and Subtract

To add or subtract unlike fractions, write equivalent fractions with common denominators. Then add or subtract the like fractions.

To add or subtract decimals, align the decimal points. Write equivalent decimals. Then add or subtract as you would with whole numbers.

Examples

Find the sum. $\frac{1}{6} + \frac{1}{2}$

A. $\frac{1}{6} + \frac{1}{2}$ Write equivalent fractions with a denominator of 6.

$\frac{1 \times 3}{2 \times 3} = \frac{3}{6}$

$\frac{1}{6} + \frac{3}{6} = \frac{4}{6}$, or $\frac{2}{3}$ Add the numerators and simplify.

Find the difference. $34.7 - 3.651$

B.   34.700   Align the decimal points.
  $-$ 3.651   Write an equivalent decimal.
   31.049   Subtract as for whole numbers.

Practice

Find the sum or difference.

1. $3.12 + 2.7$ 5.82   **2.** $1.197 - 1.09$ 0.107   **3.** $6 - 3.4$ 2.6   **4.** $2.17 + 141.8$ 143.97

5. $\frac{3}{4} + \frac{1}{6}$ $\frac{11}{12}$ **6.** $\frac{5}{8} - \frac{3}{16}$ $\frac{7}{16}$ **7.** $\frac{3}{5} + \frac{1}{4}$ $\frac{17}{20}$ **8.** $\frac{1}{3} + \frac{5}{12}$ $\frac{3}{4}$

Inverse Operations

Addition and subtraction are **inverse** operations. This means that you can check a sum or difference by using the inverse operation. You can also check a product or quotient by using the inverse operation.

Examples

Use the inverse operation to check the answer.

A.
  12   27
$+$ 15 $-$ 15
  27   12

B.
  322   142
$-$ 180 $+$ 180
  142   322

C.
   12   12
$\times$ 9 $9)\overline{108}$
 108

D.
   4   14
$14)\overline{56}$ $\times$ 4
          56

Practice

Use the inverse operation to check the answer.
Possible answers are given.

1. $23 + 15 = 38$
$38 - 15 = 23$

2. $57 - 31 = 26$
$26 + 31 = 57$

3. $8 \times 7 = 56$
$56 \div 7 = 8$

4. $144 \div 6 = 24$
$6 \times 24 = 144$

5. $14 \times 3 = 42$
$42 \div 3 = 14$

6. $366 - 218 = 148$
$148 + 218 = 366$

7. $586 + 255 = 841$
$841 - 255 = 586$

8. $250 \div 5 = 50$
$5 \times 50 = 250$

Words for Operations

Many different words and phrases can be used in numerical and algebraic expressions to represent the operations of addition, subtraction, multiplication, and division.

Examples

Write the operation described by the phrase.

A. the sum of 6 and 7

To find a sum means to add. The operation is addition.

B. the product of k and 15

To find a product means to multiply. The operation is multiplication.

Practice

Write the operation described by the phrase.

1. k greater than 75
addition

2. 42 less than m
subtraction

3. the sum of h and 6
addition

4. the quotient of 11 and b
division

5. c times w
multiplication

6. the difference of a and 45
subtraction

7. 9 increased by 7
addition

8. the product of 12 and p
multiplication

9. 2 reduced by m
subtraction

Words and Equations

You can write equations to represent some sentences. Use a variable to represent what is unknown in the sentence. Use operation signs or other mathematical signs to represent words or phrases in the sentence.

Example

Write an equation for this sentence: A number increased by 7 is 12.

Represent "a number" by a variable such as x.
Represent "increased by" with a plus sign.
Represent "is" with an equal sign.

So, the equation is $x + 7 = 12$.

Practice

Write an equation for the sentence. Variables may vary.

1. The product of a number and 7 is 49.
$y \times 7 = 49$

2. 8 less than a number is 50. $m - 8 = 50$

3. 12 and a number have a quotient of 2. $\frac{12}{b} = 2$

4. 13 times a number is 91. $13k = 91$

5. 7 more than a number is 12. $n + 7 = 12$

6. 16 divided by a number is $\frac{4}{5}$. $\frac{16}{x} = \frac{4}{5}$

7. A number reduced by 13 is 9. $m - 13 = 9$

8. 45 greater than a number is 26.
$y + 45 = 26$

Troubleshooting

Evaluate Expressions

An expression that includes one or more variables is called an **algebraic expression**. To evaluate algebraic expressions, replace the variables with the given numbers. Then evaluate as you would with a numerical expression. Follow the rules for the order of operations.

Example

Evaluate $3 + m \times 2$ for $m = 6$.

$3 + m \times 2 = 3 + 6 \times 2$ Replace m with 6.

$\qquad = 3 + 12$ Multiply before adding.

$\qquad = 15$ Add.

Practice

Evaluate the expressions for the given value of the variables.

1. $4m$ for $m = 9$ 36

2. $\frac{3}{4}p$ for $p = 8$ 6

3. $\frac{z}{24}$ for $z = 96$ 4

4. $t - 5$ for $t = 19$ 14

5. $6h$ for $h = 9$ 54

6. $5 + c$ for $c = {}^-13$ $^-8$

7. $72 \div k$ for $k = 6$ 12

8. $p - 14$ for $p = 27$ 13

9. ^-8f for $f = {}^-7$ 56

Classify Angles

You can classify angles by their sizes.

An *acute* angle has a measure greater than 0° and less than 90°.

A *right* angle forms a square corner. It measures 90°.

An *obtuse* angle has a measure greater than 90° and less than 180°.

A *straight* angle has a measure of 180°.

Practice

Classify each angle by stating whether it is *acute, obtuse, right,* or *straight.*

1. K obtuse

2. P straight

3. Z acute

4. N right

5. V acute

6. M obtuse

7. Q right

8. T acute

H18 Prerequisite Skills Review

Name Angles

You can name an angle by using one letter, three letters, or a number.

Examples

Name the angle formed by the blue rays.

Use the vertex letter to name the angle. $\angle G$

There are two angles with vertices at N. So, use three letters. $\angle ANV$ or $\angle VNA$

Use a number. $\angle 5$

Practice

Name the angle formed by the blue rays.

1. $\angle 2$

2. $\angle H$ or $\angle PHQ$ or $\angle QHP$

3. $\angle N$

4. $\angle F$

5. $\angle RPT$ or $\angle TPR$

6. $\angle 2$

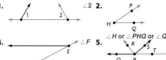

Identify Polygons

A **polygon** is a closed plane figure formed by three or more line segments. A polygon is classified by its number of sides.

Examples

State whether the figure is a polygon or not. If it is, classify it.

A. The figure is not closed, so it is not a polygon.

B. The figure is a 5-sided polygon called a pentagon.

Practice

State whether the figure is a polygon or not. If it is, classify it.

1. Yes; square or quadrilateral

2. Yes; hexagon

3. Yes; triangle or isosceles triangle

4. not a polygon

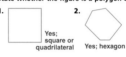

Student Handbook H19

Troubleshooting

Identify Solid Figures

A **polyhedron** is a solid figure with flat faces that are polygons. A **prism** is a polyhedron with two congruent, parallel **bases**. Its **lateral faces** are rectangles. A **pyramid** has a polygon for its base and triangles for its lateral faces.

A **cone** has a circular base. A **cylinder** has two congruent parallel circular bases. Cones and cylinders have curved lateral surfaces.

Practice

Identify each solid figure.

1. cube or square prism

2. triangular pyramid

3. cylinder

4. hexagonal prism

5. cone

6. pentagonal prism

7. hexagonal pyramid

8. triangular prism

Faces, Edges, and Vertices

Each polygon that forms a solid figure is a **face** of the figure. A line segment where two faces meet is an **edge**. A point where three or more edges meet is a **vertex**.

Example

Tell the number of faces, vertices, and edges of the cube.

The cube has 6 faces, 8 vertices, and 12 edges.

Practice

Give the number of faces, edges, and vertices of each solid figure.

1. 8; 18; 12

2. 7; 12; 7

3. 6; 10; 6

4. 8; 12; 6

H20 Prerequisite Skills Review

Write Equivalent Fractions

To write a fraction equivalent to a given fraction, multiply or divide the numerator and denominator by the same number.

Examples

Complete the number sentence to find an equivalent fraction.

A. $\frac{18}{24} = \frac{3}{\blacksquare}$

Think: To change 18 to 3, divide the numerator of $\frac{18}{24}$ by 6. Then divide the denominator by 6.

$\frac{18}{24} = \frac{18 \div 6}{24 \div 6} = \frac{3}{4}$

So, the equivalent fraction is $\frac{3}{4}$.

B. $\frac{3}{5} = \frac{\blacksquare}{20}$

Think: To change 5 to 20, multiply the denominator of $\frac{3}{5}$ by 4. Then multiply the numerator by 4.

$\frac{3}{5} = \frac{3 \times 4}{5 \times 4} = \frac{12}{20}$

So, the equivalent fraction is $\frac{12}{20}$.

Practice

Complete each number sentence to find an equivalent fraction.

1. $\frac{1}{2} = \frac{\blacksquare}{8}$ 4

2. $\frac{12}{18} = \frac{2}{\blacksquare}$ 3

3. $\frac{3}{4} = \frac{15}{\blacksquare}$ 20

4. $\frac{\blacksquare}{6} = \frac{25}{30}$ 5

5. $\frac{8}{24} = \frac{\blacksquare}{12}$ 4

6. $\frac{\blacksquare}{15} = \frac{30}{45}$ 10

7. $\frac{3}{5} = \frac{48}{80}$ 48

8. $\frac{\blacksquare}{40} = \frac{7}{8}$ 35

9. $\frac{27}{36} = \frac{\blacksquare}{12}$ 9

10. $\frac{\blacksquare}{16} = \frac{8}{32}$ 4

11. $\frac{12}{\blacksquare} = \frac{6}{10}$ 20

12. $\frac{\blacksquare}{100} = \frac{11}{20}$ 55

Solve Multiplication Equations

To solve a multiplication equation, use an inverse operation. Divide both sides of the equation by the number that multiplies the variable.

Example

Solve and check. $8n = 40$

$8n = 40$

$\frac{8n}{8} = \frac{40}{8}$ Divide both sides by 8.

$n = 5$ Simplify.

Check: $8n \stackrel{?}{=} 40$

$8 \times 5 \stackrel{?}{=} 40$

$40 = 40$ ✔

Practice

Solve and check.

1. $6k = 18$ 3

2. $3h = 27$ 9

3. $5e = 75$ 15

4. $10d = 700$ 70

5. $120 = 8m$ 15

6. $24y = 108$ 4.5

7. $40 = 160b$ $\frac{1}{4}$

8. $^-1p = 12$ $^-12$

9. $15n = 135$ 9

10. $4k = 30$ $7\frac{1}{2}$

11. $1.2\,t = 96$ 80

12. $^-5b = 35$ $^-7$

13. $198 = 18s$ 11

14. $9 = \frac{1}{2}p$ 18

15. $^-7f = {}^-98$ 14

16. $^-84 = 14q$ $^-6$

Student Handbook H21

H18–H21 Troubleshooting

Congruent and Similar Figures

Two figures are **similar** if they have the same shape. One may be an enlargement or a reduction of the other. Two figures are **congruent** if they have the same size and shape.

Examples

Tell if the figures in each pair appear to be congruent, similar, both, or neither.

A.

The figures are neither congruent or similar.

B.

The figures are similar.

C.

Both; the figures are congruent and similar.

Practice

Tell if the figures in each pair appear to be congruent, similar, both, or neither.

1.

similar

2.

neither

3.

both

Write Fractions as Decimals

To write a fraction as a decimal, divide the numerator by the denominator. Or, write an equivalent fraction with a denominator of 10, 100, or 1,000. Then rewrite the fraction as a decimal.

Example

Write $\frac{3}{4}$ as a decimal.

One Way

$$\begin{array}{r} 0.75 \\ 4\overline{)3.00} \\ -28 \\ \hline 20 \\ -20 \\ \hline 0 \end{array}$$ Divide 3 by 4. So, $\frac{3}{4} = 0.75$.

Another Way

$\frac{3}{4} = \frac{3 \times 25}{4 \times 25} = \frac{75}{100}$ Write an equivalent fraction with a denominator of 100.

$\frac{75}{100} = 0.75$ Write the equivalent fraction as a decimal.

So, $\frac{3}{4} = 0.75$.

Practice

Write the fraction as a decimal.

1. $\frac{1}{2}$ 0.5   **2.** $\frac{7}{10}$ 0.7   **3.** $\frac{1}{4}$ 0.25   **4.** $\frac{3}{8}$ 0.375   **5.** $\frac{7}{20}$ 0.35

6. $\frac{2}{5}$ 0.4   **7.** $\frac{17}{25}$ 0.68   **8.** $\frac{43}{50}$ 0.86   **9.** $\frac{48}{250}$ 0.192   **10.** $\frac{19}{50}$ 0.38

H22 Prerequisite Skills Review

Multiply with Fractions and Decimals

When multiplying decimals, the number of decimal places in the product is the total of decimal places in the two factors. When multiplying fractions, write the product of the numerators over the product of the denominators.

Examples

Find the product.

A.
$$\begin{array}{r} 2.57 \quad \text{2 decimal places} \\ \times \quad 1.2 \quad \text{1 decimal place} \\ \hline 514 \\ + \quad 2570 \\ \hline 3.084 \quad \text{2 + 1 = 3 decimal places} \end{array}$$

B. $\frac{3}{4} \times \frac{8}{9} = \frac{3 \times 8}{4 \times 9} = \frac{24}{36}$ Multiply numerators. Multiply denominators.

$\frac{24 \div 12}{36 \div 12} = \frac{2}{3}$ Simplify.

Practice

Find the product. Write the answer in simplest form. 3. 16.845; 4. 18.4275; 5. 395.5

1. 7.2 × 0.9 6.48   **2.** 8.4 × 1.1 9.24   **3.** 112.3 × 0.15   **4.** 17.55 × 1.05   **5.** 15.82 × 25

6. $\frac{1}{3} \times \frac{2}{3}$ $\frac{2}{9}$ **7.** $\frac{5}{6} \times \frac{3}{4}$ $\frac{5}{8}$ **8.** $\frac{2}{3} \times \frac{5}{12}$ $\frac{5}{18}$ **9.** $\frac{5}{8} \times \frac{3}{5}$ $\frac{3}{8}$ **10.** $\frac{1}{2} \times \frac{1}{4}$ $\frac{1}{8}$

Fractions, Decimals, and Percents

You can write a percent as a decimal and a decimal as a percent. You can write a percent as a fraction and a fraction as a percent.

Examples

A. Write 42% as a decimal.

42% = 42 ÷ 100 Divide by 100.

So, 42% = 0.42.

B. Write 0.781 as a percent.

0.781 = 0.781 × 100 Multiply by 100.

So, 0.781 = 78.1%.

C. Write 24% as a fraction.

24% = $\frac{24}{100}$ = $\frac{6}{25}$ Write the percent over 100. Simplify.

So, 24% = $\frac{6}{25}$.

D. Write $\frac{11}{25}$ as a percent.

$\frac{11}{25}$ = 11 ÷ 25 = 0.44 Divide numerator by denominator.

So, $\frac{11}{25}$ = 44%. Write the percent.

Practice

Write each decimal and each fraction as a percent. Write each percent as a decimal and as a fraction.

1. $\frac{2}{5}$ 40%   **2.** 10% 0.1, $\frac{1}{10}$ **3.** 0.34 34%   **4.** 25% 0.25, $\frac{1}{4}$ **5.** $\frac{1}{2}$ 50%

6. 0.81 81%   **7.** $\frac{7}{25}$ 28%   **8.** 60% 0.60, $\frac{3}{5}$ **9.** $\frac{18}{50}$ 36%   **10.** 0.02 2%

Certain, Impossible, Likely, Unlikely

An event is **certain** if it is sure to happen. It is **impossible** if it can never happen. It is **likely** if there is a strong chance that it will happen. It is **unlikely** if there is a strong chance that it will not happen.

Examples

Tell if the event is certain, impossible, likely, or unlikely.

A. 2 + 2 will equal 5 next Tuesday.

2 + 2 can never equal 5.

So, the event is *impossible*.

B. You toss a penny 10 times and get at least 1 head.

The probability of getting a head is $\frac{1}{2}$ each time you toss a coin.

So, the event is *likely*.

Practice

Tell if the event is certain, impossible, likely, or unlikely.

1. Rain will fall at least once this year. likely   **2.** There will be no June next year. impossible

3. You toss a quarter and get either a head or a tail. certain   **4.** A person who does not know you will guess your phone number. unlikely

Analyze Data

A **line graph** shows changes over time. How many people attended Game 2?

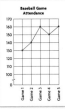

The dot on the vertical "Game 2" line is beside 140. So, 140 people attended the game.

A **circle graph** shows data as parts of a whole. How many people bought peanuts at the fair?

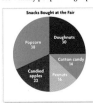

The section of the circle labeled "Peanuts" shows 16. So, 16 people bought peanuts.

Practice

For 1–2, use the line graph.

1. How many people attended Game 4? 150

2. What was the total attendance at all the games? 740

For 3–4, use the circle graph.

3. What was the most popular snack? popcorn

4. Popcorn and one other snack were half the sales. What was the other snack? candied apples

H24 Prerequisite Skills Review

Customary Units

The table shows equivalents in the customary system of measurement. To change from a larger unit to a smaller one, multiply. To change from a smaller unit to a larger one, divide.

UNITS OF LENGTH	UNITS OF CAPACITY	UNITS OF WEIGHT
12 inches (in.) = 1 foot (ft)	2 cups (c) = 1 pint (pt)	16 ounces (oz) = 1 pound (lb)
3 feet = 1 yard (yd)	2 pints = 1 quart (qt)	2,000 pounds = 1 ton (T)
5,280 feet = 1 mile (mi)	4 quarts = 1 gallon (gal)	
1,760 yards = 1 mile		

Examples

Change to the given unit.

A. 24 in. = ▓ ft **Think:** An inch is smaller than a foot. To change from inches to feet, divide by 12.

24 ÷ 12 = 2, so 24 in. = 2 ft.

B. 4 gal = ▓ qt **Think:** A gallon is larger than a quart. To change from gallons to quarts, multiply by 4.

4 × 4 = 16, so 4 gal = 16 qt.

Practice

Change to the given unit.

1. 2 yd = ▓ ft 6   **2.** 4 c = ▓ pt 2   **3.** 4 lb = ▓ oz 64   **4.** 2.5 gal = ▓ qt 10

Metric Units

The table shows how prefixes used with the basic units **meter (m)**, **liter (L)**, and **gram (g)** are related in the metric system. To change units, multiply by 10 for each place you move to the right. Divide by 10 for each place you move to the left.

kilo (k)	hecto (h)	deka (da)	BASIC UNIT	deci (d)	centi (c)	milli (m)

Examples

Change to the given unit.

A. 8 m = ▓ cm **Think:** From meter to centimeter, the move is 2 places to the right. Multiply by 10 × 10, or 100.

8 × 100 = 800, so 8 m = 800 cm.

B. 4,000 mg = ▓ g **Think:** From milligrams to grams, the move is 3 places to the left. Divide by 10 × 10 × 10, or 1,000.

4,000 ÷ 1,000 = 4, so 4,000 mg = 4 g.

Practice

Change to the given unit.

1. 2 m = ▓ dm 20   **2.** 6 L = ▓ mL 6,000   **3.** 3,000 g = ▓ kg 3   **4.** 5,000 mg = ▓ cg 500

Solve Proportions

A **proportion** is a number sentence which states that two ratios are equal. You can solve a proportion by using the fact that in a proportion, the **cross products** are equal.

 cross products

$2 \times 6 = 3 \times 4$

Example

Solve for n. $\frac{2}{3} = \frac{n}{12}$

$\frac{2}{3} \bbox{=} \frac{n}{12}$ Find the cross products.

$2 \times 12 = 3 \times n$ Use the cross products to write an equation.

$24 = 3 \times n$ Simplify.

$\frac{24}{3} = \frac{3 \times n}{3}$ Divide both sides of the equation by 3.

$8 = n$ Write the solution.

Practice

Solve for n.

1. $\frac{n}{3} = \frac{6}{9}$ $n = 2$ **2.** $\frac{4}{n} = \frac{5}{10}$ $n = 8$ **3.** $\frac{8}{10} = \frac{n}{15}$ $n = 12$ **4.** $\frac{20}{15} = \frac{12}{n}$ $n = 9$

5. $\frac{n}{6} = \frac{25}{30}$ $n = 5$ **6.** $\frac{n}{5} = \frac{9}{15}$ $n = 3$ **7.** $\frac{8}{n} = \frac{32}{16}$ $n = 4$ **8.** $\frac{48}{36} = \frac{n}{9}$ $n = 12$

Perimeter

Perimeter is the distance around a figure. To find the perimeter of a polygon, find the sum of the lengths of the sides.

Example

The opposite sides of a rectangle are congruent, so the sides of the figure that are not labeled measure 4 cm and 2 cm.

So, the perimeter is 12 cm. $P = 4\text{ cm} + 2\text{ cm} + 4\text{ cm} + 2\text{ cm}$

4 cm / 2 cm

Practice

Find the perimeter of the figure.

1. 12 cm, 3 cm, 5 cm, 4 cm   **2.** 11 cm, 44 cm   **3.** 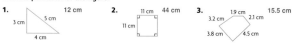 3.2 cm, 1.9 cm, 2.1 cm, 3.8 cm, 4.5 cm, 15.5 cm

4. 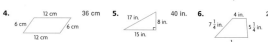 12 cm, 6 cm, 6 cm, 12 cm, 36 cm   **5.** 17 in., 8 in., 15 in., 40 in.   **6.** 4 in., $7\frac{1}{4}$ in., $5\frac{1}{4}$ in., $9\frac{1}{2}$ in., 26 in.

Change Units

When you change from one unit to another, you must decide whether there are more or fewer of the new unit. If there are more units, multiply. If there are fewer units, divide.

Examples

A rug is 4 yd long. How many feet long is this?

1 yd   1 yd   1 yd   1 yd   There will be *more* feet in the measurement than there are yards. Since 1 yd = 3 ft, multiply to find the answer.

ft: 1 1 1   1 1 1   1 1 1   1 1 1

$3 \times 4 = 12$. So, the rug is 12 ft long.

Practice

Change the measurement to the given unit.

1. a 3-ft table, to in. 36 in.   **2.** a 5-gal tank, to qt 20 qt

3. a 15-ft room, to yd 5 yd   **4.** a 1,000-m race, to cm 10,000 cm

Find the Square and Cube of a Number

The **square** of a number is the product of the number used twice as a factor. The **cube** of a number is the product of the number used three times as a factor.

Examples

A. Find the square of 5.

$5 \times 5 = 25$ Find the product, using 5 as a factor twice.

So, 5 squared is 25, or $5^2 = 25$.

B. Find the cube of 4.

$4 \times 4 \times 4 = 64$ Find the product, using 4 as a factor three times.

So, 4 cubed is 64, or $4^3 = 64$.

Practice

Find the square of each number.

1. 7 49   **2.** 14 196   **3.** 25 625   **4.** 80 6,400   **5.** 5.6 31.36

Find the cube of each number.

6. 2 8   **7.** 3 27   **8.** 5 125   **9.** 10 1,000   **10.** 0 0

11. 6 216   **12.** 11 1,331   **13.** $\frac{1}{2}$ $\frac{1}{8}$ **14.** $\frac{3}{5}$ $\frac{27}{125}$ **15.** 0.3 0.027

Areas of Squares, Rectangles, and Triangles

The area of a rectangle or square is the product of the length and the width. The area of a triangle is *half* the product of the base and the height.

l / w / $A = l \times w$ h / b / $A = \frac{1}{2} \times b \times h$

Examples

Find the area of the figure.

A. 6 ft / 5 ft

B. 9 in. / 9 in.

C. 8 cm / 12 cm

$A = 6 \times 5 = 30$, or 30 ft^2 $A = 9 \times 9 = 9^2 = 81$, or 81 in.^{2} $A = \frac{1}{2} \times 12 \times 8 = 48$, or 48 cm^2

Practice

Find the area of the figure.

1. 13 yd, 13 yd, 169 yd^2 **2.** 12 ft, 7 ft, 42 ft^2 **3.** 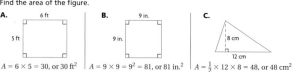 15 cm, 10.4 cm, 156 cm^2 **4.** $14\frac{1}{2}$ in., 4 in., 29 in.^{2}

Areas of Circles

The area of a circle is the product of π and the square of the radius. Use 3.14 for the value of π.

 r / $A = \pi r^2$

Examples

Find the area of the circle.

A. radius = 3 cm

$\approx 3.14 \times 3^2$
$= 3.14 \times 9$
$= 28.26$ cm^2

3 cm

B. The radius is half of the diameter, or 8 in.

$\approx 3.14 \times 8^2$
$= 3.14 \times 64$
$= 200.96$ in.^{2}

16 in.

Practice

Find the area of the circle. Use 3.14 for π.

1. 10 cm, 314 cm^2 **2.** 12 in., 452.16 in.^{2} **3.** 18 cm, 254.34 cm^2 **4.** 42 in., 1,384.74 in.^{2}

Compare Numbers

To compare integers, use a number line. The number to the right on the line is greater.	To compare decimals, align the decimal points. Then compare the digits from left to right.	To compare fractions, rename unlike fractions, then compare the numerators.

Examples

Compare. Write $<$ or $>$ for each $\bullet$.

A. $2 \bullet {}^{-}3$

-4 -3 -2 -1 0 1 2 3

2 is to the right of $^{-}3$, so $2 > {}^{-}3$.

B. $6.25 \bullet 6.179$

6.25
6.179

$0.2 > 0.1$, so $6.25 > 6.179$.

C. $\frac{1}{2} \bullet \frac{2}{3}$

$\frac{1 \times 3}{2 \times 3} = \frac{3}{6}$ $\frac{2 \times 2}{3 \times 2} = \frac{4}{6}$

$3 < 4$, so $\frac{1}{2} < \frac{2}{3}$.

Practice

Compare. Write $<$ or $>$ for each $\bullet$.

1. $485 \bullet 579$ $<$ **2.** $3.03 \bullet 3.3$ $<$ **3.** $\frac{1}{2} \bullet \frac{1}{3}$ $>$ **4.** ${}^{-}11 \bullet {}^{-}3$ $<$ **5.** $5 \bullet {}^{-}4$ $>$

6. $14.97 \bullet 14.9$ $>$ **7.** $523.6 \bullet 532.8$ $<$ **8.** $0.007 \bullet 0.01$ $<$ **9.** ${}^{-}0.5 \bullet {}^{-}0.4$ $<$ **10.** $\frac{3}{4} \bullet \frac{5}{8}$ $>$

Function Tables

To find an output value in a function table, replace the variable with an input value. Then evaluate the algebraic expression.

Example

Complete the function table.

k	$k + 4$
7	■
9	■
11	■
16	■

Replace k in $k + 4$ with 7: $k + 4 = 7 + 4 = 11$.
Replace k in $k + 4$ with 9: $k + 4 = 9 + 4 = 13$.
Replace k in $k + 4$ with 11: $k + 4 = 11 + 4 = 15$.
Replace k in $k + 4$ with 16: $k + 4 = 16 + 4 = 20$.

Input Output

k	$k + 4$
7	11
9	13
11	15
16	20

Practice

Copy and complete the function table.

1.

x	$x + 7$
9	16
13	20
18	25
24	31

2.

b	$b \times 16$
2	32
5	80
8	128
13	208

3.

m	$m \div 6$
192	32
150	25
90	15
51	8.5

4.

r	$r - 7.4$
25.8	18.4
19.2	11.8
13.05	5.65
9.1	1.7

Troubleshooting

Slides, Flips, and Turns

There are three ways that you can **transform** a figure. You can **slide,** or **translate,** the figure along a straight line. You can **flip,** or **reflect,** the figure over a line. Or you can **turn,** or **rotate,** the figure around a point.

Examples

Identify the transformation as a *slide, flip,* or *turn.*

A.

The figure has been translated along a straight line to the right. This is a *slide.*

B.

The figure has been reflected across a vertical line. This is a *flip.*

C.

The figure has been rotated clockwise around a point. This is a *turn.*

Practice

Identify the transformation as a *slide, flip,* or *turn.*

1.  turn **2.** flip or turn **3.** slide **4.** flip

Line Symmetry

A figure has **line symmetry** if it can be folded or reflected so that the two parts of the figure match, or are congruent. A figure can have more than one line of symmetry.

Examples

Is the dashed line a line of symmetry? Write *yes* or *no.*

A. 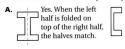 Yes. When the left half is folded on top of the right half, the halves match.

B. No. When the lower left is folded on top of the upper right, the halves do not match.

Practice

Is the dashed line a line of symmetry? Write *yes* or *no.*

1. No **2.** Yes **3.** Yes **4.** No

Measure Angles

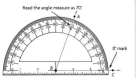
Read the angle measure as 70°.

To measure ∠*ABC* with a protractor, place the center of the protractor at *B.*

Align the 0° mark on the protractor with one ray of the angle.

Read the angle measure where the other ray passes through the scale on the protractor.

Practice

Use a protractor to measure the angle.

1. 60° **2.** 160° **3.** 100° **4.** 25°

Ordered Pairs

You can use two numbers called an **ordered pair** to locate a point on a grid. The first number tells you how far to move horizontally from (0,0). The second number tells you how far to move vertically from (0,0).

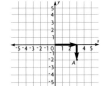

Example

Write the ordered pair for point *A.*

To reach point A from (0,0), go
⁺3 units right (horizontally) and
⁻2 units down (vertically).

So, the ordered pair is (3,⁻2).

Practice

Write the ordered pair for each point.

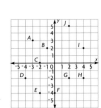

1. point *A* (⁻3,3) **2.** point *C* (⁻2,0)
3. point *D* (⁻4,⁻2) **4.** point *E* (⁻2,⁻4)
5. point *F* (0,⁻4) **6.** point *G* (2,⁻2)
7. point *I* (4,2) **8.** point *J* (2,5)
9. point *B* (⁻1,2) **10.** point *H* (4,⁻2)

CHAPTER 1

Extra Practice

Set A (pp. 16–19)

Estimate. Possible estimates are given.

1. 589 +342 900	**2.** 865 −383 500	**3.** 8,926 +1,674 10,600	**4.** 8,960 9,043 +8,756 27,000	**5.** 3,406 − 792 26,000

6. 4,496 ÷ 51 90 **7.** 47 × 98 5,000 **8.** 321 × 43 12,000 **9.** 3,552 ÷ 58 60 **10.** 6,251 ÷ 12 500

Tell whether the estimate is an overestimate or underestimate.

11. 848 + 692 ≈ 1,550 overestimate **12.** 398 × 66 ≈ 28,000 overestimate **13.** 317 − 67 ≈ 230 underestimate

Set B (pp. 20–21)

Find the sum or difference.

1. 6,343 − 1,145 5,198 **2.** 19,826 − 3,517 16,309 **3.** 22,912 + 84,718 107,630 **4.** 532,047 + 36,603 568,650

5. 6,052 + 2,791 + 3,047 + 654 12,544 **6.** 7,380 − 1,890 − 408 − 792 4,290

Set C (pp. 22–25)

Multiply or divide, writing any remainder as a fraction.

1. 83
×62
5,146 **2.** 16)869 54 5/16 **3.** 45)1,675 37 1/9 **4.** 458
×194
88,852

Set D (pp. 28–29)

Write a numerical or algebraic expression for the word expression.

1. nine dollars less than twelve dollars 12 − 9 **2.** thirteen more than a number, x x + 13 **3.** twenty-two dogs times two bowls 22 × 2 **4.** fifty-two divided by two 52 ÷ 2

Evaluate each expression.

5. 8 × a, for a = 35 280 **6.** p − 38, for p = 97 59 **7.** 175 ÷ k, for k = 5 35 **8.** 96 + m, for m = 48 144

Set E (pp. 30–31)

Determine which of the given values is the solution of the equation.

1. 5w = 70; w = 12, 13, or 14 14 **2.** 16 − a = 7; a = 8, 9, or 10 9 **3.** 48 ÷ x = 8; x = 6, 7, or 8 6

Solve each equation by using mental math.

4. 23 + c = 28 c = 5 **5.** k ÷ 9 = 5 k = 45 **6.** q − 25 = 25 q = 50 **7.** c × 6 = 426 c = 71

H32 Extra Practice

Set A (pp. 36–39)

Use mental math to find the value.

1. 26 + (4 + 18) 48 **2.** 6 × 4 × 5 120 **3.** 28 + 9 + 41 78 **4.** 83 − 36 47

5. 4 + 19 + 26 49 **6.** 38 × 6 228 **7.** 47 − 29 18 **8.** 7 + 22 + 13 42

9. 51 × 8 408 **10.** (6 × 8) × 5 240 **11.** 19 + 31 50 **12.** 92 − 29 63

13. 65 + 17 82 **14.** 10,000 ÷ 25 400 **15.** 3 × 10 × 7 210

16. 51 − 29 22 **17.** 4 × 8 × 2 64 **18.** 19 + 52 + 21 92

19. Ben has three cousins under the age of 13. The product of their ages is 336. How old are they? 8, 7, and 6 years old

Set B (pp. 40–41)

Write the equal factors. Then find the value.

1. 10⁴ 10 × 10 × 10 × 10; 10,000 **2.** 5⁶ 5 × 5 × 5 × 5 × 5 × 5; 15,625 **3.** 2³ 2 × 2 × 2; 8 **4.** 3² 3 × 3; 9 **5.** 7⁴ 7 × 7 × 7 × 7; 2,401

6. 1⁸ 1 × 1 × 1 × 1 × 1 × 1 × 1 × 1; 1 **7.** 27² 27 × 27; 729 **8.** 15¹ 15; 15 **9.** 12³ 12 × 12 × 12; 1,728 **10.** 9⁴ 9 × 9 × 9 × 9; 6,561

Write in exponent form.

11. 3 × 3 × 3 × 3 3⁴ **12.** 10 × 10 10² **13.** 5 × 5 × 5 × 5 × 5 × 5 5⁶

14. 12 × 12 × 12 12³ **15.** 1 × 1 × 1 × 1 1⁴ **16.** 21 × 21 × 21 × 21 × 21 21⁵

17. Harold was hired to take a survey of 625 people. He wants to write this number in exponent form. If the base is 5, what is the exponent? How did you arrive at your answer? 4; explanations will vary

Set C (pp. 44–45)

Give the correct order of operations.

1. 5 × 7 + 3 ÷ 2 multiply, divide, add **2.** (6 + 15) ÷ 3 × 1 − 6 parentheses, divide, multiply, subtract

3. 12² × 10 − 10³ − 100 exponents, multiply, subtract **4.** 10² + 5² ÷ 5² − 5 exponents, divide, add, subtract

Evaluate the expression.

5. 7 + (2 × 2)⁴ − 9 × 9 182 **6.** 90 × 5 − 4 × (18 ÷ 6) 438

7. 3² × (4 + 5)² − 36 693 **8.** 15² ÷ (4² + 9) + 8¹ 17

9. (8² + 3³) × (9 − 5)³ 5,824 **10.** 10³ ÷ (10² ÷ 10¹) + 10² 200

11. Scott bought 5 pounds of nails that cost $2.75 per pound and 3 pounds of screws that cost $3.50 per pound. How much did Scott spend? $24.25

Set A (pp. 52–55)

Write the value of the blue digit.

1. 6.12053 2 hundredths **2.** 0.0231 3 thousandths **3.** 8.7 7 tenths **4.** 0.849 4 hundredths

Write the number in expanded form.

5. 0.00309 0.003 + 0.00009 **6.** 5.015 5 + 0.01 + 0.005 **7.** 3.032 3 + 0.03 + 0.002

8. 20.0518 20 + 0.05 + 0.001 + 0.0008 **9.** 200.05 200 + 0.05 **10.** 5.16 5 + 0.1 + 0.06

Compare the numbers. Write <, >, or = for ●.

11. 5.099 ● 5.999 < **12.** 226.5 ● 226.4 > **13.** 251.36 ● 241.36 >

14. 18.3 ● 18.30 = **15.** 4.18 ● 4.28 < **16.** 49.089 ● 49.098 <

Write the numbers in order from least to greatest.

17. 82.16, 82, 82.15 82, 82.15, 82.16 **18.** 141.14, 114.41, 141.41 114.41, 141.14, 141.41 **19.** 5.09, 5.49, 5.23 5.09, 5.23, 5.49

Set B (pp. 58–59)

Estimate. Possible estimates are given.

1. 3.7 3.15 +2.98 10	**2.** 62.8 × 6 378	**3.** 109.7 − 53.622 56	**4.** 788.3 × 92 72,000
5. 5.92 3.15 +4.07 13	**6.** 21.513 × 9.8 220	**7.** 5.816 3.215 +1.6 11	**8.** 465.09 − 73.46 400

9. 728 ÷ 8.1 90 **10.** 8.1 − 2.456 6 **11.** 20.8 ÷ 7 3 **12.** 123.95 ÷ 61 2

Set C (pp. 60–61)

Write the decimal and percent for the shaded part.

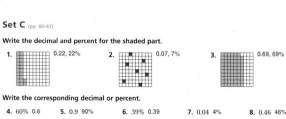

1. 0.22, 22% **2.** 0.07, 7% **3.** 0.69, 69%

Write the corresponding decimal or percent.

4. 60% 0.6 **5.** 0.9 90% **6.** 39% 0.39 **7.** 0.04 4% **8.** 0.46 46%

9. 18% 0.18 **10.** 0.41 41% **11.** 0.38 38% **12.** 7% 0.07 **13.** 90% 0.9

H34 Extra Practice

Set A (pp. 66–69)

Add or subtract. Estimate to check.

1. 12.8 − 4.1 8.7 **2.** $21.85 + $17.48 $39.33 **3.** 17.3 − 16.5 0.8

4. 8.36 + 5.216 + 0.09 13.666 **5.** 8 + 7.317 + 3.06 18.377 **6.** 5.08 − 2.261 2.819

Copy the problem. Place the decimal point correctly in the answer.

7. 13.601 − 10.311 = 329 3.29 **8.** 18.56 + 3.12 = 2168 21.68 **9.** 5 − 3.021 = 1979 1.979

Set B (pp. 70–73)

Tell the number of decimal places there will be in the product.

1. 21.3 × 18.4 2 **2.** 7.03 × 7.05 4 **3.** 9.2 × 2.13 3

Copy the problem. Place the decimal point in the product.

4. 360.05 × 12.6 = 4536630 4,536.630 **5.** 762 × 3.285 = 2503170 2,503.170 **6.** 10.11 × 1.02 = 103122 10.3122

Multiply. Estimate to check.

7. 37.5 × 10.26 384.750 **8.** 6.42 × 9.1 58.422 **9.** 0.05 × 2.9 0.145

10. 19.3 × 2.41 46.513 **11.** 2.39 × 7.6 18.164 **12.** 2 × 6.005 12.010

Set C (pp. 76–79)

Rewrite the problem so that the divisor is a whole number.

1. 16.92 ÷ 0.12 1692 ÷ 12 **2.** 661.44 ÷ 31.2 6614.4 ÷ 312 **3.** 20.2 ÷ 0.53 2020 ÷ 53

Copy the problem. Place the decimal point in the quotient.

4. 4.48 ÷ 2.8 = 16 1.6 **5.** 28.68 ÷ 1.2 = 239 23.9 **6.** 9.87 ÷ 2 = 4935 4.935

Divide. Estimate to check.

7. 9.72 ÷ 1.2 8.1 **8.** 25.0224 ÷ 3.12 8.02 **9.** 20.801 ÷ 6.1 3.41 **10.** 80.4 ÷ 4.8 16.75

Set D (pp. 82–83)

Evaluate each expression.

1. 8m for m = 4.2 33.6 **2.** 6.3 + 5.04 + k for k = 8.4 19.74 **3.** (3.4 − c) + 63 for c = 2.47 63.93

Solve each equation by using mental math.

4. p + 2.8 = 7.9 p = 5.1 **5.** k/3 = 5.6 k = 16.8 **6.** a − 17.1 = 9.5 a = 26.6

7. 6s = 7.2 s = 1.2 **8.** x + 22.6 = 30.8 x = 8.2 **9.** 15n = 4.5 n = 3

Set A (pp. 94–97)

Determine the type of sample. Write *convenience*, *random*, or *systematic*.

1. The teacher randomly selected a student and then surveyed every third student on his attendance list. systematic
2. The teacher asked students in English class about their favorite books. convenience

Set B (pp. 98–99)

A survey is to be conducted about the favorite foods of middle-school students. Tell whether the sampling method is *biased* or *unbiased*.

1. Randomly survey 10 people who get off the school bus one morning. biased
2. Randomly survey 1 of every 10 students in sixth, seventh, and eighth grades. unbiased

Set C (pp. 102–105)

Use the table at the right.

1. Copy and complete the table. Check students' tables.
2. How large was the sample size? 35

Favorite Color	Tally	Frequency	Cumulative Frequency
Blue	✕✕✕ ✕	11	11
Green	✕✕✕ ✕✕✕✕	9	20
Red	✕✕✕ ✕✕✕	8	28
Yellow	✕✕✕✕	5	33
Orange	✕✕	2	35

Set D (pp. 106–108)

Find the mean, median, and mode. Mean, median and mode are listed in order.

1. 4, 5, 7, 8, 8   6.4; 7; 8
2. 6.1, 8.1, 7.4, 7.2   7.2; 7.3; none
3. 12, 14, 18, 12, 22   15.6; 14; 12
4. 1, 1, 7, 9, 3, 4, 2, 3   3.75; 3; 1 and 3

Set E (pp. 109–111)

Use the data in table.

NUMBER OF HOURS SPENT ON HOMEWORK										
Week	1	2	3	4	5	6	7	8	9	10
Hours	8	9	10	9	7	9	8	0	7	2

1. Find the mean, median, and mode with the outliers and then without the outliers. 8.25, 8.5, 9; 6.8, 8, 9
2. How does including the outliers affect the mean? the median? the mode? mean and median decrease; mode doesn't change

Set F (pp. 112–115)

Write *yes* or *no* to tell whether the conclusion is valid. Explain.

1. The first ten females to enter a diner say their favorite drink is orange juice. You conclude that orange juice is the favorite drink of all of the customers. No. The sample is biased.
2. Two hundred students are randomly selected and asked what their favorite kind of music is. Seventy percent say pop music. You conclude that most students prefer pop music. Yes. The sample and the population are unbiased.

H36 Extra Practice

Set A (pp. 120–123)

1. Make a multiple-bar graph using the data in the table below. See Additional Answers, p. H61A.

CLUB MEETING ATTENDANCE	Sept	Oct	Nov	Dec
Male	42	31	65	61
Female	56	47	51	60

2. Make a multiple-line graph using the data in the table below. See Additional Answers, p. H61A.

AVERAGE RAINFALL (IN INCHES)	Jan	Feb	Mar	Apr
City A	4	5	3	5
City B	8	12	4	7

Set B (pp. 124–125)

1. Make a line graph using the data in the table at the right. See Additional Answers, p. H61A.
2. If the trend continues, how many miles will be traveled on the sixth day? about 265 mi

DISTANCE TRAVELED					
Day	1	2	3	4	5
Miles	45	85	129	175	220

Set C (pp. 126–128)

1. Make a stem-and-leaf plot of the data below. Find the mode and median. See Additional Answers, p. H61A.

14	22	37	41	13	18	22	29	33
36	25	21	30	48	44	19	17	28

2. Use the data in the chart below to make a histogram. See Additional Answers, p. H61A.

NUMBER OF HOURS OF MONTHLY EXERCISE					
0–2	3–5	6–8	9–11	12–15	16–18
12	15	19	22	21	6

Set D (pp. 130–131)

For 1–3, use the box-and-whisker graph. The graph shows the number of tickets sold.

1. What was the greatest number of tickets sold? 95
2. What is the median? 92
3. What are the lower and upper quartiles? 86 and 94

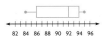

82 84 86 88 90 92 94 96

Set E (pp. 132–135)

For 1–3, use the bar graph at the right.

1. About how many times as high is the bar for Central than the bar for Lee? about 4 times as high
2. Has Central won four times as many championships as Lee? Explain. No. Central has won 60 championships while Lee has won 30 championships.
3. How can you change the graph so it is not misleading? Start the scale at zero and have equal intervals.

NUMBER OF CHAMPIONSHIPS WON

Number Won: 60 50 40 30 20 — Central, Lee — School

Student Handbook **H37**

Set A (pp. 146–147)

Tell whether each number is divisible by 2, 3, 4, 5, 6, 8, 9, or 10.

1. 80   2, 4, 5, 8, 10
2. 99   3, 9
3. 105   3, 5
4. 126   2, 3, 6, 9
5. 234   2, 3, 6, 9
6. 370   2, 5, 10
7. 591   3
8. 1,620   2, 3, 4, 5, 6, 9, 10
9. 3,048   2, 3, 4, 6, 8
10. 8,020   2, 4, 5, 10

Set B (pp. 148–149)

Use division or a factor tree to find the prime factorization.

1. 18   2 × 3 × 3
2. 40   2 × 2 × 2 × 5
3. 36   2 × 2 × 3 × 3
4. 27   3 × 3 × 3
5. 100   2 × 2 × 5 × 5
6. 150   2 × 3 × 5 × 5
7. 280   2 × 2 × 2 × 5 × 7
8. 12   2 × 2 × 3
9. 108   2 × 2 × 3 × 3 × 3
10. 420   2 × 2 × 3 × 5 × 7

Write the prime factorization of each number in exponent form.

11. 28 $2^2 × 7$
12. 420 $2^2 × 3 × 5 × 7$
13. 48 $2^4 × 3$
14. 81 3^4
15. 72 $2^3 × 3^2$
16. 80 $2^4 × 5$
17. 144 $2^4 × 3^2$
18. 221 11^2
19. 168 $2^3 × 3 × 7$
20. 1,475 $5^2 × 59$

Solve for *n* to complete the prime factorization.

21. 2 × 5 × n = 50 n = 5
22. 2 × n × 5 = 30 n = 3
23. 2 × 3 × n = 18 n = 3
24. n × 3 × 3 = 27 n = 3
25. 2 × 2 × 2 × n = 16 n = 2
26. n × 2 × 3 = 42 n = 7
27. 2 × 3 × 3 × n = 54 n = 3
28. 3 × n × 5 = 75 n = 5
29. n × n × 3 = 12 n = 2

Set C (pp. 150–153)

List the first five multiples of each number.

1. 4   4, 8, 12, 16, 20
2. 9   9, 18, 27, 36, 45
3. 14   14, 28, 42, 56, 70
4. 5   5, 10, 15, 20, 25
5. 30   30, 60, 90, 120, 150
6. 8   8, 16, 24, 32, 40
7. 12   12, 24, 36, 48, 60
8. 21   21, 42, 63, 84, 105

Find the LCM of each set of numbers.

9. 45, 54 270
10. 10, 35 70
11. 12, 20 60
12. 18, 27 54
13. 150, 60 300
14. 54, 18 108
15. 55, 33, 44 660
16. 35, 25, 49 1,225

17. Jean needs eggs and muffins for the class breakfast. Eggs come in cartons of 12 and muffins come in packages of 8. What is the least number of eggs and muffins she can buy to have an equal number of each? 24 of each

Find the GCF of each set of numbers.

18. 12, 108 12
19. 148, 84 4
20. 132, 108 12
21. 75, 105 15
22. 45, 108 9
23. 32, 128 32
24. 252, 336 84
25. 56, 280, 400 8

H38 Extra Practice

Set A (pp. 160–163)

Write the fraction in simplest form.

1. $\frac{24}{80}$ $\frac{3}{10}$
2. $\frac{14}{63}$ $\frac{2}{9}$
3. $\frac{24}{56}$ $\frac{3}{7}$
4. $\frac{15}{60}$ $\frac{1}{4}$
5. $\frac{16}{40}$ $\frac{2}{5}$
6. $\frac{50}{90}$ $\frac{5}{9}$

Complete.

7. $\frac{9}{12} = \frac{\blacksquare}{4}$ 3
8. $\frac{7}{42} = \frac{\blacksquare}{6}$ 1
9. $\frac{25}{\blacksquare} = \frac{5}{10}$ 50
10. $\frac{3}{7} = \frac{21}{\blacksquare}$ 49
11. $\frac{1}{12} = \frac{\blacksquare}{144}$ 12
12. $\frac{9}{20} = \frac{\blacksquare}{60}$ 27
13. $\frac{5}{\blacksquare} = \frac{15}{27}$ 9
14. $\frac{12}{\blacksquare} = \frac{3}{8}$ 32

Set B (pp. 164–165)

Write the fraction as a mixed number or a whole number.

1. $\frac{7}{3}$ $2\frac{1}{3}$
2. $\frac{9}{2}$ $4\frac{1}{2}$
3. $\frac{36}{5}$ $7\frac{1}{5}$
4. $\frac{72}{8}$ 9
5. $\frac{10}{2}$ 5
6. $\frac{13}{4}$ $3\frac{1}{4}$
7. $\frac{36}{6}$ 6
8. $\frac{12}{9}$ $1\frac{1}{3}$

Write the mixed number as a fraction.

9. $4\frac{1}{4}$ $\frac{17}{4}$
10. $5\frac{2}{3}$ $\frac{17}{3}$
11. $2\frac{1}{8}$ $\frac{17}{8}$
12. $7\frac{1}{9}$ $\frac{64}{9}$
13. $3\frac{4}{7}$ $\frac{25}{7}$
14. $1\frac{6}{11}$ $\frac{17}{11}$
15. $4\frac{3}{8}$ $\frac{35}{8}$
16. $15\frac{3}{4}$ $\frac{63}{4}$

Set C (pp. 166–167)

Compare the fractions. Write <, >, or = for each ●.

1. $\frac{5}{9}$ ● $\frac{1}{2}$ >
2. $\frac{3}{8}$ ● $\frac{1}{5}$ >
3. $\frac{7}{25}$ ● $\frac{3}{5}$ <
4. $\frac{3}{5}$ ● $\frac{12}{20}$ =

Order the fractions from least to greatest.

5. $\frac{1}{3}, \frac{1}{6}, \frac{1}{10}$ $\frac{1}{10}, \frac{1}{6}, \frac{1}{3}$
6. $\frac{4}{9}, \frac{2}{3}, \frac{3}{8}$ $\frac{3}{8}, \frac{4}{9}, \frac{2}{3}$
7. $\frac{1}{9}, \frac{3}{4}, \frac{5}{12}$ $\frac{1}{9}, \frac{5}{12}, \frac{3}{4}$

Set D (pp. 169–171)

Write the decimal as a fraction.

1. 0.9 $\frac{9}{10}$
2. 0.081 $\frac{81}{1,000}$
3. 0.29 $\frac{29}{100}$

Write as a decimal. Tell whether the decimal terminates or repeats.

4. $\frac{3}{8}$ 0.375, T
5. $\frac{5}{16}$ 0.3125, T
6. $\frac{1}{3}$ 0.3, R
7. $\frac{7}{9}$ 0.7, R

Compare. Write <, >, or = for each ●.

8. $\frac{3}{10}$ ● 0.03 >
9. $\frac{2}{3}$ ● 0.7 <
10. 0.79 ● $\frac{5}{8}$ >
11. 0.15 ● $\frac{3}{20}$ =

Write each fraction as a percent.

12. $\frac{6}{25}$ 24%
13. $\frac{7}{10}$ 70%
14. $\frac{9}{20}$ 45%
15. $\frac{4}{5}$ 80%

Student Handbook **H39**

Set A (pp. 176–179)

Estimate the sum or difference. Possible estimates are given.

1. $\frac{4}{7} - \frac{3}{8}$ 0
2. $3\frac{7}{9} + 1\frac{10}{11}$ 6
3. $5\frac{4}{5} - 3\frac{1}{2}$ $2\frac{1}{2}$
4. $\frac{8}{9} + \frac{3}{5}$ $1\frac{1}{2}$
5. $\frac{4}{9} + \frac{2}{5}$ 1
6. $\frac{8}{9} - \frac{5}{7}$ 0
7. $\frac{4}{9} - \frac{1}{6}$ $\frac{1}{2}$
8. $3\frac{10}{13} + 4\frac{1}{9}$ 8
9. $\frac{3}{7} + \frac{9}{12}$ $\frac{1}{2}$
10. $5\frac{3}{4} - 1\frac{1}{8}$ 5
11. $\frac{5}{9} - \frac{3}{7}$ 0
12. $8\frac{7}{8} + 5\frac{1}{2}$ $14\frac{1}{2}$

13. Shawna practiced the tuba for $\frac{5}{6}$ hr on Monday, $\frac{1}{3}$ hr on Wednesday, and $\frac{1}{4}$ hr on Friday. About how many hours did Shawna practice last week? possible answer: about 2 hours

Set B (pp. 182–185)

Write the sum or difference in simplest form. Estimate to check.

1. $\frac{3}{4} + \frac{1}{2}$ $\frac{5}{4}$, or $1\frac{1}{4}$
2. $\frac{4}{7} - \frac{3}{21}$ $\frac{5}{21}$
3. $\frac{1}{6} + \frac{5}{18}$ $\frac{4}{9}$
4. $\frac{9}{10} - \frac{2}{5}$ $\frac{1}{2}$
5. $\frac{5}{4} + \frac{1}{12}$ $\frac{13}{12}$, or $1\frac{1}{12}$
6. $\frac{6}{20} + \frac{3}{5}$ $\frac{9}{10}$
7. $\frac{5}{9} - \frac{1}{2}$ $\frac{1}{18}$
8. $\frac{7}{8} - \frac{1}{16}$ $\frac{13}{16}$
9. $\frac{3}{5} - \frac{3}{9}$ $\frac{22}{45}$
10. $\frac{5}{20} + \frac{11}{20}$ $\frac{4}{5}$
11. $\frac{11}{12} - \frac{1}{6}$ $\frac{3}{4}$
12. $\frac{1}{10} + \frac{3}{8}$ $\frac{19}{40}$

13. Rico read $\frac{1}{5}$ of a book on Saturday and $\frac{1}{3}$ of the same book on Sunday. What portion of the book does he have left to read? $\frac{7}{15}$ of the book

Set C (pp. 186–189) Check students' diagrams.

Draw a diagram to find each sum or difference. Write the answer in simplest form.

1. $2\frac{3}{8} + 1\frac{1}{4}$ $3\frac{5}{8}$
2. $2\frac{1}{3} - 1\frac{1}{6}$ $1\frac{1}{6}$
3. $1\frac{1}{5} + 1\frac{7}{10}$ $2\frac{9}{10}$
4. $3\frac{1}{3} - 1\frac{3}{4}$ $1\frac{7}{12}$

Write the sum or difference in simplest form. Estimate to check.

5. $4\frac{5}{12} - 2\frac{1}{6}$ $2\frac{1}{4}$
6. $5\frac{2}{5} - 3\frac{3}{10}$ $2\frac{1}{10}$
7. $2\frac{1}{9} + 1\frac{2}{5}$ $3\frac{23}{45}$
8. $4\frac{2}{3} + 6\frac{1}{6}$ $10\frac{5}{6}$

9. Stefan bought $1\frac{1}{2}$ lb of potato salad, $2\frac{1}{4}$ lb of coleslaw, and $4\frac{3}{4}$ lb of chicken at a deli. What is the total weight of his purchase? $8\frac{1}{2}$ lb

Set D (pp. 192–193)

Write the difference in simplest form. Estimate to check.

1. $4\frac{5}{9} - 3\frac{5}{18}$ $\frac{13}{18}$... $1\frac{13}{18}$
2. $5\frac{1}{3} - 4\frac{1}{4}$ $1\frac{2}{9}$
3. $6\frac{1}{4} - 3\frac{2}{3}$ $2\frac{7}{12}$
4. $6\frac{1}{3} - 4\frac{7}{9}$ $1\frac{5}{9}$
5. $4 - 1\frac{3}{7}$ $2\frac{4}{7}$
6. $5\frac{3}{10} - \frac{2}{5}$ $4\frac{9}{10}$
7. $7\frac{1}{6} - \frac{1}{2}$ $6\frac{2}{3}$
8. $4\frac{1}{4} - 1\frac{3}{8}$ $2\frac{5}{8}$

9. Mr. Norman had $51\frac{1}{3}$ ft of plastic pipe. He installed $25\frac{3}{4}$ ft in the bathroom. How much pipe does he have left? $25\frac{7}{12}$ ft

Set A (pp. 200–201)

Estimate each product or quotient. Possible answers are given.

1. $\frac{8}{9} \times \frac{3}{5}$ $\frac{1}{2}$
2. $\frac{1}{6} \times \frac{4}{9}$ 0
3. $5\frac{1}{2} \div \frac{5}{6}$ 1
4. $\frac{7}{9} \div \frac{3}{4}$ 1
5. $3\frac{1}{3} \times 5\frac{1}{2}$ 15
6. $8\frac{3}{5} \div 2\frac{3}{4}$ 4
7. $9\frac{7}{8} \times 10\frac{1}{2}$ 100
8. $18\frac{3}{4} \div 5\frac{1}{8}$ 3

9. Liz is making cookies to give to some new neighbors. The recipe calls for $1\frac{3}{4}$ cups of flour. About how much flour does Liz need if she makes $2\frac{1}{2}$ times the recipe? about 4 cups

Set B (pp. 202–205)

Multiply. Write the answer in simplest form.

1. $\frac{2}{4} \times \frac{3}{4}$ $\frac{3}{8}$
2. $\frac{2}{5} \times \frac{1}{4}$ $\frac{1}{10}$
3. $\frac{3}{8} \times \frac{3}{5}$ $\frac{9}{40}$
4. $3 \times \frac{7}{8}$ $2\frac{5}{8}$
5. $\frac{2}{7} \times 8$ $2\frac{2}{7}$
6. $\frac{5}{6} \times \frac{3}{8}$ $\frac{5}{16}$
7. $\frac{5}{9} \times \frac{1}{5}$ $\frac{1}{9}$
8. $\frac{1}{9} \times \frac{3}{4}$ $\frac{1}{12}$

9. To make a dye for art class, Jan needs $\frac{1}{4}$ tsp of red coloring and $\frac{1}{2}$ that amount of green coloring. How much green coloring does Jan need to make dye? $\frac{1}{8}$ tsp

Set C (pp. 206–207)

Multiply. Write the answer in simplest form.

1. $2\frac{2}{3} \times 2\frac{1}{4}$ 6
2. $2\frac{1}{2} \times \frac{1}{5}$ $\frac{1}{2}$
3. $\frac{1}{5} \times 2\frac{2}{8}$ $\frac{9}{20}$
4. $3\frac{1}{6} \times 5\frac{1}{4}$ $16\frac{5}{8}$
5. $2\frac{3}{4} \times \frac{5}{6}$ $2\frac{7}{24}$
6. $2\frac{2}{7} \times \frac{2}{5}$ $\frac{32}{35}$
7. $3\frac{2}{3} \times 2\frac{2}{5}$ $9\frac{8}{15}$
8. $6\frac{8}{9} \times 2\frac{3}{7}$ $16\frac{46}{63}$

Set D (pp. 210–213)

Find the quotient. Write the answer in simplest form.

1. $\frac{2}{9} \div \frac{1}{18}$ 4
2. $\frac{3}{8} \div \frac{1}{4}$ $1\frac{1}{2}$
3. $2 \div 2\frac{2}{3}$ $\frac{3}{4}$
4. $1\frac{11}{12} \div 1\frac{5}{6}$ $1\frac{1}{22}$
5. $\frac{3}{4} \div \frac{1}{8}$ 6
6. $\frac{5}{6} \div 1\frac{2}{3}$ $\frac{1}{2}$
7. $3\frac{3}{4} \div 2\frac{7}{12}$ $1\frac{14}{31}$
8. $\frac{5}{7} \div \frac{10}{11}$ $\frac{11}{14}$

Set E (pp. 216–217)

Evaluate the expression.

1. $3r$ for $r = \frac{1}{2}$ $1\frac{1}{2}$
2. $\frac{5}{6} + d$ for $d = \frac{3}{10}$ $1\frac{2}{15}$
3. $3\frac{3}{5} \div a$ for $a = \frac{1}{2}$ $7\frac{1}{5}$
4. $y + 3\frac{5}{8}$ for $y = 1\frac{1}{4}$ $4\frac{7}{8}$
5. $2\frac{5}{6}k$ for $k = 1\frac{1}{3}$ $3\frac{7}{9}$
6. $a \div 4\frac{1}{2}$ for $a = 3\frac{3}{5}$ $\frac{4}{5}$

Solve the equation.

7. $c + \frac{3}{4} = 1\frac{1}{4}$ $c = \frac{1}{2}$
8. $\frac{5}{9}s = \frac{5}{27}$ $s = \frac{1}{3}$
9. $x - 6\frac{1}{8} = 12\frac{1}{4}$ $x = 18\frac{3}{8}$

Set A (pp. 228–229)

Write an integer to represent each situation.

1. a temperature increase of 5° $^+5$
2. the wind speed decreases by 12 mph $^-12$
3. depositing $510 into a savings account $^+510$
4. a temperature of 7° below zero $^-7$

Write the opposite integer.

5. $^-3$ $^+3$
6. $^-12$ $^+12$
7. $^+360$ $^-360$
8. $^-1$ $^+1$
9. $^+160$ $^-160$
10. $^-3,047$ $^+3,047$
11. $^-1,119$ $^+1,119$
12. $^-942$ $^+942$

Set B (pp. 230–233)

Write each rational number in the form $\frac{a}{b}$.

1. $3\frac{1}{6}$ $\frac{19}{6}$
2. 0.5 $\frac{5}{10}$
3. 0.27 $\frac{27}{100}$
4. 13.4 $\frac{134}{10}$
5. $2\frac{2}{5}$ $\frac{12}{5}$
6. 3.18 $\frac{318}{100}$
7. 10.02 $\frac{1,002}{100}$
8. 300 $\frac{300}{1}$
9. 0.36 $\frac{36}{100}$
10. $5\frac{1}{3}$ $\frac{16}{3}$
11. 312 $\frac{312}{1}$
12. $4\frac{1}{4}$ $\frac{17}{4}$

Find a rational number between the two given numbers. Possible answers are given.

13. $\frac{3}{8}$ and $\frac{5}{6}$ $\frac{5}{12}$
14. $\frac{1}{8}$ and $\frac{1}{4}$ $\frac{3}{16}$
15. $\frac{5}{9}$ and $\frac{11}{15}$ $\frac{5}{8}$
16. 1.8 and 1.9 1.85
17. $^-1.5$ and $^-1.3$ $^-1.4$
18. 4.23 and 4.235 4.231
19. 3.8 and 3.82 3.81
20. $^-5$ and $^-4.9$ $^-4.94$
21. $^-12\frac{1}{4}$ and $^-12\frac{1}{3}$ $^-12\frac{3}{10}$

Set C (pp. 234–235)

Compare. Write <, >, or = for each ●.

1. $0.4 ● 0.38$ >
2. $\frac{2}{7} ● 0.25$ >
3. $^-0.6 ● \frac{-2}{5}$ >
4. $\frac{7}{9} ● 0.8$ <
5. $0.28 ● \frac{2}{7}$ <
6. $\frac{3}{13} ● 0.13$ >
7. $\frac{-4}{9} ● ^-3.1$ >
8. $^-3 ● 0.31$ <
9. $2\frac{1}{5} ● 2\frac{4}{13}$ <
10. $0.87 ● 0.868$ >
11. $\frac{-5}{8} ● \frac{5}{8}$ <
12. $2\frac{1}{16} ● 2\frac{1}{10}$ <

Compare the rational numbers and order them from least to greatest.

13. $\frac{1}{3}, \frac{5}{8}, 0.38, \frac{1}{2}$ $\frac{1}{3}, 0.38, \frac{1}{2}, \frac{5}{8}$
14. $\frac{2}{7}, \frac{1}{3}, 0.26$ $\frac{1}{4}, 0.26, \frac{2}{7}, \frac{1}{3}$
15. $0.92, \frac{9}{8}, 0.924$ $\frac{8}{9}, 0.92, 0.924, \frac{9}{8}$
16. $0.23, \frac{2}{9}, \frac{1}{4}, \frac{1}{5}$ $\frac{1}{5}, 0.23, \frac{2}{9}, \frac{1}{4}$
17. $\frac{-2}{5}, \frac{-1}{3}, \frac{-1}{2}$ $\frac{-3}{5}, \frac{-1}{2}, \frac{-2}{5}, \frac{-1}{3}$
18. $\frac{1}{10}, ^-3, ^-0.3$ $^-3, ^-0.3, \frac{1}{10}$
19. $^-7, 6, 1, ^-5$ $^-7, ^-5, 1, 6$
20. $^-0.1, 0.01, 10, ^-10$ $^-10, ^-0.1, 0.01, 10$
21. $\frac{1}{2}, \frac{1}{6}, 0.1$ $0.1, \frac{1}{9}, \frac{1}{6}, \frac{1}{2}$

Set A (pp. 244–247)

Write the addition problem modeled on the number line.

1.
$3 + 2 = 5$

2.
$^-4 + 9 = 5$

Find the sum.

3. $^-3 + 9$ 6
4. $1 + ^-5$ $^-4$
5. $5 + 4$ 9
6. $^-2 + 8$ 6
7. $^-9 + 17$ 8
8. $^-14 + ^-8$ $^-22$
9. $^-19 + 8$ $^-11$
10. $22 + ^-36$ $^-14$
11. $31 + 19$ 50
12. $32 + ^-45$ $^-13$
13. $63 + ^-47$ 16
14. $^-71 + 32$ $^-39$

 **Algebra** Use mental math to find the value of x.

15. $^-2 + x = ^-5$ $x = ^-3$
16. $x + ^-3 = ^-12$ $x = ^-9$
17. $x + ^-12 = ^-8$ $x = ^+4$
18. $^-9 + x = ^-2$ $x = ^+7$
19. Walter had a trading card that was worth $15 in September. In December, the card had decreased $7 in value. Write an addition problem to find the new value. $15 + ^-7$; $8
20. At 9:00 A.M., the temperature outside was $^-9$°C. By 3:00 P.M., the temperature had risen 5°C. What was the temperature at 3:00 P.M.? $^-4$°C

Set B (pp. 250–251)

Rewrite the subtraction problem as an addition problem.

1. $14 - 17$ $14 + ^-17$
2. $6 - ^-8$ $6 + 8$
3. $^-1 - ^-13$ $^-1 + 13$
4. $^-4 - 17$ $^-4 + ^-17$

Find the difference.

5. $2 - 9$ $^-7$
6. $^-8 - ^-3$ $^-5$
7. $4 - ^-2$ 6
8. $4 - 9$ $^-5$
9. $8 - 19$ $^-11$
10. $14 - ^-2$ 16
11. $^-12 - ^-12$ 0
12. $3 - 7$ $^-4$
13. $23 - 32$ $^-9$
14. $14 - 29$ $^-15$
15. $^-48 - 17$ $^-65$
16. $^-24 - ^-39$ 15

Evaluate.

17. $^-2 - ^-7 + ^-9$ $^-4$
18. $8 - ^-2 + ^-6$ 4
19. $3 - ^-9 - 12$ 0
20. $1 - ^-7 - 15$ $^-7$

21. At noon in the city of Hunterville, the temperature was 5°F. By 6:00 P.M., the temperature was $^-3$°F. What was the range of temperature from noon to 6:00 P.M.? $^-8$°F

22. The water level in the city water tower was 8 ft above normal. Three weeks later, the level was 4 ft below normal. Find the range of the water levels. 12 ft

Set A (pp. 258–259)

Find the product.

1. $^-6 \times 9$ $^-54$
2. $3 \times {}^-4$ $^-12$
3. 8×3 24
4. $^-10 \times 5$ $^-50$
5. 11×6 66
6. $^-10 \times {}^-7$ 70
7. $^-9 \times {}^-12$ 108
8. $^-9 \times 4$ $^-36$
9. $^-7 \times 6$ $^-42$
10. $^-6 \times {}^-8$ 48
11. $^-20 \times 4$ $^-80$
12. $50 \times {}^-8$ $^-400$
13. 32×10 320
14. $40 \times {}^-9$ $^-360$
15. $^-84 \times 7$ $^-588$
16. $^-71 \times {}^-15$ 1,065

17. The depth of a diver changed $^-5$ ft every 30 sec. How much of a depth change did the diver have after 2 min? $^-20$ ft

Algebra Use mental math to find the value of *y*.

18. $y \times {}^-5 = {}^-20$ $y = 4$
19. $y \times {}^-7 = 42$ $y = {}^-6$
20. $^-9 \times y = 72$ $y = {}^-8$
21. $^-5 \times y = {}^-25$ $y = 5$

Set B (pp. 260–261)

Find the quotient.

1. $^-54 \div 9$ $^-6$
2. $12 \div {}^-4$ $^-3$
3. $24 \div 3$ 8
4. $^-50 \div 5$ $^-10$
5. $63 \div 7$ 9
6. $^-42 \div {}^-6$ 7
7. $^-96 \div {}^-12$ 8
8. $^-88 \div 8$ $^-11$
9. $^-27 \div 9$ $^-3$
10. $^-64 \div {}^-8$ 8
11. $^-140 \div 10$ $^-14$
12. $225 \div {}^-25$ $^-9$
13. $360 \div 15$ 24
14. $216 \div {}^-12$ $^-18$
15. $^-980 \div {}^-14$ 70
16. $^-7,584 \div 24$ $^-316$

17. A water tower is leaking. The water level is changing $^-5$ ft per day. How many days will it take the water level to change $^-30$ ft? 6 days

Algebra Use mental math to find the value of *x*.

18. $x \div {}^-7 = {}^-4$ $x = 28$
19. $x \div {}^-6 = 8$ $x = {}^-48$
20. $^-30 \div x = 3$ $x = {}^-10$
21. $^-28 \div x = 7$ $x = {}^-4$

Set C (pp. 262–263)

Evaluate the expression.

1. $^-12 - 8 \div {}^-2 \times 10 + 40$ 68
2. $(^-8 + 6) \times 3 \div (56 - 57)$ 6
3. $5^3 + 14 - 200 \times 2$ $^-261$
4. $(^-54 + 24) \div (^-3 - {}^-8)$ $^-6$
5. $15^2 \div (^-12 + 7) \times (^-6 - 2)$ 360
6. $5 \times (30 - 42) \div 2^2$ $^-15$
7. $(^-29 + 35)^2 \div (172 - 175)$ $^-12$
8. $^-8 \times (6 - 11)^2 + 235$ 35
9. $(9 + 7 \times {}^-8) \times (^-5 + 8)^2$ $^-423$

Use a property to simplify the expression. Then evaluate the expression and identify the property you used. Possible properties are given.

10. $(645 + 19) + 11$ 675; Associative
11. $175 + 456 + 25$ 656; Commutative
12. $^-34 + 99 + 34$ 99; Commutative

Set A (pp. 274–275)

Write an algebraic expression for the word expression.

1. 9 less than *y* $y - 9$
2. 13 more than a number, *x* $x + 13$
3. $\frac{3}{4}$ increased by *y* $\frac{3}{4} + y$
4. 7 more than the quotient of 52 and *k* $\frac{52}{k} + 7$
5. Fred has 32 more than twice the number of baseball cards that José has. Write an algebraic expression for the number of baseball cards Fred has. $32 + 2b$

Write a word expression for each. Possible word expressions are given.

6. $9^2 + a$ the sum of 9 squared and *a*
7. $7x + 12$ 12 added to 7 times a number *x*
8. $24 - \frac{1}{5}c$ 24 decreased by $\frac{1}{5}c$
9. $y + \frac{1}{2}x$ *y* increased by $\frac{1}{2}x$

Set B (pp. 276–279)

Evaluate the algebraic expression for the given value of the variable.

1. $x - 6$ for $x = {}^-12$ $^-18$
2. $y + 13$ for $y = {}^-25$ $^-12$
3. $42 - k$ for $k = {}^-30$ 72
4. $^-38 + p$ for $p = 22$ $^-16$
5. $a^2 - 25$ for $a = 3$ $^-16$
6. $x^3 - 19$ for $x = 2$ $^-11$
7. $3(a + b)^2 - c$ for $a = {}^-3$, $b = 5$, and $c = {}^-8$ 20
8. $6xyz$ for $x = {}^-4$, $y = {}^-3$, and $z = {}^-6$ $^-432$
9. $3pq + r$ for $p = 2$, $q = {}^-8$, and $r = {}^-15$ $^-63$

Evaluate the algebraic expression for *x* = 2, 3, 4, and 5.

10. $7x + 12$ 26, 33, 40, 47
11. $^-4x + 10$ 2, $^-2$, $^-6$, $^-10$
12. $3x - 26$ $^-20$, $^-17$, $^-14$, $^-11$
13. $^-9x - 4$ $^-22$, $^-31$, $^-40$, $^-49$
14. $\frac{60}{x} - 14$ 16, 6, 1, $^-2$
15. $\frac{^-60}{x} - 14$ $^-44$, $^-34$, $^-29$, $^-26$

Simplify the expression. Then evaluate the expression for the given value of the variable.

16. $5x + 3x + 12$ for $x = {}^-4$ $8x + 12$; $^-20$
17. $2y + 7y - 25$ for $y = 2$ $9y - 25$; $^-7$
18. $42z - 30z - 20$ for $z = {}^-2$ $12z - 20$; $^-44$

Set C (pp. 282–283)

Evaluate the expression.

1. $\sqrt{100} - 2 + 6$ 14
2. $3 \times (9^2 - 41)$ 120
3. $4 \times \sqrt{25} - 3 \cdot 2$ 14
4. $\sqrt{36} \cdot \sqrt{36}$ 36
5. $530 \times (\sqrt{4} - 2)^2$ 0
6. $8 + \sqrt{49} - 3^2$ 6

Evaluate the expression for *a* = 16, *b* = 3, and *c* = 6.

7. $^-a + (b + c)^2$ 65
8. $\frac{c}{b} - \sqrt{a}$ $^-2$
9. $\sqrt{a + b + c}$ 5

Set A (pp. 288–289)

Write an equation for the word sentence. Choice of variable may vary.

1. $\frac{2}{3}$ of a number is 12. $\frac{2}{3}n = 12$
2. 1.6 more than a number is 5. $1.6 + n = 5$
3. $1\frac{1}{2}$ less than a number is 6. $n - 1\frac{1}{2} = 6$
4. A number divided by $^-6$ is 30. $\frac{n}{^-6} = 30$
5. 9 times a number is 53. $9n = 53$
6. 1.5 increased by a number is 4.2. $1.5 + n = 4.2$
7. $3\frac{1}{2}$ decreased by a number is $\frac{1}{2}$. $3\frac{1}{2} - n = \frac{1}{2}$
8. The quotient of a number and 3.3 is 99. $\frac{n}{3.3} = 99$
9. The sum of 11.2 and a number is 65.07. $11.2 + n = 65.07$
10. 64 divided by a number is 3.2. $\frac{64}{n} = 3.2$
11. Leroy sold 250 boxes of apples during a fund-raiser. This was 5 times as many apples as Mary sold. Write an equation that represents the situation. $5m = 250$

Set B (pp. 291–293)

Solve and check.

1. $x + 6 = 15$ $x = 9$
2. $15 = a + 2$ $a = 13$
3. $11 + k = 25$ $k = 14$
4. $z + 2.7 = 19.6$ $z = 16.9$
5. $5.7 = b + 8.6$ $b = 2.9$
6. $24.8 = 17.2 + c$ $c = 7.6$
7. $y + 8\frac{2}{3} = 16$ $y = 7\frac{1}{3}$
8. $13\frac{1}{4} = 4\frac{4}{5} + s$ $s = 8\frac{9}{20}$
9. $13\frac{3}{8} = t + 7\frac{5}{6}$ $t = 5\frac{13}{24}$
10. $13.2 = x + 7.12$ $x = 6.08$
11. $t + 7\frac{1}{3} = 10\frac{1}{12}$ $t = 2\frac{3}{4}$
12. $4.06 + r = 13.56$ $r = 9.5$
13. A carpenter cut a 72-in. board into two pieces. One of the pieces is 24 in. long. How long is the second piece? 48 in.

Set C (pp. 294–295)

Solve and check.

1. $x - 7 = 11$ $x = 18$
2. $31 = a - 7$ $a = 38$
3. $k - 10 = 42$ $k = 52$
4. $z - 3.9 = 15.8$ $z = 19.7$
5. $6.5 = b - 21.3$ $b = 27.8$
6. $56.7 = c - 19.8$ $c = 76.5$
7. $y - 5\frac{5}{6} = 13$ $y = 18\frac{5}{6}$
8. $22\frac{1}{3} = s - 4\frac{3}{4}$ $s = 27\frac{1}{12}$
9. $8\frac{3}{5} = t - 4\frac{5}{7}$ $t = 13\frac{11}{35}$
10. $a - 27 = 18$ $a = 45$
11. $60.3 = b - 8.07$ $b = 68.37$
12. $4\frac{7}{9} = x + 1\frac{2}{3}$ $x = 6\frac{4}{9}$
13. Reggie withdrew $175 from his checking account so he could go shopping for the new school year. His new balance was $234. How much was in the account before the withdrawal? $409

Set A (pp. 301–303)

Solve and check.

1. $3x = 12$ $x = 4$
2. $7k = 56$ $k = 8$
3. $\frac{p}{16} = {}^-3$ $p = {}^-48$
4. $\frac{a}{14} = 2$ $a = 28$
5. $27 = {}^-3x$ $x = {}^-9$
6. $8.8 = 2.2n$ $n = 4$
7. $4x = 24$ $x = 6$
8. $8x = {}^-32$ $s = {}^-4$
9. $9 = \frac{p}{3}$ $p = 27$
10. $56 = {}^-7p$ $p = {}^-8$
11. $21 = \frac{s}{3}$ $s = 63$
12. $45 = 9n$ $n = 5$
13. $180 = 3d$ $d = 60$
14. $46.2 = \frac{a}{3}$ $a = 138.6$
15. $1,486 = \frac{a}{2}$ $a = 2,972$
16. $\frac{c}{1.2} = 5.6$ $c = 6.72$
17. $^-12a = {}^-216$ $a = 18$
18. $3.8m = 57$ $m = 15$

For 19–20, write and solve an equation to answer the question. Variables will vary.

19. Celia divided her baseball cards equally among 4 friends. Each friend got 23 baseball cards. How many baseball cards did Celia have originally? $\frac{b}{4} = 23$; $b = 92$; 92 baseball cards

20. Julie earns $6.75 per hour at her job. She wants to save $324.00. How many hours does she have to work to earn $324.00? $6.75h = 324$; $h = 48$; 48 hours

Set B (pp. 304–307)

Use the formula *d* = *rt* to complete.

1. $d = \blacksquare$ mi
   $r = 35$ mi per hr
   $t = 4$ hr 140 mi
2. $d = 1{,}600$ km
   $r = \blacksquare$ km per min
   $t = 400$ min 4 km per min
3. $d = 2{,}100$ km
   $r = 70$ km per min
   $t = \blacksquare$ sec 30 sec
4. $d = \blacksquare$ ft
   $r = 90.7$ ft per sec
   $t = 31$ sec 2,811.7 ft
5. $d = 567$ mi
   $r = \blacksquare$ mi per hr
   $t = 17.5$ hr 32.4 mi per hr
6. $d = 4{,}850$ m
   $r = 250$ m per sec
   $t = \blacksquare$ sec 19.4 sec

Convert the temperature to degrees Fahrenheit. Write your answer as a decimal.

7. 40°C 104°F
8. 2.3°C 36.1°F
9. 14°C 57.2°F
10. 20°C 68°F

Convert the temperature to degrees Celsius. Write your answer as a decimal and round to the nearest tenth of a degree.

11. 42°F 5.6°C
12. 47°F 8.3°C
13. 79°F 26.1°C
14. 100°F 37.8°C

15. The Concorde jet has a cruising speed of 1,354 mi per hr. Suppose the Concorde maintained this speed for $3\frac{1}{2}$ hr. How far would the Concorde travel? 4,739 mi

16. The air conditioner is on only when the room temperature is greater than 75°F. Room temperature is 22°C. Is the air conditioner on? Explain. No. 22°C is equal to 71.6°F, which is less than 75°F.

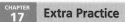

Set A (pp. 322–323)

For 1–4, use the figure at the right. Tell how many of each you can name. Then name them.

R S T W

1. points 4; *R, S, T, W*
2. line segments 6; $\overline{RS}, \overline{ST}, \overline{TW}, \overline{RT}, \overline{SW}, \overline{RW}$
3. rays 6; $\overrightarrow{RS}, \overrightarrow{ST}, \overrightarrow{TW}, \overrightarrow{WT}, \overrightarrow{TS}, \overrightarrow{SR}$
4. lines 1; Possible name: $\overleftrightarrow{RW}$

Name the geometric figure.

5. $\overline{DH}$ or $\overline{HD}$
6. possible answer: plane *GSZ*
7. $\overleftrightarrow{CK}$ or $\overleftrightarrow{KC}$
8. point *F*

Set B (pp. 326–329)

Tell if the angles are *vertical, adjacent, complementary, supplementary,* or *none of these.*

1. ∠CFD and ∠DFE adjacent
2. ∠AFB and ∠CFD vertical
3. ∠EFA and ∠CFD none of these
4. AFB and BFC supplementary and adjacent

Find the unknown angle measure. The type of angle pair is given.

5. complementary 70°
6. complementary 45°
7. supplementary 145°
8. supplementary 105°

Find the measure of each angle.

9. ∠QSP 60°
10. ∠LSR 90°
11. ∠QSN 150°
12. ∠RSP 90°
13. ∠MSN 30°
14. ∠RSN 180°

Set C (pp. 330–331)

Use the figure.

1. Name all the lines that are parallel to $\overleftrightarrow{BE}$. $\overleftrightarrow{AG}$
2. Name a line that is perpendicular to and intersects $\overleftrightarrow{BE}$. $\overleftrightarrow{AF}$
3. Name all the lines that are perpendicular to $\overleftrightarrow{AD}$. $\overleftrightarrow{BE}$
4. Name a line that is parallel to $\overleftrightarrow{AC}$. $\overleftrightarrow{GE}$
5. Name all the lines that intersect $\overleftrightarrow{GE}$. $\overleftrightarrow{AD}$, $\overleftrightarrow{AG}$, $\overleftrightarrow{BE}$,

Set A (pp. 336–339)

Find the measure of the unknown angle and classify the triangle.

1. 40°; right
2. 35°; obtuse
3. 72°; acute
4.  116°; obtuse

Set B (pp. 342–345)

Give the most exact name for the figure.

1. trapezoid
2. parallelogram
3. rectangle
4. quadrilateral

Complete the statement, giving the most exact name for the figure.

5. If a rhombus has four right angles, then it is a __?__. square
6. If a parallelogram has four congruent sides, then it is a __?__. rhombus
7. If a polygon has four sides, then it is a __?__. quadrilateral
8. If a parallelogram has four right angles, then it is a __?__. rectangle

Set C (pp. 346–347)

Draw the figure. Use square dot paper or isometric dot paper. Check students' drawings.

1. a rectangle
2. a trapezoid
3. a right triangle with all sides different lengths
4. a pentagon with no congruent sides
5. a triangle with all sides the same length
6. a rhombus

Set D (pp. 348–349)

Name the given parts of the circle.

1. center *O*
2. chords $\overline{RS}, \overline{ST}, \overline{TU}, \overline{QS}$
3. radii $\overline{OQ}, \overline{OS}, \overline{OR}$ Possible answers: $\overline{RS}, \overline{SU}, \overline{UT}$
4. diameters $\overline{QS}$
5. three arcs
6. Name a sector. Possible answer: *RS*

Set A (pp. 354–356)

Name the figure. Is it a polyhedron?

1. pentagonal prism; yes
2. rectangular prism; yes
3. cylinder; no
4. hexagonal prism; yes
5. square pyramid; yes
6. cone; no
7. triangular prism; yes
8. pentagonal pyramid; yes

Write *true* or *false* for each statement. Rewrite each false statement as a true statement. Possible true statements are given.

9. In a pentagonal prism, the bases are congruent. true
10. A cylinder may have a polygon as its base. False; a cylinder has circles as its bases.
11. All pyramids have rectangular bases. False; some pyramids have rectangular bases.
12. The lateral surface of a cylinder is curved. true
13. A prism with square bases may be a cube. true
14. An octagonal prism has six faces. False; an octagonal prism has 10 faces.

Set B (pp. 357–359)

Name the solid figure that has the given views.

1. cylinder
2. pentagonal prism
3. rectangular prism

Draw the top, front, and side views for each solid.

4.
5.
6.

Set A (pp. 374–376)

Write each ratio in fraction form. Then find the unit rate.

1. $2.50 for 10 $\frac{2.50}{10}$; $0.25
2. $2.76 for 12 $\frac{2.70}{12}$; $0.23
3. 360 people in 3 sq mi 120 people per sq mi
4. 240 miles in 6 hr $\frac{240}{6}$; 40 mi per hr
5. $2.75 for 25 $\frac{2.75}{25}$; $0.11
6. 500 miles on 20 gallons $\frac{500}{20}$; 25 mi per gal

Set B (pp. 380–383)

The figures are similar. Write the ratio of the corresponding sides in simplest form.

1. $\frac{5}{3}$
2. $\frac{3}{1}$, or 3

Tell whether the figures in each pair are similar. Write *yes* or *no*. If you write *no*, explain.

3. yes
4. No. Not all angles are congruent.

Set C (pp. 384–386)

The figures are similar. Use a proportion to find the unknown length.

1. n = 8 ft
2. n = 8 m
3. n = 52 in.

Set D (pp. 387–389)

Find the unknown dimension.

1. scale: 1 in.:5 ft drawing length: 7 in. actual length: ■ ft 35
2. scale: 1 in.:5 ft drawing length: 4 in. actual length: ■ ft 20
3. scale: 1 in.:5 ft drawing length: ■ in. actual length: 15 ft 3

Set E (pp. 390–391)

The map distance is given. Find the actual distance. The scale is 1 in. = 25 mi. $\frac{1}{25} = \frac{1.5}{n}$; 37.5 mi $\frac{1}{25} = \frac{3}{n}$; 75 mi $\frac{1}{25} = \frac{5.5}{n}$; 137.5 mi 175 mi.

1. $1\frac{1}{2}$ in.
2. 3 in.
3. $5\frac{1}{2}$ in.
4. 7 in.

Set A (pp. 396–397)

Write the percent that is shaded.

1. 50% 2. 73% 3. 75% 4. 12.5%

Set B (pp. 398–401)

Write as a percent.

1. 0.3 30% 2. 0.09 9% 3. 0.43 43% 4. $\frac{7}{20}$ 35% 5. $\frac{3}{8}$ $37\frac{1}{2}$%

Set C (pp. 402–405)

Find the percent.

1. 20% of 8 1.6 2. 30% of 90 27 3. 45% of 75 33.75 4. 50% of 58 29

5. Of all the cookies Wendy baked, 40% were chocolate chip. If she baked 200 cookies, how many were chocolate chip? 80

Set D (pp. 408–411)

Find the sale price.

1. regular price: $31.00 25% off $23.25
2. regular price: $65.00 50% off $32.50
3. regular price: $42.00 75% off $10.50

Find the regular price.

4. sale price: $45.00 25% off $60
5. sale price: $24.95 50% off $49.90
6. sale price: $14.40 20% off $18.00

Set E (pp. 412–413)

Find the simple interest.

	Principal	Rate	Interest for 1 Year	Interest for 5 Years		
1.	$65,000.00	4%			$2,600.00	$13,000.00
2.	$735.00	7%			$51.45	$257.25
3.	$1,300.00	3.9%			$50.70	$253.50
4.	$2,250.00	2.3%			$51.75	$258.75

5. Nancy put $2,500 in a savings account for 3 years at a simple interest rate of 8%. How much interest did she earn? $600

Set A (pp. 418–421)

For 1–5, use the spinner at the right. Find each probability. Write each answer as a fraction, a decimal, and a percent.

1. P(Dee) $\frac{1}{8}$, 0.125, 12.5%
2. P(Miles or Lili) $\frac{1}{4}$, 0.25, 25%
3. P(not Cara) $\frac{7}{8}$, 0.875, 87.5%
4. P(Marta) 0, 0.00, 0%
5. P(Hugo, Miwa, or Chen) $\frac{3}{8}$, 0.375, 37.5%

A number cube is labeled 5, 10, 25, 50, 100, and 2,000. Find each probability. Write each answer as a fraction.

6. P(25) $\frac{1}{6}$ 7. P(5 or 25) $\frac{1}{3}$ 8. P(a number ending in zero) $\frac{2}{3}$
9. P(1,000) 0 10. P(1,000 or 2,000) $\frac{1}{6}$ 11. P(not 500) 1

Cards showing pictures of team mascots are placed in a hat. There are 3 lions, 5 bears, 4 cheetahs, and 8 tigers. You choose one card without looking. Find each probability.

12. P(bear) $\frac{1}{4}$ 13. P(tiger or lion) $\frac{11}{20}$ 14. P(member of cat family) $\frac{15}{20}$, or $\frac{3}{4}$

A bag contains some buttons: 8 blue, 12 brown, 10 red, 4 green, and 6 yellow. You choose one button without looking. Find each probability.

15. P(yellow) $\frac{3}{20}$ 16. P(black) 0 17. P(not brown) $\frac{7}{10}$

Set B (pp. 426–427)

A spinner is divided into 5 equal sections. Each section is labeled with one of the letters A, E, I, O, and U. Anna spins the pointer 100 times and records her results in the table below.

Letter	A	E	I	O	U
Times Landed On	15	5	30	40	10

Find the experimental probability.

1. P(A) $\frac{3}{20}$ 2. P(E) $\frac{1}{20}$ 3. P(I) $\frac{3}{10}$ 4. P(O) $\frac{2}{5}$
5. P(U) $\frac{1}{10}$ 6. P(A or U) $\frac{1}{4}$ 7. P(E, I or U) $\frac{9}{20}$ 8. P(not A) $\frac{17}{20}$

9. Based on her experimental results, how many times can Anna expect the pointer to land on O in the next 20 spins? 8 times
10. Based on her experimental results, how many times can Anna expect the pointer to land on E if she spins 2,000 times? 100 times

---

Set A (pp. 434–436)

Draw a tree diagram or make a table to find the number of possible outcomes for each situation. Check students' diagrams.

1. choosing vanilla, chocolate, or strawberry yogurt, with cherry or chocolate sauce, and sprinkles or nuts 12 outcomes
2. tossing a penny and spinning the pointer on the spinner 16 outcomes

Use the Fundamental Counting Principle to find the number of outcomes for each situation.

3. a choice of pancakes, french toast, or waffles, and juice, milk, or tea 9 outcomes
4. a choice of 6 salads and 10 dressings 60 outcomes
5. rolling 2 number cubes labeled A to F 36 outcomes

Set B (pp. 437–439)

Write independent or dependent to describe the events.

1. You have a bag of 6 red marbles and 4 green marbles. You draw one marble, record the color, place the marble back in the bag, and draw again. independent
2. Ana draws one name from a box to select the winner of a movie pass and then draws another name from the same box for the winner of a CD. dependent

A box contains five cards labeled C, L, A, S, S. Without looking in the box, you select a card, replace it, and then select again. For 3–8, find the probability of each event. Then find the probability assuming the first card is not replaced.

3. P(C, L) $\frac{1}{25}$, $\frac{1}{20}$ 4. P(L, C) $\frac{1}{25}$, $\frac{1}{20}$ 5. P(A, S) $\frac{2}{25}$, $\frac{1}{10}$
6. P(S, L) $\frac{2}{25}$, $\frac{1}{10}$ 7. P(C, L or S) $\frac{3}{25}$, $\frac{3}{20}$ 8. P(C or L, S) $\frac{4}{25}$, $\frac{1}{5}$

Set C (pp. 440–441)

Seventy-five students from Park Middle School were randomly surveyed about favorite pizza toppings. The results are shown in the table.

FAVORITE PIZZA TOPPINGS	
Topping	Number of Students
Pepperoni	30
Black Olives	15
Sausage	12
Mushrooms	10
Other	8

1. Suppose there are 225 students who attend Park Middle School. Predict the number of students who prefer black olives as a pizza topping. about 45 students
2. Suppose there are 314 students at Park Middle School. Predict the number of students who prefer sausage as a pizza topping. about 50 students

---

Set A (pp. 452–453)

Use a proportion to convert to the given unit.

1. 15 ft = m yd 5 2. 12 c = r pt 6 3. 8 gal = h qt 32
4. 120 oz = x lb $7\frac{1}{2}$ 5. 6 days = b hr 144 6. 12 in. = p yd $\frac{1}{3}$

Set B (pp. 454–455)

Use a proportion to convert to the given unit.

1. 0.22 m = c km 0.00022 2. 450 mm = h cm 45 3. 0.0030 kL = p L 3
4. 1,800 g = ■ kg 1.8 5. 10,000 cm = ■ m 100 6. 0.35 L = ■ mL 350
7. Paul buys 2 L of orange juice. He drinks 250 mL with breakfast. How many milliliters are left? 1,750 mL
8. Tiffany runs 5,000 m. Ashley runs 3.5 km. Who runs farther and by how many meters? Tiffany; 1,500 m

Set C (pp. 456–457)

Use a proportion to convert to the given unit. Use the table on page 456. Round to the nearest hundredth if necessary.

1. 9 in. ≈ cm 22.86 2. 11 yd ≈ m 10.01 3. 3 mi ≈ km 4.83
4. 10 L ≈ gal 2.64 5. 55 cm ≈ ft 1.80 6. 3.5 kg ≈ lb 7.78
7. Eve weighs 51 kg. Beth weighs 116 lb. Who weighs more and by about how many pounds? Beth; about 4 lb
8. Zack has a board that is 6 ft long. He wants to cut a length that is 150 cm. About how many centimeters will be left? about 33 cm

Set D (pp. 458–461)

Measure the line segment to the given length.

1. nearest half inch; nearest inch $2\frac{1}{2}$ in.; 2 in.
2. nearest centimeter; nearest millimeter 3 cm; 33 mm

Tell which measurement is more precise.

3. 7 fl oz or 1 cup 7 fl oz 4. 2 qt or 9 c 9 c 5. 1,245 m or 1 km 1,245 m

Name an appropriate customary or metric unit of measure for each item.

6. weight or mass of a bag of sugar lb or kg 7. length of a shoelace in. or cm 8. water in a fishbowl qt or liter

Set A (pp. 469–471)

Find the perimeter.

1.
18 in. 54 in. 9 in.

2.
3.3 cm 19.8 cm
3.3 cm 3.3 cm
3.3 cm 3.3 cm
3.3 cm

3.
6.5 m 490 cm
9.8 m 21.2 m

The perimeter is given. Find the unknown length.

4. 18 cm 41 cm x = 35 cm
32 cm
x
52 cm
52 cm
P = 230 cm

5. 15 m y = 12.3 m
10 m
9 m
8.2 m y
P = 54.5 m

6. $13\frac{5}{6}$ ft g = 18 ft
g
$13\frac{2}{6}$ ft
$18\frac{1}{2}$ ft
P = 54 ft

7. Tanya wants to put a string of lights around a rectangular window that is 40 in. wide and 48 in. high. How long will the string of lights need to be to go around the window one time? 76 in.

8. Linda is building a raised flower bed $10\frac{1}{2}$ ft long and 4 ft wide. How many feet of lumber will she need to go around the flower bed? 29 ft

Set B (pp. 476–479)

Find the circumference. Use 3.14 or $\frac{22}{7}$ for π. Round to the nearest whole number.

1.
7 in. 44 in.

2.
12 ft 38 ft

3.
49 cm 308 cm

4.
$4\frac{1}{2}$ in. 28 in.

5.
2.7 cm 8 cm

6.
154 ft 968 ft

7. r = 16 ft 100 ft
8. d = 23.5 cm 74 cm
9. d = 28 ft 88 ft
10. r = 25.9 m 163 m
11. d = 82.1 mm 258 mm
12. d = 3.21 m 10 m

13. A blue circular rug in Dominique's room has a diameter of $6\frac{1}{2}$ ft. To the nearest foot, what is the circumference of the rug? 20 ft

14. A child's hat has a radius of 8 cm. To the nearest tenth of a centimeter, what is the circumference of the hat? 50.2 cm

---

Set A (pp. 484–487)

Estimate the area. Each square on the grid represents 1 cm².

1.
about 23 cm²

2.
about 7 cm²

3.
about 11 cm²

Find the area.

4.
24 cm 32 cm
384 cm²

5.
9 ft
15 ft
67.5 ft²

6.
5 in. 8 in.
20 in.²

7. 9.5 m
5.2 m
49.4 m²

Set B (pp. 488–490)

Find the area of each figure.

1.
12 yd 7 yd
84 yd²

2.
6 ft 4 ft
10 ft
32 ft²

3.
5.3 m
8.6 m
45.58 m²

4. 18 cm
12 cm
23 cm
246 cm²

5. A wall plaque is shaped like a trapezoid with a height of 6 in. and bases that measure 3.5 in. and 9.5 in. Find the area. 39 in.²

Set C (pp. 492–493)

Find the area of each circle to the nearest whole number.

1.
9 yd
254 yd²

2.
12 mm
113 mm²

3.
7 ft
154 ft²

4.
4.2 in.
55 in²

5. d = 24 cm 452 cm²
6. r = 9.2 mm 266 mm²
7. d = 8 yd 50 yd²
8. $d = 7\frac{1}{2}$ ft 44 ft²

Set D (pp. 494–497)

Find the surface area.

1.
2 in. 8 in.
5 in.
132 in.²

2.
4 m
5 in.
2 m
20 m²

3.
7 m
4 m 3 m
122 m²

4.
4 in.
5 in. 5 in.
9 in.
6 in.
168 in.²

Set A (pp. 502–505)

Find the volume.

1.
3 in. 72 in.³
6 in. 4 in.

2.
136.25 m³
10.9 m 5 m
2.5 m

3.
4.9 m
10.2 m 12.5 m
312.375 m³

Find the unknown length.

4.
6 cm 14 cm
x
V = 420 cm³ x = 5 cm

5.
x 12 cm
5.5 cm
V = 247.5 cm³ x = 7.5 cm

6.
17 in.
x 6 in.
V = 153 in.³ x = 3 in.

Set B (pp. 508–509)

Find the volume.

1.
17 ft 362.7 ft³
8 ft 8 ft

2.
9.5 m 110.8 m³
7 m 5 m

3.
79 in. 45,346 in.³
42 in. 41 in.

4. Find the volume of a rectangular pyramid with a length of 18 cm, a width of 16 cm, and a height of 12 cm. 1,152 cm³

5. Find the volume of a rectangular pyramid with a base of 300 ft² and a height of 50 ft. 5,000 ft³

Set C (pp. 511–513)

Find the volume. Round to the nearest whole number.

1.
17 ft 5 ft
about 4,537 ft³

2.
6.2 mm 4.5 mm
about 136 mm³

3.
7 cm 18 cm
about 2,769 cm³

Find the volume of the inside cylinder to the nearest whole number.

4.
6.7 cm
4 cm
1.5 cm
about 131 cm³

5.
3 ft
9 ft
13 ft
about 1,470 ft³

6.
5 mm 2 mm
9 mm
about 254 mm³

Set A (pp. 526–528)

Write a rule for each sequence.

1. 2, 6, 18, 54, . . . multiply by 3
2. $\frac{1}{10}, \frac{1}{5}, \frac{3}{10}, \frac{2}{5}, \ldots$ add $\frac{1}{10}$ and simplify
3. ⁻35, ⁻20, ⁻5, 10, . . . add 15
4. 440, 44, 4.4, 0.44, . . . divide by 10

Find the next three possible terms in each sequence.

5. $\frac{2}{5}, \frac{4}{5}, 1\frac{1}{5}, \ldots 1\frac{3}{5}, 2, 2\frac{2}{5}$
6. 2.3, 3.9, 5.5, . . . 7.1, 8.7, 10.3
7. 7, 17, 37, 67, . . . 107, 157, 217
8. 27, ⁻9, 3, ⁻1, . . . $\frac{1}{3}, ⁻\frac{1}{9}, \frac{1}{27}$

9. Vittorio practices 6 weeks for the skateboard championship. The first 4 weeks he practices $9\frac{1}{2}$ hr, $11\frac{1}{4}$ hr, 13 hr, and $14\frac{3}{4}$ hr. Following this pattern, how many hours will Vittorio practice the sixth week? $18\frac{1}{4}$ hr

Set B (pp. 529–532)

Write an equation to represent the function.

1.
x	0	1	2	3	4
y	3	4	5	6	7

y = x + 3

2.
x	10	9	8	7	6
y	6	5	4	3	2

y = x − 4

3.
x	0	1	2	3	4
y	0	8	16	24	32

y = 8x

4.
x	30	27	24	21	18
y	10	9	8	7	6

y = x ÷ 3

Set C (pp. 533–535)

Draw the next two figures in the pattern.

1.
2.

Draw the next two solids in the pattern.

3.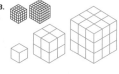

4.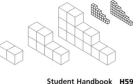

Set A (pp. 540–542)

Tell which type or types of transformation the second figure is of the first figure. Write *translation, rotation,* or *reflection.*

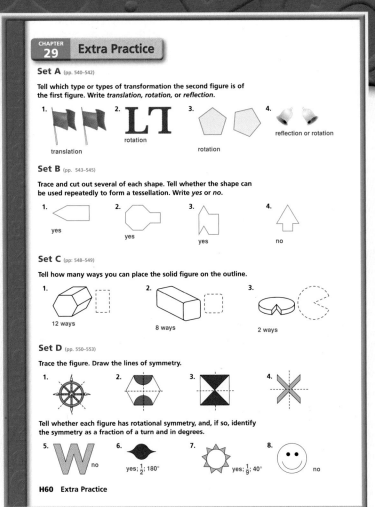

1. translation
2. rotation
3. rotation
4. reflection or rotation

Set B (pp. 543–545)

Trace and cut out several of each shape. Tell whether the shape can be used repeatedly to form a tessellation. Write *yes* or *no.*

1. yes
2. yes
3. yes
4. no

Set C (pp. 548–549)

Tell how many ways you can place the solid figure on the outline.

1. 12 ways
2. 8 ways
3. 2 ways

Set D (pp. 550–553)

Trace the figure. Draw the lines of symmetry.

1.
2.
3.
4.

Tell whether each figure has rotational symmetry, and, if so, identify the symmetry as a fraction of a turn and in degrees.

5. no
6. yes; $\frac{1}{2}$; 180°
7. yes; $\frac{1}{9}$; 40°
8. no

Set A (pp. 558–559)

Graph the solutions of the inequality. See Additional Answers, p.H61A.

1. $x < 4$
2. $x > 9$
3. $x \geq 3$
4. $x < {}^-5$

Solve the inequality and graph the solutions on a number line. See Additional Answers, p. H61A.

5. $7a \leq 14$ $a \leq 2$
6. $n + 5 > 8$ $n > 3$
7. $m - 2 < 0$ $m < 2$
8. $5c \leq 5$ $c \geq 1$

Set B (pp. 560–563)

Write the ordered pair for each point on the coordinate plane.

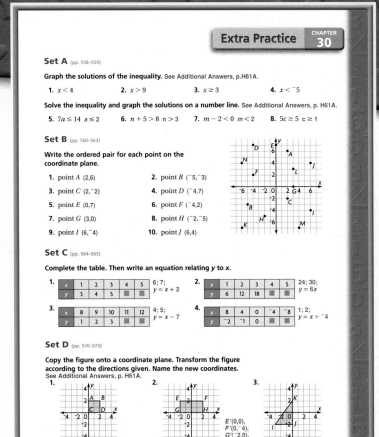

1. point A (2,6)
2. point B (${}^-5$,${}^-3$)
3. point C (2,${}^-2$)
4. point D (${}^-4$,7)
5. point E (0,7)
6. point F (${}^-4$,2)
7. point G (3,0)
8. point H (${}^-2$,${}^-5$)
9. point I (6,${}^-4$)
10. point J (6,4)

Set C (pp. 564–565)

Complete the table. Then write an equation relating y to x.

1.
x	1	2	3	4	5
y	3	4	5	■	■

6; 7;
$y = x + 2$

2.
x	1	2	3	4	5
y	6	12	18	■	■

24; 30;
$y = 6x$

3.
x	8	9	10	11	12
y	1	2	3	■	■

4; 5;
$y = x - 7$

4.
x	8	4	0	${}^-4$	${}^-8$
y	${}^-2$	${}^-1$	0	■	■

1; 2;
$y = x \div {}^-4$

Set D (pp. 570–573)

Copy the figure onto a coordinate plane. Transform the figure according to the directions given. Name the new coordinates.
See Additional Answers, p. H61A.

1.
2 units to the right
A'(2,2), B'(4,2), C'(2,0), D'(4,0)

2.
rotate 90° clockwise about (${}^-2$,0)
E'(0,0), F'(0,${}^-4$), G'(${}^-2$,0), H'(${}^-2$,${}^-4$)

3.
reflect across the y-axis
I'(3,${}^-2$), J'(0,${}^-2$), K'(0,2)

Additional Answers

Chapter 6 Extra Practice, page H37

1.

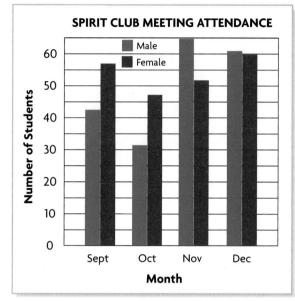

SPIRIT CLUB MEETING ATTENDANCE

2.

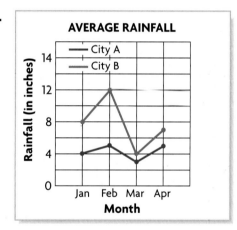

AVERAGE RAINFALL

3.

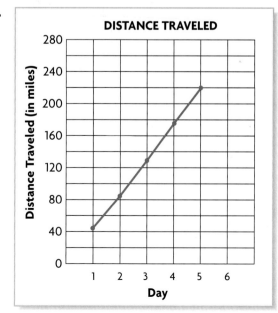

DISTANCE TRAVELED

4.

Stems	Leaves
1	3 4 7 8 9
2	1 2 2 5 8 9
3	0 3 6 7
4	1 4 8

mode: 22; median: 26.5

5.

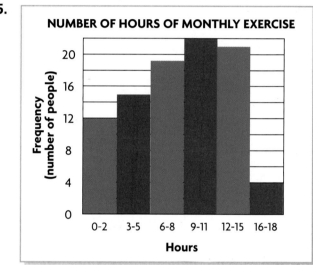

NUMBER OF HOURS OF MONTHLY EXERCISE

10.

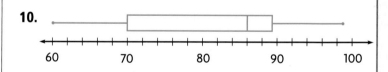

Additional Answers

Chapter 30 Extra Practice, Set A, page H61

1.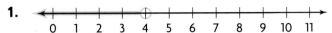

(number line with open circle at 4, ticks 0 to 11, arrow extending right)

2. (number line with open circle at 9, ticks 3 to 14, arrow extending left)

3. (number line with filled circle at 3, ticks 0 to 11, arrow extending right)

4. (number line with open circle at -5, ticks -8 to 3, arrow extending right)

5. (number line with filled circle at 2, ticks -2 to 9, arrow extending left)

6. (number line with open circle at 3, ticks -2 to 9, arrow extending right)

7. (number line with open circle at 2, ticks -2 to 9, arrow extending left)

8. (number line with filled circle at 1, ticks -2 to 9, arrow extending right)

Chapter 30 Extra Practice, Set D, page H61

1.

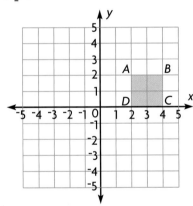

3.

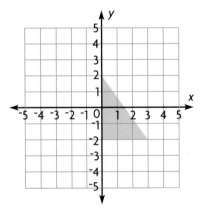

2.

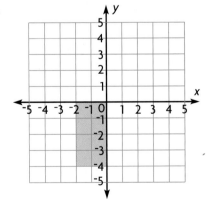

Sharpen Your Test-Taking Skills

TIPS FOR TAKING MATH TESTS

Being a good test-taker is like being a good problem solver. When you answer test questions, you are solving problems. Remember to **ANALYZE, CHOOSE, SOLVE, and CHECK.**

Analyze
Choose
Solve
Check

Analyze

Read the problem.

- Look for math terms and recall their meanings.
- Reread the problem and think about the question.
- Use the details in the problem and the question.

1. The difference between two numbers is 37. Their sum is 215. What are the numbers?

A 37 and 178   C 89 and 126

B 83 and 120   D 107 and 108

TIP! Understand the problem. The problem requires you to find two numbers for which the difference and sum are given. Reread the problem to compare the details to the answer choices. You can use estimation instead of calculating the sum and difference of each pair of numbers. The answer is **C.**

- Each word is important. Missing a word or reading it incorrectly could cause you to get the wrong answer.
- Pay attention to words that are in **bold** type, all CAPITAL letters, or *italics* and words like *round, best,* or *least to greatest.*

2. Florinda took $\frac{1}{2}$ hour to complete a race. Doris took $\frac{3}{8}$ hour and Violet took $\frac{2}{3}$ hour to complete the same race. Which lists the three runners from fastest to slowest?

F Florinda, Doris, Violet

G Doris, Violet, Florinda

H Violet, Florinda, Doris

J Doris, Florinda, Violet

TIP! Look for important words. The words *fastest to slowest* are important. The fastest runner takes the least amount of time. Think about where each fraction would be placed on a number line between 0 and 1. Then put the times in order from least to greatest. The answer is **J.**

Choose

Think about how you can solve the problem.

- See if you can solve the problem with the information given.
- Pictures, charts, tables, and graphs may have the information you need.
- You may need to recall information not given.
- Sometimes the answer choices have information to help solve the problem.

3. Jeremy wants to make a graph to see the trend of the profit in his lawn-mowing business over the past 10 months. What type of graph would best show this?

A circle graph   C line graph

B histogram   D stem-and-leaf plot

TIP! Get the information you need. The answer choices give four different types of graphs or plots. Think about each one and the kind of data that is appropriate for it. The problem states that Jeremy wants to see the trend in his profit over the past 10 months, and line graphs show trends. The answer is **C.**

- You may need to write a number sentence and solve it to answer the question.
- Some problems have two steps or more.
- In some problems you need to look at relationships instead of computing an answer.
- If the path to the solution isn't clear, choose a problem-solving strategy and use it to solve the problem.

4. A square tile with 4-inch sides is rotated along the line below. If the tile stopped so that the letter **P** appears in an upright position, which of these distances could it have been rotated?

P

F 40 in.   H 48 in.

G 44 in.   J 52 in.

TIP! Decide on a plan. From the distances given, you must find the one that could allow for complete rotations of the square tile. Since each side of the square is 4 inches long, it moves 16 inches in one complete rotation. If you *use logical reasoning,* you see that only one of the choices is a multiple of 16. The answer is **H.**

Solve

Follow your plan, working logically and carefully.

- Estimate your answer. Compare it to the answer choices.
- Use reasoning to find the most likely choices.
- Make sure you solved all the steps needed to answer the problem.
- If your answer does not match any of the answer choices, check the numbers you used. Then check your computation.

5. Glen and Doug painted a fence. It took Glen three times as long to paint one side of the fence as it took Doug to paint the other side. If *h* represents the number of hours Doug painted, which expression shows the hours Glen painted?

A $3 \div h$ C $3 + h$

B $3 - h$ D $3 \times h$

TIP! Eliminate choices. It is important to understand that *h* represents the hours it took Doug to paint one side of the fence. Since Glen painted three times as long as Doug, you can eliminate answers **A** and **B** because it does not make sense to divide by or subtract the hours Doug painted. Answer **C** means three more than *h,* so it can be eliminated. The answer is **D.**

- If your answer still does not match one of the choices, look for another form of the number, such as a decimal instead of a fraction.
- If answer choices are given as pictures, look at each one by itself while you cover the other three.
- If you do not see your answer and the answer choices include Not here, make sure your work is correct and then mark Not here.
- Read answer choices that are statements and relate them to the information in the problem one by one.

6. Tanya and her class helped plant 120 tulip and daffodil bulbs in front of the school. If 30 of the bulbs were tulips, what percent of the bulbs were daffodils?

F 90%   H 25%

G $66\frac{2}{3}$%   J Not here

TIP! Choose the answer. Since 30 of the bulbs were tulips, 90 were daffodils. The question asks what percent are daffodils so you need to find what percent of 120 is 90 (90 ÷ 120). If your answer doesn't match one of the answer choices, check your computation. If you know your work is correct, mark the letter for Not here. The answer is **J.**

Check

Take time to catch your mistakes.

- Be sure you answered the question asked.
- Check for important words you might have missed.
- Be sure you used all the information you needed.
- Check your computation by using a different method.

7. The temperature was 6°F today. A forecaster predicted that the temperature would drop by 5° each day for the next four days. Which sequence could be used to find the predicted temperatures?

A 6°F, 11°F, 16°F, 21°F, 26°F

B 6°F, 1°F, 6°F, 11°F, 16°F

C 6°F, 1°F, ⁻6°F, ⁻11°F, ⁻16°F

D 6°F, 1°F, ⁻4°F, ⁻9°F, ⁻14°F

TIP! Check your work. You need to find the sequence that shows a drop of 5° in temperature for the next four days. Draw a thermometer or a number line to check your computation. The answer is **D.**

Don't Forget!

Before the test...

- Listen to the teacher's directions and read the instructions.
- Write down the ending time if the test is timed.
- Know where and how to mark your answers.
- Know whether you should write on the test page or use scratch paper.
- Ask any questions you have before the test begins.

During the test...

- Work quickly but carefully. If you are unsure how to answer a question, leave it blank and return to it later.
- If you cannot finish on time, look over the questions that are left. Answer the easiest ones first. Then go back to answer the others.
- Fill in each answer space carefully. Erase completely if you change an answer. Erase any stray marks.
- Check that the answer number matches the question number, especially if you skip a question.

California Grade Six Mathematics Content Standards

By the end of grade six, students have mastered the four arithmetic operations with whole numbers, positive fractions, positive decimals, and positive and negative integers; they accurately compute and solve problems. They apply their knowledge to statistics and probability. Students understand the concepts of mean, median, and mode of data sets and how to calculate the range. They analyze data and sampling processes for possible bias and misleading conclusions; they use addition and multiplication of fractions routinely to calculate the probabilities for compound events. Students conceptually understand and work with ratios and proportions; they compute percentages (e.g., tax, tips, interest). Students know about π and the formulas for the circumference and area of a circle. They use letters for numbers in formulas involving geometric shapes and in ratios to represent an unknown part of an expression. They solve one-step linear equations.

Number Sense

1.0 Students compare and order positive and negative fractions, decimals, and mixed numbers. Students solve problems involving fractions, ratios, proportions, and percentages:

1.1 Compare and order positive and negative fractions, decimals, and mixed numbers and place them on a number line.

1.2 Interpret and use ratios in different contexts (e.g., batting averages, miles per hour) to show the relative sizes of two quantities, using appropriate notations ($\frac{a}{b}$, a to b, $a:b$).

Write the following as ratios:

1. The ratio of tricycles to tricycle wheels

2. The ratio of hands to fingers

3. If there are 6 tricycle wheels, how many tricycles are there?

4. If there are 45 fingers, how many hands are there?

1.3 Use proportions to solve problems (e.g., determine the value of N if $\frac{4}{7} = \frac{N}{21}$, find the length of a side of a polygon similar to a known polygon). Use cross-multiplication as a method for solving such problems, understanding it as the multiplication of both sides of an equation by a multiplicative inverse.

Joe can type 9 words in 8 seconds. At this rate, how many words can he type in 2 minutes?

Find n if:

1. $\frac{49}{21} = \frac{14}{n}$
2. $\frac{n}{3} = \frac{5}{7}$

(This problem also applies to Algebra and Functions Standard 1.1.)

Note: The sample problems illustrate the standards and are written to help clarify them.

The symbols O—n and ● identify the Key Standards for grade six.

H66 Mathematics Content Standards

Number Sense (Continued)

1.4 Calculate given percentages of quantities and solve problems involving discounts at sales, interest earned, and tips.

2.0 Students calculate and solve problems involving addition, subtraction, multiplication, and division:

    2.1 Solve problems involving addition, subtraction, multiplication, and division of positive fractions and explain why a particular operation was used for a given situation.

    2.2 Explain the meaning of multiplication and division of positive fractions and perform the calculations (e.g., $\frac{5}{8} \div \frac{15}{16} = \frac{5}{8} \times \frac{16}{15} = \frac{2}{3}$).

       1. If $\frac{11}{7}$ is divided by a certain fraction $\frac{a}{b}$, the result is $\frac{3}{8}$. What is $\frac{a}{b}$?

       2. Draw a rectangle that has a perimeter of 1 and an area that is less than $\frac{1}{30}$.

2.3 Solve addition, subtraction, multiplication, and division problems, including those arising in concrete situations, that use positive and negative integers and combinations of these operations.

    Simplify to make the calculation as simple as possible and identify the properties you used at each step:

       1. $95 + 276 + 5$

       2. $^-19 + 37 + 19$

       3. $^-16 \, (^-8 + 9)$

       4. $\left(\frac{-7}{8}\right)\left(\frac{17}{17}\right)$

       5. $(^-8)(^-4)(19)(6 + (^-6))$

2.4 Determine the least common multiple and the greatest common divisor of whole numbers; use them to solve problems with fractions (e.g., to find a common denominator to add two fractions or to find the reduced form for a fraction).

Algebra and Functions

1.0 Students write verbal expressions and sentences as algebraic expressions and equations; they evaluate algebraic expressions, solve simple linear equations, and graph and interpret their results:

1.1 Write and solve one-step linear equations in one variable.

    $6y - 2 = 10$. What is y?

Algebra and Functions (Continued)

1.2   Write and evaluate an algebraic expression for a given situation, using up to three variables.

Joe's sister Mary is twice as old as he is. Mary is 16. How old is Joe?

1.3   Apply algebraic order of operations and the commutative, associative, and distributive properties to evaluate expressions; and justify each step in the process.

1.4   Solve problems manually by using the correct order of operations or by using a scientific calculator.

2.0   **Students analyze and use tables, graphs, and rules to solve problems involving rates and proportions:**

2.1   Convert one unit of measurement to another (e.g., from feet to miles, from centimeters to inches).

Suppose that one British pound is worth $1.50. In London a magazine costs 3 pounds. In San Francisco the same magazine costs $4.25. In which city is the magazine cheaper?

When temperature is measured in both Celsius (C) and Fahrenheit (F), it is known that they are related by the following formula:

$9 \times C = (F - 32) \times 5.$

What is 50 degrees Fahrenheit in Celsius? (Note the explicit use of parentheses.)

O—¬ 2.2   Demonstrate an understanding that *rate* is a measure of one quantity per unit value of another quantity.

2.3   Solve problems involving rates, average speed, distance, and time.

Marcus took a train from San Francisco to San Jose, a distance of 54 miles. The train took 45 minutes for the trip. What was the average speed of the train?

3.0   **Students investigate geometric patterns and describe them algebraically:**

3.1   Use variables in expressions describing geometric quantities (e.g., $P = 2w + 2l$, $A = \frac{1}{2}bh$, $C = \pi d$—the formulas for the perimeter of a rectangle, the area of a triangle, and the circumference of a circle, respectively).

A rectangle has width *w*. Its length is one more than 3 times its width. Find the perimeter of the rectangle. (Your answer will be expressed in terms of *w*.)

3.2   Express in symbolic form simple relationships arising from geometry.

Measurement and Geometry

1.0   Students deepen their understanding of the measurement of plane and solid shapes and use this understanding to solve problems:

🔑 **1.1**   Understand the concept of a constant such as π; know the formulas for the circumference and area of a circle.

1.2   Know common estimates of π (3.14; $\frac{22}{7}$) and use these values to estimate and calculate the circumference and the area of circles; compare with actual measurements.

1.3   Know and use the formulas for the volume of triangular prisms and cylinders (area of base × height); compare these formulas and explain the similarity between them and the formula for the volume of a rectangular solid.

Find the volumes (dimensions are in cm).

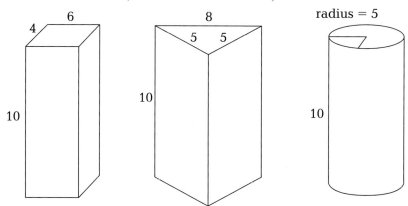

2.0   Students identify and describe the properties of two-dimensional figures:

2.1   Identify angles as vertical, adjacent, complementary, or supplementary and provide descriptions of these terms.

🔑 **2.2**   Use the properties of complementary and supplementary angles and the sum of the angles of a triangle to solve problems involving an unknown angle.

Find the missing angles.

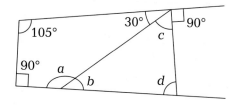

2.3   Draw quadrilaterals and triangles from given information about them (e.g., a quadrilateral having equal sides but no right angles, a right isosceles triangle).

Statistics, Data Analysis, and Probability

1.0 **Students compute and analyze statistical measurements for data sets:**

    1.1   Compute the range, mean, median, and mode of data sets.

    1.2   Understand how additional data added to data sets may affect these computations of measures of central tendency.

    1.3   Understand how the inclusion or exclusion of outliers affects measures of central tendency.

    1.4   Know why a specific measure of central tendency (mean, median, mode) provides the most useful information in a given context.

2.0 **Students use data samples of a population and describe the characteristics and limitations of the samples:**

    2.1   Compare different samples of a population with the data from the entire population and identify a situation in which it makes sense to use a sample.

    2.2   Identify different ways of selecting a sample (e.g., convenience sampling, responses to a survey, random sampling) and which method makes a sample more representative for a population.

    2.3   Analyze data displays and explain why the way in which the question was asked might have influenced the results obtained and why the way in which the results were displayed might have influenced the conclusions reached.

    2.4   Identify data that represent sampling errors and explain why the sample (and the display) might be biased.

    2.5   Identify claims based on statistical data and, in simple cases, evaluate the validity of the claims.

3.0 **Students determine theoretical and experimental probabilities and use these to make predictions about events:**

    3.1   Represent all possible outcomes for compound events in an organized way (e.g., tables, grids, tree diagrams) and express the theoretical probability of each outcome.

    3.2   Use data to estimate the probability of future events (e.g., batting averages or number of accidents per mile driven).

    3.3   Represent probabilities as ratios, proportions, decimals between 0 and 1, and percentages between 0 and 100 and verify that the probabilities computed are reasonable; know that if P is the probability of an event, $1 - P$ is the probability of an event not occurring.

Statistics, Data Analysis, and Probability (Continued)

3.4 Understand that the probability of either of two disjoint events occurring is the sum of the two individual probabilities and that the probability of one event following another, in independent trials, is the product of the two probabilities.

○━┓ **3.5** Understand the difference between independent and dependent events.

Mathematical Reasoning

1.0 Students make decisions about how to approach problems:

1.1 Analyze problems by identifying relationships, distinguishing relevant from irrelevant information, identifying missing information, sequencing and prioritizing information, and observing patterns.

1.2 Formulate and justify mathematical conjectures based on a general description of the mathematical question or problem posed.

1.3 Determine when and how to break a problem into simpler parts.

2.0 Students use strategies, skills, and concepts in finding solutions:

2.1 Use estimation to verify the reasonableness of calculated results.

2.2 Apply strategies and results from simpler problems to more complex problems.

2.3 Estimate unknown quantities graphically and solve for them by using logical reasoning and arithmetic and algebraic techniques.

2.4 Use a variety of methods, such as words, numbers, symbols, charts, graphs, tables, diagrams, and models, to explain mathematical reasoning.

2.5 Express the solution clearly and logically by using the appropriate mathematical notation and terms and clear language; support solutions with evidence in both verbal and symbolic work.

2.6 Indicate the relative advantages of exact and approximate solutions to problems and give answers to a specified degree of accuracy.

2.7 Make precise calculations and check the validity of the results from the context of the problem.

Mathematical Reasoning (Continued)

3.0   Students move beyond a particular problem by generalizing to other situations:

3.1   Evaluate the reasonableness of the solution in the context of the original situation.

3.2   Note the method of deriving the solution and demonstrate a conceptual understanding of the derivation by solving similar problems.

3.3   Develop generalizations of the results obtained and the strategies used and apply them in new problem situations.

Glossary

Pronunciation Key

a	**a**dd, m**a**p	f	**f**it, hal**f**	n	**n**ice, ti**n**	p	**p**it, sto**p**	yo͞o	**f**use, f**ew**
ā	**a**ce, r**a**te	g	**g**o, lo**g**	ng	ri**ng**, so**ng**	r	**r**un, poo**r**	v	**v**ain, e**v**e
â(r)	c**ar**e, **air**	h	**h**ope, **h**ate	o	**o**dd, h**o**t	s	**s**ee, pa**ss**	w	**w**in, a**w**ay
ä	p**a**lm, f**a**ther	i	**i**t, g**i**ve	ō	**o**pen, s**o**	sh	**sh**ure, ru**sh**	y	**y**et, **y**earn
b	**b**at, ru**b**	ī	**i**ce, wr**i**te	ô	**o**rder, j**aw**	t	**t**alk, si**t**	z	**z**est, mu**s**e
ch	**ch**eck, cat**ch**	j	**j**oy, le**dge**	oi	**oi**l, b**oy**	th	**th**in, bo**th**	zh	vi**s**ion, plea**s**ure
d	**d**og, ro**d**	k	**c**ool, ta**k**e	ou	p**ou**t, n**ow**	t͟h	**th**is, ba**th**e		
e	**e**nd, p**e**t	l	**l**ook, ru**l**e	o͝o	t**oo**k, f**u**ll	u	**u**p, d**o**ne		
ē	**e**qual, tr**ee**	m	**m**ove, see**m**	o͞o	p**oo**l, f**oo**d	û(r)	b**ur**n, t**er**m		

ə the schwa, an unstressed vowel representing the sound spelled *a* in **a**bove, *e* in sick**e**n, *i* in poss**i**ble, *o* in mel**o**n, *u* in circ**u**s

Other symbols:
• separates words into syllables
ʹ indicates stress on a syllable

A

absolute value [abʹsə•lo͞ot valʹyo͞o] The distance of an integer from zero (p. 228)

acute angle [ə•kyo͞otʹ anʹgəl] an angle whose measure is greater than 0° and less than 90° (p. 324)

acute triangle [ə•kyo͞otʹ trīʹan•gəl] A triangle with all angles less than 90° (p. 336)
Example:

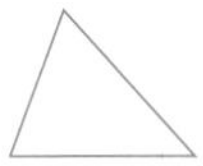

Addition Property of Equality [ə•dishʹən präʹpər•tē əv i•kwolʹə•tē] The property that states that if you add the same number to both sides of an equation, the sides remain equal (p. 294)

additive inverse [adʹə•tiv inʹvûrs] The opposite of a given number (p. 243)

adjacent angles [ə•jāʹsənt anʹgəlz] Angles that are side by side and have a common vertex and ray (p. 326)
Example:

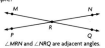

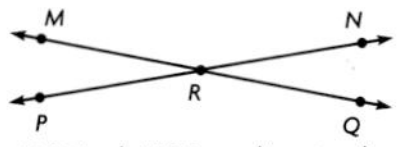
M
N
R
P
Q
∠*MRN* and ∠*NRQ* are adjacent angles.

algebraic expression [al•jə•brāʹik ik•spreʹshən] An expression that includes at least one variable (p. 28)
Examples: $x + 5$, $3a - 4$

algebraic operating system [al•jə•brāʹik äʹpə•rā•ting sisʹtəm] A way for calculators to follow the order of operations when evaluating expressions (p. 43)

angle [anʹgəl] A figure formed by two rays with a common endpoint (p. 324)
Example:

arc [ärk] A part of a circle, named by its endpoints (p. 348)
Example:

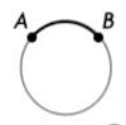
A
B
arc *AB* or $\widehat{AB}$

area [ârʹē•ə] The number of square units needed to cover a given surface (p. 484)

Associative Property [ə•sōʹshē•ā•tiv präʹpər•tē] The property that states that the way addends are grouped or factors are grouped does not change the sum or the product (p. 36)
Examples: $12 + (5 + 9) = (12 + 5) + 9$
$(9 \times 8) \times 3 = 9 \times (8 \times 3)$

axes [akʹsēz] The horizontal number line (*x*-axis) and the vertical number line (*y*-axis) on the coordinate plane (p. 560)

B

bar graph [bärʹgraf] A graph that displays countable data with horizontal or vertical bars (p. 120)

base [bās] A number used as a repeated factor (p. 40)
Example: $8^3 = 8 \times 8 \times 8$; 8 is the base.

base [bās] A side of a polygon or a face of a solid figure by which the figure is measured or named (pp. 354, 485)
Examples:

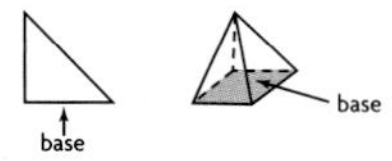
base
base

biased question [bīʹəst kwesʹchən] A question that leads to a specific response or excludes a certain group (p. 98)

biased sample [bīʹəst samʹpəl] A sample is biased if individuals or groups from the population are not represented in the sample. (p. 98)

box-and-whisker graph [bäks•ənd•hwisʹkər graf] A graph that shows how far apart and how evenly data are distributed (p. 129)

C

Celsius [səlʹsē•əs] A metric scale for measuring temperature (p. 299)

certain [sûrʹtən] Sure to happen (p. 419)

chord [kôrd] A line segment with its endpoints on a circle (p. 348)
Example:

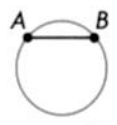
A
B
chord: $\overline{AB}$

circle [sûrʹkəl] A closed plane figure with all points of the figure the same distance from the center (p. 348)
Example:

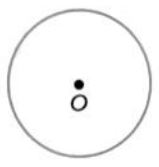
O

circle graph [sûrʹkəl graf] A graph that lets you compare parts to the whole and to other parts (p. 122)
Example:

FAVORITE HOBBIES

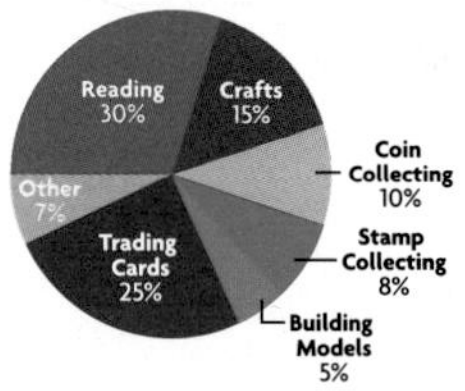
Reading 30%
Crafts 15%
Coin Collecting 10%
Stamp Collecting 8%
Building Models 5%
Trading Cards 25%
Other 7%

circumference [sûr•kumʹfər•əns] The distance around a circle (p. 474)

clustering [klusʹtər•ing] A method used to estimate a sum when all addends are about the same (p. 16)

Commutative Property [kə•myo͞oʹtə•tiv präʹpər•tē] The property that states that if the order of addends or factors is changed, the sum or product stays the same (p. 36)
Examples: $6 + 5 + 7 = 5 + 6 + 7$
$8 \times 9 \times 3 = 3 \times 8 \times 9$

compensation [kom•pən•sāʹshən] A mental math strategy for some addition and subtraction problems (p. 37)

complementary angles [kom•plə•menʹtər•ē anʹgəlz] Two angles whose measures have a sum of 90° (p. 327)
Example:

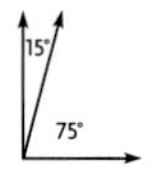
15°
75°

Multimedia Math Glossary **www.harcourtschool.com/mathglossary**

composite number [käm•päʹzət numʹbər] A whole number greater than 1 that has more than two whole-number factors (p. 145)

compound event [kämʹpound i•ventʹ] An event made of two or more simple events (p. 434)

congruent [kən•gro͞oʹənt] Having the same size and shape (p. 380)

convenience sample [kən•vēnʹyənts samʹpəl] Sampling the most available subjects in the population to obtain quick results (p. 95)

coordinate plane [kō•ôrʹdə•nit plān] A plane formed by a horizontal line (*x*-axis) that intersects a vertical line (*y*-axis) at a point called the origin (p. 560)

corresponding angles [kôr•ə•spänʹding anʹgəlz] Angles that are in the same position in different figures (p. 381)
Example:

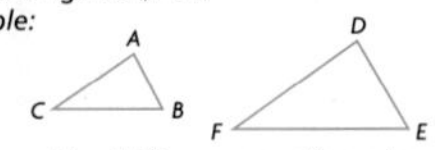
A
B
C
D
E
F
∠*A* and ∠*D* are corresponding angles.

corresponding sides [kôr•ə•spänʹding sīdz] Sides that are in the same position in different plane figures (p. 381)
Example:

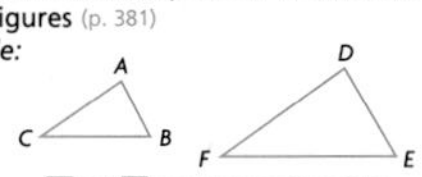
A
B
C
D
E
F
$\overline{CA}$ and $\overline{FD}$ are corresponding sides.

cube [kyo͞ob] A rectangular solid with six congruent faces (p. 354)
Example:

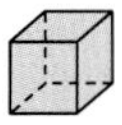

cumulative frequency [kyo͞oʹmyə•lə•tiv frēʹkwən•sē] A running total of the number of subjects surveyed (p. 103)

D

decimal [deʹsə•məl] A number with one or more digits to the right of the decimal point (p. 52)

denominator [di•näʹmə•nā•tər] The part of a fraction that tells how many equal parts are in the whole (p. 159)
Example: $\frac{3}{4}$ ←denominator

dependent events [di•penʹdənt i•vəntsʹ] Events for which the outcome of the second event depends on the outcome of the first event (p. 438)

diameter [dī•amʹə•tər] A line segment that passes through the center of a circle and has its endpoints on the circle (p. 348)
Example:

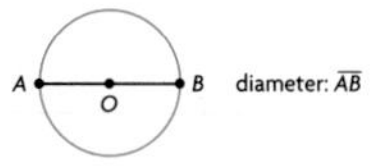
A
O
B
diameter: AB

dimension [di•menʹshən] The length, width, or height of a figure (p. 501)

discount [disʹkount] An amount that is subtracted from the regular price of an item (p. 408)

Distributive Property of Multiplication [di•stribʹyə•tiv präʹpər•tē əv mul•tə•plə•kāʹshən] The property that states that multiplying a sum by a number is the same as multiplying each addend by the number and then adding the products (p. 36)
Example: $14 \times 21 = 14 \times (20 + 1) =$
$(14 \times 20) + (14 \times 1)$

dividend [diʹvə•dend] The number that is to be divided in a division problem
Example: In $56 \div 8$, 56 is the dividend.

Division Property of Equality [di•viʹzhən präʹpər•tē əv i•kwolʹə•tē] The property that states that if you divide both sides of an equation by the same nonzero number, the sides remain equal (p. 301)

divisor [di•vīʹzər] The number that divides the dividend
Example: In $45 \div 9$, 9 is the divisor.

E

equally likely [ēʹkwə•lē līʹklē] Having the same chance of occurring (p. 418)

equation [i•kwāʹzhən] A statement that shows that two quantities are equal (p. 30)

equilateral triangle [ē•kwə•laʹtə•rəl trīʹan•gəl] A triangle with three congruent sides (p. 336)
Example:

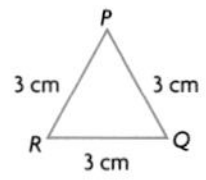
P
3 cm
3 cm
R
Q
3 cm

equivalent fractions [ē•kwivʹə•lənt frakʹshənz] Fractions that name the same amount or part (p. 160)

equivalent ratios [ē•kwivʹə•lənt rāʹshē•ōz] Ratios that name the same comparisons (p. 374)

estimate [esʹtə•mit] An answer that is close to the exact answer and that is found by rounding, by clustering, or by using compatible numbers (p. 16)

evaluate [i•valʹyo͞o•āt] Find the value of a numerical or algebraic expression (p. 28)

event [i•ventʹ] A set of outcomes (p. 417)

experimental probability [ik•sper•ə•menʹtəl prä•bə•bilʹə•tē] The ratio of the number of times an event occurs to the total number of trials or times the activity is performed (p. 426)

exponent [ik•spōʹnənt] A number that tells how many times a base is used as a factor (p. 40)
Example: $2^3 = 2 \times 2 \times 2 = 8$;
3 is the exponent.

F

face [fās] One of the polygons of a solid figure (p. 483)
Example:

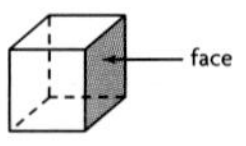
face

factor [fakʹtər] A number that is multiplied by another number to find a product

Fahrenheit [fârʹən•hīt] A customary scale for measuring temperature (p. 305)

formula [fôrʹmyə•lə] A rule that is expressed with symbols (p. 304)
Example: $A = lw$

fractal [frakʹtəl] A figure with repeating patterns containing shapes that are like the whole but of different sizes throughout (p. 533)

frequency table [frēʹkwən•sē tāʹbəl] A table representing totals for individual categories or groups (p. 103)

function [funkʹshən] A relationship between two quantities in which one quantity depends on the other (p. 529)

Fundamental Counting Principle [fun•də•menʹtəl kounʹting prinʹsə•pəl] If one event has *m* possible outcomes and a second independent event has *n* possible outcomes, then there are $m \times n$ total possible outcomes. (p. 434)

G

greatest common factor (GCF) [grāʹtəst käʹmən fakʹtər] The greatest factor that two or more numbers have in common (p. 151)

H

height [hīt] A measure of a polygon or solid figure, taken as a perpendicular from the base of the figure (p. 485)
Example:

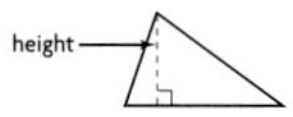
height

hexagon [heksʹə•gon] A six-sided polygon

histogram [hisʹtə•gram] A bar graph that shows the number of times data occur in certain ranges or intervals (p. 127)

I

Identity Property of Zero [ī•denʹtə•tē präʹpər•tē əv zirʹō] The property that states that the sum of zero and any number is that number (p. H2)
Example: $25 + 0 = 25$

Identity Property of One [ī•den′tə•tē prä′pər•tē əv wun] The property that states that the product of any number and 1 is that number (p. H2)
Example: 12 × 1 = 12

impossible [im•pos′ə•bəl] Never able to happen (p. 419)

independent events [in•di•pen′dənt i•vents′] Events for which the outcome of the second event does not depend on the outcome of the first event (p. 437)

indirect measurement [in•di•rekt′ mezh′ər•mənt] The technique of using similar figures and proportions to find a measure (p. 384)

inequality [in•i•kwäl′ə•tē] An algebraic or numerical sentence that contains the symbol <, >, ≤, ≥, or ≠ (p. 558)
Example: $x + 3 > 5$

integers [in′ti•jərz] The set of whole numbers and their opposites (p. 228)

isosceles triangle [ī•sä′sə•lēz trī′an•gəl] A triangle with exactly two congruent sides (p. 335)
Example:

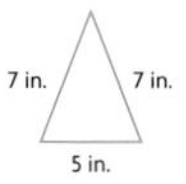
7 in.
7 in.
5 in.

L

lateral faces [lat′ər•əl fās′əz] The faces in a prism or pyramid that are not bases (p. 354)

least common denominator (LCD) [lēst kä′mən di•nä′mə•nā•tər] The least common multiple of two or more denominators (p. 182)

least common multiple (LCM) [lēst kä′mən mul′tə•pəl] The smallest number, other than zero, that is a common multiple of two or more numbers (p. 150)

like terms [līk turmz] Expressions that have the same variable with the same exponent (p. 277)

line [līn] A straight path that extends without end in opposite directions (p. 322)
Example:

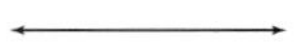

line graph [līn graf] A graph that uses a line to show how data change over time (p. 121)

line of symmetry [līn əv si′mə•trē] A line that divides a figure into two congruent parts (p. 550)

line plot [līn plät] A graph that shows frequency of data along a number line (p. 102)
Example:

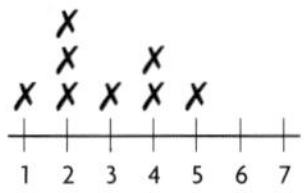
1 2 3 4 5 6 7
Miles Jogged

line segment [līn seg′mənt] A part of a line with two endpoints (p. 322)
Example:

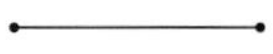

line symmetry [līn si′mə•trē] A figure has line symmetry if a line can separate the figure into two congruent parts. (p. 550)

lower extreme [lō′ər ik•strēm′] The least number in a set of data (p. 129)

lower quartile [lō′ər kwôr′tīl] The median of the lower half of a set of data (p. 129)

M

mean [mēn] The sum of a group of numbers divided by the number of addends (p. 106)

median [mē′dē•ən] The middle value in a group of numbers arranged in order (p. 106)

mixed number [mikst num′bər] A number represented by a whole number and a fraction (p. 164)

mode [mōd] The number that occurs most often in a set of data (p. 106)

multiple-bar graph [mul′tə•pəl bär′graf] A bar graph that represents two or more sets of data (p. 120)

multiple-line graph [mul′tə•pəl līn′graf] A line graph that represents two or more sets of data (p. 121)

multiple [mul′tə•pəl] The product of a given whole number and another whole number (p. 145)

Multiplication Property of Equality [mul•tə•plə•kā′shən prä′pər•tē əv i•kwol′ə•tē] The property that states that if you multiply both sides of an equation by the same number, the sides remain equal (p. 302)

N

negative integers [ne′gə•tiv in′ti•jərz] Integers to the left of zero on the number line (p. 228)

net [net] An arrangement of two-dimensional figures that folds to form a polyhedron (p. 360)
Example:

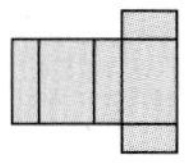

numerator [nōō′mə•rā•tər] The part of a fraction that tells how many parts are being used (p. 159)
Example: $\frac{3}{4}$ ←numerator

numerical expression [nōō•mâr′i•kəl ik•spre′shən] A mathematical phrase that uses only numbers and operation symbols (p. 28)

O

obtuse angle [äb•tōōs′ an′gəl] An angle whose measure is greater than 90° and less than 180° (p. 324)
Example:

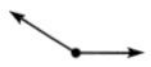

obtuse triangle [äb•tōōs′ trī′an•gəl] A triangle with one angle greater than 90° (p. 336)
Example:

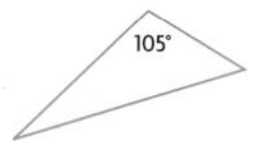
105°

opposites [ä′pə•zəts] Two numbers that are an equal distance from zero on the number line (p. 228)

order of operations [ôr′dər əv ä•pə•rā′shənz] The process for evaluating expressions: first perform the operations in parentheses, clear the exponents, perform all multiplication and division, and then perform all addition and subtraction (p. 42)

ordered pair [ôr′dərd pâr] A pair of numbers that can be used to locate a point on the coordinate plane (p. 560)
Examples: (0,2), (3,4), (⁻4,5)

origin [ôr′ə•jən] The point where the *x*-axis and the *y*-axis in the coordinate plane intersect, (0,0) (p. 560)

outcome [out′kəm] A possible result of a probability experiment (p. 418)

outlier [out′lī•ər] A data value that stands out from others in a set; outliers can significantly affect measures of central tendency. (p. 110)

overestimate [ō•vər•es′tə•mət] An estimate that is greater than the exact answer (p. 17)

P

parallel lines [pâr′ə•lel līnz] Lines in a plane that are always the same distance apart (p. 330)
Example:

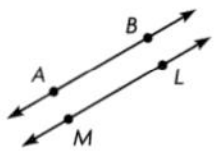
B
A
L
M

percent (%) [pər•sent′] The ratio of a number to 100; *percent* means "per hundred." (p. 60)

perimeter [pə•ri′mə•tər] The distance around a figure (p. 467)

perpendicular lines [pər•pən•dik′yə•lər līnz] Two lines that intersect to form right, or 90°, angles (p. 330)
Example:

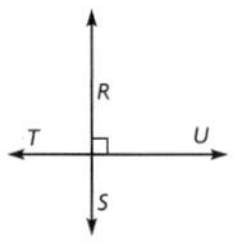
R
T
U
S

pi (π) [pī] The ratio of the circumference of a circle to its diameter; $\pi \approx 3.14$ or $\frac{22}{7}$ (p. 475)

plane [plān] A flat surface that extends without end in all directions (p. 322)

point [point] An exact location in space, usually represented by a dot (p. 322)

point of rotation [point əv rō•tā′shən] The central point around which a figure is rotated (p. 551)

polygon [pä′lē•gän] A closed plane figure formed by three or more line segments (p. 335)

polyhedron [pä•lē•hē′drən] A solid figure with flat faces that are polygons (p. 354)
Example:

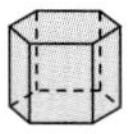
Hexagonal Prism

population [pä•pyə•lā′shən] The entire group of objects or individuals considered for a survey (p. 94)

positive integers [pä′zə•tiv in′ti•jərz] Integers to the right of zero on the number line (p. 228)

prime factorization [prīm fak•tə•ri•zā′shən] A number written as the product of all of its prime factors (p. 148)
Example: $24 = 2^3 \times 3$

prime number [prīm num′bər] A whole number greater than 1 whose only factors are 1 and itself (p. 148)

principal [prin′sə•pəl] The amount of money borrowed or saved (p. 412)

prism [priz′əm] A solid figure that has two congruent, polygon-shaped bases, and other faces that are all rectangles (p. 354)
Example:

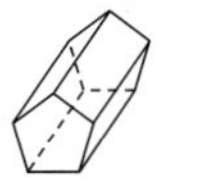

probability [prä•bə•bil′ə•tē] See *theoretical probability* and *experimental probability*

product [prä′dəkt] The answer in a multiplication problem (p. 15)

Property of Zero [prä′pər•tē əv zē′rō] The property that states that the product of any number and zero is zero (p. 35)

proportion [prə•pôr′shən] An equation that shows that two ratios are equal (p. 377)
Example: $\frac{1}{3} = \frac{3}{9}$

pyramid [pir′ə•mid] A solid figure with a polygon base and triangular sides that all meet at a common vertex (p. 355)
Example:

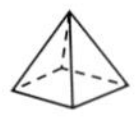

Q

quadrants [kwäd′rənts] The four regions of the coordinate plane (p. 560)

quadrilateral [kwä•drə•lat′ə•rəl] A polygon with four sides and four angles (p. 335)

quotient [kwō′shənt] The number, not including the remainder, that results from dividing (p. 23)

R

radius [rā′dē•əs] A line segment with one endpoint at the center of a circle and the other endpoint on the circle (p. 348)
Example:

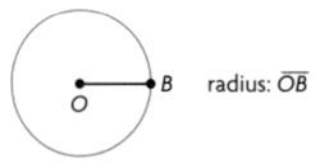
B
O
radius: $\overline{OB}$

random sample [ran′dəm sam′pəl] A sample in which each subject in the overall population has an equal chance of being selected (p. 95)

range [rānj] The difference between the greatest and least numbers in a group (p. 93)

rate [rāt] A ratio that compares two quantities having different units of measure (p. 375)

ratio [rā′shē•ō] A comparison of two numbers, *a* and *b*, written as a fraction $\frac{a}{b}$ (p. 230)

rational number [ra′shə•nəl num′bər] Any number that can be written as a ratio $\frac{a}{b}$, where *a* and *b* are integers and $b \neq 0$ (p. 230)

ray [rā] A part of a line with a single endpoint (p. 322)
Example:

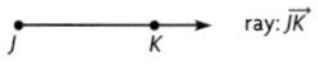
J
K
ray: $\overrightarrow{JK}$

reciprocal [ri•sip′rə•kəl] Two numbers are reciprocals of each other if their product equals 1. (p. 209)

reflection [ri•flek′shən] A movement of a figure by flipping it over a line (p. 540)

regular polygon [reg′yə•lər pä′lē•gän] A polygon in which all sides are congruent and all angles are congruent (p. 340)
Example:

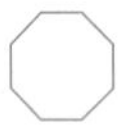

repeating decimal [ri•pēt′ing de′sə•məl] A decimal that doesn't end, because it shows a repeating pattern of digits after the decimal point (p. 169)

right angle [rīt an′gəl] An angle that has a measure of 90° (p. 324)
Example:

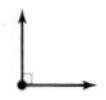

right triangle [rīt trī′an•gəl] A triangle with one right angle (p. 336)
Example:

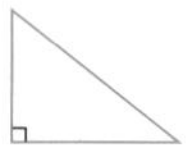

rotation [rō•tā′shən] A movement of a figure by turning it around a fixed point (p. 540)

rotational symmetry [rō•tā′shən•əl si′mə•trē] The property of a figure that can be rotated less than 360° around a central point and still be congruent to the original figure (p. 551)

S

sales tax [sālz taks] A percent of the cost of an item, added onto the item's cost (p. 410)

sample [sam′pəl] A part of a population (p. 94)

sample space [sam′pəl spās] The set of all possible outcomes (p. 418)

scale [skāl] A ratio between two sets of measurements (p. 388)

scale drawing [skāl drô′ing] A drawing that shows a real object smaller than (a reduction) or larger than (an enlargement) the real object (p. 387)

scalene [skā′lēn] A triangle with no congruent sides (p. 335)

scatterplot [skat′ər•plät] A graph with points plotted to show a relationship between two variables (p. 139)

sector [sek′tər] A region enclosed by two radii and the arc joining their endpoints (p. 348) *Example:*

sequence [sē′kwəns] An ordered set of numbers (p. 526)

similar figures [si′mə‧lər fig′yərz] Figures with the same shape but not necessarily the same size (p. 380)

simple interest [sim′pəl in′trəst] A fixed percent of the principal, paid yearly (p. 412)

simplest form [sim′pləst fôrm] The form in which the numerator and denominator of a fraction have no common factors other than 1 (p. 161)

solution [sə‧lōō′shən] A value that, when substituted for a variable in an equation, makes the equation true (p. 30)

square [skwâr] The product of a number and itself; a number with the exponent 2 (p. 280)

square [skwâr] A rectangle with four congruent sides (p. 501)

square root [skwâr rōōt] One of two equal factors of a number (p. 281)

stem-and-leaf plot [stem ənd lēf plät] A type of graph that shows groups of data arranged by place value (p. 126)

straight angle [strāt an′gəl] An angle whose measure is 180° (p. 324) *Example:*

X   Y   Z

Subtraction Property of Equality [sub‧trak′shən prä′pər‧tē əv i‧kwol′ə‧tē] The property that states that if you subtract the same number from both sides of an equation, the sides remain equal (p. 291)

sum [sum] The answer to an addition problem (p. 15)

supplementary angles [sup‧lə‧men′tə‧rē an′gəlz] Two angles whose measures have a sum of 180° (p. 327) *Example:*

100° 80°

surface area [sûr′fəs âr′ē‧ə] The sum of the areas of the faces of a solid figure (p. 494)

survey [sûr′vā] A method of gathering information about a group (p. 94)

systematic sample [sis‧tə‧ma′tik sam′pəl] A sampling method in which one subject is selected at random and subsequent subjects are selected according to a pattern (p. 95)

T

term [tûrm] Each number in a sequence (p. 526)

terms [tûrmz] The parts of an expression that are separated by an addition or subtraction sign (p. 277)

terminating decimal [tûr′mə‧nāt‧ing de′sə‧məl] A decimal that ends, having a finite number of digits after the decimal point (p. 169)

tessellation [tes‧ə‧lā′shən] A repeating arrangement of shapes that completely covers a plane, with no gaps and no overlaps (p. 543)

theoretical probability [thē‧ə‧re′ti‧kəl prä‧bə‧bil′ə‧tē] A comparison of the number of favorable outcomes to the number of possible equally likely outcomes (p. 418)

transformation [trans‧fər‧mā′shən] A movement that does not change the size or shape of a figure (p. 540)

translation [trans‧lā′shən] A movement of a figure along a straight line (p. 540)

tree diagram [trē dī′ə‧gram] A diagram that shows all possible outcomes of an event (p. 434)

Student Handbook **H81**

triangular number [trī‧an′gyə‧lər num′bər] A number that can be represented by a triangular array (p. 526)

U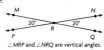

unbiased sample [un‧bī′əst sam′pəl] A sample is unbiased if every individual in the population has an equal chance of being selected. (p. 98)

underestimate [un‧dər‧es′tə‧mət] An estimate that is less than the exact answer (p. 17)

unit rate [yōō′nət rāt] A rate that has 1 unit as its second term (p. 375) *Example:* $1.45 per pound

unlike fractions [un′līk frak′shənz] Fractions with different denominators (p. 180)

upper extreme [up′ər ik‧strēm′] The greatest number in a set of data (p. 129)

upper quartile [up′ər kwôr′til] The median of the upper half of a set of data (p. 129)

V

variable [vâr′ē‧ə‧bəl] A letter or symbol that stands for one or more numbers (p. 28)

Venn diagram [ven dī′ə‧gram] A diagram that shows relationships among sets of things (p. 230)

vertex [vûr′teks] The point where two or more rays meet; the point of intersection of two sides of a polygon; the point of intersection of three or more edges of a solid figure; the top point of a cone (pp. 324, 355) *Examples:*

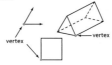
vertex   vertex

vertical angles [vûr′ti‧kəl an‧gəlz] A pair of opposite congruent angles formed where two lines intersect (p. 326) *Example:*

M   N
      20°   20°
P   Q
∠MRP and ∠NRQ are vertical angles.

volume [väl′yəm] The number of cubic units needed to occupy a given space (p. 502)

W

whole number [hōl num′bər] One of the numbers 0, 1, 2, 3, 4, ... The set of whole numbers goes on without end.

X

x-axis [eks‧ak′səs] The horizontal number line on a coordinate plane (p. 560)

x-coordinate [eks‧kō‧ôr′də‧nət] The first number in an ordered pair; it tells the distance to move right or left from (0,0). (p. 560)

Y

y-axis [wī‧ak′səs] The vertical number line on a coordinate plane (p. 560)

y-coordinate [wī‧kō‧ôr′də‧nət] The second number in an ordered pair, it tells the distance to move up or down from (0,0). (p. 560)

H82 Glossary

Chapter 1

Page 15

1. product **3.** difference **5.** sum
7. hundreds **9.** hundred thousands
11. hundred millions **13.** ten millions
15. 90,000 **17.** 300,000,000
19. 20,000,000,000 **21.** 2,000 **23.** 29,000
25. 35,000 **27.** 6,000 **29.** 135,000
31. 60,000 **33.** 50,000 **35.** 10,000
37. 640,000 **39.** 90,000

Pages 18–19

1. underestimate since both addends are
rounded down **3.** 1,500 **5.** 12,000 **7.** 600
9. 24,000 **11.** 360 **13.** 1,500 **15.** 80
17. 70 **19.** 6,000 **21.** 18,000 **23.** 350
25. 14,000 **27.** 16,000 **29.** 4,000
31. 150,000 **33.** 90 **35.** 12 **37.** 3,200,000
39. over; $400 + 700$ **41.** over; 100×20
43. over; 300×30 **45.** $>$ **47.** $<$ **49.** $<$
51. about 4,500,000 books **53.** 9,936 people
55. 235 and 345 **57.** 36 in.; 54 in.^{2} **59.** C

Page 21

3. 1,439 **5.** 26,208 **7.** 36,374 **9.** 1,111,384
11. 46,395,619 **13.** 75,125 **17.** 11,306
19. 1, 2, 3, 4, 6, 8, 12, 24 **21.** C

Pages 24–25

1. There were 102 full packages. The 18
newspapers left over were not enough to
make a full package. **3.** 792,456 **5.**
3,553,275 **7.** 54 **9.** 38,480 **11.** 850,038
13. 56 r4 **15.** 961,184 **17.** 3,496,458 **19.**
1,745,677 **21.** 26,522 **23.** 14 **25.** 19,760
27. 26 r2 **29.** 89 **31.** 1,312,800 **33.**
1,855,998 **35.** 84 **37.** $367\frac{9}{20}$ **39.** $241\frac{11}{14}$
41. 415 **43.** $159 **45.** 10 **47.** 64 **49.** B

Page 27

1. 13 apples, 27 oranges **3.** B **5.** April 26,
May 2, and May 8 **7.** 48 cards **9.** 5 min

Page 29

1. An algebraic expression has one or more
variables. **3.** $125 - 46$ **5.** $y \div 15$, or $\frac{y}{15}$
7. 46 **9.** 25×20 **11.** $76 - k$ **13.** 465
15. 9,000 **17.** 140 **19.** 3 **21.** $n + 12$
23. Deidre **25.** 215 **27.** 7,643

Page 31

1. No, because $4 + 3$ equals 7; $x = 6$
3. $f = 21$ **5.** $x = 4$ **7.** $k = 4$ **9.** $x = 5$
11. $k = 18$ **13.** $m = 9$ **15.** $x = 20$
17. $k = 29$ **19.** $v = 20$ **21.** $d = 9$
23. $p = 6$ **25.** 25 students **27.** 41
29. 4,990 **31.** D

Chapter 2

Page 35

1. 27 **3.** 64 **5.** 10,000 **7.** 512 **9.** 343
11. 256 **13.** Commutative of Addition
15. Property of Zero **17.** Associative of
Addition **19.** Distributive **21.** Identity
of Multiplication **23.** Distributive **25.** $a =$
5 **27.** $r = 3$ **29.** $t = 8$ **31.** 20 **33.** 32
35. 8 **37.** 32 **39.** 18

Pages 38–39

3. 204 **5.** 157 **7.** 56 **9.** 145 **11.** 55
13. 142 **15.** 93 **17.** 43 **19.** 168 **21.** 495
23. 185 **25.** 108 **27.** 212 **29.** 72
31. 244 **33.** 85 **35.** 45 **37.** 1,500
39. 1,028 **41.** 160 **43.** 64 **45.** 52
49. 72 CDs **51.** 18 CDs each **53.** 68 more
signatures **57.** 33,672 **59.** C

Page 41

1. 7 **3.** $2 \times 2 \times 2$; 8 **5.** $3 \times 3 \times 3 \times 3$; 81
7. $1 \times 1 \times 1 \times 1$; 1 **9.** $7 \times 7 \times 7$; 343
11. $5 \times 5 \times 5$; 125 **13.** 34×34; 1,156
15. $10 \times 10 \times 10 \times 10 \times 10 \times 10 \times 10 \times 10$;
100,000,000 **17.** $2 \times 2 \times 2 \times 2 \times 2 \times 2 \times 2 \times 2 \times 2 \times 2$; 1,024 **19.** 15×15; 225
21. 25; 25 **23.** 12^3 **25.** 4^4 **27.** n^2 **29.** 8^2
31. 10^4 **33.** 1947 **35.** Scott **37.** 36 in.
39. 745 r12

Pages 42–43

1. parentheses, exponent, multiplication,
addition; 154 **3.** multiplication, division,
addition; 16 **1.** No; 17 is the correct value,
not 9 **3.** $15 \div 3 + 12$ **5.** 29 **7.** 216
9. 31

Pages 44–45

1. $(420 - 100) \div 40 = 8$ **3.** 25 **5.** 28
7. 25 **9.** 68 **11.** 100 **13.** 1,218
15. 504 **17.** 60 **19.** 77
21. $20 - (\$3.25 + 3 \times \$1.29) = \$12.88$
23. 18,447 people **25.** 204 **27.** 32 r3

Page 47

1. Aquarium Tour, Underwater Acrobats,
Animal Acts, Whale Acts **3.** H **5.** 3 books,
4 magazines **7.** \$4,700 **9.** 24 nails

Chapter 3
Page 51

1. 0.2 **3.** 0.09 **5.** 836.23 **7.** 93,450.38
9. 306,007.06 **11.** 7 **13.** 1 tenth;
hundredths **15.** < **17.** < **19.** > **21.** >
23. > **25.** > **27.** 1 **29.** 42 **31.** 72
33. 26.4 **35.** 8.6 **37.** 14.5 **39.** 55.6

Pages 54–55

1. 2.0769 **3.** 0.007 **5.** 0.06 **7.** 0.001 +
0.00003 **9.** 300 + 40 + 2 + 0.04 + 0.006
11. = **13.** 1.351, 1.361, 1.363 **15.** 0.0007
17. 0.00006 **19.** 0.03 + 0.006 + 0.0002
21. 2 + 0.4 + 0.05 + 0.006 **23.** < **25.** =
27. > **29.** < **31.** 0.405, 1.05, 1.125, 1.25,
1.45 **33.** 8.91, 9.082, 9.285, 9.82, 9.85
35. 125.4, 125.35, 125.33, 125.3 **37.** 41.01,
$14\frac{1}{10}$, $14\frac{3}{100}$, 14.01 **39.** \$94,563,020; ninety-
four million, five hundred sixty-three
thousand, twenty **43.** 228 **45.** 29

Page 57

1. C **3.** air conditioner **5.** calculator,
\$10.50; pen, \$1.50; notebook, \$2.00 **7.** 60
cards **9.** Blaster

Page 59

3. 40 **5.** 90 **7.** 210 **9.** 32 **11.** 9
13. 50 **15.** 140 **17.** 1,800 **19.** 27,000
21. \$17,000 **23.** 36 **25.** > **27.** Possible
answer: about 24 lb **31.** 2.235, 2.325, 2.523,
2.532 **33.** 1,121 r18

Page 61

1. 18% means 18 per hundred, so 18 are red.
3. 0.06, 6% **5.** 0.7 or 0.70 **7.** 0.84 **9.** 0.5,
0.50 **11.** 0.11, 11% **13.** 0.62 **15.** 0.28
17. 0.53 **19.** 85% **21.** 40% **23.** 0.79, 79%
25. 27.5, 27.8, 27.82 **27.** 15,456 **31.** B

Chapter 4
Page 65

1. 47 **3.** 44 **5.** 10 **7.** 222 **9.** 252
11. 1,444 **13.** 4,000 **15.** 3,000 **17.** 24
19. 47 **21.** 14 **23.** 29 **25.** 43 **27.** 840
29. 19,405 **31.** 8.75 **33.** 12.5 **35.** 160.8
37. $9\frac{5}{8}$ **39.** $39\frac{2}{7}$

Pages 68–69

3. $0.63 **5.** 18.585 **7.** 20.923 **9.** 37.31
11. 124.94 **13.** 87.80 **15.** 1,438.66
17. 0.6 **19.** 287.673 **21.** 488.55
23. 287.673 **25.** 257.14 **27.** 9.42 **29.** yes
31. no **33.** 1.25 **35.** 12.3 **37.** 2.216
39. 0.090 **41.** 210; more than **43.** 3,950;
3,905; 3,590; 3,509 **45.** 0.46

Pages 72–73

3. 0.35 **5.** 2 **7.** 3 **9.** 2.87 **11.** 1.218
13. 25.84 **15.** 0.24 **17.** 3 **19.** 6
21. 194.208 **23.** 0.410 **25.** 13.8 **27.** 36.5
29. 4.92 **31.** 0.08 **33.** 0.441 **35.** 5.5080
37. 26.8467 **39.** 0.39501 **41.** 0.8934
43. $7.31 **49.** 299 r14

Page 74

1. 1.01 **3.** 0.45

Page 75

1. 6 **3.** 3 **5.** 4 **7.** 3 **9.** 8 **11.** 0.57
13. 89 r21

Pages 78–79

1. multiply by 100 **3.** 96 ÷ 16
5. 482.4 ÷ 24 **7.** 14.86 **9.** 1.97 **11.** 4.4
13. 819 ÷ 9 **15.** 239 ÷ 5 **17.** 2335.8 ÷ 102
19. 6.1 **21.** 6.9 **23.** 9.91 **25.** 0.21
27. 21.2 **29.** 8.2 **31.** 15.05 **33.** 220
35. 2.36 **37.** 3.03 **39.** 5 weeks
41. 30 pages **43.** greater than

Page 81

1. C **3.** 4 magnets **5.** 8 hr 5 min
7. 65 min, or 1 hr 5 min **9.** 108 pieces

Page 83

1. $a \times 6.45$; 12×6.45; $45.15 **3.** 11.7
5. 5.08 **7.** $m = 19$ **9.** 4.6 **11.** 14 **13.** 3.9
15. $r = 7.7$ **17.** $a = 8.2$ **19.** $p = 17.6$
21. $n \div 6$; $n = 4.8$ **23.** 4 mi **25.** 37
27. 3.08, 3.508, 3.58, 3.85

Chapter 5

Page 93

1. median **3.** range **5.** 13 more girls
7. 29 girls **9.** 8 **11.** 8.475 **13.** 28; 32
15. 11; 10.8 **17.** 6

Pages 96–97

5. population, because there are not too
many students and they are easily available
7. systematic **9.** convenience
11. population; There are not too many
basketball team members. **13.** systematic
15. convenience **21.** 9.3 **23.** 2

Pages 98–99

1. Yes. Only those in the computer club
would be represented. **3.** biased; excludes
males **5.** biased; excludes members who
did not use the gym in August **7.** biased;
excludes people who are not teenagers
9. biased; excludes males **11.** unbiased
13. biased **17.** 4 **19.** 9,000

Page 101

1. D **3.** 12 members **5.** 1 3-point,
7 2-point; 3 3-point, 4 2-point; 5 3-point,
1 2-point **7.** $42.50 **9.** 37 birds
11. Saturday

Pages 104–105

1. 1-10, 11-20; Since $2 \times 10 = 20$, you would
have 2 intervals that include 10 numbers
5. 16 **13.** 9 **15.** No, the data are categories
and not numerical **19.** unbiased

Page 107

1. The mean would become 21.2. The mean
or median would be most useful to describe
the data. **3.** 7 hours **5.** 24; 23; 22
7. 15.375 points **9.** 10 and 12 **11.** 336.8;
360; no mode **15.** Tim should divide by 4,
not 3. 6 **17.** 71 people **19.** 90%

Pages 110–111

1. The median and mode would not change. The mean would not increase as much.
3. 16; 14; 12 **5a.** Abe: mean 7.5, median 6, mode 7; Bart: mean 7.5, median 8.5, mode 0;
5b. Abe: mean 9.3, median 7, mode 7 and 20; Bart: mean 6.4, median 5, mode 0;
5c. Abe's: all increase; Bart's: mean/median decrease; mode doesn't change **7a.** 75
7b. No. With a perfect score of 100, the mean would be 65.7. **9.** 5.75; 5.5; 5 **11.** 9.5; 10; 10 and 12

Pages 113–115

1. No. The sample would be a convenience sample and not a random sample.
3. No. The sample is not representative.
5. Yes. The sample is random and representative; the question is unbiased.
7. No. The sample is not representative of the population. **9.** The interest in reading increased slightly. **11.** The interest in coin collecting decreased slightly. **13.** The interest in building models increased slightly.
15. increase: trading cards; decrease: coin collecting **17.** $5 **19.** 33; 31; 22 **21.** B

Chapter 6

Page 119

1. Saturn V, Ariane IV, Titan-Centaur, Titan IIIC **3.** about 55m **7.** about 15,000 sq mi
9. 92 **11.** 22 **13.** 3 or more **15.** 20

Pages 122–123

1. so you can tell the difference between the sets of data **3.** line graph **5.** bar graph
7. circle graph **11.** Each month, more comedies were rented. **13.** Comedy video rentals will increase and action video rentals will decrease. **17.** No. The sample is not representative of the student population.
19. 0.56 **21.** J

Page 125

1. Extend the graph until it intersects with 24 mi and find the corresponding time.
3. 5 hr **5.** 6 hr **7.** 8 hr **9.** about 45 mi
11. 5.6; 5; 4 **13.** 6.5; 7; 9 **15.** C

Pages 127–128

5. bar graph **7.** bar graph **9b.** 24.5 in.;
28 in. **13.** random **15.** 73%

Pages 130–131

1. A box-and-whisker graph shows the distribution of data, not all of the data
3. 11; 22; 11 **5.** 58; 67; 9 **7.** 85; 104; 19
9. 72 points; 97 points **13.** yes **15.** 0.02 or two hundredths

Pages 133–136

3. Yes. The question is biased and could lead people to choose the Mustangs as the best baseball team. **5.** No. Angel Falls is about 3,200 ft high while Tugela Falls is about 3,000 ft high. **7.** Yes. The question is biased and could lead people to choose oranges. **9.** No. Brand B costs $30 and Brand A costs $20.
13. Lin looked only at the graph and did not look at the scales. **15.** 43 and 55 **17.** B

Chapter 7

Page 145

1. prime number **3.** yes **5.** no **7.** yes
9. yes **11.** yes **13.** no **15.** yes **17.** no
19. yes **21.** no **23.** 16, 20, 24 **25.** 48, 60, 72 **27.** 20, 25, 30 **29.** 6, 12, 18, 24, 30
31. 30, 60, 90, 120, 150 **33.** 9, 18, 27, 36, 45
35. 1, 2, 4, 8 **37.** 1, 11 **39.** 1, 2, 3, 6, 9, 18, 27, 54

Page 147

3. 2, 4, 8 **5.** 2, 4, 8 **7.** 3 **9.** 2, 3, 4, 6, 9
11. 2, 4 **13.** 3, 5 **15.** 2, 3, 4, 6, 8 **17.** 3, 5
19. 2, 3, 6, 9 **21.** 3 **23.** T **25.** T
29. $28.88 **31.** 5% **33.** 16,302

Page 149

1. $2^2 \times 3 \times 13$ 3. $2 \times 2 \times 3$ 5. $2 \times 2 \times 2 \times 2$ 7. 3×7 9. 2×127 11. $2 \times 2 \times 2 \times 2 \times 2 \times 2$ 13. $2 \times 2 \times 19$ 15. $2 \times 3 \times 3; 2 \times 3^2$ 17. $7 \times 7; 7^2$ 19. $2 \times 2 \times 7 \times 19; 2^2 \times 7 \times 19$ 21. 2×373 23. $n = 2$
25. $n = 5$ 27. $c = 2$ or 3 31. 60% 33. 13

Pages 152–153

3. 3, 6, 9, 12, 15   5. 11, 22, 33, 44, 55   7. 21
9. 18   11. 3   13. 3   15. 4, 8, 12, 16, 20
17. 16, 32, 48, 64, 80   19. 10, 20, 30, 40, 50
21. 14, 28, 42, 56, 70   23. 24   25. 60
27. 120   29. 108   31. 2   33. 3   35. 1
37. 8   39. 9 and 12   41. a. 60   b. 4
packages of cereal samples, 3 packages of
pamphlets   43. She found the GCF instead
of LCM. The LCM is 30.   45. 124 r14

Page 155

1. October 15   3. H   5. 9 in.   7. 18 blocks

Chapter 8
Page 159

1. $>$ 3. denominator   5. $>$ 7. $<$ 9. $>$
11. 62,000; 61,600; 61,060   13. $\frac{5}{6}$ 15. $\frac{1}{3}$
17. 20% 19. 75%

Pages 162–163

1. Also multiply the denominator by 5; $\frac{10}{15}$
3. 12   5. 4   7. 1   9. 16   11. 1, 2, 4   13. 1, 2   15. $\frac{1}{8}$ 17. $\frac{1}{6}$ 19. $\frac{11}{4}$ 21. $\frac{3}{10}$ 23. 5   25. 4   27. 6   29. 8   31. 12   33. 7   35. 1   37. 1, 3   39. 1, 5   41. 1   43. $\frac{1}{6}$ 45. $\frac{1}{8}$ 47. $\frac{5}{9}$
49. $\frac{1}{5}$ 51. $\frac{2}{3}$ 53. $\frac{10}{7}$ 55. $\frac{1}{4}$ 57. $\frac{1}{5}$ 59. $\frac{1}{2}$
61. $\frac{2}{3}$ 63. $\frac{1}{4}$ 65. What fractions of the
muffins are bran?   67. 24   69. 0.035

Page 165

1. It has a whole number part and a fraction
part.   3. $3\frac{1}{2}$ 5. $3\frac{2}{3}$ 7. $\frac{5}{4}$ 9. $\frac{8}{3}$ 11. $\frac{37}{7}$
13. $4\frac{1}{2}$ 15. $5\frac{3}{4}$ 17. $5\frac{1}{6}$ 19. $12\frac{6}{7}$ 21. $16\frac{2}{3}$
23. $3\frac{2}{3}$ 25. $\frac{13}{2}$ 27. $\frac{19}{10}$ 29. $\frac{37}{4}$ 31. $\frac{53}{11}$

33. $\frac{93}{5}$ 35. no, only a fraction whose
numerator is greater than its denominator
37. $2^2 \times 3^2$ 39. 23×1

Pages 166–167

1. The denominators are the same. $4 < 5$,
so $\frac{4}{9} < \frac{5}{9}$ 3. $<$ 5. $>$ 7. $\frac{1}{4}, \frac{6}{12}, \frac{2}{3}$ 9. $>$
11. $=$ 13. $=$ 15. $>$ 17. $\frac{2}{6}, \frac{1}{2}, \frac{9}{12}$ 19. $\frac{1}{2}, \frac{7}{12}, \frac{5}{6}$ 21. $\frac{3}{10}, \frac{2}{5}, \frac{1}{2}$ 23. $\frac{1}{6}, \frac{1}{3}, \frac{1}{2}$ 25. $\frac{1}{12}, \frac{5}{8}, \frac{3}{12}$
27. 3 pieces of each pizza remain. That is $\frac{3}{8}$ of
the mushroom and $\frac{3}{12}$ cheese pizza. $\frac{3}{12} = \frac{1}{4} = \frac{2}{8}$
$< \frac{3}{8}$, so more of the mushroom pizza is left.
29. 7   31. 24

Page 168

1. 0.3   3. 0.7   5. 0.90   7. 0.4   9. 0.85

Pages 170–171

3. $\frac{7}{10}$ 5. $\frac{105}{1,000}$ 7. 0.25; T   9. 0.66666; R
11. $>$ 13. $=$ 15. 20% 17. 40% 19. $\frac{6}{100}$
21. $\frac{61}{100}$ 23. $\frac{205}{1,000}$ 25. $\frac{9}{1,000}$ 27. 0.16666; R
29. 0.625; T   31. 0.3; T   33. 0.111111; R
35. 0.36; T   37. 0.15; R   39. $=$ 41. $<$
43. $<$ 45. 75% 47. 6% 49. 50%
51. 0.5% 53. 0.72   55. Megan   57. $\frac{9}{2}$
59. 76.89

Chapter 9
Page 175

1. mixed number   3. divide   5. $\frac{3}{4}$ 7. $\frac{1}{3}$
9. $\frac{4}{3}$, or $1\frac{1}{3}$ 11. $\frac{3}{2}$, or $1\frac{1}{2}$ 13. $\frac{1}{2}$ 15. $\frac{2}{3}$ 17. $\frac{5}{3}$, or $1\frac{2}{3}$ 19. $\frac{1}{3}$ 21. $\frac{1}{2}$ 23. $\frac{5}{4}$, or $1\frac{1}{4}$ 25. $\frac{2}{3}$
27. $\frac{1}{2}$ 29. $\frac{1}{2}$ 31. $\frac{1}{3}$ 33. $\frac{5}{6}$ 35. 1   37. $\frac{2}{9}$
39. $\frac{5}{7}$

Pages 178–179

3. close to 1   5. between 0 and $\frac{1}{2}$ 7. $1\frac{1}{2}$
9. $\frac{1}{2}$ 11. $7\frac{1}{2}$ 13. 2   15. close to 1
17. close to 0   19. 2   21. $\frac{1}{2}$ 23. 17

25. 3   27. 0   29. $4\frac{1}{2}$ 31. 9 to $9\frac{1}{2}$; $9\frac{1}{4}$

33. $4\frac{1}{2}$ to 5; $4\frac{3}{4}$ 35. $5\frac{1}{2}$ to 6; $5\frac{3}{4}$ 37. about 7
39. about 6 feet   41. about 26   43. about
30   47. about $1\frac{1}{4}$ yd   49. March 15, 24;
April 2, 11, 20, 29   51. 45%

Page 181

1. $\frac{5}{12}$ 3. $\frac{1}{12}$ 5. $\frac{1}{10}$ 7. $\frac{1}{12}$ 9. $\frac{1}{8}$ 11. $\frac{1}{2}$
13. $=$ 15. $>$

Pages 183–185

1. $\frac{5}{12}$ c more 3. $\frac{7}{10} + \frac{2}{10}$ 5. $\frac{12}{15} - \frac{5}{15}$ 7. $\frac{1}{3}$
9. $1\frac{5}{12}$ 11. $\frac{1}{15}$ 13. $\frac{7}{9}$ 15. $\frac{24}{28} - \frac{21}{28}$ 17. $\frac{5}{6}$
19. $\frac{4}{5}$ 21. $\frac{3}{14}$ 23. $\frac{1}{5}$ 25. $1\frac{3}{8}$ 27. $\frac{5}{8}$ 29. $\frac{7}{15}$
31. $\frac{2}{9}$ 33. $\frac{6}{8}$, or $\frac{3}{4}$ 35. 2 37. $\frac{5}{12}$ mile
39. $r = 1$ 41. $c = \frac{3}{5}$ 43. $m = 1$ 45. $\frac{5}{8}$ tsp
47. $\frac{2}{15}$ is left; add to find the total spent and saved; subtract to find how much is left.
49. 24 and 28 51. $\frac{4}{9}$ 53. 6,132

Pages 187–189

3. $3\frac{4}{5}$ 5. $1\frac{3}{10}$ 7. $6\frac{7}{12}$ 9. $1\frac{1}{6}$ 11. $1\frac{1}{18}$
13. $2\frac{1}{2}$ 15. $8\frac{3}{10}$ 17. $10\frac{1}{8}$ 19. $4\frac{1}{10}$ 21. $11\frac{3}{20}$
23. $8\frac{3}{14}$ 25. $28\frac{1}{8}$ 27. Commutative, $2\frac{1}{4}$
29. Associative, $1\frac{5}{6}$ 31. longer; $\frac{1}{6}$ in.; subtraction; to find the difference in length
33. $9\frac{3}{4}$ c 35. 3rd prize 37. $\frac{16}{15}$, or $1\frac{1}{15}$
39. $\frac{4}{5}, \frac{2}{3}, \frac{1}{2}$

Page 191

1. $1\frac{2}{3}$ 3. $1\frac{4}{9}$ 5. $\frac{7}{10}$ 7. $\frac{11}{12}$ 9. $3\frac{3}{4}$ 11. 21.42

Page 193

1. $3\frac{1}{3} = 2\frac{4}{3}$ 3. $2\frac{1}{12}$ 5. $3\frac{9}{10}$ 7. $3\frac{17}{18}$ 9. $1\frac{11}{12}$
11. $4\frac{7}{9}$ 13. $2\frac{7}{12}$ 15. $1\frac{3}{8}$ 17. $2\frac{7}{10}$, or 2.7
19. $2\frac{4}{5}$ 21. $\frac{1}{2}$ mi shorter 25. $7\frac{1}{3}, \frac{22}{3}$
27. 55 r5

Page 195

1. $18\frac{1}{2}$ mi 3. C 5. 12 cans 7. $4\frac{3}{4}$ mi
9. Gary

Chapter 10
Page 199

1. equation 3. 0 5. $\frac{1}{2}$ 7. $\frac{1}{2}$ 9. $\frac{1}{2}$ 11. $\frac{1}{2}$
13. $\frac{1}{2}$ 15. 0 17. $\frac{1}{2}$ 19. $C = 32$ 21. $x = 0.17$ 23. $t = 14$ 25. $r = 2.6$ 27. $1\frac{1}{6}$
29. $1\frac{1}{3}$ 31. $\frac{15}{2}$ 33. $\frac{14}{5}$

Page 201

1. about 498 million pounds 3. $\frac{1}{2}$ 5. 20
7. $63\frac{3}{4}$ 9. 118 11. $\frac{1}{2}$ 13. 1 15. 4 17. 3
19. 20 21. $\frac{1}{4}$ 23. $>$ 25. about 7 min
29. $3\frac{4}{9}$ 31. 11

Pages 204–205

3. $\frac{3}{8}$ 5. $\frac{2}{10}$, or $\frac{1}{5}$ 7. $\frac{3}{10}$ 9. $\frac{12}{7}$, or $1\frac{5}{7}$ 11. $\frac{8}{3}$, or $2\frac{2}{3}$ 13. $\frac{5}{9}$ 15. $\frac{3}{16}$ 17. $\frac{1}{16}$ 19. $\frac{2}{9}$ 21. $\frac{2}{15}$
23. $\frac{7}{10}$ 25. $\frac{1}{10}$ 27. $\frac{4}{15}$ 29. 2 31. $<$
33. $<$ 35. 108 voters 37. 6 39. $b = 12.09$

Page 207

1. $3 \times 4\frac{2}{3} = (3 \times 4) + (3 \times \frac{2}{3})$; $12 + 2 = 14$.
3. $1\frac{1}{8}$ 5. $2\frac{1}{4}$ 7. $18\frac{3}{8}$ 9. $2\frac{1}{4}$ 11. $8\frac{1}{6}$
13. 33 15. 15 17. 85 19. $7\frac{1}{5}$ 21. $22\frac{1}{2}$
23. $<$ 25. $2\frac{1}{12}$ mi 29. $6\frac{7}{20}$ 31. 352,053

Page 208

1. 9 3. 4

Page 209

1. $n = 4$ 3. $n = \frac{3}{4}$ 5. 8 7. $\frac{3}{2}$, or $1\frac{1}{2}$ 9. $9\frac{9}{20}$
11. $606.64 > 606.074$

Pages 212–213

3. $\frac{3}{2}$ 5. $\frac{1}{7}$ 7. $\frac{3}{13}$ 9. $\frac{4}{5}$ 11. $\frac{1}{24}$ 13. 3
15. $1\frac{7}{32}$ 17. $\frac{1}{10}$ 19. $\frac{9}{2}$ 21. $\frac{7}{15}$ 23. $\frac{1}{9}$
25. $\frac{5}{13}$ 27. $1\frac{1}{6}$ 29. $9\frac{1}{3}$ 31. $2\frac{1}{4}$ 33. 5
35. $5\frac{1}{15}$ 37. $1\frac{8}{13}$ 39. 18 41. 32
43. $2\frac{5}{14}$ 45. $\frac{5}{18}$ 47. $\frac{4}{5}$ 49. 48 burgers
51. $1\frac{1}{4}$ yd 53. $46.90 55. $13\frac{3}{8}$

Page 215

1. $1\frac{5}{6}$ min; subtraction 3a. B 3b. H
5. $2\frac{2}{3}$ mi 7. $10\frac{1}{3}$ mi

Page 217

1. $b \times \frac{3}{4}$; $32 \times \frac{3}{4}$; 24 oz 3. $2\frac{1}{5}$ 5. $5\frac{5}{8}$
7. $y = \frac{3}{8}$ 9. $7\frac{5}{6}$ 11. $1\frac{1}{4}$ 13. $\frac{1}{20}$ 15. $\frac{3}{8}$
17. 1 19. $x = 2$ 21. $x = \frac{1}{4}$ 23. $x = 1\frac{1}{3}$
27. $\frac{3}{4}, \frac{3}{5}, \frac{3}{8}$ 29. $a = \frac{4}{5}$

Chapter 11

Page 227

1. negative numbers   **11.** 1, 2, 3, 4
13. 1, 3, 5, 7   **15.** <   **17.** =   **19.** >
21. 32°F   **23.** ⁻16°F   **25.** 60°F

Page 229

3. ⁻350   **5.** ⁻14   **7.** ⁺25   **9.** ⁻742   **11.** ⁻5
13. ⁺12,000   **15.** ⁺2   **17.** ⁺31   **19.** ⁻207
21. 28   **23.** 660   **25.** ⁻1,310 ft   **27.** $\frac{1}{5}$
29. $\frac{12}{20}$, or $\frac{3}{5}$ **31.** 13

Pages 232–233

1. All integers can be written in the form $\frac{a}{1}$
3. $-\frac{37}{100}$ **5.** $\frac{889}{1,000}$ **7.** $-\frac{22}{3}$ **9.** $-\frac{1}{2}$ **11.** 0
13. $-\frac{71}{100}$ **15.** $-\frac{21}{8}$ **17.** ⁻0.3   **19.** ⁻0.7
21. $-7\frac{1}{4}$ **23.** 16.05   **25.** $-\frac{5}{8}$ **27.** yes

29. yes   **31.** yes   **33.** 90 steps   **35.** Not all integers are whole numbers; ⁻8 is not a whole number.   **37.** 0.34; $\frac{34}{100}$

Page 235

3. <   **5.** <   **7.** <   **9.** >   **11.** <   **13.** >
15. >   **17.** 0.4, 0.46, 0.6   **19.** $-\frac{1}{4}$, ⁻0.2, 0, $\frac{1}{4}$
21. 1°, ⁻3°, ⁻5°   **23.** ⁻450   **25.** 2.096   **27.** C

Page 237

1. Jeffrey, sixth grade; Victoria, seventh grade; Arthur, eighth grade   **3.** C   **5.** Arlene, Kathy, Helene   **7.** 15   **9.** 12 mi

Chapter 12

Page 241

1. integers   **3.** ⁺62   **5.** ⁻13   **7.** ⁺12   **9.** ⁻3
11. ⁺11   **13.** ⁻8   **15.** ⁻13   **17.** ⁺4   **19.** 0

Page 242

1. ⁺13   **3.** ⁻10

Page 243

1. ⁻2   **3.** 0   **5.** ⁺7   **7.** ⁻9   **9.** ⁻6.8, ⁻6.4, ⁻6.2   **11.** ⁻3.6, $-3\frac{4}{7}$, $-3\frac{1}{2}$ **13.** B

Pages 246–247

1. Use sign of the addends.   **3.** The sum was 12, which indicates a gain of 12 yards, not a loss of 12 yards   **5.** $5 + {}^-9 = {}^-4$ **7.** ⁻7
9. ⁻2   **11.** ⁻10   **13.** 0   **15.** $^-2 + 6 = 4$
17. ⁻1   **19.** 3   **21.** ⁻20   **23.** 8   **25.** ⁻28
27. ⁻12   **29.** ⁻11   **31.** 100   **33.** $x = {}^-7$
35. $x = 5$ **37.** ⁻12°F   **39.** The Wildcats lost 2 yards.   **41.** 12 cm   **43.** greater than   **45.** C

Page 249

1. ⁻11   **3.** ⁻22   **5.** 2   **7.** ⁻5   **9.** 6   **11.** ⁻8
13. D

Page 251

1. ⁻9 + 40   **3.** 3 + 6   **5.** ⁻4 + ⁻6   **7.** ⁻5
9. ⁻7   **11.** 8 + 11   **13.** ⁻9 + ⁻11   **15.** ⁻4
17. ⁻2   **19.** 0   **21.** ⁻5   **23.** ⁻4   **25.** ⁻5
27. 5   **29.** 7°F   **31.** What was the range of temperatures?   **33.** ⁻213   **35.** $2 \times 2 \times 3 \times 7$

Chapter 13

Page 255

1. 24   **3.** 10   **5.** 4   **7.** 72   **9.** 5   **11.** 10
13. $n = 7$ **15.** $n = 54$ **17.** $n = 7$ **19.** ⁻7
21. ⁻7   **23.** ⁻17   **25.** ⁻68   **27.** ⁻47   **29.** ⁻5
31. Add 1; 6, 7, 8   **33.** Divide by 2; 8, 4, 2
35. Multiply by 2; 96, 192, 384   **37.** Subtract 8; 80, 72, 64   **39.** Rotate shaded triangle 90° clockwise.

Page 257

1. 20   **3.** ⁻18   **5.** 4   **7.** 21

Page 259

1. Neither; zero is neither positive nor negative.   **3.** ⁻54   **5.** ⁻16   **7.** ⁻21   **9.** ⁻90
11. ⁻40   **13.** 14   **15.** 84   **17.** 110   **19.** 288
21. 450   **23.** $y = {}^-3$ **25.** $y = 3$ **27.** $y = {}^-4$
29. ⁻30   **31.** The product of integers with like signs is positive; $^-5 \times {}^-2 = 10$ **33.** ⁻12
35. 364

Page 261

1. The rules are the same.   **3.** 6   **5.** ⁻8
7. 8   **9.** ⁻22   **11.** ⁻2   **13.** ⁻9   **15.** 9
17. ⁻10   **19.** ⁻17   **21.** $x = 18$ **23.** $x = $ ⁻9
25. ⁻$509   **27.** 5 weeks   **29.** ⁻96   **31.** $38\frac{1}{4}$
33. C

Pages 262–263

1. ⁻2   **3.** ⁻34   **5.** 177; Commutative
7. 576; Associative   **9.** ⁻30   **11.** 120   **13.** 13
15. 421; Commutative   **17.** $6   **19.** ⁻15
21. One; 2 is prime and is an even number.
23. 7   **25.** ⁻37

Chapter 14

Page 273

1. exponent   **3.** algebraic expression   **5.** 32
7. 125   **9.** 16   **11.** 81   **13.** 49   **15.** 216
17. 25   **19.** 7   **21.** 2   **23.** 23   **25.** 20
27. 4   **29.** 21   **31.** 1, 2, 4, 8, 16   **33.** 1, 3,
11, 33   **35.** 1, 17   **37.** 1, 2, 3, 6, 7, 14, 21, 42
39. 1, 2, 4, 5, 8, 10, 20, 40

Page 275

3. $y \div 1.5$ **5.** 54 less than 19 times x
7. $3c + 2.9$ **9.** $h \times 4j \times k$ **11.** $6.3p - 5m$
19. $14.25 + 3.5h$ **21.** $2 + 2x$ **25.** ⁻36
27. 6 and 8

Pages 278–279

1. You will have to perform fewer
computations when evaluating the
expression if you simplify it first.
3. ⁻16, ⁻11, ⁻6, ⁻1   **5.** ⁻2, 6, 14, 22   **7.** 1,
⁻2, ⁻3, ⁻2   **9.** $7x - 8$; ⁻29   **11.** ⁻16, ⁻20,
⁻24, ⁻28   **13.** $20\frac{1}{2}$, 20, $19\frac{1}{2}$, 19   **15.** ⁻5, 1, 3, 4
17. $12x - 41$; ⁻89   **19.** $356 + 6a$; 236
21. ⁻2   **23.** Associative; 67   **25.** $x = 2$
27. $x = $ ⁻1   **31.** ⁻5

Page 280

1. 4   **3.** 49

Page 281

1. 8   **3.** 14   **5.** 22   **7.** 81; 9   **9.** ⁻49
11. >

Page 283

1. Operate inside the parentheses, evaluate
$\sqrt{36}$, then multiply; 12   **3.** ⁻33   **5.** 24
7. 150   **9.** ⁻24   **11.** ⁻10   **13.** 77   **15.** >
17. 14 ft   **19.** ⁻2, ⁻6, ⁻10, ⁻14   **21.** 2, ⁻4,
⁻6, ⁻7

Chapter 15

Page 287

1. equation   **3.** 37   **5.** 23   **7.** 11.37
9. 2.7   **11.** $1\frac{7}{12}$ **13.** $\frac{1}{2}$ **15.** $7\frac{11}{12}$ **17.** $2\frac{9}{28}$
19. $43 - 19 = 24$ **21.** $16 + 3 = 19$
23. $46 + 196 = 242$ **25.** $125 \div 5 = 25$
27. $2 \cdot 6 = 12$ **29.** $21 \cdot 12 = 252$
31. $25 \cdot 16 = 400$ **33.** addition
35. subtraction   **37.** multiplication
39. subtraction

Page 289

1. any quantity that you do not know
3. $x + 7 = 20$ **5.** $5 \cdot m = 35$; or $5m = 35$
7. $14 = n + 12$ **9.** $n \div 2\frac{3}{4} = \frac{5}{6}$
11. $72,000 = 9e$ **15.** $8x - 15$; ⁻31
17. $25 + 9z$; ⁻47

Page 290

1. $x = 4$ **3.** $x = 7$ **5.** $x = 3$ **7.** $x = 1$

Pages 292–293

3. $x = 7$ **5.** $c = 2.7$ **7.** $m = 15\frac{1}{4}$ **9.** $x = 8\frac{3}{4}$
11. $k = $ ⁻41   **13.** $b = 2.9$ **15.** $y = 8\frac{3}{4}$
17. $t = $ ⁻19   **19.** $x = $ unknown length; $x +$
$12 + 10 = 29$; $x = 7$, or 7 cm   **21.** $11 = n + 8$
23. 13

Page 295

1. You add the number that is being
subtracted from the variable.   **3.** $b = $ ⁻6
5. $y = 23.2$ **7.** $d = 34\frac{7}{15}$ **9.** $a = 33$
11. $z = 17.0$ **13.** $c = 23.3$ **15.** $s = 22\frac{11}{12}$
17. $m = 11.1$ **19.** $f = \frac{19}{24}$

21. s = original amount in savings; $s - (110 + 90 + 40) = 527$; $s = 8767$ **23.** $61 - 12 - 13 - 14 + 5 - 7$ **25.** $b = 4.4$ **27.** 9, 7, 5, 3

Chapter 16

Page 299

1. Celsius **3.** $18 = n + 6$ **5.** $\frac{n}{2} = \frac{2}{3}$
7. $2x = 47$ **9.** 14 **11.** $^-73$ **13.** $^-140$
15. 9 **17.** 25 **19.** 99 **21.** 27.3 **23.** $3\frac{4}{5}$
25. $y = 5$ **27.** $a = 9$ **29.** $c = 30$
31. $q = 56$ **33.** $y = 0.04$

Page 300

1. $c = 4$ **3.** $b = 2$

Page 303

1. You use inverse operations. **3.** $x = ^-7$
5. $y = 7.2$ **7.** $k = 6$ **9.** $a = 18$ **11.** $p = 16$
13. $n = ^-5$ **15.** $a = 16.48$ **17.** $w = 2.73$
19. $a = 10$ **21.** $\frac{m}{3} = 14$; $m = 42$; 42 marbles
23. $0.45 = 0.9w$; $w = 0.5$ cm **25.** $x = 22$
27. $z = ^-12$

Pages 306–307

1. The rate of speed is in feet per minute.
5. 20 **7.** 50°F **9.** 86°F **11.** 41°F
13. 13.9°C **15.** 37.8°C **17.** 36.8 **19.** 2.5
21. 98.6°F **23.** 203°F **25.** 0°C **27.** 8.3°C
29. 34.4°C **31.** 87.5 mi per hr **33.** Yes. The shuttle would be traveling 17,550 mi per hr.
35. Earth **39.** $y = ^-6$

Page 309

1. $4x + 1 = 5$; $x = 1$ **3.** $y = 2$ **5.** Add 1 to both sides, then divide by 2; $x = 3$. **7.** 3
9. 374

Page 311

1. 18 mi **3.** C **5.** 4:20 P.M. **7.** 60 in., or 5 ft **9.** 6 students

Chapter 17

Page 321

1. angle **3.** line **5.** obtuse **7.** acute
9. straight **11.** acute **13.** $\angle MNP$ or $\angle PNM$
15. $\angle 3$ **17.** $\angle a$ **19.** $\angle PBF$ or $\angle FBP$

Pages 322–323

1. plane; point; line, line segment, or ray
3. point R **5.** point C **7.** plane DHY
9. $\overrightarrow{XY}$ **11.** $\overline{PQ}, \overline{QR}, \overline{PR}$ **13.** $\overrightarrow{PQ}, \overrightarrow{QP}, \overrightarrow{RQ},$
$\overrightarrow{QR}, \overrightarrow{RP}, \overrightarrow{PR}$ **15.** a point **17.** a point
23. $n = 96$ **25.** 2

Page 325

1. 135°; obtuse **3.** 73°; acute **5.** 180°
7. 90° **9.** 45° **11.** 90° **13.** $b = 8$ **15.** $\frac{2}{15}$

Pages 328–329

1. Vertical angles are opposite each other and do not share a common ray **3.** $\angle AED$ and $\angle BEC$, $\angle AEB$ and $\angle DEC$ **5.** $\angle AED$ and $\angle BEC$ **7.** 51° **9.** 33° **11.** $\angle DOC$
13. $\angle AOB, \angle DOC$ **15.** 18° **17.** 131°
19. 90° **21.** supplementary, adjacent
23. none of these **25.** $\angle 1, \angle 2$; $\angle 3, \angle 3$; $\angle 3,$
$\angle 4$; $\angle 4, \angle 5$; $\angle 5, \angle 1$; They are side by side and have a common vertex. **27.** $\angle 1, \angle 5$;
$\angle 4, \angle 5$; Together they form a straight line.
29. Their measures are equal. **31.** $\overleftrightarrow{PQ}$ or
$\overleftrightarrow{QP}$ **33.** $^-6$

Pages 330-331

1. perpendicular and intersecting
3. intersecting / perpendicular
5. intersecting **7.** intersecting
9. intersecting **11.** $\overleftrightarrow{AC}, \overleftrightarrow{BD}, \overleftrightarrow{CG}, \overleftrightarrow{DH}$
13. $\overleftrightarrow{BD}, \overleftrightarrow{FH}, \overleftrightarrow{CD}, \overleftrightarrow{GH}$ **17.** Perpendicular lines always intersect but intersecting lines are not necessarily perpendicular.
19. 59.2 mi per hr **21.** $\frac{5}{12}$

Chapter 18

Page 335

1. isosceles **3.** pentagon **5.** hexagon
7. quadrilateral **9.** triangle **15.** add 4; 20, 24, 28 **17.** subtract 6; 13, 7, 1 **19.** multiply by $\frac{1}{2}$; $\frac{1}{32}$, $\frac{1}{64}$, $\frac{1}{128}$

Pages 337–339

3. 49°; acute **5.** 51°; obtuse **7.** 61°; acute
9. 20°; obtuse **11.** 40°; acute **13.** 45°
15. 75° **17.** 30° **19.** 115° **21.** 120°
23. 55° **25.** 90° **27.** 46° **29.** 18°
31. 153° **33.** parallel **35.** 21

Page 341

1. 16, 22, and 29 dimes **3.** C
5. Silvia: blue; Rhoda: green; David: brown
7. about $4 billion **9.** 24 mi per gal

Pages 344–345

3. trapezoid **5.** square **7.** rectangle
or square **9.** square **11.** rectangle
13. quadrilateral **15.** rhombus **17.** square
19. quadrilateral **21.** parallelogram,
trapezoid **23.** 11 in. × 15 in. **27.** 84°
29. 0.08

Pages 346–347

13. cannot **15.** can **17.** 9 in. **19.** 55°
21. $\overrightarrow{XY}$, ray XY **23.** 0.9

Page 349

1. Divide the diameter by 2. **3.** O
7. M **9.** $\overline{MY}$, $\overline{MW}$ **11.** Possible answer:
WY **13.** The length of the radius increases.
15. 25 min **17.** trapezoid **19.** 20

Chapter 19

Page 353

1. cone **3.** rectangular prism
5. triangular prism **7.** rectangular pyramid
9. 4; 4; 6 **11.** 5; 5; 8 **13.** 7; 10; 15

Page 355

1. octagonal prism; pentagonal pyramid;
polyhedron **3.** cone; no **5.** square
pyramid; yes **7.** cylinder; no **9.** pentagonal
pyramid; yes **11.** False; a cone has one flat
surface. **13.** true **15.** False; some
pyramids have triangular bases **17.** hexagon
21. parallelogram, square, or rectangle
23. sector **25.** $3\frac{6}{7}$

Pages 358–359

3. triangular pyramid **5.** rectangular prism
7. rectangular pyramid **19.** a rectangle
21. triangular prism **23.** 0

Page 363

1. 20 balls of clay **3.** D **5.** Monday; 8°C
9. 9 sides

Chapter 20

Page 373

1. equivalent **3.** polygon **5.** 27 **7.** 20
9. 6 **11.** 5 **13.** 7 **15.** 6 **17.** $x = 7$
19. $x = 5$ **21.** $x = 26$ **23.** $x = 17$ **25.** $x = 240$ **27.** $x = 1$ **29.** neither **31.** similar
33. both

Pages 375–376

1. Multiply or divide both terms of a ratio
by the same number. **3.** $\frac{1}{2}$; $\frac{8}{16}$ **5.** $\frac{3}{4}$; $\frac{6}{8}$
7. $\frac{150 \text{ points}}{10 \text{ games}}$; 15 points per game **9.** $\frac{90 \text{ words}}{2 \text{ min}}$,
45 words per min **11.** $\frac{\$15}{6 \text{ lb}}$; $2.50 **13.** $\frac{3}{6}$
15. $\frac{2}{6}$ **17.** $\frac{12}{32}$ **19.** $\frac{15}{27}$ **21.** $\frac{\$15}{5 \text{ tapes}}$; $3 per tape
23. $\frac{60 \text{ mi}}{3 \text{ gal}}$; 20 mi per gal **25.** $\frac{\$2.10}{6 \text{ fish}}$; $0.35 per
fish **27.** $\frac{4}{2}$ **29.** 15 **31.** 60 **33.** 4:1
35. Both have 3 boxes, so look for lowest
cost. **37.** $2.10 **39.** squares of 1, 2, 3, 4…; 25
41. $2 \times 3 \times 3 \times 3$

Page 379

1. $27\frac{1}{2}$ lb **3.** 81 mi **5.** J **7.** 600 in.^{2}
9. 98 **11.** 19 salespeople **13.** 60
15. He misinterpreted the labels. Four people
sold between 21–30 cars each.

Pages 382–383

1. Yes, compare the small triangle with the large triangle: $\frac{20}{30} = \frac{2}{3}$, $\frac{12}{18} = \frac{2}{3}$, and $\frac{22}{33} = \frac{2}{3}$.
3. both **5.** both **9.** neither **13.** No; ratios are not equivalent. **15.** Yes
17. $\angle T = 70°$; $\angle Y = 110°$; ST = 3.5 m
23. 45 ft $\times$ 60 ft **27.** $y = 3$

Pages 385–386

1. The ratios of corresponding sides of similar figures are equal **3.** 12 in.
5. $x = 39$ ft **7.** $\frac{n}{8} = \frac{3}{8}$; $n = 3$ in. **9.** $\frac{30}{n} = \frac{18}{24}$; $n = 40$ cm **11.** $\frac{n}{6.2} = \frac{2.5}{5}$; $n = 3.1$ cm
13. 42 in. **15.** No. Corresponding sides do not have the same ratio. **17.** 19

Pages 388–389

1. The real bike is 36 times the bike in the drawing. **5.** 28 **7.** 30 **9.** 20 **11.** 4
13. 96 boxes **15.** Each length of 1 cm on the drawing represents a length of 2 m on the actual object. **17.** false **19.** 30

Pages 390–391

1. 20 mi **3.** 50 mi **5.** 425 mi **7.** 240 mi
9. 420 mi **11.** 1,440 mi **13.** 370 mi
15. 6 in. **17.** $2\frac{1}{2}$ in. **19.** about $2\frac{1}{2}$ hr
21. the auto club map **23.** 4 in. **25.** 9

Chapter 21
Page 395

1. ratio **3.** 0.25 **5.** 0.1 **7.** 0.8 **9.** 0.2
11. 0.81 **13.** 17.28 **15.** 26.65 **17.** 28.8
19. 34.2 **21.** $\frac{1}{6}$ **23.** $\frac{2}{21}$ **25.** $\frac{3}{5}$ **27.** $\frac{16}{21}$
29. 0.45 **31.** 14% **33.** 0.4 **35.** 0.53
37. 1 **39.** 0.03

Page 397

1. 63% **3.** 16% **5.** 31% **7.** 60% **9.** >
11. = **13.** 8% **15.** 18% **17.** 64% **19.** <
21. > **23.** 64% **25.** $2\frac{1}{2}$ in. **27.** 13.015

Pages 400–401

1. move left 2 places, move right two places
3. 25% **5.** 60% **7.** $\frac{1}{2}$ **9.** $\frac{3}{4}$ **11.** $1\frac{4}{5}$
13. 0.08 **15.** 2.4 **17.** 15% **19.** 9%
21. 0.7% **23.** 250% **25.** 12.5% **27.** $\frac{22}{25}$
29. $\frac{1}{25}$ **31.** $\frac{1}{3}$ **33.** 0.07 **35.** 2.2
37. > **39.** < **41.** 20% **43.** What percent of the instruments are woodwinds? **45.** 26 pg per hr **49.** $2 \cdot 3 \cdot 3 \cdot 5$

Pages 404–405

1. Simply double the value of 25% of the number. **3.** 6 **5.** 36 **7.** 7.8 **9.** 21
11. 20 **13.** 44 **15.** 1.08 **17.** 59.64
19. 18.48 **21.** 42.4 **23.** 15.3 **25.** 123
27. 3.85 **29.** 57 **31.** $1.20 **33.** $2.37
35. $4.83 **37.** $5 **39.** $0.80 **41.** 25%; 15
43. 10%; 0.6 **45.** 140,000,000 mi^2 **49.** 0.1%
51. similar

Pages 410–411

3. $60 **5.** $76.80 **7.** $100 **9.** $33.53
11. $46.62 **13.** $38.08 **15.** $30.72
17. $4.65 **19.** $46.20 **21.** $61.51
23. $0.68 per lb **27.** $b = 17$

Page 413

1. It is a formula to find simple interest. Interest equals principal $\cdot$ rate $\cdot$ time. **3.** $4
5. $1,728 **7.** $208 **9.** $1.40, $7.00
11. $82.80, $414.00 **13.** Bank B. At Bank A, he will owe $1,255 while at Bank B he will owe $1,200. **15.** He used 0.6 for 6%. The correct simple interest is $36. **17.** 5 in.
19. 10

Chapter 22
Page 417

1. impossible **3.** equally likely **5.** 0.5, 50%
7. 0.75, 75% **9.** 0.1, 10% **11.** 0.6, 60%
13. 0.72, 72% **15.** 0.12, 12% **17.** 0.95, 95%
19. $\frac{1}{3}$ **21.** $\frac{1}{2}$ **23.** $\frac{2}{3}$ **25.** $\frac{2}{5}$ **27.** $\frac{7}{8}$ **29.** $\frac{1}{3}$
31. $\frac{7}{12}$ **33.** $\frac{1}{4}$ **35.** certain **37.** impossible

Pages 420–421

1. 1, 2, 3, 4, 5, 6 **3.** $\frac{1}{4}$, 0.25, 25% **5.** $\frac{1}{4}$, 0.25, 25% **7.** $\frac{3}{4}$, 0.75, 75% **9.** $\frac{1}{4}$, 0.25, 25% **11.** $\frac{0}{8}$, 0, 0% **13.** $\frac{1}{2}$, 0.50, 50% **15.** $\frac{1}{6}$ **17.** $\frac{1}{3}$ **19.** $\frac{1}{2}$ **21.** $\frac{1}{3}$ **23.** 1 **25.** = **27.** > **29.** < **31.** 0.6 **33.** $\frac{5}{12}$ **35.** 77% **37.** the probability the event will not occur **41.** 9 blue; 15 red **43.** ⁻7.75, $7\frac{1}{4}$, $7\frac{3}{8}$, 7.5

Page 423

1. *too much*; $\frac{4}{7}$ **3.** *too little*; need the 1970 land speed record **5.** C **7.** 4 hr **9.** 8,528 steps

Page 425

1. $\frac{5}{8}$ **3.** 89 **5.** A

Page 427

3. $\frac{1}{5}$ **5.** $\frac{1}{10}$ **7.** $\frac{2}{15}$ **9.** $\frac{1}{4}$ **11.** $\frac{2}{5}$ **13.** $\frac{2}{5}$ **15.** 15 times **17.** number of times 4 lands ÷ total number of rolls **19.** $\frac{4}{7}$ **21.** 9.75 **23.** B

Chapter 23

Page 431

1. sample space **3.** outcome **5.** $\frac{1}{3}$ **7.** $\frac{3}{16}$ **9.** $\frac{2}{5}$ **11.** $\frac{1}{8}$ **13.** $\frac{1}{25}$ **15.** about 26 in. **17.** 100 students **19.** 16 students

Page 433

1. 12 choices **3.** B **5.** 1,870,737 **7.** 4 groups of 10; 3 groups of 8

Pages 435–436

1. 24 **3.** 9 outcomes **5.** 36 outcomes **7.** 16 outcomes **9.** 18 outcomes **11.** 216 outcomes **13.** yes; 12 · 4 · 8 = 384, and 384 > 365 **15.** $\frac{1}{5}$ **17.** 163°

Pages 438–439

1. 16%; 36%; yes, because there are more odd numbers on the spinner than even numbers, and the probability of two odd numbers is greater. **3.** dependent **5.** $\frac{1}{36}$ **7.** 0 **9.** $\frac{1}{20}$ **11.** $\frac{1}{5}$ **13.** independent **15.** $\frac{1}{36}$; $\frac{1}{30}$ **17.** $\frac{1}{6}$, $\frac{1}{5}$ **19.** $\frac{1}{9}$; $\frac{2}{15}$ **21.** $\frac{1}{27}$; 0 **23.** $\frac{1}{108}$; 0 **27.** 15 outcomes **29.** 18 outcomes

Page 441

1. Write and solve the proportion $\frac{5}{75} = \frac{n}{210}$ **3.** $\frac{7}{20}$, 0.35, or 35% **5.** about 153 sixth graders **7.** about 600 cars **9.** $\frac{5}{36}$ **11.** $\frac{1}{3}$ **13.** $\frac{1}{2}$

Chapter 24

Page 451

1. feet **3.** multiply **5.** 3 **7.** 568 **9.** 4 **11.** 24 **13.** 12 **15.** 5 **17.** 1,000 **19.** 10 **21.** 1,000 **23.** 2 **25.** 4,000 **27.** 9 **29.** $n = 45$ **31.** $n = 9$ **33.** $n = 10$

Page 453

1. Use the ratio $\frac{4 \text{ qt}}{1 \text{ gal}}$ on one side of the proportion and the number of quarts over x gallons on the other side. **3.** 4 **5.** 128 **7.** 12 **9.** $\frac{1}{2}$ **11.** $1\frac{1}{2}$ **13.** 60 **15.** $2\frac{1}{4}$ **17.** $3\frac{1}{4}$ **19.** = **21.** $4\frac{1}{2}$ yd **25.** $1\frac{13}{55}$ **27.** 2.361

Page 455

1. Use the ratio $\frac{10 \text{dm}}{1 \text{m}}$ on one side of the proportion and the number of decimeters over x meters on the other side. **3.** 0.005 **5.** 9,000 **7.** 200,000 **9.** 0.5 **11.** 1.2 **13.** 440,000 **15.** 18,000 **17.** 425 **19.** > **21.** = **25.** $\frac{1}{3}$ **27.** 40% **29.** ⁻9

Page 457

1. 1 mi; it takes 1.61 km to make 1 mi. **3.** 25.4 **5.** 427.7 **7.** 10 **9.** 76.2 **11.** 4.75 **13.** 26.37 **15.** < **17.** > **19.** 1.38 in. **21.** 18°C **23.** ⁻10 **25.** $\frac{7}{6}$

Pages 460–461

1. gram; because the gram is a smaller unit than the kilogram **3.** 2 cm; 23 mm **5.** 85 in. **7.** 8 oz **9.** meter, yard, or foot **11.** gram or ounce **13.** $1\frac{1}{2}$ in.; $1\frac{3}{4}$ in. **15.** $\frac{3}{4}$ in.; $\frac{7}{8}$ in. **17.** 8 ft **19.** 8 oz **21.** millimeter or part of an inch **23.** = **25.** = **27.** To the nearest millimeter because a millimeter is a tenth of a centimeter, which is smaller than a half centimeter. **31.** 17.055 L **33.** $^{-}96$

Page 463

1. estimate; no **3.** estimate; no **5.** C **7.** $9\frac{3}{20}$ in. **9.** $2\frac{3}{8}$ in. below **11.** 23 years old

Chapter 25

Page 467

1. perimeter **3.** 32 ft **5.** 20 cm **7.** 104 in. **9.** 4 **11.** 36 **13.** 4 **15.** 3,000 **17.** 5,000 **19.** 0.40009 **21.** 88 **23.** 2,625 **25.** 526.5 **27.** 60 **29.** 73.6

Page 471

3. 13.57 m **5.** 9 ft or 108 in. **7.** 43 m **9.** $x = 13.5$ cm **13.** 5.40 **15.** $a = 1,264$

Page 473

1. 66 in. **3.** B **7.** 42.4% **9.** 1 in.

Page 475

1. 88 in. **3.** $z = 17.6$ **5.** D

Pages 478–479

1. They both use π; one uses the diameter and the other uses 2 times the radius, which is equal to the diameter. **3.** 16 m **5.** 12 cm **7.** 283 yd **9.** 27 in. **11.** 33 cm **13.** 20 in. **15.** 9 yd **17.** 220 cm **19.** 316 in. **21.** 22 ft **23.** 16 cm **25.** 4.5 ft **27.** 9.3 cm **29.** The circumference is twice as long. **31.** 88 yd **33.** 149 m

Chapter 26

Page 483

1. square **3.** faces **5.** 144 **7.** 400 **9.** 81 **11.** 5.76 **13.** 2,401 **15.** 16,641 **17.** 25 **19.** 192 **21.** 16 **23.** 5 faces **25.** 4 faces

Pages 486–487

1. The area of the triangle is $\frac{1}{2}$ the area of the rectangle. **3.** about 20 m^2 **5.** 117 in.^{2} **7.** 45.5 in.^{2} **9.** about 6 m^2 **11.** 558.25 mm^2 **13.** 0.2 m^2 **15.** 22.5 ft^2 **17.** 273 yd^2 **19.** 12 **21.** 60%

Pages 489–490

1. $A = \frac{1}{2}h(b_1 + b_2) = \frac{1}{2} \times 4 \times (4.2 + 6.5) = 21.4$; 21.4 m^2 **3.** 10 ft^2 **5.** 102.3 m^2 **7.** 136.95 m^2 **9.** 40 ft^2 **11.** 1.008 cm^2 **15.** 24 m^2 **17.** 0.003

Page 491

1. 3 m^2 **3.** 154 m^2

Page 493

3. 28 cm^2 **5.** 1,809 ft^2 **7.** 50 yd^2 **9.** 7 m^2 **11.** 50 mm^2 **13.** 3,420 in.^{2} **15.** 77 cm^2 **17.** 804 ft^2 **19.** 100 ft^2 **21.** 3

Pages 496–497

1. Find the area of each pentagonal face and the area of the five rectangular faces and add. **3.** 184 ft^2 **5.** 336 cm^2 **7.** 340 m^2 **9.** 73.5 m^2 **11.** 108 cm^2 **13.** 69.36 cm^2 **15a.** $3 \times 6 \times 12$; 252 m^2 **15b.** $3 \times 6 \times 6$; 144 ft^2 **15c.** $10 \times 5 \times 15$; 550 in.^{2} **15d.** $2 \times 8 \times 32$; 672 cm^2 **17.** 2 cans **19.** 5 in. **21.** 113 ft^2 **23.** 0.25

Chapter 27

Page 501

1. dimensions **3.** height **5.** 64 **7.** 27 **9.** 216 **11.** 0.008 **13.** 1,728 **15.** 20 ft^2 **17.** 21 m^2 **19.** $58\frac{7}{12}$ ft^2 **21.** 52.36 m^2 **23.** 141 cm^2 **25.** 346 cm^2

Pages 504–505

1. Find $26 \times 3 \times 18$, or 1,404 cubes.
3. 24 in.^{3} **5.** 48 cm^3 **7.** 324 ft^3
9. 294 ft^3 **11.** 288 in.^{3} **13.** $x = 10$ m
15. 189 ft^3 **17.** 40 in.   **19.** 45.63

Page 507

1. twice the volume of the original container
3. B   **7.** 10 shirts, 0 shorts; 0 shirts, 8 shorts; 5 shirts, 4 shorts   **9.** Mike, Sharon, Jasmine, Hugh

Page 509

1. Both include the area of the base times the height; prism: $V = bh$; pyramid: $V = \frac{1}{3}Bh$
3. 48 m^3 **5.** 224 cm^3 **7.** 24 cm^3, or 24,000 mm^3 **9.** 4,500 ft^3 **11.** 24 yd^3, or 648 ft^3
15. 110   **17.** 0.79

Page 510

1. about 75 cm^3

Page 512–513

1. 6,029 in.^{3} **3.** πr^2 represents the area of the base and h represents the height.
5. about 346 in.^{3} **7.** about 942 in.^{3}
9. about 1,409 cm^3 **11.** about 311 cm^3
13. about 2,374 cm^3 **15.** about 7,436 ft^3
17. The volume is about eight times as large.
21. about 4 ft^3 **23.** $\frac{1}{2} \div \frac{1}{10}$

Chapter 28

Page 523

1. equation   **3.** $<$ **5.** $<$ **7.** $>$ **9.** $>$
11. $<$ **13.** $>$ **15.** $<$ **17.** $>$ **19.** 10; 21
21. 25; 25.5   **23.** 15   **25.** $^-5$ **27.** 63
29. 29   **31.** $\frac{3}{14}$ **33.** 3.1

Page 525

1. the eighth day   **3.** A   **5.** 7 videos
7. 660 ft   **9.** 40 ft^2

Pages 527–528

1. Multiply by 4; 2,048; 8,192; 32,768   **3.** Add 15 to each successive term   **5.** 43, 54, 65
7. Divide each term by 3.   **9.** Add 0.89 to each term.   **11.** 335, 485, 665   **13.** 81, 76, 70
15. 9, 12.7, 16.4, 20.1, . . .   **17.** add $54; $462
21. 754 ft^3 **23.** 264

Pages 531–532

3. $b = a - 6$ **5.** $d = c + 1.1$ **7.** $l = 4w$
9. $g = k \div 2$; 27   **11.** $d = c \div {}^-4$; $^-8$
15. in $y^2 = x$, if $x = 1$, $y = 1$ or $y = {}^-1$
17. $t = 0.75n$; $37.50   **19.** $209   **21.** $2\frac{5}{104}$

Page 535

9. $5^0, 5^1, 5^2, 5^3, \ldots$ **11.** 16 prisms; 25 prisms
13. $y = {}^-9, {}^-3, 3, 9, 15$ **15.** 5×13

Chapter 29
Page 539

1. congruent   **3.** slide   **5.** slide   **7.** turn
17. 25°   **19.** 135°

Pages 541–542

1. The figure does not change in size or shape.   **3.** rotation or reflection
5. reflection   **7.** rotation, reflection
9. rotation or translation   **11.** rotation
13. translation, reflection, reflection
19. horizontal reflection   **25.** $\frac{5}{8}$

Pages 544–545

3. yes   **5.** no   **11.** yes   **13.** no
19. 288 sq yd.   **23.** $\frac{11}{12}$

Page 547

1. triangle and square; square and octagon
3. C   **5.** 63°   **7.** a   **9.** 757 and 575

Page 549

1. Yes, the figure's size and shape do not change. **3.** 8 ways **5.** 6 ways **7.** 8 ways **9.** 12 ways **11.** rotate it 180° **13.** reflection **15.** 24 cm

Pages 552–553

1. Line symmetry means that the figure can be folded into two congruent halves that are mirror images. Rotational symmetry means that the figure matches itself when rotated less than 360°. **11.** yes; $\frac{1}{4}$; 90° **13.** yes; $\frac{1}{2}$; 180° **27.** yes; $\frac{1}{5}$; 72° **29.** no **31.** 8 pieces; yes **33.** To have rotational symmetry, it must match up with a rotation of less than 360° **35.** 125.66 in^3

Chapter 30

Page 557

1. ordered pair **3.** perpendicular **5.** = **7.** > **9.** < **11.** > **13.** ($^-$2,2) **15.** (0,0) **17.** (2,1) **19.** (0,3) **21.** ($^-$2,$^-$2)

Page 559

1. Yes. **19.** $p > {^-}11$ **21.** $a < 20{,}320$ **25.** 37.5% **27.** $\frac{3}{5}$

Pages 562–563

1. (5,4) is above the x-axis. (5,$^-$4) is below the x-axis. **3.** (2,4) **5.** (0,0) **7.** (5,$^-$5) **9.** (0,$^-$5) **11.** (2,$^-$3) **13.** A, H **15.** B **17.** (2,6) **19.** (2,$^-$2) **21.** (0,7) **23.** (3,0) **25.** (6,$^-$4) **27.** ($^-$7,$^-$6) **29.** A, L, J **31.** B, H, K **41.** triangle; 28 sq units **43.** It is 0; it is 0. **45.** $y \geq {^-}7$ **47.** 157 cm

Page 565

1. a table, a graph of ordered pairs. **7.** (45,15), (48,16), (51,17), (54,18); $w = \frac{1}{3}c$ **9.** Quadrant I **11.** 40 cm^2

Page 567

1. C **3.** $y = 9x$ **5.** 1,333 mi **7.** 11:00 A.M. **9.** about 800

Pages 572–573

3. $A'(0,3)$, $B'(2,3)$, $C'(2,1)$, $D'(0,1)$ **5.** $A'(0,0)$, $B'(^-6,0)$, $C'(^-4,2)$, $D'(^-2,2)$ **7.** $E'(0,^-1)$, $F'(3,^-1)$, $G'(3,^-4)$, $H'(0,^-4)$ **9.** $E'(1,^-3)$, $F'(4,^-3)$, $G'(4,^-1)$, $H'(1,^-1)$ **11.** No. **13.** $y = 7x$ **15.** $\frac{1}{4}$

Table of Measures

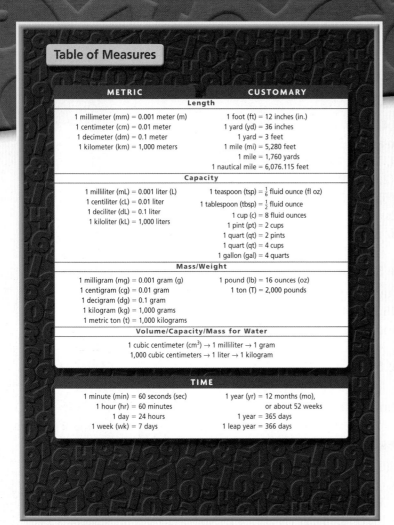

METRIC	CUSTOMARY
Length	
1 millimeter (mm) = 0.001 meter (m)	1 foot (ft) = 12 inches (in.)
1 centimeter (cm) = 0.01 meter	1 yard (yd) = 36 inches
1 decimeter (dm) = 0.1 meter	1 yard = 3 feet
1 kilometer (km) = 1,000 meters	1 mile (mi) = 5,280 feet
	1 mile = 1,760 yards
	1 nautical mile = 6,076.115 feet
Capacity	
1 milliliter (mL) = 0.001 liter (L)	1 teaspoon (tsp) = $\frac{1}{6}$ fluid ounce (fl oz)
1 centiliter (cL) = 0.01 liter	1 tablespoon (tbsp) = $\frac{1}{2}$ fluid ounce
1 deciliter (dL) = 0.1 liter	1 cup (c) = 8 fluid ounces
1 kiloliter (kL) = 1,000 liters	1 pint (pt) = 2 cups
	1 quart (qt) = 2 pints
	1 quart (qt) = 4 cups
	1 gallon (gal) = 4 quarts
Mass/Weight	
1 milligram (mg) = 0.001 gram (g)	1 pound (lb) = 16 ounces (oz)
1 centigram (cg) = 0.01 gram	1 ton (T) = 2,000 pounds
1 decigram (dg) = 0.1 gram	
1 kilogram (kg) = 1,000 grams	
1 metric ton (t) = 1,000 kilograms	
Volume/Capacity/Mass for Water	
1 cubic centimeter (cm³) → 1 milliliter → 1 gram	
1,000 cubic centimeters → 1 liter → 1 kilogram	

TIME

1 minute (min) = 60 seconds (sec)	1 year (yr) = 12 months (mo),
1 hour (hr) = 60 minutes	or about 52 weeks
1 day = 24 hours	1 year = 365 days
1 week (wk) = 7 days	1 leap year = 366 days

FORMULAS

Perimeter		Surface Area	
Polygon	P = sum of the lengths of the sides	Rectangular Prism	$S = 2(lh + lw + wh)$
Rectangle	$P = 2(l + w)$	**Volume**	
Square	$P = 4s$	Cylinder	$V = \pi r^2 h$
Circumference		Pyramid	$V = \frac{1}{3} Bh$
Circle	$C = 2\pi r$, or $C = \pi d$	Rectangular Prism	$V = lwh$
Area		Triangular Prism	$V = \frac{1}{2} lwh$ or $\frac{1}{2} Bh$
Circle	$A = \pi r^2$	**Other**	
Parallelogram	$A = bh$	Celsius (°C)	$C = \frac{5}{9} \times (F - 32)$
Rectangle	$A = lw$	Diameter	$d = 2r$
Square	$A = s^2$	Fahrenheit (°F)	$F = (\frac{9}{5} \times C) + 32$
Trapezoid	$A = \frac{1}{2} h \times (b_1 + b_2)$	**Consumer**	
Triangle	$A = \frac{1}{2} bh$	Distance traveled	$d = rt$
		Interest (simple)	$I = prt$

SYMBOLS

$<$	is less than	(4,7)	ordered pair (x,y)
$>$	is greater than	$5/hr	the rate $5 per hour
$\leq$	is less than or equal to	1:2	ratio of 1 to 2
$\geq$	is greater than or equal to	%	percent
$=$	is equal to	$\cong$	is congruent to
$\neq$	is not equal to	$\approx$	is approximately equal to
10^2	ten squared	$\perp$	is perpendicular to
10^3	ten cubed	$\parallel$	is parallel to
10^4	the fourth power of 10	$\overleftrightarrow{AB}$	line AB
2^3	the third power of 2	$\overrightarrow{AB}$	ray AB
3^{-5}	the negative fifth power of 3	$\overline{AB}$	line segment AB
$2.\overline{6}$	repeating decimal 2.666 . . .	$\angle ABC$	angle ABC
$^{+}7$	positive 7	$m\angle A$	measure of $\angle A$
$^{-}7$	negative 7	$\triangle ABC$	triangle ABC
$|^{-}4|$	the absolute value of negative 4	°	degree
$\sqrt{}$	positive square root	π	pi (about 3.14)
$^{-}\sqrt{}$	negative square root	P(4)	the probability of the outcome 4

Table of Measures

HARCOURT
Math

PROBLEM OF THE DAY

This section provides complete solutions for the **Problem of the Day** in each lesson plan. The problems include all types—one-step, multi-step, applied, process, nonroutine, open-ended, and puzzle problems—and provide options for students to develop their ability to use logical reasoning to choose and apply problem-solving strategies to varied and interesting situations.

The **Problem of the Day** for a lesson is also available on the Daily Transparency. Each Daily Transparency includes the **Problem of the Day**, the **Quick Review**, and the **Mixed Review and Test Prep** in Grades 1 and 2. In Grades 3–6, each Daily Transparency includes the **Number of the Day**, the **Problem of the Day**, and the **Lesson Quiz**.

Problem of the Day

Chapter 1 Answer Key

Lesson 1.1

Problem

Find the three-digit number that rounds to 440 and includes a digit that is the quotient of 24 ÷ 3. Is there more than one possible answer? Explain.

Solution

Strategy: Use Logical Reasoning
The numbers that round to 440 are 435, 436, 437, 438, 439, 440, 441, 442, 443, 444. One of the digits is the quotient of 24 ÷ 3 = 8. The only one of those numbers that rounds to 440 and has 8 as a digit is 438.

438; No. The numbers that round to 440 are 435–444. 24 ÷ 3 = 8. Only one of those numbers has 8 as a digit.

Lesson 1.2

Problem

Presidents George Washington, John Adams, and Thomas Jefferson lived a total of 240 years. Adams lived the longest, 23 years longer than Washington. Jefferson lived 16 years longer than Washington. How old was each president when he died?

Solution

Strategy: Predict and Test
Note that the average age is 80.
Begin by guessing, for example, that Washington is 70, Adams is 93, and Jefferson is 86. The sum of their ages is then 249, which is 9 too large. Subtract 3 from each age to get the solution.

Washington, 67; Adams, 90; Jefferson, 83

Lesson 1.3

Problem

Find the product. Compare the product with the first factor. Write a rule for multiplying a 2-digit number by 11 and a rule for multiplying greater numbers by 11.

Solution

Strategy: Find a Pattern
1. 13 × 11 = 143
2. 72 × 11 = 792
3. 326 × 11 = 3,586
4. 6,045 × 11 = 66,495

A shortcut for multiplying a 2-digit factor by 11:
34 × 11 =
1. Moving from right to left, write the ones digit of the other factor. 4
2. Write the sum of the ones and tens digits. 74
3. Write the tens digit. 374

For multiplying greater factors by 11:
1. Write the ones digit of the other factor.
2. Write the sum of the ones and tens digits, the sum of the tens and hundreds digits, etc., as necessary.
3. Write the digit in the greatest place-value position. Some students may try problems in which the sum of 2 digits is greater than 9. The pattern remains the same, but the 1 that is "carried" is added to the next pair of digits or to the first digit.

Lesson 1.4

Problem

At noon on Monday, Latisha sets her watch to the correct time. If her watch loses one minute each hour, and she does not correct it, what time will her watch show at noon on Wednesday? At noon on what day will her watch show 10:00?

Solution

Strategy: Make a Table/Write a Number Sentence
24 × 1 = 24 minutes are lost each day.
Subtract 24 minutes each day.
Results:

Monday noon:	12:00
Tuesday noon:	11:36
Wednesday noon:	11:12
Thursday noon:	10:48
Friday noon:	10:24
Saturday noon:	10:00

At noon on Wednesday her watch will show 11:12. At noon on Saturday her watch will show 10:00.

Chapter 1 Answer Key

Lesson 1.5

Problem

In a number game, when Tina says *three*, Jay says *ten*. When Tina says *five*, Jay says *sixteen*. When Tina says *nine*, Jay says *twenty-eight*. When Tina says *eight*, what does Jay say? If Jay says *one*, what number has Tina said?

Solution

Strategy: Make a Table

If Tina said the counting numbers, the numbers would have a difference of 1. Enter the given numbers and look for a pattern.

TINA	0	1	2	3	4	5	6	7	8	9
JAY	1	4	7	10	13	16	19	22	25	28

When Tina says eight, Jay says *twenty-five*.

If Jay says *one*, Tina must have said *zero*.

For discussion: Students note that when Tina says *zero*, Jay said *one*, so he must have added 1. However in the other numbers he didn't just add 1. What else did he do that made the number share a difference of 3? He multiplied by 3 and added 1. $3x + 1$.

Lesson 1.6

Problem

Martin saves *n* dollars each week. Kara saves twice as much as Martin. In 15 weeks their combined savings total $450. How much does Martin save each week? How can you use mental math to solve it?

Solution

Strategy: Use Logical Reasoning

THINK: $450 is saved in 15 weeks and the same amount is saved each week.

$450 \div 15 = 30$.

Martin and Kara save a total of $30 each week.

Kara saves twice as much as Martin, so $10 + 20 = 30$.

Martin saves $10 each week.

Chapter 2 Answer Key

Lesson 2.1

Problem

Replace the ■ with the digits 0–9 to make correct number sentences. Use each digit only once.

■ × ■ = 18

■ × ■ = 24

■ × ■ = 0

■ × ■ = 28

■ × ■ = 6

Solution

Strategy: Use Logical Reasoning

Students can write the digits 0–9, and then cross them off as they use them. Students look for a product that can have only one correct set of factors, i.e. 28. $4 \times 7 = 28$ or $7 \times 4 = 28$ (Digits may be in any order.)

Since 4 is already used,   only $3 \times 8 = 24$.

Since 3 is used,   only $2 \times 9 = 18$.

Since 2 and 3 are used,   only $6 \times 1 = 6$.

The only digits left are 5 and 0, so $5 \times 0 = 0$.

$2 \times 9 = 18$

$3 \times 8 = 24$

$5 \times 0 = 0$

$4 \times 7 = 28$

$1 \times 6 = 6$

Lesson 2.2

Problem

Replace the letters *a*, *b*, and *c* with the numbers 3, 4, and 5 to make a true sentence.

$2^a + 2^a = b^c$

Solution

Strategy: Predict and Test

$2^5 + 2^5 = 4^3$

$(2 \times 2 \times 2 \times 2 \times 2) + (2 \times 2 \times 2 \times 2 \times 2) =$ $(4 \times 4 \times 4)$

$32 + 32 = 64$

Lesson 2.4

Problem

Complete the expression using the numbers 3, 4, and 5 so that it equals 19.

_____ + _____ × _____

Solution

Strategy: Predict and Test

Substitute one of the numbers for each of the blanks and evaluate the expression:

$3 + 4 \times 5 = 3 + 20 = 23$, too big

$5 + 3 \times 4 = 5 + 12 = 17$, too small

$4 + 3 \times 5 = 4 + 15 = 19$

$4 + 3 \times 5$

Lesson 2.5

Problem

Look at the following figure. Start at point *A*. Write the sequence that allows you to go around the entire figure, covering each segment only once. Is there only one way? Can you do the same thing if you start at *B*?

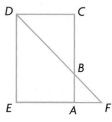

Solution

Strategy: Predict and Test

One possible answer is: Go from *A* to *F*, from *F* to *D*, from *D* to *E*, from *E* to *A*, from *A* to *C*, and from *C* to *D*. There are several others that work. Students can find a route by tracing the figure with a finger or pencil. If you start at *B*, there is no sequence of steps that allows you to trace all the segments only once.

Chapter 3 Answer Key

Lesson 3.1

Problem

The money that Mrs. Frey deposited in her bank account was in $10 bills. The sum of the digits in the amount she deposited was 18. If she had deposited $10 more, the sum of the digits would have been 1. How much did Mrs. Frey deposit?

Solution

Strategy: Use Logical Reasoning

Since the deposit was in $10 bills the amount must be a multiple of 10.

$9 + 9 + 0 = 18$

$\$990 + \$10 = \$1,000$

$1 + 0 + 0 + 0 = 1$

$990

Lesson 3.2

Problem

Jake knows that Uranus is farther from Earth than Saturn but not as far as Neptune. Match each planet with its distance from Earth.

0.744 billion mi

2.7 billion mi

1.6 billion mi

Solution

Strategy: Make an Organized List

Students can compare the three decimals and list them in order from least to greatest since all the exponent factors are the same.

0.744	Saturn
1.6	Uranus
2.7	Neptune

Once they have them in order, they can attach Saturn to the smallest number, Uranus to the next larger one, and Neptune to the largest one.

Lesson 3.3

Problem

Randall, Kira, and Sean have 100 baseball cards in all. Randall has twice as many as Kira and 10 more than Sean. How many cards does each person have?

Solution

Strategy: Predict and Test

Students can make a table and *predict and test* to find the number of cards each person has.

RANDALL	KIRA	SEAN	TOTAL
50	25	40	115
46	23	36	105
44	22	34	100

Randall has 44 cards, Kira has 22 cards, and Sean has 34 cards.

Lesson 3.4

Problem

An estimate of the sum of two decimals is 27 and an estimate of the product is 140. Give two decimals that satisfy these requirements.

Solution

Strategy: Predict and Test

Students can determine two whole numbers that satisfy the requirements, for example, 20 and 7. Then, they can select any decimals that round to 20 and to 7.

Possible answer: 6.85 and 19.61

Chapter 4 Answer Key

Lesson 4.1

Problem

Replace each [♥] with a different digit from 0–9 to make a true number sentence.

[♥].[♥] [♥] [♥] + [♥] [♥].[♥] [♥] + [♥].[♥] = 22.815

Solution

Strategy: Predict and Test

Possible answer:

$0.725 + 13.69 + 8.4 = 22.815$

Lesson 4.2

Problem

Rhonda is making an input/output table. When she sees 5 she writes 3.0. When she sees 10 she writes 6.0. When she sees 4, she writes 2.4. What will she write when she sees 12? What did she see if she wrote 4.2?

Solution

Strategy: Find a Pattern

$5 \times \underline{\hspace{1cm}} = 3.0$

$10 \times \underline{\hspace{1cm}} = 6.0$

$5 \times 0.6 = 3.0$

$10 \times 0.6 = 6.0$

Students can determine that each number Rhonda sees is multiplied by 0.6 to get the number she writes. They can determine this number by dividing 3.0 by 5 or by choosing a sensible estimate of the number and testing to see if they are correct.

Then, to find what she writes for 12:

$12 \times 0.6 = 7.2$.

To find what she saw when she wrote 4.2, divide: $4.2 \div 0.6 = 7$. 7.2; 7

Lesson 4.4

Problem

The sum of two decimal numbers is 9.3. Their difference is 4.3, and their product is 17.00. What are the numbers?

Solution

Strategy: Use Logical Reasoning

There is a 3 in the tenths place for the sum *and* the difference, so one of the digits in the tenths place must be a zero or a 5. If one tenths digit is 0, the other tenths digit is 3; if one tenths digit is 5, the other tenths digit is 8. 17.00 is divisible by 6.5 and 6.8, but not by 6.3. So the digits in the tenths place are 5 and 8.

The digit 1 may not be great enough for the ones place.

THINK: One number is 4.3 greater than the other.

Try $2.8 + 4.3 = 7.1$ (Not correct. There should be a 5 in the tenths place.)

Try $2.5 + 4.3 = 6.8$ (One number has a 5 and the other has an 8 in the tenths place.)

Check: $2.5 + 6.8 = 9.3$

$6.8 - 2.5 = 4.3$

$2.5 \times 6.8 = 17.00$

The two numbers are 2.5 and 6.8.

Some students may need the strategy *Predict and Test*.

Lesson 4.5

Problem

Marge had five 32-oz bottles of milk. Monday she drank 6 oz from the first bottle, Tuesday she drank 12 oz from the second bottle, Wednesday she drank 18 oz from the third bottle, and so on. Each day she divided the remaining milk among her five cats so that each got a whole number of ounces. She saved the remainder. On the sixth day, she drank what was left. How much did she drink on Day 6?

Solution

Strategy: Find a Pattern

In order to solve, students must first find the pattern in the amounts she drinks each day: 6, 12, 18, 24, 30. Then they can find the amount of milk she had to divide among the cats: 26, 20, 14, 8, and 2 oz.

Finally, students need to recognize that the amount she had left to drink each day is the remainder in the division problem in which the dividend is the amount left each day and the divisor is 5. The remainders are 1, 0, 4, 3, and 2, so she has 10 oz to drink on the 6th day.

10 oz

Chapter 4 Answer Key

Lesson 4.6

Problem

Lashonda and Mark each have the same number of coins. Lashonda has $8.25 in quarters. Mark has all dimes. How much more money does Lashonda have than Mark?

Solution

Strategy: Write a Number Sentence

Lashonda: $8.25 $\div$ 0.25 = 33 quarters

Mark: 33 dimes $\times$ $0.10 = $3.30

  $8.25 $-$ $3.30 = $4.95

Lashonda has $4.95 more than Mark.

Chapter 5 Answer Key

Lesson 5.1

Problem

Dana's survey showed that 3 out of 8 students preferred pepperoni pizza and 1 out of 8 students preferred cheese pizza. How many more of the 72 students surveyed by Dana liked pepperoni pizza than liked cheese pizza?

Solution

Strategy: Write a Number Sentence

18 of 72 = 9 students

38 of 72 = 27 students

27 − 9 = 18 more students liked pepperoni pizza.

Lesson 5.2

Problem

In a survey of students about a field trip to a nearby factory, 12 students were undecided, 5 times that many were in favor of the field trip, and half as many were against it as were in favor of it. How many students participated in the survey?

Solution

Strategy: Use Logical Reasoning

There are 12 students who are undecided.

$5 \times 12 = 60$, so there are 60 students in favor of the field trip.

Half of 60 is 30, so there are 30 students against the field trip.

$12 + 60 + 30 = 102$

102 students

Lesson 5.3

Problem

It takes 4 yd of material and 3 yd of trim to make 2 pumpkin decorations. Rhonda needs to make 10 decorations. How many yards of material and trim will she need?

Solution

Strategy: Make an Organized List

Students may find it helpful to organize information by making a list or table showing the number of yards of material and trim needed for 2, 4, 6, 8, and 10 decorations.

NUMBER OF DECORATIONS	MATERIAL	TRIM
2	4 yd	3 yd
4	8 yd	6 yd
6	12 yd	9 yd
8	16 yd	12 yd
10	20 yd	15 yd

20 yards of material and 15 yards of trim

Lesson 5.4

Problem

Anne's line plot of ages of students has a range of 4. Each age has twice as many x's as the previous one. If the last age has 16 x's, how many students did Anne include in her data?

Solution

Strategy: Use Logical Reasoning

If does not matter what the ages were, but there are 5 sets of ages. So work backward, dividing by 2 each time. Find the sum.

$16 + 8 + 4 + 2 + 1 = 31$ students

Lesson 5.5

Problem

A set of 9 numbers has a mean of 7. When one more number is added to the set, the mean is doubled. What number was added to the data set?

Solution

Strategy: Work Backward

The new mean is 14 and the new set has 10 numbers. So, the sum of the numbers is 10×14, or 140. The sum of the original nine numbers was 9×7 or 63. The difference between the two sums is 77, so 77 must have been added to the original set of numbers.

77

Chapter 5 Answer Key

Lesson 5.6

Problem

Rita has 1 brother and 3 sisters. If the mean age of all the children is 5 years, what will their mean age be 7 years from now?

Solution

Strategy: Use Logical Reasoning

There are 5 children in all: Rita, 1 brother, and 3 sisters. Since the mean of their current ages is 5, the total of their current ages is 5×5 years $= 25$ years.

Seven years from now each child will be 7 years older. Then the total of their ages will be $25 + 5 \times 7 = 25 + 35 = 60$. To find the mean in 7 years, use the number sentence $60 \div 5 = 12$. So in 7 years the mean of their ages will be 12 years.

12 years

Lesson 5.7

Problem

The mean of these numbers is 14. The greatest number is 21 more than the least. The mode is 18. What are the missing numbers?

3   6   9   ◆   ◆   ◆   ◆

Solution

Strategy: Use Logical Reasoning

3   6   9   ◆   ◆   ◆   24

$(3 + 21 = 24)$

There are 7 numbers with a mean of 14, so

$7 \times 14 = 98$, the total. The mode is 18. Two or three of the missing numbers must be 18. Try three 18's and find the total.

3 6 9 18 18 18 24

(Sum is 96, which is 2 less than 98.)

So try two 18's and 20 $(18 + 2)$

3 6 9 18 18 20 24

(Yes, the sum is 98.)

Chapter 6 Answer Key

Lesson 6.1

Problem

Maurie is the second-youngest of 4 teenagers, all 2 years apart in age. His mother is 3 times as old as he is and 24 years younger than her father. How old is Maurie's grandfather?

Solution

Strategy: Use Logical Reasoning

The teenagers must be 13, 15, 17, and 19 years old.

Maurie must be 15 years old.

His mother is 45 years old. (3×15)

His grandfather is 69 years old. $(45 + 24)$

Lesson 6.2

Problem

A line graph shows that the temperature at 6 A.M. was 4° warmer than at 4 A.M. In the hours between midnight and 4 A.M., the temperature had fallen an average of 3° per hour. If the temperature at 6 A.M. was 10°F, what was the temperature at midnight?

Solution

Strategy: Make a Table or a Graph

Students may reproduce the line graph to help solve. They should begin by graphing the temperature at 6 A.M., which was 10°F. Then, using the clue that this temperature was 4° warmer than at 4 A.M., they can graph 6° at 4 A.M. Because the temperature fell an average of 3° per hour for 4 hours, the temperature at midnight was $6° + 12° = 18°F$. 18°F at midnight

Lesson 6.3

Problem

What is the least number that can be divided evenly by each of the numbers 1 through 12?

Solution

Strategy: Use Logical Reasoning

Numbers 1, 2, 3, 4, and 6 are factors of 12, so if the number is divisible by 12 it is divisible by all these also. Remember, if a number is divisible by 5 and 2, it is divisible by 10. Multiply the odd numbers $5 \times 7 \times 9 \times 11 = 3,465$.

3,465 is not divisible by 8 or 12, so multiply it by 8.

$3,465 \times 8 = 27,720$ $27,720 \div 12 = 2,310$

27,720 is divisible by each of the numbers 1 through 12.

Lesson 6.5

Problem

Jason made a stem-and-leaf plot of the ages of all the adults at a family reunion. His father's age was the median age. Jason is 1 year younger than $\frac{1}{3}$ his father's age. How old is Jason?

Ages of the Adults

Stems	Leaves
2	2 6
3	0 3 7
4	2 3 3
5	5 8
6	8

Solution

Strategy: Use Logical Reasoning

Use the stem-and-leaf plot to find the median age of 42. So, Jason's father is 42 years old.

One-third of 42 is $\frac{1}{3} \times 42 = 14$.

Jason is 1 year younger than 14: $14 - 1 = 13$.

13 years old

Lesson 6.6

Problem

A circle graph shows that half of the 120 ancestors of the students surveyed came to the U.S. from Europe or South America, a quarter came from Africa, and the rest from Asia and Australia. Five times as many came from Europe as from South America. How many of the students' ancestors came from South America?

Solution

Strategy: Predict and Test

$120 \div 2 = 60$ ancestors from Europe or South America

Find 2 addends for 60, one of which must be 5 times the other. The smaller addend represents the South American ancestors.

$20 + 40 = 60$ $(40 = 2 \times 20)$ Incorrect

$15 + 45 = 60$ $(45 = 3 \times 15)$ Incorrect

$10 + 50 = 60$ $(50 = 5 \times 10)$ Correct

10 ancestors

Chapter 7 Answer Key

Lesson 7.1

Problem

Corrine is having a party. She has 45 different party favors and wants to give each guest the same number of favors. How many guests could she invite and how many favors would they get?

Solution

Strategy: Make an Organized List

Once students recognize this as a factoring problem, they can list the factors of 45:

1, 3, 5, 9, 15, and 45.

Then, to answer the question, they match pairs of factors. If Corrine invites 1 person, that person gets 45 favors, because $1 \times 45 = 45$. If she invites 3 people, each gets 15, because $3 \times 15 = 45$, and so on.

1 guest would get 45 favors; 3 guests would get 15 favors each; 5 guests would get 9 favors; 9 guests would get 5 favors; 15 guests would get 3 favors; 45 guests would get 1 favor.

Lesson 7.2

Problem

The sum of the ages of Mr. and Mrs. Olsen and their two children is 108. Their ages are sets of twin prime numbers. What are their ages? NOTE: Twin primes are two prime numbers whose difference is 2.

Solution

Strategy: Predict and Test

Students can list prime numbers and circle twin primes. They predict and test to see which sets total 108. 3, 5, 7, 11, 13, 17, 19, 29, 31, 41, 43, 59, 61, ...

Ages: $11 + 13 + 41 + 43 = 108$

Lesson 7.3

Problem

Find the least values for n and m such that the value of the first expression is twice that of the second expression.

Hint: n and m are both less than 6.

$114 \times n \qquad 95 \times m$

Solution

Strategy: Use Logical Reasoning

Students can use prime factorization to find values for n and m.

$114 \times n \qquad 95 \times m$

Prime factorization for 114: $2 \times 3 \times 19$

Prime factorization for 95: 5×19

Both expressions have the common factor of 19. If 114 is multiplied by 5 and 95 is multiplied by 3, the first expression will have a value twice that of the second expression.

$114 \times 5 = 570$ and $95 \times 3 = 285$;

$570 = 2 \times 285$

$n = 5$ and $m = 3$

Lesson 7.4

Problem

Jon is making birdhouses. He is cutting 1-in. by 6-in. boards into pieces that are 11 in. long to make the sides of the birdhouses. Which board length would produce the least waste—4 ft, 6 ft, 8 ft, or 10 ft? Explain.

Solution

Strategy: Make an Organized List

Students should first list the multiples of 11: 11, 22, 33, 44, 55, 66, 77, 88, 99, 110, and 121.

Then they can write the lengths of the board in inches:
4 ft = 48 in., 6 ft = 72 in., 8 ft = 96 in., and 10 ft = 120 in.

By comparing the multiples to the lengths, they can see that the 4-ft board provides the least waste.

4 ft long

Chapter 8 Answer Key

Lesson 8.1

Problem

John has 3 coins, 2 of which are the same. Ellen has 1 fewer coin than John, and Anna has 2 more coins than John. Each girl has only 1 kind of coin. Who has coins that could equal the value of a half-dollar?

Solution

Strategy: Use Logical Reasoning

The value of a half-dollar is 50 cents. Ellen has 1 fewer coin than John, so she has 2 coins. Two quarters have a value of 50 cents. So Ellen's coins could equal 50 cents.

Anna has 2 more coins than John, so she has 5 coins. 5 dimes have a value of 50 cents. So Anna's coins could equal 50 cents.

John has 3 coins and 2 of them are the same. There is no combination of 2 like coins and 1 other coin that would equal 50 cents. Ellen and Anna are the ones whose coins could equal the value of a half-dollar.

Lesson 8.2

Problem

At the car show, there are 20 vehicles on display. Some are motorcycles and some are cars. All 56 wheels on the vehicles need to be polished. What fraction of the vehicles are motorcycles?

Solution

Strategy: Predict and Test

Students need to find 2 numbers, a and b, which meet these conditions:

$a + b = 20$ and $2a + 4b = 56$.

Prediction 1	$a + b$	$2a + 4b$
10 motorcycles		
10 cars	$10 + 10 = 20$	$20 + 40 = 60$
Prediction 2		
12 motorcycles		
8 cars	$12 + 8 = 20$	$24 + 32 = 56$

There are 12 motorcycles and 8 cars. The fraction of vehicles that are motorcycles is $\frac{12}{20}$ or $\frac{3}{5}$.

Lesson 8.3

Problem

From 4:00 to 5:30, Jacob, Lisa, and Chelsea took turns playing the same computer game. Jacob played for $\frac{1}{2}$ hour and Lisa played for $\frac{3}{4}$ hour. For how many minutes did Chelsea play the game?

Solution

Strategy: Work Backward

Jacob, Lisa, and Chelsea played the computer game a total of 90 minutes. The amount of time left after Jacob and Lisa played is the number of minutes that Chelsea played.

Jacob played for $\frac{1}{2}$ hour or 30 minutes.

$90 - 30 = 60$ minutes

Lisa played for $\frac{3}{4}$ hour or 45 minutes.

$60 - 45 = 15$ minutes.

Chelsea played the computer game for 15 minutes.

Lesson 8.5

Problem

A pizza has 8 slices. Milton ate $\frac{1}{4}$ of the pizza. Earl ate $\frac{1}{2}$ of what was left over. Did Earl eat more or fewer than 4 pieces? Explain.

Solution

Strategy: Use Logical Reasoning

$\frac{1}{4}$ of 8 pieces = 2 pieces, so Milton ate 2 pieces of pizza.

$8 - 2 = 6$

$\frac{1}{2}$ of 6 pieces = 3 pieces, so Earl ate 3 pieces.

$3 < 4$

Earl ate fewer than 4 pieces.

Chapter 9 Answer Key

Lesson 9.1

Problem

Mike's and Kay's numbers are both less than 1. The digit in Mike's numerator is the same as the digit in Kay's denominator. Kay's number is $\frac{1}{10}$ greater than Mike's. What are Mike's and Kay's numbers?

Solution

Strategy: Predict and Test

Mike's number is less than 1 and $\frac{1}{10}$ less than Kay's.

Predict: $\frac{1}{2}$ for Kay's number.

$\frac{1}{2} = \frac{5}{10}$ $\frac{5}{10} - \frac{1}{10} = \frac{4}{10} = \frac{2}{5}$

If Kay's number is $\frac{1}{2}$, then Mike's number is $\frac{2}{5}$.

Test: The 2 in Mike's numerator is the same digit as the 2 in Kay's denominator.

Mike's number is $\frac{2}{5}$ and Kay's is $\frac{1}{2}$.

Lesson 9.3

Problem

Kim used $\frac{6}{8}$ of a tank of gas. She bought $\frac{5}{8}$ of a tank and then used $\frac{4}{8}$ of a tank. Kim was almost out of money, so she filled the tank to half full by adding $\frac{2}{8}$ of a tank of gas. What part of a tank of gas did she start with?

Solution

Strategy: Work Backward

$\frac{1}{2} = \frac{4}{8}$, so at the end she had $\frac{4}{8}$ tank of gas.

$\frac{4}{8} - \frac{2}{8} + \frac{4}{8} - \frac{5}{8} + \frac{6}{8} = \frac{7}{8}$. amount Kim started with

Kim started with $\frac{7}{8}$ of a tank of gas.

Lesson 9.4

Problem

Complete the Magic Square. The sum is $1\frac{1}{4}$.

$\frac{1}{2}$	?	$\frac{1}{6}$
?	$\frac{5}{12}$	?
?	?	?

Solution

Strategy: Write an Equation

Sample equations:

For the first row:

$\frac{1}{2} + \frac{1}{6} + n = 1\frac{1}{4}$; $n = \frac{7}{12}$.

For the second column:

$\frac{7}{12} + \frac{5}{12} + n = 1\frac{1}{4}$; $n = \frac{1}{4}$

For the diagonal:

$\frac{1}{2} + \frac{5}{12} + n = 1\frac{1}{4}$; $n = \frac{1}{3}$

If students need more help, show the answer this way.

$\frac{6}{12}$	$\frac{7}{12}$	$\frac{2}{12}$
$\frac{1}{12}$	$\frac{5}{12}$	$\frac{9}{12}$
$\frac{8}{12}$	$\frac{3}{12}$	$\frac{4}{12}$

$\frac{1}{2}$	$\frac{7}{12}$	$\frac{1}{6}$
$\frac{1}{12}$	$\frac{5}{12}$	$\frac{3}{4}$
$\frac{2}{3}$	$\frac{1}{4}$	$\frac{1}{3}$

Lesson 9.6

Problem

Melissa rides the bus $1\frac{2}{3}$ mi north and $3\frac{1}{8}$ mi east to get to school. Brandon rides his bike $2\frac{3}{4}$ mi south and $2\frac{1}{6}$ mi west to get to the same school. Who rides farther? Estimate the distances. What can you conclude?

Solution

Strategy: Write an Equation

Estimate of Melissa's distance: $2 + 3 = 5$

Estimate of Brandon's distance: $3 + 2 = 5$

Actual Distance

Melissa: $1\frac{2}{3} + 3\frac{1}{8} = 4\frac{19}{24}$

Brandon: $2\frac{3}{4} + 2\frac{1}{6} = 4\frac{11}{12}, 4\frac{22}{24}$

Brandon rides farther. From the estimates the distances appear to be the same. To answer the question you need to find the exact answer.

Lesson 9.7

Problem

Write the next 4 numbers. How does each number relate to the one before it?

A. $10, 8\frac{3}{4}, 7\frac{1}{2}, 6\frac{1}{4}$

B. $9, 7\frac{7}{8}, 6\frac{3}{4}, 5\frac{5}{8}$

C. $11\frac{7}{10}, 10\frac{2}{5}, 9\frac{1}{10}, 7\frac{4}{5}$

Solution

Strategy: Use a Pattern

For each sequence find the difference between the first and second terms. Check to make sure it is the same between the second and third terms and the third and fourth terms.

A. $10, 8\frac{3}{4}, 7\frac{1}{2}, 6\frac{1}{4}, 5, 3\frac{3}{4}, 2\frac{1}{2}, 1\frac{1}{4}$; it is $1\frac{1}{4}$ less

B. $9, 7\frac{7}{8}, 6\frac{3}{4}, 5\frac{5}{8}, 4\frac{1}{2}, 3\frac{3}{8}, 2\frac{1}{4}, 1\frac{1}{8}$; it is $1\frac{1}{8}$ less

C. $11\frac{7}{10}, 10\frac{2}{5}, 9\frac{1}{10}, 7\frac{4}{5}, 6\frac{1}{2}, 5\frac{1}{5}, 3\frac{9}{10}, 2\frac{3}{5}$; it is $1\frac{3}{10}$ less

Chapter 10 Answer Key

Lesson 10.1

Problem

A is a whole number between 55 and 60. The product of *A* and *B* is between 1,045 and 1,500. Between what two numbers is *B*?

Solution

Strategy: Work Backward

It is given that the product of *A* and *B* is between 1,045 and 1,500. Since *A* is a number between 55 and 60, then the lower range for $A \times B = 1,045$ and the upper range for $A \times B = 1,500$.

$1,045 \div 55 = 19$ and $1,500 \div 60 = 25$.

So *B* must be between 19 and 25.

between 19 and 25

Lesson 10.2

Problem

In a jump-rope marathon, Cara earns $5 for charity for each half hour or fraction of a half hour that she jumps rope. How much money will Cara earn if she jumps rope for 175 min?

Solution

Strategy: Predict and Test

$\frac{1}{2}$ hour $= 30$ minutes

$175 \div 30 = 5$ r25 or 6 half hours

$6 \times \$5 = \$30$

Lesson 10.3

Problem

It took André 1 min to fill his aquarium $\frac{1}{3}$ full. How long will it take him to fill the aquarium $\frac{3}{4}$ full?

Solution

Strategy: Draw a Picture

It takes André 1 minute to fill the aquarium one-third full. Shade one third of the picture. To fill it $\frac{3}{4}$ full, divide the aquarium into twelfths. Now each third is divided into fourths. Each section takes $\frac{1}{4}$ minute or 15 seconds to fill. $\frac{3}{4} = \frac{9}{12}$ so if he fills the aquarium $\frac{3}{4}$ full, he fills 9 sections.

4 sections $= 1$ min

1 section $= 15$ sec

9 sections $= 2$ min and 15 sec or $2\frac{1}{4}$ min

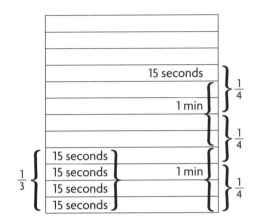

Lesson 10.5

Problem

A hawk flies $\frac{1}{3}$ mi in 30 sec. How far can the hawk fly in 1 min? How fast does it fly in miles per hour?

Solution

Strategy: Write a Number Sentence

A hawk flies $\frac{1}{3}$ mi in 30 sec, so it flies $2 \times \frac{1}{3}$ mi in 2×30 sec or $\frac{2}{3}$ mi in 60 sec, or 1 min.

If the hawk flies $\frac{2}{3}$ mi in 1 min, it flies $60 \times \frac{2}{3}$ mi in 60×1 min, or 40 mi in 60 min, or 1 hr.

So the hawk's speed is 40 miles per hour.

Lesson 10.6

Problem

Maria has $2\frac{1}{2}$ times as many trading cards as Roberto, who has $\frac{1}{4}$ as many as Julia. Karen and Tim each have 25, which is 15 fewer than Julia. Who has the most cards?

Solution

Strategy: Use Logical Reasoning

Students can start with Karen and Tim, who each have 25. That is 15 fewer than Julia, so she has 40. Roberto has $\frac{1}{4}$ as many as Julia, so he has 10; and Maria has $2\frac{1}{2}$ times as many as Roberto, so she has 25. Hence, Julia has the most.

Julia

Chapter 10 Answer Key

Lesson 10.7

Problem

Ming Li ran 90 ft from first base to second base. Each stride was about $3\frac{1}{2}$ ft long. If she takes about 2 strides per second, about how long did it take her to get to second base?

Solution

Strategy: Use Logical Reasoning

Ming Li does 2 strides per sec, so $2 \times 3\frac{1}{2} = 7$. Ming Li can cover 7 ft per sec. It is 90 ft to second base, so estimate $10 \times 7 = 70$. In 10 sec she covers 70 ft. In 3 more seconds, she covers 3×7 or 21 more feet. $70 + 21 = 91$ ft

Possible answer: about 13 sec

Chapter 11 Answer Key

Lesson 11.1

Problem

One side of Jessica's square array is 2 tiles longer than a side of Dave's square array. Together they use a total of 100 tiles. How many tiles are on each side of Dave's array?

Solution

Strategy: Predict and Test

Dave's array	$5 \times 5 = 25$	$6 \times 6 = 36$
Jessica's array	$7 \times 7 = 49$	$8 \times 8 = 64$
	74	100

There are 6 tiles on each side of Dave's array.

Lesson 11.2

Problem

I am a palindrome number, and the sum of my 7 digits is 25. My tens digit is 4 times as great as my ones digit and 4 more than my hundreds digit. My thousands digit and my thousandths digit are each 7 greater than my ones digit. What number am I?

Solution

Strategy: Predict and Test, Use Logical Reasoning

The ones digit must be less than 3 or the tens digit will be greater than the greatest digit (9). If the ones digit is 0, the tens digit will also be 0, but 0 cannot be 4 more than the hundreds digit. You are the number 8,041.408.

Lesson 11.3

Problem

Leon's number is less than Bev's.

Shannon has a negative number.

Leon's and Tony's numbers are the least and the greatest.

Who has each of these numbers:
$-2\frac{1}{5}$, $\frac{19}{18}$, 2.05, -2.25?

Solution

Strategy: Use Logical Reasoning

For help, students should write all numbers as fractions.

$-2\frac{1}{5}$, $\frac{19}{18}$, $2\frac{1}{20}$, $-2\frac{1}{4}$

Ordered from least to greatest:

-2.25,	$-2\frac{1}{5}$,	$\frac{19}{18}$,	2.05
Leon	Shannon	Bev	Tony
($<$ Bev's)	(negative)	(Boys are least and greatest)	

Leon, -2.25; Shannon $-2\frac{1}{5}$; Bev $\frac{19}{18}$; Tony, 2.05

Lesson 11.4

Problem

Cara is twice as old as Lee. In 5 years she will be $1\frac{1}{2}$ times as old as he is. How old is Lee?

Solution

Strategy: Predict and Test

In five years Cara's age will be $1\frac{1}{2}$ times Lee's age. Students may realize that Lee's present age must be an odd number. In order to multiply $1\frac{1}{2}$ by Lee's age in 5 years and get an integer, his present age would need to be an odd number.

Try 3 and 6 for their present ages.

In 5 years, the ages would be 8 and 11, which does not work.

Try 5 and 10 for the present ages. In 5 years, they would be 10 and 15, and 15 is $1\frac{1}{2}$ times 10.

5 years old

Chapter 12 Answer Key

Lesson 12.2

Problem

On a number line, the distance from 0 to a negative integer is four times as great as the distance to a positive integer. The sum of their absolute values is 35. What are the numbers?

Solution

Strategy: Predict and Test

Students may use the predict and test strategy, for example, trying 5 and ⁻20, 6 and ⁻24, and 7 and ⁻28. As an alternative, students may employ logical reasoning and divide 35 into 5 parts. The numbers are ⁻28 and 7.

Lesson 12.4

Problem

Write the missing numbers.

Each of the numbers in the first 4 rows is the sum of the two numbers below it.

```
                  ?
             ⁻3        ?
         ?       ⁻2       1
      ⁻4      ?       ?       6
  ⁻14     10      ⁻7      ?       4
```

Solution

Strategy: Write a Number Sentence

```
                  ⁻4
             ⁻3        ⁻1
         ⁻1      ⁻2       1
      ⁻4      3       ⁻5       6
  ⁻14     10      ⁻7      2       4
```

Chapter 13 Answer Key

Lesson 13.2

Problem

We are two integers. Our sum is $^-15$ and our difference is 3. Who are we?

Solution

Strategy: Predict and Test; Make an organized List

Since the difference of the two integers is positive and the sum is negative, the two integers are most likely negative. So make a list of two negative integers that have a sum of $^-15$. Then check to see if their difference is 3.

Sum	Difference
$^-1 + {}^-14 = {}^-15$	$^-1 + {}^-14 = 13$
$^-2 + {}^-13 = {}^-15$	$^-2 + {}^-13 = 11$
$^-3 + {}^-12 = {}^-15$	$^-3 + {}^-12 = 9$
$^-4 + {}^-11 = {}^-15$	$^-4 + {}^-11 = 7$
$^-5 + {}^-10 = {}^-15$	$^-5 + {}^-10 = 5$
$^-6 + {}^-9 = {}^-15$	$^-6 + {}^-9 = 3$

The two integers are $^-6$ and $^-9$.

Lesson 13.3

I am a positive integer. If I am squared, $^-5$ is added to me, $^-10$ is subtracted from me, and the remainder is divided by 2, the result is 7. What integer am I?

Solution

Strategy: Work Backward

$7 \times 2 = 14$

$14 + {}^-10 = 4$

$4 - {}^-5 = 9$

$\sqrt{9} = 3$

The integer is 3.

Lesson 13.4

Problem

Write the missing integers.

$^-2$	$\times$	?	$\times$	4	$=$	$^-24$
$\times$?	$\times$	$^-4$	$\times$	?	$=$	?
$^-10$	$\times$	?	$\times$	$^-8$	$=$	$^-960$

Solution

Strategy: Write a Number Sentence

$^-2$	$\times$	3	$\times$	4	$=$	$^-24$
$\times 5$	$\times$	$^-4$	$\times$	$^-2$	$=$	40
$^-10$	$\times$	$^-12$	$\times$	$^-8$	$=$	$^-960$

Teaching Notes

Additional Ideas:

Good Questions to Ask:

Additional Resources:

Notes for Next Time:

HARCOURT
Math

SCOPE & SEQUENCE
AND CORRELATIONS

This section contains the following:

▶ **Scope & Sequence**
The scope and sequence shows the development of all strands of math across the grades—Kindergarten through Grade 6. In addition there is a detailed scope and sequence specific to the grade level.

▶ **Correlation to Standardized Tests**
The standardized test correlations will assist you as you prepare students for the following standardized tests:

CAT–California Achievement Test
CTBS/Terra Nova–Comprehensive Test of Basic Skills
ITBS–Iowa Test of Basic Skills
MAT–Metropolitan Achievement Test
SAT–Stanford Achievement Test

▶ **Manipulatives Chart**
This chart is a correlation of the Pupil Edition and Teacher's Edition with the manipulative kits designed to accompany the program.

Scope and Sequence

NUMBER AND QUANTITATIVE REASONING	K	1	2	3	4	5	6
WHOLE NUMBERS							
Meaning of numbers	●	●	●	●	●	●	●
Read and write numbers							
to 30	●	▲					
to 100		●	●	▲	▲		
to 1,000			●	●	▲	▲	▲
in the ten thousands				●	●	▲	▲
in the millions					●	●	▲
in the billions						●	▲
Count	●	●	●	●			
Place value							
tens and ones	●	●	●				
to 100		●	●	▲	▲		
to 1,000			●	●	▲		
to 10,000				●	▲	▲	▲
in the millions					●	●	▲
in the billions						●	▲
Expanded form	●	●	●	●	●	●	▲
Compare and order							
to 10 (with objects)	●	▲					
to 100 (using symbols)		●	●	▲	▲	▲	▲
to 1,000 (using symbols)			●	●	●		
to 10,000 (using symbols)				●	●	●	▲
in the millions (using symbols)					●	●	▲
in the billions (using symbols)						●	▲
Make reasonable estimates	●	●	●	●	●	●	●
Rounding							
to nearest ten, hundred, or thousand				●	●	●	●	●
to nearest ten thousand through nearest million					●	●	●
Even/odd		●	●	●	▲	▲	▲
Ordinal numbers	●	●	●				
Multiples					●	●	●
Divisibility						●	●
Prime and composite					●	●	●
Least common multiple						●	●
Common factors						●	●
Greatest common factor						●	●
Powers and exponents						●	●
Factor whole numbers					●	●	●
Prime factors					●	●	●
Prime factorization						●	●
Square numbers and square roots					●	●	●

● Teach   ▲ Reinforce and Maintain

NUMBER AND QUANTITATIVE REASONING

WHOLE NUMBERS
Make reasonable estimates 17–19

Rounding
to nearest ten, hundred, or thousand 16
to nearest ten thousand through nearest million 16
Multiples 16–19, 150, 154–155
Divisibility 146–147, H38
Prime and composite 148, 233
Least common multiple 150–153, 180–182, H38
Common factors 151
Greatest common factor 151–153, 204, H38
Powers and exponents 40–41, 280–283, H33
  Challenge • Scientific notation 87
  Challenge • Negative exponents 267
Factor whole numbers 151–153
Prime factors 148–149, 233
Prime factorization 148–149, 150–153, H38
Square numbers and square roots
  squares 280–283, H45
  square roots 281–283, H45

Type printed in red indicates that a topic is being introduced for the first time.

NUMBER SENSE

NUMBER AND QUANTITATIVE REASONING	K	1	2	3	4	5	6
MONEY							
Identify coins	●	●	●	●			
Value of coins	●	●	●	●	▲		
count and trade amounts		●	●	●			
make change			●	●	▲		
Value of collection of coins and bills			●	●	▲		
count and trade amounts				●	▲	▲	
make change				●	▲	▲	▲
Compare amounts and prices	●	●	●	●	●	▲	▲
Equivalent amounts		●	●	●	●	▲	▲
Use decimal notation and/or dollar and cents symbols		●	●	●	●	●	▲
DECIMALS							
Meaning of decimals				●	●	●	▲
Read and write decimals							
to tenths				●	●	●	▲
to hundredths				●	●	●	▲
to thousandths					●	●	▲
to ten-thousandths						●	▲
Locate on number line				●	●	●	▲
Relate to fractions				●	●	●	●
Decimal place value							
to hundredths				●	●	●	▲
to thousandths					●	●	▲
to ten-thousandths						●	▲
Compare and order							
to hundredths				●	●	●	●
to thousandths						●	●
to ten-thousandths						●	●
Equivalent decimals					●	●	●
Relate to percent					●	●	●
Decimals greater than 1				●	●	●	▲
Round					●	●	●
Terminating/repeating decimals						●	●
Nonrepeating decimals							●
Scientific notation							●

● Teach   ▲ Reinforce and Maintain

NUMBER AND QUANTITATIVE REASONING

DECIMALS
Relate to fractions 169–171, H39

Compare and order
  to hundredths 53–55, H34
  to thousandths 53–55, H34
  to ten-thousandths 53–55
Equivalent decimals 52–55
Relate to percent 60–61, 398–401
Round 58
Terminating/repeating decimals 169–171, H39
Nonrepeating decimals (terminating decimals) 169–171
Challenge • Scientific notation 87, 267

Type printed in red indicates that a topic is being introduced for the first time.

NUMBER AND QUANTITATIVE REASONING	K	1	2	3	4	5	6
FRACTIONS							
Meaning of fractions	●	●	●	●	●	▲	▲
Part of a whole	●	●	●	●	●	▲	▲
Part of a group			●	●	●	▲	▲
Read and write fractions		●	●	●	●	▲	▲
Locate on a number line				●	●	●	▲
Relate to decimals				●	●	●	●
Compare, unit fractions			●	●	▲	▲	▲
Compare, like denominators			●	●	●	●	●
Compare, unlike denominators				●	●	●	●
Fractions equal to 1 or greater			●	●	●	●	●
Mixed numbers				●	●	●	●
locate on number line				●	●	●	▲
Equivalent fractions			●	●	●	●	●
Order, like denominators				●	●	●	●
Order, unlike denominators				●	●	●	●
Simplest form				●	●	●	●
Least common denominator						●	●
Relate to percent						●	●
Reciprocals						●	●
Rational numbers							●
INTEGERS							
Opposites						●	●
Negative numbers					●	●	●
Meaning of integers					●	●	●
Integers on the number line					●	●	●
Absolute value						●	●
Compare and order						●	●
RATIONAL NUMBERS							
Meaning of rational numbers							●
Compare and order							●
Scientific notation							●

● Teach   ▲ Reinforce and Maintain

NUMBER AND QUANTITATIVE REASONING

FRACTIONS
Relate to decimals 169–171, H39
Compare, like denominators 166–167
Compare, unlike denominators 166–167, H39
Fractions equal to 1 or greater 164
Mixed numbers 164–165, 186, H39
Equivalent fractions 160–163, H39
Order, like denominators 166–167, 231–232
Order, unlike denominators 166–167, 231–232, H39
Simplest form 161–163, H39
Least common denominator 182–185
Relate to percent 170–171, 396–397, 398–401, H39
Reciprocals 209
Rational numbers 230–232, 234–235, H42

INTEGERS
Opposites 228–229, H42
Negative numbers 228–229
Meaning of integers 228–229
Integers on the number line 228–229, 244, 246, 257
Absolute value 228–229
Compare and order 228–229

RATIONAL NUMBERS
Meaning of rational numbers 230–232
Compare and order 234–235, H42
Challenge • Scientific notation 267

Type printed in red indicates that a topic is being introduced for the first time.

NUMBER AND QUANTITATIVE REASONING	K	1	2	3	4	5	6
NUMBER SENSE							
Meaning of whole numbers	●	●	●	●	●	●	▲
Number relationships	●	●	●	●	●	●	●
Meaning of fractions		●	●	●	●	●	▲
Meaning of decimals				●	●	●	▲
Equivalent forms of numbers		●	●	●	●	●	●
Effects of operations						●	●
Meaning of percent					●	●	●
Meaning of integers					●	●	●
Meaning of rational numbers							●
MENTAL MATH							
Skip-counting			●	●	▲	▲	
Use properties		●	●	●	●	●	●
Patterns, multiples, and powers of 10				●	●	●	●
Compatible numbers					●	●	●
ESTIMATE QUANTITIES							
Benchmarks	●	●	●	●	●	●	▲
Rounding			●	●	●	●	●

● Teach ▲ Reinforce and Maintain

NUMBER AND QUANTITATIVE REASONING

NUMBER SENSE
Number relationships 60–61, 150–153, 160–163, 169–171, 230–232, 280–281, 398–401

Equivalent forms of numbers 52, 54, 60–61, 77–78, 160–163, 180–181, 230–232

Effects of operations 42–45, 202–205, 206–207, 208–209, 262–265

Meaning of percent 396–397, 401, 402–405, 406–407

Meaning of integers 228–229

Meaning of rational numbers 230–232

MENTAL MATH
Use properties 36–39, 206–207, 262–263, 278–279, 291–295, 301–303, H33
  Associative 36–39, 262–263
  Commutative 36–39, 262–263
  Distributive 36–39, 206–207, 278–279
  Equality 291–295, 301–303
  Challenge Reflexive, symmetric, and transitive properties 315
Patterns, multiples, and powers of 10
  77, 146–147, 154–155, H33
Compatible numbers 17–19, 58–59, 76

ESTIMATE QUANTITIES
Rounding
  whole numbers 16–19
  decimals 58–59
  fractions 176–179, 200–210
  mixed numbers 186–187

Type printed in red indicates that a topic is being introduced for the first time.

OPERATION AND QUANTITATIVE REASONING	K	1	2	3	4	5	6
WHOLE NUMBERS							
Addition							
Meaning of addition	●	●	●	▲	▲	▲	▲
Concrete objects, numbers less than 10	●	●					
Addition facts (sums to 10)		●	●	▲			
Addition facts (sums to 20)		●	●	▲	▲		
Basic-fact strategies							
counting on		●	●	▲			
doubles and doubles plus one		●	●	▲			
make a ten		●	●	▲			
Column addition			●	●	▲	▲	▲
Fact families/inverse relationship between + and −		●	●	▲	▲	▲	▲
Properties		●	●	●	●	●	▲
3 or more addends		●	●	●	●	●	▲
2-digit numbers, with/without regrouping		●	●	●	▲	▲	▲
using mental math			●	▲	▲	▲	▲
3-digit numbers			●	●	●	▲	▲
4-digit numbers				●	●	●	▲
Greater numbers					●	●	▲
Estimate sums			●	●	●	●	●
Subtraction							
Meaning of subtraction	●	●	●	▲	▲	▲	▲
Concrete objects, numbers less than 10	●	●					
Subtraction facts (differences from 10)		●	●	▲			
Subtraction facts (differences from 20)		●	●	▲	▲		
Basic-fact strategies							
counting back		●	●	▲			
doubles and doubles minus one			●	▲			
Missing addends			●	●	▲	▲	▲
2-digit numbers, with/without regrouping		●	●	●	▲	▲	▲
using mental math			●	▲	▲	▲	▲
3-digit numbers			●	●	▲	▲	▲
4-digit numbers				●	●	●	▲
Greater numbers					●	●	▲
With zeros		●	●	●	●	●	▲
Checking subtraction			●	●	●	▲	▲
Estimate differences			●	●	●	●	●

● Teach ▲ Reinforce and Maintain

OPERATION AND QUANTITATIVE REASONING

WHOLE NUMBERS
Addition
Estimate sums 16–19, H32
  rounding 16
  clustering 16
Subtraction
Estimate differences 16–19, H32
rounding 16

Type printed in red indicates that a topic is being introduced for the first time.

OPERATION AND QUANTITATIVE REASONING	K	1	2	3	4	5	6
Multiplication							
Meaning of multiplication			●	●	●	▲	▲
Multiplication facts for 2s, 5s, and 10s			●	●	●	▲	▲
Multiplication facts to 10 × 10				●	●	▲	▲
Multiplication facts to 12 × 12					●	▲	▲
Basic-fact strategies							
skip-counting			●	●	▲	▲	
break-apart numbers				●	●	●	
doubling				●	●		
Order Property				●	▲	▲	
Fact families/inverse relationship between × and ÷				●	▲	▲	▲
Estimate products				●	●	●	●
Multiples of 10				●	●	●	▲
Multidigit by 1-digit factor				●	●	●	▲
Multidigit by 2-digit factor					●	●	▲
Multidigit by 3-digit factor						●	▲
Multidigit by 4-digit factor						●	▲
Exponents						●	●
Properties				●	●	●	▲
Division							
Meaning of division		●	●	●	●	●	▲
Model and compute quotient			●	●	●	●	●
Division facts for 2s, 3s, 4s, 5s, 6s, 7s, 8s, 9s, 10s			●	●	●	●	●
Division facts for 11s and 12s				●	●	▲	▲
Missing factors				●	●	●	▲
Basic-fact strategies							
inverse operations				●	●	●	▲
Fact families				●	●	▲	
Remainders				●	●	●	▲
Interpret remainders				●	●	●	●
0 and 1 in division				●	▲	▲	▲
Multidigit by 1-digit divisor, no remainder				●	●	●	▲
Multidigit by 1-digit divisor, with remainder				●	●	●	▲
Multidigit by 2-digit divisor					●	●	▲
Zeros in the quotient				●	●	●	▲
Estimate quotients				●	●	●	▲
Divisibility						●	●
Determine unit cost				●	●	●	●

● Teach ▲ Reinforce and Maintain

OPERATION AND QUANTITATIVE REASONING

WHOLE NUMBERS
Multiplication
  Estimate products 17–19, H32
    rounding 17
  Exponents 40–41, H33
Division
  Model and compute quotient 23–25, H32
  Division facts for 2s, 3s, 4s, 5s, 6s, 7s, 8s, 9s, 10s 23–25
  Interpret remainders 80–81
  Divisibility 146–147, H38
  Determine unit cost 375–376, H51

Type printed in red indicates that a topic is being introduced for the first time.

NUMBER SENSE

OPERATION AND QUANTITATIVE REASONING	K	1	2	3	4	5	6
MONEY							
Add	●	●	●	●	●	●	▲
Subtract	●	●	●	●	●	●	▲
Multiply				●	●	●	▲
Divide				●	●	●	▲
Estimate sums, differences, products, quotients						●	▲
DECIMALS							
Addition							
Meaning of addition				●	●	●	▲
Sums to two decimal places				●	●	●	●
Sums to three decimal places						●	●
Sums to more than three decimal places							●
Estimate sums					●	●	●
Subtraction							
Meaning of subtraction				●	●	●	▲
Differences to two decimal places				●	●	●	●
Differences to three decimal places						●	●
Differences to more than three decimal places							●
Estimate differences					●	●	●
Multiplication							
Meaning of multiplication						●	▲
Decimal by a whole number						●	●
Decimal by a decimal						●	●
By powers of 10						●	●
Place the decimal point						●	●
Place zeros in the product						●	●
Estimate products						●	●
Round products							●
Division							
Meaning of division					●	●	●
Decimal by a whole number						●	●
Decimal by a decimal						●	●
By powers of 10						●	●
Place the decimal point						●	▲
Place zeros in the quotient						●	●
Estimate quotients (compatible numbers)						●	●
Round quotients							●
Repeating/terminating quotients							●

● Teach   ▲ Reinforce and Maintain

OPERATION AND QUANTITATIVE REASONING

DECIMALS

Addition
Sums to two decimal places 66–69, H35
Sums to three decimal places 66–69, H35
Estimate sums 58–59, 66–69, H34
  clustering 58–59

Subtraction
Differences to two decimal places 66–69, H35
Differences to three decimal places 66–69, H35
Estimate differences 58–59, 66–69, H34

Multiplication
Decimal by a whole number
  model 70
  symbolic 70–73, H35
Decimal by a decimal
  model 71
  symbolic 71–73, H35
By powers of 10
  Challenge • Scientific notation 87
  Challenge • Negative exponents 267
Place the decimal point 70–73, H35
Place zeros in the product 71–73, H35
Estimate products 58–59, H34
Round products 476–479, 492–493, 511–513

Division
Meaning of division 74–75
Decimal by a whole number 76–79, H35
Decimal by a decimal 76–79, H35
Place the decimal point 76–79, H35
Place zeros in the quotient 76–79, H35
Estimate quotients (compatible numbers) 58–59, 76, H34
Repeating/terminating quotients 169–171, H39

Type printed in red indicates that a topic is being introduced for the first time.

OPERATION AND QUANTITATIVE REASONING	K	1	2	3	4	5	6
FRACTIONS							
Addition							
Meaning of addition				●	●	●	▲
Like denominators				●	●	●	▲
Unlike denominators					●	●	●
Estimate sums					●	●	●
Mixed numbers					●	●	●
Subtraction							
Meaning of subtraction				●	●	●	▲
Like denominators				●	●	●	▲
Unlike denominators					●	●	●
Estimate differences					●	●	●
Mixed numbers					●	●	●
Mixed numbers with renaming						●	●
Multiplication							
Meaning of multiplication						●	●
Fraction by a whole number						●	●
Fraction by a fraction						●	●
Fraction and mixed number						●	●
Estimate products							●
Mixed numbers						●	●
Division							
Meaning of division						●	●
Fraction by a whole number						●	●
Whole number by fraction						●	●
Fraction by a fraction						●	●
Estimate quotients							●
Mixed numbers						●	●
INTEGERS							
Meaning of addition and subtraction						●	●
Use a number line to compute						●	●
Add						●	●
Subtract						●	●
Multiply							●
Divide							●
ESTIMATE ANSWERS							
Rounding			●	●	●	●	●
Benchmarks			●	●	●	●	▲
Compatible numbers					●	●	●

● Teach   ▲ Reinforce and Maintain

OPERATION AND QUANTITATIVE REASONING

FRACTIONS
Addition
Unlike denominators
  model 180, 182
  symbolic 182–185, H40
Estimate sums 176–179, H40
Mixed numbers
  model 186   symbolic 186–189, H40
  Challenge • Mixed numbers and time 221

Subtraction
Unlike denominators
  model 181, 183   symbolic 183–185, H40
Estimate differences 176–179, H40
Mixed numbers
  model 187, 190–191
  symbolic 187–188, 192–193, H40
Mixed numbers with renaming
  model 190–191
  symbolic 192–193, H40
  Challenge • Mixed numbers and time 221

Multiplication
Meaning of multiplication 202–203
Fraction by a whole number 202–205, H41
Fraction by a fraction 202–205, H41
Fraction and mixed number 206–207, H41
Estimate products 200–201, H41
Mixed numbers 206–207, H41

Division
Meaning of division 208–209
Fraction by a whole number 210–213
Whole number by fraction 208–209, 210–213, H41
Fraction by a fraction 208–209, 210–213, H41
Estimate quotients 200–201, H41
Mixed numbers 210–213, H41

INTEGERS
Meaning of addition and subtraction 242–243, 248–249, H43
Use a number line to compute 244, 246, 257, 258, H43
Add 242–243, 244–247, H43
Subtract 248–249, 250–251, H43
Multiply 256–257, 258–259, H44
Divide 260–261, H44

ESTIMATE ANSWERS
Rounding
  sums 16–19, 58–59, 176–179
  differences 16–19, 177–179
  products 17–19, 200–201
  quotients 17–19, 200–201
Compatible numbers 17–19, 58–59, 76, 176–179, 186–187, 200–201

Type printed in red indicates that a topic is being introduced for the first time.

ALGEBRA AND FUNCTIONS

ALGEBRA	K	1	2	3	4	5	6
CLASSIFY							
Identify and sort by attributes	●	●	●	●	●	●	●
determine objects that don't belong	●	●	●	●	●	●	●
PROPERTIES							
Of whole numbers		●	●	●	●	●	●
Associative and Commutative, of addition		●	●	▲	▲	▲	▲
Associative and Commutative, of multiplication				●	▲	▲	▲
Distributive						●	●
0 and 1			●	●	▲	▲	▲
EQUATIONS AND EXPRESSIONS							
Number sentences for addition and subtraction	●	●	●	●	●	●	●
Number sentences for multiplication and division				●	●	●	●
Use symbols: +, −, =	●	●	●	●	●	●	▲
Use symbols: x, ÷				●	●	●	▲
Missing addend				●	●	●	●
Missing factor				●	●	●	●
Write numerical expressions				●	●	●	●
Evaluate numerical expressions			●	●	●	●	●
Match problem situation and expression				●	●	●	●
Formulas				●	●	●	●
Order of operations							●
Variables					●	●	●
Use parentheses				●	●	●	●
Write and evaluate algebraic expressions					●	●	●
with one variable					●	●	●
with two variables							●
with three variables							●
Write number sentence/equation for problem situation		●	●	●	●	●	●
Create problem situation for number sentence/equation		●	●	●	●	●	●

● Teach   ▲ Reinforce and Maintain

ALGEBRA

CLASSIFY

Identify and sort by attributes
  determine objects that don't belong 354–356

PROPERTIES

Of whole numbers 36–39, 262–263, 278–279, 291–293
  Distributive 206–207

EQUATIONS AND EXPRESSIONS

Number sentences for addition and subtraction 288–289, 291–293, 294–295, H46

Number sentences for multiplication and division 300, 301–303, H47

Missing addend 291–293

Missing factor 301–303

Write numerical expressions 28–29, 282–283, H32

Evaluate numerical expressions 28–29, 262–263, 282–283, H32, H44, H45

Match problem situation and expression 274–275

Formulas
  temperature 305–307
  time and distance 124–125, 304–307
  perimeter 469
  circumference 474–479
  area 485–487, 488–490, 491, 492–493
  volume 503–505, 511–513
  surface area 494–497
  simple interest 412–413

Order of operations 42–43, 44–45, 262–263, 276–278

Variables 28–29, 274–275, 276–279, 288–289

Use parentheses 42–43, 44–45, 262–263, 276–278

Write and evaluate algebraic expressions 28–29, 82–83, 216–217, 274–275, 276–279, H32, H35, H45
  with one variable 28–29, 82–83, 274–275, 276–279, H32, H35
  with two variables 274–275, 276–279
  with three variables 274–275, 276–279

Write number sentence/equation for problem situation 288–289, 291, 294, 303, 378–379, 408–411, H46

Create problem situation for number sentence/equation 289, 307

Type printed in red indicates that a topic is being introduced for the first time.

ALGEBRA AND FUNCTIONS

ALGEBRA	K	1	2	3	4	5	6
Solve equations							
1-step addition and subtraction equations		●	●	●	●	●	●
1-step multiplication and division equations				●	●	●	●
modeling 2-step equations							●
equations with two variables					●	●	●
with integers						●	●
with rational numbers							●
linear equations					●	●	●
Use number sentence/equation to solve problem		●	●	●	●	●	●
Relate graphs and equations					●	●	●
Relate tables, graphs, and rules					●	●	●
INEQUALITIES							
Compare numbers	●	●	●	●	●	●	●
Inequality symbols: <, >		●	●	●	●	●	●
Algebraic inequality							●
Write inequality for problem situation							●
Solve inequalities							●
Use to solve problem							●

● Teach   ▲ Reinforce and Maintain

ALGEBRA

EQUATIONS AND EXPRESSIONS

Solve equations

1-step addition and subtraction equations 290, 291–293, 294–295, H46

1-step multiplication and division equations 300, 301–303, H47

modeling 2-step equations 308–309

equations with two variables 529–532, 564–565, 566–567, 568–569, H59, H61

with integers 290, 291–293, 294–295, H46

with rational numbers 290, 291–293, 294–295, H46

linear equations 568–569

Use number sentences/equation to solve problem 291–293, 294–295, 301, 303, 304–307, 378–379, H46

Relate graphs and equations 564–565, 566–567, 568–569, H61

Relate tables, graphs, and rules 564–565, 566–567, 568–569, H61

INEQUALITIES

Compare numbers 53–55, 166–167, 228–229, 231–232, 234–235, 396–397, H34, H39, H42

Inequality symbols: <, > 53, 166–167, 234–235, 396–397, 558

Algebraic inequality 558–559, H61

Write inequality for problem situation 558–559

Solve inequalities 558–559, H61

Use to solve problem 53, 167, 235, 396

Type printed in red indicates that a topic is being introduced for the first time.

ALGEBRA AND FUNCTIONS

ALGEBRA	K	1	2	3	4	5	6
PROPORTIONAL REASONING							
Ratio						●	●
concept						●	●
read and write						●	●
equivalent ratios						●	●
cross products							●
rates, unit rates							●
Proportion							
meaning of proportion							●
solve proportions							●
applications							
indirect measurement							●
scale drawings						●	●
similar figures						●	●
Percent							
meaning of percent						●	●
percent and decimals						●	●
percent and fractions						●	●
percents greater than 100%/less than 1%						●	●
find percent of a number						●	●
find percent one number is of another						●	●
estimate percents							●
applications							
circle graph						●	●
sales tax						●	●
simple interest							●
discount							●
NUMBER LINE							
Locate		●	●	●	●	●	●
Compare and order		●	●	●	●	●	●
Operations		●	●	●	●	●	●

● Teach   ▲ Reinforce and Maintain

ALGEBRA

PROPORTIONAL REASONING

Ratio 374–376, H51
  concept 374–376
  read and write 374–376
  equivalent ratios 374–376
  similar figures 384–385, H51
  cross products 378
  rates, unit rates 375–376, H51

Proportion
  meaning of proportion 377
  solve proportions 378–379, H51
  applications
    indirect measurement 384–386, H51
    scale drawings 387–389, 390–391, H51
    similar figures 384–386, H51

Percent
  meaning of percent 396–397, 398–401, H52
  percent and decimals 398–401, H52
  percent and fractions 170–171, 398–401, H52
  percents greater than 100%/less than 1% 398–401
  find percent of a number 402–405, H52
  Challenge • Find percent one number is of another • Percent of Increase and Decrease 445
  estimate percents 402–405
  applications
    circle graph 406–407
    sales tax 408–411
    simple interest 412–413, H52
    discount 408–411, H52

NUMBER LINE
  Locate 53–55, 166–167, 176–178, 228–229, 231–232
  Compare and order 166–167, 231–232, 234–235
  Operations 244, 246, 257, 258

Type printed in red indicates that a topic is being introduced for the first time.

ALGEBRA AND FUNCTIONS

ALGEBRA	K	1	2	3	4	5	6
GRAPHING ON A NUMBER LINE							
Whole numbers					●	●	●
Integers					●	●	●
Rational numbers					●	●	●
Inequalities							●
COORDINATE GRAPHING							
Ordered pairs			●	●	●	●	●
Coordinate plane							
1 quadrant				●	●	●	▲
4 quadrants						●	●
Relations						●	●
Functions					●	●	●
Linear equations					●	●	●
Nonlinear equations							●
FUNCTIONS AND RELATIONS							
Solve problems involving functions				●	●	●	●
Input-output tables		●	●	●	●	●	●
Graphs of functions					●	●	●
Write a rule			●	●	●	●	●
Graph from a rule					●	●	●
Linear functions							
with whole numbers					●	●	●
with integers						●	●
Applications							
measurement conversions					●	●	●	●
rates							●
proportions							●
distance/speed/time							●
unit cost				●	●	●	●

● Teach   ▲ Reinforce and Maintain

ALGEBRA

GRAPHING ON A NUMBER LINE
Integers 228–229, 244, 246, 257
Rational numbers 53–55, 231–232
Inequalities 558–559, H61

COORDINATE GRAPHING
Ordered pairs 560–563, 564–565
Coordinate plane 560–563, 564, 570–573
  4 quadrants 560–563, 564, 570–573
Relations 564–565
Functions 529, 564
Linear equations 568–569
Nonlinear equations 568–569

FUNCTIONS AND RELATIONS
Solve problems involving functions 529–532, 564–565, 566–567
Input-output tables 529–532
Graphs of functions 564–565
Write a rule 529–532, 564–565, 566–567, H61
Graph from a rule 568–569
Linear functions
  with whole numbers 568–569, H61
  with integers 569
Applications
  measurement conversions 305–307, 452–453, 454–455, 456–457, H55
  rates 375–376, H51
  proportions 378–379, 384–386, 387–389, 390–391, H51
  distance/speed/time 124–125, 304–307
  unit cost 375–376, H51

Type printed in red indicates that a topic is being introduced for the first time.

MEASUREMENT AND GEOMETRY

MEASURING OBJECTS	K	1	2	3	4	5	6
CONCEPTS							
Choose appropriate tools/units to measure or draw			●	●	●	●	●
angles					●	●	●
parallel and perpendicular lines					●	●	▲
polygons and circles					●	●	▲
Precision/accuracy					●	●	●
LENGTH							
Meaning of linear measurement	●	●	●	●	●	●	●
Nonstandard units	●	●	●	●	●		
Compare and order	●	●	●	●	●	●	▲
Estimate	●	●	●	●	●	●	▲
Customary units		●	●	●	●	●	●
measure to the nearest inch			●	●	▲	▲	▲
measure to fractional part of an inch				●	▲	▲	▲
Metric units		●	●	●	●	●	●
measure to the nearest centimeter			●	●	▲	▲	▲
measure to the nearest millimeter						●	●
Relate units			●	●	●	●	●
choose appropriate units			●	●	●	●	●
Change units within a system				●	●	●	●
Compare/convert units between systems							●
Apply distance formula							●
CAPACITY							
Meaning of capacity	●	●	●	●	●	●	▲
Nonstandard units	●	●	●	●			
Compare and order	●	●	●	●	●	●	▲
Estimate	●	●	●	●	●	●	▲
Customary units			●	●	●	●	▲
Metric units			●	●	●	●	▲
Relate units				●	●	●	●
choose appropriate units				●	●	●	▲
Change units within a system				●	●	●	●
Compare/convert units between systems							●

● Teach   ▲ Reinforce and Maintain

MEASURING OBJECTS

CONCEPTS
Choose appropriate tools/units to measure or draw 458–461, H55
   angles 324–325, H31
Precision/accuracy 458–461, H55

LENGTH
Meaning of linear measurement 458–461, H55
Customary units 452–453, H55
Metric units 454–455, H55
   measure to the nearest millimeter 458–461
Relate units 452–453, 454–455, H55
   choose appropriate units 458–461, H55
Change units within a system
   customary units 452–453, H55
   metric units 454–455, H55
Compare/convert units between systems 456–457, H55
Apply distance formula 124–125, 304–307

CAPACITY
Relate units 452–453, 454–455, H55
Change units within a system
   customary units 452–453, H55
   metric units 454–455, H55
Compare/convert units between systems 456–457, H55

Type printed in red indicates that a topic is being introduced for the first time.

MEASUREMENT AND GEOMETRY

MEASURING OBJECTS	K	1	2	3	4	5	6
WEIGHT/MASS							
Meaning of weight/mass	●	●	●	●	●	●	▲
Nonstandard units	●	●	●	●			
Compare and order	●	●	●	●	●	●	▲
Estimate	●	●	●	●	●	●	▲
Customary units			●	●	●	●	▲
Metric units			●	●	●	●	▲
Relate units				●	●	●	●
choose appropriate units				●	●	●	▲
Change units within a system				●	●	●	●
Compare/convert units between systems							●
TEMPERATURE							
Meaning of temperature			●	●	●	▲	▲
Read a thermometer: Fahrenheit and Celsius			●	●	●	●	▲
Meaning of negative numbers					●	●	●
Computing temperature changes					●	●	●
Change units between systems: Fahrenheit/Celsius						●	●

MEASURING OBJECTS

WEIGHT/MASS

Relate units 452–453, 454–455, H55

Change units within a system
    customary units 452–453, H55
    metric units 454–455, H55

Compare/convert units between systems
456–457, H55

TEMPERATURE

Meaning of negative numbers 228–229, H42

Computing temperature changes 247, 250–251

Change units between systems:
Fahrenheit/Celsius 305–307

● Teach   ▲ Reinforce and Maintain

Type printed in red indicates that a topic is being introduced for the first time.

MEASUREMENT AND GEOMETRY

MEASURING TIME	K	1	2	3	4	5	6
Concept of time	●	●	●	●	●	▲	▲
CLOCK							
As tool to measure time	●	●	●	●	●		
Sequence events	●	●	●	●	●		
Identify the times of everyday events	●	●	●	●	▲		
Tell and show time							
to the hour and half hour	●	●	●	●	▲		
to the quarter hour			●	●	▲		
to 5-minute and 1-minute intervals			●	●	●		
A.M. and P.M.			●	●	●	▲	▲
Relate minutes/hours, days/months, weeks/years			●	●	▲		
Estimate time	●	●	●	●	▲		
Elapsed time			●	●	●	●	
Add and subtract units			●	●	●	●	
Schedules		●	●	●	●	●	
CALENDAR							
As tool to measure time	●	●	●	●	▲	▲	
Days of the week	●	●	●	●	▲		
Read	●	●	●	●	●		
Elapsed time			●	●	●	●	

● Teach   ▲ Reinforce and Maintain

Type printed in red indicates that a topic is being introduced for the first time.

MEASUREMENT AND GEOMETRY

MEASURING FIGURES	K	1	2	3	4	5	6
PERIMETER							
Meaning of perimeter			●	●	●	●	●
Measure			●	●	●	●	●
Add to find			●	●	●	●	●
Multiply and add to find				●	●	●	●
Apply formulas							
square, rectangle, and compound figures					●	●	●
polygon/regular polygon					●	●	●
Use appropriate units of measure					●	●	●
CIRCUMFERENCE							
Estimate					●	●	●
Meaning of circumference					●	●	●
Find diameter or radius					●	●	●
Meaning of pi						●	●
Apply formula						●	●
Compare calculated and estimated							●
AREA							
Meaning of area				●	●	●	●
Estimate and measure with nonstandard units				●	●	●	●
Derive and apply formulas					●	●	●
squares, rectangles, and compound figures					●	●	●
parallelograms and triangles						●	●
trapezoids							●
circles							●
surface areas						●	●
nets						●	●
Use appropriate units of measure					●	●	●
Relate area and perimeter				●	●	●	●

● Teach   ▲ Reinforce and Maintain

MEASURING FIGURES

PERIMETER
Meaning of perimeter 468, 469–471, H56
Measure 468, 469
Estimate 468
Add to find 469–471, H56
Multiply and add to find 469–471, H56
Apply formulas
   square, rectangle, and compound figure 469–471, H56
   polygon/regular polygon 469–471, H56
Use appropriate units of measure 468

CIRCUMFERENCE
Estimate 474–475
Meaning of circumference 474–475, 476–479
Find diameter or radius 478–479
Meaning of pi 79, 474–475,
Apply formula 475, 476–479, H56
Compare calculated and estimated 474–475

AREA
Meaning of area 484–487, H57
Derive and apply formulas
   squares, rectangles, and compound figures 484–487, H57
   parallelograms and triangles 484–487, 488–490, H57
   trapezoids 488–490, H57
   circles 491, 492–493, H57
   surface areas 494–497, H57
   nets 360–361, 502, 508
Use appropriate units of measure 484–487
Relate area and perimeter 487

Type printed in red indicates that a topic is being introduced for the first time.

MEASUREMENT AND GEOMETRY

MEASURING FIGURES	K	1	2	3	4	5	6
SURFACE AREA							
Meaning of surface area						●	●
Estimate and measure with nonstandard units				●			●
Construct a cube and rectangular prism as patterns						●	▲
Apply formulas						●	●
prism						●	●
pyramid							●
Use appropriate units of measure					●	●	●
VOLUME							
Meaning of volume				●	●	●	●
Estimate and measure with nonstandard units				●	●		
Estimate and measure					●	●	●
Apply formulas							
prisms					●	●	●
pyramids							●
cylinders							●
Compare formulas: rectangular prism/triangular prism/cylinder							●
Use appropriate units of measure						●	●
Relate perimeter, area, and volume						●	●
ANGLES							
Compare to right angle (greater than, less than, equal to)				●	●	●	●
Identify and classify				●	●	●	●
right, acute, obtuse				●	●	●	●
vertical, adjacent, complementary, supplementary							●
Relate to $\frac{1}{4}$, $\frac{1}{2}$, and $\frac{3}{4}$ turns					●	●	●
Measure, draw, and construct						●	●
triangle: sum of measures of angles is 180°						●	●
rectangle: sum of measures of angles is 360°						●	▲
other polygons: sum of measures						●	▲
ALGEBRAIC THINKING							
Indirect measurement							●
similar figure applications							●

● Teach   ▲ Reinforce and Maintain

Type printed in red indicates that a topic is being introduced for the first time.

MEASUREMENT AND GEOMETRY

GEOMETRIC IDEAS	K	1	2	3	4	5	6
CONCEPTS							
Position	●	●	●				
Attributes	●	●	●	●	●	●	●
Sides, vertices, edges, and faces		●	●	●	●	●	●
Points, lines, segments, angles, rays				●	●	●	●
parallel, perpendicular, and intersecting lines				●	●	●	●
Congruence		●	●	●	●	●	●
Symmetry		●	●	●	●	●	●
line (bilateral)		●	●	●	●	●	●
point (rotational)					●	●	●
Transformations			●	●	●	●	●
Similarity					●	●	●
SOLID FIGURES							
Attributes and properties	●	●	●	●	●	●	●
Identify and describe common geometric objects	●	●	●	●	●	●	●
Identify, describe, and classify	●	●	●	●	▲	▲	▲
sphere, pyramid, cube, prism	●	●	●	●	▲	▲	▲
cone, cylinder	●	●	●	●	▲	▲	▲
Represent and visualize	●	●	●	●	●	●	▲
Build/take apart				●	●	●	▲
Identify or draw different views						●	●
Make nets				●	●	●	●
Measure							
volume				●	●	●	●
surface area				●		●	●

● Teach ▲ Reinforce and Maintain

GEOMETRIC IDEAS

CONCEPTS

Attributes
  triangles 336–339, H49
  quadrilaterals 342–345, H49
  solid figures 354–356, 357–359, 362–363, H50

Sides, vertices, edges, and faces 362–363, H50

Points, lines, segments, angles, rays 322–323, 324–325, 326–329, H48
  parallel, perpendicular, and intersecting lines 330–331, H48

Congruence 380–383, H51

Symmetry
  line (bilateral) 550–553, H60
  point (rotational) 550–553, H60

Transformations
  translations, reflections, and rotations 540–542, 548–549, 570–573, H60, H61
  Challenge • Dilations (Stretching) 577
  tesselations 543–547, H60

Similarity
  identify similar figures 380–383, H51
  write a proportion to find an unknown measure 384–386, H51
  indirect measurement 384–386, H51

SOLID FIGURES

Attributes and properties 354–356, 357–359, 362–363, H50

Identify and describe common geometric objects 354–356, H50

Identify or draw different views 357–359
  Challenge • Perspective 367

Make nets 360–361, 502, 508

Measure
  volume 502–505, 508–509, 510–513, H58
  surface area 494–497, H57

Type printed in red *indicates that a topic is being introduced for the first time.*

MEASUREMENT AND GEOMETRY

GEOMETRIC IDEAS	K	1	2	3	4	5	6
PLANE FIGURES							
Attributes and properties	●	●	●	●	●	●	●
triangle	●	●	●	●	●	●	●
quadrilaterals (rect., square, parall., rhombus, trap.)		●	●	●	●	●	●
Identify and describe common geometric objects	●	●	●	●	●	●	●
Identify, describe, and classify	●	●	●	●	●	●	●
rectangle, square, triangle, circle	●	●	●	●	●	●	●
pentagon, hexagon, octagon				●	●	●	●
Represent and visualize	●	●	●	●	●	●	●
Build/take apart			●	●	●	●	▲
Draw with appropriate tools							
parallel and perpendicular lines					●	●	●
angles					●	●	●
rectangles						●	●
triangles						●	●
quadrilaterals						●	●
Measure with appropriate tools							
angles					●	●	●
perimeter/circumference			●	●	●	●	●
area				●	●	●	●
Parts of a circle (radius, diameter, chord, arc, central angle)				●	●	●	●
ALGEBRAIC THINKING							
Formulas				●	●	●	●
Graphing figures						●	●
Scatterplots							●
Correlations							●
Similar figure applications							●
indirect measurement							●

● Teach   ▲ Reinforce and Maintain

GEOMETRIC IDEAS

PLANE FIGURES

Attributes and properties
  triangle 336–339, H49
  quadrilaterals (rect., square, parall., rhombus, trap.) 340, 342–345, H49

Identify and describe common geometric objects 336–339, 342–345, H49

Identify, describe, and classify
  rectangle, square, triangle, circle; pentagon, hexagon, octagon 336–339, 342–345, 348–349, H49

Represent and visualize 346–347

Draw with appropriate tools
  parallel and perpendicular lines 330
  angles 346–347
  rectangles 346–347
  triangles 346–347
  quadrilaterals 346–347

Measure with appropriate tools
  angles 324–325
  perimeter/circumference 468, 474
  area 484

Parts of a circle (radius, diameter, chord, arc, central angle) 348–349, H49

ALGEBRAIC THINKING

Formulas 485–487, 488–489, 492–493, 494–497, 508–509, 511–513

Graphing figures 570–573, H61
  Challenge • Dilations (Stretching) 577
  Challenge • Scatterplots 139
  Challenge • Correlations 139

Similar figure applications 384–386, 387–389, 390–391
  indirect measurement 384–386, H51

Type printed in red indicates that a topic is being introduced for the first time.

MEASUREMENT AND GEOMETRY

SPATIAL SENSE	K	1	2	3	4	5	6
VISUAL THINKING							
Patterns	●	●	●	●	●	●	●
tessellations				●	●	●	●
nets				●	●	●	●
Congruence		●	●	●	●	●	●
Symmetry		●	●	●	●	●	●
line (bilateral)		●	●	●	●	●	●
point (rotational)				●	●	●	●
Similarity					●	●	●
Transformations							
translations, reflections, and rotations			●		●	●	●
dilations							●
Representing							
building, drawing 3-D figures					●	●	●
different views						●	●
Perspective							●
Networks							●
COORDINATE GEOMETRY							
COORDINATE PLANE							
Ordered pairs				●	●	●	●
Graph points and figures					●	●	●
Graph linear relationships					●	●	●
Relate length of horizontal line segment to *x*-coordinates					●	▲	▲
Relate length of vertical line segment to *y*-coordinates					●	▲	▲
Graph equations					●	●	●
Relations and functions					●	●	●
Identify functions							
linear functions					●	●	●
nonlinear functions							●
Translations, reflections, rotations						●	●

● **Teach**   ▲ **Reinforce and Maintain**

SPATIAL SENSE

VISUAL THINKING
Patterns 533–535, H59
   tessellations 543–545, 546–547, H60
   nets 360–361, 502, 508
Congruence 326, 380–383
Symmetry
   line (bilateral) 550–553, H60
   point (rotational) 550–553
Similarity 380–383, 384–386, 387–389, H51
Transformations
   translations, reflections, and rotations 540–542, 548–549, 570–573, H60, H61
   Challenge • Dilations (Stretching) 577
Representing
   building, drawing 3–D figures 357–359
   different views 357–359
   Challenge • Perspective 367
   Challenge • Networks 517

COORDINATE GEOMETRY

COORDINATE PLANE
Ordered pairs 560–563, 564–565, H61
Graph points and figures 560–563, 564–565, 570–573, 577, H61
Graph linear relationships 564–565
Graph equations 564–565, 568–569
Relations and functions 564–565, 568–569, H61
Identify functions
   linear functions 568–569
   nonlinear functions 568–569
Translations, reflections, rotations 570–573, H61

Type printed in red indicates that a topic is being introduced for the first time.

STATISTICS, DATA ANALYSIS, AND PROBABILITY

STATISTICS AND DATA ANALYSIS	K	1	2	3	4	5	6
COLLECTING DATA							
Use systematic way to record			●	●	●	▲	▲
Pose question/collect data	●	●	●	●	●	▲	▲
Formulate question			●	●	●	▲	▲
Analyze question					●	●	●
Conduct survey		●	●	●	●	●	●
Sampling							●
determine when appropriate							●
bias/errors							●
select in different ways (convenience, random, systematic)							●
determine most representative							●
ORGANIZING DATA							
Sort objects/data and describe categories	●	●	●	●			
Tally table/chart	●	●	●	●	▲	●	▲
Frequency table/chart			●	●	▲	●	▲
cumulative frequency					●	●	▲
Organized list			●	●	●	●	●
Stem-and-leaf plot					●	●	▲
Line plot				●	●	●	▲
DISPLAYING DATA							
Objects/pictures	●	●					
Picture graph	●	●	●				
Pictograph			●	●	▲	▲	
Bar graph	●	●	●	●	●	●	▲
Line graph				●	●	●	▲
identify ordered pairs				●	●	●	▲
write ordered pairs				●	●	●	▲
graph ordered pairs					●	●	●
Circle graph					●	●	●
Histogram						●	●
Box-and-whisker graph							●
Scatterplot							●
Represent same data in different ways		●	●	●	●	●	●
Choose an appropriate graph					●	●	●

● Teach   ▲ Reinforce and Maintain

STATISTICS AND DATA ANALYSIS

Type printed in red indicates that a topic is being introduced for the first time.

STATISTICS, DATA ANALYSIS, AND PROBABILITY

STATISTICS AND DATA ANALYSIS	K	1	2	3	4	5	6
ANALYZING DATA							
Ask/answer questions about data	●	●	●	●	●	▲	▲
Interpret one-variable graphs	●	●	●	●	●	●	▲
Interpret two-variable graphs					●	●	●
Interpret tables	●	●	●	●	●	●	▲
Compare data		●	●	●	●	●	▲
Compare data sets of different sizes						●	▲
Compare/choose appropriate representations					●	●	●
Identify misleading graphs						●	●
Choose scale					●	●	●
Identify outliers					●	●	●
Find range			●	●	●	●	▲
Measures of central tendency							
find mean (average)					●	●	▲
find median					●	●	▲
find mode			●	●	●	●	▲
compare/analyze measures						●	●
determine effects on measures of adding data						●	●
determine effects of outliers							●
Relate to conclusions the way data is displayed						●	●
Evaluate conclusions based on data					●	●	●
Make predictions				●	●	●	●
Misleading graphs							●

● Teach   ▲ Reinforce and Maintain

STATISTICS AND DATA ANALYSIS

ANALYZING DATA

Interpret two-variable graphs 568–569

Compare/choose appropriate representations 94–97, 120–123, 126–128, 132–135

Identify misleading graphs 132–135, H37

Choose scale 120

Identify outliers 110–111, H36

Measures of central tendency
    compare/analyze measures 106–108, H36
    determine effects on measures of adding data 109–111, H36
    determine effects of outliers 110–111, H36

Relate to conclusions the way data is displayed 112–115, H36

Evaluate conclusions based on data 112–115, H36

Make predictions 124–125

Misleading graphs 132–135, H37

Type printed in red indicates that a topic is being introduced for the first time.

STATISTICS, DATA ANALYSIS, AND PROBABILITY

PATTERNS	K	1	2	3	4	5	6
GEOMETRIC PATTERNS							
Identify and describe		●	●	●	●	●	●
Extend		●	●	●	●	●	●
Generate		●	●	●	●	●	●
COLOR/NUMERIC/RHYTHMIC PATTERNS							
Write a rule				●	●	●	●
Identify and describe		●	●	●	●	●	●
Extend	●	●	●	●	●	●	●
Generate	●	●	●	●	●	●	●
LINEAR NUMBER							
Identify and describe		●	●	●	●	●	●
Extend	●	●	●	●	●	●	●
Generate			●	●	●	●	●

● Teach   ▲ Reinforce and Maintain

PATTERNS

GEOMETRIC PATTERNS
Identify and describe 533–535, H59
Extend 533–535, H59
Generate 533–535, H59

COLOR/NUMERIC/RHYTHMIC PATTERNS
Write a rule 526–528, H59
Identify and describe 526–528
Extend 526–528, H59
Generate 526–528

LINEAR NUMBER
Identify and describe 529–532, H59
Extend 529–532
Generate 529–532

Type printed in red indicates that a topic is being introduced for the first time.

PROBABILITY	K	1	2	3	4	5	6
CONCEPTS							
Likelihood of events				●	●	●	●
certain, likely, unlikely, impossible				●	●	●	●
more likely, equally likely, less likely				●	●	●	●
Fairness				●	●	●	▲
Randomness							●
FINDING OUTCOMES							
Outcomes			●	●	●	●	●
Tree diagram					●	●	●
Table/grid					●	●	●
Sample spaces							●
Combinations							●
Fundamental Counting Principle							●
THEORETICAL PROBABILITY							
Meaning					●	●	●
Simple events				●	●	●	●
Compound events							●
Independent/dependent events							●
EXPERIMENTAL PROBABILITY							
Record possible outcomes				●	●	●	●
organized list				●	●	●	●
table/grid				●	●	●	●
tree diagram					●	●	●
Record outcomes during trials				●	●	●	●
Summarize/display results				●	●	●	●
Express verbally and numerically				●	●	●	●
Predict based on experiment or prior data				●	●	●	●
Simulations						●	●
Random numbers							●
REPRESENT PROBABILITY							
Verbally and numerically				●	●	●	●
Ratio, proportion, decimal, percent							●
Verify reasonableness							●
Of event not occurring (1 – P)							●

● Teach   ▲ Reinforce and Maintain

Type printed in red indicates that a topic is being introduced for the first time.

PROBLEM SOLVING PROCESS	K	1	2	3	4	5	6
SET UP/APPROACH PROBLEM							
Determine strategy	●	●	●	●	●	●	●
Determine materials	●	●	●	●	●	●	●
Model problem	●	●	●	●	●	●	●
Analyze problem							
relationships				●	●	●	●
relevant/irrelevant information		●	●	●	●	●	●
sequencing/prioritizing				●	●	●	●
patterns		●	●	●	●	●	●
Determine when to break into simpler parts				●	●	●	●
Formulate conjectures based on problem							●
SOLVE PROBLEM							
Use concrete objects	●	●	●	●	●	●	●
Use pictorial representation	●	●	●	●	●	●	●
Make calculations	●	●	●	●	●	●	●
Use results of simpler problem				●	●	●	●
Use mathematical notation/terms/clear language				●	●	●	●
Estimate solution graphically							●
EXPLAIN/JUSTIFY REASONING OR SOLUTION							
Explain reasoning with concrete objects	●	●	●	●	●	●	●
Explain reasoning with pictorial representations	●	●	●	●	●	●	●
Explain reasoning using a variety of methods				●	●	●	●
Defend reasoning		●	●	●	●	●	●
Check solution based on context	●	●	●	●	●	●	●
Justify procedure used		●	●	●	●	●	●
Use estimation to check			●	●	●	●	●
Defend solutions verbally and symbolically				●	●	●	●
Exact vs. estimated answers				●	●	●	●
GENERALIZE							
Between problems		●	●	●	●	●	●
Apply solution to similar problem				●	●	●	●
State/apply generalizations				●	●	●	●
Evaluate reasonableness in context of problem				●	●	●	●

● Teach   ▲ Reinforce and Maintain

PROBLEM SOLVING PROCESS

SET UP/APPROACH PROBLEM

Determine strategy 12, 27, 57, 101, 155, 195, 237, 311, 341, 363, 379, 433, 473, 507, 525, 547

Determine materials 13, 34, 92, 158, 198, 226, 254, 272, 298, 320, 334, 352, 372, 394, 416, 450, 466, 556

Model problem 2, 3, 56–57, 194–195, 339, 341, 345, 347, 356, 359, 361, 472–473, 506–507, 543–545, 564–565

Analyze problem

  relationships 7, 10, 12, 304–307, 340–341, 378–379, 384–386, 387–389, 390–391, 456–457, 568–569

  relevant/irrelevant information 349, 422–423

  sequencing/prioritizing 6, 29, 46–47, 138, 154–155, 205, 421, 432–433

  patterns 7, 340–341, 524–525

Determine when to break into simpler parts 9, 13, 362–363

Formulate conjectures based on problem 149, 347, 479, 516, 566–567

SOLVE PROBLEM

Use concrete objects 3, 280–281, 286, 290, 357, 360–361, 491, 502, 506–507, 508, 522, 543–545, 546, 568–569

Use pictorial representation 2, 194–195, 198, 314, 331, 334, 366, 367, 450, 472–473, 500

Make calculations 13, 45, 80–81, 185, 207, 213, 214–215, 221, 266, 283, 304–307, 310–311, 314, 394, 444, 445

Use results of simpler problem 9, 314, 340–341, 362–363, 378–379, 474, 491, 506–507, 524, 576

Use mathematical notation/terms/clear language 10, 34, 86, 138, 275, 372, 378–379, 492

  Challenge • Scientific notation 87, 267

Estimate solution graphically 124–125, 139, 577

EXPLAIN/JUSTIFY REASONING OR SOLUTION

Explain reasoning with concrete objects 280–281, 290, 308, 355, 357–358, 360–361, 502, 508, 522, 543–546, 546, 568–569

Explain reasoning with pictorial representations 2, 194–195, 314, 334, 366, 450, 472–473, 490, 500, 506–507, 517, 524–525, 538

Explain reasoning using a variety of methods 99, 104, 111, 123, 289, 290, 346, 362, 366, 376, 385, 386, 444, 474, 490, 497, 505, 531

Defend reasoning 99, 104, 111, 123, 289, 290, 346, 362, 366, 376, 385, 386, 444, 474, 487, 497, 531

Check solution based on context 80–81, 144, 310–311

Justify procedure used 214–215

Use estimation to check 68, 404, 502

Defend solutions verbally and symbolically 99, 104, 111, 123, 289, 290, 346, 366, 376, 385, 386, 444, 474, 487

Exact vs. estimating answers 462–463, 466, 482

GENERALIZE

Between problems 149, 347, 479, 566–567

Apply solution to similar problem 9, 362–363

State/apply generalizations 566–567

Evaluate reasonableness in context of problem 57, 80–81, 566–567

Type printed in red indicates that a topic is being introduced for the first time.

MATHEMATICAL REASONING

PROBLEM SOLVING STRATEGIES/SKILLS	K	1	2	3	4	5	6
HEURISTIC		●	●	●	●	●	●
STRATEGIES							
Use logical reasoning	●	●	●	●	●	●	●
Predict and test				●	●	●	●
Make a table or graph	●	●	●	●	●	●	●
Find a pattern	●	●	●	●	●	●	●
Draw a picture or diagram	●	●	●	●	●	●	●
Write a number sentence		●	●	●			
Work backward				●	●	●	●
Break a problem into simpler parts/solve a simpler problem				●	●	●	●
Make a model or act it out	●	●	●	●	●	●	●
Write an equation					●	●	●
Make an organized list				●	●	●	●
Choose a strategy		●	●	●	●	●	●
SKILLS							
Identify relationships			●	●	●	●	●
Estimate or exact answer	●	●	●	●	●	●	●
Sequence events			●	●	▲	▲	▲
Too much/too little information		●	●	●	●	●	●
Multistep problems		●	●	●	●	●	●
Choose the operation			●	●	●	●	●
Draw conclusions		●	●	●	●	●	●
Interpret the remainder				●	●	●	●
Use a graph	●	●	●	●	●	●	●
Make generalizations				●	●	●	●
Sequence information				●	●	●	●
Evaluate reasonableness of answers		●	●	●	●	●	●
Use a table		●	●	▲	▲	▲	▲
Use a formula						●	●
Make decisions						●	●
Sequence and prioritize information						●	●
Relevant or irrelevant information						●	●
APPLICATIONS							
Number Sense	●	●	●	●	●	●	●
Algebra and Functions	●	●	●	●	●	●	●
Measurement and Geometry	●	●	●	●	●	●	●
Statistics, Data Analysis, and Probability	●	●	●	●	●	●	●

● Teach   ▲ Reinforce and Maintain

PROBLEM SOLVING STRATEGIES/SKILLS

HEURISTIC

STRATEGIES

Use logical reasoning 11, 111, 205, 236–237, 306, 349, 405, 421, 490, 507, 542, 567

Predict and test 4, 26–27

Make a table or graph 8, 14, 56–57, 100–101, 118, 158, 272, 372, 394

Find a pattern 7, 340–341, 522, 524–525, 576

Draw a picture or diagram 2, 194–195, 198, 339, 341, 345, 347, 356, 359, 361, 472–473, 543–545, 556, 564–565, 568–569

Work backward 5, 310–311

Break a problem into simpler parts/solve a simpler problem 9, 13, 362–363

Make a model or act it out 3, 174, 187, 286, 377, 506–507, 546–547

Write an equation 10, 293, 295, 298, 303, 378–379, 386, 389, 391, 411, 479, 490, 493, 509, 513

Make an organized list 6, 92, 154–155, 226, 416, 432–433, 430

Choose a strategy 12, 27, 57, 101, 155, 195, 237, 311, 341, 363, 379, 433, 473, 507, 525, 547

SKILLS

Identify relationships 7, 10, 12, 304–307, 340–341, 378–379, 384–386, 387–389, 390–391, 456–457

Estimate or exact answer 462–463, 466, 482

Too much/too little information 422–423

Multistep problems 13, 308–309

Choose the operation 21, 25, 69, 185, 189, 214–215, 263, 303, 401, 507

Draw conclusions 112–115

Interpret the remainder 80–81

Use a graph 47, 55, 120–123, 124–125, 126–128, 130–131, 132–135

Make generalizations 272, 566–567

Sequence information 46–47

Evaluate reasonableness of answers 68

Use a formula 124–125, 304–307, 412–413, 469–471, 476–479, 485–487, 488–490, 492–493, 494–497, 503–505, 508–509, 511–513

Make decisions 26–27, 46–47, 80–81, 187, 214–215, 231, 236–237, 398, 402, 404, 409–410, 462–463, 482

Sequence and prioritize information 46–47

Relevant or irrelevant information 422–423

APPLICATIONS

Number sense 39, 45, 47, 57, 61, 69, 73, 79, 81, 83, 185, 189, 193, 205, 213, 263

Algebra and Functions 266, 289, 293, 295, 303, 304–307, 383, 384–386, 387–389, 390–391, 412–413, 529–532

Measurement and Geometry 331, 347, 359, 453, 455, 457, 471, 479, 490, 493, 497, 505, 509, 513, 538

Statistics, Data Analysis, and Probability 101, 105, 108, 111, 123, 125, 128, 131, 135, 416, 421, 427, 430, 436

Type printed in red indicates that a topic is being introduced for the first time.

MATHEMATICAL REASONING

REASONING	K	1	2	3	4	5	6
CRITICAL THINKING AND LOGICAL REASONING							
Classify and sort	●	●	●	●	●	●	●
Identify, extend, and use patterns	●	●	●	●	●	●	●
Order and sequence	●	●	●	●	●	●	●
Make generalizations			●	●	●	●	●
Compare and contrast	●	●	●	●	●	●	●
Draw conclusions			●	●	●	●	●
Use logical reasoning	●	●	●	●	●	●	●
Make and test predictions	●	●	●	●	●	●	●
Explain and justify answers	●	●	●	●	●	●	●
Evaluate evidence and conclusions				●	●	●	●
Interpret charts, tables, and graphs	●	●	●	●	●	●	●
Check reasonableness of results	●	●	●	●	●	●	●
VISUAL THINKING AND LOGICAL REASONING							
Spatial relationships	●	●	●	●	●	●	●
Visual patterns	●	●	●	●	●	●	●
Use visual representations to solve problems	●	●	●	●	●	●	●
DECISION MAKING							
Decide when to estimate				●	●	●	●
Decide on a computation method				●	●	●	●
Decide whether answer is reasonable		●	●	●	●	●	●
Choose from options or alternatives		●	●	●	●	●	●
CREATIVE THINKING							
Solve nonroutine problems			●	●	●	●	●
Generate problems	●	●	●	●	●	●	●
Choose alternative ways to solve problems		●	●	●	●	●	●

● Teach ▲ Reinforce and Maintain

REASONING

CRITICAL THINKING AND LOGICAL REASONING
Classify and sort 135, 324–325, 326–329, 330–331, 336–339, 342–345, 354–356

Identify, extend, and use patterns 77, 258–259, 340–341, 360–361, 522, 524–525, 526–527, 529–532, 533–535, 543–547, 576

Order and sequence 14, 29, 46–47, 92, 138, 158, 205, 226, 372, 394, 405, 421, 556

Make generalizations 149, 272, 347, 479, 566–567

Compare and contrast 12, 78, 147, 170, 334, 344, 355, 360, 388, 478, 490, 507, 509, 513

Draw conclusions 112–115, 286, 298, 416

Use logical reasoning 11, 69, 236–237

Make and test predictions 4, 26–27

Explain and justify answers 99, 104, 111, 123, 289, 290, 346, 366, 376, 385, 386, 444, 474, 487, 497, 505, 531

Evaluate evidence and conclusions 112–115

Interpret charts, tables, and graphs 120–123, 124–125, 126–128, 130–131, 132–135

Check reasonableness of results 66–69

VISUAL THINKING AND LOGICAL REASONING
Spatial relationships 357–359, 533–534, H60

Visual patterns 340–341, 360–361, 533–535, 543–547, H60

Use visual representations to solve problems 2, 194–195, 472–473, 506–507, 533–535

DECISION MAKING
Decide when to estimate 462–463

Decide on a computation method 187, 214–215, 231, 398, 404, 409–410

Decide whether answer is reasonable 66–69

Choose from options or alternatives 402, 404, 482

CREATIVE THINKING
Solve nonroutine problems 4, 5, 9, 26–27, 310–311, 362–363, 384–386

Generate problems 21, 59, 73, 101, 125, 163, 179, 195, 229, 275, 289, 307, 341, 397, 423, 441

Choose alternative ways to solve problems 362–363, 432–433

Type printed in red indicates that a topic is being introduced for the first time.

MATHEMATICAL REASONING

PROCESSES	K	1	2	3	4	5	6
COMMUNICATION							
Drawing	●	●	●	●	●	●	●
Writing		●	●	●	●	●	●
Talking	●	●	●	●	●	●	●
CONNECTIONS							
Mathematical	●	●	●	●	●	●	●
Cross-curricular	●	●	●	●	●	●	●
Everyday	●	●	●	●	●	●	●
MULTIPLE REPRESENTATIONS							
Different manipulatives	●	●	●	●	●	●	●
Different models	●	●	●	●	●	●	●
Manipulatives and models	●	●	●	●	●	●	●
Manipulatives, words, and symbols	●	●	●	●	●	●	●
Models, words, and symbols	●	●	●	●	●	●	●
TOOLS							
Calculator							●
Software	●	●	●	●	●	●	●
Manipulatives	●	●	●	●	●	●	●
Measuring tools	●	●	●	●	●	●	●
ruler		●	●	●	●	●	●
protractor					●	●	●
Compass					●	●	●

● Teach   ▲ Reinforce and Maintain

PROCESSES

COMMUNICATION

Drawing 2, 194–195, 472–473

Writing 19, 29, 47, 69, 97, 128, 149, 171, 201, 220, 263, 314, 331, 366, 389, 461, 521, 563

Talking 21, 41, 78, 99, 122, 149, 187, 204, 232, 246, 261, 283, 292, 404, 441

CONNECTIONS

Mathematical 193, 247, 263, 289, 293, 307, 405, 559, 563

Cross-curricular 20, 25, 69, 102, 120, 135, 154, 166, 186, 200, 234, 250, 279, 336, 345, 374, 405, 430, 505, 538, 563

Everyday 50, 52, 174, 298, 394, 406, 408, 412

MULTIPLE REPRESENTATIONS

Different manipulatives 242–245

Different models 180–181, 543–544

Manipulatives and models 568–569

Manipulatives, words, and symbols 70, 74–75, 168, 180–181, 190–191, 208–209

Models, words, and symbols 194–195, 233, 279, 354, 357, 472, 506

TOOLS

Calculator 43, 77, 280, 281, 403, 425, 475, 477

Software 24, 53, 122, 171, 183, 188, 260, 302, 327, 338, 349, 438, 544

Manipulatives 70–72, 74–75, 160–163, 180–181, 190–191, 242–243, 256, 290, 300, 308, 346–347, 354, 357, 358, 377, 402, 424, 502–503, 543–545, 568–569

Measuring tools
   ruler 360–361, 387, 468–469, 474
   protractor 324, 336, 406–407

Compass 406–407, 474, 491, 406–407, 474, 491

Type printed in red indicates that a topic is being introduced for the first time.

Standardized Test Correlations

LEARNING GOALS FOR GRADE 6		CAT	CTBS/ TERRA NOVA	ITBS	MAT	SAT
Chapter 1	**Whole Number Applications**					
1A	To write whole number estimates	CAT	CTBS/Terra Nova	ITBS	MAT	SAT
1B	To write whole number sums, differences, products, and quotients	CAT	CTBS/Terra Nova	ITBS	MAT	SAT
1C	To evaluate expressions and to use mental math to solve equations involving addition, subtraction, multiplication, or division	CAT	CTBS/Terra Nova	ITBS	MAT	SAT
1D	To solve problems by using an appropriate problem solving strategy such as *predict and test*				MAT	
Chapter 2	**Operation Sense**					
2A	To write whole number sums, differences, products, and quotients using number properties and mental math	CAT	CTBS/Terra Nova	ITBS	MAT	SAT
2B	To evaluate expressions using exponents	CAT	CTBS/Terra Nova	ITBS	MAT	SAT
2C	To evaluate expressions using order of operations	CAT	CTBS/Terra Nova	ITBS	MAT	SAT
2D	To solve problems by using an appropriate problem solving skill such as *sequence and prioritize the information*	CAT	CTBS/Terra Nova	ITBS	MAT	SAT
Chapter 3	**Decimal Concepts**					
3A	To write, compare, and order decimals	CAT	CTBS/Terra Nova	ITBS	MAT	SAT
3B	To write estimates of decimal sums, differences, products, and quotients	CAT	CTBS/Terra Nova	ITBS	MAT	SAT
3C	To write decimals as percents and percents as decimals	CAT	CTBS/Terra Nova			
3D	To solve problems by using an appropriate problem solving strategy such as *make a table*		CTBS/Terra Nova			
Chapter 4	**Decimal Operations**					
4A	To write sums, differences, products, and quotients of decimals	CAT	CTBS/Terra Nova	ITBS	MAT	SAT
4B	To evaluate expressions and use mental math to solve equations involving decimals		CTBS/Terra Nova			SAT
4C	To solve problems by using an appropriate problem solving skill such as *interpret the remainder*	CAT	CTBS/Terra Nova	ITBS	MAT	SAT
Chapter 5	**Collect and Organize Data**					
5A	To identify types of samples and determine if they are representative of a given population or biased, and to draw conclusions about a set of data					
5B	To organize, read, interpret, and analyze data in frequency tables and line plots		CTBS/Terra Nova	ITBS	MAT	
5C	To calculate and compare measures of central tendency with and without outliers	CAT			MAT	
5D	To solve problems by using appropriate problem solving strategies such as *make a table*		CTBS/Terra Nova			
Chapter 6	**Graph Data**					
6A	To make and analyze different kinds of graphs and visual displays including circle graphs, bar graphs, stem-and-leaf plots, histograms, and box-and-whisker graphs	CAT	CTBS/Terra Nova	ITBS	MAT	SAT
6B	To estimate and solve for unknown values by using a graph, arithmetic, logical reasoning, and algebraic techniques	CAT	CTBS/Terra Nova	ITBS	MAT	SAT
6C	To compare different types of graphs to determine if they are appropriate or misleading		CTBS/Terra Nova		MAT	
Chapter 7	**Number Theory**					
7A	To write and apply divisibility rules	CAT		ITBS	MAT	SAT
7B	To write and apply prime factorization in exponent form					
7C	To write and apply greatest common factors and least common multiples	CAT	CTBS/Terra Nova	ITBS	MAT	SAT
7D	To solve problems by using an appropriate problem solving strategy such as *make an organized list*					
Chapter 8	**Fraction Concepts**					
8A	To write fractions in equivalent and simplest form	CAT	CTBS/Terra Nova		MAT	
8B	To convert between, compare, and order fractions and mixed numbers	CAT	CTBS/Terra Nova	ITBS	MAT	SAT
8C	To represent and use equivalent representations for fractions, decimals, and friendly percents	CAT		ITBS	MAT	SAT
Chapter 9	**Add and Subtract Fractions and Mixed Numbers**					
9A	To write estimates of sums and differences of fractions and mixed numbers			ITBS	MAT	SAT
9B	To write fraction and mixed number sums and differences	CAT	CTBS/Terra Nova	ITBS	MAT	SAT
9C	To solve problems by using an appropriate problem solving strategy such as *draw a diagram*		CTBS/Terra Nova			
Chapter 10	**Multiply and Divide Fractions and Mixed Numbers**					
10A	To estimate products and quotients of fractions and mixed numbers			ITBS		SAT
10B	To write products and quotients of fractions and mixed numbers	CAT		ITBS	MAT	SAT
10C	To evaluate expressions and to use mental math to solve equations involving addition, subtraction, multiplication, or division of fractions	CAT		ITBS	MAT	SAT
10D	To solve problems by using an appropriate problem solving skill such as *choose the operation*	CAT	CTBS/Terra Nova	ITBS	MAT	SAT

Standardized Test Correlations

LEARNING GOALS FOR GRADE 6		CAT	CTBS/ TERRA NOVA	ITBS	MAT	SAT
Chapter 11	**Number Relationships**					
11A	To identify and write integers, opposites, and absolute values	CAT		ITBS	MAT	SAT
11B	To identify and represent relationships among sets of numbers by using a variety of methods including number lines	CAT	CTBS/Terra Nova		MAT	SAT
11C	To compare and order rational numbers	CAT	CTBS/Terra Nova	ITBS	MAT	SAT
11D	To solve problems by using an appropriate problem solving strategy such as *use logical reasoning*	CAT	CTBS/Terra Nova	ITBS	MAT	SAT
Chapter 12	**Add and Subtract with Integers**					
12A	To write sums of integers by using a variety of methods including models and number lines	CAT			MAT	SAT
12B	To write differences of integers by using a variety of methods including models	CAT				
Chapter 13	**Multiply and Divide with Integers**					
13A	To write products of integers	CAT	CTBS/Terra Nova		MAT	SAT
13B	To write quotients of integers	CAT	CTBS/Terra Nova		MAT	SAT
13C	To perform a combination of operations with integers	CAT	CTBS/Terra Nova		MAT	SAT
Chapter 14	**Expressions**					
14A	To write and evaluate algebraic expressions	CAT			MAT	
14B	To evaluate expressions with squares and square roots				MAT	
Chapter 15	**Addition and Subtraction Equation**					
15A	To write verbal sentences as equations					
15B	To use models to solve one-step equations	CAT	CTBS/Terra Nova	ITBS	MAT	SAT
15C	To solve addition and subtraction equations	CAT	CTBS/Terra Nova	ITBS	MAT	SAT
Chapter 16	**Multiplication and Division Equations**					
16A	To solve multiplication and division equations, and to use models to solve multiplication equations	CAT	CTBS/Terra Nova	ITBS	MAT	SAT
16B	To solve real-world problems by using formulas	CAT	CTBS/Terra Nova	ITBS		SAT
16C	To use models to solve two-step equations		CTBS/Terra Nova			SAT
16D	To solve problems by using an appropriate strategy such as *work backward*	CAT	CTBS/Terra Nova	ITBS	MAT	SAT
Chapter 17	**Geometric Figures**					
17A	To identify, classify, and draw points, rays, lines, and planes	CAT	CTBS/Terra Nova	ITBS	MAT	SAT
17B	To identify, classify, measure, and draw angles	CAT	CTBS/Terra Nova	ITBS	MAT	SAT
17C	To recognize the relationships among angles		CTBS/Terra Nova	ITBS	MAT	SAT
Chapter 18	**Plane Figures**					
18A	To identify, classify, and draw triangles, quadrilaterals, and other two-dimensional figures	CAT	CTBS/Terra Nova	ITBS	MAT	SAT
18B	To identify and measure parts of a circle	CAT		ITBS	MAT	SAT
18C	To solve problems by using appropriate strategies such as *find a pattern*	CAT	CTBS/Terra Nova	ITBS	MAT	SAT
Chapter 19	**Solid Figures**					
19A	To identify, classify, and draw solid figures		CTBS/Terra Nova	ITBS	MAT	SAT
19B	To identify solid figures from different points of view					
19C	To identify nets and patterns for solid figures					
19D	To solve problems by using an appropriate strategy such as *solve a simpler problem*	CAT	CTBS/Terra Nova	ITBS	MAT	SAT
Chapter 20	**Ratio and Proportion**					
20A	To write ratios, rates, unit rates, and proportions	CAT		ITBS	MAT	SAT
20B	To use ratios and proportions to solve problems involving similar figures, scale drawings, and maps	CAT	CTBS/Terra Nova	ITBS	MAT	SAT
20C	To solve problems by using an appropriate strategy such as *write an equation*			ITBS		SAT
Chapter 21	**Percent and Change**					
21A	To write ratios as percents		CTBS/Terra Nova	ITBS	MAT	SAT
21B	To write equivalent forms of percents, decimals, and fractions	CAT	CTBS/Terra Nova	ITBS	MAT	SAT
21C	To solve real-life and application percent problems such as those involving tips, discounts, sales tax, and simple interest, and to estimate and find the percent of a number	CAT		ITBS	MAT	SAT
21D	To make circle graphs using percents	CAT		ITBS		
Chapter 22	**Probability of Simple Events**					
22A	To calculate the likelihood of an event, to find the theoretical probabilities of simple events, and to express probabilities as fractions, decimals, and percents	CAT		ITBS	MAT	SAT
22B	To make predictions based on experimental probabilities		CTBS/Terra Nova	ITBS	MAT	SAT
22C	To solve problems by using an appropriate skill, such as *too much or too little information*	CAT	CTBS/Terra Nova	ITBS	MAT	SAT

Standardized Test Correlations

LEARNING GOALS FOR GRADE 6		CAT	CTBS/ TERRA NOVA	ITBS	MAT	SAT
Chapter 23	**Probability of Compound Events**					
23A	To identify and find the probabilities of compound, independent, and dependent events by using a variety of methods					
23B	To find probabilities, and to make predictions by using sample data	CAT	CTBS/Terra Nova	ITBS	MAT	SAT
23C	To solve problems using an appropriate strategy such as *make an organized list*					
Chapter 24	**Units of Measure**					
24A	To convert between customary measures of length, weight, and capacity and to convert between metric measures of length, mass, and capacity	CAT	CTBS/Terra Nova			SAT
24B	To estimate and write conversions between units in customary and metric systems	CAT	CTBS/Terra Nova			SAT
24C	To measure to a given degree of precision using appropriate units and tools		CTBS/Terra Nova			
24D	To solve problems using an appropriate skill such as *estimate or find exact answer*	CAT	CTBS/Terra Nova	ITBS	MAT	SAT
Chapter 25	**Length and Perimeter**					
25A	To estimate, measure, and calculate perimeters of plane figures	CAT	CTBS/Terra Nova	ITBS	MAT	SAT
25B	To find the circumference of a circle					
25C	To solve problems by using an appropriate strategy such as *draw a diagram*		CTBS/Terra Nova			
Chapter 26	**Area**					
26A	To estimate and write the area of polygons	CAT	CTBS/Terra Nova	ITBS		SAT
26B	To estimate and write the area of a circle					
26C	To write the surface area of prisms and pyramids					
Chapter 27	**Volume**					
27A	To estimate and write the volume of triangular and rectangular prisms		CTBS/Terra Nova			
27B	To estimate and write the volume of triangular and rectangular pyramids		CTBS/Terra Nova			
27C	To estimate and write the volume of cylinders					
27D	To solve problems by using an appropriate strategy such as *make a model*		CTBS/Terra Nova			
Chapter 28	**Patterns**					
28A	To identify, extend, and make number patterns in function tables and sequences and to write a rule to define a pattern	CAT	CTBS/Terra Nova	ITBS	MAT	SAT
28B	To identify and extend geometric patterns, and to write a rule to define a pattern	CAT	CTBS/Terra Nova	ITBS	MAT	SAT
28C	To solve problems by using an appropriate strategy, such as *find a pattern*					
Chapter 29	**Geometry and Motion**					
29A	To identify, analyze, and draw transformations of plane and solid figures		CTBS/Terra Nova	ITBS		
29B	To identify, analyze, and build or make tessellations					
29C	To identify and analyze line and rotational symmetry in geometric figures		CTBS/Terra Nova	ITBS	MAT	SAT
29D	To solve problems by using an appropriate strategy, such as *make a model*		CTBS/Terra Nova			
Chapter 30	**Graph Relationships**					
30A	To write, solve, and graph algebraic inequalities on a number line					
30B	To identify, locate, and graph points, relations, and transformations on a coordinate plane, and to write a rule for relations by using tables and graphs	CAT	CTBS/Terra Nova	ITBS	MAT	SAT
30C	To identify linear and nonlinear relationships					
30D	To solve problems by using an appropriate skill such as *make generalizations*	CAT	CTBS/Terra Nova	ITBS	MAT	SAT

Manipulatives Chart

MANIPULATIVES	KIT SOURCES	PUPIL EDITION PAGES	TEACHER EDITION PAGES
Algebra Tiles	Core Manipulative Kit Teacher Modeling Kit Build-A-Kit® Module N	290, 300, 308, 309	
Base-Ten Units (1 cm)	Core Manipulative Kit Teacher Modeling Kit Build-A-Kit® Module E	358, 502–503, 506	20B, 40B, 146B
Square Tiles	Core Manipulative Kit Teacher Modeling Kit Build-A-Kit® Module M	280–281, 568, 569	40B, 280–281, 382, 568–569
Equabeam™ Balance	Teacher Modeling Kit		
Fraction Circles	Core Manipulative Kit Teacher Modeling Kit Build-A-Kit® Module J	208	208
Fraction Bars	Core Manipulative Kit Teacher Modeling Kit Build-A-Kit® Module I	160–161, 180–182, 186–187, 190–191	160, 180–181, 182B, 182, 184, 190–191
Fraction Tower	Core Manipulative Kit Teacher Modeling Kit		
Geoboards (11 x11)	Core Manipulative Kit Teacher Modeling Kit Build-A-Kit® Module Q		
Pattern Blocks	Core Manipulative Kit Build-A-Kit® Module L	543	543, 550B, 552
Spinners	Core Manipulative Kit Teacher Modeling Kit Build-A-Kit® Module K	55, 108, 424	38, 58B, 202B, 420, 424, 426B
Two-Color Counters	Core Manipulative Kit Teacher Modeling Kit Build-A-Kit® Module C	242–243, 248–249, 256, 377, 402	294B, 377, 402, 524B, 526B

HARCOURT Math

PROFESSIONAL HANDBOOK

Marvelous Decimals

by Roger Howe

It is hard to see clearly how wonderful something as familiar as our decimal number system really is, but pause a moment to contemplate its marvels.

Of the many virtues of the decimal system, consider the following six:

1 **Efficiency** It represents numbers with astounding (in a sense, perfect) compactness and efficiency.

2 **Sophistication** It is highly sophisticated. It uses all the operations of basic algebra (addition, multiplication, and exponentiation [raising to powers]) merely to represent numbers.

3 **Ease of calculation** It makes calculations fast and simple to perform. More technically, it supports efficient, general, easily implemented algorithms for calculation.

4 **Ease of comparison** It is compatible with our ideas of ordering and magnitude. We can easily tell which of two decimal numbers is larger.

5 **Ease of approximation** It deals smoothly with errors and approximation.

6 **Scale independence** It scales easily, allowing representation of arbitrarily small numbers as well as arbitrarily large ones by essentially the same scheme. The arithmetic operations are scale-independent.

That the decimal system does so much so well and so easily makes it a marvel for users, but it presents a challenge for educators. All the structure built into decimals, and all the benefits they confer, are hard to appreciate without

both extended practice and extended thought. It takes a long time for a student to unpack the intellectual treasure chest we know as the decimal place-value number system, and it takes careful guidance from teachers to strike the right balance between helping students master the mechanics of decimal computation and providing them with insight into the various computational recipes that have been developed. However, done right, attention to concepts can provide a solid foundation for computation. It can make the sometimes seemingly arcane procedures of arithmetic appear as pragmatic solutions to essential problems.

History of the Decimal Place-Value System

Let's look briefly at the history of the development of the decimal number system and its possible effects on mathematics and science. The decimal system took a long time to develop. After several thousand years of precursors, this way of writing numbers was invented in India in about A.D. 500. It was adopted and developed by Islamic scholars and finally introduced into Europe in the late Middle Ages. An early pioneer and promoter of decimal notation in Europe was Leonardo of Pisa, also known as Fibonacci. Before Fibonacci, Roman numerals were used to keep records and calculation was done with a counting board. Use of decimals gradually displaced Roman numerals and became standard by the fifteenth century. Although the effects of a change of practice such as the transition from Roman numerals to decimals are diffuse and subtle to gauge, some writers attribute to decimals both a significant role in the European commercial boom of the late Middle Ages and Renaissance and a great stimulus to science and mathematics.

This collection of articles surveys a few highlights of the features of the decimal system listed above. This article discusses the first two items—efficiency and sophistication. The following articles discuss how the sophisticated structure built into decimal numbers promotes efficient arithmetic and how it allows for estimation.

The Efficiency of the Decimal Place-Value System

Writing Numbers Let's look first at writing numbers. The earliest representations of numbers were simple tallies: one mark for one object of some sort. So to indicate 10, it would take 10 tally marks: I I I I I I I I I I. Our decimal system represents up to 9 objects with just one symbol, but that does not begin to reveal its efficiency. As we use more digits, the system gets increasingly efficient. Each additional digit increases our descriptive reach *tenfold*. One digit can tell us the number of people in a typical nuclear family. With two digits, we can name the number of people in an extended family or in a typical school classroom. With three digits, we can specify the number of students in a moderate-sized school. Four digits allow us to name the populations of a large public high school, a moderate-sized college, or a small town. Five digits can number the largest campuses of state universities or large towns and small cities. With six digits, we can count the populations of sizable cities (San Francisco, Cleveland) and some states (Delaware, Wyoming). Seven digits allow us to name the populations of New York City and Paris, most states, and many countries. Using eight digits, we can number the populations of the largest cities (Tokyo, Mexico City, São Paulo), states (California, New York), and most countries (England, Canada, Argentina, Nigeria). Nine digits count the people in large countries like the United States, Japan, or Indonesia—all but China and maybe India. With ten digits, the same number as tallies to count our fingers, we can record the entire human population of the world. With ten digits, we can also write an arbitrary U.S. telephone number. This efficient representation lets us dial anyone in the country in a matter of seconds. (Of course, we will probably get the person's answering machine.)

The principle behind this efficiency is the same principle that makes language work. Start with a small set of basic symbols and create an arbitrarily large vocabulary by making lists formed from the basic symbols—that is, by putting several basic symbols in sequential order. Thus, spoken words

are sequences (in time) of basic sounds (called phonemes by linguists). In English and other languages that use an alphabet, the same system governs writing. Each written word is a sequence (on the page) of letters that encode spoken sounds. So, the decimal system is merely the application to numbers of a general technique for presenting information. We can call it the *alphabetic principle* or *digitization*. The decimal system, however, embodies digital representation at its ultimate. It represents every (positive whole) number, with no exceptions and in exactly one way for each—no misses, no repetitions. This contrasts with the situation for language. There are many sequences of letters and many sequences of syllables that do not make words, but rather only nonsense. Additionally, there is more than one way to pronounce or spell some words.

The Sophistication of the Decimal Number System

Very Round Numbers Admirable as it is, the representational efficiency of our decimal notation hardly touches on the sophistication of the system as a way of representing numbers specifically, rather than some other indefinitely large collection, such as words or telephone numbers. In assigning telephone numbers, we are not really using the numbers as numbers—they are just labels. It doesn't make any sense to add, multiply, or round off telephone numbers. We could just as well use any collection of symbols to write telephone numbers. There still is a (redundant) labeling of the telephone buttons also by letters, which these days is exploited by firms with 800 numbers to provide customers with a catchy mnemonic for remembering how to call them—for example, 1-800-CALL-XYZ. Numbers are convenient for labeling things, but they are much more. They have a rich structure—arithmetic operations, ordering, and magnitude—that makes them much more valuable than a simple list. The decimal system is admirably compatible with all these structures. This compatibility comes out of the sophisticated way the decimal system uses algebraic operations and principles for the mere task

of writing numbers. The basis of the system is numbers of a very special type—a single digit followed by zeros. We will call such numbers "very round." Thus, 7,000; 30; 600,000; 200; 5; and 800,000,000,000 are very round numbers.

Every positive whole number is a sum of very round numbers—one for each decimal place. Indeed, the digits in a given number tell us how to express it as a sum of very round numbers. The following examples show 742 and 3,805 expressed in this way. When we teach children to express numbers in this way, we call it *expanded form*.

$$742 = 700 + 40 + 2$$
$$3,805 = 3,000 + 800 + 5$$

Notice that in 3,805 the zero in the tens place indicates that no very round number with only one zero is needed. This is the place-value principle in action. We record the absence of the multiple of 10 in order to signal that the 8 is representing 800, not 80. Very round numbers are the purest expression of the place-value principle. They are the elements from which all numbers are formed. Thus the zero, which might seem wasteful since it stands for nothing, is the key to making decimal place-value representation work. We will call the very round numbers used to form a general decimal whole number the *very round components* of the number. Thus, the very round components of 742 are 700, 40, and 2.

Structure of Very Round Numbers The use of addition in writing numbers is supplemented by the use of multiplication in forming the very round numbers. Each very round number is the product of a digit times a power of 10 as shown in the following examples.

$$700 = 7 \times 100$$
$$40 = 4 \times 10$$
$$3,000 = 3 \times 1,000$$

Of course, this is also true for the single digits such as $2 = 2 \times 1$, etc., but we don't usually bother to make this explicit.

Each very round number with digit 1 is a power of 10—the product of 10 multiplied by itself repeatedly. The number of multiplications by 10 is just the number of zeros as shown in the following examples.

$$1 = 10^0$$
$$10 = 10^1$$
$$100 = 10 \times 10 = 10^2$$
$$1{,}000 = 10 \times 10 \times 10 = 10^3$$

Polynomials in the Variable "10" If we take into account the multiplicative structure of the very round numbers, in addition to the additive structure of non-round numbers, we see that every decimal number is composed from a very limited collection of basic components. In fact, every decimal number is made by combining just the digits and 10 by means of the basic operations of algebra—addition, multiplication, and exponentiation (raising to powers). Here is how this looks for our examples of 742 and 3,805.

$$742 = 700 + 40 + 2$$
$$= (7 \times 100) + (4 \times 10) + (2 \times 1)$$
$$= 7 \times 10^2 + 4 \times 10^1 + 2 \times 10^0$$
$$3{,}805 = 3{,}000 + 800 + 5$$
$$= (3 \times 1{,}000) + (8 \times 100) + (5 \times 1)$$
$$= 3 \times 10^3 + 8 \times 10^2 + 5 \times 10^0$$

Thus, simply to record numbers, our decimal system implicitly uses all the operations of basic algebra. Furthermore, the expressions we use to write decimal numbers are of a kind familiar from algebra. A quantity that is formed by taking some number, raising it to various powers, and multiplying by some coefficients and summing is referred to as a *polynomial*. Thus, we see that decimal notation is a shorthand device for expressing numbers as "polynomials in 10." This way of describing our familiar decimal notation may seem to be making something simple complicated, but the similarity is not superficial. There are strong parallels between decimal numbers and polynomials, not only in the way of writing them but also in calculations and other properties. The standard procedures for addition, multiplication, and so forth, exploit the structure just elaborated. Furthermore, the "Laws of Algebra" are heavily involved in justifying and comparing algorithms for computation. Understanding and appreciation of the decimal system is greatly enhanced by recognition of this pervasive role of algebra.

Doing Decimal Arithmetic: Addition

by Roger Howe

The article "Marvelous Decimals" (pp. PH1–PH4), describes the algebraic sophistication that our standard decimal notation brings to the writing of numbers. Decimal numbers implicitly treat ordinary whole numbers as "polynomials in 10." What do we get from this algebraic sophistication? We get remarkable power, not only to record but also to manipulate numbers, to perform the usual operations of arithmetic. We get *ease of calculation in the form of efficient, easily implemented algorithms*. Addition and multiplication are essentially combinations of single-digit operations (plus keeping track of decimal places). More exactly, we add or multiply general numbers by appropriate combinations of additions or multiplications of very round numbers, and these essentially amount to calculations with single-digit numbers. Let's see what this means for addition.

Adding Very Round Numbers

Remember that a "very round number" is a number with a single digit followed by zeros: 9; 40; 100; 20,000; 600,000,000, and so forth. The general principle behind addition of decimal numbers is that every addition can be done by an appropriate combination of additions of very round numbers. So, let's examine the sum of two very round numbers.

Let's call the number of digits in a very round number the *length of the number*. Adding very round numbers is interesting only when both numbers have the same length. To add very round numbers of different lengths, all we do is to put the leading digit of each number in its place in the sum. For example, 7,000 + 40 = 7,040. This procedure holds for the sums of many very round numbers, as long as they all have different lengths. For example, 3,000 + 800 + 5 = 3,805. This is, of course, the basic principle that is used to express a general whole number as a sum of its very round components. Students refer to this expression of a number as *expanded form*. However, when we add two very round numbers of the same length, such as 3,000 + 2,000 = 5,000; or 40 + 40 = 80; or 700 + 600 = 1,300, it is not a simple matter of recording digits in appropriate places. Instead, we see that we essentially have to do a single-digit addition and also keep track of the number of zeros in the very round summands. Treating the above examples more formally, we see these processes taking place:

$$3{,}000 + 2{,}000 = (3 \times 1{,}000) + (2 \times 1{,}000) = (3 + 2) \times 1{,}000 = 5 \times 1{,}000 = 5{,}000$$

$$40 + 40 = (4 \times 10) + (4 \times 10) = (4 + 4) \times 10 = 8 \times 10 = 80$$

$$700 + 600 = (7 \times 100) + (6 \times 100) = (7 + 6) \times 100 = 13 \times 100 = 1{,}300$$

The crucial fact we need to know to find the sum is a single-digit addition—an "addition fact." Another way of thinking about factoring out the power of 10 is to treat the power of 10 as a unit. Thus, for $3{,}000 + 2{,}000 = 5{,}000$, we can say, "Three thousands plus two thousands makes five thousands," in analogy with "Three apples plus two apples makes five apples." If the sum of the digits of the numbers we are adding is less than 10, the sum will again be very round and will be the same length as the two original numbers. However, if the sum of the digits is 10 or larger, the sum of the very round numbers will be longer than the original numbers and may not be very round. If we have to do further calculations with it, we should decompose it into a sum of its very round components. This would lead us to write:

$$700 + 600 = 1{,}300 = 1{,}000 + 300$$

We can now continue the computation, using the 1,000 and the 300 individually, as called for. This, of course, is the source of "carrying," or "regrouping."

Adding Any Whole Numbers

To add two general numbers, we decompose each of them into their very round components and add components with the same length. Thus, to compute $26 + 53$, we write:

$$26 + 53 = (20 + 6) + (50 + 3) =$$
$$(20 + 50) + (6 + 3) = 70 + 9 = 79$$

This example is very simple. It has only two-digit addends and requires no carrying or regrouping. Before looking at more complicated examples, the following points should be made. First, although we have written everything on a line, with liberal use of parentheses, what we have done, in essence, is the same as the standard procedure for this addition. Standard procedure tells us to line the numbers up one under the other and add each column:

$$\begin{array}{r} 26 \\ +53 \\ \hline 79 \end{array}$$

We see that the process of alignment and column-wise operation forces us to add the 6 and 3 and the 20 and 50 (represented only by the digits, with the zeros being implicit in the location of the digit in the tens column). Thus, the standard procedure is a way to achieve automatically what we have done explicitly. Although we will not do it in each case, all the illustrations that follow also translate in similar fashion into the standard format.

Second, we should take note of all the rearrangement we have done to get from $(20 + 6) + (50 + 3)$ to $(20 + 50) + (6 + 3)$. These rearrangements are, of course, recognized as being legitimate by anyone experienced with arithmetic. More formally, they are justifiable by means of some of the Laws of Algebra. Specifically, this rewriting used the Commutative and Associative Laws for addition several times. Also, as discussed above, in the addition $20 + 50 = 70$, we are implicitly invoking the Distributive Law, which connects addition and multiplication. The Distributive Law is the law that allows us to factor out the 10 in the process.

$$20 + 50 = (2 \times 10) + (5 \times 10) =$$
$$(2 + 5) \times 10 = 7 \times 10 = 70$$

Since the purpose of this article is not to give a formal treatment of arithmetic, but only to discuss some key ideas, we usually do not mention these Laws of Algebra again. However, they are implicitly involved in virtually all arithmetic calculations, and a full understanding of decimal arithmetic does involve fluency with these Laws.

As previewed on page PH6, sometimes the sum of two digits is 10 or larger, and results in a sum that and has one more digit than the original numbers. This results in "carrying," or "regrouping." We must decompose the result into its very round components and combine the longer one with the original components of that length. Thus,

$$76 + 53 = (70 + 6) + (50 + 3) =$$
$$(70 + 50) + (6 + 3) =$$
$$120 + 9 = 100 + 20 + 9 = 129$$

This is quite a transparent process if the carrying only affects the largest power of 10 as above. If the overflow occurs in a smaller place, the overflow from one sum must be combined with the sum for the next higher place-value position.

$$26 + 57 = (20 + 6) + (50 + 7) =$$
$$(20 + 50) + (6 + 7) = 70 + 13 =$$
$$70 + (10 + 3) = (70 + 10) + 3 =$$
$$80 + 3 = 83$$

In adding multi-digit numbers, the need to carry, or regroup, may affect several places, and there may be a cascade effect, whereby an overflow at one place affects several larger places, as in

$$146 + 57 = (100 + 40 + 6) + (50 + 7) =$$
$$100 + (40 + 50) + (6 + 7) =$$
$$100 + 90 + 13 = 100 + 90 + (10 + 3) =$$
$$100 + (90 + 10) + 3 = 100 + 100 + 3 =$$
$$200 + 3 = 203$$

Despite these complications, the principle is clear. All additions can be done by suitable combinations of additions of very round numbers.

Ease of Calculation

It is also important that this "suitable combination" involves only a fairly small number of additions. To add any two num-

bers under 1,000 (three-digit numbers), we need at most three basic additions and perhaps three more to allow for carrying, or regrouping (six at most). To add two numbers under 10,000, it is only slightly worse—a maximum of eight one-digit additions. Compare this with the effort of counting the objects in a set made by joining two sets, each with several thousand objects! Just as it eases the labor of writing numbers, decimal notation reduces the effort needed for addition. Furthermore, we should remember that all the complications are inherent already in one-digit addition—$7 + 6 = 13$ is greater than 10, and we can't help that. Our decimal system accommodates this fact of life as gracefully as one could hope.

Extra Efficiency of the Standard Algorithm

The standard format for doing the last addition is:

$$\begin{array}{r} {}^{1\,1} \\ 146 \\ +\ 57 \\ \hline 203 \end{array}$$

The ones above the 4 and the 1 represent the regroupings. They remind us to convert 10 ones to a ten and 10 tens to a hundred and to then add these newly created larger units to the ones already there.

The standard algorithm is much more compact and involves much less writing than the computation above. The reason for the compactness is twofold.

- First, rather than explicitly performing the space-consuming decomposition of each number into very round numbers, the standard procedure forces this by lining up the numbers according to their place values and prescribing column addition.

- Second, the standard procedure goes from right to left, adding the ones and regrouping a 10, if necessary, *before* adding the tens, with this process being repeated similarly for each place-value position.

This short-circuits the space-consuming recombination and recalculation steps in our first version. **Thus, the standard procedure is designed for compactness and efficiency of exact calculation.**

Flexibility for Mental Math and Estimation

However, the principle that our computation emphasizes—that multi-digit addition is a combination of additions of very round numbers of the same length—is worth understanding. For one thing, it allows us to think flexibly about addition. It shows us that the operations needed to compute the sum may be done in many orders—thanks to the Commutative and Associative Laws. The standard procedure picks one order— the order that keeps rewriting to a minimum. However, other orders are possible and may sometimes be useful. In particular, with mental math, it often seems more natural to start by adding the places farthest to the left, since these are the largest parts of the numbers being added. Thus, to add 146 and 57 mentally, many people would start by adding $140 + 50$ to get 190, and then add the $6 + 7 = 13$ to the result, getting $190 + 13 = 203$. The point is that the 190 is much larger than the 13, so with just that part of the addition completed, you already know "most of" the answer. If you did not need to know the exact answer, but just approximately how large the sum is, you could say that it is "about 190" or "about 200" (since it is clearly more than 190, and 200 is a very round number). By contrast, the standard procedure starts by computing the ones place, which is the smallest part of the answer, and doesn't find the main part of the result until the end of the calculation. The same ideas let us quickly estimate the size of a multi-digit sum, so that we can check an answer on a calculator for reasonableness. This is discussed more thoroughly in "Estimation and Arithmetic" (pp. PH17–PH20).

Doing Decimal Arithmetic: *Multiplication*

by Roger Howe

In the article "Doing Decimal Arithmetic—Addition" (pp. PH5–PH8), we saw how decimal notation provides a framework for efficient addition. The story with multiplication is similar, but in some ways more remarkable. Everything again depends on combining operations on very round numbers.

Multiplying Very Round Numbers

Recall that very round numbers are numbers consisting of a single digit followed by some zeros. Examples are 2,000 and 4 and 90. They may also be described as a single-digit number times a power of 10. Multiplying very round numbers amounts to multiplying the digits, plus keeping track of the powers of 10. More precisely, to multiply two very round numbers, we multiply their digits, then on the right we append as many zeros as are in both factors together. Here are some examples of multiplications of very round numbers:

$$20 \times 40 = (2 \times 10) \times (4 \times 10) = (2 \times 4) \times (10 \times 10) = 8 \times 100 = 800;$$
$$30 \times 3{,}000 = (3 \times 10) \times (3 \times 1{,}000) = (3 \times 3) \times (10 \times 1{,}000) = 9 \times 10{,}000 = 90{,}000;$$
$$600 \times 7 = (6 \times 100) \times 7 = (6 \times 7) \times 100 = 42 \times 100 = 4{,}200 = 4{,}000 + 200$$

As the last example shows, when the product of the two digits is 10 or more, the product of the very round numbers may not be very round, and in any case will have one more digit than when the product is less than 10. This is not an essential problem, but it is one source of regrouping in the standard procedures for multiplication.

One case that might cause confusion is when one of the digits is 5 and the other is even. When this happens, the product of the digits will be a multiple of 10 and so the whole product will be very round, and it will seem to have an extra zero. But this case is computed in the same way as all the others. The "extra" zero is contributed by the product of the digits. Thus, in the examples below, the extra zero in the second product results because $5 \times 4 = 20$:

$$50 \times 300 = (5 \times 10) \times (3 \times 100) = (5 \times 3) \times (10 \times 100) = 15 \times 1{,}000 = 15{,}000, \text{ but}$$
$$50 \times 400 = (5 \times 10) \times (4 \times 100) = (5 \times 4) \times (10 \times 100) = 20 \times 1{,}000 = 20{,}000$$

Multiplying Any Whole Numbers

Once we know how to multiply very round numbers, the Distributive Law tells us what to do to multiply general multi-digit numbers. To multiply two

numbers, we should multiply every very round component of one factor by every very round component of the other and add the products together. As an example, take first a one-digit by two-digit multiplication:

$$2 \times 34 = 2 \times (30 + 4) = 60 + 8 = 68$$

Here all the single-digit products were less than 10. If some product is more than 10, it must be decomposed into its very round components, resulting in regrouping:

$$2 \times 37 = 2 \times (30 + 7) = 60 + 14 =$$
$$60 + (10 + 4) = (60 + 10) + 4 = 70 + 4 = 74$$

To multiply a pair of multi-digit numbers, we must remember to multiply *each* term of one by *each* term of the other and then add *all* the products together. Thus,

$$21 \times 23 = (20 + 1) \times (20 + 3)$$
$$= 20 \times 20 + 1 \times 20 + 20 \times 3 + 1 \times 3$$
$$= 400 + 20 + 60 + 3 = 400 + 80 + 3 = 483$$

If one wants to proceed very carefully, the second equality can be accomplished in stages:

$$21 \times 23 = 21 \times (20 + 3) = 21 \times 20 + 21 \times 3$$
$$= (20 + 1) \times 20 + (20 + 1) \times 3$$
$$= 20 \times 20 + 1 \times 20 + 20 \times 3 + 1 \times 3$$

Comparing with the Standard Algorithm

As with addition, our way of writing the multiplication parallels the standard procedure. For the standard procedure, we write the numbers under one another just as we did for addition. Then we multiply the top number by each digit of the bottom number and "move the product to the left" in order to take account of the fact that we are really multiplying not only by a single digit but also by a power of 10. The moving-over

procedure is the bookkeeping step that reminds us of the power of 10, which is an implicit factor in the product.

$$\begin{array}{r} 21 \\ \times\ 23 \\ \hline 63 \\ +\ 42 \\ \hline 483 \end{array}$$

Here the 42 really means $420 = 400 + 20$, the first two summands in our expanded computation, and $63 = 60 + 3$ accounts for the last two summands. Thus, the standard procedure automatically organizes several summands from the extended form of the product into single multi-digit numbers, which are then added according to the standard procedures for addition. Perhaps we should emphasize that we could add the four products, 400, 20, 60, and 3, in any order whatsoever without changing the answer—the rules of addition let us do that. We have written them in the order we did, precisely to allow easy comparison with the standard algorithm.

The Need for Regrouping

In this example, we used small digits to avoid the complications of regrouping. Regrouping comes from two sources:

1. when we need to decompose a product larger than 10

2. when the sum of terms with a given power of 10 is greater than 10

(Note that the first problem is essentially the same as in addition, but it is more prominent with multiplication than with addition because the product of two one-digit numbers tends to be larger than the sum.) For example,

$$24 \times 41 = (20 + 4) \times (40 + 1) =$$
$$= 800 + 160 + 20 + 4 = 800 + (100 + 60) + 20 + 4$$
$$= (800 + 100) + (60 + 20) + 4 = 900 + 80 + 4 = 984$$

Here the product 4×4 is greater than 10. Even if all products are less than 10, however, the fact that several products are multiplied by the same power of 10 can produce regrouping:

$$23 \times 32 = (20 + 3) \times (30 + 2)$$
$$= 600 + 90 + 40 + 6 = 600 + 130 + 6$$
$$= 600 + (100 + 30) + 6$$
$$= (600 + 100) + 30 + 6 = 700 + 30 + 6 = 736$$

Here, the products involving the factor 10 are 3×30 and 20×2. Although each is less than 100, they sum to more than 100, resulting in regrouping.

Typically, both causes of regrouping will occur in the same product, making even a two-digit calculation fairly lengthy if carried out in the step-by-step manner we have been using. Here is an example.

$$36 \times 67 = (30 + 6) \times (60 + 7)$$
$$= 1{,}800 + 360 + 210 + 42$$
$$= 1{,}800 + (300 + 60) +$$
$$(200 + 10) + (40 + 2)$$
$$= 1{,}000 + (800 + 300 + 200) +$$
$$(60 + 10 + 40) + 2$$
$$= 1{,}000 + 1{,}300 + 110 + 2$$
$$= 1{,}000 + (1{,}000 + 300) + (100 + 10) + 2$$
$$= (1{,}000 + 1{,}000) + (300 + 100) + 10 + 2$$
$$= 2{,}000 + 400 + 10 + 2 = 2{,}412$$

Comparing this with the standard procedure helps us to appreciate the high degree of compression the latter achieves.

(Note that the relation between our long procedure and the standard one is the same as in the first examples: the first two products of the long method, 1,800 and 360, sum to make 2,160, and the second two products, 210 and 42, sum to make 252. These are the two partial products of the standard procedure, which are added

$$\begin{array}{r} 36 \\ \times\ 67 \\ \hline 252 \\ +216 \\ \hline 2{,}412 \end{array}$$

to find the full product. All the intermediate steps in the long method are to accomplish the needed regrouping.) The downside of this compacting of the task of multiplication is that the final procedure is far from transparent. It takes considerable time and effort on the part of the teacher to make sure that students understand why it works.

Multiplication Is More Complex than Addition

We see in the previous examples that the tendency of products of one-digit numbers to be larger than their sums complicates multiplication by producing more regrouping. There is another more fundamental way in which multiplication is more complex than addition. To add two multi-digit numbers, the number of very round additions (not including regrouping) that must be done is only the number of digits in the smaller of the summands. However, to multiply the same two numbers, the number of one-digit multiplications that must be done is the *product* of the number of digits in the two numbers. Further, the multiplications must be followed by a roughly equal number of additions. The following examples, in which each digit is a 1, involve no regrouping, so each product of very round components contributes a 1 to some digit of the product. The sum of the digits in the final product therefore tells us the total number of very round multiplications involved.

$$11 \times 11 = (10 + 1) \times (10 + 1) = 100 + 10$$
$$+ 10 + 1$$
$$= 100 + 20 + 1 = 121$$

$$111 \times 111 = (100 + 10 + 1) \times (100 + 10 + 1)$$
$$= 10{,}000 + 1{,}000 + 100$$
$$+ 1{,}000 + 100 + 10$$
$$+ 100 + 10 + 1$$
$$= 10{,}000 + 2{,}000 + 300 + 20 + 1$$
$$= 12{,}321$$

In the first product, the digit sum is $1 + 2 + 1 = 4$, and in the second it is $1 + 2 + 3 + 2 + 1 = 9$. Thus, multiplying two 3-digit numbers involves 9 very round multiplications, more than twice as much work as the four multiplications for multiplying two 2-digit numbers. Multiplying two 4-digit numbers will require 16 multiplications, or four times as many as for 2-digit numbers. (The reader may enjoy finding the product $1,111 \times 1,111$.)

Flexibility for Mental Math and Estimation

Thus multiplication is intrinsically more complex than addition; but it can still be accomplished with remarkably little work relative to the size of the numbers involved, and just as in the writing of numbers, this efficiency improves as the size of the numbers increases. When the necessary operations are organized for efficiency by following one of the standard algorithms, the multiplication of three- and four-digit numbers—yielding products into the tens of millions—can be accomplished quickly by hand.

Hence, with multiplication as with addition, the decimal system supports efficient arithmetic. This is probably the feature of it that is most explicitly appreciated, and it forms the core of mathematics instruction in the elementary grades. In teaching, it is important to keep in mind that the compactness and sophistication that make the decimal system so powerful also present roadblocks for most children as they try to learn it. The considerable structure, both explicit and implicit, used in building the decimal system must be unpacked mentally by each child and then repacked. Failure to grasp, at least in some implicit form, the features discussed above, as well as the underlying Laws of Algebra, will impede further learning.

Just as for addition, the "long form" of multiplication that we have used in our discussion is, of course, a good deal more cumbersome than the usual method taught for finding products. It has also the same advantages, both for letting us see what is going on in forming a product and for promoting flexible thinking about multiplication. As with addition, one advantage with the long form is that we can use it to relate the usual procedure to mental math. In this multiplication:

$$21 \times 23 = 20 \times 20 + 1 \times 20 + 20 \times 3 + 1 \times 3 = 400 + 20 + 60 + 3 = 400 + 80 + 3 = 483$$

the usual procedure begins with computing $60 + 3 = 63$. This is done for the same reason that addition is done from left to right—to minimize rewriting. But as in addition, this means that we are paying attention to the smallest parts of the product first. If one is interested in knowing how large something is, it makes sense to pay attention to the largest parts first. In the multiplication above, it is clear that the product 20×20, of the longest very round components, is the largest. Next in size are the products of the longest very round component of one number with the next-to-longest component of the other number. The product of the single digits is the smallest of the four terms. So, if we were multiplying 21×23 mentally, we would first compute $20 \times 20 = 400$, and we would already have an idea of the size of the number. Then we would make a correction by adding $1 \times 20 + 20 \times 3 = 20 + 60 = 80$. Finally, we would add the $1 \times 3 = 3$. If the product of the digits in the smaller products is greater than 10, regrouping is necessary, and the largest digit may be affected. Still, the simple one-digit multiplication of the two longest very round components can give us an idea of what the total product will be. This provides a useful check that the numbers we get from a calculator are plausible. These ideas are discussed more carefully in "Estimation and Arithmetic" (pp. PH17–PH20).

ESTIMATION and Approximation

by Roger Howe

In the articles "Doing Decimal Arithmetic: Addition" and "Doing Decimal Arithmetic: Multiplication" (pp. PH5–PH12), we see how decimal notation makes arithmetic easy. Ease of computation is very important, but the decimal system does much more for us. Estimation and approximation are almost as important as exact calculation. Many decisions we make depend on knowing only a number's approximate size—roughly how large it is—rather than knowing exactly what the number is. But estimation is not merely practical. In fact, we cannot avoid dealing with approximation and estimation. Essentially all real-life numbers—numbers that come from measurements or from some sort of data collection process—are not exact. They are subject to errors of many kinds—errors of measurement, errors of processing, and so on. They may even refer to quantities that are not well defined, that is, quantities that refer to an *ideal* situation can only be approximated in real life.

One example of approximation is the measurement of the "radius of the Earth." To mention the radius of the Earth is to implicitly treat the Earth as a sphere. But it is not exactly a sphere in the mathematical sense. It is slightly flattened at the poles, and it has a bulge near Hawaii. And, of course, it has wrinkles—mountain ranges and deep undersea trenches. (Mount Everest would fit easily into the Marianas Trench near the Philippines and still be well underwater.) It also has bumps—volcanoes such as Mauna Loa in Hawaii. These deviations from the shape of a sphere are small in a relative sense. If the Earth were the size of a billiard ball, it would look as round as the billiard ball and be even smoother. But the deviations do limit the accuracy with which we can speak of "the radius of the Earth." They mean that the "radius of the Earth" is not a definite number. That does not mean that it is not a useful number to think and talk about, but it does mean that we have to tolerate imprecision in this phenomenon, as in most. The ability to think approximately is more valuable in many situations than the ability to calculate exactly, although it is much less represented in the mathematics curriculum.

MAGNITUDE

The decimal system readily adapts to dealing with magnitude, error, and approximation. Just as with arithmetic, the very round numbers are the key. Very round numbers are numbers with a single leading digit followed by zeros—numbers like 70; 50,000; and 200. Every number is a sum of very round numbers encoded by the digits of the number. For example,

2,345 = 2,000 + 300 + 40 + 5. We call 2,000 and 300 and 40 and 5 the *very round components* of 2,345. (See "Marvelous Decimals," pp. PH1–PH4 for more details about very round numbers.)

ORDERING NUMBERS

The basis for dealing with magnitude, error, and approximation is this very simple principle: **Of the very round components of a number, the longest is the largest.** In fact, it is larger than all of the shorter very round components put together. This is true, no matter what the components are—even if the digit in the longest component is only a 1 and the digit in the next component is a 9. (Of course, this is more obvious if the situation is reversed!) Thus, the most important piece of information about the size of a (positive, whole) decimal number is the number of digits needed to represent it—the more digits, the larger the number. Any two-digit number is larger than any one-digit number, any three-digit number is larger than any two-digit number, and so on. The extreme cases are $10 > 9$, or $100 > 99$, or $1,000 > 999$, etc. In recognition of the key role that the number of digits plays in determining the size of numbers, it is sometimes referred to as the *order of magnitude* of the number. In the less formal language of the financial world, the idea is captured in terms like "six-figure salary."

After order of magnitude, the next most important item is the leading, or first, or leftmost, digit—the digit of the longest very round component. Among numbers of the same order of magnitude, the one with the larger leading digit is larger. For example,

$$6,048 > 5,873 \qquad 60,481 > 58,738$$
$$604,813 > 587,386$$

If a four-digit number begins with 2, it is at least 2 times as large as any three-digit number. If it begins with 6, it is at least six times as large, and so forth.

Making finer distinctions between numbers is not much harder. If two numbers have the same order of magnitude and the same leading digit, then the one with the larger second (from left) digit is the larger number: $85 > 83$ and $8,524 > 8,396$. If the first two digits are the same, then size is determined by the third digit, and if these are also the same, by the fourth digit, then the fifth, etc. For example,

$$854 > 852 \qquad 85,475 > 85,468$$
$$8,547,521,673 > 8,547,511,384$$

Except for the restriction that the numbers should have the same length, this is the same principle of ordering used in dictionaries—*lexicographic order.* However, in mathematics it is not an arbitrary convention, but a natural consequence of the meaning of decimal notation.

APPROXIMATION

The principles used for comparing numbers also help us approximate numbers effectively. We can rephrase the main observation about magnitude by saying that the longest very round component of a number contains most of the information about its size. Indeed, the longest very round component of a number is always more than half of the number. For example, in the following decompositions, the first term is always larger than the second:

$$154 = 100 + 54 \qquad 7,633 = 7,000 + 633$$
$$100 > 54 \qquad 7,000 > 633$$
$$495,852 = 400,000 + 95,852$$
$$400,000 > 95,852$$

This means that, if we just drop the second term, we still have most of the original number left. (The larger the first digit, the truer this is. If the first digit is a 9, we still have at least 90 percent of the number left.) In short, the information provided by just the first digit already gives us a reasonable idea of what the actual number is.

If we retain more digits of the number, the accuracy of the approximation improves rapidly. If we retain the first two digits, we will always have at least 90 percent of the number. If we retain

the first three digits, we have at least 99 percent of the number, and at least 99.9 percent of it with the first four digits. For example,

$$400,000 > 95,852 \qquad 490,000 > 10 \times 5,852$$
$$495,000 > 100 \times 852$$

In fact, these statements are very conservative, because they must remain true for the worst cases, such as 19 or 109 or 1,009, when the first few digits are as small as they can be and the remaining digits are as large as they can be. This conservatism is imposed on us by the fact that single digits can represent a nine-fold range in size. Frequently, the first digit by itself will give 90 percent of the number, and the first two digits will give close to 99 percent. In any case, retaining only the first few digits of a decimal number already captures most of the number, and the accuracy of approximation increases rapidly with the additional number of digits retained. Specifically, the possible error decreases by a factor of 10 with each additional retained digit. The approximation process consisting of replacing the rightmost digits of a number with zeros is commonly called *rounding*, or more specifically, *rounding down*, since dropping the final digits always gives a number smaller than the original one. There are other types of rounding, including "rounding up" and "rounding to the nearest," that give slight refinements and that are useful in some situations, but all three types of rounding are qualitatively similar.

Absolute and Relative Accuracy

How good an approximation is good enough? This depends on context. Approximation is inherently a thornier issue than equality, because it is not a "yes-no" kind of issue. It involves matters of judgment. It involves consideration of context. In order to say whether one number is a "good approximation" of another number, we need to know what we want from the number, what we will use it for, what kind of inference might be made from it, and similar issues. A whole field of applied mathematics, known as numerical analysis, is devoted to understanding issues of approximation. Despite possible pitfalls, we cannot escape dealing with approximation because all numbers derived from measurement are necessarily known only approximately. Automatic computation also requires attention to error and approximation because computers can represent numbers only to a certain level of accuracy.

In situations involving error and approximation, there is frequently an implicit unit. Something is large or small according to whether it is larger or smaller than this unit. Confusion can result when people discussing an issue have different ideas about what the unit is. Thus, in a discussion of waste in government, people usually get excited when they hear that "millions of dollars" are being wasted on something. This is because, in thinking about "millions of dollars," people tend to compare this figure with amounts they are familiar with, such as their own salary. Relative to most people's everyday experience, a million dollars is a lot of money. However, the federal budget is currently well over a trillion dollars ($1,000,000,000,000), and a million dollars ($1,000,000) is only one-millionth of a trillion. I do not wish in any way to defend waste in government, but I would argue that here the relevant unit is the total federal budget, and the question to ask is "What portion of the total is being wasted?" If you expect government spending to be 99 percent efficient, which is probably never the case, you would still expect it to waste 10 billion dollars ($10,000,000,000) out of a trillion. Millions just don't show up. If the government is wasting only a few million, we should be overjoyed.

Even when we know clearly what the correct unit is, there are other issues. An important one is the kind of computation that will be done using a given number. In some spectacular examples from numerical analysis, a seemingly simple computation blows up a seemingly negligible error to such an extent that the answer becomes meaningless. This kind of magnification can also happen

in the real world—for example, in weather. Future weather can be very sensitive to small changes in current conditions. This sensitivity may put a serious limit on how good our weather predictions can possibly be. Thus, the issue of approximation in general is complex.

We can discuss only a few general principles and simple situations. Two quite different types of accuracy are used frequently in discussing approximation. It is important to be able to distinguish between them and to tell whether one or the other is appropriate. One is *absolute accuracy*, in which errors are compared to a fixed number and amounts smaller than the fixed number are ignored. This is seen often in financial statements, which often give figures stated in units of a thousand dollars. The other kind is *relative accuracy,* in which errors are compared to the number being approximated. Relative accuracy is what is proposed above as the appropriate kind of accuracy to be considered in a discussion of government waste.

In rounding numbers, absolute accuracy refers to the number of digits that we neglect. Relative accuracy refers to the number of digits we retain. The retained digits are called *significant digits.* For example, if we round 4,286,419 to 4,286,000, we have absolute accuracy to the thousands and relative accuracy to four significant digits. The type of accuracy that is the more relevant depends on the context.

We should note a possible ambiguity in rounding. The usual convention in dealing with rounded numbers is that the non-zero digits are accurate (except that the last digit may be off by one) and that the digits represented by zeros could have been more or less anything. However, it might happen that the last significant digit is a zero. Then the number appears to be less accurate than it is. Thus, 4,280,419 rounded to the thousands is 4,280,000, and under usual conventions, this looks as if it is rounded to ten thousands. Sometimes context can tell us that some zeros at the end of a rounded number are in fact significant, but without further information, one assumes that they represent deleted or unknown digits.

Equipped with the language of significant digits, we again ask, "How accurate is accurate enough?" When measuring physical quantities, each additional significant digit is hard won. In many situations, one or two significant digits are enough to be useful. The usefulness of percents is based on the fact that, frequently, when discussing amounts that are part of some whole, anything less than one one-hundredth of the total is small enough to be negligible. Specifying percentages is akin to having two significant figures of accuracy. To have more than four significant digits takes painstaking work, and frequently even four-digit significance is not realistic. Consider again the example of the radius of the Earth. Since this is approximately 4,000 miles, four significant figures would specify it to at least the nearest mile. However, the difference in altitude between the deepest sea trenches and the highest mountains is over 10 miles. In this situation, and many others involving physical quantities, four significant figures of accuracy are simply not attainable.

ESTIMATION and Arithmetic

by Roger Howe

In the article "Estimation and Approximation" (pp. PH13–PH16), the issues of approximation and, in particular, the technique of rounding are discussed. The present article will discuss how rounding interacts with arithmetic—specifically, with the basic operations of addition and multiplication of positive whole numbers.

ROUNDING SIMPLIFIES ARITHMETIC

Since all decimal arithmetic is based on single-digit arithmetic, rounding simplifies the mechanics of the arithmetic operations. In the addition of round numbers, the zeros can just be carried along. For example:

$$87 + 37 = 124 \text{ and } 87{,}000 + 37{,}000 = 124{,}000$$

This means that when we round off numbers, it becomes less work to add them. It is easier to add 87,000 and 37,000 than to add 87,266 and 37,495.

Zeros on the end of rounded numbers are also easy to deal with in multiplication. They can just be deleted and then reinserted after the multiplication is done. The total number of added zeros in the product is the sum of the numbers of zeros ending the two factors. For example:

$$200 \times 34 = (2 \times 100) \times 34 = (2 \times 34) \times 100 = 68 \times 100 = 6{,}800$$
$$20 \times 340 = (2 \times 10) \times (34 \times 10) = (2 \times 34) \times (10 \times 10) = 68 \times 100 = 6{,}800$$
$$2 \times 3{,}400 = 2 \times (34 \times 100) = (2 \times 34) \times 100 = 68 \times 100 = 6{,}800$$

So, rounding simplifies multiplication. It is easier to compute 20×340 than to compute 23×345. As with multiplication of very round numbers, zeros created by the product of the non-round parts of the numbers may seem to be "extra zeros." They make it seem that there are more zeros than normal. But they do not change the process. One simply has to keep in mind that the "extra" zeros come from the multiplication of the retained digits. In the multiplication $20 \times 350 = (2 \times 10) \times (35 \times 10) = (2 \times 35) \times (10 \times 10) = 70 \times 100 = 7{,}000$, the final result has three zeros. One zero came from the product 2×35, and the other two zeros, one from the 20 and one from the 350, were appended to the end of the 70.

ACCURACY OF ROUNDED ARITHMETIC

Although rounding simplifies arithmetic, it introduces a new issue. If we add or multiply numbers that are only approximations of actual quantities, we must ask how well the result approximates the actual sum or product. Since a full discussion of this question gets rather involved, only a few basic observations are given here.

Recall the two types of accuracy—absolute and relative—discussed in "Estimation and Approximation." Although both apply to the same rounding process, they are quite different ways of thinking about error. *Absolute error* refers to the number of decimal places ignored in rounding, while *relative error* refers to the number of decimal places that are retained. Suppose we round 49,248 down to 49,200. To describe the absolute accuracy of this, we would say we have rounded (down) to the hundreds place. To describe the relative accuracy, we would say that we have retained three significant digits.

In doing addition, absolute accuracy is the relevant consideration. The main point is that the absolute accuracy of a sum can be no better than the worst absolute accuracy of the addends. For example, consider the sum 4,300 + 280 = 4,580. This sum appears to be rounded to the tens place. However, since 4,300 is standing for any number between 4,300 and 4,399 (since we are talking about rounding down), and 280 means a number between 280 and 289, all we know about the true sum is that it is between 4,580 and 4,688. This cannot actually be represented by a single rounded number according to standard conventions, but we frequently fudge it and write it as 4,600. If we decide to represent it by a single decimal number, 4,600 is the best choice. Certainly the third digit of accuracy that is implied by the formal sum is unwarranted.

This principle is the source of humor in the story of a family visiting a natural history museum. After looking at the skeleton of a huge dinosaur, they approached the guard in the room to ask how old it was. He answered, "70 million and 12 years."

They replied, "Oh, that's very old! How do you know?"

He answered, "Well, when I started working here, they told me that it was 70 million years old, and I've been here 12 years, so now it must be 70 million and 12."

In a case in which two numbers of substantially different sizes are being added, the need to round both to the same absolute accuracy can result in seemingly paradoxical situations that involve ignoring fairly large numbers. For example, in adding the rounded numbers 40,000 + 2,800, where 40,000 has been rounded to the nearest 10,000, the 2,800 must also be rounded to that place, which means that it will round to 0! It can be very difficult to round 42,800 back to 40,000, completely writing off the 2,800. However, retaining the extra digits in the formally correct sum creates a false impression of accuracy.

For products, the parallel principle is that *relative* accuracy of a product can be no better than the *least* relative accuracy of the factors. In standard arithmetic, $80 \times 74 = 5,920$. However, if 80 is standing for some number between 80 and 89, then even if the 74 is completely accurate, the number 5,920 is standing for some number between 80×74 and $89 \times 74 = 6,586$. We see from the large range of possibilities in the hundreds and smaller places that it makes no sense to state a result with more than one significant digit. Even the first digit may not be completely certain, but if we want to represent the product by a single number, 6,000 is as good as we can do. The extra digits of implied accuracy in the value 5,920 are quite misleading. When using a calculator, we need to make extra effort to keep in mind that most of the digits in the rapidly produced result of a multiplication may be meaningless.

If nothing further is to be done with a number, retaining meaningless digits may do little harm—it produces some unnecessary mental clutter, but there is no reason to think that the four-digit number 5,920 is a worse approximation of the

actual number it represents than 6,000 is. The real problem with retaining meaningless digits is that they may produce a false sense of accuracy, leading us to use them in calculations whose results are meaningless and misleading. This is particularly likely to happen when we do subtraction. Suppose we have two numbers, 5,920 and 6,160, neither of which is accurate to more than one significant digit but for which we have retained three digits. If we now subtract them, we get 240, but since the two numbers involved are, in fact, only accurate to the nearest 1,000, this number is totally meaningless—none of its digits represent any reality. If we now use this number in further computations, whatever we produce will be nonsense. Calculators are quite willing to produce this kind of nonsense at the push of a button. It is up to us to know when to round off.

BALLPARK ESTIMATES USING ROUNDING

We can use the fact that rounding simplifies arithmetic to estimate a sum or a product by doing the same operation on rounded numbers. This gives us the opportunity to check that a calculation done on a calculator is roughly correct. Such checks can guard against gross errors when we punch in the numbers to be operated on. We can simplify the arithmetic as much as we want, depending on how accurate we want our check to be. The fewer digits we retain, the easier our check computation will be. Unfortunately, it will also be less accurate. The simplest thing to check would be when we retain only the largest very round component of a number. As we have noted already in "Doing Decimal Arithmetic: Addition" and "Doing Decimal Arithmetic: Multiplication," the sum or the product of the largest very round components represents the largest single contribution to the sum. However, due to regrouping, this single very round contribution may not determine even the leading digit in the actual sum. This problem

is worse for multiplication than for addition. Consider the product for

$$14 \times 65 = (10 + 4) \times (60 + 5)$$
$$= (10 \times 60) + (4 \times 60) + (10 \times 5) + (4 \times 5)$$
$$= 600 + 240 + 50 + 20$$
$$= 910$$

We see that, of the four products of very round components, the largest is $10 \times 60 = 600$. However, the next two terms, $4 \times 60 = 240$ and $10 \times 5 = 50$, raise the amount from 600 to near 900, and the last term, $4 \times 5 = 20$, actually puts the total over 900. Thus, although the leading product gives a substantial chunk of the final product, the other terms contribute enough so that it is a matter of judgment as to whether the 600 is a "good approximation" of the actual product. Such judgments might be challenging to young students just learning multiplication.

One way to eliminate the need for such judgments is to sandwich the actual result between two products of rounded approximations to the original factors. This would create a "ballpark" in which the exact answer should lie. This strategy relies on the following basic properties of addition and multiplication:

- When adding two numbers, if either number increases, the sum also increases.

- When multiplying two positive numbers, if either number increases, the product also increases.

These facts are referred to as *monotonicity* of addition and multiplication, respectively. The monotonicity properties suggest the following strategy for getting "ballparks" in which a sum or a product of two numbers should lie. This strategy involves rounding up as well as rounding down. Rounding up is slightly more complicated than rounding down but is still quite simple. To round down, drop the last (meaning rightmost) digits of a number and replace them with zeros. In rounding up, do the same but also add a 1 to the last non-rounded digit of the number. This will

always produce a number larger than the original. Thus, 47,283 rounded down to the thousands is 47,000. Rounded up to the thousands, it is 48,000. Effectively, we have written 47,283 = 47,000 + 283, and replaced 283 by 1,000 to do the rounding up. Rounded down to the hundreds, 47,283 is 47,200; rounded up it is 47,300. Occasionally, rounding up will create a regrouping situation, and one or more digits could turn over, creating zeros that actually represent significant digits. Thus, 49,936 rounded up to the thousands is 49,000 + 1,000 = 50,000. Rounded up to the hundreds, it is 49,900 + 100 = 50,000—the same as rounding up to the thousands. In our application, this will not cause problems.

Here is the "ballpark estimation strategy" for sums or products of two positive whole decimal numbers.

---

1. Round the numbers down (to any desired accuracy).

2. Round the numbers up (to any desired accuracy).

3. Do the same operation (that is, add or multiply) on the rounded numbers (on the two rounded up numbers and on the two rounded down numbers) as specified for the original numbers.

4. The actual sum or product should lie between the two answers calculated in Step 3 above.

Of course, the simplest arithmetic will result if the rounding leaves only one significant digit. Here are some examples. For the product $14 \times 65 = 910$, the rounded down product is $10 \times 60 = 600$ and the rounded up product is $20 \times 70 = 1,400$. We have $600 < 910 < 1,400$, showing that the product is in the right ballpark. Of course, in this case, 1,400 is more than twice as large as 600, so the ballpark is rather large! But this is to some extent unavoidable. When the leading digit is a 1, the longest very round component says less about the number than when the leading digit is greater than 1.

Here is another example, using larger leading digits. Consider the product $43 \times 826 = 35,518$. Round up and down to one significant digit. Rounding down gives $40 \times 800 = 32,000$. Rounding up gives $50 \times 900 = 45,000$. We do indeed have $32,000 < 35,518 < 45,000$, as we must if we had done the actual multiplication correctly. If we round 826 to two significant digits, the ballpark rounded down is $40 \times 820 = 32,800$ and rounded up is $50 \times 830 = 41,500$. So, we have $32,800 < 35,518 < 41,500$. If we round 826 to one significant digit and leave 43 at two significant digits, the ballpark is $43 \times 800 = 34,400$ and $43 \times 900 = 38,700$. If we retain two significant digits in both factors, the ballpark is $43 \times 820 = 35,260$ and $43 \times 830 = 35,690$. With one-digit accuracy in both factors, the ballpark includes numbers with a leading digit of either 3 or 4. It did not completely determine even the first digit, although it limited the possibilities to 3 or 4. With two-digit accuracy in both factors, we also have two-digit accuracy in the product. Thus, we can narrow the ballpark as much as we want at the price of doing more work. The true answer must always lie in the ballpark.

A "BLIND SPOT"
IN THE ORDER OF OPERATIONS

by Liping Ma

Liping Ma is a mathematics educator and researcher. She was an elementary school teacher in China before moving to the United States in 1988. She later attended Michigan State University and Stanford University as a doctoral student. In addition to her experiences as a mathematics teacher, she is the mother of two children who attend schools in the United States. Her many experiences with the educational systems of both countries have given her a unique perspective. In the following essay, she shares her concern about a "blind spot" she has noticed in the way many American educators address the order of operations in expressions or equations.

Many teachers in the United States are fond of using the mnemonic phrase "**P**lease **E**xcuse **M**y **D**ear **A**unt **S**ally." This mnemonic is intended to be a helpful reminder of the order in which operations should be addressed in expressions or equations. "Always do **p**arentheses first, **e**xponents second, then **m**ultiplication, then **d**ivision, then **a**ddition, and then **s**ubtraction." However, using this mnemonic can cause confusion and can lead to an incorrect answer. Consider, for example, this problem.

$$5 - 3 + 2 = \blacksquare$$

If we follow the mnemonic, it means that we should add $3 + 2$ first and then subtract that answer from 5. Then our result would be 0, which is incorrect. The correct answer is 4. Do $5 - 3$ first, then add 2. To help clarify the rationale for the priority of the operations, I've provided the following hypothetical discussion between two teachers.

Teacher A: This morning, one of my students asked me why we use "Please Excuse My Dear Aunt Sally" to determine the order of operations. I wasn't really sure of the answer. Is the priority order of operations really so arbitrary?

Teacher B: I don't think it is arbitrary. In fact, I think using that mnemonic can sometimes lead to errors. First, let's think about the four basic operations: addition, subtraction, multiplication, and division. If I asked you to put the four operations into two groups, what would you do?

Teacher A: I would put addition and subtraction in one group, since I know they are closely related: $2 + 3 = 5$ gives you $5 - 3 = 2$ or $5 - 2 = 3$. I would put multiplication and division in another group. They are also closely related: $2 \times 3 = 6$ gives you $6 \div 3 = 2$ or $6 \div 2 = 3$. Also, children learn addition and subtraction first at about the same time, and then they learn multiplication and division.

Teacher B: There is a name for the relationship of the operations in each group—*inverse operation*. Addition and subtraction are a pair of inverse operations, and multiplication and division are another pair of inverse operations. And the operation of squaring a number, for example $2^2 = 4$, and the operation of finding a square root, for example $\sqrt{4} = 2$ forms yet another pair of inverse operations.

Teacher A: Inverse operations? So we put operations that are inverses of each other in the same group? Interesting!

Teacher B: Have you ever noticed that subtracting a number is the same as adding its negative?[1] For example, $5 - 3 = 5 + (^-3)$. On the other hand, dividing a number is equivalent to multiplying by its reciprocal. For example, $10 \div 2 = 10 \times \frac{1}{2}$.

Teacher A: I see! In this sense, we can say that addition and subtraction are essentially the same operation, and multiplication and division are essentially the same operation. That is why there is no priority between addition and subtraction and between multiplication and division! But I still don't understand why some operations have priority over others.

Teacher B: Well, you just mentioned that addition and subtraction are closely related, and so are multiplication and division. How about addition and multiplication? Do you see any connections between them?

Teacher A: Yes. Multiplication is like adding the same number many times. But I think multiplication is much more powerful than addition. For example, to know how much 7 times 5 is, we do $5 + 5 + 5 + 5 + 5 + 5 + 5$ with addition and 7×5 with multiplication. The latter is much more efficient—not to mention what would happen if we were using big numbers.

Teacher B: Now let me ask you to solve a word problem. Suppose that your school has 45 fourth graders and 32 fifth graders, and each fourth grader has 4 books and each fifth grader has 7 books. How many books do all the fourth and fifth graders have?

---

[1] This is why in an equation with only addition and subtraction, the position of a number can be changed if the number is given the appropriate sign.

Teacher A: This is a three-step problem. I first do $45 \times 4 = 180$, get the number of fourth graders' books, then do $32 \times 7 = 224$, get the number of fifth graders' books, and then do $180 + 224 = 404$ to get all the books for the two grades.

Teacher B: But can you put the three steps in one equation?

Teacher A: I haven't thought about it.

Teacher B: Putting them together you get $45 \times 4 + 32 \times 7 = 404$ books. Doesn't this look more efficient and concise than the three separate equations?

Teacher A: Now I see. Because multiplication has priority over addition, we are able to deal with two chunks of computation in one equation. Otherwise, we can only deal with individual operations. So, this equation has two layers— one layer deals with multiplication and the other deals with addition.

Teacher B: I like the word "chunk." The problems that mathematics deals with may be much more complicated than the word problem I just gave you. But with the priority system, an equation can have many more layers. So it can deal with chunks, sub-chunks, even several layers of sub-chunks.

Teacher A: Oh, I remember what I learned in high school. In addition to parentheses ( ), there are also brackets [ ] and braces { }. They all have priority over all operations, though there is no fixed order in which they are handled. When parentheses, brackets, and braces are in an equation, there can be as many as six "layers" in the equation.

Teacher B: Yes. Of course, in elementary school our students learn a brief version of this priority system with only three layers.

Teacher A: This short version is: do parentheses first, multiplication *and* division second, and addition *and* subtraction last. I believe that once students learn this version well and feel comfortable with it, they will be ready to face the whole operation system when they learn more advanced mathematics.

Teacher B: I think your brief version makes lots of sense. From this version, young students will learn an important concept of mathematics operations.

Teacher A: Actually, it is from your explanation! Thank you so much!

Models for FRACTIONS

The study of fractions is the deepest and most interesting part of elementary school arithmetic. It builds on all the work that has happened earlier and sets the stage for algebra. A teacher should have several models handy to help students understand the basic concepts. With practice one gets better at seeing which model will help a given student the most in a certain situation.

BY TOM ROBY

The "slices of pie" model (or "pizza" model, though pizzas come in different shapes) is almost a cliché—but for good reason. It's easier to visualize $\frac{1}{3}$ of a circle accurately and distinguish it from $\frac{1}{4}$ of a circle than it is to grasp the same fractions in a bar model. At some level this seems to be hardwired into students' minds, but it also is trained by the clock reading that students begin as soon as they get to school. The "pie" shape also works well for adding fractions since it is easy to visualize and conceptualize pieces of pie being subdivided into smaller pieces to form common denominators.

Another important model for fractions is the number line. It helps students see how the new numbers they are learning relate to familiar ones. It gives a geometric feeling to addition in that adding $\frac{1}{3}$ to $\frac{1}{2}$ can be seen as starting $\frac{1}{3}$ to the right of zero and proceeding another $\frac{1}{2}$ unit to the right. The number line also becomes essential later in the mathematical sequence when working with positive and negative fractions. The slice of pie can still be used, but only if one can convince students to think of "pie demerits," or some way that a slice of pie can count negatively!

For a concrete practical model, it's hard to beat money. Students can draw on their direct experience. It is probably worth asking students to think about why we call the twenty-five cent piece a "quarter." For a student having trouble with some concept, asking a similar question in a monetary context can pay real dividends. For example, if adding fractions is a stumbling block, give students the problem $\frac{1}{2} + \frac{1}{4}$. Ask them to tell you what they would get if they added a half-dollar to a quarter. When they answer "seventy-five cents," respond with "Good, now what's that in quarters?" "How can we see it, thinking only in quarters?" "Can I trade my half-dollar for something equivalent?" The disadvantage of money is that it only models well those fractions corresponding to the kinds of money we have—halves, fourths, tenths, twentieths, and

hundredths. Just try modeling $\frac{1}{3} + \frac{1}{7}$ using money! This illustrates why it is critical for students to move beyond this model to more general ones as soon as they are able.

For a hands-on practical model, use strips of paper. Students can draw lines to divide a strip into three equal segments and then shade the first two segments. Now fold the paper along the $\frac{1}{3}$ line so that the shaded portion is folded on top of itself. Fold that in half again. When unfolded, the paper will have fold marks at $\frac{1}{6}$, $\frac{2}{6}$ (or $\frac{1}{3}$), and $\frac{3}{6}$ (or $\frac{1}{2}$). This helps students see the equivalent fractions. An extra folding in half will produce twelfths, and so on.

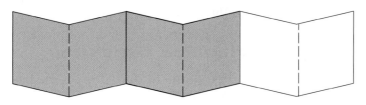

Paper or geometric models are excellent for helping students understand the reason underlying the rule for multiplication of fractions:

$$\text{product} = \frac{\text{product of numerators}}{\text{product of denominators}}$$

For example, to model $\frac{3}{4} \times \frac{2}{3}$, divide a (not too thin) strip of paper into thirds, starting from the left edge. Fold it in half, this time top to bottom, so that the fold runs through the middle of the strip. One more top-to-bottom fold will place fold marks at heights $\frac{1}{4}$, $\frac{1}{2}$, and $\frac{3}{4}$. Now unfold the paper and shade the small rectangles that fall within the lower three horizontal strips and the leftmost two vertical strips. You should get something like this:

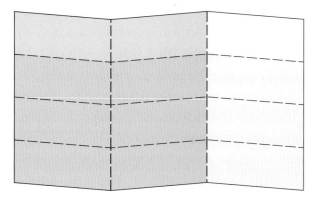

In this example, $\frac{3}{4}$ represents the fraction along the left side, and $\frac{2}{3}$ represents the fraction running along the bottom. So, the product of the numerators represents the number of rectangles that get shaded, and the product of the denominators represents the total number of small rectangles.

$$\frac{3}{4} \times \frac{2}{3} = ?$$

$$\frac{3 \times 2}{4 \times 3} \quad \begin{array}{l}\text{number of shaded rectangles} \\ \text{total number of small rectangles}\end{array}$$

We divide the number of shaded rectangles by the total number of rectangles to get the product.

$$\frac{3 \times 2}{4 \times 3} = \frac{6}{12}, \text{ or } \frac{1}{2}$$

Actual paper isn't necessary to show this model to students—a carefully drawn picture will do. This is faster when reviewing the concept, but the paper folding drives the concept home when students are learning it for the first time. It's important that students work with strips of paper on their own to model a couple of multiplication problems after they have seen it presented. Then they will never have any trouble with the rule for multiplying fractions.

Visual models are helpful even for whole numbers and their operations. Because fractions are harder to conceptualize, few students can be successful in using them without the benefits of visual models of several types.

GEOMETRY
and Measurement

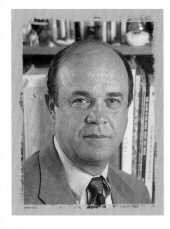

by David G. Wright

Geometry is visual and beautiful. It is a strand in mathematics in which precise definitions give meaning to shapes, measurements, and even addition and multiplication of numbers. In this article we look at understanding measurement of length, area, and volume and developing spatial sense.

Linear Measurement—Measuring One Dimension

The number of units needed to measure a line segment depends on the basic unit chosen. The basic unit can be an inch, a foot, a yard, a centimeter, a meter, or a kilometer. It can even be the length of a paper clip. Whatever the basic unit of length, students should know that a length of 3 means that when 3 of the basic units are abutted, the total length is the length of the object being measured. The 3 units cover the whole length, but they do not overlap. As simple as this idea is, it must be completely understood by students before any other discussion of measurement of length, area, or volume takes place.

What do we mean when we say that an object has a length of $3\frac{2}{7}$? If one of our unit lengths is divided into seven equal pieces, the length of any one of them is $\frac{1}{7}$. The length of two of them abutted has a length of $\frac{2}{7}$. Thus, a length of $3\frac{2}{7}$ means that if three unit lengths and two $\frac{1}{7}$ lengths are abutted, the resulting length is the same as that of the object being measured. So, we see that linear measurement gives a geometric understanding to fractions. It also gives a geometric meaning to the addition of fractions. The sum of $\frac{4}{3}$ and $\frac{7}{2}$ is simply the length of two line segments of lengths $\frac{4}{3}$ and $\frac{7}{2}$ when they are abutted. Linear measure is also used to measure the perimeter of a polygon and the circumference of a circle.

Area Measurement—Measuring Two Dimensions

Now let us consider measurement of area—a measurement of two dimensions. The unit of measurement is now a square with a side length of 1. We call such a square a *unit square*. Thus, measuring the area of a shape is the same as saying how many unit squares are needed to exactly fill the shape so that the squares abut but do not overlap. This is best understood in the case of a rectangle in which the lengths of the sides are counting numbers. For instance, a rectangle with sides of lengths 2 and 3 can be covered with no overlaps by two rows of 3 copies of the unit square with a side length of 1. Thus, the area of this rectangle is 2×3, or 6 square units.

In order to teach geometry to young children, teachers must develop competence in the following areas:

- **Developing spatial sense, including an understanding of one, two, and three dimensions,**

- **Understanding basic shapes and their properties,**

- **Communicating geometric ideas,**

- **Understanding length, area, and volume.**

CBMS Mathematical Education of Teachers Project, Draft Report March, 2000

In general, the area of a rectangle is the product of the lengths of the sides, or the dimensions of length and width. This works even for fractional lengths and gives meaning to the multiplication of fractions. For instance, consider a rectangle with sides of lengths $\frac{2}{7}$ and $\frac{3}{5}$. What could the area of this rectangle be? The first thing that should be noticed is that it must be less than 1 square unit because it fits inside a unit square. So, the answer should be a fraction of a unit square. But what fraction is it? Consider a unit square and divide the vertical side into 7 equal pieces (the denominator of one dimension—$\frac{2}{7}$) and the horizontal side into 5 equal pieces (the denominator of the second dimension—$\frac{3}{5}$). Using the divisions on the vertical side, slice the square into 7 equal rectangles. Now, using the divisions on the vertical side, slice each of the 7 equal rectangles into 5 equal pieces. Thus, we have $5 \times 7 = 35$ equal rectangles that do not overlap filling the unit square. So, the area of any one of these rectangles must be $\frac{1}{35}$. Furthermore, a rectangle with sides of lengths $\frac{2}{7}$ and $\frac{3}{5}$ is filled up with 6 of these rectangles (the product 2×3), each of which has an area of $\frac{1}{35}$. So, we can see that the area of the rectangle is $\frac{6}{35}$, or the product $\frac{2}{7} \times \frac{3}{5}$. This example gives a geometric meaning to the product of two fractions.

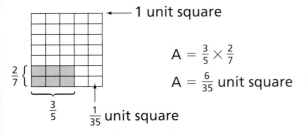

$A = \frac{3}{5} \times \frac{2}{7}$

$A = \frac{6}{35}$ unit square

Area is also used to measure triangles. A triangle cannot be filled up by unit squares without some cutting. A simpler way to get the area of a right triangle is to find the area of two copies. These two copies can fit together to form a rectangle. The area of each right triangle is half the area of the rectangle.

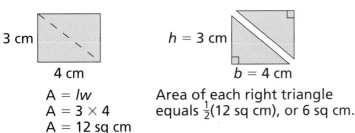

$A = lw$
$A = 3 \times 4$
$A = 12$ sq cm

Area of each right triangle equals $\frac{1}{2}$(12 sq cm), or 6 sq cm.

In general, knowing how to find the area of right triangles enables you to find the area of any triangle by looking at the sum or difference of areas of right triangles. The area of the following triangle BDF placed inside a rectangular grid can be found by computing the area of the rectangle and then subtracting the area of the right triangles.

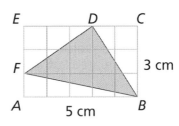

Area of $\triangle BDF$ equals area of rectangle $ABCE$ minus the sum of the areas of $\triangle ABF$, $\triangle BCD$, and $\triangle DEF$.

Area also measures other plane shapes, like parallelograms, trapezoids, and other polygons. These areas can be computed by breaking the shape, or an even larger shape, into triangles or rectangles that do not overlap and then computing the area of each piece.

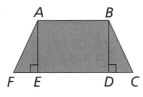

Area of trapezoid $ABCF$ equals the sum of the areas of $\triangle AEF$, $\triangle BDC$, and rectangle $ABDE$.

We also find area of a circle (technically inside the circle). The area of a circle cannot be computed as above. A precise description about how area is computed requires the ideas of calculus, but the following picture shows that a circle can be cut to almost form a rectangle whose height is the radius and whose base is half the circumference. The area of this "rectangle" is the area of the circle. Since the circumference is $2 \times \pi \times$ radius, we can see that the formula for the area of the circle is πr^2.

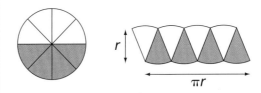

Area also measures the surface of a solid. This is most easily done for a solid like a square pyramid, where the faces are triangles and the base is a

square. Finding the surface area of a solid requires finding the area of each of the faces of the solid and finding the sum of the areas.

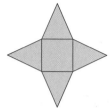

Surface area of a square pyramid equals area of square base plus the sum of the areas of the four triangular faces.

Volume Measurement— Measuring Three Dimensions

The volume of a solid is computed by finding how many unit cubes (where each edge is length 1) are needed to fill the solid with no gaps or overlaps. This is most easily done for a rectangular prism (box) where each of the edges has a natural number for a length. For example, a box whose edge lengths are 2, 3, and 4 has two layers, each of which contains $3 \times 4 = 12$ cubes. So the total volume is $2 \times 3 \times 4 = 24$ cubic units.

We measure volume for other solid objects, such as cones, pyramids, and spheres (filled in). If the previous examples are well understood, the idea of volume should not be too difficult. However, except for the rectangular prism, the volume formulas are a bit harder to explain.

Developing Spatial Sense— Understanding One, Two, and Three Dimensions

Spatial sense is "the ability to form a mental image of an object or set of objects, to recognize the structure of such objects, and to decompose those objects into component parts and recombine them in correct relation to one another" (CBMS Mathematical Education of Teachers Project, Draft Report,

March 2000). Much of what went on in our discussion of understanding length, area, and volume also required the use of spatial sense. Here is an excellent problem that will help develop spatial sense.

> *A number of white cubes with an edge length of 1 are fitted together to build a cube with an edge length of 3. The outside of this cube is painted red. How many unit cubes have been painted on*
> > *at least one face?*
> > *exactly one face?*
> > *exactly two faces?*
> > *exactly three faces?*

Repeat the problem for cubes with edge lengths of 4, 5, or some other number greater than 3.

There are various strategies for solving the first question. One is to carefully count the painted unit cubes in some order so as to find the total and not have any repetitions. A simpler strategy is to notice that the volume of the cube is 27. When the painted cubes are taken away, there is only one cube remaining. So, the number of painted cubes is 26.

Basic two- and three-dimensional shapes have mathematical definitions. A rectangle, for instance, is a quadrilateral (four-sided polygon) with right angles. From this definition, it follows that a square is also a rectangle. It is important for students to know that a square is a special kind of rectangle. A square is a rectangle in which all the sides have equal length. A rectangle may or may not be a square depending on whether the sides have equal length. A triangle is a polygon with 3 sides. Since the definition says nothing about equal sides, students need to be exposed to a variety of triangles so that they do not get the idea that all triangles must be equilateral. Through such experience students can learn to communicate geometric ideas and to form mental images of shapes so that they understand the component parts of the shapes and their relationships.

CONCEPTUAL UNDERSTANDING
The Power of Models and Visuals

by Evan Maletsky

Conceptual understanding is the foundation upon which mathematical thinking is built. For students to be good critical thinkers and effective problem solvers in mathematics, they need both understanding and skill in dealing with the concepts they have been taught. How do we build a solid understanding of mathematical concepts in our classrooms?

Models—Powerful Tools for Building Understanding

Many abstract concepts have their beginnings in concrete, hands-on experiences. This is especially true when it comes to the learning process that takes place in the mathematics classroom. Models offer powerful tools for developing solid understanding of mathematical concepts.

Sometimes, the best models for the classroom are made from the simplest of things. A 2-in. × 8-in. strip of paper may not look like much to work with at first glance. But it may, in fact, be just the needed visual model to give meaning to an otherwise abstract concept.

Have students fold the strip in half and in half again, open it up, and look at the unfolded strip. What mathematical ideas would you want your students to see when they look at this unfolded strip?

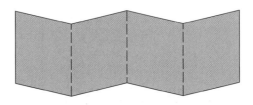

Compare the areas of the newly formed squares with that of the original rectangle. Each of the 2-in. squares has $\frac{1}{4}$ the area of the original rectangle, but it does not have $\frac{1}{4}$ of the perimeter. Many students confuse area with perimeter, and many think that the terms mean the same thing. Understanding the one-dimensional property of perimeter and comparing it with the two-dimensional property of area is fundamental to an understanding of the concepts of both perimeter and area. This model can serve to reinforce these key concepts.

Of course, there is much more that students need to see in this folded strip of paper. For example, everyone sees the 4 squares, but not everyone sees the other 6 rectangles that are there. To help students see all 10 rectangles, label the four square parts, in order, as A, B, C, and D. Then use the letters to name the different rectangles.

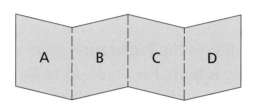

Rectangles: **ABCD, ABC, BCD**
AB, BC, CD, A, B, C, and D

Identify 1 rectangle made from all four squares, 2 rectangles from three squares, 3 rectangles from two squares, and 4 rectangles from one square. One quickly sees the sum of the number of rectangles, $1 + 2 + 3 + 4 = 10$. If the strip were folded into five parts, there would be $1 + 2 + 3 + 4 + 5 = 15$ rectangles. As shown in the table, the number of rectangles shows a nice pattern involving the triangular numbers.

Number of creases	0	1	2	3	4	5	6
Number of parts	1	2	3	4	5	6	7
Number of rectangles	1	3	6	10	15	21	28

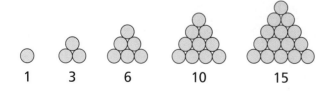

In general, fold the strip into n connected parts and use the formula $\frac{n(n + 1)}{2}$ to find the total number of rectangles. This number is a triangular number.

This same two-dimensional flat strip can easily be folded into models that are three-dimensional when studying the concept of volume. Use 1-inch wooden cubes as units of volume. Fill the models of a 2-in. cube and a 1-in. × 3-in. × 2-in. rectangular prism. Use these volumes to estimate that of a triangular prism.

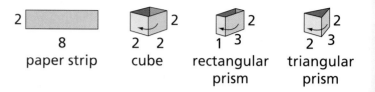

This activity sets in motion the development of the relationship of linear dimensions to volume. With different folding patterns, prisms of other shapes can easily be constructed and explored by your students. This same strip of paper, folded in different ways, creates models of prisms with different volumes. Fold it into eight equal 1-in. parts to form a prism with a regular octagon as a base. Its volume will be greater than that of the cube. For the maximum volume, don't fold it at all. Just curl it around to form a cylinder.

Models help bring in the dynamics of geometry. Only by seeing the action and change that comes from forming these different solids will students really begin to understand fully the concept of volume.

Visuals—A Way of Seeing Mathematics

Many arithmetic and algebraic concepts are abstractions in the eyes of the students because they don't see any reality in these concepts. Here is where models can offer visual support to numerical ideas.

Consider for a moment the concept of percent. Many students struggle with percent. They've been taught the computational algorithms, but what do they see? Even many of those who get the correct numerical results to percent problems have little if anything to say about what those numbers mean.

Think again about our folded strip. If the whole strip represents 100 percent, then

each of the four squares is a visual model for 25 percent. The squares can be combined with the eye to show 50 percent and 75 percent as well.

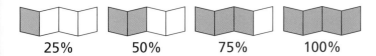

Of course, if a small square represents the whole, or 100 percent, then, from the very same model, we can see 100 percent, 200 percent, 300 percent, and 400 percent. But then, we can assign any value at all to the squares or to the strip. Suppose we call the whole strip the number 12. Then, through areas, we quickly see the numbers 3, 6, and 9 as well.

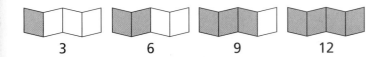

Maybe your students see even more. The same number of squares are shaded to show both 9 and 75 percent. Does this mean that 75 percent of 12 is 9? Clearly, it does.

On one of the past National Assessment of Educational Progress tests, eighth graders were asked to find 75 percent of 12. Sadly, less than half answered correctly. One wonders what it was that they saw, if anything, in trying to do this problem.

Our students need to develop good number sense. That comes from more than just practice in computation. It requires a vast and varied set of experiences that include concrete models and visual images of number relationships. This is especially important when it comes to estimation.

As an example, consider again our paper strip. Have each student fold it at some random point of their choice. Then assign some number to the area of the original strips and have the students estimate the corresponding number for the areas of the two parts. Watch how they work. Note if they do any computation. Ask them to write down the process they use. See if they use rounding or compatible numbers or just wild guesses. The results may well be very revealing.

If the original rectangle were assigned an area of 492, how would you go about estimating the areas of the two parts shown below?

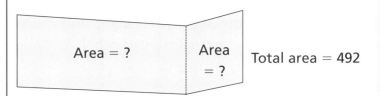

Concrete to Pictorial to Abstract

Models and visuals play a critical part in the concrete and pictorial stages of learning. They are essential to building the conceptual understanding that is needed, ultimately, to do abstract thinking. In *Harcourt Math* the approach to building mathematical concepts is to provide learning experiences based on reasoning before presenting practice. Throughout the years, mathematics has been the model for logic and reasoning. The foundation for success in this arena is built on the understanding of the basic concepts developed in the elementary school years.

Think again about our folded strip. This time, number the squares 1, 2, 3, and 4 on one side and 5, 6, 7, and 8 on the other side, with the 8 behind the 1. Now tear the strip apart into four squares, numbered front and back. Think of the numbers as digits, and ask some arrangement questions to reinforce the concept of place value.

• How many two-digit numbers can be formed with the digit 2 in the tens place?

• Do you see why the number 27 cannot be formed?

- What are the 24 different three-digit numbers possible with 2 in the tens place?

- What are the 48 different four-digit numbers possible with 2 in the tens place?

Adapt the example to any grade level you desire. Simplify the problem by using only the digits 1, 2, 3, and 4 on one side. At a more challenging level, make the problem a cooperative learning activity in which students use the digits 1 through 8 and count all possible arrangements with 1, 2, 3, or 4 digits.

one-	two-	three-	four-digit choices
$8 +$	$8 \times 6 +$	$8 \times 6 \times 4 +$	$8 \times 6 \times 4 \times 2$

$$= 8 + 48 + 192 + 384 = 632$$

Moving from a simple modeling of two-digit numbers and the place-value concept at the concrete stage, this activity can quickly take us into the visual and abstract stages of mathematical reasoning.

At every level, a mathematics program must offer a rich blend of concept development, skill-oriented activities, and problem-solving opportunities. *Harcourt Math* captures these ideas in a new and refreshing way. It is the best way to reach and teach our students mathematics.

Mathematics and the mathematical experience must tickle the senses as well as sharpen and stretch the mind. It is through handling, seeing, and thinking experiences that students can sense the excitement, appreciate the beauty, and share in the creativity of the subject.

References

National Council of Teachers of Mathematics (1989). *Curriculum and Evaluation Standards for School Mathematics.* Reston, Virginia.

National Council of Teachers of Mathematics (2000). *Principles and Standards for School Mathematics.* Reston, Virginia.

National Council of Teachers of Mathematics (1991). *Professional Standards for Teaching Mathematics.* Reston, Virginia.

Sobel, M., and E. Maletsky (1999). *Teaching Mathematics: A Sourcebook of Aids, Activities, and Strategies.* Needham Heights, Massachusetts: Allyn and Bacon.

Effective Practice:
Memorizing the Number Facts

by Grace M. Burton

Almost everyone agrees that children need to memorize the number facts. Indeed, when teachers and parents talk, one of the most frequently asked questions about school mathematics is, "How can I get the children to stop counting on their fingers?" After nearly a century of educational research, some strategies for assuring memorization have been developed. You may wish to consider them as you plan your mathematics program. To encourage the memorization of number facts:

- **Build understanding first.** All of us memorize more easily when we understand what is to be memorized. This necessary understanding can be developed when children have many chances to model the facts with real objects and to illustrate the meaning of the facts with pictures.

$3 \times 5 = \underline{15}$

- **Make clear that the goal is memorization.** When children are told to "learn their facts," it may not be obvious to them that adults mean they should immediately produce a sum or product when given two numbers. While there is a time in early instruction when "figuring out" is important, direct recall is the final goal, and children should be aware of this.

- **Have children thoroughly explore the Commutative and the Identity Properties for addition and multiplication.** When children truly believe that 3×6 and 6×3 (or $3 + 6$ and $6 + 3$) have the same answer, their memorization task is cut in half. When they accept that the sum of any number plus 0 is the number they started with (and that any number times 1 is the number they started with), there are 19 fewer addition or multiplication facts to be memorized.

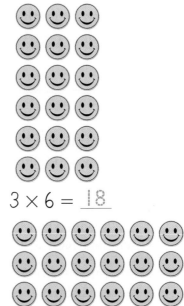

$3 \times 6 = \underline{18}$

$6 \times 3 = \underline{18}$

$3 + 6 \qquad 6 + 3$

- **Assign memorization of the easier facts first.** Facts with 1, 2, or 3 as addends or factors provide important helps in memorization.

Easier Facts

+	0	1	2	3	4	5	6	7	8	9
0	0	1	2	3	4	5	6	7	8	9
1	1	2	3	4	5	6	7	8	9	10
2	2	3	4	5	6	7	8	9	10	11
3	3	4	5	6	7	8	9	10	11	12
4	4	5	6	7	8	9	10	11	12	13
5	5	6	7	8	9	10	11	12	13	14
6	6	7	8	9	10	11	12	13	14	15
7	7	8	9	10	11	12	13	14	15	16
8	8	9	10	11	12	13	14	15	16	17
9	9	10	11	12	13	14	15	16	17	18

- **Focus on only a small group of facts at a time.** Anyone faced with memorizing 100 items might feel overwhelmed. Asking that five or fewer items be memorized seems (and is) a much more doable assignment. These might be a fact family or a set of addends that have the same sum.

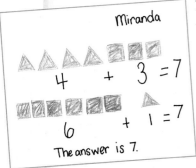

Miranda

4 + 3 = 7

6 + 1 = 7

The answer is 7.

- **Encourage parents to "hear" a few facts frequently.** You may wish to provide parents with an assigned "fact family" or set of facts for each week and suggest that they use some of the time they are in the car with their children or doing chores together to review these facts.

- **Have children keep a private record of the facts that they have memorized.**

Facts I Know by Heart

×	0	1	2	3	4	5	6	7	8	9
0										
1										
2						10	12	14	16	18
3					12	15	18	21	24	27
4				12	16	20	24	28	32	36
5			10	15	20	25	30	35	40	45
6			12	18	24	30	36	42	48	54
7			14	21	28	35	42	49	56	63
8			16	24	32	40	48	56	64	72
9			18	27	36	45	54	63	72	81

By providing children with these strategies for memorizing addition and multiplication facts, teachers and parents can work together to empower children with a potent tool for mathematics investigation and problem solving.

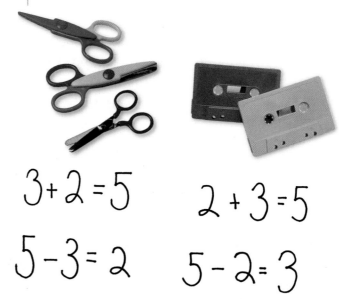

$3 + 2 = 5$ $2 + 3 = 5$

$5 - 3 = 2$ $5 - 2 = 3$

References

Ashlock, Robert B. (1998). *Error Patterns in Computation.* Seventh Edition. Columbus, Ohio: Merrill.

Rathmell, Edward C. "Using Thinking Strategies to Teach the Basic Facts." In *Developing Computational Skills,* edited by Marilyn N. Suydam. Reston, Virginia: NCTM, 1978.

Thornton, Carol A. and Smith, Paula J. "Action Research: Strategies for Learning Subtraction Facts," *Arithmetic Teacher,* 35 (April 1988), 8–11.

Thorndike, E. L. (1925). *The Psychology of Arithmetic.* New York: Macmillian.

Van de Walle, John A. (1998). *Elementary and Middle School Mathematics: Teaching Developmentally.* Third Edition. New York: Longman.

Effective Practice:
Building Computational and Procedural Efficiency

by Grace M. Burton

Some teachers and parents believe that when children are learning to use the whole-number algorithms for addition, subtraction, multiplication, and division, the more practice they do, the more likely they will learn. Educational research suggests that there are more effective strategies to accomplish efficiency with the whole-number algorithms. While practice is indeed important, there are ways to structure this practice so that children develop competency with the standard algorithms in an efficient way.

To encourage efficiency in the use of whole-number algorithms, you may wish to incorporate some of these research-based ideas:

- **Use realistic contexts to build understanding.** When children see a need for mathematics in their own lives, they are more apt to believe that there is a reason to apply themselves to learning. Teachers can help children appreciate the usefulness of algorithms when they present story problems of interest and when they ask children to write story problems for which a given algorithm is appropriate.

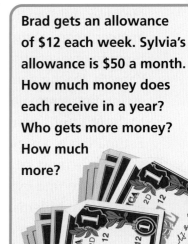

Brad gets an allowance of $12 each week. Sylvia's allowance is $50 a month. How much money does each receive in a year? Who gets more money? How much more?

- **Ensure that the required number facts have been memorized.** Even children who "know their facts" profit from practice on a regular basis. Setting a time for a quick review of a few facts, such as first thing every morning, helps them keep facts "at the ready." Playing games that require the use of number facts is also a good idea. Instant recall of the facts allows children to concentrate on the steps in the algorithms without having to stop to figure out a needed number fact.

- **Choose models that closely mirror the base-ten system.** When the link between the model and the written symbols is clear, children more easily make the connection between actions with real objects and the written record of those actions. Therefore, using materials based on our base-ten system that illustrate that one 10 equals ten 1s, etc., is crucial. Efficient teaching of the standard algorithms calls for extensive use of materials, such as base-ten blocks, sticks of ten connecting cubes, or bean sticks. The most effective way to use these materi-

als is to have children model the problem with the materials, write the algorithm to be completed, and then record step-by-step what they do with the materials.

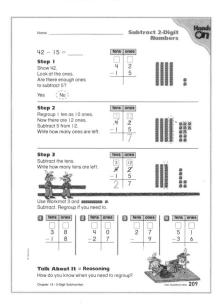

- **Encourage children to estimate answers before computing or to check the reasonableness of their computation.** Helping children decide what a reasonable answer to an example might be will help alert them to answers that are not reasonable. Directly teaching and frequently reviewing estimation strategies encourage students to thoughtfully consider their answers. Estimation is a particularly important real-life skill, since most adults estimate rather than compute to find exact answers to solve everyday problems.

- **Check for understanding after a few examples have been completed.** Whenever children practice a skill, it is easier to acquire proficiency if errors are caught early. The same is true when children are developing computational proficiency. Teachers who provide guided practice and diagnose for errors are supported in this strategy by years of research. In *Harcourt Math*, students are given exercises in which they must find and correct an error—an effective way to check whether students understand the concept or procedure well enough to detect and correct errors. Teachers are provided a *Common Error Alert* in some lesson plans in the *Teacher's Edition* to assist in the process of diagnosing and analyzing students' errors.

▶ Check

1. **Explain** how you can use estimation to help you decide whether 903 ÷ 3 = 31 is reasonable. 900 ÷ 3 = 300, so 31 is not reasonable for the quotient.

Tell where to place the first digit. Then divide.

2. 6)38 ones   3. 4)81 tens

4. 2)182 tens   5. 5)85 tens

6. 6)771 hundreds

> In a lesson on **Placing the First Digit in the Quotient,** the Check provides diagnostic information before practice is assigned.

- **Provide appropriate remedial instruction.** Once an error has been detected, it is often helpful to ask the child to model the algorithm with real materials, recording each step with pencil and paper. Diagnosing children's errors quickly is critical in order to prevent extensive repetition of that same error.

- **Enlist parents in your educational plan.**
  Keeping parents informed of your expectations and the strategies you use to meet them will help make you and the child's family partners in his or her learning.

- **Review all algorithms at frequent intervals.**
  Providing mixed reviews at regular intervals is a potent force to solidify what has been previously learned. You will want to do it often.

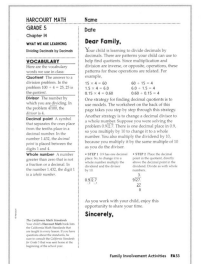

The practice exercises and suggested activities in *Harcourt Math* were developed by the authors based on a study of the research. Therefore, as you use the program, you will have many options for presenting appropriate practice based on each individual student's mathematical strengths and weaknesses and their preferred learning modalities. The conceptual understanding of each of the algorithms is carefully developed prior to presenting practice on applying the procedure. Multifaceted practice requires that students demonstrate conceptual understanding, skill proficiency, and the ability to choose the correct algorithm and apply it in problem-solving situations. Review of the algorithm and its applications are woven throughout the program so that students can maintain their skill proficiency. When you use ideas from research to plan efficient practice in the whole-number algorithms, children, even those with special needs, are more likely to achieve success with this important mathematical goal.

Mixed Review and Test Prep

30. $68 + 25 = \blacksquare$ 93   **31.** $71 - 29 = \blacksquare$ 42

32. Use mental math to find the sum $15 + 8 + 2 + 5$. 30

33. How many sides does a quadrilateral have? 4 sides

34. **TEST PREP** In which number does the digit 2 have the least value? (p. 18) D

A 2.564   **C** 5.264

B 4.256   **D** 6.524

Mixed Review

Find the sums.

5️⃣ $6 + 4 = \underline{10}$ $3 + 9 = \underline{12}$ $0 + 11 = \underline{11}$

$4 + 6 = \underline{10}$ $9 + 3 = \underline{12}$ $11 + 0 = \underline{11}$

References

Ashlock, Robert B. (1998). *Error Patterns in Computation.* Seventh Edition. Columbus, Ohio: Merrill.

Bley, Nancy, and Carol Thornton. (1989). *Teaching Mathematics to the Learning Disabled.* Second Edition. Austin: Pro-Ed.

Fuson, Karen, C. (1992). "Research on Whole Number Addition and Subtraction." In *Handbook of Research on Mathematics Teaching,* edited by Douglas A. Grows. New York: Maxwell Macmillan.

Suydam, Marilyn N. (ed.). (1978). *Developing Computational Skills.* Reston, Virginia: National Council of Teachers of Mathematics.

Van de Walle, John A. (1998). *Elementary and Middle School Mathematics: Teaching Developmentally.* Third Edition. New York: Longman

Developing Algebraic Thinking
Preparation for
Algebra Begins in Kindergarten

by Angela Giglio Andrews

Traditionally, algebra has been seen as a high school course—and as a significant mathematics hurdle that *only some* students successfully clear (Carroll). However, in today's world algebra can no longer be thought of as a subject for a select few. All students need to develop reasoning and problem-solving skills built upon exploration, conjecturing, modeling, explaining, and generalizing. These skills lay the foundation for the formal study of algebra (Steen, 1992). The responsibility for implementing these algebraic thinking skills begins with the kindergarten teacher. Fortunately, students already possess some natural algebraic understandings when they come to kindergarten. For instance, a kindergarten student, counting buttons in a collection, commented to her friend, "You know, I was just thinking. Whenever you add one to any number, you get the next number!" Her generalization about the patterns and relationships of the numbers she was exploring was intuitively algebraic in nature. Our responsibility is to recognize these natural algebraic intuitions and expand upon them.

As with any concept or skill, algebraic thinking will best develop when students experience it in various contexts and situations. We want our students to develop a feeling for and comfort with algebra that they will carry with them throughout their schooling. To reach this goal, we must pick and choose from a variety of activities that flow naturally from the mathematics we already have been teaching. We make these choices better when we recognize the algebraic potential of each activity.

We begin introducing the roots of algebra to our students when we have them **classify, pattern, and work with numbers.**

Classifying and Patterning

If mathematics is the study of patterns (Steen, 1988), then algebra is the mathematics of making *generalizations* about those patterns and relationships. Classification is about generalizing—the first step in algebra. When students classify, they must generalize attributes that are common to all the members of the set. A good way to help students learn to pattern objects by size, shape, texture, type, and other attributes is to do lots of sorting. Every sorting and classifying lesson contributes to our students' understanding of patterning which is

the foundation for algebraic thinking. Patterns help develop inductive reasoning and make it possible to predict what is supposed to happen in math. If we do not teach students to look for patterns as a basic approach to understanding, learning math becomes much more difficult than it need be. For instance, the student who is learning to count to 100 and doesn't see the pattern of our base-ten number system has the hard task of learning 100 separate tasks in order. Starting in kindergarten, we immerse our students in the concept of pattern at calendar time, with rhythms and chants at music time, and with pattern cards in the interest center. Students generalize patterns with connecting cubes, orientations of craft sticks, and shapes of buttons. Using letters in order to provide a link between seemingly unrelated materials, we describe the patterns they create. (AAB may be their first algebraic expression in which symbols stand for relationships.) Patterning helps students begin to recognize "isomorphisms," or things that have the same structure but may not look the same. For instance, we help students translate color patterns such as "blue, blue, red," into shape patterns "circle, circle, square." Teachers need to help students expand their patterning skills to include reasoning about more complex patterns and explaining the generalizations they make about patterns in our base-ten number system (Kenney).

Working with Numbers

As students develop their understanding of arithmetic operations, they can be led to investigate properties of numbers and operations. While learning the doubles facts for addition, for example, a first grader noted that the sum of all doubles had to be even, because "they would always have a partner." Even young students make some generalizations about the properties of numbers. For instance, a kindergarten child may notice while constructing sums with connecting cubes that $2 + 3 = 5$ and $3 + 2 = 5$. The teacher might then ask if this could be true for all numbers. By verifying with concrete objects, the student would see that observation does not depend on any par-

ticular properties of these two numbers but rather the generalization also applies to any other pairs of numbers. The Order Property $a + b = b + a$, which the child is exploring informally, will later form the basis for memorizing basic addition and multiplication facts and even later to solving algebraic equations. The teacher's well-timed questions can lead students to see that the thinking they are doing about particular numbers can be generalized to many numbers. As teachers, we need to recognize that helping students to make such generalizations about numbers creates a bridge from arithmetic to algebraic thinking.

No other skill has been as closely tied to algebra as solving equations. The concept of representing unknown quantities can begin in kindergarten, using concrete objects, verbal descriptions, pictures, boxes ($3 + \blacksquare = 5$) or blanks ($\_ + 2 = 5$). Teachers can model and help students translate between these different representations. In working with equations, teachers should emphasize the equal ($=$) symbol as representing the concept of balance. (Younger students who may not understand balance can understand that *equals* means "is the same as.") Students' misunderstanding of the meaning of the equal sign is often a barrier to solving equations successfully. Many students believe that $4 + 5 =$ means "add $4 + 5$," rather than "find the number that balances the equation."

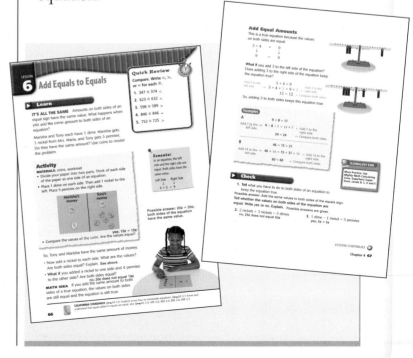

Test results show (Kieran) that students are much more successful solving equations when they have had experiences with number models with missing numbers in various formats, such as

$$\_\_\_ = 8 + 2 \qquad 4 + \_\_\_ = 10 \qquad \_\_\_ + 5 = 10 + 2$$

$$3 + 10 = \_\_\_ + 7 \qquad \blacksquare + 5 = 9 + 2$$

In *Harcourt Math,* the development of algebraic thinking is a focus at every grade level. Algebra is a way of thinking, and the goal of the program is to develop children's abilities to think algebraically about the concepts and skills of mathematics and to apply algebraic thinking to solving problems of all types. Helping students understand mathematics from a perspective of identifying and describing patterns in both number and shape, making and testing generalizations, understanding the concept of equivalence as they memorize basic facts, developing proficiency with the algorithms, relating geometric concepts to algebraic concepts, and exploring the idea of function are some of the many ideas that are threads throughout the program.

The algebraic thinking introduced in the program beginning in kindergarten prepares the way for later formal instruction in algebra. By providing opportunities for our students to build confidence and competence, we help students see that algebra is something they can understand—not a hurdle to clear, but just another step along the way to mathematical literacy.

References

Carroll, Bill. *University of Chicago School Mathematics Project.*

Kenney, Patricia, and Silver, Ed. Eds. (1997) *Results from the 6th Mathematics Assessment of the National Assessment of Educational Progress.* Reston, Va.: NCTM.

Kieran, C. (1992) "The learning and teaching of school algebra." *Handbook of Research on Mathematics Teaching and Learning.* New York: Macmillan.

Steen, L. A. (1992) "Does everybody need to study algebra?" *Basic Education 37.*

———(1988) "The science of patterns." *Science* 240.

Problem Solving:
The Reason to Teach Mathematics

by Jan Scheer

Gerry and I have been friends since before his son, Jeremy, started school. Jeremy always had problems in math, and Gerry frequently called to ask for my advice, which was usually ignored. (You're never a hero in your own family or with your closest friends.) The trouble persisted, and Jeremy was sent to an "after-school program" where memorization was the primary learning approach.

Jeremy was at my home recently. Knowing that his class of 30 students would be taking a big bus trip, I inquired as to the number of buses that would be needed if a bus holds 20 students. Without taking a breath, Jeremy responded by saying, "That's easy! One and a half." While I stood dumbfounded, his dad marveled at how much Jeremy had learned at his "after-school program." I composed myself and asked Jeremy if he would take the half of the bus with the driver or the half without! Jeremy informed me that I was confusing him and left in a huff.

This incident really disturbed me. Although Jeremy could, indeed, divide 30 by 20 and get an answer of $1\frac{1}{2}$, he had no understanding of the problem. Understanding and application would indicate that in this case $\frac{30}{20}$ should proffer an answer of 2, not $1\frac{1}{2}$.

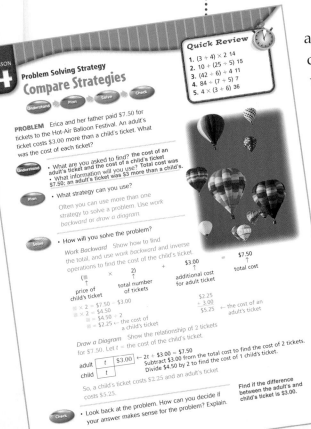

In real life, when do we solve problems? I have never observed anyone in any place take out a pencil and paper to solve a long division problem. I have never seen anyone in a supermarket whip out base-ten blocks to figure which can of soup is the better buy. Nor have I seen anyone use fraction circles to determine what stock to purchase. But every day I see people who are using their mathematical understanding, experiences, and skills to deal with problem situations. They **understand** what the problem is; they **make a plan;** they **solve** the problem; and, finally, they **check** to be sure that their answer is reasonable. If Jeremy had followed this plan, he would have known that his answer was not reasonable.

In *Harcourt Math*, problem solving is part of every lesson. Many lessons present a problem as the vehicle for teaching a skill so that children can see the connection between the skill they are learning and its application. There are lessons devoted specifically to teaching children to use a problem solving strategy and helping them understand

the types of problems for which that strategy is a good choice. Children practice problem solving in every lesson—problems that require skills taught earlier in their mathematics experiences, that require two or more steps to solve, that require reading and analyzing data, that require logical reasoning, and that apply the skill presently being taught.

The program helps children develop their abilities to think through a problem by focusing on questions that guide their understanding of the problem, their development of a plan as to which strategy to try or what approach to take, their solution of the problem, and their reflection on whether or not their answer is reasonable in the context of the problem. Reminders to use this process—**Understand, Plan, Solve,** and **Check**—are in every chapter. A Problem Solving Think Along provides a recording device for students as they address each of the above processes. This encourages the "stop and think"

approach to solving problems rather than just random attempts. The teaching support that is part of *Harcourt Math* includes a Problem of the Day for every lesson—a rich problem that requires application of this thinking process. In addition, exercises in the practice sets for lessons require students to write their own word problems; write a question from given information; and explain, prove, and/or justify their solutions.

Harcourt Math has a strong focus on problem solving so that as children are becoming proficient with basic facts and the algorithmic procedures, they are seeing the usefulness of mathematics in solving problems that relate to their everyday experience. Children need to be taught that sometimes there can be more than one right answer; often, there can be more than one way to get the answer. They need to be able to use a variety of problem solving strategies. In short, we always need to be teaching children to **think.** *Problem solving is not one reason to teach mathematics; it is the only reason to teach mathematics.*

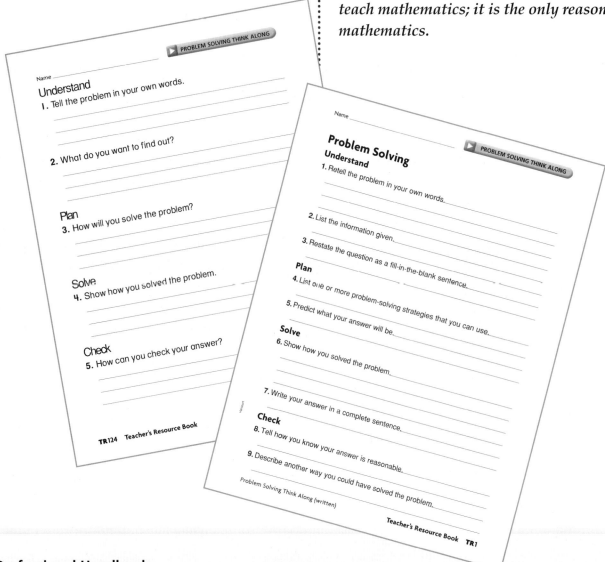

Instructional STRATEGIES:

BEST PRACTICES DEFINED BY RESEARCH

by Joyce McLeod

Instructional strategies used in the classroom usually mirror what teachers think about how children learn. So, choosing instructional strategies from among the best practices defined by research is based upon assumptions about learning and should reflect what is known about learning. The following research-based statements answer the question "What is learning?"

- Learning is goal–oriented.
- Learning is linking new information to prior knowledge.
- Learning is organizing information.
- Learning is acquiring a repertoire of cognitive and metacognitive structures.
- Learning occurs in phases yet is nonlinear.
- Learning is influenced by development (Jones, et al., 1987).

Best practices reflect these statements about learning. As we have learned more about how the brain functions as a learning organ and how learning modalities play a critical role in learning, our repertoire of best practices has been refined to reflect these understandings about learners.

Choosing appropriate instructional strategies in mathematics is a critical factor in ensuring that students make continuous progress. The hierarchical nature of the mathematics curriculum makes it imperative that teachers diagnose and intervene quickly to prevent severe deficits in children's mathematical development. In order to provide a balanced program, best practices for developing conceptual understanding, skill and procedural fluency, and reasoning and problem solving abilities must be aligned with the content. In addition, strategies that focus on effective learning modalities and memory strategies to ensure automaticity with the basic facts must be a part of the teacher's repertoire. Among the best practices for teaching mathematics, the following stand out:

- practice
- explicit instruction
- questioning strategies
- use of visuals
- reading and vocabulary development strategies
- use of manipulatives
- intervention

Let's look briefly at each of these best practices and how they are implemented in *Harcourt Math.*

Practice

Practice is important for reinforcing students' knowledge and for preparing students to move on to new topics and new types of problems. Review helps students retain knowledge and improve performance. In a review of research, Geary (1994) concludes that practice is essential for mastering skills and developing the automaticity that will allow these skills to be used routinely in other situations. Bahrick and Hall (1991) studied the life span retention of content acquired in math courses. Their study found that talent and achievement had some impact, but the primary variable for success was practice that had occurred over time. Individuals who had learned the math content over a short period without practice over time showed declines in performance.

Daily Routine

In *Harcourt Math*, practice and review are designed to reflect these research findings. In Grades 1 and 2, the Daily Routine in each lesson helps children review prior-taught skills, and spaced reviews throughout the student text provide ongoing review of critical skills. In Grades 3 through 6, every lesson begins with a Quick Review and ends with a Mixed Review and Test Prep. These reviews of lesson prerequisite skills and of prior-taught skills cover a wide range of key mathematical topics and represent a mixture of procedures and skills.

Models that show the step-by-step application of algorithmic procedures and worked examples showing the variety of possible types of problems within a procedure are included throughout the program. These models are often accompanied by pictures of manipulatives to allow students to deepen their conceptual understanding of a procedure as they apply the steps in the procedure. At the end of a group of chapters that cover a major mathematical topic, a Study Guide and Review shows worked examples of the types of problems in which students should develop automaticity, with page references to help students review if necessary.

In Grades 3 through 6, practice exercises for every lesson include a variety of problems. Basic drill-type items are included in lessons emphasizing basic fact acquisition and procedural fluency. Thought-provoking word problems that apply the procedure, skill, or concept taught in the lesson and that review prior-taught skills are included in every lesson. The emphasis in many of these problems is using logical reasoning; solving multistep problems; and explaining, justifying, and proving solutions. Exercises that require writing questions given a possible solution, writing problems with given conditions, and analyzing errors develop students' conceptual and procedural knowledge of mathematics.

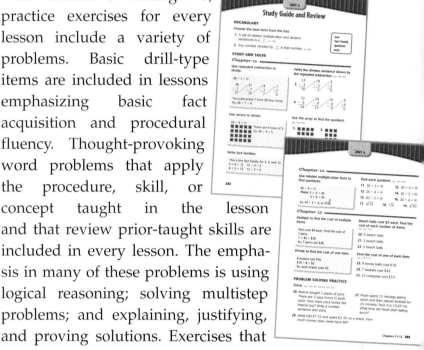

Explicit Instruction

Explicit instruction is one of many terms that describe a teaching practice focused on making specific skills or strategies known to a learner. Explicit instruction involves explaining, demonstrating, and/or modeling mathematical concepts and procedures to students.

Liping Ma, in her book *Knowing and Teaching Elementary Mathematics,* emphasizes that in order for a teacher to instruct in mathematics, he or she must have these four properties of understanding:

- **Basic ideas** are the "simple but powerful basic concepts and principles of mathematics" that should be revisited and reinforced.

- **Connectedness** is the understanding of the connections between mathematical ideas that prevents students' learning from being fragmented and helps them see that math is a unified body of knowledge.

- **Multiple perspectives** are the different facets of an idea, the various approaches to the solution of a problem, and the explanations that students make of the different facets.

- **Longitudinal coherence** is the understanding of the whole mathematics curriculum that helps teachers understand what students have studied previously and what they are going to learn later (Ma, p. 122).

Guided Instruction
- *Read Green Thumb with students. Then direct students' attention to the model.* **When using a model, how do you know that 12 is the least common denominator?** The $\frac{1}{12}$ fraction bars are equivalent to the sum of the $\frac{2}{3}$ and $\frac{3}{4}$ bars.
- *Discuss the least common multiple.* **How do you find the LCM of 3 and 4?** Possible answer: List multiples of both numbers until you find a common multiple. **How can you rename a fraction to an equivalent fraction?** Multiply the numerator and denominator by the same number to keep the value of the fraction the same.
- *Refer students to the answer.* **How do you know that the answer is in simplest form?** Possible answer: The numerator and denominator have no common factors except 1.
- *Have students apply reasoning skills.* REASONING **What would the least common denominator be for $2 - \frac{7}{8}$?** Explain. 8; $2 = \frac{2}{1}$, so the least common multiple of the denominators 1 and 8 is 8.

In *Harcourt Math,* explicit instruction is facilitated by clear development in every lesson. In Grades 3–6, the instructional part of the student's lesson consists of vocabulary development, models and/or examples, and questions that help students connect new learning to previous learning, consider different approaches to thinking about a basic idea in mathematics, or choose different solution methods for a given problem. In Grades 1–2, the students' lessons show models and reinforce vocabulary. In the *Teacher's Edition* for all grade levels, explicit instruction is developed through Guided Instruction, which includes questions that help students connect the lesson topic to previously learned material, facilitate conceptual understanding and efficient skill development, and help students avoid common errors.

Questioning Strategies

All learning begins with questions. Questions cause interactions, and the quality of those interactions is determined by the character of the question. Questions are fundamental to teaching because they provide information, help students become more actively involved in a lesson, and guide students toward the highest levels of learning in which they apply what they have learned in a variety of ways.

Good questions focus students' attention on concepts, generalizations, laws, and principles and help them think critically and see relationships. In any one lesson, four or five good, open-ended questions challenge students to analyze, apply, react to, or reflect on content. Providing students time to answer (usually about a three- to four-second lapse following a question) results in more comprehensive, higher-quality answers (Rowe 1974).

In *Harcourt Math,* questions that guide students' thinking and help them analyze concepts and skills are included in the Pupil Edition. These questions are designed to help students develop strategies for solving problems and for memorizing basic facts, procedural processes, and key mathematical definitions. We know that memorizing something that is not understood or that has little meaning to an individual is virtually an impossible task. Think, for example, about your Social Security number. Memorizing and retaining that sequence of numbers in your long-term memory if it had no relevance to you would be impossible. You would have to memorize that sequence again and again if you were asked to repeat it at random or to use it in some isolated example. It would only become a part of your long-term memory and easily accessed if it had relevance for you and was connected to other experiences in your memory. So, good questions form the basis for helping students make connections and store information in their long-term memories so that they can easily access it when needed. The basic facts form a large part of the memories that we need to make permanent in students' long-term memories, and since memorizing what we do not understand is almost impossible, questioning for understanding forms the basis for memory.

Use of Visuals

Research clearly shows that the use of visuals enhances learning. Visuals help learners:

- isolate and identify important material.

- recall prior knowledge.
- provide interaction with content.
- enhance information acquisition (Dwyer, 1994).

Picture viewing is more exploratory than reading. Fixation durations are generally longer in picture viewing. Visuals serve as aids to memory because information received from visuals appears to remain longer in memory. Visuals also provide motivation when they give a real-life meaning to the mathematics. However, the most important aspect to remember about using visuals is that it is not the visual itself that causes gains in learning, but rather the instructional strategy in which the visual is embedded.

In *Harcourt Math*, visuals and accompanying questions and teaching suggestions are included throughout the program. Visuals are used to help teachers provide critical scaffolds to understanding and, therefore, memory. They are also used to help students appreciate the usefulness of mathematics in everyday activities. Our students live in a visual world, but many of these visuals pass rapidly before their eyes with very little learning occurring. So, teaching children to read visuals and to link visuals and text is a critical part of the focus in the program. The adage "Before you can see to learn, you must first learn to see," is taken seriously by the authors of this program.

Reading and Vocabulary Development Strategies

Reading in mathematics is critical for students' success. Mathematics is a language and a way of thinking. Therefore, teaching students to read mathematics for understanding and developing the unique vocabulary of mathematics are essential for success. Students' reading abilities in mathematics can be helped by relating their personal knowledge and experience to the information in the text, relating one part of the text to another, provid-

ing the lesson objective to students at the beginning of the lesson, and discussing the meaning of important new words (Ornstein, 1995).

In *Harcourt Math*, development of students' content reading skills forms a focus in the presentation of each lesson. Some of the helps to content-area reading include providing instructional objectives to focus students' thinking, providing a key question to guide the lesson development, identifying and defining key mathematical terms used in the lesson, and providing prompts to help students remember prior-taught material necessary for understanding the lesson. Review exercises throughout the program reinforce the content-area reading developed around each topic.

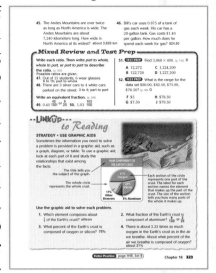

Use of Manipulatives

Research supports the use of manipulatives to increase students' conceptual understanding and achievement in mathematics. Two main points that emerge from the research are:

- Long-term use of manipulatives is important for success.
- Teachers need to have clear purposes for using manipulatives in a particular situation (Sowell, 1989).

In *Harcourt Math*, manipulatives and the pictorial representations of manipulatives are used throughout the grade levels. Concepts are introduced through manipulative activities accompanied by questions that help students see the link between the concrete material or a pictorial representation and the mathematical idea being modeled. These structured manipulative activities demonstrate the purpose for using the manipulative and provide support to teachers in making the most efficient and effective use of manipulatives.

Basic-fact strategies and the procedures for each of the computational algorithms are developed through the use of manipulatives. These activities support memorization of basic facts and procedures because they provide concrete visuals that children can use to link related facts and procedures and, therefore, make the task of memorization easier. In the beginning, memorization of basic facts is best facilitated by use of basic-fact strategies supported by concrete experiences. As the goal of automaticity with the basic facts is reached, the basic-fact strategies are no longer used in the process of memorization but remain in the students' memories to act as helps for solving word problems. The same premise holds true as children develop automaticity with the basic algorithmic procedures.

Intervention

Intervention refers to a given set of strategies used by a teacher to accommodate the diverse skill levels, interests, and learning preferences of students. In order to meet the learning needs of all students, attention must be given to tailoring instruction so that the needs of auditory, visual, and kinesthetic learners are met; students' personal interests are considered; and instruction begins where students are. Carol Tomlinson, in her book *The Differentiated Classroom,* makes the following recommendations for differentiating instruction in the classroom:

- Build instruction around the essential concepts, principles, and skills of a subject.

- Attend to individual differences.

- Use assessment as today's means of understanding how to modify tomorrow's instruction.

- Use assessment data to modify the content students are to learn, the processes through which content is to be taught, and the product by which the students demonstrate what they have learned.

In *Harcourt Math,* intervention is woven through the program as the means by which teachers differentiate instruction. The variety of assessment instruments provides effective tools

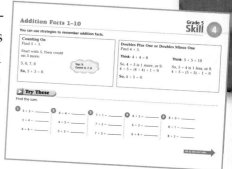

that help teachers diagnose students' strengths and weaknesses and allow them to make informed decisions about the classroom curriculum. In Grades 3–6, a Student Handbook in the back of the *Pupil Edition* provides intervention activities and exercises. *Intervention Strategies and Activities* links intervention activities to the grade-level content and, therefore, allows teachers to present grade-level content differentiated to meet the needs of all learners.

The instructional strategies used in the classroom are an important determinant of students' achievement. The instructional strategies developed in *Harcourt Math* will help you make instructional decisions based on the goals of your classroom curriculum as mandated by your school or district, by the needs of each of your students, and by preparation for tests that your students are required to take.

References

Bahrick, H. P., & Hall, L. K. (1991). "Lifetime maintenance of high school mathematics content." *Journal of Experimental Psychology: General,* 120: 22–23.

Chuska, Kenneth. (1995). *Improving Classroom Questions.* Bloomington, Indiana: Phi Delta Kappa Educational Foundation.

Dwyer, Francis M., with Morre, David M. (1994). *Visual Literacy: A spectrum of visual learning.* Englewood Cliffs, New Jersey: Education Technology Publications.

Geary, D. C. (1994). *Children's Mathematical Development: Research and Practical Applications.* American Psychological Association. Washington, D.C.

Jones, B., Palincsar, A., Ogle, D., & Carr, E. (1987). *Strategic Teaching and Learning: Cognitive Instruction in the Content Areas.* Alexandria, Virginia: Association for Supervision and Curriculum Development.

Ma, Liping. (1999). *Knowing and Teaching Elementary Mathematics.* Mahwah, New Jersey: Lawrence Erlbaum Associates, Publisher.

Ornstein, Allan. (1995). *Strategies for Effective Teaching* (2nd Ed). Chicago: Brown & Benchmark Publishers.

Rowe, Mary Budd. "Wait-time and rewards as instruction variables: Their influence on language, logic, and fate control: Part I: Wait-time." *Journal of Research in Science Teachings* 11, no. 2: 81–84.

Sowell, E. J. (1989). "Effects of manipulative materials in mathematics instruction." *Journal for Research in Mathematics Education,* 29 (2), 121–142.

Tomlinson, Carol. (1999). *The Differentiated Classroom: Responding to the Needs of All Learners.* Alexandria, Virginia. Association for Supervision and Curriculum Development.

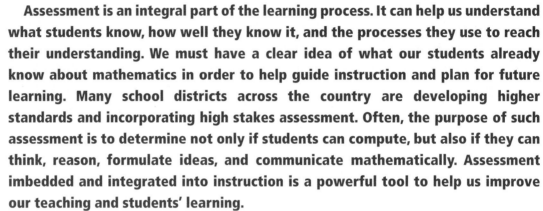

ASSESSMENT
An Integral Part of the Learning Process

by Lynda Luckie

Assessment is an integral part of the learning process. It can help us understand what students know, how well they know it, and the processes they use to reach their understanding. We must have a clear idea of what our students already know about mathematics in order to help guide instruction and plan for future learning. Many school districts across the country are developing higher standards and incorporating high stakes assessment. Often, the purpose of such assessment is to determine not only if students can compute, but also if they can think, reason, formulate ideas, and communicate mathematically. Assessment imbedded and integrated into instruction is a powerful tool to help us improve our teaching and students' learning.

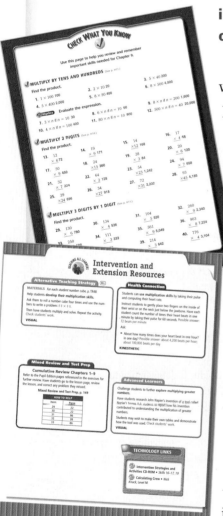

Entry-Level assessment is included in *Harcourt Math* to determine whether students enter a grade level with weaknesses and gaps in their skill proficiency and understanding or whether students show strengths and are, therefore, capable of thriving in a challenging curriculum. This entry-level assessment, designed to determine where students are in their skill development, conceptual understanding, and ability to solve problems, is provided at the beginning of each year. In addition, the *Check What You Know* at the beginning of each chapter provides an entry-level assessment for the content in that chapter. This assessment is linked to diagnostic and prescriptive information to assist the teacher in intervening to prevent students from experiencing failure with new material.

Progress monitoring is a part of every lesson. The third step of the lesson plan in *Harcourt Math* provides activities to check students' conceptual understanding and skill development, providing immediate diagnostic information to the teacher and immediate feedback to the student. In addition, end-of-chapter and end-of-unit progress monitoring provides students, their parents, and their teachers information as to whether students' learning has been connected with related mathematical ideas, can be used to solve problems, and, for skills, is progressing toward the level of automaticity.

Summative evaluation occurs at the end of each chapter, at the end of each unit, and at the end of the year. There are a variety of types of assessment instruments—multiple-choice tests, free-response tests, performance tasks, portfolio suggestions, and writing prompts—that may be used for summative evaluation. The assessment program in *Harcourt Math* is designed to develop a complete portrait of each student's mathematical development—conceptual development, skill proficiency, and problem solving ability. The underlying philosophy of the assessment program is described below.

Varied assessment tools help students value mathematics.

While a good assessment program helps teachers develop a solid plan for instruction and learning, it should also help students learn to value mathematics. Students' definitions and understanding of assessment dictate their perceptions of what we value. For instance, if assessment consists solely of computation-driven tests, then students will believe that is all we value. On the other hand, if we want students to value development of problem solving skills, reasoning, and mathematical communication, then we must find ways to make these connections more explicit for students (Davinoy, Bliem, and Mayfield). If we value strategies and thought processes, we must look at not only the "what" but also the "how."

Just as a balanced diet includes more than one food group, so does a balanced assessment program use more than one format. Students should be given opportunities in multiple formats to demonstrate what they know and can do. While the importance of computational skills should not be minimized, it is almost impossible to accurately assess students' understanding of the big ideas of mathematics without a variety of assessment tools. Indeed, some elements of mathematics learning can only be measured in ways other than multiple-choice tests (Stenmark, Mathematics Assessment NCTM). One of the most powerful arguments for implementing various assessment techniques is the value it has as a diagnostic tool for improved instruction.

Varied assessment tools prepare students for standardized tests.

Some useful assessment models include performance assessments, portfolios, math journals, individual or small-group projects, formal tests that include multiple-choice and free-response items, and self-assessment instruments. Good teaching also includes some informal student assessment such as observations and student interviews. Anecdotal record sheets and checklists can be very useful for this kind of documentation. Included in a balanced assessment program is a good preparation for local or national standardized testing. Exposure to and familiarity with the format and types of problems can be the key to building students' fluency and self-confidence in their abilities to take tests and perform well. Then the high-stakes tests will not be something for students to dread, but rather another opportunity to show what they know and can do.

Varied assessment tools provide useful diagnostic information to teachers about students' strengths and weaknesses.

Portfolios can be one of the best ways to present a clear, visible, continuous, and comprehensive picture of students' progress. It can be a way to showcase students' work. You may want to include several different types of assessment in portfolios, such as performance assessment tasks, paper-and-pencil tests, projects, and students' writing about mathematics. A suggestion for a writing piece is for students to record how they view themselves as mathematicians, both at the beginning and toward the end of the school year. You may see a huge difference in their perceptions over time. Many teachers find that students particularly enjoy selecting their best work to include in their portfolios. Moreover, a student portfolio can provide an invaluable communication tool as you conference with parents about their child's progress.

Performance Assessment consists of presenting a mathematical task or project for students to work on and then making a determination of what they know and can do. This

Name _____
Date _____

PORTFOLIO GUIDE

A Guide to My Math Portfolio

What is in My Portfolio	What I Learned
1.	
2.	
3.	
4.	
5.	

I organized my portfolio this way because _____
_____

Portfolio Guide (Student)   Assessment Guide AG xix

can be accomplished by using any combination of observations, student interviews, and rubrics that can be developed by teachers and/or by students. Performance assessments often incorporate a wide variety of mathematical skills and give evidence of a rich mathematics curriculum. As students work on these tasks, they become engaged in the activities and quickly learn that math is more than just learning how to complete an algorithm. They also learn that there is often more than one right answer and more than one way to solve a problem.

Math Journals provide invaluable insight into a student's progress. They can reveal understanding as well as attitudes and perceptions. Entries in a journal can be as simple and unstructured as responding to a prompt or can become more complex as students are asked to explain a mathematical process or justify an answer. As in their portfolios, students might record their changing view of themseves as mathematicians. Students should be encouraged to use pictures and diagrams to help explain their thinking. Many teachers use a math journal as a personal communication tool by responding in a student's journal and developing an ongoing conversation about mathematics. One caution to be considered is that students need to know that a journal entry is a viable part of the classroom mathematics program. If journals are never reviewed and never receive affirmation, then they will likely become just another chore in the minds of students.

Standardized and Free-Response Format Tests provide one way to diagnose your students' abilities to apply the skills and procedures of mathematics. These tests can be used before instruction on a topic is begun, to determine whether

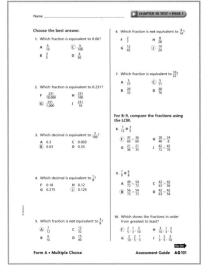

or not each student has the prerequisite skills for the new content. They can be used at the end of a sequence of lessons on a topic to determine whether an appropriate skill level has been attained. These tests can also assess students' abilities to apply skills and concepts in problem solving situations. Cumulative Review tests are a valuable way to measure remembering and retention over time of both conceptual and procedural knowledge and the ability to apply that knowledge in problem solving situations.

Self-Assessment tools help you understand the attitudes and perceptions your students have about mathematics, their assessment of their own abilities to do mathematics, and their preferred ways of working. For many students, cooperative learning groups are an effective way for students to develop their problem solving abilities and their abilities to

communicate about mathematics they are learning and to practice in order to develop skill and procedural fluency. Other students may work better individually for some of these types of activities. Self-assessment tools give you valuable information not only about the mathematics students are learning but also about the ways in which they prefer to learn.

References

Stenmark, J. K. (1989). *Mathematics Assessment: Myths, Models, Good Questions, and Practical Suggestions.* Berkley, California: University of California.

Davinroy, K. H., Bliem, C. L., & Mayfield, V. (1995) "How Does My Teacher Know What I Know?: Third Graders' Perceptions of Math, Reading, and Assessement." Boulder, Colorado: CRESST (National Center for Research on Evaluation, Standards, and Student Testing), University of Colorado.

The purpose of assessment should be to help students see the real-life application of mathematics.

As you develop your assessment program, keep in mind the big ideas. For example, what you want to assess should help you decide on the assessment tool. Whichever form you choose should embrace an "authentic assessment" mentality. In other words, assessment should help foster making a transition from what students learn in school to the mathematics they will need to know in "real life." There is also a very real place in your program for daily and periodic review of what students are learning. Curriculum should spiral and revisit ideas within the context of new material. For example, finding the area of given parcels of land can be imbedded in a problem solving task that involves representing data in a graph about national parks.

Building a Comprehensive Assessment Program in Your Classroom

If you are already using multiple forms of assessment, then you already realize the benefits. If not, one of the purposes of this article is to encourage you to begin to make some changes. The decision to make changes comes slowly and with deliberate effort. Some suggestions include:

- Take small steps.

- Try one new thing at a time.

- Allow yourself to make mistakes and adjustments.

- Collaborate with fellow teachers, parents, and students.

- Persevere until it becomes a natural, integrated component of your teaching.

Harcourt Math provides a varied toolbox of assessment instruments designed to provide ongoing diagnostic information about your students' strength and weaknesses. Students can only make progress in mathematics when teachers have varied sources of information about the abilities of their students. Your choice of assessment instruments should be linked to the kinds of information that you need to make your mathematics classroom a rich experience for your students; to prepare students for the standardized assessment required by your state, district, or school; and to provide both the student and his or her family members with a complete profile of the student's mathematical competency. The choices are many and varied and will allow you to continue to modify your assessment program to meet your needs and your students' needs and to document to parents, school administrators, and the community the richness of your classroom mathematics program.

Keep in mind that assessment should not be something we "do" after we "teach." Often we can assess students' learning in the process of teaching. Teachers do this every day. We watch students develop new skills and strategies as they become problem solvers. We know that we can imbed skill practice within tasks that are interesting and exciting for our students. We watch as students learn from each other and construct their own understanding on the foundation of what they already know, enabling them to transfer that knowledge to new situations. Based on these ongoing and informal observations that are supported in the daily lessons in *Harcourt Math*, teachers can make good choices as to which of the many and varied assessment options included with the program are right for their classroom. When teachers allow students to experience success in a variety of assessment formats, they confirm their belief that all students can learn, and they empower students to view themselves as mathematicians.

Technology
Pathways to Teaching and Learning

by Howard Johnson

Increasingly today, children are using computers for what we have long considered traditional activities of childhood. They use this technology to play, learn, communicate, and develop relationships. Historically, education has centered around a model of learning that focuses on presenting information that students are to learn. Then, through repetition and practice, it was assumed that facts, concepts, and skills were stored and integrated to form knowledge structures. Testing could then measure certain outcomes and behaviors to assess the degree to which the material had been learned.

Recently, however, it has become clear that learner-centered education improves students' motivation to learn. This shift changes the teacher's role to that of creating and structuring the learning environment so that interaction with the teacher, with other students, and with all types of instructional materials and technology are practiced. Teachers are even more critical and valued in this learning setting because they diagnose students' strengths and weaknesses and use all of the instructional tools they have to reach each individual student. Indeed, as pointed out by Banchoff, "The future potential of the Internet . . . will change the way we do mathematics, the way we write about it, and the way we present it in our classrooms at all levels. It is a very exciting time to be a teacher."

Technology as a Tool for Learning

The benefits students receive from using technology are determined by how their teachers connect its use to the classroom curriculum. In every case, however, these tools provide an effective alternative means of representing mathematical concepts, skills, and ideas. Technology can be used to help students engage in problem solving experiences with real data—problems that students themselves may encounter in the world, problems that can be approached with a variety of strategies, and problems that may have more than one solution. Jensen and Williams report that using technology has a positive effect on "both problem solving achievement and attitudes toward the activity of problem solving." The computer can be an invaluable tool to help the problem solver focus on generating ideas, trying out various approaches, and checking hunches. Computers put students in the position of being able to test their

conjectures since the machine can produce an endless stream of output that students can use as data for testing and revising their conjectures.

Careful planning is essential in using technology in classrooms. Campbell and Stewart offer the following guidelines for teachers to consider:

- Use technology to enhance your curriculum goals, not for its own sake.

- Use technology to supplement manipulative activities, not to replace them.

- Use software that is developmentally appropriate.

- Use interactive software that capitalizes on the potential of the computer.

- Encourage students to question and help each other.

- Help students determine when technology is appropriate and when other approaches are more appropriate or efficient.

Technology as a Tool for Teaching

In *Harcourt Math,* technology is linked directly to the lessons in the program and is designed to reinforce and extend content, to provide practice on basic skills, to provide activities that help students see the relevance of mathematics to their daily lives, and to diagnose and intervene to help those students who are not ready for grade-level instruction. The following technology components are for student use:

Harcourt Learning Site (www.harcourtschool.com), which provides the following resources:

- a multimedia glossary

- activities for each grade level, designed to present interesting situations and to provide practice in problem solving and computation

- *News Breaks* that provide articles to help students see the relevance of mathematics to solving everyday problems

- *Video Updates* that provide timely information and link mathematics to world events

- *E-Lab,* a series of activities that support the hands-on lessons in the textbook by providing a slightly different perspective on the concept being developed

Mighty Math, a series of six CD-ROMs that provide support for concept development, computation practice, and problem solving experiences:

- *Carnival Countdown* and *Zoo Zillions*— Kindergarten through Grade 3

- *Calculating Crew* and *Number Heroes*— Grades 3–6

- *Astro Algebra* and *Cosmic Geometry*— Grade 6

Intervention Strategies and Activities is a series of six CD-ROMs (one for each grade level, 1–6) that provide instruction, practice, and a short assessment for critical skills. Students work on skills and concepts from prior-taught topics that they had difficulty with, as shown by their performance on the Check What You Know inventory for every chapter in the program. Students are provided immediate feedback that focuses not only on the wrong answer but also on the error made. Each activity includes the following:

- *Show Me* section, which teaches the skill using oral and visual prompts

- *Try These* section, which provides scaffolded support in doing the skill

- *Practice* section, to reinforce the skill

- *Check* section, which is a short assessment

Technology as a Planning and Management Tool

To assist teachers in planning lessons and in developing assessment instruments tailored to their individual classroom requirements, the following technology components are provided:

Lesson Planner CD-ROM, which provides templates that you can use to customize your lesson plans so they match your local curriculum.

Harcourt Electronic Test Bank: Math Practice and Assessment, which provides features that allow you to:

- construct alternative tests and practice sets by using the item bank
- assign the Chapter Review/Test found in the *Pupil Edition* to the entire class or to individuals
- have students take the test on the computer with all multiple-choice answers scored electronically
- weight answers and weight the test score in relation to the overall grade
- present items one at a time on the screen to help those students with special needs

Intervention Strategies and Activities, described above, has the following features to help teachers manage the intervention program:

- assign the Check What You Know diagnostic inventory for each chapter
- set up specific activities as class work or as individual assignments
- view and/or print class or individual reports showing scores on activities
- view and/or print skill reports for the complete list of skills for the entire grade level

There is no longer a question as to whether or not technology should be used in the learning and teaching of mathematics. Teachers will have the time-saving convenience of technology to help with lesson planning, meeting the learning needs of each student, and developing assessment instruments aligned with the classroom curriculum. Students will have these powerful tools to enhance mathematics learning and prepare them for this century with the skills and knowledge they will need to be competitive in their work world and in their everyday lives.

References

Banchoff, Thomas F. (2000). The Mathematician as a Child and Children as Mathematicians. *Teaching Children Mathematics,* Vol. 6, Number 6, 350–356.

Campbell, P., & E. Stewart, (1993). Calculators and Computers. In R. J. Jensen (ed.), *Research Ideas for the Classroom: Early Childhood Mathematics* (pp. 251–268). New York, NY: Macmillan.

Jensen, R., & B. Williams. (1993). Technology: Implications for Middle Grades Mathematics. In D. T. Owens (ed.), *Research Ideas for the Classroom: Middle Grades Mathematics* (pp. 225–243). New York, NY: Macmillan.

Linking Home and School

Making Mathematics Part of the Family's Daily Routine

by Vicki Newman

School-home communication is one of the key components of an effective mathematics program. Parents have a better understanding of their child's mathematics program and become more supportive of a standards-based curriculum when the communication between school and home is ongoing. With a clear picture of what their child is learning at school and how they can provide support at home, families play a vital role in their child's mathematics education.

Children benefit when parents and teachers work together to emphasize the importance of mathematics in their children's daily lives. If children see a reason for studying math at school, they learn to value mathematics and develop a positive attitude and interest. The link between school and home is essential in ensuring a successful mathematics program. The following suggestions may help you foster the link between school and home and provide valuable information to parents.

■ Identify grade-level mathematics content standards to provide parents with an outline of essential concepts and skills their child should know.

■ Explain the goals of a balanced mathematics program through parent newsletters, parent conferences, or school bulletin boards. Have children share classroom projects and daily work that reflect how their mathematics program provides a balance between conceptual competence, computational and procedural competence, and mathematical reasoning.

■ Help parents recognize their role and their child's role in learning mathematics. Suggest ways parents can support mathematics learning at school and extend learning experiences at home. Identify strategies parents can use at home to help their children with homework.

■ Share information with parents regarding their child's progress in mathematics. Include samples of daily work and share the variety of assessment tools you frequently use to identify their child's progress.

■ Encourage parents and the community to become involved in mathematics education by letting them know that their comments, concerns, and suggestions are valued.

The school-home link in *Harcourt Math* will help you implement these suggestions as you share the following materials with parents:

■ **Family Involvement Activities** in kindergarten through Grade 2 outline the mathematics taught in each chapter, provide a list of the math vocabulary (with definitions) that will be introduced and reviewed, and give examples of the types of questions and problems children will be working on in the classroom. One important component of the school-home link is helping family members understand the thinking their child must do in order to be successful with the skills, concepts, and problem solving activities presented in the chapter. The Family Involvement materials include problems that children and their parents can solve together and a Family Fun activity that helps children see that mathematics can be fun

and that solving math problems is a real-life skill. In addition, at the bottom of each of the lesson pages in the Pupil Edition, there is a Home Activity that describes the mathematics the child is learning and provides a suggestion for a way parents can help. All of these school-home links provide practical information that will help you involve parents as partners in supporting their child's progress in meeting mathematics standards.

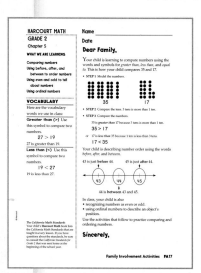 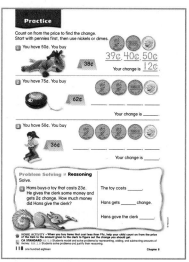

■ **Family Involvement Activities** for Grades 3 through 6 also include a description of what the child will be learning, a list of vocabulary terms and definitions, and suggested ways for parents to help, including activities that provide more practice and a game that helps families have fun while helping their child with the mathematics they are learning at school.

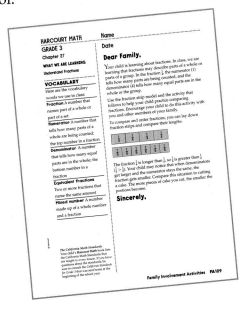

Making Mathematics Part of the Family's Daily Routines

Parents can work with teachers to help their children see the relevance of mathematics in their everyday lives. When parents are filling out a mail-order form, figuring out how many days until a special family event, or calculating the mileage on a family trip, they can involve their children in these mathematical moments. "Parents' attitudes toward mathematics have an impact on how mathematics will be viewed by their children. The child whose parents show enthusiasm for mathematics in the home will be more likely to develop enthusiasm" (Brosnan et al., 329).

As children solve word problems in contexts that are meaningful, they become more confident in applying their math skills. When parents listen to their children explain how they solved a problem, they become more aware of the math concepts and skills their child is mastering. By helping their child apply classroom lessons in their home environment, parents become advocates of their child's education and develop a partnership with teachers that links school and home. The materials in *Harcourt Math* are designed to help you build that critical school-home link.

References

Brosnan, Patricia; Diamantis, Maria; and Hartog, Martin D. Feb. 1998. "Doing Mathematics with Your Child," *Teaching Children Mathematics,* Vol. 4, No. 6, pp. 326–330.

California Department of Education. 1999. *Mathematics Framework for California Schools, Kindergarten Though Grade Twelve.*

Ensign, Jacque. Feb. 1998. "Parents, Portfolios, and Personal Mathematics," *Teaching Children Mathematics,* Vol. 4 No. 6, pp. 331–337.

Follmer, Robin; Ford, Marilyn Sue; and Litz, Kathleen K. Feb. 1998. "School-Family Partnerships: Parents, Children, and Teachers Benefit!" *Teaching Children Mathematics,* Vol. 4, No. 6, pp. 310–312.

Moldavan, Carla C. Feb. 2000. "A Parent's Portfolio: Observing the Power of Matt, the Mathematician," *Teaching Children Mathematics,* Vol. 6, No. 6, pp. 372–374.

HARCOURT

Math

BIBLIOGRAPHY AND INDEX

The following bibliography contains references to:

► **Fiction and nonfiction books for students**
► **Technology resources**
► **Professional books and magazines**

These materials will assist you in creating an interesting learning environment. The references to literature are provided to help you work through your media center to acquire literature selections that you can use with *Harcourt Math.* The math activities developed to correlate to these books will help you build a math curriculum to meet the needs of all students.

The index contains information for both the Pupil Edition and Teacher's Edition. The italicized entries are found in the Teacher's Edition.

Bibliography

Books for Students

The Alaska Purchase. Cohen, Daniel. Millbrook, 1996.

The Amazing Book of Shapes. Sharman, Lydia. Dorling Kindersley, 1994.

American History Math: 50 Problem-Solving Activities That Link Math to Key Events in U.S. History. Glasthal, Jacqueline B. Scholastic, 1996.

"Hockey" by Scott Blaine in *American Sports Poems.* Knudson, R.R., and May Swenson, eds. Orchard Books, 1995.

Arithmetricks: 50 Easy Ways to Add, Subtract, Multiply, and Divide Without a Calculator. Julius, Edward H. John Wiley & Sons, 1995.

Bats, Bugs, and Biodiversity: Adventures in the Amazonian Rain Forest. Goodman, Susan E. Atheneum Books, 1995.

"Mother and Daughter" in *Baseball in April and Other Stories.* Soto, Gary. Harcourt, 1990.

The Circuit. Jimenez, Francisco. University of New Mexico Press, 1997.

"Up the Slide" in *The Complete Short Stories of Jack London.* London, Jack. Stanford University Press, 1993.

The Diary of Anne Frank. Goodrich, Frances, and Albert Hackett. Heinemann, 1995.

Exploring the Night Sky. Dickinson, Terrence. Camden House, 1987

Exploring the Titanic. Ballard, Robert D. Scholastic, Inc., 1988.

Face on the Milk Carton. Cooney, Caroline B. Laurel Leaf, 1994.

The Facts On File Children's Atlas. Wright, David & Jill. Facts on File, Inc., 1993.

Force & Motion: Eyewitness Science. Lafferty, Peter. Dorling Kindersley, 1992.

From the Mixed-Up Files of Mrs. Basil E. Frankweiler. Konigsburg, E.L. Atheneum, 1987.

Funny and Fabulous Fraction Stories. Greenberg, Dan. Scholastic, 1996.

G Is for Googol. Schwartz, David M. Tricycle Press, 1998.

The Gilded Cat. Dexter, Catherine. William Morrow & Company, 1992.

Go Figure! The Numbers You Need for Everyday Life. Hopkins, Nigel J., John W. Mayne, and John R. Hudson. Gale Research Inc., 1992.

"Raymond's Run" in *Gorilla, My Love.* Bambara, Toni Cade. Random House, 1992.

Gulliver's Travels. Swift, Jonathan. Running Press Book Publishers, 1992.

I Have A Dream: The Life and Words of Martin Luther King, Jr. Haskins, James. Millbrook Press, 1992.

Incredible Comparisons. Ash, Russell. Dorling Kindersley, 1996.

Island of the Blue Dolphins. O'Dell, Scott. Houghton Mifflin, 1990.

Janice Van Cleave's Math for Every Kid. Van Cleave, Janice. John Wiley & Sons, 1991.

Jigsaw Jackson. Birchman, David F. Lothrop, Lee & Shepard, 1996.

King of the Wind. Henry, Marguerite. Macmillan, Inc., 1991.

The Librarian Who Measured the Earth. Lasky, Kathryn. Little, Brown and Company, 1994.

Life by the Numbers. Devlin, Keith. John Wiley & Sons, 1998.

Little Farm in the Ozarks. MacBride, Roger Lea. HarperCollins, 1994.

"The School Play" in *Local News.* Soto, Gary. Harcourt, 1993.

The Maltese Cat. Kipling, Rudyard. Creative Education, Inc., 1991.

The Math Chef. D'Amico, Joan, and Karen Eich Drummond, R. D. John Wiley & Sons, 1997.

Math Mini Mysteries. Markle, Sandra. Atheneum, 1993.

Melisande. Nesbit, E. Harcourt, 1989.

"Tranquility Base" in *Men from Earth.* Aldrin, Buzz. Bantam Books, 1991.

Mountains. Simon, Seymour. Morrow Junior Books, 1994.

Nearer Nature. Arnosky, Jim. Midaya Press, 1996.

A New Way of Life (formerly titled *The Vietnamese in America*). Rutledge, Paul. Lerner Publications Company, 1991.

Not for a Billion, Gazillion Dollars. Danzinger, Paula. Delacorte Press, 1992.

Nothing But the Truth. Avi. Avon, 1991.

Number the Stars. Lowry, Lois. Houghton Mifflin, 1989.

The Phantom Tollbooth. Juster, Norton. Random House, 1989.

Pyramid. Macaulay, David. Houghton Mifflin, 1975.

The Red Pony. Steinbeck, John. Viking Penguin, 1992.

Real-Life Math Investigations. Lee, Martin, and Marcia Miller. Scholastic, 1997.

Robinson Crusoe. Defoe, Daniel. Running Press Book Publishers, 1990.

Secrets of the Shopping Mall. Peck, Richard. Dell, 1991.

The Secrets of Vesuvius Bisel, Sara C. Madison Press, 1990.

She Flew No Flags. Manley, Joan B. Houghton Mifflin Company, 1995.

Skinnybones. Park, Barbara. Bullseye Books, 1995.

Snow Bound. Mazer, Harry. Dell, 1990.

The Star Fisher. Yep, Laurence. William Morrow & Company, 1991.

Sticks. Bauer, Joan. Delacorte Press, 1996.

Summer Ice: Life along the Antarctic Peninsula. McMillan, Bruce. Houghton Mifflin, 1995.

"Dog of Pompeii" by Louis Untermeyer in *Teach Your Children Well: A Parent's Guide to the Stories, Poems, Fables, and Tales That Instill Traditional Values.* Allison, Christine, ed. Delacorte Press, 1993.

The Tarantula in My Purse. George, Jean Craighead. HarperCollins, 1996.

"Emergency Landing" from *Visiting Mrs. Nabakov and Other Excursions.* Williams, Ralph. Vintage Books, 1995.

Volcano: The Eruption and Healing of Mount St. Helens. Lauber, Patricia. Bradbury Press, 1986.

The Walrus and the Carpenter. Carroll, Lewis. Penguin Books USA Inc., 1992.

What Hearts. Brooks, Bruce. HarperCollins, 1992.

What Is a Wall, After All? Allen, Judy. Candlewick Press, 1993.

Where Am I? The Story of Maps and Navigation. Smith, A. G. Stoddart Kids, 1997.

The Whipping Boy. Fleischman, Sid. William Morrow & Company, 1986.

The Widow and the Parrot. Woolf, Virginia. Harcourt, 1992.

Math Software

TITLE	PUBLISHER	DESCRIPTION	SYSTEM REQUIREMENTS
JumpStart Adventures 4th Grade: Haunted Island (Windows/Macintosh Hybrid CD-ROM)	Knowledge Adventure	Students apply lessons in math, and other curriculum areas to rescue 13 lost friends before they turn into freakish fiends forever! **Math Topics** • Equations • Division • Multiplication • Addition • Subtraction • Decimals • Fractions • Units of Measure	**PC:** 486 or Pentium or higher. Windows 3.1 or 95/98. 256 color SVGA monitor, 8 MB RAM, 9 MB hard disk space, 2X CD-ROM drive, sound card and speakers **Macintosh:** 68040 processor; System 7.1 or higher, 256 color monitor 640 × 480, 8 MB RAM, 9 MB hard disk space, 2X CD-ROM drive.
JumpStart Adventures 5th Grade: Jo Hammet, Kid Detective (Windows/Macintosh Hybrid CD-ROM)	Knowledge Adventure	While visiting the museum on a field trip, Jo Hammet uncovers a sinister plot to destroy all of the city's factories! Her mission (with student help) is to find clues leading to the capture of the mad genius Dr. X. **Math Topics** • Fractions • Decimals • Equations • Division • Multiplication • Geometry • Ratios	**PC:** 486 or Pentium or higher. Windows 3.1 or 95/98. 256 color SVGA monitor, 16 MB RAM, 15 MB hard disk space, 2X CD-ROM drive, sound card and speakers. **Macintosh:** 68040 processor; System 7.1 or higher, 256 color monitor 640 × 480, 8 MB RAM, 15 MB hard disk space, 2X CD-ROM drive.
MathKeys (Windows/Macintosh Hybrid CD-ROM)	The Learning Company	Students calculate probability by operating spinners, coin flippers, and other playful machines. They can see data in graph, chart, number, and word sentence forms. **Math Topics** • Whole Numbers • Probability • Geometry • Measurement • Fractions	**PC:** 486; Windows 95 or higher; 4 MB RAM; hard disk; 256 color graphics; Windows Compatible sound card; mouse **Macintosh:** 68020 processor; Mac OS 7.0 or higher; 4 MB RAM; hard disk; 256 colors; mouse
Mighty Math Calculating Crew (Windows/Macintosh Hybrid CD-ROM)	Edmark	This program teaches students the concepts, facts, and thinking skills necessary to build math confidence and develop a strong, lasting understanding of math. **Math Topics** • Multiplication • Division • Decimals • Number Lines • 3-D Solids • Money Transactions	**PC:** 486DX or better, 8 MB RAM, and 5 MB hard disk, 2X CD-ROM drive, Windows 3.1 or 95. 256 Color SVGA monitor **Macintosh:** 68030/25 MHz or better. 8 MB RAM, 2X CD-ROM drive, 14" or larger color monitor, System 7.0.1 or higher
Mighty Math Number Heroes (Windows/Macintosh Hybrid CD-ROM)	Edmark	The combined programs include over 250 reading and math activities, hundreds of animations, and five original songs. Each activity offers hints and includes three levels of difficulty. **Math Topics** • Multiplication • Division • Fractions • 2-D Geometry • Probability	**PC:** 486DX or better, 8 MB RAM, and 5 MB hard disk, 2X CD-ROM drive, Windows 3.1 or 95. 256 Color SVGA monitor **Macintosh:** 68030/25 MHz or better. 8 MB RAM, 2X CD-ROM drive, 14" or larger color monitor, System 7.0.1 or higher
The ClueFinders 5th Grade Adventure (Windows/Macintosh Hybrid CD-ROM)	Mattel	A sudden tsunami has shipwrecked the gang on an uncharted volcanic island, and Owen and Leslie have disappeared! Students collect the mysterious Cryp Tiles to solve the mystery before the volcano blows! **Math Topics** • Multiplication • Division • Geometry	**PC:** Pentium or better; Windows 95/98; 16 MB RAM; 25 MB hard disk space; VGA/SVGA monitor; 256 colors; Supports mouse & sound card **Macintosh:** Power Mac; Hard Drive System 7.1 and up, 16 MB RAM, 25 MB hard disk space; 4X CD-ROM drive; 256 colors
The ClueFinders 6th Grade Adventures (Windows/Macintosh Hybrid CD-ROM)	Mattel	The 9 interactive puzzles, customized workbooks, and 50 printable activities help students learn important skills in math in addition to a full curriculum of subjects. **Math Topics** • Decimals • Percents • Fractions • Statistics • Estimations • Ratios	**PC:** Pentium or better; Windows 95/98; 16 MB RAM; 25 MB hard disk space; VGA/SVGA monitor; 256 colors; Supports mouse & sound card **Macintosh:** Power Mac; Hard Drive System 7.1 and up, 16 MB RAM, 25 MB hard disk space; 4X CD-ROM drive; 256 colors

Math Software

TITLE	PUBLISHER	DESCRIPTION	SYSTEM REQUIREMENTS
The ClueFinders 6th Grade Math Adventures (Windows/Macintosh Hybrid CD-ROM)	Mattel	Students travel to a small village high in the Himalayas to solve the mystery of the disappearing treasures. The software continually adjusts the program to match students' growing abilities. **Math Topics** • Multiplication • Division • Geometry • Problem Solving	**PC:** 486 processor or better; Windows 95/98; 16 MB RAM; 25 MB hard disk space; VGA/SVGA monitor; 256 colors; Supports mouse & sound card **Macintosh:** Power Mac; Hard Drive System 7.1 and up, 16 MB RAM, 25 MB hard disk space; 4X CD-ROM drive; 256 colors
Carmen Sandiego Math Detective (Windows/Macintosh Hybrid CD-ROM)	Broderbund	The program includes three levels of over 250 activities with thousands of math problems, as well as over 400 word problems and customizable problem sets. **Math Topics** • Numeration • Geometry • Measurement • Problem Solving	**PC:** 586 processor & up; Windows 3.1 & up; 20 MB hard drive space, 8 MB RAM; VGA/SVGA monitor; 2X CD-ROM drive; sound card **Macintosh:** 68040 processor; System 7.1 & up, 6 MB RAM, 20MB hard disk space, 2X CD-ROM drive, 256 colors
Community Construction Kit (Windows/Macintosh Hybrid CD-ROM)	Tom Snyder Productions	An opportunity for students to develop and create their own communities by designing historically accurate buildings and landscaping. **Math Topics** • Geometry • Map Skills • 3-D Concepts	**PC:** 386 processor & up; Windows 3.1 & up; 14 MB hard disk space, 4 MB RAM; VGA/SVGA monitor; 2X CD-ROM, sound card **Macintosh:** 68020 processor and up, System 7.0 & up, 4 MB RAM, 8 MB hard disk space, 2X CD-ROM drive, 256 colors
CornerStone Mathematics – Level B (Windows/Macintosh Hybrid CD-ROM)	Skillsbank	The process includes: Warm-up, Review, Quiz, Take Five, and Worksheet to demonstrate, guide, test, reinforce, and provide extra practice of concepts. **Math Topics** • Number Concepts • Estimation • Whole Number Computation • Decimals • Fractions • Percents • Data and Graphs	**PC:** 486 processor & up; Windows 3.1 & up; 10 MB hard disk space, 8 MB RAM; VGA/SVGA monitor; 2X CD-ROM drive; sound card **Macintosh:** 68030 processor, System 7.0 & up, 8 MB RAM, 5 MB hard disk space, 2X CD-ROM drive, 256 colors
The Cruncher (Windows/Macintosh Hybrid CD-ROM)	Knowledge Adventure	Program features include a full-featured spreadsheet, step-by-step animated tutorials, ten real-world projects and templates, colorful charts, and graphs. **Math Topics** • Spreadsheets • Graphs • Statistics • Surveys • Investments	**PC:** 386; Windows 3.1 or 95; 4 MB RAM; 14 MB hard disk space; 2X CD-ROM drive; SVGA; sound card **Macintosh:** 68020/16 MHz; System 7.0; 4 MB RAM; 8 MB hard disk space; 2X CD-ROM drive; 256 colors
Fraction Operations (Windows/Macintosh Hybrid CD-ROM)	Tenth Planet	Fraction Operations combines hands-on techniques with multimedia technology. Math concepts are presented in a variety of ways to accommodate a range of learning styles and ability levels. **Math Topics** • Common Denominators • Addition • Equivalent Fractions • Subtraction • Dividing Fractions • Multiplication	**PC:** 386 processor & up; Windows; 14 MB hard disk space, 4 MB RAM; VGA/SVGA monitor; 2X CD-ROM drive **Macintosh:** 68020 processor; System 7.0 & up, 4 MB RAM, 8 MB hard disk space, 2X CD-ROM drive, 256 colors
Geometer's Sketchpad (Windows/Macintosh Hybrid CD-ROM)	Key Curriculum Press	The software includes specific lessons for investigations, explorations, demonstrations, and constructions. Geometric figures designed by the student can be manipulated, transformed, and distorted while preserving geometric relationships. **Math Topics** • Geometry • Visualization • Analysis • Informal Deduction	**PC:** 386/25 MHz; DOS 3.1 or later; 1 MB RAM; 7 MB hard drive space; VGA. **Macintosh:** MacPlus or better, with 1 MB RAM or more, running System Software Version 6.0 or better
The Graph Club (Windows/Macintosh Hybrid CD-ROM)	Tom Snyder Productions	The Graph Club is an easy-to-use graphing tool that can be used for self-directed exploration, lessons, and presentations, or creative class projects. **Math Topics** • Gather, Sort, and Classify • Interpret Tables and Graphs • Analyze Data and Graph	**PC:** Windows 3.1: CPU 386SX / 16 MHz; 8 MB RAM; Monitor: 13" VGA 640 × 480 256 Colors **Macintosh:** LC II or better: System 7.1; 16 MHz; 4 MB RAM; Monitor: 13" 640 × 480 resolution, 256 Colors

Math Software

TITLE	PUBLISHER	DESCRIPTION	SYSTEM REQUIREMENTS
Interactive Math Journey (Windows/Macintosh Hybrid CD-ROM)	The Learning Company	Children take a trip through five math lands to learn key concepts. **Math Topics** • Patterns and Shapes • Addition • Measurement • Subtraction • Fractions • Multiplication	**PC:** 486DX/66 MHz; Windows; 256 color SVGA monitor; 8 MB RAM; sound card, 8 MB hard disk space; 2X CD-ROM drive **Macintosh:** 68030 processor; System 7.01; 256 Color Monitor; 8 MB RAM; 8 MB hard disk space; 2X CD-ROM drive, 13" display
Reader Rabbit's Math Ages 6–9 (Windows/Macintosh Hybrid CD-ROM)	The Learning Company	Students help Reader Rabbit escape from a pirate-infested island by outwitting pirates by using their outstanding math abilities. **Math Topics** • Addition • Subtraction • Geometry • Place Value • Problem Solving	**PC:** 486DX/66 MHz; DOS 5; 256 color SVGA monitor; 8 MB RAM; sound card, 20 MB hard disk space; 4X CD-ROM drive **Macintosh:** Power PC, System 7.1; 256 Color Monitor; 8 MB RAM; 20 MB hard disk space; 4X CD-ROM drive, 13" display
Logical Journey of the Zoombinis (Windows/Macintosh Hybrid CD-ROM)	Broderbund	A map displays students' progress on the journey and provides access to options for turning on/off background music, dialog, sound effects, and transition screens. The randomly generated puzzle solutions automatically adjust to a player's skill level. **Math Topics** • Relationships • Patterns • Grouping • Sorting • Matching • Graphing • Deductive Reasoning	**PC:** 386DX/66 MHz; Windows; 256 color SVGA monitor; 4 MB RAM; sound card, 14 MB hard disk space; 2X CD-ROM drive **Macintosh:** 68020 processor; System 7.0; 256 Color Monitor; 4 MB RAM; 8 MB hard disk space; 2X CD-ROM drive, 12" display
The Lost Mind of Dr. Brain (Windows/Macintosh Hybrid CD-ROM)	Knowledge Adventure	The program's story line is based on an experiment gone awry in which Dr. Brain has transferred too much of his brain to Rathbone, his lab rat. The student's mission is to repair Dr. Brain's brain and restore Rathbone to his ordinary cheese-loving state. **Math Topics** • Problem Solving • Data Analysis • Logical and Deductive Reasoning • Visual/Spatial Relationships	**PC:** 386/33 MHz; Windows 3.1 or 95; 8 MB RAM; 14 MB hard disk space; 2X CD-ROM drive; SVGA; sound card **Macintosh:** 68020/16 MHz; System 7.0; 4 MB RAM; 8 MB hard disk space; 2X CD-ROM drive; 256 colors
Math Blaster Ages 9–12 (Windows/Macintosh Hybrid CD-ROM)	Knowledge Adventure	Student progress can be charted using the math skills screen, which keeps track of mastered subjects and levels. The program automatically adjusts to individual student levels. Online help and math tips provide explanations upon request. **Math Topics** • Addition • Subtraction • Multiplication • Division • Multi-Digit Numbers • Fractions • Decimals • Percents	**PC:** 386/33 MHz; Windows 3.1 or 95; 4 MB RAM; 14 MB hard disk space; 2X CD-ROM drive; SVGA; sound card **Macintosh:** 68020/16 MHz; System 7.0; 4 MB RAM; 8 MB hard disk space; 2X CD-ROM drive; 256 colors
Math Blaster Pre-Algebra (Windows/Macintosh Hybrid CD-ROM)	Knowledge Adventure	Earth's inhabitants are being "zapped" of their mathematical abilities by the magnetic brain invented by Dr. Dabble, the mad scientist. Students solve word problems involving pre-algebra and logical-thinking skills as they attempt to locate the disembodied brain in Dr. Dabble's mansion. **Math Topics** • Decimals • Factors • Integers • Fractions • Prime Numbers • Multiples • Percents	**PC:** 386/33 MHz; Windows 3.1 or 95; 4 MB RAM; 14 MB hard disk space; 2X CD-ROM drive; SVGA; sound card **Macintosh:** 68020/16 MHz; System 7.0; 4 MB RAM; 8 MB hard disk space; 2X CD-ROM drive; 256 colors
Math for the Real World (Windows or Macintosh CD-ROM)	Knowledge Adventure/ Kaplan	Students solve practical real-world problems as they travel the country with an up-and-coming rock band. **Math Topics** • Time • Charts • Logic • Fractions • Money	**PC:** 386/33 MHz; Windows 3.1 or 95; 4 MB RAM; 14 MB hard disk space; sound card; 2X CD-ROM drive **Macintosh:** 68020 processor; System 7.0 or later; 4 MB RAM; 8 MB hard disk space; 256 colors; 2X CD-ROM drive

Math Software

TITLE	PUBLISHER	DESCRIPTION	SYSTEM REQUIREMENTS
Math Workshop™ Deluxe (Windows/Macintosh Hybrid CD-ROM)	Broderbund	Interface divides activities into beginning (downstairs) and more advanced (upstairs). Custom play option allows teachers to create their own "problem sets." **Math Topics** • Computation • Estimation • Logical Reasoning • Fractions • Spatial Visualization	**PC:** 486/33 MHz; 256 color SVGA monitor; 8 MB RAM; Soundcard, 4MB hard disk space; CD-ROM drive **Macintosh:** Power PC; 256 Color Monitor; 12 MB RAM; 25 MB hard disk space; CD-ROM drive
Snootz Math Trek (Windows/Macintosh Hybrid CD-ROM)	Theatrix Interactive	"Snootian Translator" allows students to share secret messages with friends and aliens. The program provides several levels of difficulty for activities. **Math Topics** • Sequencing • Map Reading • Shapes • Symbols • Cause and Effect	**PC:** 386/33MHz; Windows 3.1 or 95; 4 MB RAM; 14 MB hard disk space; 2X CD-ROM drive; SVGA; sound card **Macintosh:** 68020/16 MHz; System 7.0; 4 MB RAM; 8 MB hard disk space; 2X CD-ROM drive; 256 colors
Thinkin' Things Collection 2 (Windows/Macintosh Hybrid CD-ROM)	Edmark	Students are led to use logical reasoning and creative imagination as they perform various tasks in this engaging program. **Math Topics** • Critical Thinking • Spatial Awareness • Problem Solving • Perspective	**PC:** 386/33 MHz; Windows 3.1 or 95; 4 MB RAM; 14 MB hard disk space; 2X CD-ROM drive; SVGA; sound card **Macintosh:** 68020/16 MHz; System 7.0; 4 MB RAM; 8 MB hard disk space; 2X CD-ROM drive; 256 colors
Thinkin' Things Collection 3 (Windows/Macintosh Hybrid CD-ROM)	Edmark	This program allows students to use logical reasoning to solve various activities. They are encouraged to be creative in their solutions. **Math Topics** • Logical Reasoning • Analyze and Synthesize Information	**PC:** 386/33 MHz; Windows 3.1 or 95; 4 MB RAM; 14 MB hard disk space; 2X CD-ROM drive; SVGA; sound card **Macintosh:** 68020/16 MHz; System 7.0; 4 MB RAM; 8 MB hard disk space; 2X CD-ROM drive; 256 colors
Widget Workshop (Windows/Macintosh Hybrid CD-ROM)	Maxis	A hands-on laboratory that allows students to produce experiments and inventions while exploring principles of science, mathematics, logic, computer science, and physics. **Math Topics** • Logic • Puzzles • Math Functions • Logic Gates • Random Numbers	**PC:** 386/33 MHz; Windows 3.1 or 95; 4 MB RAM; 14 MB hard disk space; 2X CD-ROM drive; SVGA; sound card **Macintosh:** 68020/16 MHz; System 7.0; 4 MB RAM; 8 MB hard disk space; 2X CD-ROM drive; 256 colors
Mathville Starway (Windows/Macintosh Hybrid CD-ROM)	Ingenuity Works	Ten skill-testing activities from all areas of Grades 5–7 math curriculum will keep students intrigued and interested in learning. The software supports National Council of Teachers of Mathematics' standards. **Math Topics** • Composite Numbers • Fractions • Number Lines • Percents • Angles • Coordinates	**PC:** 486 or higher, Windows 3.x or Windows 9x, SVGA, 640 × 480, 256 color monitor, 8 MB RAM CD-ROM drive, sound card **Macintosh:** System 7 or higher, 640 × 480 color monitor, 8 MB RAM, CD-ROM drive
Mathville Waterway (Windows or Macintosh CD-ROM)	Ingenuity Works	The program contains a virtual water world that overflows with TWELVE entertaining and skill-testing math activities. It is designed to stretch student abilities by challenging them to apply skills to a variety of new problem-solving situations. **Math Topics** • Decimals • Fractions • Transformations • Coordinates • Number Patterns • Metric Units • Probability and Data • Logic • Problem Solving	**PC:** 486 or higher, Windows 3.x or Windows 9x, SVGA, 640 × 480, 256 color monitor, 8 MB RAM CD-ROM drive, sound card **Macintosh:** System 7 or higher, 640 × 480 color monitor, 8 MB RAM, CD-ROM drive

Books for Teachers

Baratta-Lorton, M. *Mathematics Their Way: An Activity-Centered Mathematics Program for Early Childhood Education.* Addison-Wesley, 1995.

Baratta-Lorton, R. *Mathematics: A Way of Thinking.* Addison-Wesley, 1977.

Benson, D. *The Moment of Proof: Mathematical Epiphanies.* Oxford University Press, 1999.

Berk, L., and A. Winsler. *Scaffolding Children's Learning: Vygotsky and Early Childhood Education.* National Association for the Education of Young Children, 1995.

Bloomer, A., and P. Carlson. *Activity Math: Using Manipulatives in the Classroom.* Addison-Wesley, 1993.

Bresser, R., and C. Holtzman. *Developing Number Sense—Grades 3–6.* Math Solutions Publications, 1999.

Bright, G., and J. Harvey. *Basic Math Games.* Dale Seymour Publications, 1987.

Brodie, J. P. *Constructing Ideas About Large Numbers.* Creative Publications, 1995.

Burk, D., A. Snider, and P. Symonds. *Box It or Bag It Mathematics: Teachers' Resource Guide, First–Second.* The Math Learning Center, 1988.

Burns, M. *About Teaching Mathematics.* Math Solutions Publications, 1993.

Burns, M. *About Teaching Mathematics: A K–8 Resource.* Math Solutions Publications, 1992.

Burns, M. *A Collection of Math Lessons from Grades 6–8.* Math Solutions Publications, 1990.

Burns, M. *Math and Literature (K–3).* Math Solutions Publications, 1992.

Burns, M. *Math By All Means: Division, Grades 3 and 4.* Math Solutions Publications, 1994.

Burns, M. *Math By All Means: Multiplication, Grade 3.* Math Solutions Publications, 1994.

Burns, M. *Math By All Means: Probability, Grades 3 and 4.* Math Solutions Publications, 1994.

Burns, M. *MATH: Facing an American Phobia.* Math Solutions Publications, 1998.

Burns, M. *Probability, Grades 2–3.* Math Solutions Publications, 1994.

Burns, M. *This Book Is About Time.* Yolla Bolly Press, 1978.

Burton, G. *Towards a Good Beginning: Teaching Early Childhood Mathematics.* Addison-Wesley, 1985.

Burton, G., D. Clements, et al. *Addenda Series, Grades K–6.* NCTM, 1991–1992.

Burton, G., et al. *Addenda Series, Grades K–6, Number Sense and Operations.* NCTM, 1993.

Butterworth, B. *The Mathematical Brain.* Macmillan, 1999.

Caine, R. and G. *Unleashing the Power of Perceptual Change: The Potential of Brain-Based Teaching.* ASCD, 1997.

Carpenter, T., E. Fennema, M. Franke, L. Levi, and S. Empson. *Children's Mathematics—Cognitively Guided Instruction.* Heinemann, 1999.

Cathcart. W., Y. Pothier, J. Vance, and N. Bezuk. ***Learning Mathematics in Elementary and Middle Schools.*** Merrill, 2000.

Childs, L., and L. Choate. ***Nimble with Numbers.*** Dale Seymour Publications, 1999.

Clapham, C. ***Concise Dictionary of Mathematics.*** Oxford University Press, 1996.

Coates, G., and J. Stenmark. ***Family Math for Young Children.*** Lawrence Hall of Science, 1997.

Coburn, T., et al. ***Addenda Series, Grades K–6, Patterns,*** NCTM, 1993.

Cohen, J. "The First 'R': Reflective Capacities." ***Educational Leadership,*** Vol. 57, ASCD, September 1999.

Cooney, M., ed. ***Celebrating Women in Mathematics and Science.*** NCTM, 1996.

Copley, J., ed. ***Mathematics in the Early Years.*** NCTM, 1999.

Cowan, T., and J. Maguire. ***Timelines of African-American History: 500 Years of Black Achievement.*** Berkley Publishing Group, 1994.

Crawford, M. and M. Witte. "Strategies for Mathematics: Teaching in Context." ***Educational Leadership,*** Vol. 57, ASCD, November 1999.

Curcio, F. "Developing Number Sense in the Middle Grades," ***Addenda Series.*** NCTM, 1991.

Curcio, F., and N. Bezuk, et al. ***Addenda Series, Grades 5–8, Understanding Rational Numbers and Proportions.*** NCTM, 1994.

Danielson, C., and L. Abrutyn. ***An Introduction to Using Portfolios in the Classroom.*** ASCD, 1997.

Del Grande, J., and L. Morrow, ***Addenda Series, Grades K–6, Geometry and Spatial Sense,*** NCTM, 1993.

Drake, S. ***Planning Integrated Curriculum.*** ASCD, 1993.

Eby, J., and E. Kujawa. ***Reflective Planning, Teaching and Evaluation: K–12.*** Merrill, 1994.

Elliott, P., ed. ***Communication in Mathematics, K–12 and Beyond (1996 Yearbook).*** NCTM, 1996.

Fennelland, F., and D. Williams. "Decimal Dash" in ***The Arithmetic Teacher.*** NCTM, 1986.

Ferrini-Mundy, J., K. Graham, L. Johnson, and G. Mills, eds. ***Making Change in Mathematics Education: Learning from the Field.*** NCTM, 1998.

Flournoy, V., et al. ***The Patchwork Quilt.*** Scholastic, 1996.

Forte, I., and S. Schurr. ***Interdisciplinary Units and Projects for Thematic Instruction.*** Incentive Publications Inc., 1994.

Franco, B., et al. "Geometry Concentration" in ***Understanding Geometry.*** Great Source Education Group, 1998.

Franco, B., et al. ***Understanding Geometry.*** Great Source Education Group, 1998.

Fuson, K. C., and Y. Kwon. "Korean Children's Understanding of Multidigit Addition and Subtraction," ***Child Development,*** Vol. 63, 491–506, 1992.

Garland, T. ***Fibonacci Fun: Fascinating Activities with Intriguing Numbers.*** Dale Seymour Publications, 1998.

Geary, D. C. ***Children's Mathematical Development: Research and Practical Applications.*** American Psychological Association, Washington, D.C., 1994.

Geary, D. C. "Reflections of Evolution and Culture in Children's Cognition: Implications for Mathematics Development and Mathematics Instruction," *American Psychologist,* Vol. 50, 24–27, 1995.

Geary, D. C., C. C. Bow-Tomas, and Y. Yao. "Counting Knowledge and Skill in Cognitive Addition: A Comparison of Normal and Mathematically Disabled Children," *Journal of Experimental Child Psychology,* Vol. 54, 372–91,1992.

Geary, D. C., et al. "A Biocultural Model of Academic Development," in *Global Prospects for Education: Development, Culture, and Schooling.* Edited by S. G. Paris and H. M. Wellman, Washington, D.C.: American Psychological Association, 1998.

Geary, D. C., et al. "Development of Arithmetical Competencies in Chinese and American Children: Influence of Age, Language, and Schooling," *Child Development,* Vol. 67, 2022–44, 1996.

Geary, D. C., and K. F. Widamin. "Numerical Cognition: On the Convergence of Componential and Psychometric Models," *Intelligence,* Vol. 16, 47–80, 1992.

Geddes, D., et al. *Addenda Series, Grades 5–8, Geometry in the Middle Grades.* NCTM, 1992.

Geddes, D., et al. *Addenda Series, Grades 5–8, Measurement in the Middle Grades.* NCTM, 1994.

Gelfand, I., and A. Shen. *Algebra.* Birkhauser, 1993.

Glassman, B., ed. *Macmillan Visual Almanac.* Blackbirch Press, 1996.

Glatzer, D., and J. Glatzer. *Math Connections.* Dale Seymour Publications, 1989.

Goldsmith, L., and J. Mark. "What Is Standards-Based Mathematics Curriculum?" *Educational Leadership*, Vol. 57, ASCD, November 1999.

Greenes, C., and G. Immerzeel. *Problem Solving Focus: Time and Money.* Dale Seymour Publications, 1993.

Grouws, D., ed. *Handbook of Research on Mathematics Teaching and Learning.* Macmillan, 1992.

Han, S. T., and B. Ford. *The Master Revealed—A Journey with Tangrams.* Cuisenaire.

Heaton, R. *Teaching Mathematics to the New Standards: Relearning the Dance.* Teachers College Press, 2000.

Henderson, J. *Reflective Teaching: Becoming an Inquiring Educator.* Macmillan, 1992.

Hiebert, J., T. Carpenter, E. Fennema, K. Fuson, D. Wearne, H. Murray, A. Olivier, and P. Humam. *Making Sense: Teaching and Learning Mathematics with Understanding.* Heinemann, 1997.

Hoffman, P. *The Man Who Loved Only Numbers: The Story of Paul Erdos and the Search for Mathematical Truth.* Hyperion, 1998.

House, P., and A. Coxford. *Connecting Mathematics Across the Curriculum.* NCTM, 1995.

Hynes, M. E., ed. *Mission Mathematics: K–6.* NCTM, 1997.

Irvin, J., ed. *What Current Research Says to the Middle Level Practitioner.* National Middle School Association, 1997.

Jacobs, H. *Interdisciplinary Curriculum: Design and Implementation.* ASCD, 1989.

Jurgens, H., E. Maletsky, H. O. Peitgen, T. Perciante, D. Saupe, and L. Yunker. *Fractals for the Classroom: Strategic Activities, Vols. 1 & 2.* NCTM. Copublished with Springer-Verlag, 1991-1992.

Kamii, C., and L. Housman. *Young Children Reinvent Arithmetic: Implications of Piaget's Theory.* Teachers College Press, 1999.

Kaplan, J. *Basic Decimals.* Educational Design, Inc., 1996.

Kaplan, J. *Basic Fractions.* Educational Design, Inc., 1996.

Kaplan, J. *Strategies for Solving Math Word Problems.* Educational Design, Inc., 1996.

Kenney, P., and E. Silver. *Results from the Sixth Mathematics Assessment of the National Assessment of Educational Progress.* NCTM, 1997.

Krause, M. *Multicultural Mathematics Materials.* NCTM, 1993.

Lamancusa, J. *Kid Cash: Creative Money-Making Ideas.* TAB Books, 1993.

Lee, M., and M. Miller. *Great Graphing.* Scholastic Professional Books, 1993.

Leutzinger, L., ed. *Mathematics in the Middle.* NCTM, Copublished with the National Middle School Association, 1998.

Levia, M., et al. "Oh How We've Changed!" in *Addenda Series: Fourth Grade.* NCTM, 1992.

Lindquist, M., et al. *Making Sense of Data. Addenda Series, Grades K–6.* NCTM, 1992.

Ma, Liping. *Knowing and Teaching Elementary Mathematics.* Lawrence Erlbaum Associates, 1999.

Madfes, T., Project Director. *Learning from Assessment: Tools for Examining Assessment through Standards.* (Includes PBS Mathline Video). NCTM, 1999.

Maletsky, E. *Teaching with Student Math Notes.* NCTM, 1993.

Mamchur, C. *A Teacher's Guide to Cognitive Type Theory and Learning Style.* ASCD, 1996.

The Math Learning Center. "Fractions on a Geoboard," in *Opening Eyes to Mathematics, Volume 3.* 1995.

McIntosh, A., B. Reys, R. Reys, and J. Hope. *Number SENSE: Simple Effective Number Sense Experiences, Grades 4–6.* Dale Seymour Publications, 1997.

Means, B., C. Chelener, and M. Knapp. *Teaching Advanced Skills to At-Risk Students.* Jossey-Bass Inc., 1991.

Mendlesohn, E. *Teaching Primary Math with Music.* Dale Seymour Publications, 1990.

Merrill, W. *A Calculator Tutorial.* Dale Seymour Publications, 1996.

Miller, D., and A. McKinnon. *The Beginning School Mathematics Project.* ASCD, 1995.

Miller, E. *Read It! Draw It! Solve It! Problem Solving for Primary Grades.* Dale Seymour Publications, 1997.

Morrison, P., and P. Morrison. *Powers of Ten.* W. H. Freeman and Morrison Company, 1982.

Morrow, L., ed. *The Teaching and Learning of Algorithms in School Mathematics (1998 Yearbook).* NCTM, 1998.

Moses, B. *Algebraic Thinking, Grades K–12: Readings from NCTM's School-Based Journals and Other Publications.* NCTM, 1999.

Myren, C. *Posing Open-Ended Questions in the Primary Classroom.* Teaching Resource Center, 1997.

Newman, V. *Math Journals, Grades K–5.* Teaching Resource Center, 1994.

Newman, V. *Numbercises—A Fitness Program: Strategies for Addition and Subtraction.* Teaching Resource Center, 1998.

Norton-Wolf, S. *Base-Ten Block Activities.* Learning Resources, 1990.

O'Connor, V., and M. Hynes, *Mission Mathematics: 5–8.* NCTM, 1997.

Ohanian, S. *Garbage, Pizza, Patchwork Quilts, and Math Magic.* W. H. Freeman and Company, 1992.

Olson, A. *Mathematics Through Paper Folding.* NCTM, 1975.

Pappas, T. *Fractals, Googols and Other Mathematical Tales.* Wild World Publishing/Tetra, 1993.

Pappas, T. *The Magic of Mathematics—Discovering the Spell of Mathematics.* Wild World Publishing/Tetra, 1994.

Parker, M., ed. *She Does Math!—Real-Life Problems from Women on the Job.* The Mathematical Association of America, 1995.

Perrone, V., ed. *Expanding Student Assessment.* ASCD, 1991.

Phillips, E., et al. *Addenda Series, Grades 5–8, Patterns and Functions.* NCTM, 1991.

Phillips, L. M., ed. *Mathematics: Teacher Resource Handbook.* Kraus International Publications, 1993.

Piccirilli, R. *Mental Math: Computation Activities for Anytime.* Scholastic Professional Books, 1996.

Pohl, V. *How to Enrich Geometry Using String Designs.* NCTM, 1986.

Pollard, J. *Building Toothpick Bridges.* Dale Seymour Publications, 1985.

Project AIMS. *AIMS Activities.* AIMS Educational Foundation, 1988–1995.

Reys, B., et al. *Addenda Series, Grades 5–8.* NCTM, 1991.

Rich, D. *MegaSkills.* Houghton Mifflin, 1992.

Richardson, K. *Developing Number Concepts: Book 1, Counting, Comparing and Patterns.* Dale Seymour Publications, 1999.

Richardson, K. *Developing Number Concepts: Book 2, Addition and Subtraction.* Dale Seymour Publications, 1999.

Richardson, K. *Developing Number Concepts: Book 3, Place Value, Multiplication, and Division.* Dale Seymour Publications, 1998.

Ringenberg, L. *A Portrait of 2.* NCTM, 1995.

Rommel, Carol A. *Integrating Beginning Math & Literature.* Incentive Publications, Inc., 1991.

Satariano, P. *Storytime, Mathtime: Math Explorations in Children's Literature.* Dale Seymour Publications, 1997.

Schechter, B. *My Brain Is Open: The Mathematical Journeys of Paul Erdos.* Simon & Schuster, 1998.

Scheidt, T. *Fantasy Baseball.* Giant Step Press, 1994.

Schifter, D., and C. Fosnot. *Reconstructing Mathematics Education: Stories of Teachers Meeting the Challenge of Reform.* Teachers College Press, 1993.

Schoenfeld, A. "When Good Teaching Leads to Bad Results: The Disasters of Well-Taught Mathematics Courses," *Educational Psychologist,* Vol. 23, 145–66, 1998.

Schullman, D., and E. Rebeka. *Growing Mathematical Ideas in Kindergarten.* Math Solutions Publications, 1999.

Schultz, K., et al. *Mathematics for Every Young Child.* Merrill, 1990.

Seymour, D. *Getting Smarter Every Day.* Prentice Hall, 1999.

Seymour, D. *Probability Model Masters.* Dale Seymour Publications, 1990.

Sheffield, L. *Developing Mathematically Promising Students.* NCTM, 1999.

Silverman, R., W. Welty, and S. Lyon. *Case Studies for Teacher Problem Solving.* McGraw-Hill, Inc., 1992.

Singer, Margie, et al. *Between Never and Always*. Dale Seymour Publications, 1997.

Skinner, P. *It All Adds Up!* Math Solutions Publications (Adapted by permission of Addison-Wesley Longman, Australia), 1999.

Skinner, P. *What's Your Problem? Posing and Solving Mathematical Problems, K–2.* Heinemann, 1990.

Slavin, R. E., N. L. Karweit, and B. A. Wasik, eds. *Preventing Early School Failure: Research, Policy, and Practice.* Allyn and Bacon, 1994.

Sobel, M., and E. Maletsky. *Teaching Mathematics: A Sourcebook of Aids, Activities, and Strategies.* Allyn & Bacon, 1998. Sonnabend, T. *Mathematics for Elementary Teachers—An Interactive Approach.* Saunders College Publishing, Harcourt Brace College Publishers, 1993.

Steen, L., ed. *On the Shoulders of Giants—New Approaches to Numeracy.* National Research Council, 1990.

Steen, L., ed. *Why Numbers Count—Quantitative Literacy for Tomorrow's America.* NCTM, 1997.

Stenmark, J., V. Thompson, and R. Cossey. *Family Math.* University of California, 1986.

Stenmark, J., ed. *Mathematics Assessment: Myths, Models, Good Questions, and Practical Suggestions.* NCTM, 1991.

Sternberg, R., and W. Williams. *How to Develop Student Creativity.* ASCD, 1996.

Stevenson, F. *Exploratory Problems in Mathematics.* NCTM, 1992.

Stewart, K., and K. Walker. *20 Thinking Questions for Base-Ten Blocks, Grades 3–6.* Creative Publications, 1995.

Stiff, L., and F. Curcio, eds. *Developing Mathematical Reasoning in Grades K–12 (1999 Yearbook).* NCTM, 1999.

Sylvester, R. *A Celebration of Neurons—An Educator's Guide to the Human Brain.* ASCD, 1995.

A Teacher's Guide to Performance-Based Learning and Assessment. Educators in Connecticut's Pomperaug Regional School District 15. ASCD, 1996.

Thiessen, D., and M. Mathias. *The Wonderful World of Mathematics: A Critically Annotated List of Children's Books in Mathematics.* NCTM, 1992.

Thornton, C., and N. Bley, eds. *Windows of Opportunity: Mathematics for Students with Special Needs.* NCTM, 1994.

Threewit, F. *Estimation Destinations.* Cuisenaire, 1994.

Tomlinson, Carol Ann. *How to Differentiate Instruction in Mixed-Ability Classrooms.* ASCD, 1995.

Trafton, P., and D. Thiesen. *Learning Through Problems: Number Sense and Computational Strategies/A Resource for Teachers.* Heinemann, 1999.

Van Cleave, J. "Graphing," in Van Cleave's *Math for Every Kid: Easy Activities That Make Learning Math Fun.* Wiley, 1991.

Van Cleave, J. *Math for Every Kid.* Wiley, 1991.

Van de Walle, J. *Elementary and Middle School Mathematics: Teaching Developmentally, Third Edition.* Dale Seymour Publications, 1997.

Walter, M. *Boxes, Squares, and Other Things.* NCTM, 1995.

Webb, N., and T. Romberg. *Reforming Mathematics Education in America's Cities: The Urban Mathematics Collaborative Project.* Teachers College Press, 1994.

Welchman-Tischler, R. *How to Use Children's Literature to Teach Mathematics.* NCTM, 1992.

Wu, H. "The 1997 Mathematics Standards War in California," in *What Is at Stake at the K–12 Standards Wars.* Edited by S. Stotsky. New York: Peter Lang Publishers, 1999.

Zaslavsky, C. *Fear of Math—How to Get Over It and Get On with Your Life.* Rutgers University Press, 1994.

Zaslavsky, C. *Multicultural Math: Hands-On Math Activities from Around the World.* Scholastic Professional Books, 1994.

Zawojewski, J., et al. *Addenda Series, Grades 5–8, Dealing with Data and Chance.* NCTM, 1991.

Zemelman, S., H. Daniels, and A. Hyde. *Best Practice: New Standards for Teaching and Learning in America's Schools.* Heinemann, 1998.

Index

of solid figures, 354–359, 362–363, H50

Unit prices. *See* Unit rates

Unit rates, 375–376, H51

Units, converting, 452–457

Universal Access

Advanced Learners, 14F, 20B, 22B, 26B, 44B, 70B, 76B, 80B, 92F, 94B, 106B, 109B, 126B, 130B, 144F, 146B, 164B, 182B, 192B, 206B, 216B, 226B, 250B, 266, 272F, 276B, 294B, 310B, 320F, 326B, 336B, 348B, 357B, 362B, 372F, 384B, 406, 408B, 412B, 426B, 432B, 450F, 452B, 469B, 492B, 506B, 511B, 522F, 524B, 543B, 550B, 564B, 569, 570B

Alternative Teaching Strategy, 16B, 18, 20B, 22B, 24, 26B, 28B, 30B, 36B, 38, 40B, 44B, 46B, 52B, 54, 56B, 58B, 60B, 66B, 68, 70B, 72, 76B, 78, 80B, 82B, 87, 94B, 96, 98B, 100B, 102B, 104, 106B, 109B, 112B, 114, 120B, 122, 124B, 126B, 130B, 132B, 134, 146B, 148B, 150B, 152, 154B, 160B, 162, 164B, 166B, 169B, 176B, 178, 182B, 184, 186B, 188, 192B, 194B, 200B, 202B, 204, 206B, 208, 210B, 212, 214B, 216B, 228B, 230B, 232, 234B, 236B, 244B, 246, 250B, 256, 258B, 260B, 262B, 274B, 276B, 278, 282B, 288B, 291B, 294B, 301B, 304B, 306, 308, 310B, 322B, 326B, 328, 330B, 336B, 338, 340B, 342B, 344, 346B, 348B, 354B, 357B, 362B, 374B, 378B, 380B, 382, 384B, 387B, 390B, 396B, 398B, 400, 402B, 404, 408B, 410, 412B, 418B, 420, 422B, 426B, 432B, 434B, 437B, 440B, 452B, 454B, 456B, 458B, 460, 462B, 469B, 472B, 476B, 478, 484B, 486, 488B, 492B, 494B, 496, 502B, 504, 506B, 508B, 511B, 524B, 526B, 529B, 531, 533B, 540B, 543B, 546B, 548B, 550B, 552, 558B, 560B, 562, 564B, 566B, 570B, 572, 577

Art Connection, 274B, 360, 476B, 508B

Block Scheduling, 14F, 92F, 144F, 226F, 272F, 320F, 372F, 450F, 522F

Career Connection, 16B, 28B, 70B, 112B, 130B, 154B, 166B, 206B, 402B, 494B, 540B, 560B

Early Finishers, 14G, 20B, 28B, 46B, 56B, 58B, 66B, 76B, 92G, 100B, 102B, 132B, 144G, 150B, 160B, 180, 194B, 200B, 214B, 221, 226G, 243, 260B, 272G, 282B, 308, 320G, 330B, 340B, 361, 367, 372G, 378B, 396B, 398B, 402B, 422B, 437B, 450G, 454B, 462B, 468, 484B, 502B, 522G, 526B, 529B, 546B, 560B

English Language Learners, 14G, 30B, 40B, 56B, 60B, 80B, 82B, 92G, 98B, 100B, 102B, 120B, 144G, 148B, 160B, 169B, 194B, 200B, 210B, 214B, 226G, 228B, 234B, 244B, 260B, 272G, 274B, 288B, 301B, 320G, 325, 330B, 342B, 357B, 372G, 374B, 380B, 390B, 398B, 424, 437B, 444, 450G, 458B, 469B, 476B, 484B, 511B, 522G, 533B, 548B, 570B

Fine Arts Connection, 314, 322B, 456B, 472B

Health Connection, 50, 174

History Connection, 154, 166, 430

Interdisciplinary Suggestions, 14F, 92F, 144F, 226F, 272F, 320F, 372F, 450F, 522F

Language Arts Connection, 176B, 346B, 380B, 548B

Literature Connection, 14G, 86, 92G, 144G, 226G, 272G, 320G, 372G, 450G, 522G

Math Connection, 516, 576

    Algebra, 42, 150B, 210B

Geometry, 230B, 280, 526B

    Measurement, 190

Physical Education Connection, 139, 166B, 282B, 440B

Practice Game, 14G, 92G, 144G, 226G, 272G, 320G, 372G, 450G, 522G

Reading Strategy, 26B, 46B, 80B, 100B, 214B, 236B, 310B, 340B, 362B, 378B

Science Connection, 22B, 44B, 82B, 186B, 257, 267, 288B, 304B, 374B, 387B, 418B, 434B, 458B, 524B, 564B

Social Studies Connection, 26B, 60B, 66B, 98B, 124B, 301B, 342B, 354B, 390B, 406, 494B

Special Needs, 14F, 30B, 36B, 52B, 74, 92F, 109B, 120B, 144F, 146B, 154B, 169B, 182B, 190, 192B, 202B, 220, 226F, 236B, 242, 248, 256, 258B, 262B, 272F, 280, 294B, 310B, 320F, 324, 326B, 346B, 360, 362B, 372F, 384B, 387B, 396B, 426B, 432B, 450F, 454B, 474, 492B, 502B, 522F, 529B, 543B, 568

Technology, 46B, 52B

Vocabulary Strategy, 36B, 94B, 228B, 324, 340B, 348B, 366, 418B, 434B, 462B, 508B, 550B, 558B

Writing in Mathematics, 16B, 40B, 58B, 74, 106B, 112B, 124B, 126B, 132B, 148B, 164B, 176B, 180, 186B, 202B, 208, 216B, 230B, 250B, 262B, 276B, 291B, 304B, 322B, 336B, 354B, 378B, 408B, 412B, 422B, 440B, 452B, 472B, 474, 488B, 506B, 533B, 546B, 566B, 568

Unlike fractions, 180–181

Unlikely outcomes, 419, H24

Upper quartile, 129–131, H37

Use Logical Reasoning strategy, 11, 236–237

Using Data, *14, 34, 50, 64, 92, 118, 144, 158, 174, 198, 226, 240, 254, 272, 286, 298, 320, 334, 352, 372, 394, 416, 430, 450, 466, 482, 500, 522, 538, 556 See also* Data

Variables, 28–29, 274–279, 288–295, 300–309

Venn diagrams, 230, 233

Vertical angles, 326–329, 337, H48

Vertices, 362–363, H20

Visual Arts Connection, *488B, 540B*

Vocabulary, *16A, 16, 28A, 28, 30A, 30, 36A, 36, 40A, 40, 42, 60A, 60, 94A, 94, 98A, 98, 102A, 102, 106, 109A, 109, 120A, 120, 126A, 126, 129, 146, 148A, 148, 150A, 150, 160A, 160, 164A, 164, 169A, 169, 176, 180, 182A, 182, 186, 208, 228A, 228, 230A, 230, 242, 244, 262, 276A, 276, 280, 288, 291A, 291, 294A, 294, 301A, 301, 322A, 322, 324, 326A, 326, 330A, 330, 336A, 336, 340A, 340, 346, 348A, 348, 354A, 354, 360, 374A, 374, 377, 378, 380A, 380, 384A, 384, 387A, 387, 398, 408A, 408, 412A, 412, 418A, 418, 426A, 426, 434A, 434, 437A, 437, 440, 454, 474, 484A, 484, 494A, 494, 502A, 502, 526A, 526, 529A, 529, 533A, 533, 540A, 540, 543A, 543, 548, 550A, 550, 558A, 558, 560A, 560, 570*

Vocabulary Cards, *14I, 34B, 50B, 92I, 118B, 144I, 158B, 174B, 198B, 226I, 240B, 272I, 286B, 298B, 320I, 334B, 352B, 372I, 394B, 416B, 430B, 466B, 482B, 500B, 522I, 538B, 556B*

Vocabulary Development, *14I, 34B, 50B, 64B, 92I, 118B, 144I, 158B,*

Teaching Notes

Additional Ideas:

Good Questions to Ask:

Additional Resources:

Notes for Next Time:

HARCOURT

Math

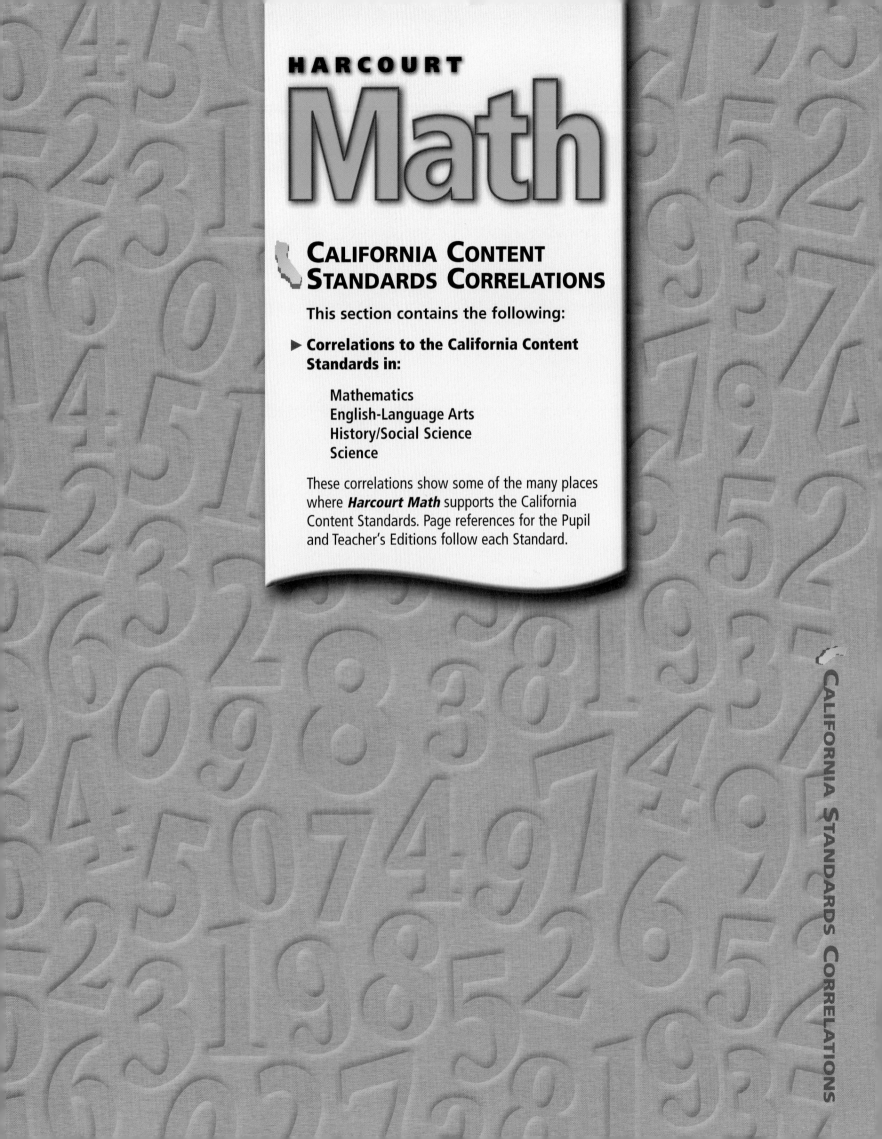

CALIFORNIA CONTENT STANDARDS CORRELATIONS

This section contains the following:

▶ **Correlations to the California Content Standards in:**

    Mathematics
    English-Language Arts
    History/Social Science
    Science

These correlations show some of the many places where **Harcourt Math** supports the California Content Standards. Page references for the Pupil and Teacher's Editions follow each Standard.

California Correlations

CALIFORNIA MATHEMATICS CONTENT STANDARDS	PUPIL EDITION AND TEACHER'S EDITION PAGES
NUMBER SENSE	
NS 1.0 Students compare and order positive and negative fractions, decimals, and mixed numbers. Students solve problems involving fractions, ratios, proportions, and percentages:	52–55, 60–61, 166–167, 169–171, 176–179, 182–189, 192–195, 200–207, 210–213, 230–235, 374–376, 378–391, 396–405, 408–413, 452–453, 454–457, 506–507
NS 1.1 Compare and order positive and negative fractions, decimals, and mixed numbers and place them on a number line.	52–55, 166–167, 230–233, 234–235
NS 1.2 Interpret and use ratios in different contexts (e.g., batting averages, miles per hour) to show the relative sizes of two quantities, using appropriate notations (a/b, a to b, $a{:}b$).	374–376, 380–383, 387–389, 390–391, 506–507
NS 1.3 Use proportions to solve problems (e.g., determine the value of N if $\frac{4}{7} = \frac{N}{21}$, find the length of a side of a polygon similar to a known polygon). Use cross-multiplication as a method for solving such problems, understanding it as the multiplication of both sides of an equation by a multiplicative inverse:	378–379, 384–386, 387–389, 390–391, 452–453, 454–455, 456–457
NS 1.4 Calculate given percentages of quantities and solve problems involving discounts at sales, interest earned, and tips.	402–405, 408–411, 412–413
NS 2.0 Students calculate and solve problems involving addition, subtraction, multiplication, and division.	20–25, 28–29, 66–83, 180–193, 202–213, 242–251, 256–263, 301–303
NS 2.1 Solve problems involving addition, subtraction, multiplication, and division of positive fractions and explain why a particular operation was used for a given situation.	180–181, 182–185, 186–189, 190–191, 192–193, 202–205, 206–207, 208–209, 210–213, 214–215
NS 2.2 Explain the meaning of multiplication and division of positive fractions and perform the calculations (e.g., $\frac{5}{8} \div \frac{15}{16} = \frac{5}{8} \times \frac{16}{15} = \frac{2}{3}$).	202–205, 206–207, 208–209, 210–213, 214–215, 216–217
NS 2.3 Solve addition, subtraction, multiplication, and division problems, including those arising in concrete situations, that use positive and negative numbers and combinations of these operations.	242–243, 244–247, 248–249, 250–251, 256–257, 258–259, 260–261, 262–263
NS 2.4 Determine the least common multiple and the greatest common divisor of whole numbers; use them to solve problems with fractions (e.g., to find a common denominator to add two fractions or to find the reduced form for a fraction).	150–153, 160–163, 166–167, 180–195, 202–213, 221

CALIFORNIA MATHEMATICS CONTENT STANDARDS	PUPIL EDITION AND TEACHER'S EDITION PAGES
ALGEBRA AND FUNCTIONS	
AF 1.0 Students write verbal expressions and sentences as algebraic expressions and equations; they evaluate algebraic expressions, solve simple linear equations, and graph and interpret their results.	28–31, 82–83, 216–217, 274–279, 282–283, 288–295, 300–303, 378–379, 568–569
AF 1.1 ⊶ Write and solve one-step linear equations in one variable.	30–31, 82–83, 288–289, 290, 291–293, 294–295, 300, 301–303
AF 1.2 Write and evaluate an algebraic expression for a given situation, using up to three variables.	28–29, 274–275, 276–279
AF 1.3 Apply algebraic order of operations and the commutative, associative, and distributive properties to evaluate expressions and justify each step in the process.	36–39, 42–43, 44–45, 262–263, 276–279, 282–283
AF 1.4 Solve problems manually by using the correct order of operations or by using a scientific calculator.	42–43, 44–45, 262–263, 276–279
AF 2.0 Students analyze and use tables, graphs, and rules to solve problems involving rates and proportions.	124–125, 304–307, 374–376, 380–383
AF 2.1 Convert one unit of measurement to another (e.g., from feet to miles, from centimeters to inches).	452–453, 454–455, 456–457
AF 2.2 ⊶ Demonstrate an understanding that rate is a measure of one quantity per unit value of another quantity.	374–376
AF 2.3 Solve problems involving rates, average speed, distance, and time.	124–125, 304–307
AF 3.0 Students investigate geometric patterns and describe them algebraically.	469–471, 474–475, 476–479, 484–487, 488–490, 491, 494–497
AF 3.1 Use variables in expressions describing geometric quantities (e.g., $P = 2w + 2l$, $A = \frac{1}{2}bh$, $C = \pi d$, formulas for the perimeter of a rectangle, the area of a triangle, and the circumference of a circle, respectively).	469–471, 474–479, 484–487, 488–490, 491, 492–493, 494–497
AF 3.2 Express in symbolic form simple relationships arising from geometry.	469–471, 474–475, 476–479, 484–487, 488–490, 491, 492–493
MEASUREMENT AND GEOMETRY	
MG 1.0 Students deepen their understanding of measurement of plane and solid shapes and use this understanding to solve problems:	324–325, 458–459, 468–479, 484–490, 494–497, 502–513
MG 1.1 ⊶ Understand the concept of a constant such as π; know the formulas for the circumference and area of a circle.	474–475, 476–479, 491, 492–493

MEASUREMENT AND GEOMETRY *(continued)*

MG 1.2	Know common estimates of π (3.14; $\frac{22}{7}$) and use these values to estimate and calculate the circumference and the area of circles; compare with actual measurements.	474–475, 476–479, 491, 492–493
MG 1.3	Know and use the formulas for the volume of triangular prisms and cylinders (area of base $\times$ height); compare these formulas and explain the similarity between them and the formula for the volume of a rectangular solid.	502–505, 508–509, 510, 511–513
MG 2.0	Students identify and describe the properties of two-dimensional figures.	322–323, 336–339, 342–345, 348–349
MG 2.1	Identify angles as vertical, adjacent, complementary, or supplementary and provide descriptions of these terms.	326–329
MG 2.2 ⚷	Use the properties of complementary and supplementary angles and the sum of the angles of a triangle to solve problems involving an unknown angle.	326–329, 336–339
MG 2.3	Draw quadrilaterals and triangles from given information about them (e.g., a quadrilateral having equal sides but no right angles, a right isosceles triangle).	346–347

STATISTICS, DATA ANALYSIS, AND PROBABILITY

SDAP 1.0	Students compute and analyze statistical measurement for data sets.	102–105, 106–108, 109–111
SDAP 1.1	Compute the range, mean, median, and mode of data sets.	102–105, 106–108, 109–111
SDAP 1.2	Understand how additional data added to data sets may affect these computations of measures of central tendency.	109–111
SDAP 1.3	Understand how the inclusion or exclusion of outliers affects measures of central tendency.	109–111
SDAP 1.4	Know why a specific measure of central tendency (mean, median, mode) provides the most useful information in a given context.	106–108
SDAP 2.0	Students use data samples of a population and describe the characteristics and limitations of the samples.	94–97, 98–99
SDAP 2.1	Compare different samples of a population with the data from the entire population and identify a situation in which it makes sense to use a sample.	94–97

STATISTICS, DATA ANALYSIS, AND PROBABILITY (continued)

CALIFORNIA MATHEMATICS CONTENT STANDARDS	PUPIL EDITION AND TEACHER'S EDITION PAGES
SDAP 2.2 〇━┓ Identify different ways of selecting a sample (e.g., convenience sampling, responses to a survey, random sampling) and which method makes a sample more representative for a population.	94–97
SDAP 2.3 〇━┓ Analyze data displays and explain why the way in which the question was asked might have influenced the results obtained and why the way in which the results were displayed might have influenced the conclusions reached.	98–99, 132–135
SDAP 2.4 〇━┓ Identify data that represent sampling errors and explain why the sample (and the display) might be biased.	94–97, 98–99
SDAP 2.5 〇━┓ Identify claims based on statistical data and, in simple cases, evaluate the validity of the claims.	112–115
SDAP 3.0 Students determine theoretical and experimental probabilities and use these to make predictions about events.	418–421, 426–427, 440–441, 437–439
SDAP 3.1 〇━┓ Represent all possible outcomes for compound events in an organized way (e.g., tables, grids, tree diagrams) and express the theoretical probability of each outcome.	432–433, 434–436
SDAP 3.2 Use data to estimate the probability of future events (e.g., batting averages or number of accidents per mile driven).	426–427
SDAP 3.3 〇━┓ Represent probabilities as ratios, proportions, decimals between 0 and 1, and percentages between 0 and 100 and verify that the probabilities computed are reasonable; know that if P is the probability of an event, $1-P$ is the probability of an event not occurring.	418–421, 437–439, 440–441
SDAP 3.4 Understand that the probability of either of two disjoint events occurring is the sum of the two individual probabilities and that the probability of one event following another, in independent trials, is the product of the two probabilities.	418–421, 437–439
SDAP 3.5 〇━┓ Understand the difference between independent and dependent events.	434–436, 437–439

CALIFORNIA MATHEMATICS CONTENT STANDARDS		PUPIL EDITION AND TEACHER'S EDITION PAGES
MATHEMATICAL REASONING		
MR 1.0	Students make decisions about how to approach problems.	3, 12, 26–27, 46–47, 56–57, 80–81, 100–101, 154–155, 166–167, 186–189, 194–195, 214–215, 230–233, 236–237, 310–311, 340–341, 362–363, 378–379, 398–401, 402–405, 422–423, 432–433, 462–463, 472–473, 506–507, 524–525, 546–547, 566–567
MR 1.1	Analyze problems by identifying relationships, distinguishing relevant information from irrelevant, identifying missing information, sequencing and prioritizing information, and observing patterns.	7, 46–47, 120–123, 258–259, 340–341, 362–363, 422–423, 524–535, 565, 568–569
MR 1.2	Formulate and justify mathematical conjectures based on a general description of the mathematical question or problem posed.	146–147, 258–259, 268, 336–339, 474–475, 488–490
MR 1.3	Determine when and how to break a problem into simpler parts.	13, 36–39, 206–207, 340–341, 484–487, 494–497
MR 2.0	Students use strategies, skills, and concepts in finding solutions.	2–13, 26–27, 42–43, 46–47, 56–57, 74–75, 80–81, 100–101, 129, 154–155, 168, 180–181, 190–191, 194–195, 208–209, 214–215, 236–237, 242–243, 248–249, 256–257, 280–281, 290, 300, 308–311, 324–325, 340–341, 360–363, 377, 378–379, 406–407, 422–425, 432–433, 462–463, 472–475, 491, 506–507, 510, 524–525, 546–547, 566–569
MR 2.1	Use estimation to verify the reasonableness of calculated results.	20–25, 66–73, 76–79, 182–189, 192–193, 202–207, 210–213
MR 2.2	Apply strategies and results from simpler problems to more complex problems.	9, 120–123, 276–279, 336–339, 362–363, 469–471
MR 2.3	Estimate unknown quantities graphically and solve for them by using logical reasoning and arithmetic and algebraic techniques.	124–125
MR 2.4	Use a variety of methods, such as words, numbers, symbols, charts, graphs, tables, diagrams, and models, to explain mathematical reasoning.	3, 74–75, 132–135, 168, 180–181, 190–191, 194–195, 256–257, 280–281, 300, 308–309, 354–359, 360–361, 377, 406–407, 468, 491, 506–507
MR 2.5	Express the solution clearly and logically by using the appropriate mathematical notation and terms and clear language; support solutions with evidence in both verbal and symbolic work.	28–31, 40–41, 274–279, 469–471, 476–479, 484–497, 502–505, 508–513, 558–559
MR 2.6	Indicate the relative advantages of exact and approximate solutions to problems and give answers to a specified degree of accuracy.	458–461, 462–463
MR 2.7	Make precise calculations and check the validity of the results from the context of the problem.	4, 5, 26–27, 310–311, 508–509, 511–513

CALIFORNIA MATHEMATICS CONTENT STANDARDS		PUPIL EDITION AND TEACHER'S EDITION PAGES
MATHEMATICAL REASONING (continued)		
MR 3.0	Students move beyond a particular problem by generalizing to other situations.	2–13, 26–27, 46–47, 56–57, 80–81, 100–101, 154–155, 194–195, 214–215, 236–237, 310–311, 340–341, 362–363, 378–379, 422–423, 432–433, 462–463, 472–473, 506–507, 524–525, 546–547, 566–567
MR 3.1	Evaluate the reasonableness of the solution in the context of the original situation.	4, 5, 26–27, 80–81, 310–311, 508–509, 511–513
MR 3.2	Note the method of deriving the solution and demonstrate a conceptual understanding of the derivation by solving similar problems.	2–13, 26–27, 46–47, 56–57, 80–81, 100–101, 154–155, 194–195, 214–215, 236–237, 310–311, 340–341, 362–363, 378–379, 422–423, 432–433, 462–463, 472–473, 506–507, 524–525, 546–547, 566–567
MR 3.3	Develop generalizations of the results obtained and the strategies used and apply them in new problem situations.	2–13, 26–27, 46–47, 56–57, 80–81, 100–101, 154–155, 194–195, 214–215, 236–237, 310–311, 340–341, 362–363, 378–379, 422–423, 432–433, 462–463, 472–473, 506–507, 524–525, 546–547, 566–567

CALIFORNIA ENGLISH-LANGUAGE ARTS CONTENT STANDARDS		TEACHER'S EDITION PAGES
READING		
1.0	Word Analysis, Fluency, and Systematic Vocabulary Development (Grade Six) Students use their knowledge of word origins and word relationships, as well as historical and literary context clues, to determine the meaning of specialized vocabulary and to understand the precise meaning of grade-level-appropriate words.	30B, 94B, 98B, 100B, 102B, 148B, 169B, 176B, 228B, 274B, 291B, 301B, 418B, 434B
1.2	Identify and interpret figurative language and words with multiple meanings.	214B
2.4	Clarify an understanding of texts by creating outlines, logical notes, summaries, or reports.	56B, 69, 79, 100B, 153, 213, 233, 279, 339, 405, 421, 432B, 461, 472B, 479, 487, 505, 532, 563
WRITING STRATEGIES		
	b. Develop the topic with supporting details and precise verbs, nouns, and adjectives to paint a visual image in the mind of the reader.	322B

CALIFORNIA HISTORY/SOCIAL SCIENCE CONTENT STANDARDS		TEACHER'S EDITION PAGES
6.2	Students analyze the geographic, political, economic, religious, and social structures of the early civilizations of Mesopotamia, Egypt, and Kush, in terms of:	
	1. the location and description of the river systems, and physical settings that supported permanent settlement and early civilizations	390B
	5. Egyptian art and architecture	342B, 452B, 494B

CALIFORNIA SCIENCE CONTENT STANDARDS	TEACHER'S EDITION PAGES
PLATE TECTONICS AND EARTH'S STRUCTURE	
f. how to explain major features of California geology in terms of plate tectonics (including mountains, faults, volcanoes).	370
ENERGY IN THE EARTH SYSTEM	
e. differences in pressure, heat, air movement, and humidity result in changes of weather.	448
ECOLOGY — LIFE SCIENCE	
d. different kinds of organisms may play similar ecological roles in similar biomes.	520–521
RESOURCES	
a. the utility of energy sources is determined by factors that are involved in converting these sources to useful forms and the consequences of the conversion process.	90–91
b. different natural energy and material resources, including air, soil, rocks, minerals, petroleum, fresh water, wildlife, and forests, and classify them as renewable or nonrenewable.	142–143, 224–225, 458B
INVESTIGATION AND EXPERIMENTATION	
a. develop a hypothesis	342B, 418B
b. select and use appropriate tools and technology (including calculators, computers, balances, spring scales, microscopes, and binoculars) to perform tests, collect data, and display data	244B
c. construct appropriate graphs from data and develop qualitative statements about the relationships between variables.	270–271

Teaching Notes

Additional Ideas:

Good Questions to Ask:

Additional Resources:

Notes for Next Time:

Teaching Notes

Additional Ideas:

Good Questions to Ask:

Additional Resources:

Notes for Next Time:

Teaching Notes

Additional Ideas:

Good Questions to Ask:

Additional Resources:

Notes for Next Time: